1984

W9-CZM-963

ADVANCED CELL BIOLOGY

ADVANCED CELL BIOLOGY

LAZAR M. SCHWARTZ and MIGUEL M. AZAR, Editors

Khalil Ahmed*
Leonard Baskin
Jacob Joseph Blum
Jeffrey L. Blumer
Diethelm H. Boehme
Robert Bowman
Henry Brezenoff
Theresa Campana*
Thomas S. Chen
Connie Clark
Elias Cohen
John T. Crosson
Ronald A. Eckhardt*
Ronald L. Felsted
Becca Fleischer
Sidney Fleischer
Richard E. Giles
Said A. Goueli
Morley D. Hollenberg*
Akira Kaji*
Muriel W. Lambert
W. Clark Lambert
Reuben Lotan
Neville Marks
James L. Matthews
Kenneth S. McCarty

Kenneth S. McCarty, Jr.
John J. Mieyal
Elaine L. Mills
Keith Moffat
Garth L. Nicolson
Michiko Okamoto
James J. O'Leary
Byung H. Park
John T. Penniston
Paul G. Quie
Michael S. Risley
Frank H. Ruddle
Fritz Sieber
Akhouri A. Sinha
Hans L. Spiegelberg
Clifford J. Steer
Randolph C. Steer
Elton Stubblefield*
George P. Studzinki*
Roy V. Talmage
Carole J. VanderWiel
Carlo M. Veneziale
Michael J. Wilson
Tatsuo Yamamoto
Chung S. Yang*

*Section Editor

ADVISORY PANEL:
Khalil Ahmed, Nicholas R. Bachur, Theresa Campana, Ronald A.
Eckhardt, Morley D. Hollenberg, Toby C. Rodman, Herman S. Shapiro,
Paul Szabo

VAN NOSTRAND REINHOLD COMPANY
NEW YORK　CINCINNATI　ATLANTA　DALLAS　SAN FRANCISCO
LONDON　TORONTO　MELBOURNE

Van Nostrand Reinhold Company Regional Offices:
New York   Cincinnati   Atlanta   Dallas   San Francisco

Van Nostrand Reinhold Company International Offices:
London   Toronto   Melbourne

Library of Congress Catalog Card Number: 80–15853
ISBN: 0–442–27471–8

Manufactured in the United States of America

Published by Van Nostrand Reinhold Company
135 West 50th Street, New York, N.Y. 10020

Published simultaneously in Canada by Van Nostrand Reinhold Ltd.

15 14 13 12 11 10 9 8 7 6 5 4 3 2 1

Library of Congress Cataloging in Publication Data

Main entry under title:

Advanced cell biology.

  Includes index.
  1. Cytology. I. Schwartz, Lazar M. II. Azar,
Miguel M. [DNLM: 1. Cells. QH581.2 A244]
QH581.2.A37   574.87   80–15853
ISBN 0–442–27471–8

Contributors

Khalil Ahmed, Ph.D.

Professor of Laboratory Medicine and Pathology, University of Minnesota, Veterans Administration Medical Center, Minneapolis, Minnesota

Miguel M. Azar, M.D., Ph.D.

Professor of Laboratory Medicine and Pathology, University of Minnesota, Chief, Laboratory Services, Veterans Administration Medical Center, Minneapolis, Minnesota

Nicholas R. Bachur, M.D., Ph.D.

Chief, Clinical Biochemistry Laboratory, Baltimore Cancer Research Program, National Institute of Health, Baltimore, Maryland

Leonard Baskin, Ph.D.

Research Associate Department of Biochemistry, College of Medicine and Dentistry of New Jersey, New Jersey Medical School, Newark, New Jersey

Jacob Joseph Blum, Ph.D.

Professor of Physiology, Duke University, Durham, North Carolina

Jeffrey L. Blumer, M.D., Ph.D.

Assistant Professor of Pediatrics and Pharmacology, Case Western Reserve University, School of Medicine, Cleveland, Ohio

Diethelm H. Boehme, M.D.

Chief Laboratory Services, Veterans Administration Medical Center, East Orange, N.J., Professor of Pathology, New Jersey College of Medicine and Dentistry, Newark, New Jersey.

Robert Bowman, M.D.

Assistant Professor of Laboratory Medicine and Pathology, University of Minnesota, Minneapolis, Minnesota

Henry Brezenoff, Ph.D.

Associate Professor of Pharmacology, College of Medicine and Dentistry of New Jersey, New Jersey Medical School, Newark, New Jersey

Theresa Campana, Ph.D.

Associate in Medicine, Yeshiva University, Albert Einstein College of Medicine, New York, New York

Thomas S. Chen, M.D.

Associate Professor of Pathology, College of Medicine and Dentistry of New Jersey, New Jersey Medical School, Newark, New Jersey

Connie Clark, Ph.D.

Assistant Professor of Laboratory Medicine and Pathology, University of Minnesota, Veterans Administration Medical Center, Minneapolis, Minnesota

Elias Cohen, Ph.D.	Associate Chief Cancer Research Scientist, Laboratory Medicine, Roswell Park Memorial Institute, Buffalo, New York
John T. Crosson, M.D.	Associate Professor of Laboratory Medicine and Pathology, University of Minnesota; Director of Clinical Immunology, Hennepin County Medical Center, Minneapolis, Minnesota
Ronald A. Eckhardt, Ph.D.	Professor of Biology, Brooklyn College of The City University of New York, Brooklyn, New York
Ronald L. Felsted, Ph.D.	Research Chemist, Baltimore Cancer Research Institute, National Institute of Health, Baltimore, Maryland
Becca Fleischer, Ph.D.	Research Associate Professor, Department of Molecular Biology, Vanderbilt University, Nashville, Tennessee
Sidney Fleischer, Ph.D.	Professor of Molecular Biology, Vanderbilt University, Nashville, Tennessee
Richard E. Giles, Ph.D.	Fellow, Department of Microbiology and Immunology, University of Michigan Medical School, Ann Arbor, Michigan
Said A. Goueli, Ph.D.	Research Associate, Toxicology Research Laboratory, Department of Laboratory Medicine and Pathology, University of Minnesota, Veterans Administration Medical Center, Minneapolis, Minnesota
Morley D. Hollenberg, D.Phil., M.D.	Professor and Chairman, Division of Pharmacology and Therapeutics, University of Calgary Faculty of Medicine, Calgary, Alberta, Canada
Akira Kaji, Ph.D.	Professor of Microbiology, University of Pennsylvania, Philadelphia, Pennsylvania
Muriel W. Lambert, Ph.D.	Assistant Professor of Pathology, College of Medicine and Dentistry of New Jersey, New Jersey Medical School, Newark, New Jersey
W. Clark Lambert, M.D., Ph.D.	Assistant Professor of Pathology, College of Medicine and Dentistry of New Jersey, New Jersey Medical School, Newark, New Jersey
Reuben Lotan, Ph.D.	Senior Scientist, Department of Biophysics, The Weizmann Institute of Science, Rehovot, Israel
Neville Marks, Ph.D.	Principal Research Scientist, Center for Neurochemistry, Rockland Research Institute. Wards Island, N.Y.; Associate Professor, Dept. of Psychiatry, New York University, New York, New York
James L. Matthews, Ph.D.	Associate Dean, Baylor University Medical Center, and Special Professor of Physiology, University of Texas, South Western Medical School, Dallas, Texas

Kenneth S. McCarty, Ph.D. — Professor of Biochemistry, Duke University, Durham, North Carolina

Kenneth S. McCarty, Jr., M.D., Ph.D. — Assistant Professor of Internal Medicine and Pathology; Director, Endocrine Oncology Laboratory, Duke University, Durham, North Carolina

John J. Mieyal, Ph.D. — Associate Professor of Pharmacology, Case Western Reserve University, Cleveland, Ohio

Elaine L. Mills, M.D. — Assistant Professor of Pediatrics, University of Minnesota, Minneapolis, Minnesota

Keith Moffat, Ph.D. — Associate Professor of Biochemistry, Cornell University, Ithaca, New York

Garth L. Nicolson, Ph.D. — Professor, Department of Tumor Biology, University of Texas System Cancer Center, M. D. Anderson Hospital and Tumor Institute, Houston, Texas

Michiko Okamoto, Ph.D. — Professor of Pharmacology, Cornell University Medical College, New York, New York

James J. O'Leary, M.D., Ph.D. — Fellow, Department of Laboratory Medicine and Pathology, University of Minnesota, Veterans Administration Medical Center, Minneapolis, Minnesota

Byung H. Park, M.D. — Professor of Pediatrics, Microbiology, and Immunology, State University of New York, School of Medicine, Buffalo, New York

John T. Penniston, Ph.D. — Professor of Biochemistry, Mayo Medical School, Rochester, Minnesota

Paul G. Quie, M.D. — Professor of Pediatrics and Microbiology, University of Minnesota, Minneapolis, Minnesota

Michael S. Risley, Ph.D. — Assistant Professor of Anatomy, Cornell University Medical College, New York, New York

Toby C. Rodman, Ph.D. — Associate Professor of Anatomy, Cornell University Medical College; Adjunct Associate Professor, Rockefeller University, New York, New York

Frank H. Ruddle, Ph.D. — Professor of Cell Biology and Human Genetics, Yale University, New Haven, Connecticut

Lazar M. Schwartz, M.D. — Clinical Associate Professor of Pathology, College of Medicine and Dentistry of New Jersey, New Jersey Medical School, Newark, New Jersey; Veterans Administration Medical Center, East Orange, New Jersey

Herman S. Shapiro, Ph.D. — Associate Professor of Biochemistry, College of Medicine and Dentistry of New Jersey, New Jersey Medical School, Newark, New Jersey

Fritz Sieber, Ph.D. — Associate Professor of Medicine, Johns Hopkins University School of Medicine, Baltimore, Maryland

Akhouri A. Sinha, Ph.D. — Associate Professor of Genetics and Cell Biology, University of Minnesota, Veterans Administration Medical Center, Minneapolis, Minnesota

Hans L. Spiegelberg, M.D. — Member, Department of Immunopathology, Scripps Clinic, La Jolla, California

Clifford J. Steer, M.D.　　Clinical Associate, Division of Liver Diseases, National Institute of Arthritis, Metabolism, and Digestive Diseases, National Institutes of Health, Bethesda, Maryland

Randolph C. Steer, M.D.　　Post-Doctoral Fellow, Department of Laboratory Medicine and Pathology, University of Minnesota, Veterans Administration Medical Center, Minneapolis, Minnesota

Elton Stubblefield, Ph.D.　　Professor of Biology, The University of Texas System Cancer Center, M. D. Anderson Hospital and Tumor Institute, Houston, Texas

George P. Studzinski, M.D., Ph.D.　　Professor and Chairman, Department of Pathology, College of Medicine and Dentistry of New Jersey, New Jersey Medical School, Newark, New Jersey

Paul Szabo, Ph.D.　　Research Associate, Memorial Sloan Kettering Cancer Center, New York, New York

Roy V. Talmage, Ph.D.　　Professor of Surgery and Pharmacology, University of North Carolina, Medical School, Chapel Hill, North Carolina

Carole J. VanderWiel, Ph.D.　　Assistant Professor of Surgery, University of North Carolina, Medical School, Chapel Hill, North Carolina

Carlo M. Veneziale, M.D., Ph.D.　　Professor of Biochemistry, Mayo Medical School, Rochester, Minnesota

Michael J. Wilson, Ph.D.　　Assistant Professor of Laboratory Medicine and Pathology, University of Minnesota, Veterans Administration Medical Center, Minneapolis, Minnesota

Tatsuo Yamamoto, Ph.D.　　Assistant Professor of Bacteriology, Juntendo University, Tokyo, Japan

Chung S. Yang, Ph.D.　　Professor of Biochemistry, College of Medicine and Dentistry of New Jersey, New Jersey Medical School, Newark, New Jersey

Introduction

Miguel M. Azar

Cell biology is one of the youngest divisions of the life sciences. The term "cell" was first used by Robert Hooke in the latter half of the seventeenth century and derives from the Latin *cella*, which means a hollow space. The idea that living beings are composed of cells and their products was established more than a century ago by Schleiden and Schwann. With the contributions of Virchow, Flemming, Golgi, and others, it became increasingly apparent that the "hollow spaces" of living organisms were in fact not hollow at all, but, rather, structures composed of poorly understood parts that were capable of producing extraordinary changes under a variety of conditions. In 1892, Hertwig published *Die Zelle and das Gewebe*, which attempted to relate the structure and function of living cells in a coherent manner. With that, the branch of biological sciences then known as cytology and presently called cell biology came into being.

Professor Albert Claude, in the lecture he delivered in Stockholm in 1974, when he received the Nobel Prize for Physiology and Medicine, stated that "until 1930 or about then, biologists were in the same situation as astronomers and astrophysicists, who were permitted to see the objects of their interest, but not to touch them; the cell was as distant from us as the stars and galaxies were from them. More dramatic and frustrating was that we knew that the instrument was at our disposal; the microscope, so efficient in the nineteenth century, had ceased to be of any use, having reached, irremediably, the theoretical limit of its resolving power."

It is now 1980, and no longer are we unable to touch the objects of our scientific interest. No longer do we believe that the cell, that tiny unit of living matter, does not exert a great influence on the state of the whole organism. Biology and medicine have shown us the opposite, often with tragic clarity. Indeed, the cell is no longer as distant from us as the stars and galaxies. As the student of astronomy must learn to speak the language of his discipline, that is, to understand the concepts of measurement and interpretation of the structure and function of the physical universe, so must the student of cell biology learn to speak his own language, so that he also may know to measure and interpret the dimensions of the complicated and mysterious universe that is contained within every living cell.

How does the student learn to speak the language of cell biology? The answer seems clear. He must learn as he would learn to speak the language of a foreign country. First he must learn the simple vocabulary of the cell. Then he must learn to express those words in a meaningful way. Should he desire more than just fluency in his new language, that is, if he seeks to master it, he must develop a new skill—one that is more important; he must learn to ask questions and to approach their solutions. In that regard he must be well aware of the methods of investigation available to him. Thus, it seems appropriate that the first section of *Advanced Cell Biology* be devoted to principles of investigation.

Advances in cell fractionation and the use of the electron microscope have been of greatest importance in cell biology. Electrochemical, optical, and immunologic methods have allowed us to ascertain with great sensitivity and specificity the identities and characteristics of molecules that are fundamental to the maintenance of structure and function of many types of cells and tissues. Information derived from cell culture, X-ray, and resonance methods has added greatly to our understanding of cellular activities.

Once he is equipped with the powerful tool of understanding the application of investigative methods, if the student is to ask the most important questions, it is advantageous, if not essential, for him to understand what is presently known about the cell as a whole; that is, as a collection of many different structures, all of which accomplish specific tasks. He must endeavor to learn and to assimilate what is known about the plasma membrane, mitochondria, Golgi apparatus, cytoplasm, ribosomes, nucleus, nucleolus, and so forth. *Advanced Cell Biology* includes up-to-date discussions of the structural and functional aspects of these cellular components as they contribute to the normal and abnormal functions of living cells.

To the student unfamiliar with the role of the cell membrane, it will become readily apparent that the contribution of that "organelle" is far greater than that of merely serving as a barrier to contain the materials of the intracellular milieu, as scientists once believed. That the cell surface is a rich domain of receptors whose presence or absence and behavior confer critical features to cells is extensively described in Section 3.

The transport, secretion, and storage of molecules of biologic importance are discussed in Section 4. Where appropriate, mention is made of abnormalities in these functions, although abnormal cellular activity is not the main theme of the text.

The recurrent theme of *Advanced Cell Biology* is an emphasis on the structural and metabolic compartmentation that exists within living cells. It is this unique architecture of the cell that allows it to collectively effect its role in the function of the living organism at the systemic level.

Extensive consideration of the specific functions of the various subcellular components is included in Sections 4 through 11. Familiarity with the ultra-structural organization of the cell is of critical importance because most of the biochemical transformations occur at the molecular level. The student will receive an important message throughout the book: that the structure and function in cells are inseparable. Concise discussions of coenzymes, electron transport and phosphorylation mechanisms in mitochondria, microsomes, and microsomal oxidations are considered in Section 5.

The physiological aspects of the nucleus and of protein synthesis are considered in detail and with great clarity. Discussions of the forms and functions of DNA, its associated enzymes, and mechanisms of replication provide the student with a broad and coherent survey of the field. The nature of these and other events is considered in both prokaryote and eukaryote cells in some chapters, thus providing the student with information that may be used for comparison. Such combined information on both levels of cells is obtainable in few texts presently available.

Section 11, on the cell cycle, provides an extensive consideration of recent observations in this area. It should be of great interest to cell biologists as well as clinical scientists and clinicians who are involved in the application of chemotherapeutic agents used in the treatment of cancer. Finally, Section 12, dealing with the eukaryotic chromosome, provides excellent discussions of the chromosome concept in general, genetic control, somatic cell hybridization, cytologic mapping, and the molecular localization of DNA classes. Each of these areas is clearly defined in terms of its relevance to molecular genetics and is unquestionably important if one is to understand the normal and abnormal activity of the cell nucleus.

Throughout *Advanced Cell Biology* there are chapters that provide consideration of topics of interest in addition to the "core" topics included within the major sections. Some provide consideration of the molecular pathology of cells, whereas others discuss quantitative considerations of certain subjects. In each case, they provide concise and useful additions to the text. Of equal value is the abundance of recent review articles and books listed in the reference sections of some chapters of the book. These publications have been sited for their clarity, accuracy, and completeness; as such they are valuable to students of cell biology at both the intermediate and advanced levels.

Advanced Cell Biology is a collection of discussions prepared by scientists representing many of the related areas of biological science such as biochemistry, microbiology, genetics, physiology, pathology, pharmacology, and anatomy. The combination of these varied backgrounds and approaches to modern problems in cell biology provides the student with a unique mixture of viewpoints that it is hoped will serve as a source of intellectual pleasure and, above all, as an inspiration to further learning.

Acknowledgments

The editors dedicate this work to their beloved wives Paula and Silvia, in recognition of their continuing understanding and support. To all our contributing colleagues, we express our thanks. The efforts made in sharing their knowledge and experience in the respective fields will be appreciated by teachers and students alike. We also express our gratitude to the Research Committees of Veterans Administration Medical Center for their approval of this project.

The guidance of Mrs. Sara A. Finnegan, Chief Editor, Williams & Wilkins Co., Baltimore, MD., in the initial stage of preparation, and of Mr. Ashak M. Rawji, formerly Senior Editor, and of Ms. Susan Munger, present Senior Editor of Van Nostrand Reinhold, New York, is gratefully acknowledged. The excellent technical presentation is due to the personal involvement of a number of dedicated people of Van Nostrand, namely, Ms. Alberta W. Gordon, Managing Editor, Ms. Anne Dempsey, Asst. Editor, Mrs. Connie MacDonald, Copy Editor, and Mr. Fred Eckert, illustrator. Mr. Calvin A. Zamarelli, Ms. Judith Grace, Ms. Sheila Watson, Mrs. Juliette Ratner, and Mr. David F. Madden, Librarians, are also thanked for their assistance.

We are much obliged to the many authors and publishing houses who kindly granted permission to reproduce illustrations and tables from their publications. We have made every effort to trace the copyright holders for borrowed material. If inadvertently, we have overlooked any, we will be pleased to make the necessary corrections at the first available opportunity.

Lazar M. Schwartz
Miguel M. Azar

Contents

Section 3. Cell Receptors, Morley D. Hollenberg, Section Editor

Section 4. Transport, Secretion, and Storage, Khalil Ahmed, Section Editor

Section 5. Biological Oxidations and Energy Metabolism, Chung S. Yang, Section Editor

Section 6. DNA and Associated Enzymes, Theresa Campana, Section Editor

Section 7. DNA Replication and Associated Phenomena, Theresa Campana and Lazar M. Schwartz

Section 13.   Perspectives for Cell Biology, George P. Studzinski

ADVANCED CELL BIOLOGY

SECTION 1
PRINCIPLES OF
INVESTIGATION
IN CELL BIOLOGY

MIGUEL M. AZAR, SECTION EDITOR

1.1. The Isolation of Homogeneous Preparations of Mammalian Cells and of Intracellular Organelles

Carlo M. Veneziale and John T. Penniston

ISOLATION OF HOMOGENEOUS CELLS

In recent years freshly isolated preparations of pure cells have been used for experiments in which cellularly heterogeneous intact organs, slices, or minces would formerly have been used. Such preparations are valuable because measurements of ions, metabolites, proteins, or enzyme activities can be made on a single cell type without interference due to the presence of other kinds of cells. A second advantage of isolated pure cells is that multiple experiments and their controls can be done with the cells obtained from one organ, whereas usually only a single experiment is possible with an isolated perfused organ. These advantages have been realized in the study of the liver, which contains parenchymal epithelial, and other cells. Parenchymal cells isolated from liver have been especially useful for studies on the regulation of gluconeogenesis. For example, the use of parenchymal cells has made it easier to confirm and elaborate on observations made originally with perfused livers regarding the hormonal stimulation of gluconeogenesis from certain substrates (1–4).

The preparation of isolated cells has usually been accomplished by the digestion of tissues with proteolytic enzymes. By this method intact cells can be liberated from solid tissues. Because collagen is important in holding together most tissues, the enzyme collagenase is usually used. However, absolutely pure collagenase is ineffective in dispersing tissues because most organs also utilize proteins other than collagenase to hold cells together. Usually, crude preparations of collagenase containing additional proteolytic enzymes, not always identified, have been used. A common experience is that the amount of collagenase required varies from one lot to another. Recently, collagenases with specific impurities have become available (Worthington Enzymes, Freehold, New Jersey) so that preparations may be tailored to the tissue to be digested.

Whereas most tissues require enzymic digestion, some do not. Seminal vesicle is an example of tissue whose individual cell types can be isolated by a simple nonenzymic procedure; only blunt dissection is required to isolate the highly androgen-dependent columnar epithelium of guinea pig seminal vesicle from its underlying smooth muscle.

In this section we describe in some detail the isolation of intact homogeneous cells from four different tissues, thereby providing prototypic information of possible use in the isolation of other cells. In addition we sketch the isolation procedures for seven other cell lines (Table 1).

Preparation of Hepatic Parenchymal Cells

The earliest methods for the isolation of rat liver parenchymal cells employed mechanical disruption in the presence of chelating agents (5–8). Subsequently, enzyme digestion by perfusion and incubation with collagenase and hyaluronidase were reported (9–11). In 1972 Ingebretsen and Wagle (12) reported a very satisfactory enzyme-digestion method for the isolation of rat liver parenchymal cells in high yield. Theirs was the first preparation of cells to give rates of gluconeogenesis comparable to the rates given by isolated perfused liver. We have used the following modified enzyme digestion method (4).

Table 1. Isolation of Pure Cell Types.

CELL TYPES	BASIS OF ISOLATION PROCEDURE	REFERENCES
Nonparenchymal hepatic sinusoidal	Liver perfusion and incubation with pronase	25
Kidney glomeruli	Renal perfusion in situ; sieving of minced cortex through phosphor bronze sieve	26
Intestinal mucosa cells	Vibration of inverted intestine in special medium	27
Adrenal cortex cells	Mechanical agitation in trypsin solution	28
Mammary gland parenchymal cells	Collagenase digestion, sieving, and pelleting in hypertonic solution	29
Gastric parietal cells	Collagenase digestion of gastric mucosa, sieving, and density gradient centrifugation	30
Islets of Langerhans	Collagenase digestion of pancreas, dilution, and sedimentation under unit g	31, 32

Livers were excised from 24-hr-fasted male Sprague-Dawley rats (200–300 g) and were connected to a perfusion apparatus primed with 180 ml of perfusate, of which the first 50 ml was discarded. Perfusate was allowed to flow through the portal vein at 50 ml/min and consisted of calcium-free Krebs-Ringer bicarbonate solution gassed with 95% O_2:5% CO_2 and containing 10 mM sodium pyruvate and 25 mg collagenase (Boehringer Mannheim No. 15412). After 40 min of perfusion the liver was transferred to a plastic beaker containing 10 mg collagenase, 10 mM pyruvate, and 1.5% gelatin in 20 ml calcium-free Krebs-Ringer bicarbonate solution. Capsular tissue was teased away with a spatula, and the disrupted organ was incubated at 37°C for 15 min in a Dubnoff shaker gassed as before. The mixture was then filtered through nylon (250-μm mesh), which permitted only parenchymal cells to pass. The cells were isolated by centrifugation (50×g for 90 sec) and washed twice before being suspended (5.6% cells) in Krebs-Ringer bicarbonate solution containing 1.5% gelatin. Electron microscopic studies of this preparation indicated a homogeneous population of intact hepatocytes.

The cells thus prepared have been entirely satisfactory for studies of gluconeogenesis. In liver perfusion experiments reported by Ross et al. (13) with a mixture of 10 mM lactate and 3 mM pyruvate as substrate, glucose formation was 42 μmoles/g/30 min; with our isolated cells and a total lactate plus pyruvate concentration of only 3.6 mM (lac/pyr, 10/1), glucose formation was 11.3 μmoles/g/30 min, which was almost exactly comparable. Moreover, with cells prepared in this manner it was possible to demonstrate very subtle hormonal effects. For example, glucagon and epinephrine each stimulated gluconeogenesis from dihydroxyacetone, but of the two hormones only glucagon inhibited the assayable activity of phosphofructokinase and pyruvate kinase (4).

Isolation of Adipocytes

The classic contribution of Rodbell (14) on adipocyte isolation by collagenase digestion provided the opportunity for penetrating endocrine studies (15, 16). With the isolated cells, hormone responses, including stimulation of the adenylate cyclase system, could be studied. Development of the isolation procedure deserves special praise because it predated widespread application of enzyme digestion to many tissues for isolation of specific cells. In principle, cells are released from adipose tissue that has been incubated with crude collagenase (125–150 units/mg). Because they float, the adipocytes are easily separated from other cells and constituents. Greater detail and additional references pertinent to the procedure to be described can be found elsewhere (17).

Rats were killed by decapitation, and wetted epididymal fat pad or other fat tissue was minced and transferred to a 25-ml plastic vial containing 3 ml of a buffered incubation medium plus 0.1 ml of collagenase solution. The tissue was incubated with shaking for 1 hr at 37°C. The buffer consisted of 2% albumin in salt solution of the following composition: 125 mM NaCl, 5 mM KCl, 1.0 mM $CaCl_2$, 2.5 mM $MgCl_2$, 1.0 mM KH_2PO_4 and 25 mM tris-HCl of pH 7.4. The collagenase solution comprised 15–30 mg/1.0 ml buffered solution.

The incubation mixture was expressed by means of a plunger through nylon or silk screening, which dispersed clumps of fat cells and separated cells from unwanted stromal and undigested tissue. The cell suspension was centrifuged at approximately $130 \times g$ for 15 sec, and the material below the packed floating fat cells discarded by suction. The cells were washed twice in 5 ml of buffer and collected each time as the fraction found floating after centrifugation. The cells were sieved again as described above, collected, and after appropriate dilution were ready to use.

Isolation of Renal Tubules

Isolated tubules have been used for studies on Na^+ and K^+ flux, effects of parathormone, regulation of gluconeogenesis, metabolism of vitamin D metabolites, and uptake of sugars, amino acids, and p-amino-hippurate. Suspensions of separated rabbit renal tubules were first prepared in 1966 using collagenase (18). A modification of the original procedure yielded 500–750 mg of tubules per rabbit kidney (19). The suspension consisted mostly of proximal tubules, some isolated cells, and glomeruli. We present a similar procedure, which was originally used for the isolation of rat renal tubules (20). Light and electron microscopic examination of the preparation disclosed fragments of both proximal and distal tubules, of which denatured aqueous extracts had an ATP:ADP of 7.95:2.16 (nmoles/mg protein). In addition, when incubated with a variety of substrates, suspensions of the isolated tubules formed glucose at rates that compared favorably to control kidney cortex slices.

Under anesthesia, the abdominal aorta of a rat was exposed through a lower midline incision. Coeliac artery, abdominal aorta, and inferior vena cava were ligated just below the diaphragm. The kidneys were perfused through the abdominal aorta below the renal arteries with 10 ml of calcium-free Hanks' solution containing 4 mg collagenase and 10 mg hyaluronidase. After removal of the kidneys and excision of the medullary portions, cortices from four to six of the organs were combined and minced. The minces were suspended in 10 ml of fresh perfusion solution in a 250-ml Erlenmeyer flask and gassed with 95% O_2 : 5% CO_2 for 60 min at 37°C in a metabolic shaker. The contents of the flask were then diluted with cold saline-free Hanks' solution to make 50 ml and filtered first through a single layer of nylon stocking and then through nylon mesh of 60-μm pore size. The tubules were collected by centrifugation for 60 sec at 50×g and 4°C. The supernatant was discarded and the pellet washed twice with calcium-free Hanks' solution and collected each time by centrifugation at 30×g for 60 sec. The loosely packed pellet of tubules, which contained approximately 60–70 mg protein/ml, was then ready for use.

Isolation of Guinea Pig Seminal Vesicle Epithelium

The prostate has been used most widely for studies on the mechanisms of androgen action. However, it is cellularly heterogeneous, and its androgen-dependent epithelial cells comprise only 30–40% of the entire tissue. A strong contemporary interest in the mechanism(s) of androgen action stimulated a search for a more suitable experimental target tissue. Guinea pig seminal vesicle mucosa was evaluated because it consists of a monolayer of apparently homogeneous columnar epithelial cells, which are exquisitely sensitive to androgen deprivation and replacement. It proved to be a most suitable tissue (21). In vitro the isolated epithelium retains its impressive anabolic properties, including the capability to maintain an ATP:ADP:AMP of 2.5:0.3:0.2 (μmoles/g) and to synthesize small molecules such as citrate and fructose and large molecules such as its four intrinsic, soluble, secretory proteins. The proteins have been used as genetic markers in experiments designed to elaborate on the nature of androgen control (22, 23). The tissue was first isolated in 1955 by Levy and Szego (24), who evaluated some of its metabolic characteristics. What follows is a description of the isolation techniques that we found suitable for in vitro studies on energy metabolism, biosynthetic processes, steroid interconversions, and androgen binding.

Each animal was anesthetized with ether and shaved; the abdomen was then rapidly opened by a lower midline incision, the seminal vesicles were isolated and severed at their junction with the vas, and the animal was killed. The seminal vesicles were immediately plunged into ice-cold 0.154 M NaCl solution, slit open longitudinally with a pair of fine scissors, and swirled in the saline to dislodge the seminal plasma. The organs then were transferred immediately to a second cold saline bath and pinned to cardboard under the liquid surface. With the blunt edge of a pair of fine forceps, the mucosa was gently stripped from the muscle by pressure applied in the mucosa–muscle plane. Stripping of the mucosa of both seminal vesicles required approximately 2–3 min. The isolated epithelium was then ready for experimentation.

In Table 1 we have outlined the procedural approaches for the isolation of seven other cell types. Details and extensive references can be found elsewhere (*Methods in Enzymology*, Vol. 32, Part B, 1974). The worker who desires to isolate a new cell type can choose from among the techniques of enzyme digestion by perfusion or simple incubation, mechanical agitation, sieving, differential centrifugation, and density gradient centrifugation. Two or three techniques in combination have usually proved satisfactory for a particular cell from any given tissue. Current techniques are adequate for the isolation of homogeneous preparations of many different cell types.

In isolating a new cell type, it is necessary to offer evidence that the resultant cells are viable; most authors offer the exclusion of trypan blue as proof of cell viability, and in some cases this may be adequate. More compelling evidence would be proof of normal energy metabolism, as, for example, the maintenance of a normal ATP:ADP ratio and total adenine nucleotide concentrations in cells provided adequately with substrate, oxygen, and pH buffering capacity. Alternatively the demonstration of energy-requiring metabolic activity might suffice.

ISOLATION OF ORGANELLES

In order to utilize tissue for the preparation of subcellular fractions, it is necessary, first of all, to disperse the tissue by mechanical means. This is usually accomplished by (listed in order of increasing severity) homogenization with a rotating pestle, homogenization with a rotating blade, or sonication. These methods not only disperse the tissue, but also break open the cells. When the starting material consists of cells that are already dispersed, the cells may be broken open by any of the mechanical methods mentioned above, or by osmotic lysis.

Rotating Pestle

Most soft tissues, such as liver, kidney, central nervous system, reproductive, adipose, lung, and endocrine tissue, can be effectively homogenized by a rotating pestle. Tissues of this sort should, in general, not be treated by more severe methods, which will cause unnecessary disruption of the organelles and perhaps destruction of biological function.

Rotating-Blade Blender

Some tissues require more stringent treatment than can be provided by rotating-pestle homogenization. Muscle tissue is tough and must be dispersed by a high-speed rotating-blade blender. Often a special blender of unusual efficiency (a polytron) is used for this purpose. The presence of myofibrils in large numbers interferes with the isolation of most other components of muscle cells. It is necessary, therefore, to remove the myofibrils either by filtration through a set of wire screens or by extraction with high concentrations of salt such as potassium chloride or lithium bromide (33).

Sonication

Platelets are difficult to disrupt because of their small size and special properties. It is generally necessary to employ sonication or to use homogenization with an ultratight pestle in order to disrupt platelets. Although sonication is used to disrupt platelets, it is more widely used to break up organelles than cells.

Lysis

Osmotic lysis has a limited usefulness because it usually does not disrupt cells sufficiently to allow subsequent separation of membrane fractions. It is widely used for preparation of the plasma membranes of human erythrocytes, in which there are no intracellular membranes to cause contamination. This technique has the advantage that the resultant "ghosts" retain the morphology of the intact cell. Similar "ghosts" have been prepared from adipose cells, but that preparation is contaminated with other membranes which have been retained within the plasma membrane envelope.

General Comments

The most commonly used methods for separating subcellular particles are differential centrifugation, which is based on the rate of sedimentation of the particles through the suspending solution, and density gradient centrifugation, which is based on the flotation of the subcellular particles in dense sucrose solutions. Table 2 shows some examples of the sizes of intact subcellular organelles, the pelleting force required to bring the particles down, and their equilibrium density as determined by flotation in sucrose solutions. This table is shown mainly as background for discussion, since the parameters given vary from species to species and even more drastically from organ to organ. Although in Table 2 and throughout this chapter we have discussed centrifugal forces and times without regard to specific types of rotors, the worker who desires to reproduce the published results should follow the original procedures as closely as possible. Such factors as the tube angle and size and whether a swinging bucket or fixed-angle rotor is used can influence the degree of separation; even in the same rotor, the same total $g \cdot min$ applied at high speed and at low speed may produce different results. The influence of rotor parameters on separations has been discussed by Gram (36).

Table 2. Characteristics of Cell Fractions from Rat Liver (34, 35).

FRACTION	PROTEIN (%)	DIAMETER (μ)	PELLETING FORCE ($g \cdot MIN$)	EQUILIBRIUM DENSITY (g/ML)	CHARACTERISTIC ENZYME ACTIVITIES
Liver cells	100	15–20	10^3	~1.20	
Nuclei	15	5–11	5–10×10^3	~1.32	DNA polymerase, RNA polymerases, high DNA content
Mitochondria	25	0.7–1.1	10^5	1.18–1.21	Cytochrome oxidase, succinate-cytochrome c reductase
Golgi apparatus	2	1–3	3×10^5	1.06–1.14	N-acetylglucosamine galactosyltransferase
Lysosomes	2	0.4–0.6	4×10^5	1.20–1.22	Acid phosphatase
Peroxisomes	2.5	0.4–0.6	4×10^5	1.22–1.24	Catalase, urate oxidase
Rough endoplasmic reticulum	12	0.05–0.2	3–10×10^6	1.13–1.25	Rotenone-insensitive NADH–cytochrome c reductase, glucose-6-phosphatase, protein synthesis
Smooth endoplasmic reticulum	8	0.05–0.3	3–10×10^6	1.10–1.20	Rotenone-insensitive NADH–cytochrome c reductase, glucose-6-phosphatase
Plasma membranes	2				Ouabain-sensitive Na^+-K^+ ATPase, adenylcyclas, hormone and lectin binding
from "nuclear" fraction		2–10	10^4	1.16–1.18	
from "microsomal" fraction		0.1–0.7	10^5–10^7	1.12–1.15	
Soluble proteins	30	<.01	$>10^8$	~1.30	Soluble enzymes, such as lactic dehydrogenase

It can be seen from Table 2 that the pelleting force required to bring particles down is inversely proportional to the size of the particles, whereas the equilibrium density is independent of the size of the particles. Because of the relationship between pelleting force and particle size, the distribution of subcellular organelles after centrifugation will depend on the degree to which the organelles have been broken up by homogenization. The pelleting forces given refer to the subcellular organelles in their most intact and most easily sedimented state. Some organelles are easily broken by homogenization, and therefore require a high pelleting force. The rough and smooth endoplasmic reticulum, for example, are a network of membranes extending throughout the cell; it is impossible to homogenize a cell and release its contents without breaking this network. Therefore, the endoplasmic reticulum always appears in homogenates as very small vesicles that pellet with difficulty.

While the investigator has little control over the size of isolated endoplasmic reticulum vesicles, the plasma membranes and the Golgi apparatus can be separated in varying degrees of intactness, depending upon the homogenization. The Golgi apparatus can be obtained nearly intact by a very gentle homogenization with a loose-fitting pestle, whereas more vigorous homogenization generally causes it to appear as a contaminant of the microsomal fraction. Similarly, the plasma membranes can appear both in the nuclear fraction and in the microsomal fraction, with the distribution depending, to some extent, upon the intensity of the homogenization.

Another factor that governs the sedimentation of organelles is the concentration of Mg^{2+} and Ca^{2+}. Too much of these ions, particularly Ca^{2+}, can cause aggregation, resulting in more rapid sedimentation and difficulty in the separation of organelles. On the other hand, in some situations, omission of Mg^{2+} can cause partial disintegration of membranes, leading to an inadequate preparation. These factors must be balanced against each other, and the appropriate solution found for every situation. Thus the development of an isolation procedure for a particular organelle is an art that must be adapted to each organ, each organelle, and each species.

The development of such an isolation procedure usually begins with the division of the cell homogenate into four fractions, representing the organelles which pellet with increasing difficulty. These fractions are nuclear, mitochondrial, microsomal, and soluble; the first three spin down at 10^4, 10^5, and 10^7 $g \cdot min$ respectively, while the soluble fraction is not pelleted. The nuclear fraction usually contains nuclei, plasma membranes, and intact cells, whereas the mitochondrial fraction contains predominantly mitochondria, with lysosomes and peroxisomes. The composition of the microsomal fraction is more complex, and the difficulties facing those who attack it have been discussed (37). Rough endoplasmic reticulum can be pelleted from the microsomal fraction by further centrifugation. However, this separation is imperfect, and methods utilizing preferential interaction of the rough endoplasmic reticulum with substances such as CsCl, have been developed to provide better separation. Depending on the organ used, the smooth microsomal fraction which remains in suspension contains various organelles. When the smooth microsomal fraction has been obtained from liver, it contains predominantly smooth endoplasmic reticulum, whereas fractionation of cells from other tissues may yield microsomal fractions containing mainly Golgi elements or plasma membranes (37). The subfractionation of smooth microsomal fractions is usually accomplished by density gradient centrifugation.

Alterations in the Properties of Subcellular Components Due to the Isolation Procedure

Enzymic Activity.   The membrane isolation techniques discussed in this chapter yield organelles with enzymic activities of a type and amount appropriate to the organelles' function. However, because the enzymic activity in situ is not known, it is difficult to evaluate changes caused by the isolation procedure. Frequently, the changes in enzymic activity caused by a particular technique are understood only after a superior technique has been developed. An example of this is shown in Table 3; plasma membranes isolated directly from adipose tissue have higher enzymic activities than those isolated from collagenase-treated adipocytes.

Morphology.   Since the morphology of organelles in situ is known, a direct comparison with isolated organelles is possible. The morphological integrity of isolated organelles is rather variable; nuclei and mitochondria can be isolated in a form that appears to be nearly intact, and recent work on Golgi apparatus (38) has succeeded in obtaining the characteristic form of Golgi. Because it is an enclosing membrane, the plasma membrane is difficult to prepare in a morphologically intact form. Only from mammalian erythrocytes, which have no internal organelles, is this possible. From other tissues it is possible to obtain plasma membranes as large sheets, or as small closed vesicles that have been chopped up by homogenization. The various subcellular granules, such as chromaffin granules, lysosomes, and peroxisomes, can be isolated in a morphologically intact form, but the smooth and rough endoplasmic reticulum are disintegrated by preparation methods. The effect of preparation methods on the internal morphology of mitochondria is discussed below.

Permeability and Fluidity.   More subtle alterations are the changes in the permeability of the membrane and in the fluidity of the phospholipid bilayer portion of the membrane. In most membranes, these parameters cannot be compared between in situ and isolated organelles, but a comparison is

Table 3. Isolation of Plasma Membranes.

STARTING MATERIAL	BASIS	COMMENTS	REFERENCES
Erythrocytes	15:1 hemolysate of washed red cells, 20 mM PO_4, pH 7.4.	Repeated centrifugation (8×10^5 $g \cdot min$) in 20 mM PO_4, pH 7.4 until white.	Cleanest and easiest plasma membrane preparation.	54, 55
Liver	"Nuclear" fraction, pelleted from rat liver homogenate in (1.5×10^4 $g \cdot min$) $NaHCO_3$ medium (1 mM, pH 7.5).	Wash $3 \times$ (10^4 $g \cdot min$); take upper part of pellet each time; then suspend in sucrose to d = 1.20; step gradient formed above suspension; spin 6×10^6 $g \cdot min$; collect from d 1.16/1.18 interface.	A widely used method; many others available and may give cleaner membranes.	56
Skeletal muscle	10^4 $g \cdot min$ supernatant from polytron homogenate in sucrose EDTA medium.	Treat overnight with 0.5 M LiBr; spin for 2.5×10^4 $g \cdot min$, recover super, and pellet membranes at 3×10^5 $g \cdot min$. Resuspend and pellet $2 \times$ more. Suspend in 50% sucrose; step gradient (30–50% sucrose) formed above suspension, and spun 10^7 $g \cdot min$.	Gives a plasma membrane with the expected properties; see ref. 19 for alternative. Large amount of myofibrils causes difficulty.	57
Adipose cells	Microsomal supernatant from adipose tissue homogenate in sucrose-EDTA medium, after 4×10^5 $g \cdot min$.	Pellet at 6×10^6 $g \cdot min$, resuspend, layer atop sucrose (d = 1.13), and spin (5×10^6 $g \cdot min$). Plasma membranes stay atop sucrose.	Preparation direct from adipose tissue gives higher activity of membrane enzymes than preparation from dispersed cells.	58
Cultured cells	Total particulate pellet from fibroblast homogenate in isotonic saline (4×10^6 $g \cdot min$).	Suspend in 68% sucrose, and form linear sucrose gradient above sample. Spin (9×10^7 $g \cdot min$), recover top two bands, pellet (8×10^6 $g \cdot min$), and resuspend.	A method based on toughening of the membrane with various reagents is also available (22).	59

possible in the erythrocyte. Highly purified erythrocyte membranes have lost their impermeability to Na^+ and K^+ (39), and their fluidity, as measured by spin-labeled phosphatidylcholine, is greater (40). It is possible to make resealed erythrocyte membranes, with the fluidity and Na^+-K^+ permeability of intact erythrocytes, but only by restoring the lysed ghosts to isotonicity in the presence of the diluted cell contents, a procedure that seals much hemoglobin into the membrane (41).

Plasma Membranes

The isolation of pure plasma membranes presents difficulties because of the existence of specialized regions of varying composition on different portions of the surface of a cell. Because of the different properties of these specialized regions, plasma membranes are found in more than one fraction upon centrifugation of cellular homogenates. Their position depends upon the extent to which they are broken up (whether small vesicles or large sheets), and upon their density, which is increased by the presence of tight junctions.

One laboratory has recently reported the division of the plasma membranes of rat liver into three categories (42). This study, using complex preparative procedures, found that the plasma membranes that face the bloodstream were in a "microsomal" fraction and banded at the relatively light density of 1.12–1.13 on sucrose gradients. The plasma membranes that face the bile duct were also of low density but were isolated from a "nuclear" pellet. The plasma membranes from the regions of intercellular contact also came from a "nuclear" pellet, but had a heavier density in sucrose gradients (1.16–1.18). It is apparent from this study that the isolation of all of the components of plasma membrane is likely to be a very complex procedure, and the relatively simple procedures used to date have probably isolated only a particular portion of the plasma membrane. The investigator who wishes to prepare plasma membranes is, therefore, advised to consult the literature on the tissue of interest.

The traditional marker enzymes for plasma membranes have been 5'-nucleotidase and alkaline phosphodiesterase. These enzymes, which are easy to assay, are present in high specific activity in plasma membranes. However, recent work (43, 44) has shown that the localization of hormone or lectin binding sites, adenylate cyclase, and the ouabain-sensitive $Na^+ + K^+$ ATPase are better markers of plasma membranes. Radio-labeled hormones or lectins appear to be useful for the detection of small amounts of plasma membranes (41); this is an advantage, because the yield of plasma membranes from cells is often quite small, and the availability of the cells themselves may be limited.

Table 3 summarizes some simple procedures for making plasma membranes from the more abundant mammalian tissues. The reader should bear in mind the many pitfalls that exist in the preparation of plasma membranes. In addition to the methods summarized in this table, there also exist methods for the isolation of plasma membranes from pancreas (44, 45), kidney (46), HeLa cells (47), platelets (48, 49), synaptosomes (50, 51), thyroid (52), and myelinated nerve (53).

Isolation of Nuclei

Many of the techniques used for the isolation of nuclei are modifications of that designed by Chauveau et al. (60), who homogenized rat liver in 2.2 M sucrose and centrifuged at 40,000×g for 60 min. Purified nuclei formed the pellet because they have a density greater than that of the sucrose solution. Other cytoplasmic components appeared as floating debris because they are less dense than the sucrose solution. For example, mitochondria, lysosomes, and microbodies have densities of 1.18–1.24 at 4°C, whereas 2.29 M sucrose solution has a density of 1.291 at 20°C and 1.300 at 0°C (61). The original technique had the drawback that homogenization was difficult in the dense sucrose solution, and cell breakage was often incomplete. The method of Maggio et al. (62) addressed this particular problem. The tissue was first homogenized in 0.88 M sucrose containing 1.5 mM $CaCl_2$, filtered through cheesecloth, layered over 2.2 M sucrose containing 0.3 mM $CaCl_2$, and centrifuged at 53,000×g for 90 min. The pellet was resuspended in 2.0 ml 0.88 M sucrose and layered over 1.5 ml 1.5 M sucrose, which was layered over 2.2 M sucrose. Centrifugation at 30,000×g for 45 min gave highly purified preparations. Either Ca^{2+} or Mg^{2+} was effective in preventing clumping, swelling, and fragmentation. The use of a neutral detergent such as Triton X-100 during the preparation, for example, during the first resuspension, would eliminate the outer nuclear membrane and its attached ribosomes should this be necessary for a given experiment.

The method of Chauveau et al. (60) or some modification thereof appears to be the best general approach to nuclei isolation. Satisfactory preparations of nuclei from many different tissues have thus been obtained. This method, even in its most simple form, gave relatively well-purified nuclei from guinea pig seminal vesicle epithelium (21, 63). A description of the method as we applied it to this tissue follows: The epithelium, usually 700 mg, was finely minced and homogenized in 25 ml of the homogenization medium with a Potter-Elvehjem homogenizer, using two to four strokes at 300 rpm. The composition of the medium was as follows: 2.2 M sucrose, 25 mM KCl, 5 mM $MgCl_2$, and 5 mM tris-HCl, pH 7.5. The homogenate was filtered through a double layer of cheesecloth, layered on top of 15 ml pure homogenization medium, and centrifuged for 75 min at 40,000×g in a Beckman SW 27 rotor. The supernatant was discarded by suction, and the pellet resuspended in a storage solution composed of 25% glycerol (w/v), 1 mM $MgCl_2$, and 10 mM tris-HCl, pH 7.9. The pellet was then homogenized by hand in a small Potter-Elvehjem homogenizer and could be stored at $-25°C$ until needed. Nuclei prepared in this way were satisfactory for studies on the assayable activity of RNA polymerases.

For suggestions on how to improve yield and purity and for a complete resume of methods to be found in the literature, the reader is referred to Roodyn (64) and Spelsberg et al. (65).

Isolation of Mitochondria

Mitochondria are characterized by the presence of any one of several enzymes unique to the inner membrane; usually cytochrome oxidase is chosen. The purity of a mitochondrial preparation can be assessed by thin section electron microscopy, since mitochondria have a characteristic morphology. The morphology of mitochondria as they exist in the ascites tumor cell has been shown to depend on the metabolic state of the cells. Cells respiring at a resting rate contained mitochondria in the orthodox configuration, that is with an expanded matrix and a narrow intracristal space, whereas cells in which oxidative phosphorylation was stimulated contained condensed mitochondria, that is, with a greatly contracted matrix and an expanded intracristal space (66).

Procedures for the isolation of mitochondria have been developed for many tissues (67). Mitochondria are usually isolated under conditions that give P/O ratios near 3 for NADH-linked substrate oxidation and a high respiratory control ratio. These conditions include the use of 0.25 M sucrose in the preparation, which gives condensed mitochondria, similar to those observed in the living cell during active phosphorylation of ADP.

Mitochondria are usually prepared from heart or liver. Those from liver can be prepared quickly in good yield, with a high respiratory control ratio. However, liver mitochondria are unstable, showing changes when stored longer than 2–4 hr in the cold, and thus are not usually suitable as a starting material for preparing submitochondrial fractions. On the other hand, the preparation of heart mitochondria requires more time, and yields fewer mitochondria; also, those obtained have a lower respiratory control ratio. However, they are stable, and their protein composition includes a higher proportion of respiratory chain and phosphorylation components. Thus, they have been preferred for the purification of the various components of the oxidative phosphorylation system. The phosphorylating ATPase (68), phosphorylation cofactors (69), and electron transfer complexes (70) have been purified from heart mitochondria. For the preparation of large quantities of heart mitochondria both large swinging bucket centrifuges and continuous flow centrifuges are desirable (71).

The small-scale preparation of heart mitochondria from slaughter-house material (72) will be described. For this procedure, one or two beef hearts are obtained from the slaughter house and chilled immediately. Surrounding fat and connective tissue are removed; right and left ventricular tissue are cut into chunks and passed through a cold meat grinder. The ground beef heart is suspended in 0.25 M sucrose, 0.01 M Tris, pH 7.8. The pH must be continually raised to 7.8 throughout the procedure because the tissue produces acid. The suspended ground beef heart is freed from the sucrose solution by squeezing in cheesecloth. The neutralized ground beef heart is then homogenized in the sucrose–Tris medium utilizing a loose-fitting rotating pestle in a Potter-Elvejhem homogenizer, neutralized, and centrifuged for 24,000 $g \cdot$ min to remove the nuclear fraction. The supernatant is saved, and its lipid granules are removed by filtering through cheesecloth. The filtrate is then centrifuged for 100,000 $g \cdot$ min, and the supernatant discarded. The buff-colored layer on the top of the pellet is discarded. The remaining dark-brown layer, which consists of "heavy" beef heart mitochondria, is resuspended and recentrifuged. For maximum purity a third centrifugation can be performed. The average yield of intact heavy beef heart mitochondria is about 1 mg protein/g wet weight of starting ground beef heart.

Methods for the isolation of liver mitochondria are based on the method of Schneider (73), which has been evaluated by Hogeboom (74). The medium usually used is 0.25 M sucrose buffered to a pH of 7.0–7.4, although some workers have used solutions of mannitol. The liver is homogenized with a rotating pestle in cold medium until the tissue is fully dispersed. The homogenate is centrifuged for 6000 $g \cdot$ min and the supernatant fraction retained. Some mitochondria may be recovered from the pellet by resuspension and repelleting. The combined supernatants are then centrifuged for 75,000 $g \cdot$ min and the supernatant, together with any lightly packed pink microsomes, discarded. Mitochondria thus obtained may be purified by one or two further washes with cold medium.

Procedures such as the one just described give liver mitochondria with a condensed matrix, but a more recent method (75), in which the liver is homogenized with clean sand, involves exposure of the mitochondria to the sucrose medium for only 1 hr or less, which appears to result in mitochondria with an orthodox configuration.

Endoplasmic Reticulum

In liver cells, the microsomal fraction is dominated by smooth and rough endoplasmic reticulum membranes. The usual preparations of these membranes are well established and widely used despite the modest amounts of contamination by plasma membranes, Golgi apparatus, and so forth.

In preparing the endoplasmic reticulum from liver, the commonly used methods are based either on the method of Rothschild (76) or the similar method of Dallner (77). The Rothschild method starts with a homogenate from liver in 0.88 M sucrose. The nuclear fraction is then removed by two centrifugations of 2.5×10^6 $g \cdot min$ each. The supernatant is diluted with water and lysed over a 1.31 M sucrose solution. After centrifugation for 5×10^7 $g \cdot min$, the smooth microsomes gather at the interface at the top of the 1.31 M sucrose solution, while the rough microsomes are pelleted to the bottom of the tube. The smooth microsomes can be removed from the interface, resuspended, and pelleted.

The method of Dallner (77) is rather similar, except that the supernatant fluid from the low-speed centrifugation is made 15 mM in CsCl, and the centrifugation over the 1.30 M sucrose cushion needs to be only 1.5×10^7 $g \cdot min$. The shorter centrifugation time is much more convenient, and is made possible by the Cs^+-caused aggregation of the rough endoplasmic reticulum. A critical discussion of the merits of the two methods has been presented by Gram (36).

The sarcoplasmic reticulum in muscle is a highly specialized form of smooth endoplasmic reticulum. The reticulum from skeletal muscle can be purified by differential centrifugation alone, since the amount of plasma membrane and Golgi apparatus that might contaminate it is minimal. However, the removal of myofibrils requires salt extraction of the microsomal fraction. A widely used procedure is that of Martonosi (78). In this procedure, the skeletal muscle is homogenized with a blender in 0.1 M KCl buffered at pH 7.3. Myofibrils are removed by centrifugation for 2×10^4 $g \cdot min$, and mitochondria are then removed by centrifugation for 1.6×10^5 $g \cdot min$. The microsomal fraction containing the sarcoplasmic reticulum is then brought down by centrifugation for 1.7×10^6 $g \cdot min$. The microsomal pellet is resuspended, the suspension made 0.6 M in KCl and incubated 1 hr in the cold. This extraction with high salt dissolves the myofibrils, and the sarcoplasmic reticulum can then be pelleted by centrifugation at 4.8×10^6 $g \cdot min$. This extraction and centrifugation can be repeated once again, and the final pellet is a reasonably pure sample of sarcoplasmic reticulum.

Meissner (48) has developed a technique using linear gradients to make a more highly purified preparation of sarcoplasmic reticulum; he has also been able to fractionate sarcoplasmic reticulum vesicles into light and heavy fractions by isopycnic centrifugation in a linear sucrose gradient. The heavy vesicles contained interior soluble proteins, whereas the light vesicles were empty (79).

Isolation of Lysosomes

By density equilibration in sucrose gradient the lysosomes of normal liver were found to have a median density of 1.22 (80). The median density of mitochondria has been reported to be 1.19, and of peroxisomes, about 1.24. The size and density of lysosomes can be changed by the parenteral administration of Dextran 500 or Triton Wr-1339 to intact animals. Such foreign substances when taken into cells by endocytosis accumulate within lysosomes. Triton WR-1339, which accumulates in liver lysosomes, decreases their density to approximately 1.11 (81, 82). Thus, by sucrose gradient centrifugation, lysosomes from Triton WR-1339 treated rats can be separated from mitochondria and peroxisomes, the organelles that contaminate lysosomes prepared by differential centrifugation alone.

In Table 4 we present the procedures for the isolation of both liver and kidney lysosomes. Purification of the latter also requires density gradient centrifugation, but alteration of density by pretreatment with Triton WR-1339 is unnecessary. The equilibrium density of kidney lysosomes differs greatly from that of kidney mitochondria: 1.21–1.26 for the lysosomes and 1.17–1.19 for the mitochondria (85). Acid phosphatase, which is abundant in lysosomes of both liver and kidney, has served as a major marker enzyme in purification procedures.

Isolation of Granules

Only recently has a significant amount of literature appeared on the isolation of intracellular granules from a variety of tissues. Secretory granule-containing tissues, being so specialized and uniquely differentiated, vary greatly from one another in many respects. Therefore, it is difficult to generalize about methods except to say that differential centrifugation and density gradient centrifugation of appropriate cell fractions have provided the main approach. In Table 5 we summarize the salient features of procedures that have been applied to six tissues, hoping thereby to offer useful prototypic approaches to the isolation of granules in other tissues also.

Concluding Comments

In this chapter we have provided a guide to procedures for the isolation of organelles used by a majority of cell biologists and biochemists. The procedures utilize a wide array of techniques that may also be applicable in the preparation of the less commonly studied cell components. We have not presented procedures for the isolation of all the organelles found in eukaryotic animal cells. Those omitted include nucleoli (95), nuclear membranes (96),

Table 4. Isolation of Lysosomes.

STARTING MATERIAL	BASIS OF SEPARATION	COMMENTS	REFERENCES
Livers (90 g) of Triton WR-1339 injected rats	(1) Supernatant diluted with equal volume of 0.25 M sucrose, 340,000 g·min applied. Pellet suspended and recentrifuged.	Pellet comprised of mitochondria, peroxisomes, and lysosomes.	83
20% homogenate free of nuclei, plasma membranes, and unbroken cells by 5000–6500 g·min centrifugation.	(2) Pellet suspended in 45% (w/v) sucrose (1 ml sucrose:1 g liver), of which 30 ml forms bottom layer of a gradient, 20 ml 34.5% sucrose the intermediate and 10 ml 14.3% sucrose the top layer. Centrifuged at 25,000 rpm for 120 min in SW 25.2 rotor (Beckman-Spinco).	Lysosomes float to interface of upper two sucrose solutions. Only 5% of the isolated lysosomal protein is mitochondrial, and 1% is peroxisome in origin.	
Cortices of six rat kidneys	(1) Supernatant centrifuged at 9000×g for 3 min.	Results in three layers. Upper referred to as brush border fraction; white in color. Middle consists of mitochondria; yellow-brown. Lowest layer comprised of semipurified lysosomes; dark brown.	84, 85
11% homogenate of bloodless cortical tissue free of nuclei, plasma membrane, and unbroken cells by centrifugation at 143×g for 10 min.	(2) Semipurified fraction suspended in 2–3 ml and layered onto 24–25 ml of continuous gradient made from 2.1 M sucrose (11.7 ml) and 1.1 M sucrose (13.0 ml). Centrifuged 113,000×g for 150 min.	Lowermost of three bands consists of purified lysosomes.	

Table 5. Isolation of Granules.

	STARTING MATERIAL	BASIS FOR SEPARATION	COMMENTS	REFERENCES
Pancreatic β granules	800×g supernatant of homogenized islets.	Centrifugation on discontinuous gradient of 0.6 M sucrose 1% ficoll and 2.0 M sucrose 5% ficoll for 5×10^5 g·min.	Yields intact granules with some E.R. vesicles, M_w, and lysozymes.	86
Adrenal chromaffin granules	380×g supernatant fraction of homogenized medulla.	After centrifugation at 8720×g, supernatant centrifuged 80,790×g. Pellet suspended in 0.3 M sucrose, layered on 1.6 M sucrose and centrifuged 80,790×g.	Yields pink sediment containing granules.	87–89
Anterior pituitary	10,500×g supernatant of homogenized bovine glands.	After centrifugation at 140,000×g, sediment suspended and layered on discontinuous ficoll gradient.	Larger and denser granules containing prolactin and growth hormone separated.	90
	900×g supernatant of homogenized bovine glands centrifuged at 5000×g, and supernatant passed through millipore filters.	Filtrate centrifuged 140,000×g; pellet suspended, layered on 10–40% continuous sucrose gradient, and centrifuged 75,000×g. An intermediate fraction diluted, layered on 50–55% gradient, and centrifuged 105,000×g.	Yields pellet of small granules containing TSH, FSH, and FH.	91
Melanin granules	600×g supernatant of homogenized mouse melanoma tissue.	11,000×g sediment suspended in dilute sucrose, layered on 1.7 M sucrose, and centrifuged 37,000×g. Sediment suspended and layered on 2.0 M sucrose and centrifuged 37,000×g.	Final centrifugation into 2.0 M sucrose removes contaminating mitochondria from sedimented granules.	92

Table 5. Continued

STARTING MATERIAL	BASIS FOR SEPARATION	COMMENTS	REFERENCES
Mast cell granules	Mast cells from thorax and abdomen lyzed in water and centrifuged $350\times g$.	Supernatant centrifuged $3000\times g$.	Sedimented granules retain capacity to store inorganic cations and biogenic amines.	93
Posterior pituitary granules	$1100\times g$ supernatant of homogenized bovine glands; centrifuged $3900\times g$.	Supernatant centrifuged at $26,000\times g$; sediment suspended and layered on continuous nonlinear sucrose density gradient from 1.3 to 3.0 M.	Both vasopressin and oxytocin granules isolated above densest portion of gradient.	94

chromosomes (97), and tight junctions (51). Because of space limitations we could not provide a resume of the techniques employed for the purification of these organelles but instead supply appropriate references.

Several specific comments concerning the experimental use of purified organelles for purposes other than protein purification work are indicated. It is generally true that the knowledge to be gained from experiments that utilize a pure preparation of an organelle is limited by the imagination of the investigator with respect to his experimental design and by the qualitative and quantitative analytical techniques available to him. Perhaps a more compelling limitation rests with the fact that when removed from its native environment the organelle usually behaves in a manner quite different from its physiologic behavior. The "biochemical face" it assumes depends both on the degree to which the isolated organelle retains its physiological morphology, permeability, and enzymic activities, and on the generally unnatural environment to which it is subjected. For example, isolated mitochondria will convert pyruvate to malate and citrate or to acetoacetate, depending on the concentrations of K^+ and Pi in the external medium (98). In addition to the regulation exerted by ionic constituents of the medium, the effects of other components, such as sucrose, mannitol, Tris, and proteins, remain undefined. Thus the investigator is at great risk. He may make observations dictated primarily by his experimental conditions and fail to make the more correct observations that are forthcoming only when the intracellular milieu has been more precisely simulated. From these comments one can appreciate the fact that proper use of isolated organelles creates as many difficulties as those, already discussed, that arise from their isolation. What is the nature of the intracellular environment? What are all the physiologic effector molecules for a given process under study? What are all the mechanisms of regulation? These questions also present a major challenge.

REFERENCES

1. Veneziale, C. M. 1971. *Biochemistry* 10:3443.
2. Veneziale, C. M. 1972. *Biochemistry* 11:3286.
3. Veneziale, C. M., and Lohmar, P. 1973. *J. Biol. Chem.* 248:7786.
4. Veneziale, C. M., Deering, N. G., and Thompson, H. J. 1976. *Mayo Clin. Proc.* 51:624.
5. Anderson, W. G. 1953. *Science* 117:627.
6. Longmuir, I. S., and Rees, W. A. 1962. *Nature (London)* 177:453.
7. Jacob, S. T., and Bhargava, P. M. 1962. *Exp. Cell Res.* 27:453.
8. Takeda, Y., Ichihara, A., Tanioka, H., and Inoue, H. 1964. *J. Biol. Chem.* 239:3590.
9. Howard, R. B., Christensen, A. K., Gibbs, F. A., and Pesch, L. A. 1967. *J. Cell Biol.* 35:675.
10. Howard, R. B., and Pesch, L. A. 1968. *J. Biol. Chem.* 243:3105.
11. Berry, M. N., and Friend, D. S. 1969. *J. Cell. Biol.* 43:506.
12. Ingebretsen, W. R., and Wagle, S. R. 1972. *Biochem. Biophys. Res. Commun.* 47:403.

13. Ross, B. D., Hems, R., Freedland, R. A., and Krebs, H. A. 1967. *Biochem. J.* 105:869.
14. Rodbell, M. 1964. *J. Biol. Chem.* 239:375.
15. Birnbaumer, L., and Rodbell, M. 1969. *J. Biol. Chem.* 244:3477.
16. Rodbell, M., Birnbaumer, L., and Pohl, S. L. 1970. *J. Biol. Chem.* 245:718.
17. Rodbell, M., and Krishna, G. 1974. *Methods Enzymol.* 31:103.
18. Burg, M. B., and Orloff, J. 1966. *Am. J. Physiol.* 211:1005.
19. Rorive, G., and Kleinzeller, A. 1974. *Methods Enzymol.* 32:658.
20. Nagata, N., and Rasmussen, H. 1970. *Biochim. Biophys. Acta* 215:1.
21. Veneziale, C. M., Steer, R. C., and Buchi, K. 1977. In *Regulatory Mechanisms Affecting Gonadal Hormone Action, Advances in Sex Hormone Research,* Vol. 3, J. A. Thomas and R. L. Singhal, eds., pp 1–50. University Park Press, Baltimore.
22. Veneziale, C. M. 1977. *Biochem. J.* 166:155.
23. Veneziale, C. M., Burns, J., Lewis, J. C., and Buchi, K. A. 1977. *Biochem. J.* 166:167.
24. Levy, H. A., and Szego, C. M. 1955. *Am. J. Physiol.* 182:507.
25. Bissell, D. M., Hammaker, L., and Schmid, R. 1972. *J. Cell Biol.* 54:107.
26. Fong, J. S. C., and Drummond, K. N. 1969. *Lab. Invest.* 20:512.
27. Harrison, D. D., and Webster, H. L. 1969. *Exp. Cell Res.* 55:257.
28. Sayers, G., Swallow, R. L., and Giordano, N. D. 1971. *Endocrinology* 88:1063.
29. Pitelka, D. R., Kerkof, P. R., Gagne, H. T., Smith, S., and Abraham, S. 1969. *Exp. Cell Res.* 57:43.
30. McDogual, W. S., and DeCosse, J. J. 1970. *Exp. Cell Res.* 61:203.
31. Moskalewski, S. 1965. *Gen. Comp. Endocrinol.* 5:342.
32. Lacy, P. E., and Kostianovsky, M. 1967. *Diabetes* 16:35.
33. Schapira, G., Dobocz, I., Piau, J. P., and Delain, E. 1974. *Biochem. Biophys. Acta* 345:348.
34. Steck, T. L. 1972. In *Membrane Biology,* C. F. Fox and D. D. Keith, eds., p. 81. Sinauer Assoc., Stamford, Connecticut.
35. Fleischer, S., and Kervina, M. 1974. *Methods Enzymol.* 31:24.
36. Gram, T. E. 1974. *Methods Enzymol.* 31:225.
37. Dallner, G. 1974. *Methods Enzymol.* 31:191.
38. Fleischer, B. 1974. *Methods Enzymol.* 31:180.
39. Johnson, R. M. 1975. *J. Membr. Biol.* 22:231.
40. Tanaka, K. -I., and Ohnishi, S. -I. 1976. *Biochim. Biophys. Acta* 426:218.
41. Bodemann, H., and Passow, H. 1972. *J. Membr. Biol.* 8:1.
42. Wisher, M. H., and Evans, W. H. 1975. *Biochem. J.* 146:375.
43. Chang, K. J., Bennett, V., and Cuatrecasas, P. 1975. *J. Biol. Chem.* 250:488.
44. Lernmark, A., Nathans, A., and Steiner, D. F. 1976. *J. Cell Biol.* 71:606.
45. Suoboda, M., Robberecht, P., Camus, J., Deschodt-Lanckman, M., and Christophe, J. 1976. *Eur. J. Biochem.* 69:185.
46. Ebel, H., Aulbert, E., and Merker, H. J. 1976. *Biochem. Biophys. Acta* 433:531.
47. Johnson, S., Stokke, T., and Prydz, H. 1974. *J. Cell Biol.* 63:357.
48. Meissner, G. 1974. *Methods Enzymol.* 31:238.
49. Baenziger, N. L., and Majerus, P. W. 1974. *Methods Enzymol.* 31:149.
50. Jones, D. H., and Matus, A. I. 1974. *Biochim. Biophys. Acta* 356:276.
51. Bartfai, T., Berg, P., Schultzberg, M., and Heilbronn, E. 1976. *Biochim. Biophys. Acta* 426:186.
52. Yamashita, K., and Field, J. B. 1974. *Methods Enzymol.* 31:144.
53. Norton, W. T. 1974. *Methods Enzymol.* 31:435.
54. Dodge, J. T., Mitchell, C. D., and Hanahan, D. J. 1963. *Arch. Biochem. Biophys.* 100:119.
55. Hanahan, D. J., and Ekholm, J. E. 1974. *Methods Enzymol.* 31:168.
56. Emmelot, P., Bos, C. J., van Hoeven, R. P., and van Blitterswijk, W. J. 1974. *Methods Enzymol.* 31:75.

57. Schapira, G., Dobocz, I., Piau, J. P., and Delain, E. 1974. *Biochem. Biophys. Acta* 345:348.
58. Giacobino, J. -P., and Chmelar, M. 1975. *Biochem. Biophys. Acta* 406:68.
59. Perdue, J. F. 1974. *Methods Enzymol.* 31:162.
60. Chauveau, J., Moule, Y., and Rouiller, C. H. 1956. *Exp. Cell Res.* 11:317.
61. Mahler, H. R., and Cordes, E. H., eds. 1966. *Biological Chemistry*. Harper and Row, New York and London.
62. Maggio, R., Siekevitz, P., and Palade, G. E. 1963. *J. Cell Biol.* 18:267.
63. Büchi, K., and Veneziale, C. M. 1977. *Andrologia,* 9:237.
64. Roodyn, B. D. 1972. In *Subcellular Components,* G. D. Birnie and S. M. Fox, eds., p. 15. Butterworth, London.
65. Spelsberg, T. C., Knowler, J. T., and Moses, H. L. 1974. *Methods Enzymol.* 26:263.
66. Hackenbrock, C. R., Rehn, T. G., Weinbach, E. C., and Lemasters, J. J. 1971. *J. Cell Biol.* 51:123.
67. Estabrook, R. W., and Pullman, M. E. 1967. *Methods Enzymol.* 10:74.
68. Serrano R., Kanner, B. I., and Racker, E. 1976. *J. Biol. Chem.* 251:2453.
69. Kagawa, Y. 1972. *Biochem. Biophys. Acta* 265:297.
70. Green, D. E., and Silman, H. I. 1967. *Annu. Rev. Plant Physiol.* 18:147.
71. Blair, P. V. 1967. *Methods Enzymol.* 10:78.
72. Smith, A. L. 1967. *Methods Enzymol.* 10:81.
73. Schneider, W. C. 1948. *J. Biol. Chem.* 176:259.
74. Hogeboom, G. H. 1955. *Methods Enzymol.* 1:16.
75. Guerra, F. C. 1974. *Methods Enzymol.* 31:299.
76. Rothschild, J. 1963. *Biochem. Soc. Symp.* 22:4.
77. Dallner, G. 1963. *Acta Pathol. Microbiol. Scand. Suppl.* 166.
78. Martonosi, A. 1968. *J. Biol. Chem.* 243:71.
79. Meissner, G. 1975. *Biochem. Biophys. Acta* 389:51.
80. Beaufay, H. 1972. *Lysosomes, A Laboratory Handbook,* G. T. Dingle, ed., p. 1. North-Holland Publ., Amsterdam.
81. Wattiaux, R., Wibo, M., and Baudhuin, P. 1963. Lysosomes, in *Ciba Found. Symp.,* p. 176.
82. Wattiaux, R. 1966. In *Etude experimentale de la surcharge des lysosomes,* Duculot, Gembloux, Belgium.
83. Trouet, A. 1974. *Methods Enzymol.* 31:323.
84. Maunsbach, A. B. 1966. *J. Ultrastruct. Res.* 16:13.
85. Maunsbach, A. B. 1974. *Methods Enzymol.* 31:330.
86. Kemmler, W., and Steiner, D. F. 1970. *Biochem. Biophys. Res. Commun.* 41:1223.
87. Blaschko, H., Born, G. V. R., D'Iorio, A., and Eade, N. R. 1956. *J. Physiol.* 133:548.
88. Smith, A. D., and Winkler, H. 1967. *Biochem. J.* 103:480.
89. Bartlett, S. F., and Smith, A. D. 1974. *Methods Enzymol.* 31:379.
90. LaBella, F., Krass, M., Fritz, W., Vivian, S., Shin, S., and Queen, G. 1971. *Endocrinology* 89:1094.
91. Tesar, J. T., Koenig, H., and Hughes, C. 1969. *J. Cell Biol.* 40:225.
92. Menon, I. A., and Haberman, H. F. 1974. *Methods Enzymol.* 31:389.
93. Uvnas, B. 1974. *Methods Enzymol.* 31:395.
94. Hope, D. B., and Pickup, J. C. 1974. *Methods Enzymol.* 31:403.
95. Zalta, J., and Zalta, J. P. 1973. In *Methods in Cell Biology,* Vol. VI, D. M. Prescott, ed., pp. 317–24. Academic Press, New York.
96. Kasper, C. B. 1974. *Methods Enzymol.* 31:279.
97. Hanson, C. V. 1973. In *New Techniques in Biophysics and Cell Biology,* Vol. 2, R. M. Pain, and B. J. Smith, eds., pp. 43–83. John Wiley and Sons, New York.
98. Schaefer, P., and Veneziale, C. M. 1973. *Eur. J. Biochem.* 35:18.

108,847

1.2. Cell Culture

Clifford J. Steer

The understanding of specific cellular functions has been greatly enhanced by the development of cell culture. Isolated cells are being used increasingly in the study of biological phenomena. By controlling the medium surrounding cells in culture, it is possible to do intra- and extracellular biochemical measurements simultaneously from single batches of cells. The use of isolated cells in culture has permitted extensive studies of membrane phenomena such as binding and transport processes. By controlling pH, osmotic pressure, temperature, and other variables involved in the maintenance of cellular integrity and function, the pairing of test and control cells has allowed for more sensitive detection of significant test variables. Whereas in organ culture special measures are taken to prevent the tissue from becoming disorganized, no such precaution is made in tissue culture. Certain cells, for example, macrophages and white blood cells, are highly motile and begin to migrate from tissue explants soon after culture begins. The rationale for organ culture is, in fact, preservation of the three-dimensional relationship of the parent organ and investigation of the functional activities of organized tissues in vitro. Today the most prevalent mode is cell culture in which the tissue is intentionally disorganized by disrupting it into individual cells. This permits the study of functions specific to a particular cell type without intervening epithelial and vascular barriers. This review will primarily concern isolated cell culture.

Two general stages of cell culture are defined: primary culture and serially propagated cell culture. The former consists of dispersed cells newly isolated from intact tissue and established on a substratum in nutrient medium. Usual substrata include glass and plastic. Serially propagated cells are, of course, also initiated as primary culture. However, the cells are allowed to proliferate for a variable period of time after which they are either physically or enzymatically (e.g., trypsinization) removed from substrate and replated. The interval of optimal subculture is, of course, dependent on the rate of cellular proliferation. As soon as cells have been transferred in this manner, the culture is designated a *cell strain*. Those cell strains that can be indefinitely subcultured in this way are termed *established cell lines*. At times the transition from the primary culture to an established cell line formation is smooth and gradual. At other times, a dramatic event termed "crisis" or "transformation" occurs during which a cell line distinct from the originally isolated cell is established. Genetic, morphologic, biochemical, and growth characteristics of the "established" or "transformed" cell line are frequently different from those of the primary cell line. The loss of density-dependent inhibition, disorganized growth habit, a decrease in cell adhesiveness, and the appearance of tumor-specific surface antigens are examples of properties shared by cells transformed in culture to an established cell line. The human skin fibroblast is an example of a particularly stable primary cell strain. Although it has potential for being subcultured for many months, it does not frequently undergo a "spontaneous" change to an established cell line. On the other hand, mouse skin fibroblasts almost invariably undergo a "spontaneous" transition to form established cell lines.

Prior to development of functional characterization, morphology had been a major means of identifying cells in culture. However, morphologic identification alone can be a deceptive method. For example, it has long been assumed that cells with the appearance of fibroblasts (spindle-shaped) originate from connective tissue, whereas those of epithelial shape originate from parenchyma. On this basis, it has been claimed that liver-derived cells with epithelial morphology represent hepatic parenchymal cells in culture. Investigators have, however, recognized that liver-derived cells with epithelial appearance may represent a line of nonparenchymal cells (e.g., sinusoidal lining cells). Conversely, hepatocytes in culture that have been characterized with certainty by specific markers, may appear in the culture environment to be fibroblastic in morphology. It is apparent that beyond the stage of early cell culture, hepatocytes may lose some of the distinctive morphologic characteristics of liver parenchymal cells in vivo. Investigators now more frequently rely on specific functions of isolated cells in culture as means of characterization, examples of which include biochemical and cell surface receptor parameters. A typical example is the production of serum albumin as a means to identify hepatocytes in culture; this protein appears to be produced exclusively by the liver parenchymal cell in vivo. Borenfreund transformed an established monolayer culture of albumin-secreting epithelioid cells from normal rat liver with methylazoxymethanol acetate, a chemical carcinogen. The result was a malignant line of cells exhibiting an irregular, piling growth pattern and spindle-shaped appearance. The cells were then injected intradermally into nude mice and developed into tumors within 12 days. Cells from the tumor were isolated and reestablished in culture. They again exhibited an epithelial-like morphology and secreted albumin. Other examples of specific hepatocyte enzymes include pyruvate kinase L and aldolase B. In monolayer cultures, these enzymes may be released into the medium with the synthesis of similar but less characteristic or liver-specific enzymes such as pyruvate kinase K and aldolases A and C.

Certain cells maintain characteristic biochemical functions even after overt transformation. For example, fibroblasts usually retain the capacity to secrete collagen; malignant mast cells in culture usually retain the capacity to secrete histamine; and tumors of endocrine origin usually retain the ability to secrete polypeptide and steroid hormones. There is no doubt that some retention of the differentiated phenotype in certain cell lines does exist.

The composition of the medium is by far the most important single factor in maintaining cells in culture. Cell viability is dependent on such conditions as pH, osmotic pressure, and nutrients—all properties of the medium. In 1916 Harrison, the founder of modern tissue culture, was able to maintain viable frog embryo nerve fibers by using clotted lymph as his nutrient medium. Since that time there has been development of the "physiologic salt solutions," formulated to resemble the ionic components of blood and lymph. Common to the many synthetic mixtures produced was the incorporation of serum factors essential for life. Cell lines that are highly selective for their ability to grow in rigorously defined media have been developed. Characteristic of almost all those cell lines is the need for serum protein. For survival beyond several hours, cells need more than a simple balanced salt solution.

All physiologic salt solutions have been derived from that originally defined by Ringer. Tyrode's solution was the first developed specifically for support of mammalian cell metabolism. Usual buffering agents include phosphate and bicarbonate. Other buffers used in this laboratory include HEPES (N-2-hydroxyethylpiperazine-N-ethanesulfonic acid) and Tris (tris-(hydroxy-methyl)-aminomethane). Earle's balanced salt solution is an example of one requiring a 5% CO_2 tension for equilibration to maintain pH stability in the physiologic range (6.9–7.8). The salt solutions developed by Krebs are frequently used for metabolic studies. The most interesting feature of his solutions is incorporation of Krebs cycle intermediates.

The first systematic studies of "synthetic" media were initiated by Albert Fischer, who, using dialyzed plasma as basal medium, showed that the small molecular fraction could be adequately replaced by a mixture of amino acids similar to those found in fibrin. His work culminated in the publication of his medium V-605 in 1948. The earliest media shown to be able to support growth of certain cell lines in the absence of added serum were medium 858 and medium MCTC 109. Media are developed for specific cells with particular requirements for growth and metabolism. Electrolytes are no longer considered to provide only a salt mixture similar in composition to that of serum, but rather to have specific roles in ion transport and effects on metabolic pathways. For example, the concentration of potassium in the medium can affect the beating rhythm of isolated cardiac cells. On the other hand, the potassium concentration, compartmentalization, and permeability in growing and quiescent chick embryo fibroblasts are not different, suggesting that the regulation of growth of these cells does not involve a significant alteration of general potassium metabolism. Mouse strain L cells can grow in an apparently normal fashion for months without added magnesium, whereas omission of calcium can cause changes in morphology, cessation of growth, and even cell death.

The use of carbohydrates such as glucose, maltose, and fructose and the addition of keto acids, carboxylic acids, purines, pyrimidines, and trace metals such as iron, copper, and zinc have become important factors as more highly purified components are used to make media. Galactose, when added under defined conditions, allows normal cell growth to be maintained for some cells in the absence of glucose. The use of coenzyme A, nicotinic acid, riboflavin, folic acid, and thiamine is shared by the majority of cells in culture. The role of insulin in cell culture media is probably multifaceted, affecting membrane integrity, glucose utilization, and incorporation of amino acids. Jeejeebhoy, using a model of isolated hepatocytes in suspension, showed that in the absence of insulin, glucose transport into the cell, intracellular glucose and glycogen levels, and albumin synthesis are not fully maintained. The addition of thyroxine appears not to be important in either cell viability or growth in the majority of cell lines tested. Bailey found that most of the cell lines studied grew well in the absence of polyunsaturated fatty acids. With the exception of HeLa-S3 and embryonic rat heart cells, multiple cell lines tested showed normal growth rates and morphologic appearance by light and electron microscopy. Harary demonstrated that rat heart cells in lipid-deficient media ceased to beat; he attributed this effect to probable mitochondrial dysfunction. Cell cultures of hepatocytes from 16-day fetal livers of C57BL/6J mice require an adrenocorticosteroid hormone for long-term culture in defined media. Jeejeebhoy, using hepatocyte suspensions, showed that a mixture of glucagon, cortisol, triiodothyronine, and growth hormone enhanced fibrinogen synthesis. Freund, using Morris hepatoma cells, showed powerful growth inhibition in the presence of low concentrations of a glucocorticoid hormone. Also noted by Freund were marked changes in surface morphology as well as a striking increase in cell adhesiveness, which appeared to be induced by synthesis of characteristic surface proteins.

The phrase "isolated cells in culture" implies a method of tissue disaggregation. Physical disruption is infrequently used because it causes too much cellular damage. The method of tissue disaggregation most commonly employed today involves enzymatic treatment. Examples of enzymes frequently used include trypsin (the most commonly used agent), collagenase (the most effective agent to dissolve fibrous components of tissue), elastase, papain, and pronase. The isolation of hepatocytes in our laboratory is accomplished by perfusion of intact liver with 0.03% collagenase in calcium-free Krebs-Henseleit solution. Further enrichment of the suspension with Kupffer cells is accomplished by pronase digestion of the hepatocytes. The surface receptors on Kupffer cells, however, may be injured by pronase, as evidenced by the inability to detect complement receptors and Fc receptors for immunoglobulins immediately after isolation. These surface receptors are restored, however, after the cells have remained in monolayer culture for 12–24 hr. We have also recently found that pronase injures Kupffer cell receptors for specifically modified glycoproteins. From the above examples it is evident that disaggregation techniques may produce injury to cells, which may not always be restored in subsequent culture.

The majority of cells in culture are established in monolayer systems, suspension, or systems analogous to those of tissues. Cell lines in monolayer culture are usually grown directly on glass or plastic surfaces. They are maintained in vessels having a flat surface on which cells can settle. Examples include T-flasks, Carrel flasks, Petri dishes, and Erlenmeyer flasks. Collagen is being more extensively used as a substratum. Primary cultures of liver cells on collagen-coated plates and floating collagen membranes show markedly prolonged viability, and morphologic and functional features reminiscent of hepatocytes in vivo. An example is the prolonged induction of tyrosine aminotransferase, a specific liver cell enzyme marker, by cyclic nucleotides and steroids in hepatocytes cultured on floating collagen membranes. Interestingly, it appears that the free surface of an attached epithelium does not provide a suitable substratum for the attachment and locomotion of either fibroblastic or epithelial cells.

It is generally considered that cell culture by suspension system is an ideal way to study biochemical functions, particularly for large populations of cells. Sampling is more accurate than that involved in monolayer systems. Spinner vessels, the most common vehicle to maintain cells in suspension, should be rotated at minimum speed to ensure uniform suspension of cells with minimal damage. Optimal concentrations of inoculum usually lie in the range between 10^5 and 10^6 cells/ml. Macromolecules such as methylcellulose or polyglycol, are frequently used to inhibit cell aggregation, particularly in a ring around the culture vessel at the surface of the medium. In a prolific cell line, medium must be supplemented to keep cell density optimal for cell growth. In a suspension system, renewal of medium is frequently a difficult problem. Attempts have been made to develop a system of continuous medium replacement, but most have been fraught with difficulties.

A new approach to the provision of suitable physical conditions for cells in culture is that established by Knazek, who devised an artificial capillary system for tissue culture. This consists of a glass tube through which run a combination of 340 μm O.D. (outer diameter) polymeric capillaries and 260 μm O.D. silicone polycarbonate capillaries. Cells are grown within the tube in the spaces between the capillaries. The polymeric capillaries are permeable to molecules of less than 50,000 mw, while the silicone polycarbonate capillaries are permeable to gases.

The essential manipulations involved in maintaining cell lines are medium renewal or "feeding" and subculture or "transfer." Feeding can frequently be accomplished by simple removal and replacement of media with a pipette or syringe. Subculture requires that cells be brought into suspension before transfer can occur. Cells growing in monolayer can be suspended by physical means (shaking, rubber policeman), chelating agents, or proteolytic enzymes. Trypsin is the most common example of the last. A simple transfer might involve the following sequence: Cells are present as a monolayer on glass, plastic, or other substratum; medium is removed, and a preparation of trypsin is added. Usually after a short period of incubation the cells are in suspension and can be taken up by pipette or syringe, washed of proteolytic enzyme, and transferred to new culture medium and substratum. The mechanism of action of chelating agents such as EDTA (diamino-ethane-tetra-acetic acid) involves binding of calcium and magnesium, which are important in the attachment of cell to substratum.

During the last decade a wide variety of studies have demonstrated the usefulness of cell culture systems in elucidation of the biochemistry and cellular functions of cyclic nucleotides. Important relationships have been noted between cyclic AMP and such cellular phenomena as cell proliferation, density, interaction, and differentiation. There is evidence that the morphologic changes induced by cyclic AMP are mediated by effects on the microtubular-microfibrillar system. It has been suggested that cyclic AMP causes assembly, stabilization, and orderly alignment of the microtubular system, resulting in morphologic alteration of the cell surface and cell shape. Examples of agents commonly found to stimulate adenylate cyclase activity or cyclic AMP formation include glucagon, histamine, and catecholamines. Various cell lines exhibit variable responses to these stimulating agents. For example, catecholamine-stimulated HeLa, Chang, and 3T6 mouse embryo fibroblasts exhibit moderate and transient elevation of cyclic AMP levels, whereas cultured human fibroblasts and C-6 astrocytoma cells display marked and prolonged elevation. This difference may result from activation of catecholamine receptors that are either dormant or nonexistent in vivo.

Much less information is available concerning cyclic GMP levels and receptor-mediated stimulation of cyclic GMP in cultured cells. Epidermal growth factor (EGF), fibroblast growth factor (FGF), certain plant lectins, as well as prostaglandins, insulin, and serum proteases are examples of substances capable of stimulating intracellular levels of cyclic GMP. There appears to be good evidence for an inverse relationship between the levels of cyclic GMP and cyclic AMP. Numerous investigators have noted the inhibitory effect of cyclic AMP and stimulative effect of cyclic GMP on cell proliferation. It appears that the cell culture system presents a unique advantage for future elucidation of receptor-mediated modulation of cyclic nucleotide formation and the effects of these nucleotides on cellular transformation, growth, metabolism, and differentiation.

Cell culture offers a unique system to study a wide variety of factors responsible for the control of cellular growth. The factors that cause "normal" cells in culture to exhibit orderly, restricted, definable growth, and those that cause their transformed counterparts to exhibit impressive loss of that control, are not totally known. Normally, cells in culture follow a density-dependent regulation; that is, they grow to a certain saturation density and then stop. The quiescent cells, primarily in the G_0 and G_1 phase of the cell cycle, can remain healthy for long periods of time. Recent evidence suggests that quiescence is not a result of contact inhibition by surrounding cells as previously thought. Instead, arrest of mammalian cell growth appears to be the result of limitation of one or more of a variety of materials in the surrounding medium. There is evidence that cells are arrested in growth at the same "restriction point" whether the limiting factor is a low-molecular-weight nutrient or a macromolecular serum factor. Skehan noted two separate but interacting mechanisms regulating the growth rate of rat C_6 glioma cells in culture. The first mechanism appears to be an endogenous program that specifies the time-base of growth events, a mechanism not subject to density-dependent regulation. The second mechanism determines the amplitude of the growth rate at all times following the end of the lag phase and is quite sensitive to density-dependent regulation. Skehan suggests that the inhibition of growth is mediated not through density-dependent regulation, but rather by an endogenous mechanism. He further suggests the possibility of applying the concept of this control system to other cell lines.

Among the long list of substances that appear to influence cellular growth, certain polypeptides appear to represent the more important natural macromolecular factors. Examples include the submaxillary gland extracts "nerve growth factor" and "epidermal growth factor," the pituitary extracts "ovarian growth factor" and "fibroblast growth factor," the somatomedins, colony stimulating factor, nonsuppressible insulinlike activities, and embryonic rat fibroblast growth factors S_1 and S_2. Other substances affecting cell line growth include lectins, antigens, peptides, and lipopolysaccharides. Certain of these above-mentioned factors appear to be released by cells into the culture medium.

The earliest changes following growth stimulation of cells in culture involve intracellular levels of cyclic nucleotides and changes in the membrane permeability and transport of nutrients. Whether initiation of growth is dependent on an increasing cyclic GMP to cyclic AMP ratio or a change in membrane permeability is only speculative. These variables, however, are not as easily defined when examining the growth characteristics of transformed cells. There appears to be a lack of density-dependent regulation as well as a decreased requirement for the above-mentioned macromolecular growth factors. The latter may be the direct result of altered membrane properties modifying the interaction between circulating hormones and membrane receptors, as well as less rapid utilization of those growth factors. Transformed cells have been shown to release increased amounts of growth-stimulating proteases into culture medium. Some of these proteases may be capable of releasing the cell line from density-dependent inhibition of growth. The inhibition of cell growth in vitro by protease inhibitors strengthens this argument. It is evident that patterns of cell growth are complex and reflect the interplay of numerous modulating factors.

The ability to isolate and maintain cells in culture has provided a tremendously useful tool for the study of mammalian cell metabolism, growth, and ultrastructure. This in vitro model greatly facilitates investigations on the toxicity of chemicals, viral transformation, and chemical carcinogenesis. Cell culture systems are being used increasingly in the fields of immunology and cytogenetics. As an example, recently in this laboratory a protein on the surface of hepatocytes cultured in monolayer was shown to be a mitogen capable of inducing increased cellular cytotoxocity by desialylated lymphocytes. During the past 50 years we have seen impressive progress in the field of cell culture. It would certainly appear that the scope of application of this tool during the next 50 years will be even greater.

REFERENCES

1. Jeejeebhoy, K. N., and Phillips, M. J. 1976. Isolated mammalian hepatocytes in culture. *Gastroenterology* 71:1086–96.
2. Bissell, D. M. (1976). Study of hepatocyte function in cell culture. In *Progress in Liver Diseases,* Vol. V, Hans Popper and Fenton Schaffner, eds., pp. 69–82. Grune and Stratton, New York.
3. Gospodarowicz, D., and Moran, J. S. 1976. Growth factors in mammalian cell culture. In *Annual Review of Biochemistry,* Vol. 45, Esmond E. Snell, Paul D. Boyer, Alton Meister, and Charles C. Richardson, eds. pp. 531–58. Annual Reviews, Inc. Palo Alto, California.
4. Rothblat, G. H., and Cristofalo, V. J. 1972, 1977. *Growth, Nutrition and Metabolism of Cells in Culture,* Vol. I, II, III. Academic Press, New York.
5. Paul, John. 1975. *Cell and Tissue Culture,* 5th ed. Churchill Livingstone, London.
6. Earle, W. R. 1948. Tissue culture. In *Laboratory Technique in Biology and Medicine,* 2nd ed., E. V. Cowdry, ed. Williams and Wilkins, Baltimore.
7. Waymouth, C. 1954. The nutrition of animal cells. *Int. Rev. Cytol.* 3:1–68.
8. Rothblat, G. H., and Kritchevsky, D., eds. 1967. "Lipid metabolism in tissue culture cells, Wistar Inst. Symp., Monograph No. 6. Wistar Inst. Anat. Biol., Philadelphia.

9. Higuchi, K. 1973. Cultivation of animal cells in chemically defind media—A review. *Adv. Appl. Microbiol.* 16:111–36.
10. Skehan, P. 1976. On the regulation of cell growth in culture. *Exp. Cell Res.* 97:184–92.
11. Holley, R. W. 1975. Control of growth of mammalian cells in cell culture. *Nature* 258: 487–90.
12. Fogh, J., Holmgren, N. B., and Ludovici, P. P. 1971. A review of cell culture contaminations. *In Vitro* 7(1):26–41.
13. Chlapowski, F. J., Kelly, L. A., and Butcher, R. W., 1975. Cyclic nucleotides in cultured cells. *Adv. Cyclic Nucleotide Res.* 6:245–338.
14. Cox, R. P., and King, J. C. 1975. Gene expression in cultured mammalian cells. *Int. Rev. Cytol.* 43:281–351.
15. Ham, R. G. 1974. Nutritional requirements of primary cultures. A neglected problem of modern biology. *In Vitro* 10:119–29.
16. Pitot, H. C. 1976. Cell–carcinogen interaction in tissue culture. Introduction. Symposium, *Am. J. Pathol.* 85(3):705–8.
17. Kruse, Paul F., Jr., and Patterson, M. K., Jr., eds. 1973. *Tissue Culture—Methods and Applications.* Academic Press, New York.
18. Stulberg, C. S., Paterson, W. D., Jr., and Simpson, W. F. 1976. Identification of cells in culture. *Am. J. Hematol.* 1(2):237–42.
19. Knazek, R. A. Gullino, P. M., Kohler, P. O., and Dedrick, R. L. 1972. Cell culture on artificial capillaries: An approach to tissue growth, *in vitro. Science* 178:65–66.
20. Fischer, A., Astrup, T., Ehrensvärd, G., and Øhlenschläger, V. 1948. Growth of animal tissue cells in artifical media. *Proc. Soc. Exp. Biol. Med.* 67:40–46.
21. Harary, I., McCarl, R., and Farley, B. 1966. Studies *in vitro* on single beating rat heart cells. IX. The restoration of beating by serum lipids and fatty acids. *Biochim. Biophys. Acta* 115:15–22.
22. Bailey, J. M., and Dunbar, L. M. 1973. Essential fatty acid requirements of cells in tissue culture: A review. *Exp. Mol. Pathol.* 18(2):142–61.
23. Borenfreund, E., Higgins, P. J., Steinglass, M., and Bendich, A. 1975. Properties and malignant transformation of established rat liver parenchymal cells in culture. *J. Natl. Cancer Inst.* 55(2):375–84.
24. Freund, J. S., Dempsey, E. W., Loeb, J. N., and Borek, C. 1975. Scanning electron microscopy of glucocorticoid treated hepatocytes and hepatoma cells in culture. *Proc. Soc. Exp. Biol. Med.* 150(1):14–19.
25. Leffert, H. L., Moran, T., Boorstein, R., and Koch, K. S. 1977. Procarcinogen activation and hormonal control of cell proliferation in differentiated primary adult rat liver cell cultures. *Nature* 267: 58–61.

1.3.   Microscopy: Instruments and Techniques*

Akhouri A. Sinha

In recent years, the development of a variety of microscopes and microscopic techniques has led to a complex discipline in which biomedical scientists are constantly faced with the problems of selecting appropriate tools and techniques to study complex biological phenomena. For example, with the advent of the electron microscope biological/pathological specimens can now be magnified to over one million times. To utilize such a powerful microscope numerous new techniques have been developed during the last two decades (25, 26, 35, 21). This work has resulted in a bridging of the classical boundaries between the morphological and biochemical disciplines by molecular cytologists. In a chapter such as this, I intend to provide only a brief description of the different types of microscopes, their usefulness, and their shortcomings, as well as some comments on specific techniques that have been used in my laboratory. In addition, appropriate references are provided to facilitate selection of microscopes and associated techniques.

THE OPTICAL MICROSCOPE

The Light Microscope

The light microscope, often called the conventional, compound, regular, bright-field, or optical microscope, continues to be one of the most important and basic microscopes in biomedical laboratories. It is composed of mechanical and optical parts. In a light microscope the transmitted light is projected through a condenser to translucent and stained tissue sections (about 4 to 10 μm thick) to the objective lens, which enlarges the specimen to the eyepiece, which in turn further magnifies the images to the eye or camera (Figure 1). The total magnification is obtained by multiplying the magnifying power of the objective and eyepiece lenses; the magnification is independent of resolving power, which is usually about 0.2 μm. The microscope provides only

---

* This research was supported by Minneapolis V.A. Hospital.

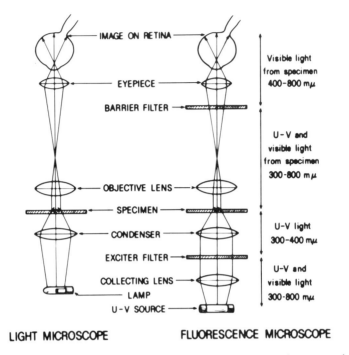

Figure 1. A schematic illustration to compare light and fluorescence microscopes, their light sources, and optics.

two-dimensional images of the specimens. The resolving power is limited because of the objective lens and the visible light rays (about 0.4–0.8 μm wavelength) used in microscopy. For example, a blurred image of two particles separated by the smallest distance at a given magnification indicates their poor resolution. In general, light microscopes have three aberrations: curvature of the field, chromatic, and spherical aberrations. Most manufacturers have corrected these defects by improving lenses. For example, by buying an apochromatic or chromatic, flat-field objective lens one can resolve most of the lens aberrations.

THE SPECIALIZED OPTICAL MICROSCOPES

The light microscope can be modified with suitable accessories into specialized optical microscopes such as phase contrast, Nomarski or interference, fluorescence, dark-field, and polarizing microscopes. The inverted microscope by its design is distinct from the above microscopes. It is an essential tool for tissue and organ culture studies.

The Phase Contrast Microscope

The living or unstained biological specimens are essentially transparent, hence unsuitable for examination by a light microscope, and the chemical fixatives often used for preparations of tissues are unsuitable for living specimens. Therefore, the phase microscope has become a tool of choice for studying living specimens, cells in culture, viruses, bacteria, cell cytology, and blood. The principal basis for the phase contrast microscope is the exaggeration of minute differences in the refractive indexes of living specimens by advancing or retarding the light waves. In simplistic terms, by optical manipulations the microscope converts phase or optical path differences into visible differences of a light microscope. To obtain suitable results, a special condensor and objective are required in the phase microscopy. Additional theoretical and practical considerations have been discussed by Pluta (50) and Humason (30).

Nomarski Differential Interference Microscope

The Nomarski interference optics are improvements over the ordinary phase contrast optics. The Nomarski optics eliminate the "halo" around cells that is observed in ordinary phase contrast microscopy. This microscope is most suited for studying living cells, blood, chick embryos, chromosomes, smears of culture cells, spermatozoa, ova, and so on. It permits optical sectioning of relatively thick biological objects. Nomarski microscopy does not depend upon the object producing the interference of light rays, but generates its own interfering rays. For additional details, see the reviews (33, 23, 2).

The Polarizing Microscope

The polarizing microscope is often used to identify birefrigence of bone tissues, collagen, muscle and nerve fibers, cilia, and endogenous and exogenous crystals. Most of the soft animal tissues are monorefrigent—and are examined by a light microscope. In general, polarizing occurs in substances that have periodic arrangements in their atoms. In this microscope calcite or Nicol prisms permit passage of the polarized light, but eliminate ordinary rays. One needs a powerful light source for obtaining appropriate reflections of specimens (30, 32).

The Fluorescence Microscope

In the fluorescence microscope a specially prepared specimen is used to convert the invisible ultraviolet rays (about 365 μm) into visible rays of longer wavelengths (Figure 1). Here the ultraviolet light excites certain dyes known as "fluorochromes" to emit light of longer wavelengths, which is then observed as "fluorescence." The microscope is very useful in studying bacteria, cancer cells, fungi, heavy metals, and antigen–antibody reactions in blood and tissues. Techniques for tissue, reagents, and antisera preparations are exacting, and shortcuts should be avoided. In general, photomicrography is difficult, but with high-speed film, appropriate photometers, and a high-intensity light source excellent micrographs can be taken. Now the standard fluorescence microscope can be converted to a phase contrast fluorescence microscope by using an aplanatic phase contrast fluorescence condensor. Formalin-fixed paraffin sections are suitable for some fluorescent staining, but long fixations as well as wrong fixatives should be avoided because of autofluorescence problems in the specimens (30, 32).

The Inverted Microscope

In the inverted microscope, the arrangement of optics and mechanical parts is diametrically opposite to that in the light microscope (Figure 2). Here the light source is at the top instead of the bottom as in a light microscope (Figure 1). This microscope is essential for tissue and organ culture studies. A dish of tissue culture specimens is placed on the stage, and the light passes through the specimen to the objective lens and to the eyepiece. The construction of this microscope facilitates observing specimens in a culture dish without the risk of contamination.

THE ELECTRON MICROSCOPES

There are two distinct types of electron microscope, the transmission electron microscope (TEM) and the scanning electron microscope (SEM). Recently some manufacturers have combined the two microscopes into a scanning-transmission electron microscope (STEM). Some additional modifications have been made to investigate specific biological problems.

Transmission Electron Microscope

The TEM is almost directly analogous to an optical microscope except for focusing, which is achieved by varying the lens current. A metallic filament mounted on an electron gun produces electrons (light source) when heated at high temperature. Electrons are then condensed by electromagnetic condenser lenses, the object is magnified by the electromagnetic diffraction and

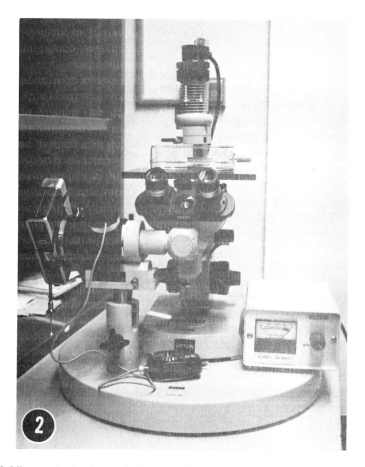

Figure 2. Micrograph of an inverted microscope illustrates the optics and photographic arrangement.

intermediate lenses, and the image is projected onto a viewing fluorescent screen by the projector lens (67, 1) (Figures 3 and 4). The instrument is enclosed in a rigid tube with the interior maintained at constant high vacuum. The microscope provides two-dimensional images much as the light microscope does. The thin sections are often about 200–400 Å thick. The current embedding and sectioning methods are limiting factors for obtaining thinner sections consistently. In general, point-to-point resolving power of a TEM is about 3 Å. Tissues are usually fixed in buffered glutaraldehyde and then in osmium tetroxide, embedded in epoxy resin, and cut with an ultramicrotome using a glass or diamond knife. The images are usually photographed,

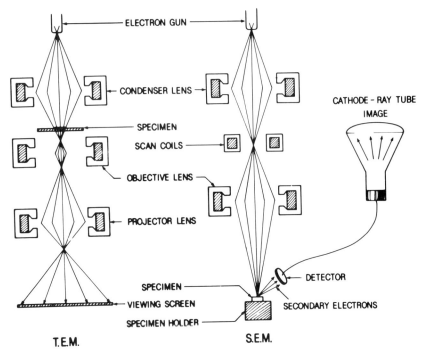

Figure 3. A schematic diagram of transmission and scanning electron microscopes illustrates the light sources, the lenses, and viewing screens. Compare the arrangements with the light microscope.

and the negatives are further enlarged photographically, sometimes up to one million or more times (Figure 5).

Modifications such as (a) dark-field TEM to study DNA and RNA polymerase attached to DNA molecules (16, 17) and (b) high voltage TEM (650–1200 kV) to study thick sections as well as chromosomes, have been developed (51, 24). The high voltage TEM provides three-dimensional features of whole mounts, bacteria, and specimens in relatively thick sections. The high voltage TEM has been of limited use because of poor contrast in specimens.

The Scanning Electron Microscope

Unlike the TEM, in SEM the electrons do not pass through the specimen, which is often thick and large, but the surface of the specimen is scanned for secondary electrons with a series of amplifiers that in turn produce televisionlike images on a cathode ray tube screen (Figure 3). The microscope is

Figure 4. The micrograph illustrates a typical electron microscope with a high voltage electron gun for the light source at the top and a viewing screen at the center of the panel.

excellent for three-dimensional studies of blood cells, bacteria, tissues, and organs (Figure 6). The resolving power of most commercial SEMs is in the range of 100 Å. It has depth of focus about 500 times that of a light microscope. The SEM works in the range of 10 to 100,000 times magnification and fills the void left by the light transmission electron microscopes. The SEM can

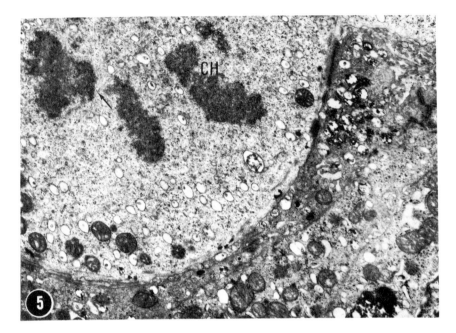

Figure 5. The electron micrograph of an acinus from a human prostatic carcinoma patient illustrates a dividing cell with its chromosomes (CH), microtubules (arrow), and adjacent columnar cells showing organelles and inclusions. ×11,500.

be modified to accommodate X-ray analysis of specially prepared specimens (57). Samples are prepared by special methods for conducting the charges (27, 28, 18, 26, 12).

SOME TECHNIQUES ASSOCIATED WITH MICROSCOPY

Examination of Living Tissues and Organisms

Living tissues or organisms are usually suspended in isotonic saline or appropriate serum media for examination by a phase contrast microscope. Cells in culture are examined by an inverted microscope. Sometimes specimens are stained with vital dyes such as neutral red, Janus green B, trypan blue or red (30, 38). These dyes either enhance the cytological details or distinguish the viable and nonviable cells in tissue culture. The living tissues eventually die because of autolysis and hence are not suitable for long-term studies.

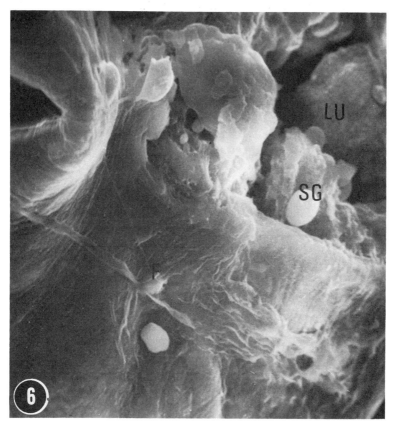

Figure 6. The SEM micrograph illustrates a lateral view of a mouse prostate tubule, its acinar lumen (LU), secretory granule (SG), and a fibroblast (F). ×730.

Fixation of Tissues by Physical Methods

In this technique, the tissues are quickly frozen in liquid nitrogen, in Freon "22," or sometimes on dry ice for histochemical, immunocytochemical, and light electron microscopic autoradiography of water-soluble and diffusible radioactive compounds. Freezing prevents autolysis in the tissues, and frozen specimens are then sectioned by a refrigerated cryostat for light microscopy or by a modified cryoultramicrotome for electron microscopy. Frozen sections are often somewhat thicker (about 10 μm) than the chemically fixed specimens; hence they do not provide optimum resolution for cytological details (Figure 7). Furthermore, formation of ice crystals often damages some cellular

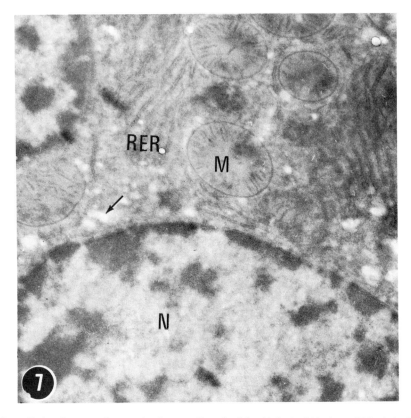

Figure 7. An electron micrograph of mouse liver fixed for ½ hr in 3% glutaraldehyde in 0.1 M phosphate buffer, then frozen in liquid nitrogen and sectioned with a diamond knife by a modified LKB III cryoultramicrotome at −45°C, shows well-preserved nucleus (N), mitochondria (M), rough endoplasmic reticulum (RER), and occasional ice crystals (arrow). Compare with Figure 5, where tissue was processed by chemical methods. ×12,700.

details. The cryoultramicrotomy techniques are very time-consuming and are still being developed (52, 10, 3, 46).

Fixation of Tissue by Chemical Methods

The chief aim of chemical fixation is to coagulate or precipitate the constituents of protoplasm, especially the proteins, by crosslinking quickly in a state as close to living as possible. The practical aspects of the procedure are well established (25, 35, 42, 30, 49, 39). A good fixative quickly penetrates the tissues and prevents autolysis and postmortem changes. The choice of fixative is often determined by the purpose for which the specimen is being preserved. One of the most widely used fixatives is 10% neutral buffered formalin, which penetrates the tissue rapidly and is compatible with most of the stains necessary in light microscopy. For electron microscopy 3% phosphate buffered glutaraldehyde and buffered osmium tetroxide are most often used as a fixative. One should be aware of artifacts produced by the actions of fixatives. For example, there are many factors affecting the fixations, such as pH of solutions, type of buffer, concentration of fixative, size of tissue, temperature, and rate of fixative penetration (25, 35, 49). In general, a specimen perfused with a fixative is better fixed than the one fixed by immersing in a fixative (Figure 5). For a consistently good result, the volume ratio of fixative to tissue should be about 20 to 1. The ultrastructural features of well-preserved tissues are provided in Table 1.

Some chemically fixed tissue can be used for histo- and cytochemistry, in light and electron microscopic autoradiography. However, tissues fixed by physical methods are usually better for histochemistry and immunocyto-chemistry than those fixed by chemical methods. After fixation the specimens are dehydrated, cleared, and embedded either in paraffin for light microscopy or epoxy resin for electron microscopy. The sections are usually stained for

Table 1. Ultrastructural Appearance of Cellular Components in Well-fixed Mammalian Tissues.

COMPONENT	APPEARANCE
Plasma membrane	Dense and intact
Cytoplasmic ground substance	Finely granular without empty spaces
Rough endoplasmic reticulum	Uniformly arranged flattened cisternae in long profiles with attached ribosomes
Smooth endoplasmic reticulum	Cisternae membranes intact and not associated with ribosomes
Golgi complex	Intact arrays of smooth membranes and associated vesicles
Mitochondria	Outer double membrane, intact cristae and dense matrix, mitochondria neither swollen nor shrunken
Nuclear envelope	Double membranes with pores, the outer membrane studded with ribosomes
Nuclear contents	Uniformly dense with masses of chromatin and scattered heterochromatin, besides the nucleolus

both light and electron microscopy. One can readily obtain specific techniques from the above references.

Freeze Fracture Technique

Freeze fracture and freeze etching techniques were first introduced by Steere (63). The specimens are immediately fixed in 3% glutaraldehyde in 0.1 M phosphate buffer at pH 7.3 for 2 hr, washed and soaked overnight in 20–30% glycerin, frozen with Freon "22" in liquid nitrogen, freeze-cleaved at −105°C on a Balzer's apparatus, shadowed with platinum at a 45° angle, and carbon-coated at a 90° angle. The replicas are cleaned with dimethyl-

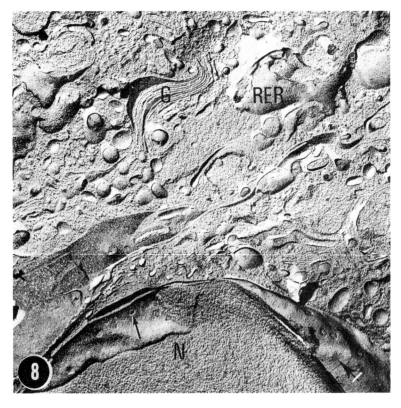

Figure 8. The freeze fracture replica from a human patient having benign prostatic hypertrophy shows cross-fractured nucleus (N), remnants of nuclear membranes, and nucleopores (arrow), the membranes of Golgi complex (G), rough endoplasmic reticulum (RER), and plasma membranes. The crossed bold arrow indicates the direction of shadow. ×18,770.

formamide for 10 min and with 25% Chlorox bleach (sodium hypochlorite) for 1 hr, rinsed in water, and mounted on copper grids for electron microscopy. The technique is most suited to study membranes, junctional complexes, and distribution of particles on the plasma membranes (Figure 8). It can also provide unique information regarding the nature of suspensions, colloids. and other mixed-phase systems which cannot be easily fixed, embedded, and sectioned. Additional reviews on the freeze-cleave techniques are provided in the references (44, 62, 7, 52, 59).

Techniques for Cell Surface Labeling

The plant lectin concanavalin A (Con A) binds to the cell membranes of animal cells and possibly agglutinates preferentially the transformed cells (31). The plasma membrane is believed to play an important role in cell communication. Cell surface treated with horseradish peroxidase and Con A can be readily examined by an electron microscope (47, 11, 61). In recent years Con A has been increasingly used to study cell surfaces of dividing cells (19, 11, 48). Techniques are available to localize ^{3}H Con A by autoradiographic methods (15) (Figure 9).

In addition to the above surface-labeling technique, ruthenium red and violet have been used extensively to label extracellular mucopolysaccharides, plasma membranes, and junctions (40, 41, 29, 22). The surface coat of cells when labeled with ruthenium red is readily visualized by the electron microscope. The cell surfaces appear to play a crucial role in antigen–antibody interactions, which can also be readily visualized when labeled (34, 45).

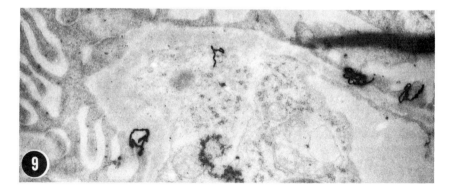

Figure 9. Electron microscopic autoradiograph illustrates localization of ^{3}H Con A grains in the glomerular basement membrane subjacent to the podocytes of a dog kidney. ×22,830.

Autoradiographic Techniques

Both light and electron microscopic autoradiography are based upon the same physical principles, since both use a thin layer of photographic emulsion closely applied to the specimen for detecting emitted radiation. The technique has become almost indispensable in biomedical studies (20, 54, 4, 8, 53).

For light microscopic autoradiography, specimens containing a radioactive isotope, approximately 0.3 μc of ^{3}H thymidine or cytidine/g body weight, are usually washed first with 0.1 M phosphate buffer and then fixed in 10% buffered neutral formalin. Tissues are then processed for paraffin embedding, sectioning, and mounting on a glass slide. The slide is deparaffinized and passed through a series of graded ethanols to an aqueous medium prior to being coated with a nuclear track emulsion in a dark room equipped with a wratten 2 series red safelight. Usually NTB 2 or 3 nuclear emulsions (Eastman Kodak Co.) are used for dip-coating of slides, which are allowed to air dry before being stored in a black Bakelite slide box containing some drierite in a plastic bag. The box is sealed with tape and refrigerated at 4°C, but not frozen, usually for 2 to 3 weeks. After the desired exposure, the slide box is brought in the darkroom, developed photographically usually in Kodak Microdol-X developer, fixed in 30% sodium thiosulfate, and washed in water. The slides can then be examined for the localization of isotopic grains (Figure 10) or can be stained to enhance contrast of cellular details. The technique permits distinction of radioactive particles that are about 1 μm apart. For additional details consult Baserga and Malamud (4) and Rogers (53). There are several variations of the above theme, which provide individual flexibility and choice in techniques (55).

For electron microscopic autoradiography the specimen containing the desired isotope is fixed in glutaraldehyde and processed for electron microscopy. Thin sections can be either mounted on copper grids and coated with fine grain nuclear track emulsion such as Illford L-4 emulsion (Illford, England) using a loop method (8, 9) or mounted on celloidin-coated glass slides and coated with emulsion using a dipping method (56, 36, 37, 60). The slides are air-dried and stored in a Bakelite slide box containing some drierite and then refrigerated at 4°C for 8 to 10 weeks. The slides are developed in Kodak Microdol-X for 3 to 4 min, fixed in 30% sodium thiosulfate, and washed; sections are floated on water and then mounted on grids. The thin sections are examined for localization of grains by an electron microscope (Figure 11). Epon-embedded thick sections are often processed for light microscopic autoradiography. Special autoradiographic techniques have been developed for water- and lipid-soluble isotopic compounds (64, 65, 6).

Autoradiography as a quantitative method is one of the best tools in molecu-

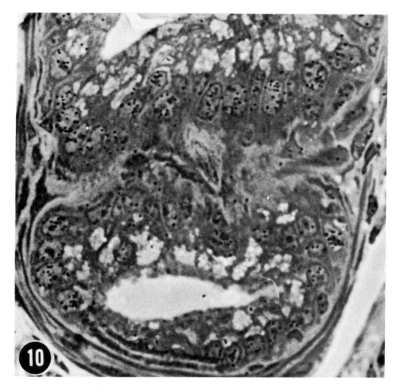

Figure 10. A light microscopic autoradiograph illustrates localization of ^{3}H cytidine in the nuclei of acinar cells from a mouse prostate. ×1100.

lar cytology for identifying cell populations, cell cycles, and cells actively incorporating isotopic compounds while maintaining in situ cell organization (43). The technique requires meticulous care at every step; otherwise many artifacts can be introduced into the result.

Examination of Ultracentrifugation Fractions by Electron Microscopy

Biochemical studies, though specific and quantitative, usually disrupt tissue organization and cellular components from normal and pathological specimens. Morphological criteria are often needed to determine the purity of centrifuged fractions before confidence can be placed in the analyses. Differential centrifugation is a physical process in which centrifugal force is used

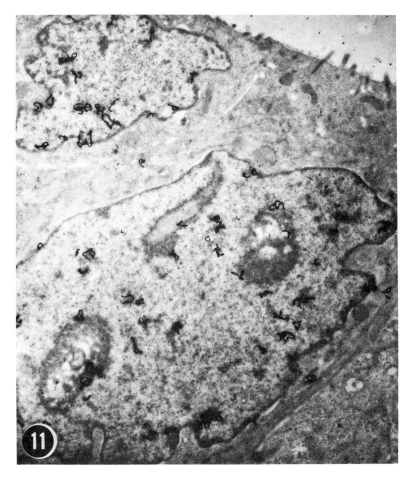

Figure 11. An electron microscopic autoradiograph illustrates localization of ^{3}H thymidine in the nuclei of acinar columnar cells of a human prostate patient having prostatitis. ×10,100.

to separate organelles and cellular inclusions (Figure 12). Sedimentation of particles depends on their size, form, and density, and the viscosity of the medium. Specific fractions are obtained after centrifugation or ultracentrifugation and spun into a pellet, which is then fixed by glutaraldehyde and processed for electron microscopy as described earlier. Information obtained from morphological studies of fractions is now increasingly compared with the results of biochemical studies. This useful technique has considerably aided the efforts to correlate structure and function at the subcellular level (13, 5, 66, 14, 58).

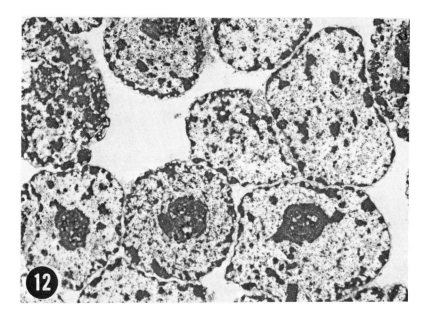

Figure 12. The micrograph illustrates nuclei of rat hepatocytes isolated by a technique of differential centrifugation. Note the absence of cytoplasmic organelles and inclusions in the preparation examined by an electron microscope. ×20,500.

ACKNOWLEDGMENT

The author wishes to thank Dr. Robert F. Hammer, Department of Veterinary Biology, University of Minnesota for the use of the scanning electron microscope and Dr. Ross G. Johnson, Department of Genetics and Cell Biology, University of Minnesota for the use of Balzer's apparatus and associated facilities. I greatly appreciate the technical help of Frank Pomroy and the assistance of Ms. Joan C. Korkowski.

REFERENCES

1. Agar, A. W., Alderson, R. H., and Chescoe, D. 1974. *Principles and Practice of Electron Microscope Operation.* North-Holland American Elsevier Co. Inc., New York.
2. Allen, R. D., David, G. B., and Nomarski, G. 1969. *Z. Wiss. Mikrosk. Mikrosk. Tech.* 69:193.
3. Bernhard, W., and Viron, A. 1971. *J. Cell Biol.* 49:731.
4. Baserga, R., and Malamud, D. 1969. *Modern Methods in Experimental Pathology,* Harper and Row, New York.
5. Blobel, G., and Potter, V. R. 1966. *Science* 154:1662.
6. Boyenval, J., and Droz, B. 1976. *J. Microsc. Biol. Cell.* 27:129.

7. Bullivant, S. 1973. In *Advanced Techniques in Biological Electron Microscopy,* J. K. Koehler, ed. Springer-Verlag, New York.
8. Caro, L. G. 1964. In *Methods in Cell Physiology,* Vol. I, D. M. Prescott, ed. Academic Press, New York.
9. Caro, L. G., and Vantubergen, R. P. 1962. *J. Cell Biol.* 15:173.
10. Christensen, A. K. 1971. *J. Cell Biol.* 51:772.
11. Collard, J. G., and Temmink, J. H. M. 1974. *Exp. Cell Res.* 86:81.
12. Crewe, A. V. 1971. *Sci. Am.* 224:26.
13. DeDuve, C., Pressman, B. C., Gianette, R., Wattliaux, R., and Applemans, F. 1955. *Biochem. J.* 60:604.
14. Deter, R. L. 1973. In *Principles and Techniques of Electron Microscopy: Biological Applications,* M. A. Hayat, ed. Van Nostrand Reinhold, New York.
15. DeWolf, W. C., Bentley, M., Staley, N. A., Sinha, A. A., and Miller, J. 1976. *Transplantation* 22:406.
16. Dubochet, J. 1973. In *Principles and Techniques of Electron Microscopy: Biological Applications,* M. A. Hayat, ed. Van Nostrand Reinhold, New York.
17. Dubochet, S., Ducommun, M., Zollinger, M., and Kellenberger, E. J. 1971. *J. Ultrastruct. Res.* 35:147.
18. Everhart, T. E., and Hayes, T. L. 1972. *Sci. Am.* 226:55.
19. Garrido, J. 1975. *Exp. Cell Res.* 94:159.
20. Gautier, A. 1976. *Int. Rev. Cytol.* 44:113.
21. Glauert, A. M. 1974. *Practical Methods in Electron Microscopy.* North Holland Publishing Co., Amsterdam–Oxford.
22. Gordon, M., Fraser, L. R., and Dandekar, P. D. 1975. *Anat. Rec.* 181:95.
23. Hale, A. J. 1958. *The Interference Microscope.* E. S. Lingstone Ltd., Edinburgh.
24. Hama, K. 1973. In *Advanced Techniques in Biological Electron Microscopy,* J. K. Koehler, ed. Springer-Verlag, New York.
25. Hayat, M. A. 1970. *Principles and Techniques of Electron Microscopy: Biological Applications,* Vol. 1. Van Nostrand Reinhold, New York.
26. Hayat, M. A. 1974. *Principles and Techniques of Scanning Electron Microscopy,* Vol. 1. Van Nostrand Reinhold, New York.
27. Hayes, T. L. 1973. In *Advanced Techniques in Biological Electron Microscopy.* J. K. Koehler, ed. Springer-Verlag, New York.
28. Hollenberg, M. J., and Erickson, A. M. 1973. *J. Histochem. Cytochem.* 21:109.
29. Huet, C., and Herzberg, M. 1973. *J. Ultrastruct. Res.* 42:186.
30. Humason, G. L. 1967. *Animal Tissue Techniques,* 2nd ed. Freeman, San Francisco.
31. Inbar, M., and Sachs, L. 1969. *Proc. Natl. Acad. Sci. U.S.A.* 63:1418.
32. Jungueira, L. C., Carneiro, J., and Contopoulos, A. M. 1977. *Basic Histology,* 2nd ed. Lange Medical Publ., Los Altos, California.
33. Kayden, H. T., and Bessis, M. 1970. *Blood* 35:427.
34. Kent, S. P., and Wilson, D. V. 1975. *J. Histochem. Cytochem.* 23:169.
35. Koehler, J. K. 1973. *Advanced Techniques in Biological Electron Microscopy.* Springer-Verlag, New York.
36. Kopriwa, B. M. 1967. *J. Histochem. Cytochem.* 14:923.
37. Kopriwa, B. M. 1973. *Histochem.* 37:1.
38. Kruse, P. F., Jr. and Patterson, M. K., Jr. 1973. *Tissue Culture: Methods and Applications.* Academic Press, New York.
39. Lillie, R. D. 1965. *Histopathological Technique and Practical Histochemistry,* 3rd ed. McGraw-Hill, New York.
40. Luft, J. H. 1971a. *Anat. Rec.* 171:347.

41. Luft, J. H. 1971b. *Anat. Rec.* 171:369.
42. Luft, J. H. 1973. In *Advanced Techniques in Biological Electron Microscopy.* J. K. Koehler, ed. Springer-Verlag, New York.
43. Mai, J. K., and Junger, E. 1977. *Cell Tiss. Res.* 183:221.
44. McNutt, M. S., and Weinstein, R. S. 1973. *Prog. Biophys. Mol. Biol.* 26:45.
45. Morris, R. E., and Fritz, R. B. 1975. *J. Histochem. Cytochem.* 23:855.
46. Nei, T. 1974. In *Principles and Techniques in Scanning Electron Microscopy: Biological Applications,* Vol. 1. M. A. Hayat, ed. Van Nostrand Reinhold, New York.
47. Nicolson, G. L., and Singer, S. J. 1971. *Proc. Natl. Acad. Sci. U.S.A.* 68:942.
48. Nicolson, G. L., Yanagimachi, R., and Yangimachi, H. 1975. *J. Cell Biol.* 66:263.
49. Pearse, A. G. E. 1968. *Histochemistry: Theoretical and Practical,* 3rd ed. Little Brown & Co., Boston.
50. Pluta, M. 1968. *J. Microscopy* 89:205.
51. Ris, H. 1969. *J. Microscopie* 8:761.
52. Robards, A. W. 1974. *Sci. Prog. Oxford* 61:1–40.
53. Rogers, A. W. 1973. *Techniques of Autoradiography,* 2nd ed. Elsevier. Amsterdam, Netherlands.
54. Salpeter, M. M., and Bachman, L. 1972. In *Principles and Techniques of Electron Microscopy: Biological Applications,* Vol. 2, M. A. Hayat, ed. Van Nostrand Reinhold, New York.
55. Salpeter, M. M., and McHenry, F. A. 1973. In *Advanced Techniques in Biological Electron Microscopy,* J. K. Koehler, ed. Springer-Verlag, New York.
56. Salpeter, M. M., Bachmann, L., and Salpeter, E. E. 1969. *J. Cell Biol.* 41:1.
57. Saubermann, A. J., and Echlin, P. 1975. *J. Microscopy* 105:155–191.
58. Sinha, A. A., and Mizuno, N. S. 1977. *Cell Tiss. Res.* 183:191.
59. Sinha, A. A., Bentley, M. D., and Blackard, C. E. 1977. *Cancer* 40:1182.
60. Sinha, A. A., Blackard, C. E., Doe, R. P., and Seal, U. S. 1973. *Cancer* 31:682.
61. Smith, S. B., and Revel, J. P. 1972. *Dev. Biol.* 27:434.
62. Staehelin, L. A. 1974. *Int. Rev. Cytol.* 39:191.
63. Steere, R. L. 1957. *J. Biophys. Biochem. Cytol.* 3:45.
64. Stumpf, W. E., and Roth, L. J. 1965. *Cryobiology* 1:227.
65. Stumpf, W. E., and Roth, L. J. 1966. *J. Histochem. Cytochem.* 14:274.
66. Wibo, M., Amar-Costesec, A., Berthet, J., and Beaufy, H. 1971. *J. Cell Biol.* 51:52.
67. Wischnitzer, S. 1973. In *Principles and Techniques of Electron Microscopy: Biological Applications,* M. A. Hayat, ed. Van Nostrand Reinhold, New York.

1.4.   Electrophoretic Methods

Ronald L. Felsted

The migration of substances (colloids, cells, macromolecules, ions, etc.) in an electric field is called electrophoresis. When biological materials are suspended in an aqueous solvent, they acquire a surface charge due to the ionization of acidic and/or basic groups. For example, amino acids and proteins become charged primarily by the ionization of carboxyl and amino groups. Being amphoteric, these molecules can have a net positive, negative, or zero charge, depending on the pH of the surrounding medium. If solutions of these charged molecules are placed in an electric field, they will migrate with an electrophoretic mobility dependent on the field strength and their individual charge densities. The positively charged molecules will migrate toward the cathode, and the negatively charged molecules toward the anode. The pH at which the electrophoretic mobility is zero is called the isoelectric point. This is to be distinguished from the isoionic point, where the concentrations of positive and negative ionized groups are equal (i.e., the net charge of the molecule is zero).

FREE BOUNDARY AND ZONE ELECTROPHORESIS

In the 1930s Tiselius first described the practical and theoretical applications of free or moving boundary electrophoresis (electrophoresis in a homogeneous medium) (Figure 1). Moving boundary electrophoresis was originally used to analyze protein mixtures and components of blood serum. This method has the disadvantages of requiring complicated and expensive equipment and large quantities of sample, and, because of the nature of the experimental design, complete separation of protein mixtures is never achieved. It is, however, the best method for the measurement of electrophoretic mobilities of macromolecules.

Because of the above disadvantages, the vast majority of applications of electrophoresis in cell biology utilize the principles of zone electrophoresis (Figure 2). Whereas free boundary electrophoresis takes place in a homogeneous solution, zone electrophoresis takes place within a stabilizing matrix. Advantages of zone electrophoresis include the potential complete separation of all electrophoretically different components, the requirement for simpler,

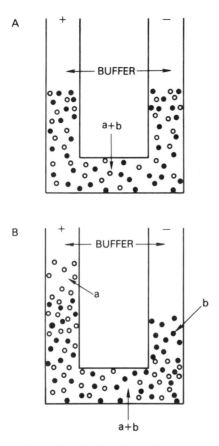

Figure 1. Moving boundary electrophoresis of a mixture of two components, *a* and *b*. (A) Initial conditions before electrophoresis. (B) Conditions after application of an electric current for a time sufficient to partially separate *a* and *b*.

less expensive equipment, the requirement for smaller amounts of sample, and the application to a wide range of macromolecules or simple molecules.

FACTORS AFFECTING ELECTROPHORETIC MOBILITY AND RESOLUTION

In general, separation by electrophoresis depends on the ionic strength and pH of the buffer and on the net charge and solubility of the solutes. Although the conditions for electrophoresis are usually determined experimentally, typical ionic strengths in the range of 0.05 to 0.1 allow for adequate mobilities and separations. In addition, consideration must be given to the specific nature

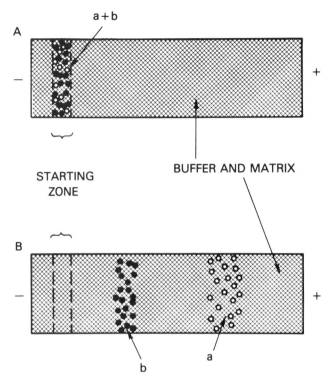

Figure 2. Zone electrophoresis of a mixture of two components *a* and *b*. (A) Before electrophoresis with *a* and *b* applied in a narrow starting zone. (B) Conditions after application of an electric current for a time sufficient to completely resolve *a* and *b*.

of the solute and solvent. For example, an electrolyte of borate ions will form complexes with uncharged sugars, resulting in sugar complexes that migrate during electrophoresis.

A major limitation to resolution is the inevitable broadening of migrating zones as a result of molecular diffusion. Diffusion is a greater problem with small ions than with macromolecules. Serious diffusion problems with small ions are usually overcome by high voltage electrophoresis. This results in faster migrations and consequently lower diffusion, but special precautions for cooling must be provided.

The use of a stablizing matrix in zone electrophoresis does introduce several potential anomalies. Because electrophoretic mobilities depend on an electric field, any electrophoresis experiment will result in heat from the applied current. Besides increasing electrophoretic mobilities, this temperature increase results in evaporation from the aqueous medium. Losses due to evaporation result in a capillary flow of buffer through the supporting matrix from the electrode reservoirs. This liquid flow may distort electrophoretic migration. In addition, evaporation results in increased electrolyte concentration, causing a decrease of electrophoretic mobility. Evaporation losses are usually controlled by enclosing the apparatus in a container or by direct cooling of the electrophoresis matrix.

Another anomaly arises when the supporting matrix itself carries a charge. In that event, a flow of the electrolyte solution relative to the supporting matrix results (electro-osmosis or endo-osmosis). For example, a negatively charged support will exert a force vector toward the anode. However, because it cannot move, an equal but opposite force vector (consisting of electrolyte) will move in the opposite direction. If a negatively charged protein is present in the electrolyte, its expected migration toward the anode will be slightly retarded owing to the opposite electro-osmotic flow. The extent of this backward flow is proportional to the charge on the matrix and can be determined by adding an unchanged substance such as dextran to the experiment and noting its displacement during electrophoresis.

The supporting matrix may also affect the apparent electrophoretic mobilities by forcing the migrating species and electrolytes to travel a tortuous path quite different from that expected in a homogeneous medium. This geometric effect may result in a separation based on molecular size instead of or as well as electrophoretic mobility.

Nonspecific adsorption of the migrating species by the supporting matrix is another possible complication arising in zone electrophoresis. This is generally undesirable because of the resulting trailing effect of the migrating substance. Also, general adsorption will retard the total migration and result in incomplete separation. In special cases where adsorption is specific for a particular species, biospecific adsorption may actually facilitate the analysis of samples not otherwise resolved during electrophoresis.

A COMPARISON OF MATRIX MATERIALS
IN ZONE ELECTROPHORESIS

One of the first matrix materials used in zone electrophoresis was filter paper. Paper electrophoresis is carried out on a horizontal or a vertical apparatus and is the most common matrix for high voltage applications. Most papers have an anionic character and display electro-osmosis. Paper has the advantage of easy sample application and easy detection of migration species with specific stains. Although as many as seven major proteins of serum can be resolved, paper application to macromolecules is generally limited owing to poor resolution and adsorption. Paper electrophoresis is best used for the analysis of small molecules such as sugars, nucleotides, amino acids, peptides, and natural products.

Electrophoresis on cellulose acetate membrane is basically similar to paper electrophoresis. Cellulose acetate is a continuous sheet of cellulose in which most of the hydroxyl groups have been modified. This makes the gel nonadsorptive, and separations of protein mixtures are obtained without trailing. It is chemically pure, being nitrogen-free, and is resistant to alcohols, ether, benzene, and dilute acids. Electro-osmosis is greater in cellulose acetate than filter paper. Because the cellulose acetate strips hold less liquid, evaporation and drying out are more severe than for filter paper. As a result, separations must be carried out at lower current densities in a water-saturated atmosphere.

One of the better media for zone electrophoresis is made with starch gel prepared from potato starch. Because positively charged proteins are slightly absorbed, the pH of the buffer solutions are usually adjusted to the alkaline side of their isoelectric point. Protein resolution is enhanced because of molecular sieving and low diffusion of the migrating zones in the tight gel matrix. From 15 to 17 different components are detected in human serum. The major limitations are the time required for preparation and the fact that the carbohydrates cannot be stained specifically.

Agar and agarose gel electrophoresis have been widely used in immunological studies. Agar is made up of agaropectin and agarose. Its undesirable characteristics such as turbidity, reactivity with basic proteins and lipoproteins, and electro-osmosis are due to the agaropectin. The agarose purified from agar is cleaner, exhibits no adsorption, and shows little electro-osmosis. Resolution is superior to that with filter paper, but not as good as that with starch gels. For example, serum is resolved into about five separate zones. Protein electrophoretic mobilities in agarose are similar to free boundary electrophoresis because the pores are large enough to allow even the largest proteins to pass unrestricted. As a result, agarose is the preferred matrix for the electrophoresis of the largest molecules such as viruses or protein complexes.

Polyacrylamide gel is one of the most effective matrix materials used in zone electrophoresis. It has the following advantages over starch gel; (1) electro-osmosis is absent (all serum proteins move toward the anode in an alkaline buffer); (2) the gels are transparent and allow direct measurement of zone patterns by spectrophotometry; (3) the average pore size and the extent of molecular sieving can be controlled by varying the acrylamide and cross-link concentrations; (4) the gel structures can be prepared reproducibly; and (5) the gel is mostly chemically inert, a factor that facilitates differential staining. Further versatility is obtained by inclusion of reagents (i.e., urea, sucrose, cofactors, reducing agents, and nonionic detergents) into gels. Because polymerization is accomplished by a free radical mechanism, artifacts sometimes result from interaction of these residual reagents with macromolecules during electrophoresis.

SPECIFIC ELECTROPHORESIS METHODS

Two-Dimensional Electrophoresis

When complex mixtures of macromolecules or smaller species such as amino acids, peptides, or nucleotides are insufficiently resolved by a single electrophoresis, electrophoresis performed in a different buffer at right angles to the first separation enhances separation. A similar application for the analysis of amino acids or peptides on filter paper is accomplished by electrophoresis in one direction followed by chromatography in the second dimension. This procedure is called fingerprinting, and the electrophoresis is typically carried out at high voltage. Similar resolution at lower voltage with smaller amounts of sample is also possible on thin layers of cellulose or silica gel on a glass or plastic backing. Two-dimensional analysis of macromolecules is usually performed in polyacrylamide, starch, or agarose gels. An example is the resolution of complex protein mixtures by the two-dimensional combination of electrophoresis and isoelectric focusing (see below).

Disc Gel Electrophoresis

Disc gel electrophoresis utilizes a discontinuous buffer system to increase the resolution of zone electrophoresis. Through the principles of the "Kohlrausch regulating function," buffer conditions are designed that concentrate a protein mixture into a narrow starting zone as it migrates through a large-pore gel. Once this narrow sample zone is formed, it then enters a smaller-pore gel where different buffer conditions permit the separation on the basis of electrophoretic mobility and molecular sieving. Starting with a narrow sample zone offers the advantage that a separation is obtained in a short period of time before diffusion begins to limit resolution. A number of discontinuous buffer systems are available with polyacrylamide as the matrix material. With this technique, up to 25 different components of serum can be resolved.

A similar initial zone-sharpening effect is obtained by using a continuous electrophoresis buffer system but applying the sample to the top of the gel in a mixture of glycerol or sucrose (to stabilize against mixing) and the same buffer at a lower ionic strength. Although the concentrating capacity of this approach is not as great as that with the discontinuous buffer method, it does allow greater flexibility in the selection of buffer and pH conditions.

Both of these procedures can be adapted for electrophoresis in glass tubes or in flat sheets. With the latter approach, numerous samples can be electrophoresed simultaneously, thus facilitating a comparison of relative migrations.

Procedures are available for using disc gel polyacrylamide electrophoresis to distinguish between size or charge macromolecule isomers. Also, because the slopes of plots of relative migration versus acrylamide concentrations are a linear function of protein size, molecular weights can be estimated by comparison to appropriate standards.

Sodium Dodecyl Sulfate (SDS)–Polyacrylamide Electrophoresis

Polyacrylamide electrophoresis of proteins in the presence of the anionic detergent SDS is an important method for the determination of polypeptide molecular weights. In the presence of SDS and upon reduction of disulfide bonds, multisubunit proteins are converted into individual SDS–polypeptide complexes that assume conformations proportional to polypeptide or macromolecule (subunit) molecular weights. Because the bound SDS masks the intrinsic protein charge, most of these complexes have identical charge densities. With the same charge densities and conformations proportional to size, electrophoresis through a molecular sieving matrix, such as polyacrylamide gel, results in migrations proportional to polypeptide molecular weight. By comparison to proteins of known size, the molecular weight of unknown polypeptides can be determined. Since SDS denaturation usually destroys biological activity, this procedure requires the use of purified proteins. Otherwise, the identification of the polypeptide of interest in the presence of contaminating species is difficult. SDS–polyacrylamide electrophoresis is usually used for determination of molecular weights in the range of 10,000 to 80,000 daltons. However, procedures are available for extending the useful range to as low as 1,000 daltons.

The SDS procedure depends on a uniform charge density produced in the SDS–polypeptide complex. Some glycoproteins and lipoproteins do not bind characteristic ratios of SDS, and some proteins whose intrinsic charge is not completely masked by the anionic SDS result in complexes of different charge densities and, therefore, give incorrect molecular weights. Also, proteins that are resistant to denaturation in SDS and thus assume atypical conformations give anomalous results.

Polyacrylamide Gradient Gel Electrophoresis

In all electrophoresis procedures described above, resolution is limited by molecular diffusion. Because of this limitation, maximum resolution is usually achieved by narrow starting zones. In gradient gel electrophoresis, where the matrix pore size gradually decreases in the direction of electrophoresis, it is not necessary to have a narrow starting zone because of a zone-sharpening effect during migration. Zone sharpening occurs because the trailing edge of the zone moves faster in the large-pore gel than the leading edge of the zone moving in the smaller-pore gel. Eventually, the gel pore becomes so small that the zone stops migrating. As electrophoresis continues, proteins of low charge density will catch up to proteins of similar size but higher charge density. The result is that a mixture of proteins is resolved into discrete sharp bands where the influence of the protein charge on its final migration position is minimized, and the protein's final migration position is determined by its shape (molecular weight). This allows molecular weight to be determined by comparing the migration distance with those of standard proteins. This procedure actually measures molecular size rather than molecular weight. It assumes the unknown protein has a molecular size and molecular weight relationship similar to the standards. In the case of a standard curve made with globular proteins, an unknown protein that is not globular will yield an incorrect molecular weight. For example, it is known that elongated proteins align during gradient gel electrophoresis and migrate to a pore-size position consitent with the smallest dimension of the molecule and thus give a low molecular weight estimate. This technique is good for obtaining apparent molecular weights in the molecular weight range of 70,000 to 3,000,000 daltons. By combining SDS and polyacrylamide gradient gel electrophoresis, the effective molecular weight range is extended to as low as 20,000 daltons.

If electrophoresis is discontinued before all molecules have traveled to their molecular weight limits, molecules of identical size and different charge densities will be resolved. As many as 40 components of serum are distinguished by limited electrophoresis in polyacrylamide gradient gels.

Immunoelectrophoresis

Electrophoresis combined with radial immunodiffusion is called immunoelectrophoresis. First electrophoresis is carried out in agar or agarose, which separates the antigen mixture into various zones. A longitudinal trough parallel to the direction of electrophoresis is then cut in the gel and filled with antiserum against the antigen mixture. A double diffusion where antiserum diffuses into the gel from the trough and the antigens diffuse radially in all directions from the electrophoretic zones then takes place for 24–48 hr in a humidified chamber. Precipitates in the form of arcs occur at the equivalence point where antigens and antibodies combine. The number of precipitin arcs formed corresponds to the number of separate antigens. Similar procedures can be carried out on cellulose acetate membrane with the advantages that no preparation of the support is necessary, and very low sample volumes are used. The disadvantage of cellulose acetate membrane is that visualization requires staining, and because the time required for optimum precipitin arc formation is not known in advance, one does not know when to stain.

Although immunoelectrophoresis is essentially an analytical tool, quantification is obtained by two-dimension (Laurell) immunoelectrophoresis. In this method the antigens are first electrophoresed in agarose. A strip of gel containing the separated antigens is then immersed in a new agarose gel containing antiserum. The antigens are electrophoresed at right angles to the original separation into the new antibody-containing gel. As the antigens migrate into the gel, they are precipitated by the antiserum. As long as the antigen is in excess, it will continue to migrate into the antibody-containing gel, forming a rocket-shaped precipitate pattern. The amount of antigen within the leading boundary edge is gradually diminished until a stable precipitate forms at the leading edge and thereafter remains stationary. The area under the protein peak is directly proportional to the concentration of the antigen and is used to quantify the antigen present.

Isoelectric Focusing

The electrophoresis of proteins is usually carried out at a constant pH where electrophoretic mobility (if unhindered by molecular sieving, adsorption, etc.) is determined by the isoelectric point of the protein. Isoelectric focusing, however, is carried out in a pH gradient where the lowest pH value is at the anode and the highest pH value is at the cathode. When samples are added to this pH gradient, each will acquire a different charge, depending on its isoelectric point and the pH at that point of the gradient where it is located. In an electric field, migration toward the appropriate electrode will depend on the net charge of the molecule. As the molecule passes through the changing pH gradient, it will eventually reach a point where the surrounding pH is identical to its isoelectric point, and its migration will end. Isoelectric focusing can resolve proteins with differences in isoelectric points as little as 0.02 pH unit. This is possible because of the continuing concentration effect, which counteracts diffusion of each species.

The pH gradients are made with low-molecular-weight synthetic aliphatic amino carboxylic acids having different isoelectric points, compounds that are called ampholytes. The pH gradient is formed by an electric field, which causes each ampholyte to migrate to its respective point. Once formed, the gradient is stabilized against convection by a sucrose density gradient or a matrix such as polyacrylamide. The major advantage of isoelectric focusing is its superb resolving power. By combining isoelectric focusing in one dimension with electrophoresis or immunoprecipitation in a second direction, extremely complex mixtures have been analyzed. The major disadvantage of isoelectric focusing is that many proteins are insoluble or denatured at their isoelectric point. Sometimes solubility is increased by use of high ampholyte concentrations, which compensates for the requirement of salt-free conditions. Also, certain solubilizing as well as nonionic denaturing and reducing agents can be included into the pH gradient for particular applications.

Electrophoretic methods are usually of greatest value in cell biology as analytical tools. Because these methods reflect such properties as electrophoretic mobility, molecular weight, and isoelectric point, they are powerful criteria for the purity of macromolecules. One or more of the above techniques are usually used to define the state of purity of purified macromolecule preparations.

It is usually assumed that the presence of more than one electrophoretic zone is an indication of heterogeneity. Although this is usually true, a homogeneous protein interacting reversibly and rapidly with a small electrophoretically neutral component of the buffer can also result in multiple zones. Such an interaction could also cause a broad trailing similar to that seen when the supporting matrix shows adsorption of the sample. Similarly, multiple electrophoretic zones may result from isomerization or complexing between the same or different macromolecules. When encountering multiple zones, one is advised to be cautious before concluding that the sample is heterogeneous.

PREPARATIVE APPLICATIONS

Finally, it should be pointed out that several electrophoretic methods have been extended to preparative applications. One early method for the preparative separation of electrically charged molecules by paper electrophoresis is called curtain or continuous electrophoresis. In this case, separation is accomplished by the gradual addition of sample to the top of a paper chromatograph fed by a continuously flowing buffer solution. At the same time, a uniform electrical field is applied at right angles to the electrolyte flow. The individual components will then migrate in a path continuously determined by buffer flow and electrophoretic mobility, and are recovered as they elute from the bottom of the chromatograph (Figure 3).

Excellent preparative methods are also available with starch gel and disc gel polyacrylamide electrophoresis as well as isoelectric focusing. Although the resolving power of the analytical methods is usually not duplicated in the preparative applications, these methods are nonetheless powerful tools in the purification of macromolecules.

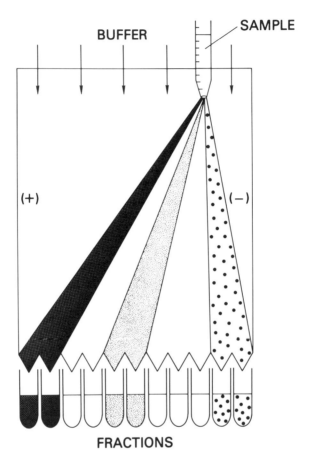

Figure 3. Separation of three components by continuous electrophoresis on a sheet of filter paper.

REFERENCES

Bier, M. 1959. *Electrophoresis.* Academic Press, New York.

Chrambach, A., and Rodbard, D. 1971. *Science* 172:440–51.

Lambrin, P., Rochu, D., and Fine, J. M. 1976. *Anal. Biochem.* 74:567–75.

Leach, S. J., ed. 1969. *Physical Principles and Techniques of Protein Chemistry,* Part A. Academic Press, New York.

Moore, D. H., ed. 1968. *Physical Techniques in Biological Research,* Vol. II, Part A, 2nd ed. Academic Press, New York.

Niederwiesar, A., and Pataki, G., eds. 1971. *New Techniques in Amino Acid, Peptide and Protein Analysis.* Ann Arbor Science Publishers Inc., Ann Arbor, Michigan.

1.5.   Optical Methods

Ronald L. Felsted

Optical techniques are essential tools in cell biology. In the following chapter, primary emphasis is directed toward the essentials of absorption spectrophotometry as one of the most important tools for quantitative work in cell biology. Reference to three additional less commonly used optical methods is also included. For more details the reader is referred to several excellent summaries in the literature.

ABSORPTION SPECTROPHOTOMETRY

All optical methods involve the interaction of electromagnetic radiation with matter. In this interaction most materials will absorb some part of the radiation. The part absorbed will depend upon the molecular structure of the matter; and it is the measurement of this fraction of absorbed radiation that is the basis of spectrophotometric analysis.

Planck showed that there is a strict proportion between the energy of radiation E and its frequency v:

$$E = hv$$

where h is Planck's constant. For example, the low frequency (long wavelength) radiowave radiation contains relatively little energy, while the high frequency (short wavelength) gamma radiation contains a great deal of energy. The absorption of radiation by matter occurs only if the energy of the radiation (frequency) corresponds to the energy required to raise the molecules of the matter to a higher energy state. For monoatomic atoms or ions, the excitation energies are very narrowly defined, and these species absorb very narrow frequency radiations. On the other hand, the radiation absorbed by more complex organic molecules is much broader and complex because of the several possible ways in which energy can be absorbed.

In the ultraviolet (UV) and visible (VIS) spectrum (wavelengths of 200–750 nm), this absorption of energy lifts orbital electrons from their stable ground state to higher-energy (activated) states as follows:

$$M + h\nu \rightarrow M^*$$

where M is the absorbing molecule and M* is the molecule in a higher energy level after absorption of radiant energy $h\nu$. In most cases, the excited state M* is unstable, and the absorbed energy (radiation) is quickly (10^{-8} sec) dissipated in the form of heat as the displaced electrons fall back to their normal energy levels. The excited molecule then returns to its ground state as follows:

$$M^* \rightarrow M + \text{heat}$$

Although this is the most common process, the absorbed energy can also be reemitted as radiation in a process called fluorescence (see below). In this latter case, the excited electron will dissipate a portion of its absorbed energy as heat and then reemit the remaining lower energy as lower-frequency (i.e., longer-wavelength) radiation.

Laws of Light Absorption

The quantitative measurement of light (radiation) absorption is based on two formalized laws. The first is Lambert's law, which states that the proportion of light absorbed by a transparent medium is independent of the intensity of the incident light and that each successive unit layer of the medium absorbs an equal fraction of the light passing through it. As an example, if the intensity of incident light is 1.0 and each successive unit thickness of medium absorbs 1/10 of the incident light, the light intensity will be diminished successively on passing through each unit path length of sample as follows: 1.0, 0.9, 0.81, 0.73, 0.6 . . . , etc. The gradual weakening of light intensity through the medium is expressed mathematically as equation (1):

$$I = I_0 \cdot \exp\left[-k' b\right] \tag{1}$$

where I_0 is the incident light intensity, and I is the intensity of light transmitted through thickness b. The constant k' depends upon the temperature, the wavelength for a given absorbing substance, and a given concentration and solvent if the absorbing substance is in solution. $T = I/I_0$ is defined as the transmittance, and percent transmission is simply $T \cdot 100$.

Since most analytical applications deal with solutions, the relationship between transmittance and concentration is covered by the second formalized law of light absorption, Beer's law, which states that light absorption is proportional to the number of molecules of absorbing substance through which the light passes. For example, light transmitted through a solution of concentration c and length b has the same intensity as light passing through a solution of the same substance at concentration $c/2$ and length $2b$. The mathematical expression of Beer's law is similar to Lambert's law, and is shown in equation (2):

$$I = I_0 \cdot \exp [-k'''c] \tag{2}$$

where k'' is dependent on the solvent, temperature, pathlength, and wavelength.

When both b and c are variable, from equations (1) and (2) the combined Beer-Lambert law becomes:

$$I = I_0 \cdot \exp [-k'''bc]$$

or, more commonly:

$$I = I_0 \, 10^{-abc}$$

where $k''' = 2.3 \, a$. Absorbance A is defined as;

$$A = \log I_0/I = abc \tag{3}$$

Since A is dimensionless, the absorptivity, a, will have the units of $1/bc$. Thus, if the concentrations are expressed as molar, and the pathlength is in centimeters, the units of the absorptivity would be M^{-1} cm^{-1}, and it would be called a molar absorptivity ϵ. Where the molecular weight is unknown, the term $E_{1\,cm}^{1\%}$, (absorbance measured through a 1-cm solution of 1% solute) is frequently used to compare absorption intensities. A summary of terms commonly used in spectrophotometry is compiled in Table 1. In practice

Table 1. Spectrophotometry Nomenclature.

NAME	SYMBOL	DEFINITION
Absorbance	A	$A = -\log_{10} T$
Absorptivity or extinction coefficient	a	$a = A/bc$ $c =$ concentration in g/l
Molar absorptivity	ϵ	$\epsilon = a \cdot$ (molecular weight)
Pathlength	b	Light path through the sample in cm
Transmittance	T	I/I_0, ratio of intensity of transmitted radiation to intensity of incident radiation.
"E-value"	$E_{1\,cm}^{1\%}$	Absorbance of a 1% solution through a 1-cm pathlength. $10 = E_{1\,cm}^{1\%} \cdot$ (molecular weight)
Percent transmission	$\% \, T$	$100 \cdot T$

log I_0/I is not determined directly by the measurement of I_0 and then I on the solution alone. Rather, the solution is compared to a suitable solvent blank in an identical sample container (cuvette). Then I_0 is obtained from the solvent blank, and I is obtained from the sample solution. In this way, one also corrects for factors affecting the decrease of light intensity, other than absorption of solute, as it passes through the solution (see below). It is emphasized that the above laws are valid only for monochromatic light. Practical limitations in instrumentation and anomalies that have an apparent bearing on the validity of these laws will be considered below.

Basic Instrumentation

Instruments used in spectrophotometric analysis usually have the following minimum components: (1) a source of radiant (light) energy, (2) a means of selecting the radiant energy of interest, and (3) a radiation detector (photomultiplier). In addition some means of insertion of liquid, gas, or solid sample into the selected radiant band is also provided. Light absorption can be measured either with a wide band of radiation using a colorimeter or with a narrow band of radiation using a spectrophotometer. The colorimeter utilizes a system of filters to select a broad band of wavelengths in the vicinity of the absorption maxima, whereas the spectrophotometer uses a monochromator and slit system, respectively, to disperse the light and select a band of light with a narrow range of wavelengths. Usually the more expensive instruments allow resolution of the light into a narrower spectral band. The essential features of the spectrophotometer are presented in Figure 1.

The light source must be a source of radiation of the range of wavelengths required for analysis. It must be intense enough so that, after passing through the monochromator and slits, the selected band of light will be of sufficient energy to be detected. In addition, the intensity must be stable at least through

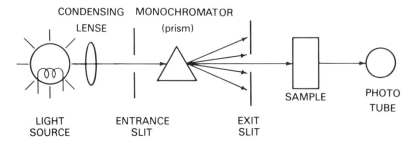

Figure 1. The basic features of a spectrophotometer: (1) light source, (2) monochromator, and (3) phototube.

the course of the experiment. Light with wavelengths in the VIS and near infrared (300–2500 nm) is typically provided by tungsten or tungsten-iodine lamps. For UV analysis, high pressure hydrogen or deuterium lamps with quartz envelopes emit continuous high intensity radiation in the 180–380 nm range.

The radiation from the light source is focused by a condensing lens or concave mirror through an entrance slit, which directs all entering light onto a monochromator (prism or diffraction grating). White light (mixture of all wavelengths) entering the monochromator is dispersed into a spectrum of distinguishable wavelength bands. The spectrum from a prism is discontinuous, with the short-wavelength UV light resolved better than the longer-wavelength VIS light. The diffraction grating has the advantage of producing a linear dispersion of the spectrum, but precautions must be taken to eliminate overlapping light from higher-order spectra. Some of the better instruments pass the light through two monochromators to achieve a spectrum of high optical purity. The spectrum emerging from the monochromator is then passed through an exit slit, which defines the wavelength band width (chromatic purity) of the incident light. With prism instruments, it is necessary to have a changing slit width in order to maintain a particular spectral band width throughout the discontinuous spectrum. Generally, the narrower the slit, the greater the resolution of the instrument. However, there is a minimum slit width, which depends on the design of the instrument, below which no further resolution may be gained. If the light is not sufficiently pure (i.e., broad slit width), a narrow absorption band will appear broadened, and the absorbance of the sample will not obey Beer's law (see below).

Every spectrophotometer requires a means of detecting the light emerging from the exit slit. There are several types of radiation detectors, but each responds more strongly in some regions of the spectrum than in others. A lack of adequate detector sensitivity can limit the minimum slit widths and therefore the spectral band purity attainable with a particular instrument. The signal from the detector can usually be amplified in order to increase the instrument sensitivity; however, this is usually accompanied by increased noise and requires more expensive circuitry.

Precautions in Spectrophotometry

The linearity between concentration and absorbance predicted by the Beer-Lambert law is subject to many anomalies. A number of these deviations can be explained by changes in the composition of sample with concentration, pH, and so on. For example, many solutions of acids, bases, or salts are more completely ionized in dilute than concentrated solution. Since absorption of the ionized species may differ from the un-ionized species, deviations from the Beer-Lambert law may result. Other sample-solvent-related deviations can be explained by light scattering, fluorescence, decomposition, or aggregation.

Deviations of a more general nature can also occur. When a beam of radiation passes through a sample, the incident radiation will always be more intense than the transmitted light. Although we assume that the decrease in light intensity is due strictly to true absorption of incident light by the sample, apparent absorption can also result from reflection of incident light. In the case of a liquid sample, there are four reflective surfaces (i.e., two glass–air and two glass–liquid interfaces). Even greater reflections may occur within the instrument itself from the surface of the slits or the surface of the photo cell. For analytical work, apparent deviations from the Beer-Lambert law can be alleviated largely by the use of clean cuvettes, suitable solvent blanks, and calibration curves.

It should be reemphasized that the Beer-Lambert law is valid only with monochromatic light. Although an instrument may be set at a particular wavelength, the light coming from the exit slit may actually include not only the desired wavelength but additional radiation of longer and shorter wavelengths. The resulting absorbance is then an average absorbance of all the chromophores included within the band of nonmonochromatic light. These effects are minimized by making absorbance measurements at wavelengths corresponding to the middle of broad maximum absorption regions. In this way not only is the sensitivity of the measurement maximized, but the average absorbance recorded from the nonmonochromatic light will be very close to the absorbance that would be obtained if true monochromatic light were used. Under conditions of nonmonochromatic light, conformity to the Beer-Lambert law is no assurance that correct values are being obtained. A sure test is provided only by measuring absorbance as a function of slit width.

The presence of stray light is really a special case of nonmonochromatic light just discussed. Stray light results from various instrument design limitations, including surface reflections, diffraction effects, and imperfections in optics. Radiation that results from these effects can be at wavelengths outside the spectral band defined by the monochromator. If we assume that this stray light is not significantly absorbed compared to the monochromatic light, the larger the percentage of nonabsorbable incident light (stray light), the lower the maximum percentage of incident light that can be absorbed by the true chromophore. In the absence of stray light, the absorbance is given by equation (3):

$$A = \log \frac{I_0}{I}$$

With stray light contributing equally to sample and reference and no stray light being absorbed by the sample:

$$A_{app} = \log \frac{I_0 + \text{stray light}}{I + \text{stray light}}$$

where A_{app} is the apparent absorbance. As the concentration of the absorbing solute is increased, I approaches zero until:

$$A_{app} \approx \log \frac{I_0 + \text{stray light}}{\text{stray light}} = \text{constant}$$

The effect is that the larger the percentage of stray light is, the greater the depression of measured absorbance (Figure 2). Spectrophotometers with a single monochromator typically have about 0.1% stray light. This limits the maximum practical measurable absorbance to about 1.7. More expensive instruments utilizing double monochromators and filters can reduce stray light to lower than 0.0001% and will allow measurements up to an absorbance

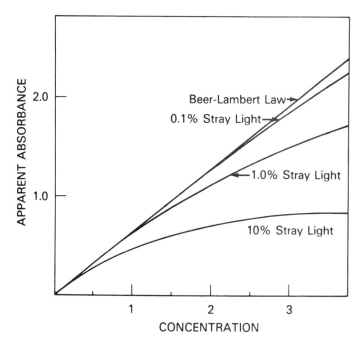

Figure 2. The effect of stray light on the Beer-Lambert relationship.

of about 6. Stray-light errors are most serious near the wavelength limits of the spectrophotometer and, naturally, at very high absorbances.

Applications

Since molecular structure determines the wavelength of light that is absorbed, absorption spectra are sometimes used in the qualitative identification of unknown materials. Absorption spectra are usually presented by plotting absorbance (ordinant) as a function of wavelength (abscissa) (Figure 3). Identification is facilitated by reference to collections of UV-VIS spectra.

Most organic molecules encountered in cell biology exhibit rather broad absorption characteristics, which limit precise qualitative application. On the other hand, because of the relationship between absorption and concentration, spectrophotometry is very useful for quantitative analysis. The sensitivity

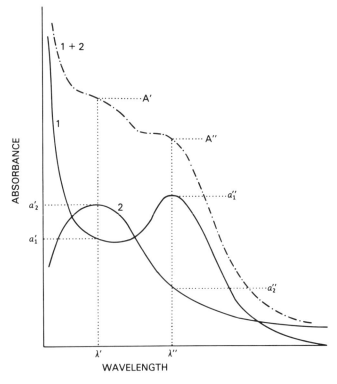

Figure 3. The absorbance spectra of a two-component mixture (—.—) and individual components 1 and 2 (——). At wavelengths of λ' and λ'', components 1 and 2 exhibit absorbances of A' and A'' and individual absorptivities of a'_1 and a'_2, and a''_1 and a''_2, respectively.

of this method is determined by the size of the absorptivity and the minimal absorbance that can be determined practically. For example, if the molar absorptivity for a compound is $10^4 M^{-1}$ cm^{-1}, and the minimum detectable absorbance is 0.01, then for a 1-cm pathlength, the minimum concentration that can be detected from the Beer-Lambert law, equation (3), is:

$$c = \frac{A}{ab} = \frac{0.01}{(10^4 M^{-1}\ cm^{-1})\,(1\ cm)} = 10^{-6} M$$

Greater sensitivity can be achieved by using longer-pathlength cells.

Usually, the absorbances of different molecules are independent of each other, and thus the total absorption is the sum of that of each contributing absorbing molecule. Because of this additive property, mixtures of n components can sometimes be analyzed by measuring n absorbances at n different wavelengths where the absorbances of the individual components at those wavelengths are known. For a two-component system (Figure 3) where the pathlength b is constant:

$$A' = a_1' \ c_1 \ b + a_2' \ c_2 \ b$$
$$A'' = a_1'' \ c_1 \ b + a_2'' \ c_2 \ b$$

where A' and A'' are the observed absorbances at the wavelengths λ' and λ'', a_1' and a_2' are the absorbances of components 1 and 2 at wavelength λ', a_1'' and a_2'' are the absorbances of components 1 and 2 at wavelength λ'', and c_1 and c_2 are the unknown concentrations of components 1 and 2. These two equations can be solved simultaneously for the two unknowns.

Another common application of spectrophotometry is for the determination of reaction rates. For example, consider the oxidation of ethyl alcohol by nicotinamide adenine dinucleotide (NAD^+) and alcohol dehydrogenase (ADH):

$$\text{ethyl alcohol} + NAD^+ \xrightarrow[\text{ADH}]{} \text{acetaldehyde} + NADH + H^+$$

The reduced cofactor, NADH, absorbs strongly at 340 nm, whereas none of the other substrates or products has any significant absorption at this wavelength. Therefore, the rate of enzymatic oxidation of ethyl alcohol (or reduction of NAD^+) is conveniently measured by following the increase in absorption at 340 nm as a function of time as the product NADH accumulates.

Other possible applications include the study of chemical equilibrium reactions, difference spectroscopy, and measurements in the far UV (below 190 nm) and the near infrared (above 800 nm).

FLUORESCENCE

As described above, the reemission of absorbed radiation at a longer wavelength is called fluorescence. The ratio of the total emitted light to the total absorbed light is called the quantum efficiency and is characteristic of each molecule. Therefore, both the amount of light absorbed and the amount of light reemitted are proportional to concentration. Since the quantum efficiency and the shape of the emission spectrum are independent of the wavelength of the absorbed light, only the intensity and not the shape of the emission spectrum will change if the absorbed light is at a wavelength different from the wavelength of the absorption maximum of the molecule. A nonfluorescent molecule has a quantum efficiency of zero.

Since a fluorescent molecule also must absorb incident light, in theory, this molecule can be quantified by a measurement of absorbance or fluorescence. The measurement of fluorescence, however, has the advantage of being from 10^2 to 10^3 times more sensitive than absorbance measurements. This increase in sensitivity is partly explained by the fact that the emitted light is measured directly and may be increased or decreased by increasing or decreasing the intensity of the light absorbed. In spectrophotometry, on the other hand, the concentration is a measure of the loss of light as it passes through the sample. This indirect measurement limits the concentrations that can be determined because of inaccuracies of measuring small differences of light intensities.

Another advantage of fluorescence is its specificity. The presence of an absorbing but nonfluorescent contaminant is a direct interference in spectrophotometry but does not necessarily interfere in fluorescence measurements. In addition, even if two fluorescent compounds absorb at the same wavelength, they need not necessarily emit at the same wavelength.

The basic schematic of a fluorometer is presented in Figure 4. If the excitation and emission light are selected by filters, the instrument is known as a filter fluorometer. If, instead, monochromators are used to establish the excitation and emission wavelengths, it is called a spectrofluorometer. An excitation spectrum is obtained from the latter instrument by setting the emission monochromator at a wavelength at or near the emission peak of a sample and scanning the excitation monochromator; reversing the process gives an emission spectrum. For quantitative work the desired excitation and emission wavelengths are selected, and the relative fluorescence of unknowns compared to the fluorescence of standards. The emission spectra obtained from these instruments are uncorrected and are really a composite of the true emission spectra plus instrumental errors defined by the nature of the light source, the monochromator efficiency, and the phototube sensitivity at various wavelengths. These spectra, however, are generally useful for rough comparisons

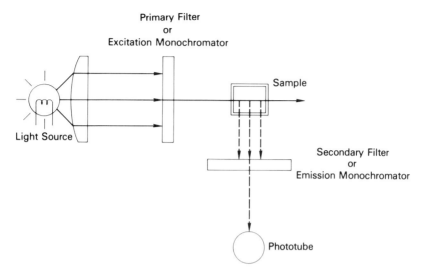

Figure 4. The basic features of a filter fluorometer (equipped with primary and secondary filters) and a spectrofluorometer (equipped with excitation and emission monochromators).

of spectra from different instruments. Absolute spectrofluorometers are now on the market, which automatically correct for these instrument variations and provide very useful corrected or absolute emission spectra.

OPTICAL ROTARY DISPERSION AND CIRCULAR DICHROISM

Plane-polarized light can be resolved into right-handed and left-handed circularly polarized component vectors. These two circularly polarized vectors exhibit different indices of refraction (or velocities) and different molar absorptivities as they pass through asymetric molecules. This difference in refraction results in rotation of the composite plane of polarized light and is termed circular birefringence. The variation of circular birefringence with the wavelength of light is called optical rotary dispersion (ORD), and the difference in absorption of the left and right circularly polarized component vectors by the asymetric molecule is called circular dichroism (CD). These methods have been most useful in the study of protein structure and provide basically the same information.

Both ORD and CD have been used to distinguish differences between the random-coil form and the helical form of synthetic polypeptides, and the differences in secondary structure of native and denatured proteins. Estimates of helical content have been commonly obtained from the Moffit-Yang equation:

$$[m'] = \frac{a_0\lambda^2}{\lambda^2 - \lambda_0^2} + \frac{b_0\lambda^4}{(\lambda^2 - \lambda_0^2)^2}$$

where $[m']$ is the reduced mean residue rotation, λ is wavelength, and a_0, b_0, and λ_0 are constants. Values of b_0 are known to vary from about -630 for perfectly α-helical polymers to zero for random coils. Therefore, a percent estimate of helix content in polymers and proteins is obtained from 100 $b_0/630$. This calculation is, however, an oversimplification because in proteins a number of complications arise.

REFERENCES

Clark, G. L., ed. 1961. *The Encyclopedia of Spectroscopy.* Reinhold Publishing Corp., New York.

Gillam, A. E., and Stern, E. S. 1955. *Electronic Absorption Spectroscopy.* Edward Arnold Publishers Ltd., London.

Jergensons, B. 1973. *Optical Activity of Proteins and Other Macromolecules.* Springer-Verlag, New York.

Kolthoff, I. M., and Elving, P. J., eds. 1964. *Treatise on Analytical Chemistry,* Part I, Vol. 5. Interscience Publishers, New York.

Leach, S. J., ed. 1973. *Physical Principles and Techniques of Protein Chemistry,* Part C. Academic Press, New York.

Oster, G., and Pollister, A. W., eds. 1955. *Physical Techniques in Biological Research,* Vol. I. Academic Press, New York.

Udenfriend, S. 1962. *Fluorescence Assay in Biology and Medicine,* Vol. I. Academic Press, New York.

Udenfriend, S. 1969. *Fluorescence Assay in Biology and Medicine,* Vol. II. Academic Press, New York.

1.6. Immunological Methods*

Hans L. Spiegelberg

ABBREVIATIONS

Ig, immunoglobulins—all antibodies are immunoglobulins, but not all immunoglobulins necessarily have antibody activity.
C, complement.
PBS, phosphate-buffered 0.15 M NaCl, pH 7.2–7.4.
SAS, saturated ammonium sulfate.
RIA, radioimmunoassay.

INTRODUCTION

In the past 25 years, immunology has been one of the fastest-growing fields in biology. In addition to major breakthroughs that have occurred within this discipline it has made a great impact on other areas of biology. First, immunological phenomena have provided means for studying protein–protein interactions, genetic regulation of protein synthesis, cell differentiation, cell–cell interactions, cell membrane receptors, and so on. Second, antibodies have been shown to be highly specific reagents that can be used to detect, characterize, and quantitate small quantities of biological substances and, therefore, serve as invaluable tools for investigators outside the field of immunology. It is this second impact of immunology with which this chapter deals. It is impossible to cover all immunological methods; therefore, emphasis is placed on how to prepare antibodies, isolate them, and use them in the most common techniques. Additional information with respect to both detailed procedures and specialized use of some of the techniques should be sought in such books as *Methods in Immunology* by Campbell et al. (1), *Manual of Clinical Immunology* edited by Rose and Friedman (2), *In Vitro Methods in Cell-Mediated and Tumor Immunity* edited by Bloom and Davis (3), *Experimental Immunochemistry* edited by Kabat and Mayer (4), *Methods in Immunology and Immunochemistry* edited by Williams and Chase (5), and so on.

* Publication no. 1427 from the Immunology Departments of the Research Institute of Scripps Clinic. The work was supported by USPHS grant AI–10734–01.

Preparation of Hyperimmune Sera

Antibodies or immunoglobulins (Ig) of mammals can be divided into five classes, IgG, IgA, IgM, IgD, and IgE, according to antigenic and structural differences. IgG is the major class and, except for IgM, is almost always used for immunological test systems. IgM is favored in complement (C) fixation and hemagglutination tests because it is more efficient than IgG in these two systems.

In order to produce large quantities (3–5 mg/ml or more) of high-affinity IgG antibodies, the antigen to be injected should be mixed with a so-called adjuvant. The most commonly used adjuvant is Freund's adjuvant (6), which consists of a mixture of a mineral oil (e.g., Bayol F., Esso Co.) and an emulsifier (e.g., Arlacel C. Atlas Chemical Co.) in proportion v/v 9:1. It is easily prepared in the laboratory or can be obtained commercially as a mixture (e.g., from Difco Lab). The oil–emulsifier mixture is called incomplete adjuvant. In contrast, complete Freund's adjuvant also contains heat-killed mycobacteria (e.g., *M. tuberculosis* H37RA, Difco Lab). The mycobacteria cause an inflammation at the injection site depending on the dose. Adjuvant containing 0.1 mg/ml bacteria usually results in a mild reaction, whereas 0.2–1.0 mg/ml can cause severe abscesses. Incomplete adjuvant is used when "strong" antigens are injected, and the experimental animal is boosted periodically over months or years. Complete adjuvant is preferred when either "poor" antigens or mixtures of many antigens with differing concentrations, such as whole serum, are used for the inoculation. Guinea pigs produce two subclasses of IgG, depending on the nature of the adjuvant, one that fixes complement and the other that fixes to mast cells and causes anaphylactic reactions (7). However, in rabbits, goats, and sheep that are most commonly used for hyperimmune serum production, this is not the case. Rabbits show only one subclass of IgG. Goats or sheep form several IgG subclasses, but it is unpredictable what subclass predominates in an individual animal.

The antigens to be injected are usually dissolved in phosphate-buffered 0.15 M NaCl of pH 7.2–7.4 (PBS). The quantity depends on the availability and can vary from 10 μg to 10 mg/ml. Equal volumes of Freund's adjuvant and antigen are mixed in a blender or other device and vigorously mixed until a thick emulsion is formed. A thick emulsion is important in order to avoid rapid leaking of the antigen out of the adjuvant. A good adjuvant preparation does not separate into the oil and water phases for several weeks if stored at 4°C. The adjuvant is injected either subcutaneously or intramuscularly at several sites over the neck and back area. Rabbits are also injected into the footpads. The initial injection is followed by biweekly booster injections near the initial sites. The footpads of rabbits are injected only once because of possible ulceration. Sera from animals demonstrating a good antibody response contain precipitating antibody 4 weeks after the initial injection and reach a maximum after 6 to 8 weeks. If they do not yield a good antiserum at this time, it is better to start a new animal than to continue with booster injections; poor initial responders seldom change into good antibody producers.

In general, injection of the antigen in a form that remains at the injection site for long periods of time and causes a local inflammatory response, appears to be the best approach for obtaining antisera of high antibody content. Methylated bovine serum albumin, pertussis vaccine, and other substances have also been shown to have a good adjuvant effect.

ISOLATION OF IgG AND ITS F(ab')$_2$ AND Fab FRAGMENTS

The IgG fraction of a hyperimmune serum, which contains most of the antibodies, can easily be isolated in pure form. First, the globulin fraction of the serum is precipitated at a 50% saturated ammonium sulfate (SAS) concentration and washed in 50% SAS until the supernatant is colorless. This step eliminates albumin and free hemoglobin, which is often present in animal sera because of the hemolysis occurring during blood and serum collection. Free hemoglobulin isolates in later steps with IgG and therefore must be eliminated. The precipitated globulin fraction is dissolved in water and dialyzed against 0.015 M phosphate buffer, pH 8.0. It is then applied on a DEAE-cellulose column equilibrated with the same buffer. The majority of the IgG is eluted with this buffer in pure form. Goat or sheep antisera sometimes contain a lot of γ1-type IgG antibodies, and a second stepwise elution with 0.035 M PO$_4$ buffer, pH 8.0 should be performed and tested for antibody activity. In addition to the IgG, the 0.035 M fraction also contains β proteins, which can be separated by Sephadex G-200 gel filtration. The isolated IgG is concentrated by vacuum dialysis. A simple device for this purpose, which can be assembled in any laboratory, is shown in Figure 1.

IgG has a tendency to aggregate and to bind nonspecifically to many surfaces. The portion of the molecule that is responsible for this is called the Fc fragment. It does not participate in the antibody combining site but mediates secondary biological functions, such as C fixation and binding to Fc cell receptors (8). Because the nonspecific "sticking" of IgG can interfere with certain test systems (e.g., immunofluorescence or isolation of antigens by immunoadsorbent columns), the F(ab')$_2$ or Fab fragments, which contain the antibody combining site but not Fc fragment, are prepared. The F(ab')$_2$ fragment, a divalent antibody fragment that still precipitates and agglutinates antigens, is prepared by pepsin digestion (3% w/w) of IgG in a pH 4.0 acetate buffer (9). Pepsin degrades the Fc fragment into mostly dialyzable

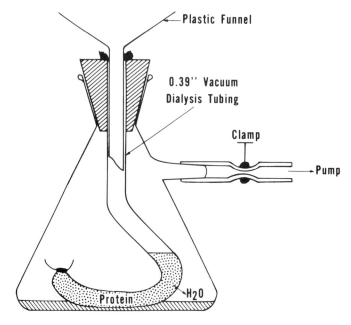

Figure 1. Protein concentration device. Special dialysis tubing is closed with a double knot, led through a rubber stopper, and pushed over the tip of a plastic funnel. The tubing and funnel tip are then pushed into the stopper and placed on top of a side arm flask. The funnel is filled with the protein solution to be concentrated, and a strong vacuum is applied. The excess tubing on top of the stopper prevents the dialysis tubing from being pulled into the flask. The flask is closed with clamp and kept at 4°C until the protein solution is concentrated to the desired volume. The protein that adheres to the wall of the tubing is pushed off by massaging the tubing, and the concentrated protein dialyzed against PBS in the same dialysis bag used for concentration.

peptides. Theoretically, the $F(ab')_2$ fragment should have the same precipitin and agglutinin activity as the parent IgG. However, empirically, $F(ab')_2$ of the equivalent of about twice the amount of original IgG is needed to obtain equal reactions. The $F(ab')_2$ fragment can be reduced in Tris buffer, pH 8.2 with 0.02 M dithiothreitol (3.09 mg/ml) for 2 hr at room temperature and then alkylated with 0.05 M iodoacetamide (10 mg/ml) to form univalent Fab' fragments, each containing one antibody combining site.

When both Fab and Fc fragments are required, the IgG is digested with 1% w/w papain in the presence of 0.02 M cysteine hydrochloride (1.5 mg/ml) and 0.002 M EDTA-tetrasodium salt (0.75 mg/ml) at pH 7.0 (10). Rabbit Fab and Fc fragments are then separated by CM-cellulose chromatography (10). Fab and Fc fragments of all other species are isolated by DEAE-cellulose chromatography. The Fab fragments elute from such columns with 0.005

M PO$_4$ buffer, pH 8.0, and the Fc fragments with the same buffer at a higher molarity (0.05–0.1 M).

PURIFICATION OF ANTIBODIES

In many investigations it is advantageous or even necessary to have not only the IgG serum fraction but a pure antibody preparation. Many methods have been described for this; some are derived from other techniques (11) but none is absolutely satisfactory. They are all based on insolubilization of the antigen, reaction of the antiserum with the insoluble antigen, and washing off the nonantibody protein, followed by dissociation of the antibodies from the insoluble antigen with acidic buffers or chaotropic agents. Theoretically, the procedure is simple, but practically many problems arise. First, the antigen is no longer native with respect to all its antigenic determinants after insolubilization and, therefore, may not absorb all antibodies; second, the insoluble antigen nonspecifically adsorbs serum proteins that cannot be completely washed off; third, a small portion of the antigen becomes soluble during elution of the antibodies; and fourth, the dissociation conditions alter the antibodies and cause irreversible aggregation and loss of some of its activity. Nevertheless, if relatively large quantities of antigen and antibodies are available, relatively pure antibodies can be produced by a number of methods.

At present, coupling of the antigen to CNBr-activated Sepharose-4B (Pharmacia Fine Chemicals Co.) appears to be the most commonly used method. The CNBr-treated Sepharose-4B is activated with dilute HCl, 10 mg protein added per g, and mixed overnight. The reaction is stopped with ethanolamine and the Sepharose-4B–antigen complex thoroughly washed. Heat-inactivated antiserum (to prevent binding of C) is then added, the nonantibody protein is washed off, and the antibodies are eluted with either 0.2 M glycine buffer, pH 2.5 or 3.5 M Na-thiocyanate, pH 7.0. The eluted antibodies are immediately dialyzed against PBS and concentrated by pressure dialysis (Figure 1).

The reverse procedure is used for isolation of antigens. If available, purified antibodies (because they have a much higher capacity to bind antigen than the IgG fraction) are coupled to Sepharose-4B. A mixture of antigens is then added, and material that does not bind to the antibodies is washed off. The specifically bound antigen is then eluted from the immunoadsorbent as described above.

GEL DIFFUSION PRECIPITIN REACTIONS

Addition of hyperimmune antiserum to a soluble antigen results in the formation of a lattice of antigen–antibody molecules that becomes visible as a white insoluble precipitate. When the amount of antigen added to a constant amount of antiserum is varied, different amounts of precipitate are formed; the plot of this reaction is called a precipitin curve (Figure 2) (12). In antibody excess, all antigen is precipitated, the excess antibodies remaining in the supernatant. A "zone of equivalence" is then reached at the optimal antibody–antigen ratio, where over 98% of the antibody and antigen is precipitated. Addition of more antigen (antigen excess) results in solubilization of the precipitate and formation of soluble antigen–antibody complexes in the supernatant. The shape of the precipitin curve depends mainly on the nature of the antigen. In general, small molecules have a high antibody–antigen ratio at equivalence, and the precipitate is dissolved completely at relatively small antigen excess. In contrast, high-molecular-weight antigens show a broad precipitin curve (Figure 2). The most accurate means of quantitating the amount of precipitating antibody in a given antiserum is by determining

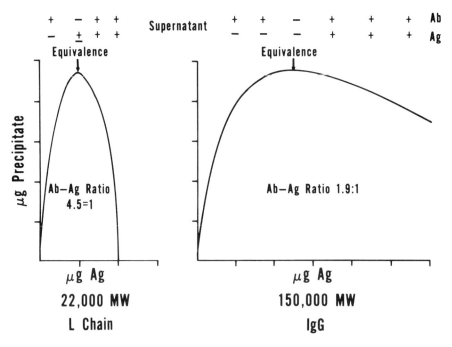

Figure 2. Two types of precipitin curves. On the left side, Ig light chains and on the right side IgG were added in increasing quantities to a constant amount of antiserum. As more antigen is added, more precipitate is formed until equivalence (optimal antibody–antigen concentration) is reached. Addition of more antigen results in formation of soluble complexes with the appearance of both antibodies and antigen in the supernatant. In general, small-molecular-weight antigens (e.g., light chain) show a higher antibody–antigen ratio at equivalence than high-molecular-weight antigens (e.g., IgG) and dissolve more rapidly in antigen excess.

the precipitin curve. Another application of the precipitin reaction in solution is the measurement of the turbidity that is created after an antigen–antibody precipitin reaction. It has recently been adapted for automated equipment designed to measure antigen concentrations in serum.

The most widely used applications of the precipitin reaction, however, are the precipitin reactions performed in semisolid media such as agar or agarose. The advantages of these gel precipitin analyses are that only small amounts of reagents are necessary because of their high sensitivity, the ability to compare different antigens to each other, and, last but not least, the simplicity of the methods, allowing their performance in any laboratory. The three most commonly used variations of gel precipitin reactions are Ouchterlony analysis (13), immunoelectrophoresis (14), and antigen quantitation by the Mancini method (15). For the Ouchterlony analysis (Figure 3), 1% agar or agarose is dissolved in PBS containing merthiolate or sodium azide as antibacterial agent, employing a boiling water bath. Three milliliters agar is then poured onto a microscope slide or into a Petri dish and allowed to solidify in a moist chamber in the cold. A pattern of wells, usually a center well with four to eight surrounding wells, is cut with one of the many commercially available cutting devices. The agar is removed from the well by suction. The center well is filled with the antiserum, and surrounding wells are filled with antigens. After incubation in a moist chamber at 4°C, room temperature, or 37°C for 18–48 hr, lines of precipitate form in the agar. When two antigens are placed in adjacent wells and a polyvalent antiserum is placed in the center, three major patterns can be observed. First, antigenic identity of two substances is characterized by complete fusion of the two precipitin lines (Figure 3, wells 2 and 3). Second, partial antigenic identity is shown by fusion of the lines and a "spur" formation of the antigen that has more antigenic determinants than the other (Figure 3, wells 1 and 2, 3 and 4, 3 and 5, 1 and 6). Third, antigenic nonidentity is shown by crossing of the two precipitin lines (Figure 3, wells 5 and 6). If more than one antigen is detected by the antiserum, two or more parallel precipitin lines are formed. The precipitin line is located halfway between the two wells when optimal antigen–antibody concentrations are present. The line is located more toward the antiserum well in antigen excess and vice versa. Faint and diffuse lines are seen with weak antisera. Depending on the size of the wells and distance between them and the nature of antigen and antiserum, proteins at concentrations as low as a few μg/ml can be detected. If a large antigen excess exists, a precipitin line can appear early after the wells are filled (3–4 hr) and disappear thereafter in complete antigen excess. This is particularly the case for low-molecular-weight antigens (e.g., light chains of Ig). The reason for this was explained above and in Figure 2. The sensitivity of the Ouchterlony reaction can be increased at least tenfold if radioactive reagents are used.

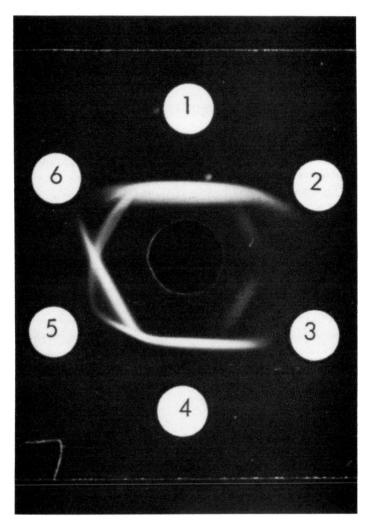

Figure 3. Typical patterns of double gel diffusion (Ouchterlony) analysis. Center well contains the antiserum (polyvalent anti-IgG). The antigen in well 1 (IgG and IgM) forms two poorly separated lines appearing as a diffuse line. The line shows one "spur" over protein in well 2 (IgM) and three spurs over protein in well 6 (Fc fragment of IgG). It also forms a line of "partial identity" with the precipitin line of well 6 (IgG has more determinants than its Fc fragment but shares common determinants). Proteins in wells 2 (IgM) and 3 (IgM) form weak precipitin lines because of small antibody content to IgM, and show line of "identity." Protein in well 4 (IgG) shows line of partial identity and a spur over proteins in wells 3 (IgM) and 5 (Fab fragment of IgG). The spur of IgG over the Fab fragment shows line of identity to the Fc fragment in well 6. The proteins in wells 5 (Fab) and 6 (Fc) show line of "nonidentity." The protein concentration was 1 mg/ml for IgG and IgM and 0.25 mg/ml for the Fab and Fc fragments.

For this, the Ouchterlony plate is washed, dried, and examined by incubation or on X-ray film.

In the immunoelectrophoresis method (Figure 4), gel diffusion precipitation is combined with electrophoresis. The antigen can therefore be characterized by both its mobility in an electric field and antigenic behavior. The agar is dissolved at a 2% concentration in 0.05 ionic strength barbital buffer, pH 8.2 and poured onto a miscroscope slide (14). Wells are cut, filled with the antigen solutions, and immediately subjected to electrophoresis. Troughs are then cut between the wells in the direction of electrophoresis and filled with antiserum. After incubation for 6–18 hr, precipitin arcs appear along the troughs (Figure 4). Precipitin arcs of high-molecular-weight substances are located farther away from the troughs than low-molecular-weight antigens. Antigen excess results in localization of the arc near the trough. The immuno-electrophoresis method is particularly useful for mixtures of antigens.

Immunoelectrophoresis

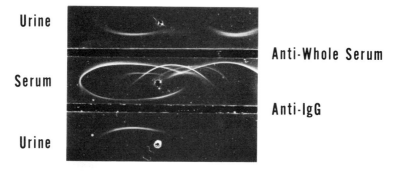

Urine

Serum

Urine

Anti-Whole Serum

Anti-IgG

Mancini Plate

Figure 4. Immunoelectrophoresis (top) and radial diffusion (Mancini) (bottom) analysis. Serum and urine of a patient with nephrosis were placed in the wells of an immunoelectrophoresis slide and separated for 1 hr. Troughs were filled with antiserum to human serum (top) and to IgG (bottom). The urine contains a cathodal component (IgG) and an anodal component (albumin), whereas the serum contains many proteins. In the Mancini analysis, IgG of three known concentrations (10, 5, and 2.5 mg/ml) was filled in wells 1–3 to the left and three samples of unknown concentration to the left. The agarose contained anti-IgG antibodies. The diameter of the precipitin rings is proportional to the antigen concentration.

Antigens can be accurately quantitated by the radial gel diffusion method described by Mancini et al. (15) (Figure 4). In this technique monospecific antibody is mixed with 3% molten agar at 56°C and poured into plastic dishes. Wells are cut and filled with antigen solutions of known as well as unknown concentrations. A precipitin ring will form around the well. The ring will expand until all antigen has reacted with the antibody present in the agar. The diameter of the ring is proportional to the antigen concentration. A standard curve is made by plotting the concentration on a semilogarithmic scale versus the diameter of the precipitin ring on a linear scale.

A typical protocol in which gel diffusion methods are used as tools for isolation of an unknown protein having a given function (e.g., enzymatic activity) is as follows. First, an antiserum is made to the mixture containing the enzyme. Second, the mixture of proteins is separated by electrophoresis, column chromatography, adsorption chromatography, and so on, and the individual fractions are analyzed for enzyme activity and number of proteins by immunoelectrophoresis and Ouchterlony analysis. Different protein isolation procedures are used until a fraction is obtained that contains only one protein having the enzyme activity. A monospecific antiserum is then made against the pure enzyme, and this antiserum used for quantitation of the enzyme-protein by the Mancini method. The antiserum is also used to search for the presence of the enzyme in various biological fluids employing Ouchterlony analysis.

HEMAGGLUTINATION

One of the most sensitive immunological tests for detection of antibodies and antigens is hemagglutination and hemagglutination inhibition (16). It has been shown that 0.03 μg/ml antibody concentrations can still cause an agglutination reaction. Although agglutination of cells can be seen under the microscope, the settling of erythrocytes in a glass tube or a conical well of a plastic tray (Figure 5) is a more sensitive, accurate, and practical procedure to determine agglutination. Nonreactive erythrocytes settle as a sharply delineated small button, whereas agglutinated cells evenly cover the bottom of the tube or well. Usually doubling dilutions of the antiserum are tested, and the result is expressed in a semiquantitative manner as titer, the highest dilution of the antiserum that causes complete agglutination of a 0.5% concentration of red cells. In order to obtain equal sedimentation conditions in wells containing different antiserum dilutions or no antibody, the protein concentration should be similar in all wells. Therefore, 1 or 2% normal serum or 1 mg/ml bovine serum albumin is added to the diluent. The antiserum dilutions are first added to the wells, followed by the red cell suspension. After mixing, the cells are allowed to settle for several hours before the

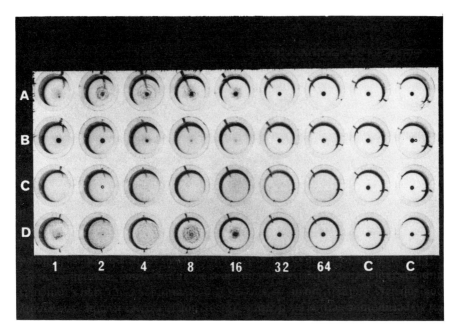

Figure 5. Hemagglutination reaction. Doubling dilutions (1, 2, 4, 8, etc.) of four rabbit anti-ox erythrocyte antisera (A, B, C, D) were tested for agglutinating antibodies to ox erythrocytes. The last two rows contained diluent (3 mg bovine serum albumin in PBS) as a negative control (C). The agglutination titer of sera A, B, and D is 1:16, although they show different patterns probably related to different IgM and IgG concentrations. The serum C has a titer of >1:64. A negative reaction is shown by a sharp cell button in the middle of the conical well, and a positive reaction by an even or a crenated layer of red cells. Antiserum B shows a "prozone" phenomenon, that is, absence of agglutination at the highest antibody concentrations.

reaction is read. If the end titer is unclear, the cells can be mixed again and allowed to settle a second time, a procedure that often yields a more clear-cut result. Some sera show a "prozone" phenomenon (Figure 5, row B); that is, no agglutination occurs at the highest concentrations because of antibody excess.

Since antibodies directed to red cells are not often used, indirect hemagglutination tests have been developed in which protein or carbohydrate antigens are coupled to the red cells. In such a system the red cells are not the antigen but serve as the indicator for an unrelated antigen–antibody agglutinin reaction. For adsorption of antigens to red cells, the cells are treated with either tannic acid (16) or pyruvic aldehyde and/or formaldehyde (17). The cells treated with the latter have the advantage that they can be stored for long periods of time. The antigen can also be covalently coupled to red cells with $CrCl_2$ (18) or with bis-diazotized benzidine (16).

A modification of the hemagglutination method used for detection of small quantities of antigen is the hemagglutination inhibition assay. The red cells are coated with a known antigen and agglutinated with a constant amount of antibody. For the detection of the antigen in an unknown sample, serial dilutions of the sample are mixed with a constant amount of antibody before addition of the antigen-coated red cells. If the antigen is present in the unknown sample, it will react with the antibodies and inhibit the hemagglutination reaction in a dose-dependent manner.

ROSETTE ASSAY

Recently, the sensitive and simple rosette assay has found wide applications for the detection of cell membrane receptors or other cell membrane components. Initially, it was observed that sheep red cells bind specifically to human T lymphocytes by attaching around the lymphocyte to form a "rosette" (19). "Receptors" for heterologous red cells can be detected by this assay; however, this reaction is of limited interest. In contrast, when red cells that do not react with other cells are coated with a specific protein to which the other cells have receptors, the rosette assay gains a wide application. Rosette assays for only a few cell surface components have been designed thus far, but it is likely that use of this method will increase in the future through many modifications.

Examples for the detection of specific cell receptors are given in Figure 6. Ox red cells do not react with human white cells and can therefore be used as indicator cells for other substances. If they are coated with IgG, they form rosettes with cells that have receptors for the Fc fragment of IgG such as lymphocytes (Figure 6, A) and monocytes (Figure 6, C). Similarly, if they are coated with IgE, they detect certain lymphocytes (Figure 6, B) and basophils (Figure 6, D), both having Fc receptors for IgE. To demonstrate specificity of these reactions, soluble proteins are added, which inhibit the rosette formation.

Theoretically, many proteins and carbohydrates could be attached to red cells, and the coated cells could be used as indicator cells for receptors either on cell surfaces or in tissues by layering the indicator cells onto tissue sections. We have recently modified a method described by Strausbach et al. (20) for bridging proteins or purified antibody F(ab')$_2$ fragments directed to cell surface components for the rosette assay (Figure 7) (21). Fab fragments of rabbit anti-ox erythrocyte antibodies were coupled with gluteraldehyde to Fc fragments of IgE and used for detection of Fc-receptors for IgE. We have also coupled Fab anti-ox fragments to purified F(ab')$_2$ anti-IgM or anti-IgD and detected the membrane-bound surface immunoglobulin sIgM and sIgD on lymphocytes (Figure 7). The Fab anti-ox red cell fragment is used

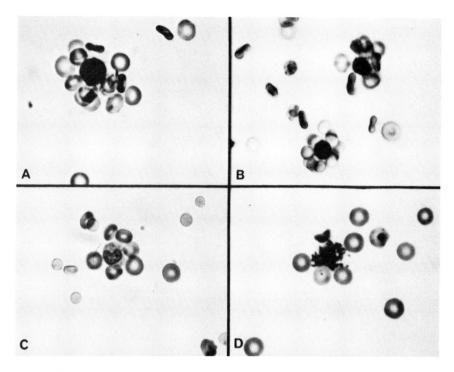

Figure 6. Rosette formation. Ox erythrocytes coated with immunoglobulins were added to different white blood cells in order to detect receptors for the Fc fragment of the Ig. If the white cells have receptors, the red cells attach to the white cells to form a "rosette." (A) Lymphocyte forming a rosette with IgG and (B) with an IgE-coated cell. (C) Monocyte forming a rosette with IgG and (D) basophilic granulocyte with IgE-coated erythrocyte.

because it provides a stronger bond between protein and red cell than simple adsorption of protein onto red cells whose surface has been altered by treatment with tannic acid or pyruvic aldehyde. In the future it should be possible to link any protein to indicator red cells with the Fab anti-ox red cell bridge for the study of protein–cell interactions.

COMPLEMENT FIXATION

The complement (C) fixation test is an indirect way to measure and quantitate antigen–antibody reactions. It is used most frequently to detect antibodies to ill-defined antigens present in tissue extracts or virus-containing culture fluids. The C fixation test is based on the observation that IgG and IgM antibodies activate the complement system (4, 8) and during that process

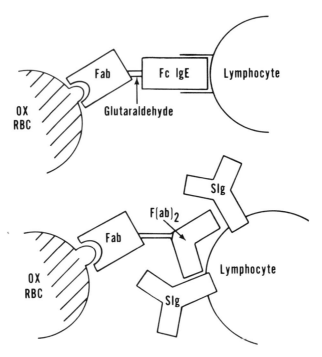

Figure 7. Fab bridge for rosette assay. In order to detect cell membrane components by the rosette assay, "artificial antibodies" can be produced for coating the indicator erythrocytes employing Fab anti-erythrocyte antibodies coupled with glutaraldehyde to the specific indicator protein. Fc fragments of IgE were coupled to Fab anti-ox antibodies for detection of Fc receptors (top) and F(ab)₂ anti-Ig antibodies to detect surface immunoglobulin of lymphocytes.

inactivate or "fix" the complement components. Basically, a limited quantity of C is added to the antibody–antigen system, and after its "fixation" the remaining C activity is titrated. In the first step antiserum that has been heated at 56°C to inactivate its own C is added to the antigen together with a given quantity of guinea pig serum as the source of C. After incubation for 1 hr at 37°C, sheep erythrocytes coated with rabbit anti-sheep antibodies (amboceptor) that consist predominantly of IgM anti-sheep erythrocyte antibodies are added. The mixture is incubated again at 37°C for 30 min or 1 hr. The amount of sheep erythrocytes lysed depends on the amount of C that remained in the system. The degree of lysis is quantitated by measuring the optical density of the hemoglobulin released into the supernatant. Control tubes consist of either antiserum or antigen solution alone, which should not fix significant amounts of complement. If the antiserum contains aggregated IgG or soluble immune complexes, the antiserum fixes C without addition of antigen. Such sera are called "anticomplementary." The best-known application of the C fixation test is the screening of sera for syphilis. Patients thus afflicted have antibodies against a phospholipid present in beef or human heart extracts.

IMMUNOFLUORESCENCE

Immunofluorescence is a histochemical procedure for locating antigens in tissue sections and on cell surfaces of single cell suspensions. The globulin fraction or preferably the isolated IgG of hyperimmune antisera are conjugated to a fluorescent dye. The labeled antibodies are then added to the tissue section or cell suspension, and after incubation the nonantibody proteins are washed off. The tissue is then examined with a microscope to which an ultraviolet light source is attached. Tissue components that contain the antigen will fluoresce against a dark background (Figure 8). The main difficulty of the immunofluorescence method is the nonspecific absorption of fluorescei- nated proteins to the tissue, which is overcome by absorption of the labeled antibody fraction with tissue powders or by fractionation of the fluoresceinated IgG on DEAE-cellulose columns. Also, proper control experiments have to be performed. They consist of blocking the reaction with native unlabeled antigen, unlabeled specific antibodies, and by demonstrating the absence of a fluorescence reaction with an unrelated fluoresceinated antiserum (22).

Immunofluorescence is performed as either a direct or an indirect proce- dure. In the direct method, the antiserum to the tissue antigen is fluoresce- inated, added to the tissue, and its reaction "directly" observed. In the indirect method, which is considerably more sensitive, unlabeled antiserum (e.g., rabbit antiserum) is added first and the tissue washed. A second fluoresceinated antiserum to the immunoglobulins of the first antiserum (e.g., goat anti-rabbit Ig) is then added. The antibodies of the first antiserum offer more sites for attachment of the fluoresceinated second antibodies and thus make the fluores- cence stronger at the reaction site. Obviously, control experiments are even more important in the indirect method.

Tissue sections have to be in a native state. Lightly fixed sections of frozen tissue are therefore used. Fluorescein isothyocyanate, which fluoresces green, and rhodamine B isothyocyanate, which fluoresces red, are the most com- monly used dyes. They can either be used alone or used together to detect two antigens simultaneously. This double-labeling technique is particularly valuable for following independent movement of two proteins on cell surfaces.

RADIOIMMUNOASSAYS

Radioimmunoassays employ the antibody–antigen reaction for quantitating proteins that are present in body fluids at minute concentrations (i.e., 5–

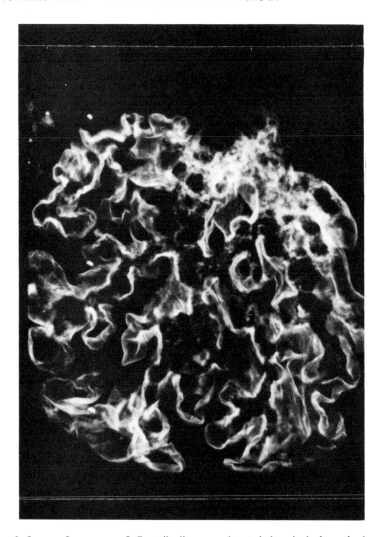

Figure 8. Immunofluorescence. IgG antibodies were detected deposited along the basement membrane of a monkey kidney glomerulus with fluorescein isothiocyanate labeled goat anti-monkey IgG antiserum fraction (photo courtesy of Dr. C. B. Wilson, ref. 23).

100 ng/ml). The antigen is radiolabeled with ^{125}I by the chloramine T method. An antibody–antigen equilibrium (e.g., 50% binding of a certain antigen) is then established using very small amounts of antigen. Unlabeled antigen is then added to disturb this equilibrium, and the competitive effect of the unlabeled material quantitated by measuring the radioactivity of the remaining reacting labeled antigen. A calibration curve is first established by adding

known quantities of unlabeled antigen and measuring how much radioactive antigen is displaced by it. The effect of samples of unknown antigen concentration can then be tested and their antigen displacement compared to the standard curve. The radioimmunoassay (24, 25) is used for the determination of hormones such as insulin, growth hormone, and so forth. It is also used for quantitating the IgE concentration of sera of patients with allergies. It is applicable to any experimental system where pure antigens that can be radiolabeled are available. Many variations have been described. Radiolabeled soluble antibody–antigen complexes that are precipitated can be competitively inhibited with unlabeled antigen. The antibody can be attached to Sepharose-4B, radiolabeled antigen with and without unlabeled competitor added, and, after washing, the amount of radioactivity attached to the insolubilized antibody determined.

ACKNOWLEDGMENTS

The author thanks Ms. Gloria Portillo for reviewing and Mrs. Margaret Stone for preparing the manuscript.

REFERENCES

1. Campbell, D. H., Garvey, J. S., Cremer, N. E., and Sussdorf, D. H. 1970. *Methods in Immunology,* 2nd ed. W. A. Benjamin, Inc., New York.
2. Rose, N. R., and Friedman, H., eds. 1976. *Manual of Clinical Immunology.* Am. Soc. Microbiology, Washington, D.C.
3. Bloom, B. R., and David, J. R., eds. 1976. *In Vitro Methods in Cell-Mediated and Tumor Immunity.* Academic Press, New York.
4. Kabat, E. A., and Mayer, M. M., eds. 1961. *Experimental Immunochemistry,* 2nd ed. Charles C. Thomas, Springfield, Illinois.
5. Williams, C. A., and Chase, M. W., eds. 1967–1976. *Methods in Immunology and Immunochemistry,* Vols. I–V. Academic Press, New York.
6. Freund, J. 1947. Some aspects of active immunization. *Ann. Rev. Microbiol.* 1:291.
7. Benacerraf, B., Ovary, Z., Bloch, K. J., and Franklin, E. C. 1963. Properties of guinea pig 7S antibodies. I. Electrophoretic separation of two types of guinea pig 7S antibodies. *J. Exp. Med.* 117:937.
8. Spiegelberg, H. L. 1974. Biological activities of immunoglobulins of different classes and subclasses. *Adv. Immunol.* 19:259.
9. Nisonoff, A., Wissler, F. C., Lipman, L. N., and Woernli, D. L. 1960. Separation of univalent fragments from bivalent rabbit antibody molecules by reduction of disulfide bonds. *Arch. Biochem. Biophys.* 89:230.
10. Porter, R. R. 1959. The hydrolysis of rabbit gamma globulin and antibodies with crystalline papain. *Biochem. J.* 83:119.
11. Cuatrecasas, P., Wilcheck, M., and Anfinsen, C. B. 1968. Selective enzyme purification by affinity chromatography. *Proc. Natl. Acad. Sci.* 61:636.
12. Heidelberger, M., and Kendall, F. E. 1934. Quantitative studies on the precipitin reaction. *J. Exp. Med.* 59:519.

13. Ouchterlony, O. 1964. Gel diffusion techniques. In *Immunological Methods,* J. F. Ackroyed, ed. F. A. Davis, Philadelphia, p. 55.
14. Scheidegger, J. J. 1955. Une micro-methode de l'immunoelectrophorese. *Int. Arch. Allergy* 7:103.
15. Mancini, G., Carbonara, A. O., and Heremans, J. F. 1965. Immunochemical quantitation of antigens by single radial immunodiffusion. *Immunochemistry* 2:235.
16. Stavitsky, A. B. 1964. Hemagglutination and hemagglutination inhibition reactions with tannic acid and bis-diazotized benzidine–protein conjugated erythrocytes. In *Immunological Methods,* J. F. Ackroyed, ed., p. 363. F. A. Davis, Philadelphia.
17. Hirata, A. A., and Brandriss, M. W. 1968. Passive hemagglutination procedures for protein and polysaccharide antigens using erythrocytes stabilized by aldehydes. *J. Immunol.* 100:641.
18. Gold, E. R., and Fudenberg, H. H. 1967. Chromic chloride, a coupling reagent for passive hemagglutination reactions. *J. Immunol.* 99:859.
19. Coombs, R. R. A., Gurner, B. W., Wilson, A. B., Holm, G., and Lindgren, B. 1970. Rosette formation between human lymphocytes and sheep red cells not involving immunoglobulin receptors. *Int. Arch. Allergy Appl. Immunol.* 39:658.
20. Strausbach, P., Sulica, A., and Givol, D. 1970. General method for the detection of cell producing antibodies against haptens and proteins. *Nature (London)* 227:68.
21. Gonzalez-Molina, A., and Spiegelberg, H. L. 1977. A subpopulation of normal human peripheral B lymphocytes that bind IgE. *J. Clin. Invest.* 59:616.
22. Coons, A. H. Fluorescent antibody methods. In *General Cytochemical Methods,* J. F. Danielli, ed., p. 399. Academic Press, New York.
23. Wilson, C. B. 1976. Immunohistopathology of the kidney. In *Manual of Clinical Immunology,* N. R. Rose and H. Friedman, eds., p. 692. Am. Soc. Microbiology, Washington, D.C.
24. Jaffe, B. M., and Behrman, H. R. 1974. *Methods of Hormone Radioimmunoassay.* Academic Press, New York.
25. Gill, T. J. 1976. Principles of radioimmunoassay. In *Manual of Clinical Immunology, 3N. R. Rose and H. Friedman, eds., p. 169. Am. Soc. Microbiology, Washington, D.C.*

1.7. X-Ray Methods

Keith Moffat

The belief that the three-dimensional structure of macromolecules and macro-molecular assemblies determines their function, and conversely that function must ultimately be explained in terms of structure, is one of the central features of molecular biology. The way in which X-rays, electromagnetic radiation of wavelengths around 1 Å, interact with macromolecules has proved to be one of the most useful means of examining their structure. Indeed, in the most favorable cases the complete, three-dimensional atomic structures of macromolecules such as enzymes and transfer RNA can be obtained, and used to explain in atomic detail their mechanism of action.

When a highly collimated beam of X-rays falls on a macromolecular sample, each individual electron is accelerated by the electric field component of the radiation, and reradiates X-rays equally in all directions. That is, radiation is scattered or diffracted by the sample. The overall angular distribution of this scattered radiation depends on the way in which the electrons are arranged in space because interference will occur between the X-rays scattered from individual electrons. Thus, from measurements of this angular distribution, information about the electronic structure of the sample can ultimately be obtained.

Two main factors govern this angular distribution: the arrangement of the electrons within each molecule in the sample (i.e., the electronic structure of the molecule), and the arrangement of the molecules in the sample. For example, the molecules may be arranged in a completely regular three-dimensional array, as in a single crystal of hemoglobin; or in a regular sheetlike two-dimensional array, as in the membrane proteins bacteriorhodopsin and cytochrome oxidase; or in rodlike, essentially one-dimensional arrays as in DNA fibers or filamentous viruses; or they may exhibit no regular array at all, as in a solution of the multienzyme complex fatty acid synthetase.

The total scattering from the sample, which depends on both factors, is experimentally observable, yet only the first factor is usually of interest. The more regular the array in which the molecules are arranged, the more readily can this first factor be extracted and the electronic structure of the molecules be determined; the less regular the array, the more limited is the structural information that can be obtained.

For this reason, physical biochemists usually go to great lengths to obtain samples in which the molecules are as well ordered as possible. Unfortunately, few interesting biological systems are obliging enough to form well-ordered arrays under physiological conditions. This introduces the grave danger that the nonphysiological solution conditions necessary to promote the formation of well-ordered arrays such as crystals, sheets, or fibers may themselves produce conformational changes in the molecules, and loss of biological activity. Structural information obtained on such samples is likely to be of less value. However, biological activity need not be lost; crystals of many enzymes are known in which the molecules in the crystal are still enzymatically active, as shown by their ability to catalyze the chemical transformation of substrates that are diffused into the crystals.

Mathematically, the scattering of X-rays by a sample described by the electron density function $\rho(r)$ is given by a particular kind of weighted integral of $\rho(r)$:

$$F(s) = \int_{-\infty}^{\infty} \rho(r) \exp[2\pi i r \cdot s] \, dr \tag{1}$$

The meaning of the symbols is shown in Figure 1 and its legend; an excellent description of how this expression is derived is given in the article by Holmes and Blow referred to at the end of this chapter. This integral has the form of a Fourier transform; thus, the expression states that "$F(s)$ is the Fourier transform of $\rho(r)$." We may then make use of an important property of Fourier transforms, inversion, and state that "$\rho(r)$ is the inverse Fourier transform of $F(s)$," or mathematically:

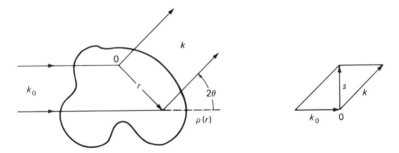

Figure 1. A beam of X-rays characterized by the wave vector k_0 falls on an arbitrary object $\rho(r)$, and some of the X-rays are scattered in the direction characterized by the wave vector k. As shown on the right, the scattering vector s is defined by $s = k - k_0$. Since k_0 is fixed, as k varies, so does s. The larger the scattering angle 2θ, the larger is the magnitude of s, and the finer are the details of the structure responsible for the scattering. The intensity of X-rays scattered in the direction k is proportional to $|F(s)|^2$, where $F(s)$ is given by equation (1).

$$\rho(r) = \int_{-\infty}^{\infty} F(s) \exp\left[-2\pi i r \cdot s\right] ds \qquad (2)$$

Thus, to determine the desired structure $\rho(r)$, it is necessary to obtain the quantity $F(s)$, called the scattering function or scattering factor, and then to compute the integral in equation (2). If $F(s)$ could be measured experimentally, this would be relatively straightforward. Unfortunately, $F(s)$ is a complex (or vector) quantity, characterized by both a scattering amplitude $|F(s)|$ and a phase α; only the scattered intensity $|F(s)|^2$ can be measured experimentally, and the phase is lost. This constitutes the *phase problem*, the heart of the difficulty in structure determination. All the subsequent chemical and mathematical manipulations in macromolecular structure determination are designed to recover this phase information by indirect means.

Before we consider one way in which this may be achieved for crystalline samples, the form of $F(s)$ should be examined. As noted above, the overall scattering $F(s)$ depends on two factors, the molecular structure and the way in which the molecules are arranged in the sample. This may be expressed mathematically by stating that $\rho(r)$ in the sample may be regarded as the convolution of the electron density function describing the molecules, $\rho_{mol}(r)$, and a distribution function describing the arrangement and orientation of the molecules in space, which we will denote D. That is:

$$\rho_{sample}(r) = \rho_{mol} * D$$

where the asterisk denotes the mathematical operation of convolution. Another fundamental property of Fourier transforms may then be used: the Fourier transform of the convolution of two functions is given by the product of the Fourier transforms of the two functions. Hence:

$$F_{sample}(s) = F_{mol}(s) \times G(s)$$

and

$$F_{mol}(s) = F_{sample}(s)/G(s)$$

where $G(s)$ is the Fourier transform of the distribution function D. The form of $G(s)$ will vary, depending on how the molecules are arranged. If, for example, the sample is a single, well-ordered crystal, then all the molecules lie on a regular lattice, the so-called real lattice. It turns out that $G(s)$ has a particularly simple form; it is also a lattice, the reciprocal lattice, whose values are 1 for integral values of s, and zero elsewhere. In this case

$$F_{sample}(s) = F_{mol}(s)$$

for integral values of s, and

$$F_{\text{sample}}(s) = 0$$

elsewhere. That is, scattering from crystals occurs only in certain directions given by integral values of s; the scattering or diffraction pattern consists solely of a series of spots or reflections, one for each integral value of s (Figure 2A). If the sample is only partially ordered, containing fibers or sheets, then $G(s)$ will take different forms, depending on the exact nature of the partial ordering, and will similarly influence $F_{\text{sample}}(s)$. Examples of such diffraction patterns are shown in Figures 2B and 2C. Some spots are seen, superimposed on a more or less continuous background scattering. Finally, if the sample is a solution of macromolecules, in which all possible orientations are found, then the total intensity of scattering $|F_{\text{sample}}(s)|^2$ is the average of the intensity of scattering from each molecule, taken over all orientations:

$$|F_{\text{sample}}(s)|^2 = \langle \, |F_{\text{mol}}(s)|^2 \, \rangle \text{ all orientations}$$

Scattering occurs at all values of s, not just integral ones; no spots are seen. Thus, a fairly cursory examination of the form of the diffraction pattern will give information about the order of the sample. Spots will only be seen if there is some regular ordering, and their location will give some information about the nature of this ordering.

Two possible strategies can be followed beyond this point. If the sample is very well ordered (e.g., a single crystal, or a highly ordered gel, fiber, or membrane), then attempts can be made to recover the phase of $F(s)$ by indirect means. If this can be done, then these phases can be combined with the experimentally measured values of $|F(s)|$ to yield the vectors $F(s)$, which can then be inserted in equation (2). Computation of the integral then yields the desired structure $\rho(r)$. One indirect means of recovering these phases, which has proved most effective, is known as the method of isomorphous replacement. Briefly, it is necessary to prepare chemical derivatives of the sample, by attaching various heavy atoms such as mercury, platinum, or samarium to it in such a way that the tagged molecules retain basically the same structure as the native, unreacted molecule. That is, these molecules must all be "isomorphous." If the scattering of X-rays from crystals of each of these derivatives is compared with that from the native, then it may be possible first, to locate the heavy atoms; second, to calculate their contribution to the overall scattering; and third, to use this information to determine the phases of $F(s)$ for the native molecule. A fairly straightforward explanation of how this is achieved is given in the article by Holmes and Blow. Application

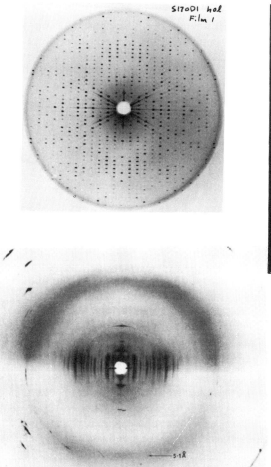

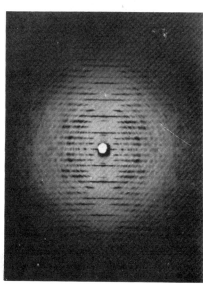

Figure 2. Examples of X-ray diffraction patterns of samples differing in their extent of order. *(A)* The single-crystal diffraction pattern of a well-ordered crystal of bovine intestinal calcium-binding protein. (Photo courtesy of Dr. Marian Szebenyi) *(B)* The fiber diffraction pattern of a partly ordered gel of the rod-shaped virus tobacco mosaic virus. The long axes of the virus particles are vertical. The diffraction pattern is concentrated on horizontal lines, layer lines, whose spacing is related to the pitch of the helix that the coat protein and RNA form (photograph taken from Holmes et al. Nature *254,* 192 (1975): reprinted by permission of MacMillan and Co.). *(C)* The membrane diffraction pattern of a partly ordered two-dimensional sheetlike array of the membrane protein bacteriorhodopsin. The plane of the membrane is horizontal. The most prominent features of the diffraction pattern are the vertical streaks that run through a horizontal line through the center of the pattern; these arise from the regularity of the side-by-side packing of the bacteriorhodopsin molecules in the plane of the membrane (photograph taken from Henderson, *J. Mol. Biol.,* 93, 123 (1975), reprinted by permission of Academic Press).

of this isomorphous replacement strategy has led to the determination of the molecular structure of 70 or so macromolecules.

A second strategy does not require experimental determination of the phases. Here, an intelligent guess is made about the structure of the molecules, perhaps based on chemical or other structural evidence, and this is combined with some experimentally determined knowledge of the state of ordering of the molecules in the sample. In this way, a model for the electron density distribution $\rho_{model}(r)$ can be formulated. By application of equation (1) to $\rho_{model}(r)$, the X-ray scattering $F_{model}(s)$ can be calculated, as can $|F_{model}(s)|$. This can then be compared with the experimentally determined $|F_{sample}(s)|$, and the parameters of the model adjusted until the best agreement between the two is obtained. As will readily be appreciated, this strategy will only be effective if the starting model is reasonably accurate, or if the model is described by only a few parameters that can be systematically adjusted. This strategy was followed by Crick and Watson in their classic proposal for the structure of DNA. They combined chemical information that suggested base pairing with a belief that helical structures were likely, and demonstrated that a two-stranded helical molecule with certain helical parameters was consistent with the X-ray diffraction patterns obtained by Franklin and Wilkins on partially ordered fibers of DNA. At a more mundane level, this strategy has also been used to demonstrate that the molecular structures are very closely similar in different crystal forms of hemoglobin, and to demonstrate that the overall conformation of molecules in solution, as examined by low-angle X-ray scattering from solutions, is consistent with their structure in the crystalline state.

Molecular biologists are generally not concerned with structure for structure's sake; rather, they are concerned with what structure can tell them about the molecular mechanism of action of the macromolecules. Macromolecules are by no means rigid structures, and, indeed, changes in structure are absolutely central to such biological processes as enzyme catalysis, DNA replication, and membrane transport. What they would therefore like to know is exactly what the structure of the macromolecule is at each stage of its mechanism of action—to have a movie, as it were, of the structure. Unfortunately, structural studies by X-ray scattering techniques at present cannot provide movies, but only very blurred snapshots. The reason for this is that the structure actually determined is essentially static, both a space average of the structure of all the molecules in the sample (which may be as many as 10^{15} molecules), and a time average of all the structures present during X-ray data collection, which may take hours or even days. This data collection time is very much longer than the lifetime of most interesting structures. For example, the turnover number of most enzymes is high, and the catalytically interesting structures are therefore all very short-lived, in the millisecond (or even shorter) time range. That is, these catalytically interesting structures cannot be examined directly; molecular movies cannot be made. In order to circumvent this problem, crystallographers often study stable complexes believed to be structurally related to the catalytically interesting but experimentally inaccessible structures. Examples of such complexes include enzyme–product or enzyme–inhibitor complexes. Alternatively, they may attempt to slow down the rates of the reactions, by working at unfavorable pH values, using poor substrates, or drastically lowering the temperature. In this way the lifetime of the interesting structural intermediates may be extended to many hours, enabling them to be studied directly. Structural studies at temperatures approaching that of liquid nitrogen have been initiated on some proteolytic enzymes, and are particularly promising. Despite these ingenious approaches, the difficulty remains that the crystallographer is finally forced to deduce the structures of the catalytically interesting, short-lived complexes from the structures of a series of static complexes—to construct the movie from a series of snapshots, where some may be missing, and others are of not quite the same scene. It is perhaps not surprising that this has proved to be exceptionally difficult; only a handful of mechanisms of action of enzymes can be said to be fully understood in molecular detail.

Finally, from the point of view of mechanism, it should be stressed that X-ray structure analysis is necessary, but not sufficient. Enzymologists have supplemented structural results with those derived from such other techniques as enzyme kinetics, specificity studies, chemical modification of the active site, bio-organic mechanisms, and nuclear magnetic resonance spectroscopy, to deduce molecular mechanisms of action. Molecular anatomy is a prerequisite to an understanding of the molecular physiology, but it alone is not enough.

SUGGESTED READING

Holmes, K. C., and Blow, D. M. 1965. *The Use of X-ray Diffraction in the Study of Protein and Nucleic Acid Structure. Methods of Biochemical Analysis*, Vol. XIII, pp. 113–240. D. Glick, ed., Wiley Inters. New York. An excellent review, written for biologists and biochemists, of the principles of macromolecular structure determination.

Pilz, I. 1973. Small-angle X-ray scattering. In *Physical Principles and Techniques of Protein Chemistry*, Part C, S. J. Leach, ed., pp. 141–245. Academic Press, New York. A detailed review of the type of structural information that can be derived from X-ray studies of macromolecules in solution.

Attention should also be drawn to the review articles that appear frequently in such series as *Annual Review of Biochemistry* and *Annual Reviews of Biophysics and Bioengineering*, which generally deal especially with the structural and mechanistic results obtained by X-ray techniques.

1.8. Magnetic Resonance Methods

Keith Moffat

Nuclear magnetic resonance (NMR) and electron paramagnetic resonance (EPR) are powerful, versatile, and to a large extent complementary techniques for studying aspects of the structure of molecules, especially in solution. Unlike X-ray methods, they involve few constraints on the physical state of the sample, and changes in structure may be readily investigated.

The basic principles are common to both NMR and EPR, but there are considerable differences in the nature of the magnetic interactions involved, the way in which structural information is obtained, and the generality of the two techniques as applied to biological systems. We will consider NMR first, then move on to a somewhat briefer treatment of EPR.

NUCLEAR MAGNETIC RESONANCE

All nuclei with odd mass number, and many with even mass number, possess the property of spin. Since such nuclei are charged, this confers a magnetic moment μ on them, which is proportional to the magnitude of their spin I:

$$\mu = g_N \beta_N I$$

where g_N is a dimensionless constant, the nuclear g-factor, and β_N is the nuclear magneton, a unit of magnetic moment. If such nuclei are placed in a static magnetic field of magnitude H, they experience a force and tend to orient themselves with the magnetic field, much as tiny bar magnets do. However, quantum theory demands that only certain orientations are possible; that is, the spins are spatially quantized. The number of values is $(2I + 1)$, where I is the spin number. For example, for the proton ^1H and ^{13}C, the magnitude of I is $1/2$, and only two orientations are possible, which are referred to as aligned with and against the magnetic field. Since the potential energy of the interaction of a magnetic moment μ with a magnetic field H is $-\mu H$, these two orientations correspond to potential energies of $-1/2$ $g_N \beta_N H$ $(I = +1/2)$ and $+1/2$ $g_N \beta_N H$ $(I = -1/2)$, and the energy difference between them is $g_N\beta_N H$ (Figure 1). Transitions between these energy levels, or flipping of the spins, can then be induced by subjecting the system to an oscillating magnetic field of frequency ν such that the resonance condition

$$h\nu = g_N\beta_N H \tag{1}$$

is satisfied, where h is Planck's constant. A net absorption of energy from the oscillating magnetic field will occur provided the number of spins in the two orientations is unequal. This is normally the case, as thermal equilibrium ensures there will be very slightly more spins in the lower energy level than in the higher.

Equation (1) shows that absorption could be detected either by varying the frequency ν at a fixed field H, or by varying the field at a fixed frequency. The resonance conditions at a fixed field for a number of biologically important nuclei are given in Table 1. An important consequence of the very small difference in the number of spins in the two orientations is that extremely small amounts of energy are absorbed. Furthermore, the natural abundance of certain useful isotopes such as ^{13}C and ^{15}N is also low. High sample concentrations, in the millimolar range, and sophisticated data acquisition and analysis systems are therefore necessary.

The reason that magnetic resonance experiments yield structural information is that the effective magnetic field H_{eff} at each nucleus depends not merely on the static applied field H, but also on additional magnetic fields that are generated by its structural environment. Electrons in the same atom shield the nucleus from the applied field; circulating ring currents in nearby aromatic groups such as the side chains of tyrosine, phenylalanine, and tryptophan generate an additional field, as may nearby paramagnetic ions. That is, the resonance frequency ν will differ from nucleus to nucleus, in a structure-

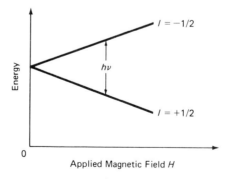

Figure 1. A simple illustration of the splitting of nuclear spin labels in a magnetic field H.

Table 1. Magnetic Resonance Data for Some Nuclei of Importance in Biological Systems.*

NUCLEUS	NMR FREQUENCY (MHZ)	APPROXIMATE SENSITIVITY	NATURAL ABUNDANCE (%)	NUCLEAR SPIN
^{1}H	42.58	1.00	99.98	1/2
^{13}C	10.71	0.02	1.11	1/2
^{15}N	4.32	0.001	0.37	1/2
^{17}O	5.77	0.03	0.04	5/2
^{19}F	40.06	0.83	100.00	1/2
^{23}Na	11.26	0.09	100.00	3/2
^{31}P	17.24	0.07	100.00	1/2
^{33}S	3.27	0.002	0.74	3/2

* Values are calculated for a magnetic field of 10,000 gauss. The sensitivity is expressed relative to the same number of protons. (Adapted from *Nuclear Magnetic Resonance in Biochemistry* by T. L. James.)

dependent manner. These differences in ν are described by the chemical shift δ, a dimensionless number:

$$\delta = \frac{\nu_s - \nu_{ref}}{\nu_{ref}}$$

where ν_s and ν_{ref} are the resonance frequencies of the sample and a reference compound. Usually, δ is multiplied by 10^6 and expressed as parts per million (ppm).

Each NMR absorption line may then be characterized by three parameters: its chemical shift δ, its area (proportional to the number of nuclei with that chemical shift or magnetic environment), and its line width. The line width is related to the lifetimes of the nuclear spin states, which are governed by various relaxation processes that are also structure-dependent. Each relaxation process is associated with a correlation time τ, such as τ_E (chemical exchange), τ_R (overall tumbling or rotational motion), τ_M (local motion), or τ_S (the so-called electron spin-lattice relaxation). Thus, the overall correlation time τ_C is given by

$$\frac{1}{\tau_C} = \frac{1}{\tau_E} + \frac{1}{\tau_M} + \frac{1}{\tau_R} + \frac{1}{\tau_S} \tag{2}$$

Note that τ_C will be dominated by the smallest of τ_E, τ_M, τ_R, and τ_S; their magnitudes will of course vary from system to system. Two nuclear relaxation parameters are usually measured experimentally, in separate experiments: the longitudinal or spin–lattice relaxation time T_1 (related to reorientation of the nuclear spins parallel to the applied magnetic field H), and the transverse or spin–spin relaxation time T_2 (related to reorientation in the plane normal to H). The relationship between T_1, T_2, and τ_C is shown in Figure 2; note that $T_2 \leq T_1$.

NMR studies of macromolecules have generally sought a structural interpretation of either chemical shift data or (to a lesser extent) relaxation data. Unfortunately, three factors conspire to make chemical shift data from proton NMR spectra of macromolecules difficult to interpret. First, macromolecules naturally contain a large number of protons, and hence must contain a large number of absorption lines; second, the magnetic environments of these protons do not differ very much, their range of chemical shifts is small, and the lines tend to overlap; and third, the line widths of each proton absorption are fairly large, which also makes the lines tend to overlap. A typical macromolecular proton NMR spectrum thus consists of a large absorption envelope, resulting from the superposition of numerous broad individual proton absorption lines (Figure 3). This places the experimenter in a frustrating position: all the desired structural information is present in the spectrum, but it is extremely hard to extract! The overall goal in the interpretation of NMR spectra is to assign each spectral line to a particular chemical group, and then to account for the properties of that line—chemical shift, intensity, and line width—in structural terms. In practice, most studies have concentrated on the chemical shift, but, for the reasons noted above, this is by no means easy.

A number of strategies have been employed to simplify chemical shift data. Much useful information has emerged from studying those proton reso-

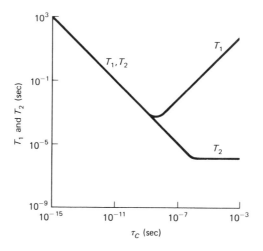

Figure 2. The theoretical dependence of T_1 and T_2 on τ_C.

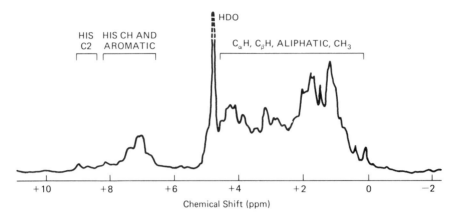

Figure 3. The proton NMR spectrum of a 1.1 mM solution of the enzyme lysozyme, in D_2O. The spectrum was recorded at 270 MHz, using Fourier transform techniques, in about 1 min. Without Fourier transform techniques, a spectrum of comparable quality would have required several hours to record. Certain regions of the spectrum are identified with particular classes of protons. The resonances between 0 and −2 ppm have been assigned to certain methyl protons that X-ray crystallographic results show to be near tryptophan, tyrosine, and phenylalanine residues. The additional magnetic field due to the circulating ring currents in these aromatic side chains has shifted the resonances of these protons upfield. The very large peak at +4.77 ppm arises from the protons of residual water in the sample. The chemical shift is expressed in ppm, relative to the reference compound known as DSS. (Spectrum courtesy of Dr. G. W. Feigenson).

nances that, because of an unusual magnetic environment, have large chemical shifts and are thus well resolved from the main proton absorption envelope. For example, the C2 protons of the imidazole side chains of histidine generally have large chemical shifts that are pH-dependent. As the state of protonation of the imidazole nitrogens changes, so does the magnetic environment of the C2 protons. It has proved possible not merely to determine the pK values of each histidine side chain in ribonuclease, but also to assign each pK value to a particular histidine in the sequence. As a further example, proton resonances arising from those protons involved in hydrogen bonding between base pairs in tRNA could be identified. The total number of such protons agreed with that predicted by the cloverleaf model for the structure of tRNA, thus providing an early confirmation of the correctness of that model. Many proteins contain structural features such as paramagnetic metal ions, porphyrins, or flavins that produce unusually large magnetic fields, and enhance the chemical shift of proton resonances that are normally buried in the main absorption envelope. For example, separate resonances for certain valine methyl groups can be observed in hemoglobin proton NMR spectra, and identified with those particular valines that are known from X-ray crystallographic data to be near the heme groups. In order to simplify the spectra still further, it is sometimes possible to obtain macromolecules in which certain protons are removed, either by deuteration (all exchangeable protons are replaced by deuterium by soaking in D_2O), or by selective synthesis with deuterated amino acids (the proton resonances arising from only those amino acids will be absent), or by studying mutants (resonances arising from the altered amino acid will differ in the mutant and the wild type).

Much useful information has also been obtained by studying the simpler and better-resolved proton NMR spectra of smaller molecules, and the way in which they interact with macromolecules. For example, consider the binding of a reversible inhibitor I to an enzyme E:

$$E + I \underset{k_2}{\overset{k_1}{\rightleftharpoons}} EI$$

The inhibitor protons may experience magnetic environments in the EI complex that differ from those free in solution, I; if so, their chemical shifts will differ. It might therefore be expected that two separate absorption lines would be seen for each inhibitor proton, whose intensities would be proportional to [I] and [EI]. It turns out that this is true, in cases where the chemical exchange rates, given by $1/\tau_{EI} = k_2$, $1/\tau_I = k_1 [E]$, are lower than the chemical shift frequency difference (Figure 4a). If, however, the chemical exchange rate is slowly increased, then the two lines broaden (Figure 4b) and move toward one another until they merge into one broad line (Figure 4c), which finally sharpens (Figure 4d). That is, the line shape and width give information about the rate constants involved, k_1 and k_2. This is an example of the information that may be derived from relaxation processes (in this case, chemical exchange).

Another example of the use of relaxation measurements comes from NMR studies of biological membranes. Measurements of T_1 and T_2 and interpretation of results in terms of structural and motional parameters has resulted in a picture of the phospholipid bilayer in a state of restricted molecular motion that is intermediate in frequency between a solid and a liquid.

In view of the difficulties inherent in interpreting proton NMR spectra of macromolecules, it is not surprising that biophysicists have begun to explore the structural information that can be obtained with the other nuclei. This has only been possible recently, when technological advances such as Fourier-transform NMR greatly increased the rate at which NMR spectra of other nuclei could be measured. This area of research seems certain to expand greatly.

The most promising of these other nuclei is ^{13}C, since two factors simplify

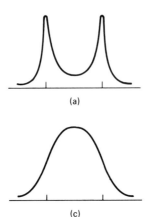
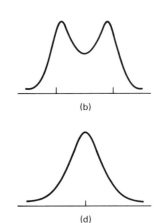

Figure 4. Theoretical line shapes expected for a proton exchanging between two different magnetic environments. In this example, the two environments are equally populated. The spectra have been adjusted to have the same height. (a) Exchange rate much less than the chemical shift frequency difference. (b) Rate comparable to but less than the frequency difference. (c) Rate comparable to but greater than the frequency difference. (d) Rate greater than the frequency difference.

its spectra: its chemical shifts are about ten times larger than those for protons, and of course macromolecules contain fewer carbon atoms than protons. A limitation is that ^{13}C is present in low natural abundance (Table 1). This barrier can be overcome by preparing molecules or regions of molecules selectively enriched in ^{13}C, either by chemical synthesis or by biosynthesis. Other nuclei that have been successfully employed include ^{31}P and ^{19}F. The last has been introduced either by chemical modification of macromolecules with the appropriate fluorine-containing reagent, or by growing bacteria on media containing fluorotyrosine or fluorotryptophan.

ELECTRON PARAMAGNETIC RESONANCE

Like the proton, the electron has a spin of 1/2, and its energy levels are also split into two when placed in a magnetic field H. In a manner exactly analogous to the NMR case (equation 1), the EPR resonance equation may be obtained:

$$h\nu = g_S\beta_S H \tag{3}$$

where g_S is dimensionless (the electronic g-factor) and β_S is a unit of magnetic moment. For a free electron, $g \sim 2.00$, but considerable deviations from this value occur if the electron experiences orbital motion that is not spherically symmetric. That is, spin–orbit coupling alters the g-value. The constraints of chemical bonding also affect the spatial orientation of the electronic orbitals, so that the g-value varies with orientation with respect to the applied magnetic field H; the g-factor is anisotropic. Finally, the effective magnetic field experienced by the electron will be influenced by nearby nuclei that may also possess a magnetic moment. This leads to a splitting of an EPR absorption line into $2I + 1$ components, where I is the magnitude of the nuclear spin responsible for the splitting. The magnitude of the splitting is expressed by a hyperfine splitting factor, A, which may also be anisotropic. Thus, an EPR spectrum is sensitive to the chemical and structural environment of the unpaired electron. Some representative EPR spectra (which are generally measured and plotted as the first derivative of the absorption) are shown in Figure 5. Just as in the NMR case, the shape of EPR absorption

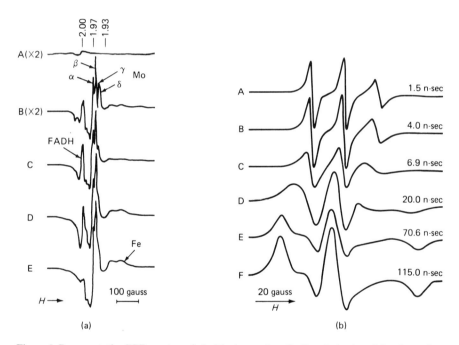

Figure 5. Representative EPR spectra, plotted (as is usual) as the first derivative of the absorption spectra. (a) The rather complex EPR spectra obtained on the enzyme xanthine oxidase, before (spectrum A) and during (spectra B–E) reaction with its substrate xanthine. The origin of several paramagnetic signals is indicated: molybdenum (Mo, components α, β, γ, and δ), the semiquinone form of the coenzyme flavin, adenine dinucleotide (FADH), and iron (Fe) (taken from Palmer et al., 1964, *J. Biol. Chem.* 239:2657–66). (b) Spectra of a simple spin label in solutions of viscosity that increase from spectrum A to spectrum F. Each spectrum is identified by the tumbling time of the spin label characteristic of rotational diffusion (courtesy of Dr. I. C. P. Smith).

lines may also be modified by relaxation processes, which depend on the dynamics of molecular motion.

Although the EPR resonance condition, expressed as equation (3), is identical in form to the NMR resonance condition, equation (1), there are striking differences between EPR and NMR in their application to biological systems. The most important of these differences is that the number of unpaired electrons in most biological systems is very small (and may of course be zero). Common examples of unpaired electrons include certain paramagnetic transition metal ions such as iron, copper, and manganese, and certain coenzymes such as the semiquinone form of flavins. Hence, EPR spectra of biological systems, which detect only the unpaired electrons, are very much simpler than NMR spectra of the same system, containing far fewer absorption lines. For this reason and because the energies involved in EPR transitions are larger than those in NMR transitions (though still very small), EPR is a considerably more sensitive technique than NMR, and can be carried out effectively on dilute solutions. A further advantage of EPR is that the unpaired electrons, as in the above examples, are generally associated very directly with a catalytically important part of the molecule. EPR thus provides a clear "window" into the active site. For example, the anisotropy of the EPR spectrum of the heme iron was used to determine the orientation of the heme groups in crystals of both myoglobin and hemoglobin before their crystal structures were known.

The scarcity of unpaired electrons may of course be a hindrance; perhaps the molecule or system of interest does not contain any, or they are not located in a region of interest. This difficulty has been elegantly overcome by the use of spin labels, stable organic free radicals of the general form shown in Figure 6. The beauty of spin labels lies in the fact that the R group can take almost any form. For example, spin labels have been prepared in which the R group is designed to react chemically with particular amino acid side chains; in others the R group mimics lipids, or steroids, or carbohydrates. The EPR spectra of spin labels are very sensitive to this state of motion, as illustrated in Figure 5, and they may therefore serve as dynamic probes. This property has been exploited to the full in studying the fluidity of membranes, or the flexibility of particular regions of proteins.

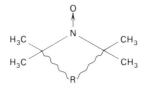

Figure 6. General form of stable organic free radicals.

Finally, in some systems considerable advances have been made by utilizing both EPR and NMR techniques. Certain protein kinases bind both Mg and ATP. Magnesium does not exhibit an EPR spectrum, but it can be effectively replaced by Mn, which does. A detailed study of the EPR spectra of various forms of the Mn-containing enzymes could then be coupled with a proton NMR study of the nucleotide binding, and important quantities such as the binding constants for the metal and the nucleotides, and the distances between the metal and certain nucleotide protons, could be calculated.

SUGGESTED READING

Knowles, P. F. 1972. The application of magnetic resonance methods to the study of enzyme structure and action. In *Essays in Biochemistry,* Vol. 8, pp. 79–106. P. Campbell and G. D. Grewille, Series eds., Academic Press, New York. A brief review of the principles of NMR and EPR, with examples of their application to various systems.

Metcalfe, J. C. 1970. Nuclear magnetic resonance spectroscopy. In *Physical Principles and Techniques of Protein Chemistry,* Part B, S. J. Leach, ed., pp. 175–361. Academic Press, New York. A somewhat more extensive review of NMR techniques.

James, T. L. 1975. *Nuclear Magnetic Resonance in Biochemistry.* Academic Press, New York. A detailed description of NMR techniques useful in biophysics and biochemistry.

1.9. Some Representative Mathematical Plots in Biological Research

Said A. Goueli and Randolph C. Steer

Modern cellular biology is a complex subject that demands of its students a variety of analytical and interpretive skills, among the most important of which is the ability to understand data presented in graphical form. Because of the strong emphasis on the biochemistry of transport, enzymes, and receptors, several particular data plots appear quite frequently in the literature. With this in mind, we have chosen to provide in brief outline a discussion of some of these representations. This will provide the student an exposure to the appearance and general concept of each plot. References are included that provide for more extensive consideration of the theoretical basis of each subject.

ARRHENIUS PLOT

This is a valuable plot for determining the activation energy of a reaction (E_a) or the change in heat of activation ($\Delta H^{\neq}$). From these parameters, $\Delta S^{\neq}$ and $\Delta G^{\neq}$ (change in entropy and free energy of the reaction respectively) can be determined. In this plot, log K (the reaction rate constant) is plotted against $1/T$:

$$\log K = \frac{-E_a}{2.3R} \cdot \frac{1}{T} + \log A \tag{1}$$

From equation (1), the slope will be equal to $\frac{-E_a}{2.3R}$ where R is the gas constant, 1.98 cal/dg (Figure 1, Curve A). Also, by integration of equation (1) we obtain:

$$\log \frac{K_2}{K_1} = \frac{E_a}{2.3R} \left(\frac{T_2 - T_1}{T_1 T_2} \right) \tag{2}$$

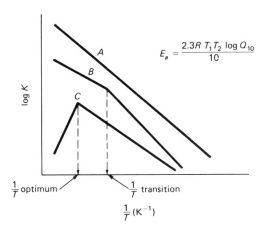

Figure 1. Arrhenius plot.

where K_1 and K_2 are specific reaction rate constants at temperatures T_1 and T_2, respectively. Because K_2/K_1 is a ratio (i.e., no absolute value is required), any function of the rate constants or apparent values could be substituted for them. From this equation, a plot of log (K_2/K_1) against $(T_2 - T_1)/(T_1 T_2)$ will give a slope of $E_a/2.3R$. Also, a value of log (K_2/K_1) will give an indication of the effect of temperature on the reaction constant (4, 12).

If the plot of log K versus $1/T$ is not linear, this is an indication of more than one rate-limiting step, or at the same temperature a different step becomes rate-limiting. (Figure 1, Curve B). If there is a sudden drop on the curve, this indicates enzyme inactivation. (Figure 1, Curve C).

The plot is helpful in distinguishing between two different reactions by the difference in their slopes, and in determining the effect of other variables such as pH by plotting the activity at different temperatures for two or more sets of pH values.

Also, Q_{10} (temperature coefficient), which is the factor by which the rate constant is increased by raising the temperature $10°C$, can be determined:

$$E_a = \frac{2.3R\, T_1 T_2 \log Q_{10}}{10} \tag{3}$$

ENZYME KINETIC PLOTS

For a simple enzymatic reaction,

$$E + S \underset{K_{-1}}{\overset{K_1}{\rightleftharpoons}} ES \xrightarrow{K_2} E + P \tag{4}$$

Michaelis and Menten developed the following equation:

$$V_{max} = \frac{K_2\,(E_o)\,[S]}{K_m + [S]}$$

or:

$$= \frac{V_{max}\,[S]}{K_m + [S]} \tag{5}$$

where:

v = initial velocity
V_{max} = maximum velocity = $K_2[E]$
K_m = Michaelis-Menten constant $\approx \dfrac{K_2 + K_{-1}}{K_1}$
$[S]$ = substrate concentration
$[E_o]$ = total enzyme concentration

This equation, which is called the steady-state rate equation, describes a rectangular hyperbola with asymptotes at $[S] = -K_m$ and $v = V_{max}$ (Figure 2).

The center of this cone section is at the point $(-K_m, V_{max})$; in enzyme kinetics, interest is in that portion of the curve where $[S]$ has positive values.

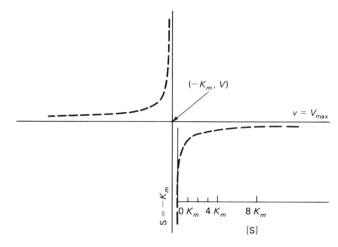

Figure 2. Michaelis-Menten plot.

The initial velocity $(v) = V_{max}$ when [S] increases to an infinite volume. Under these conditions the reaction velocity is constant and is independent of substrate concentration. This is an example of zero-order kinetics.

On the other hand, if $[S] \ll K_m$, then equation (5) becomes:

$$v = \frac{V_{max}\,[S]}{K_m} \tag{6}$$

This means that the reaction velocity has V_{max}/K_m as a reaction constant. This is an example of first-order kinetics. Also, values of [S] between 0.1 K_m and 10 K_m (which are characteristic of first- and zero-order kinetics, respectively) represent reactions that are intermediate between zero- and first-order kinetics. Finally, when $[S] = K_m$

$$v = \frac{V_{max}}{2} \tag{7}$$

This defines K_m as the value of [S] in molar concentration that gives v a value of $V_{max}/2$. It follows that the lower the K_m value, the higher the affinity of the enzyme to the substrate, and the higher the K_m, the lower the affinity (i.e., simply, better binding—better catalysis). Since it is only practical to experiment with finite substrate concentrations, it will be impossible to measure V_{max} and K_m accurately from a plot of [S] versus v because the asymptotes cannot be drawn closely enough.

Michaelis and Menten (1913) recognized this difficulty and developed a representation in which v is plotted against log [S] (Figure 3). The curve has an inflection point where $[S] = K_m$. Although this method is statistically

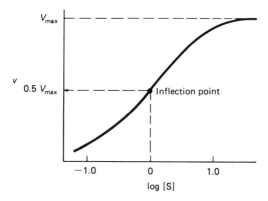

Figure 3. Semilogarithmic Michaelis-Menten plot.

correct, because the plot is curved biochemists tried to develop easier methods to plot the results to obtain values for K_m and V_{max}. (8, 11)

Linear transformations of the Michaelis-Menten equation may take several forms which are summarized as follows:

$$\frac{1}{v} = \frac{K_m}{V} \cdot \frac{1}{[S]} + \frac{1}{V} \quad \text{[Lineweaver-Burk reciprocal plot]} \qquad (8)$$

$$\frac{[S]}{v} = \frac{1}{V} \cdot [S] + \frac{K_m}{V} \quad \text{[Hanes-Woolf plot]} \qquad (9)$$

$$\frac{v}{[S]} = \frac{-1}{K_m} v + \frac{V}{K_m} \quad \text{[Eadie-Scatchard plot]} \qquad (10)$$

$$v = -K_m \frac{v}{[S]} + V \quad \text{[Woolf-Augustinsson-Hofstee plot]} \qquad (11)$$

These equations are similar to the equation of a straight line $y = a + mx$, where a is the intercept and m is the slope. These equations can be translated into the graphs depicted in Figure 4a–d. From these plots, we obtain the kinetic parameters K_m and V_{max}. If these plots have more than one slope, this indicates the presence of more than one enzyme in the system or that there is an interaction between multiple sites on the same enzyme.

INHIBITION KINETICS

The preceding section on linearization of the Michaelis-Menten equation may also be applied to study and characterize inhibitory effects on enzyme reactions (10, 12, 15). If a Lineweaver-Burk plot were used, three different plots would characterize the three most common types of inhibition—*competitive, noncompetitive*, and *uncompetitive* inhibition—as shown in Figure 5a–c. The same use may be made of the other linear forms of the equation.

The most pronounced difference between competitive and noncompetitive inhibition is that in competitive inhibition the maximum velocity is reached in the presence of the inhibitor if the substrate concentration is increased, but it will never be attained in the case of noncompetitive inhibition, no matter how high the substrate concentration (2). In contrast, the K_m for the system is the same for noncompetitive inhibition, as compared to the absence of the inhibitor, and this is not the case in competitive inhibition. In other words, competitive inhibition depends on affinity, but noncompetitive

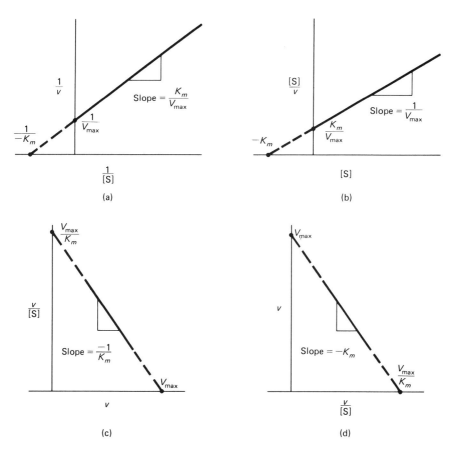

Figure 4. (a) Lineweaver-Burk plot (b) Hanes-Woolf plot. (c) Eadie-Scatchard plot. (d) Woolf-Augustinsson-Hofstee plot.

inhibition does not, since the inhibitor binds to a site other than the substrate binding site. In noncompetitive inhibition, the inhibitor does not prevent binding of the substrate and vice versa. This is opposite to what happens in competitive inhibition. In the case of noncompetitive inhibition, the inhibitor binds to the [ES] complex as well as to [E]; in competitive inhibition, the inhibitor binds only to the free enzyme, [E].

On the other hand, if the inhibitor binds only to the [ES] complex (i.e., no binding site on the enzyme until a molecule of substrate has bound to the enzyme), this is called *uncompetitive inhibition*. In this type of inhibition both V_{max} and K_m are reduced by the factor $1 + ([I]/K_I)$ where $[I] =$ inhibitor concentration and K_I is the inhibition constant.

In 1953, Dixon (5) developed a plot by which K_I can be determined. In

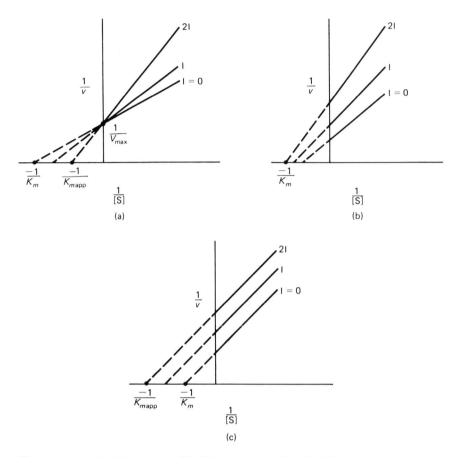

Figure 5. Competitive (a), noncompetitive (b), and uncompetitive (c) inhibition, using Lineweaver-Burk plot.

the Dixon plot, $1/v$ is plotted against $[I]$ for a series of substrate concentrations. The point of intersection of any two lines occurs where $I = -K_I$, on the $[I]$ axis.

Using the Dixon plot for all different types of inhibition, we obtain Figure 6a–d.

There are, however, disadvantages to this plot. First, it does not distinguish between competitive and mixed inhibition. Second, it cannot determine K_I for an uncompetitive inhibitor. Therefore, Cornish-Bowden (3) developed a plot in which $[S]/v$ is plotted against $[I]$ (Figure 7). In this case, the plot will not give K_I in the case of competitive inhibition, but it will distinguish between competitive and mixed inhibition. Also, it gives the value of K_I

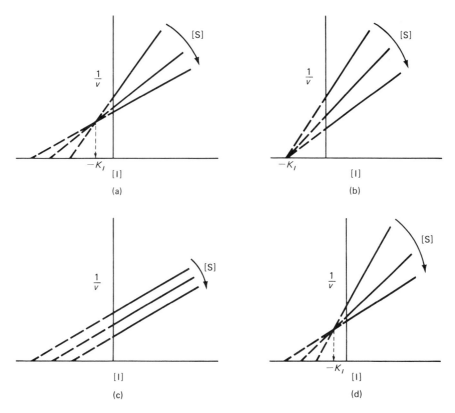

Figure 6. Dixon plots. (a) Competitive inhibition. (b) Noncompetitive inhibition. (c) Uncompetitive inhibition. (d) Mixed inhibition.

for an uncompetitive inhibition. Thus, by combining the information from the Dixon plot and the Cornish-Bowden plot we obtain the kinetic parameter K_I, and are able to distinguish between different types of inhibition.

A COMMENT ON THE USE OF VARIOUS LINEAR FORMS OF THE MICHAELIS-MENTEN EQUATION

For comparison of results obtained under different experimental conditions and for a proper evaluation of the results on theoretical grounds, graphical methods do not determine precise values of the kinetic parameters. Therefore, Wilkinson (1961) developed a statistical procedure in which the weighted and nonlinear regression methods were used. He demonstrated that the plot of $[S]/v$ versus $[S]$ is preferable to that of $1/v$ versus $1/[S]$.

Cornish-Bowden and Eisenthal (4, 5, 9) developed a plot, called the *direct*

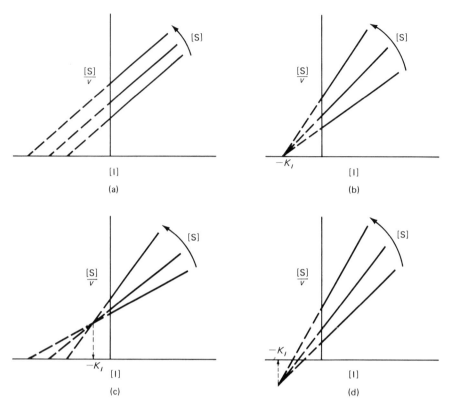

Figure 7. Cornish-Bowden plots. (a) Competitive inhibition. (b) Noncompetitive inhibition. (c) Uncompetitive inhibition. (d) Mixed inhibition.

linear plot, in which attention was focused on K_m V_{max} rather than [S] and v as the essential parameters. Using this plot, a reliable estimate of K_m and V_{max} was obtained.

Dowd and Riggs (6) claimed that the plot of $1/v$ versus $1/[S]$ is the least reliable of all linear transformations of the Michaelis-Menten equation. Even when the error in v is small, this plot is the poorest of all linear transformations of the equation because the smallest value of v plays an extraordinary part in determining the position of the fitted line, thus yielding totally worthless estimates of V_{max} and K_m. Also, they indicated that the plot of $[S]/v$ versus [S] was somewhat better than that of v versus $v/[S]$. However, both yielded reasonably accurate estimates of the kinetic parameters, although the latter was preferred when the error in v was large.

For detection of deviations from the classical model of enzyme kinetics, Walter (16) indicated that the plot of v versus $v/[S]$ is the best in detecting any curvature. To distinguish an order-one model (one binding site) from an order-two model (more than one binding site), the plots of $1/v$ versus $1/[S]$ and $[S]/v$ versus $[S]$ were inferior to that of v versus $v/[S]$. Both of the former two methods tend to make the order-two model look more like the order-one model. Finally, Atkins and Nimmo (1) recommended that unless the error is definitely known to be normally distributed and of constant magnitude, the direct linear plot is the one to use.

HILL PLOT

In 1910, Hill developed an equation that explained the sigmoidal behavior of hemoglobin binding to oxygen (15). The same equation was exploited later to explain the behavior of allosteric enzymes as follows:

$$v = \frac{V[S]^{nh}}{K + [S]^{nh}} \tag{12}$$

where

$v =$ initial velocity of the reaction
$V =$ substrate concentration
$nh =$ Hill coefficient
$K =$ Reciprocal of an overall equilibrium constant

Then

$$\log \left(\frac{v}{V - v} \right) = nh \log [S] - \log K \tag{13}$$

A linear regression of $\log (v/V - v)$ versus $\log [S]$ allows the two constants nh and K to be determined (Figure 8).

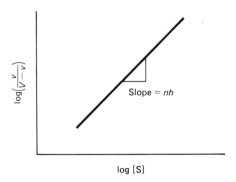

Figure 8. Hill plot.

In sigmoidal kinetics, $K' = [S]_{50}^{nh}$, which is different from K_m in classical Michaelis-Menten kinetics, where the substrate concentration is equal to K_m is the $[S]_{50}$ value. The ratio of substrate concentrations required to achieve 90% and 10% of V_{max} equals 81 for classical Michaelis-Menten kinetics, but is less than that for sigmoidal kinetics (12, 15).

The Hill plot should be used with the understanding that a fractional value for nh indicates that the rules for deriving the Hill equation have not been met.

SCHILD PLOT

In 1947, Schild suggested the use of pA as a measure of drug antagonism (14). He defined pA as the negative logarithm to base 10 of the molar concentration of an antagonistic drug that will reduce the effect of a multiple dose (x) of an active drug to that of a single dose.

For example, if we say that pA_2 pethidine–histamine $= -5.8$, we mean that $10^{-5.8}$M pethidine is required to reduce the effect of 2 μg histamine to that produced in the absence of pethidine by 1 μg histamine.

In order to get a reliable result, a constant submaximal response to the stimulant drug must be produced before addition of the antagonist. A single pA value is not sufficient to fully characterize an antagonist. To have a complete description of the relation between a given antagonist and an active drug, it would be necessary to state both the time–action and the concentration–action relations of the system. The difference between pA_2 and pA_{10} provides a quantitative test for the hypothesis that antagonists compete with drugs for receptors according to simple mass action. In a first-order reaction, a ninefold increase of antagonist corresponds to a fivefold increase of active drug between pA_2 and pA_{10}. pA is used to define the activity and specificity of an antagonist, its time–action relations, and the trend of its concentration–action curve. pA values are additive; for example, in order to express the total activity of an antagonist against two drugs, the respective values may be added together.

Factors that affect the determination of pA of an antagonist on an isolated preparation should be studied. Variables such as experimental preparation, concentration of the antagonistic drug, time of contact with the antagonistic drug, concentration of the active drug, effect produced by the active drug alone, composition of Ringer's fluid, temperatures, and so forth, should be considered. The first two or three variables are more significant than the others.

Because neither the concentration of an active drug nor the effect produced by that drug has always been defined for pA determination, the use of pA as an independent measure does not have a practical value. This is the case

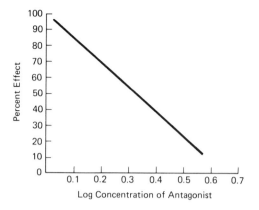

Figure 9. Schild plot.

when dealing with drugs that show pA dependency on the above-mentioned variables.

Therefore, Schild suggested that, in most cases, pA be measured when the effect is 50% maximal. In this case, pA can be used as a practical measure of antagonistic activity, even when it is dependent on the concentration of active drug. (A Schild plot is shown in Figure 9.)

SCATCHARD PLOT

Scatchard developed the following equation to describe ligand binding to a macromolecule:

$$\frac{\bar{N}}{[L]} = \frac{n - \bar{N}}{K_d} = \frac{n}{K_d} - \frac{\bar{N}}{K_d} \tag{14}$$

where

$$\bar{N} = \frac{[PL]}{[P]_0} = \frac{n[L]}{K_d + [L]} \tag{15}$$

K_d = dissociation constant of the ligand protein complex

L = ligand concentration

n = number of binding sites per molecule of protein, having similar K_d

$[PL]$ and $[P]_0$ = bound protein and total protein concentrations, respectively

So, if we plot $\bar{N}/[L]$ versus $\bar{N}$, this gives a straight line with slope $= -1/K_d$; when $(\bar{N}/[L]) = 0$, then $(n/K_d) = (\bar{N}/K_d)$, i.e., $n - \bar{N}$. In other words, the intercept gives the value of n, the number of binding sites per molecule of protein (10, 13). So, if we measure the concentration of ligand bound to protein at a series of values of concentrations of free ligand in a solution containing a fixed total protein concentration of $[P]_0$, we are able to draw the Scatchard plot.

The protein-bound ligand $[PL]$ is the difference between the concentration of total ligand and free ligand, which can be determined by equilibrium dialysis. For each value of $[L]$, the ratio $[PL]/[P]_0$ is calculated; this is equal to the above-mentioned $\bar{N}$. $\bar{N}$ represents the number of ligand molecules bound by the protein molecule. Then plotting $\bar{N}/[L]$ versus $\bar{N}$ gives a straight line, as stated. (See Figure 10.)

If the plots are linear (Figure 10, Curve A) and extrapolate to an integral number of binding sites, this gives a good indication that one is dealing with a specific set of identical binding sites. There is, however, the possibility that the sites may actually be different in terms of their protein structure, but able to bind the ligand with the same dissociation constant.

If, however, the plot is not linear, one has the impression of dealing with more than one type of binding site on the protein. This will give more than one value of K_d, as in Figure 10, Curve B.

The Scatchard plot is also used in enzyme kinetics where it corresponds to what was referred to above as the Eadie-Scatchard plot, where $v/[S]$ was plotted against v with a slope of $-1/K_m$, and a vertical intercept of V_{max}/K_m. The horizontal intercept V_{max}, corresponds to the number of substrate binding sites per molecule of enzyme.

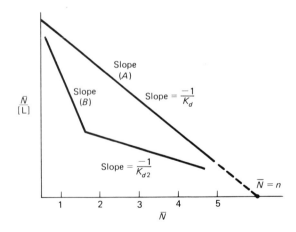

Figure 10. Scatchard plot.

In cases of cooperativity between the binding sites, or where different intrinsic affinities for the ligand to the different active sites exist, the plot will not be linear.

In summary, the Scatchard plot is valuable in determining the number of binding sites on the protein or enzyme molecule, and also in calculating the binding constant of those sites to the ligand. Also, the plot can be used to indicate if there is more than one active site with the same intrinsic affinity or with different intrinsic affinities. Finally cooperativity can be seen by analyzing the plot carefully (10).

REFERENCES

1. Atkins, G. L., and Nimmo, I. A. 1975. A comparison of seven methods for fitting the Michaelis-Menten equation. *Biochem J.* 149:775–77.
2. Ault, A. 1974. An introduction to enzyme kinetics. *J. Chem. Ed.* 51:381–86.
3. Cornish-Bowden, A. 1974. A simple graphical method for determining the inhibition constants of mixed, uncompetitive and non-competitive inhibitors. *Biochem. J.* 137:143–44.
4. Cornish-Bowden, A. 1976. *Principles of Enzyme Kinetics.* Butterworth, London and Boston. 206 pp.
5. Cornish-Bowden, A., and Eisenthal, R. 1974. Statistical considerations in the estimation of enzyme kinetics parameters by the direct linear plot and other methods. *Biochem. J.* 139:721–30.
6. Dixon, M. 1953. The determination of enzyme inhibitor constants. *Biochem. J.* 55:170–71.
7. Dowd, J. E., and Riggs D. S. 1965. A comparison of estimates of Michaelis-Menten kinetic constants from various linear transformations. *J. Biol. Chem.* 240:863–69.
8. Eadie, G. S. 1943. The inhibition of cholinesterase by physostigmine and prostigmine. *J. Biol. Chem.* 146:85–93.
9. Eisenthal, R., and Cornish-Bowden, A. 1974. The direct linear plot. A new graphical procedure for estimating enzyme kinetic parameters. *Biochem. J.* 139:715–20.
10. Ferdinand, W. 1976. *The Enzyme Molecule.* John Wiley & Sons, London and New York. 289 pp.
11. Hofstee, B. H. J. 1952. On the evaluation of the constants Vm and K_m in enzyme reactions. *Science* 116:329–31.
12. Roberts, D. V. 1977. *Enzyme Kinetics.* Cambridge University Press, London and New York. 326 pp.
13. Scatchard, G. 1949. The attractions of proteins for small molecules and ions. *Ann. N.Y. Acad. Sci.* 51:660–72.
14. Schild, H. O. 1947. pA, a new scale for the measurements of drug antagonism. *Br. J. Pharmacol.* 2:189.
15. Segel, I. H. 1975. *Enzyme Kinetics.* John Wiley & Sons, New York and London. 957 pp.
16. Walter, C. 1974. Graphical procedures for the detection of deviations from the classical model of enzyme kinetics. *J. Biol. Chem.* 249:699–703.
17. Wilkinson, G. N. 1961. Statistical estimations in enzyme kinetics. *Biochem. J.* 80:324–32.

SECTION 2
PLASMA MEMBRANES AND CELL WALLS

AKIRA KAJI, SECTION EDITOR

2.1. Plasma Membranes of Eukaryotes

Reuben Lotan and Garth L. Nicolson

All cells are separated from their environment by a membrane that encapsulates the cytoplasm and is called a cell membrane or plasma membrane. The plasma membrane is the primary site for the control of cell growth, division, development, communication, movement, differentiation, and death. In addition to boundary functions, the plasma membrane also serves as an essential, selective barrier that regulates the passage of nutrients and stimuli into the cell and waste products or secretions out of the cell. Eukaryotic cells also possess other barriers, intracellular membranes that surround organelles such as the nucleus, Golgi apparatus, lysosomes, peroxisomes, mitochondria, vacuoles, chloroplasts, and others. Each of these intracellular membrane systems is functionally specialized for digestion, respiration, biosynthesis, or secretion. Most eukaryotic cells have additionally an interconnecting network of intracellular membranes, the endoplasmic reticulum, which is involved in biosynthesis, secretion, storage, and transport of proteins and lipids. This chapter will concentrate on the structure and composition of the plasma membrane with emphasis on the dynamics and regulation of cell membrane organization. The physiologic functions of plasma membranes in transport of nutrients and transduction of extracellular stimuli as well as their role in cellular motility and cell–cell interactions will be discussed in other chapters of this book.

PLASMA MEMBRANE ISOLATION AND PURIFICATION

Most of the direct approaches to the determination of the composition and molecular structure of plasma membranes require their isolation and purification from other cellular organelles. Although a variety of methods for the isolation of plasma membrane have been developed, this is not a straightforward endeavor. The cell surface membrane must be disrupted before isolation, and common techniques include: mechanical homogenization or shear, nitrogen cavitation or gas-bubble nucleation, and hypoosmotic lysis. Unfortunately, these methods are indiscriminate and cause some disruption of intracellular organelle membranes as well as the plasma membrane. This may lead to adsorption of organellar components to the disrupted plasma membrane and partial degradation of plasma membrane components by released lysosomal hydrolases. Entrapment of soluble cytoplasmic components in vesicles formed from fragments of the plasma membranes is another source of contamination. Treatment of cells with agents that stabilize the plasma membrane (e.g., Zn^{2+}) before homogenization or addition of sucrose to cell homogenates prevents extensive plasma membrane fragmentation and allows their isolation as large envelopes.

The separation of plasma membrane vesicles and fragments from other membranes and organelles of the disrupted cells is usually based on differences in charge, density, and/or size. The latter types of separation are accomplished by differential rate centrifugation or differential (isopycnic) density gradient centrifugation (see Chapter 1.1). Separation according to surface charge and other properties of membrane components may be achieved by phase separation in aqueous solutions of mixed polymers such as dextran and polyethylene glycol. A more novel approach to purifying plasma membranes makes use of their specific surface receptors. Membrane fragments bearing specific receptors can be purified by centrifugal affinity density perturbation where receptor–ligand interactions modify the density of the plasma membrane fragments.

Once the plasma membrane fraction has been isolated, its purity must be assessed. Electron microscopy can be employed to follow the progress of the isolation and purification procedures. Morphological observations can detect contamination by intracellular membranes or organelles. However, many cellular membranes tend to form smooth vesicles after cell disruption; so contamination by intracellular membranes may be unnoticed. Therefore, additional quantitative methods have been developed. Determination of purity is better achieved by analysis of endogenous biochemical markers that are preferentially localized in the plasma membrane such as the enzymes 5'-nucleotidase, alkaline phosphatase, and Na^+, K^+-dependent ATPase, membrane antigens, or virus receptors. Another approach is to first covalently label membrane components on intact cells by chemical or enzymatic techniques. These procedures usually employ charged, and therefore presumably nonpermeant, reagents that label externally exposed membrane components. The ^{35}S-labeled diazonium salt of sulfanilic acid is an example of a reagent capable of labeling plasma membrane proteins by reacting with exteriorly exposed amino, sulfhydryl, tyrosyl, or histidyl groups. Because small organic reagents are almost never completely nonpermeant, enzymatic methods have been developed to label membrane surface proteins. The most widely used enzyme is lactoperoxidase, which, in the presence of $Na^{125}I$ and H_2O_2, catalyzes iodination of accessible tyrosine residues of membrane proteins. Labeling of membrane glycoproteins and glycolipids may be achieved by oxidation of galactosyl or N-acetylgalactosaminyl residues with the enzyme galactose oxidase followed by reduction with tritiated borohydride. The labeling of membrane components with radioactive isotopes allows not only an easy quantitation of membrane purity during isolation, but also analysis of the labeled components following membrane isolation.

PLASMA MEMBRANE COMPOSITION AND ORGANIZATION

All cell membranes are composed of protein, lipid, and carbohydrate in variable quantities (see Table 1). Membrane carbohydrate is found primarily in glycoproteins and to a lesser extent in glycolipids. Membrane proteins and glycoproteins normally constitute 60–70% of the plasma membrane mass, and they associate with lipids and glycolipids by noncovalent forces. Although the chemical composition of a particular membrane is usually distinct, different regions of the same membrane (e.g., in cells of solid tissues) may have different compositions owing to regional specialization such as in hepatocyte membranes facing bile canaliculi or neural cell membrane synapses. Additionally, cell differentiation, maturation and aging, and variation in cell environment such as temperature or nutritional status, as well as exposure to hormones or drugs, may lead to changes in membrane composition.

MEMBRANE PROTEINS

Isolation and Characterization

While studies on the organization of proteins in membranes require their examination in situ, the chemical characterization of individual membrane

Table 1. Chemical Composition of Different Cellular Membranes

	APPROXIMATE PERCENT OF DRY MASS		
MEMBRANE	PROTEIN	LIPID	CARBOHYDRATE
Plasma membrane:			
Red blood cell	49	44	10
Nerve myelin	70	17	13
Liver cell	54	36	10
Nuclear membrane	66	32	2
Endoplasmic reticulum	62	27	1
Golgi	64	26	10
Mitochondria:			
Inner membrane	78	22	—
Outer membrane	55	45	trace

proteins cannot be achieved without their isolation from purified membranes. For operational purposes plasma membrane proteins and glycoproteins have been divided into two main classes: integral and peripheral. Integral membrane proteins and glycoproteins are characterized by their lipid interactions which are due to the favorable entropy gained from sequestering hydrophobic protein structures away from the aqueous environment. These integral membrane proteins are intercalated into the plasma membrane interior to various depths, some spanning the entire membrane. In contrast, peripheral membrane proteins are only weakly bound to the surfaces of plasma membranes, and their presence is not dependent on protein–lipid hydrophobic interactions. Because of the disparate properties of integral and peripheral membrane, differing techniques have been utilized for their isolation and purification.

The isolation of integral membrane proteins requires disruption of protein–lipid interactions, resulting in radical changes in protein conformation in order to reach thermodynamic equilibrium with the altered environment. It is difficult to extract integral membrane proteins in a monomolecular soluble form because these proteins often occur in complexes with other proteins or lipids in the membrane or when isolated. Because the associations between integral membrane proteins and lipids as well as between integral membrane proteins themselves involve—in addition to hydrophobic forces—ionic interactions, the agents used for extraction must disrupt both of these interactions without altering membrane protein composition. Alternatively, peripheral membrane proteins are released from membranes by single ionic manipulations such as raising or lowering the ionic strength or the pH, removal of divalent cations, or extraction with high concentrations of salt. Under these conditions most of the integral membrane proteins are markedly insoluble and require more drastic extraction procedures to remove them from their favored hydrophobic environments. Strong chaotropic agents like urea and guanidine hydrochloride or inorganic ions (e.g., SCN^-, ClO_4^-, I^-) disorganize the arrangement of water molecules, thereby enhancing the solubility of apolar groups in water, and may, in addition, also rupture hydrogen bonds and unfold soluble globular proteins into random polypeptide chains. Such agents have been used with varying success to extract integral membrane proteins and glycoproteins. Partial release of integral membrane proteins can be achieved with organic solvents such as ethanol, chloroethanol, butanol, N-pentanol, acidified phenol, or aqueous pyridine. These solvents extract lipids into the organic phase, leaving most of the integral membrane proteins insoluble or in the aqueous phase. In many instances a considerable proportion of the membrane lipid, in the form of protein–lipid aggregates, can partition into the aqueous phase. One disadvantage of organic solvents, however, is that they do not efficiently disaggregate protein–protein aggregates.

By far the most efficient class of membrane-solubilizing agents are surfactants (detergents). These amphiphilic compounds exhibit high affinities for both membrane lipids and integral membrane proteins and are effective at low concentrations. Membrane-disrupting surfactants are classified according to their charge into nonionic (Triton X-100, Nonidet P-40), zwitterionic (dimethyl dodecyl glycine), anionic (bile salts, lithium diiodosalicylate, sodium dodecylsulfate), and cationic (cetyl trimethylammonium bromide) detergents. The nonionic detergents are not always effective, and a considerable number of integral membrane proteins remain insoluble after treatment. More efficient solubilization can be achieved with the widely used anionic detergent sodium dodecylsulfate (SDS). This detergent forms soluble complexes with both lipids and integral membrane proteins stabilized primarily by hydrophobic interactions and dissociates most integral proteins to their monomeric polypeptide chains. Owing to similar binding on a weight basis of SDS by different proteins, a constant charge-to-relative-molecular-mass ratio can be obtained, allowing separation of membrane proteins according to their size by gel filtration or electrophoresis in the presence of SDS. A disadvantage in using SDS is that this detergent inactivates most proteins. Therefore, nonionic detergents are used in the isolation of membrane proteins when it is desirable to recover enzymatic, receptor, or antigenic activities.

Once solubilized and stabilized in buffered detergent solutions, membrane proteins and glycoproteins can be purified by conventional methods like gel filtration and ion exchange chromatography (in nonionic detergents only). Recently sugar-binding proteins called lectins have been insolubilized on inert carriers and have been successfully used for affinity chromatography of plasma membrane glycoproteins from various cell types.

The application of polyacrylamide gel electrophoresis in SDS buffers offers excellent resolution and sensitivity in detection of minute amounts of membrane proteins, especially if the proteins are prelabeled with radioactive isotopes and detected on the gels by autoradiography. Such procedures have revealed that membranes may contain numerous heterogeneous proteins differing in electrophoretic mobility. For example, six major and nine minor proteins have been separated after solubilization of human erythrocyte ghosts, and as many as 50 polypeptide bands resolved after solubilization of HeLa cell plasma membranes. The subunit molecular weights of the various membrane polypeptides are in the range 10,000 to 250,000 daltons.

Chemical Properties of Membrane Proteins

Many integral membrane proteins are glycoproteins, containing oligosaccharide side chains covalently attached to their polypeptide backbones. Plasma membranes usually contain between 2 and 10% by weight carbohydrate, much of which is present on glycoproteins. The major neutral sugars found in membrane glycoproteins are galactose, mannose, and fucose, and the principal amino sugars are N-acetylglucosamine, N-acetylgalactosamine, and N-acetylneuraminic acid. Glycoprotein carbohydrate side chains are usually branched heterooligosaccharides comprised of between 2 and 60 sugar residues. The major linkages between the sugar and the peptide chains are alkali-labile O-glycosidic bonds between N-acetylgalactosamine and serine or threonine hydroxyl groups, and alkali-stable N-glycosidic bonds between N-acetylglucosamine and asparagine amide (Figure 1). Evidence indicates that all sugars and their associated peptide moieties lie at the outer surface of plasma membranes and protrude off the exterior of the cells, whereas the nonglycosylated part of the molecule is at least partly embedded in the lipid bilayer.

Analyses of the amino acid composition of various integral membrane glycoproteins suggest that they may have a lower proportion of polar amino

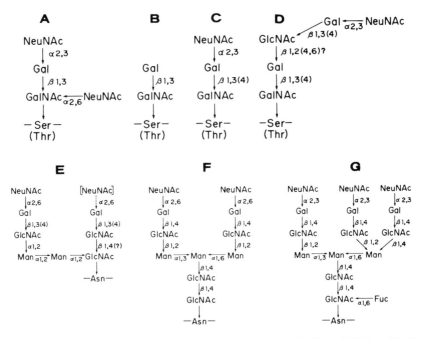

Figure 1. Examples for O-glycosidically bound oligosacchardies (A–D) and N-glycosidically bound oligosaccharides (E–G) found in glycopeptides isolated from: (A) human red blood cell membrane glycophorin; (B–D) mammary carcinoma (TA-3) cell surface epiglycanin; (E) human red blood cell membrane glycophorin; (F) serum transferrin; (G) human diploid fibroblast surface, vesicular stomatitis viral envelope glycoprotein.

acids compared to peripheral membrane proteins. Otherwise the composition is not strikingly different from that of soluble glycoproteins and does not alone provide insight into the ability of membrane proteins to strongly associate with membrane lipids. A more unique and important property of integral proteins is the presence of specialized amino acid sequences. In particular, the nonrandom distribution of nonpolar and polar amino acid residues along the polypeptide chain renders them amphipathic or asymmetric with respect to the hydrophobic and hydrophilic portions of their structure. For example, the 55,000-dalton subunit of glycophorin, the major human erythrocyte integral membrane glycoprotein, has been sequenced completely and contains 131 amino acids. This includes a region of 23 amino acid residues of relatively hydrophobic character, which form a stable α-helix, located between a carboxyl-terminal sequence relatively rich in charged amino acids and a polypeptide region bearing hydrophilic oligosaccharide side chains. Glycophorin contains about 55% carbohydrate arranged in 15 O-glycosidically bound tetrasaccharide side chains and one longer and more complex N-glycosidically bound oligosaccharide chain in each glycophorin polypeptide chain near the amino-terminal end. There is ample evidence that the polypeptide chain of glycophorin spans the entire membrane displaying the carboxyl-terminal end at the inner surface and the sugar-bearing amino-terminal end protruding from the cell at the outer surface. An analogous nonrandom distribution of hydrophilic and hydrophobic amino acids and the presence of a stretch of hydrophobic amino acids between hydrophilic segments was recently found in human histocompatibility antigens. It is likely that the hydrophobic sequence of amino acids is important in achoring these molecules in the lipid bilayer. Other integral membrane proteins may be only partially embedded in the lipid bilayer, leaving hydrophilic parts of their structures in contact with the exterior or interior environment.

Biological Properties of Membrane Proteins

Plasma membrane proteins fulfill many diverse biological functions. Many proteins possess enzymatic activity (e.g., 5'-nucleotidase, adenylate cyclase, ATPase), whereas others are involved in active transport of nutrients and formation of ion channels. Specific integral membrane proteins exposed at the surface of the plasma membrane serve as receptors for hormones, lectins, or viruses. The interactions of cells with neighboring cells are also mediated via specialized surface components. Membrane proteins can be antigens which appear to function in cellular recognition, and some lymphoid cells carry antibodylike immunoglobulins on their surfaces. Many membrane proteins will be discussed in detail in other chapters.

MEMBRANE LIPIDS

Extraction and Isolation

Membrane lipids are often difficult to extract with simple solvents like ether. However, diverse solvent mixtures such as chloroform–methanol or ethanol–ether are very effective in extracting membrane lipids. The separation of lipids from contaminating proteins and peptides with apolar characteristics can be achieved by gel permeation chromatography on lipophilic Sephadex. When isolated, different classes of lipids can be resolved by thin layer or column chromatography on silicic acid, aluminum oxide, cellulose, or controlled-pore glass beads. The complete chemical characterization of isolated individual molecular species of lipids is now possible by using a combination of gas–liquid chromatography and mass spectrometry.

Physico-Chemical Properties of Membrane Lipids

Membrane lipids form the matrix of the plasma membrane and are the major contributors to the hydrophobic character of cell membranes. The asymmetric distribution of hydrophobic and hydrophilic groups confers on lipids an amphipathic structure. When they are added to an aqueous system, their solubility is limited, and above a certain concentration they segregate their hydrophobic moieties from the solvent by self-aggregation. The aggregates, known as micelles, can form a sphere, ellipsoid, cylinder, or bilayer. In the bilayer form, two parallel amphipathic lipid layers are arranged such that their polar groups face the aqueous environment. The driving force for micelle formation is a positive entropy change that is nonspecific in the sense that micelles containing mixtures of different amphiphilic molecules are formed with the same entropy change. The formation of bilayers by amphiphiles is greatly enhanced when the molecules contain two alkyl chains per polar group because there is no reduction in surface area per polar group as is the case with single-chain amphiphiles. As will be described below, the predominant type of lipid molecules found in biological membranes (except cholesterol) contains two hydrocarbon chains per polar head group and forms bilayers. X-ray diffraction analysis, as well as electron microscopy and optical diffraction methods, indicated that the thickness of the bilayer of biological membranes is in the range 4 to 10 nm, depending on the extent of hydration. On the basis of chemical structure the lipids found in eukaryotic plasma membrane can be classified into three major groups: glycerophosphatides, sphingolipids and glycolipids, and sterols.

The most abundant class of membrane lipids, the glycerophosphatides, are derivatives of glycerol and bear two long-chain fatty acids esterified to two glycerol hydroxyl groups at carbons 1 and 2 and phosphoric acid esterified to the primary hydroxyl group at carbon 3. The phosphate residue is banded in a diester linkage with choline, serine, ethanolamine, glycerol, or myoinositol. These diester-linked hydrophilic groups may lack a net charge at physiological pH (phosphatidylcholine) or bear a negative charge (phosphatidylserine, phosphatidylglycerol, phosphatidylinositol). The long-chain fatty acids are unbranched; they contain 10 to 20 carbon atoms and are either unsaturated (with *cis* double bonds) or saturated (Figure 2).

A separate subgroup of glycerophosphatides are the glyceryl ether phosphatides or plasmalogens, which contain an alkali-stable, ether-linked paraffinic group at the 1-carbon position of the glycerol. Minor amounts of lysoglycerophosphatides may be found occasionally in plasma membranes. Because these compounds contain only one fatty acyl residue, they possess detergent-like properties. Lysoglycerophosphatides can also be formed by the lytic action of phospholipases (A_1 or A_2) on intact cells.

Sphingolipids resemble glycerolipids except that they contain a long-chain amino alcohol, sphingosine, or dihydrosphingosine instead of glycerol (Figure 2). The long-chain fatty acid is attached to the amino group via an amide linkage, and the hydroxyl may carry an additional hydrophilic group. Ceramides are a class of sphingolipids that have a free hydroxyl group at the 1-carbon position. When this hydroxyl is esterified with a monosaccharide such as galactose, the resulting compound is a cerebroside, and when a complex oligosaccharide containing neutral and amino sugars (including N-acetylneuraminic acid) is esterified through the hydroxyl, the compound is a ganglioside. The terminal hydroxyl group of sphingosine in ceramides may carry

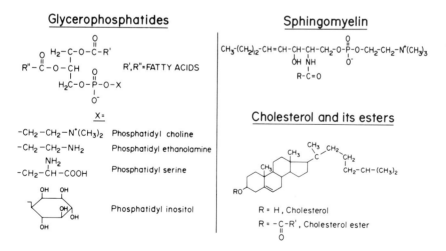

Figure 2. The structures of three types of membrane lipids.

a phosphate ester of choline as in sphingomyelin, which is a ceramide 1-phosphorylcholine. The fatty acyl groups of sphingolipids are derived mainly from saturated or unsaturated 24-carbon-long fatty acids (e.g., lignoceric, nervonic).

The third class of lipids found in membranes is the sterols (Figure 2). The most abundant sterol is cholesterol, usually nonesterified. Neutral glycerides, cholesterol esters, and free fatty acids are only occasionally observed as minor components in plasma membrane lipid extracts.

The proportions of the major lipid classes in the plasma membrane of different cell types are usually similar; however, the molecular species within each of the lipid groups may be dissimilar (Table 2). In addition, the length of the fatty acyl substituents on phospholipids and the extent of saturation may vary with the particular physical requirements of the membrane. In comparison with other membranes of the cell, the plasma membrane contains most of the cellular glycolipids and also contains a high proportion of the total cell membrane cholesterol. The molar ratio of cholesterol to phospholipid is about 1.0 for plasma membranes of various cells, whereas in the nuclear and mitochondrial membranes, the ratios are 0.1 to 0.2 and 0.02 to 0.05, respectively.

Biological Activities of Membrane Lipids

In addition to the general function of lipids in the formation of a bilayer into which membrane proteins are intercalated, there are a few more specific activities carried out by certain types of lipids. Several glycolipids carry blood group specificity (ABH or Lewis) or antigenic activity (Forssman antigen), and certain gangliosides act as binding sites for cholera enterotoxin and tetanus

Table 2. Phospholipid Composition of Plasma Membranes of Different Cell Types

| | APPROXIMATE PERCENT OF TOTAL PHOSPHOLIPID[a] | | | | |
SOURCE OF MEMBRANE	PE	PS	PI	PC	SPH
Human erythrocyte	28	14	1	29	28
Rat liver cell	25	4	7	46	17
Baby hamster kidney cell line 21	18	9	2	44	18
Mouse 3T3 fibroblasts	27	6	3	52	7
Human diploid fibroblasts cell line WI-38	12	12	13	56	7

[a] PE, phosphatidyl ethanolanine; PS, phosphatidyl serine; PI, phosphatidyl inositol; PC, phosphatidyl choline; SPH, sphingomyelin.

toxin. The activities of various membrane-bound enzymes and transport systems appear to be regulated by the "fluidity" of their microenvironment, which is determined by the bulk fluidity of the membrane lipids and also by specific lipids that are tightly bound to these membrane structures. Because the bulk fluidity of the membrane depends on the ratio of cholesterol to phosphatides, cholesterol may be important as a regulator of certain enzymatic activities. It is noteworthy, however, that lipid fluidity affects enzyme activity even in membranes that have no cholesterol.

PLASMA MEMBRANE ORGANIZATION: SUMMARY

An overwhelming amount of data accumulated over the last few years indicates that the structures of cellular membranes conform to a number of basic principles set forth by the fluid mosaic model of Singer and Nicolson: (1) The major membrane lipids, such as the phospholipids, are arranged in a planar bilayer configuration that is predominantly in a "fluid" state under physiological conditions. (2) The lipid bilayer is not a continuous structure and is interrupted by numerous proteins, which are inserted or intercalated to various degrees into the bilayer. (3) In most membranes the arrangement of lipids, glycolipids, proteins, and glycoproteins is asymmetric with respect to the distribution of specific molecules in the inner and outer halves of the bilayer. (4) The proteins and glycoproteins of cell membranes are quite heterogeneous with respect to their structure and state of aggregation. (5) Integral membrane proteins and glycoproteins are globular, bimodal molecules that interact with both the hydrophobic (hydrocarbon) and hydrophilic regions of the membrane and are characterized by their strong interactions with membrane lipids. (6) The degree of intercalation of integral plasma membrane proteins into the lipid bilayer is determined by the amino acid sequence and the three-dimensional folding of the proteins. (7) Some integral membrane proteins span the entire bilayer and have portions of their structures protruding at both the inner and outer membrane surfaces. (8) Certain integral proteins are thought to exist as oligomeric complexes, and there is evidence indicating that a number of these integral proteins interact with peripheral membrane proteins at the external or cytoplasmic membrane surface. (9) Peripheral membrane proteins and glycoproteins are only weakly bound to the surface of biological membranes, and their interaction with the membrane is not highly dependent upon hydrophobic forces for stable bonding. (10) Peripheral membrane proteins probably associate with integral membrane proteins, glycoproteins, and perhaps also lipids and glycolipids by ionic interactions or by weak nonionic interactions such as Van der Waals and London dispersion forces.

DYNAMICS OF CELL MEMBRANE COMPONENTS

According to the fluid mosaic model the plasma membrane is visualized as a two-dimensional solution of lipid in which a mosaic of integral membrane proteins is embedded, with peripheral proteins bound loosely to either surface (see Figure 3). Maintenance of the striking asymmetry of the plasma membrane requires that components localized in either the inner or outer surface of the lipid bilayer not be able to rotate at appreciable rates from one side of the membrane to the other (flip-flop). The main obstacle that limits transmembrane rotation is the tremendous thermodynamic barrier, which tends to prevent the passage of hydrophilic molecules or polar regions of glycolipids and glycoproteins through the hydrophobic matrix of the membrane.

The lipid hydrocarbon chains in natural membranes are generally in a fluid state, which allows for some freedom of lateral motion of integral membrane proteins, lipoprotein complexes, and individual lipids within the plane of the membrane. Whereas some cell surface components diffuse quite rapidly and apparently freely in the membrane, others move much more slowly. The spectrum of mobilities observed for different receptors on the surface membrane and even within specific limited areas on the cell surface suggests that specific controlling mechanisms exist that restrict the mobility of certain receptors in order to maintain specific topographic arrangements or patterns

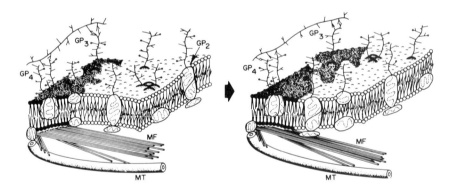

Figure 3. Modified version of the fluid mosaic model of membrane structure, showing transmembrane control over the distribution and mobility of cell surface receptors by peripheral and membrane-associated cytoskeletal components. In this hypothetical model the mobility of integral glycoprotein complexes, GP_3 and GP_4, is controlled by outer surface peripheral components and also by membrane-associated cytoskeletal elements at the inner surface. In addition, complexes GP_3 and GP_4 are shown to be sequestered into a specific lipid domain, indicated by the shaded area, whereas complex GP_2 exists in a free or unaggregated state and is capable of free lateral motion. MF, microfilaments; MT, microtubules. (From G. L. Nicolson, 1976, *Biochim. Biophys. Acta* 475:57–108, by permission.)

on the surface of the cell. The topographic display of surface receptors may change rapidly and reversibly in response to stimuli from outside the cells or from within the cell. It is possible that such changes may play an important role in transmembrane-mediated communication.

Consideration of the dynamics of membrane components should not be limited to the complex structural and topographic rearrangements exhibited by different membrane components. Equally important is the flow of membrane components into and out of the membrane: the synthesis, assembly, and turnover of different membrane constituents. All the above aspects of membrane dynamics will be discussed individually in the subsequent sections.

A. Dynamics of Membrane Lipids

The motion of lipids in cell membranes is determined by factors such as lipid chain flexibility, rotational and lateral diffusion, viscosity, phase separation, and interactions with other lipids or with membrane proteins.

1. Lipid Viscosity. Most biological lipid bilayer membranes are stabilized by hydrophobic interactions between the lipid hydrocarbon chains. The matrix of the membranes is formed mainly from fluid-state lipids that have a viscosity similar to that of light machine oil. The use of physical techniques such as nuclear magnetic resonance and electron spin resonance allows estimation of the bending and flexing of fatty acid hydrocarbon chains in the lipid matrix. Studies with unperturbed lipid bilayers indicate that hydrocarbon chain flexing and bending is relatively constant down the acyl chains; however, a rapid change occurs near the methyl end. Under physiological conditions phospholipid acyl chains undergo rapid rotation and kinking (*trans-gauche* isomerization about carbon–carbon bonds), and the kinks that form appear to fluctuate rapidly up and down the acyl chains. These anisotropic acyl chain motions determine, to a large extent, the fluidities of membranes. Although it cannot be excluded that the viscosity of biological membranes may be affected by proteins or protein–lipid complexes, it is very likely that lipids account for the bulk fluid characteristics of cellular membranes. Evidence has been obtained in many systems indicating that artificial lipid bilayers formed from lipids extracted from biological membranes possess similar viscosities to those of the membranes from which they were extracted.

Membrane viscosities can be measured by a variety of methods. The most popular technique has been fluorescence polarization measurements on the rotational diffusion of small organic fluorescent probes in the membrane apolar environment. These measurements analyze the properties of the membrane near the probe, and therefore may not reflect the bulk properties of membranes. Using this method various investigators have obtained values of

1–10 poise for the microviscosities of diverse types of plasma and intracellular membranes.

Cholesterol plays an important role in determining membrane fluidity. Close-apposition molecular models of cholesterol and phospholipids with the cholesterol hydroxyl group near the phosphate group show that the remainder of the sterol molecule lies close to the phospholipid hydrocarbon chain, and an equimolar complex can easily be formed by apolar interactions. In such a complex the mobility of the hydrocarbon chain should be limited. Indeed, cholesterol interacts with certain phospholipid fatty acids and sphingolipids and causes a reduction in their lateral molecular spacing and in the flexibility of the carboxyl half of the phospholipid acyl chains (between carbons 2 and 10). Although cholesterol–phospholipid interactions appear to rigidify biological membranes at physiological temperatures, those interactions do not convert membranes to solid phase states. The presence of cholesterol in biological membranes serves to create an intermediate fluid condition in either fluid or solid phases. Consequently most biological membranes usually show decreased phospholipid hydrocarbon chain mobility and flexing as compared to artificial phospholipid dispersions in the absence of cholesterol.

2. Lipid Motion within Membranes.   The lateral diffusion of lipids in natural membranes has been measured by various physical techniques such as nuclear magnetic resonance spin exchange, and values for diffusion constants in the range $D = 1 \times 10^{-8}$ to 12×10^{-8} cm^{2}sec^{-1} have been calculated. The variability of the values has depended on the type of spin label, lipid composition, divalent cation concentration, the method of measurement, and the assumptions made before calculations. The values indicate that the lateral diffusion rate of phospholipids is quite high, permitting a single molecule to move a few micrometers per second when the membrane is in the fluid state.

Since membrane lipids are amphipathic molecules and are distributed asymmetrically in the plasma membrane, their perpendicular motion in the membrane from one side to another (flip-flop) is energetically unfavorable and must only occur at very low rates. Studies with human erythrocyte membranes using chemical labeling of lipids or enzymatic hydrolysis of phospholipids have demonstrated that sphingomyelin, phosphatidylethanolamine, and phosphatidylserine are localized predominantly in the inner cytoplasmic half of the membrane, whereas phosphatidylcholine is found at higher concentrations in the outer half. A high rate of flip-flop motion would have randomized the distribution of these phospholipids in both membrane halves. Flip-flop motion of phosphatidylcholine across artifical phospholipid bilayers measured by spin-labeling techniques is not very rapid, with a half-time of several hours at 30°C. Using different methods and biological membranes, it has been shown that rat erythrocyte ghosts exchange nearly 75% of their phosphatidylcholine rapidly and nearly 25% slowly to phospholipid ∶ cholesterol vesicles. In contrast, inverted ghost vesicles (inside out) exchanged 37% of the phosphatidylcholine rapidly and 76% at a slower rate. Based on these studies, flip-flop half-times of 2.3 hr and 5.3 hr were calculated for right-side-out and inside-out ghost vesicles, respectively. Spin-labeling studies on the movement of phospholipids in a phospholipid bilayer indicated that neighbor-exchange across the bilayer (flip-flop) was about 10^{10} times slower than lateral exchange.

3. Lipid Phase Separation.   The movements of phospholipid acyl chains are dependent on temperature. For each phospholipid a transition temperature exists below which the hydrocarbon chains are relatively rigid, extended, and packed in parallel. At or above the phase transition temperature the phospholipid acyl chains become more fluid or liquid–crystalline in nature and undergo cooperative chain movements such as flexing, bending, twisting, or lateral motions. As a result of these changes the lipids proceed from a relatively "solid" phase (at the lower temperatures) to a "fluid" state, the thickness of the bilayer is reduced, and the area occupied by each lipid molecule is increased (for example, in dipalmtoyl phosphatidylcholine from about 48 to 60 Å^2). The phase transitions are strongly dependent on lipid composition, the length of the acyl chains, the nature of the polar head group, the degree of unsaturation, and the presence of divalent cations. The transition is endothermic and can be determined by differential scanning calorimetry, which measures the differential heat required to maintain a constant rate of temperature change. Mixtures of phospholipids (with different transition temperatures) in bilayers exhibit complex and broad phase transitions that are due to the coexistence of fluid and solid phases of differing lipid compositions, with resultant lipid lateral segregation and long-range molecular motion in the bilayer plane.

The solid and fluid phases of some artificial binary lipid bilayers can be visualized by freeze-cleavage electron microscopy. Solid lipid phases appear as smooth surfaces with "banded" linear repeating ridges, and the fluid phase appears completely smooth. Similar observations have been made with biological membranes that undergo lateral phase separations. However, in biological membranes numerous intercalations or particles, not observed in model membranes of pure lipids, are visualized. These intramembranous particles most probably represent proteins. When lipid phase transitions occur in biological membranes, the distribution of the intercalated particles is changed; during slow cooling they are sequestered into the fluid-phase lipids and are excluded from the solid-phase lipids. Cholesterol can modify the formation of lipid domains and induce protein particle rearrangements. Inclusion of 20 mole

% of cholesterol in dimyristoyl phosphatidylcholine vesicles abolishes the bands seen in freeze-cleavage electron microscopy which usually represent solid-phase lipid. However, electron spin resonance reveals the presence of different lipid phases in these same vesicles. Vesicles containing protein and 10 mole % cholesterol show two protein particle populations in lipid phases below but near the transition temperature (15°C): a particle-rich phase and a particle-poor phase. Increasing the cholesterol content to 20 mole % causes the particles to rearrange and form stringlike linear arrays which disperse above the phase transition temperature. These lipid phase characteristics can have a profound influence on the distribution and topography of integral membrane protein complexes, even in the presence of a significant concentration of cholesterol.

Lipid motion in membranes may have specific cellular functions. For example, in many biological membranes with broad lipid phase transition changes, local lipid domain formation may lead to protein segregation, sequestration, or clustering, which may have biological significance in modifying the topographic display of specific receptors or in modifying states of association or aggregation. The fluidity of the lipid matrix in plasma membranes may be of considerable importance in regulating a number of cell membrane functions such as transport, adhesion, endocytosis, fusion, and others.

B. Effects of Calcium on Biological Membranes

Calcium may play an important role in determining the properties of biological membranes by modifying the mobility of lipids within the membrane. Calcium ions cause condensation of phospholipid bilayers and restrict the mobility of certain phospholipids as well as the mobility of lipids as shown by the lateral motion of electron paramagnetic spin labels in rat liver plasma membranes. Introduction of Ca^{2+} into erythrocyte membranes during hemolysis results in increased lipid mobility as well as aggregation of membrane proteins, which suggests that Ca^{2+} decreases protein–lipid interaction and increases protein–protein aggregation. Binding of Ca^{2+} to membranes can modify the charge and decrease repulsion between negatively charged membrane components, and thus may induce structural reorganizations. Because alterations in Ca^{2+} mobilization and membrane interactions occur rapidly and reversibly, this ion is well suited to play a regulatory role in modulating membrane properties. Indeed, changes in membrane Ca^{2+} binding are induced by a variety of regulatory molecules such as cyclic nucleotides, ATP, neurotransmitters, and certain hormones. Calcium influx is probably an important transmembrane signal, as it occurs during activation of cells by mitogens, transmitters, and some hormones.

C. Protein and Glycoprotein Motion

The fluid nature of membrane bilayers implies that integral proteins and glycoproteins should be able to move laterally in the membrane. Indeed, it is now well established that integral membrane proteins and glycoproteins can undergo dynamic changes and topographical rearrangements with respect to other membrane components. On the other hand, translational movement or flip-flop motion of proteins or glycoproteins is unfavorable because of the same thermodynamic considerations mentioned previously for lipids. Specific proteins have been shown to rotate about an axis perpendicular but not parallel to the plane of the membrane. For example, the visual pigment rhodopsin, a glycoprotein, can rotate in the retinal rod disc membrane with a measured rotational relaxation time of 20 nsec. Therefore the major movements of membrane proteins are rotational and lateral (in the plane of the membrane) and not translational (flip-flop).

1. Lateral Mobility of Membrane Proteins and Glycoproteins. Qualitative evidence on the lateral mobility of proteins in biological membranes has been obtained by examination of freeze-cleaved erythrocyte membrane preparations. Intramembranous protein particles, which are usually distributed randomly in the membrane at physiological pH, can aggregate when the pH is lowered to 5.5. The aggregation process is completely reversible because readjusting the pH back to 7.4 restores the original particle distribution. The aggregations of the intramembranous particles in erythrocyte membranes at low pH is accompanied by changes in the display of specific glycoproteins exposed on the cell surface of the membrane. For example, labeling negatively charged groups on the cell surface (mostly contributed by N-acetylneuraminic acid on the major sialoglycoprotein) with positively charged electron-dense particles also reveals aggregation of these surface components at low pH, returning to a random distribution at neutral pH. A wide variety of treatments can induce redistribution of erythrocyte intramembranous particles, including temperature changes, alterations in membrane lipid composition, enzyme treatment (trypsin after addition of lysolecithin), and membrane-active drugs.

Quantitative studies on the lateral mobility of proteins and glycoproteins have involved introduction of covalent labels such as fluorescent reagents. Binding of fluorescent antibodies to cell surface antigens or fluorescent lectins to cell surface oligosaccharides in combination with methods such as fluorescence recovery after photobleaching has allowed calculation of the rates of lateral motion. Although the lateral mobilities of membrane proteins and glycoproteins appear to be much slower than those of phospholipids, they are nonetheless significant. Labeling of histocompatibility antigens on human and mouse cells with specific antibodies tagged with different fluorescent reagents followed by fusion of the cells to obtain human–mouse heterokaryons permitted visualization of the redistribution of the antigens in the hetero-karyon membrane. Shortly after fusion the antigens were segregated in differ-ent halves of the fused cell membrane. However, after incubation at 37°C for 40 min, the antigens were randomly distributed and completely intermixed. The randomized distribution was not dependent on energy supply and was attributed to lateral diffusion of the proteins in the lipid bilayer with a calcu-lated diffusion constant of $D = 2 \times 10^{-10}$ cm^{2}sec^{-1}. Fluorescent Fab' monova-lent antibodies applied to a spot on the membrane of muscle fibers spread in the membrane with a $D = 1$–2×10^{-9} cm^{2}sec^{-1}, whereas intact bivalent antibody molecules bound to surface antigens diffuse on the plasma membrane at about 1% the rate compared to the monovalent Fab'. Slow lateral mobility of membrane glycoproteins on intact human erythrocytes ($D = {<}3 \times 10^{-12}$ cm^{2}sec^{-1}) occurs after labeling surface membrane proteins nonspecifically with fluorescein isothiocynate. These data suggest the existence of peripheral or transmembrane mechanisms that may impede lateral movement. Lateral diffusion coefficients in the range 3×10^{-11} cm^{2}sec^{-1} to 3×10^{-12} cm^{2}sec^{-1} have been measured by fluorescence recovery after photobleaching of fluores-cent concanavalin A (tetravalent) or succinylated concanavalin A (divalent) bound to mannose-containing glycoproteins at the surface of mouse fibroblasts and rat myoblasts. In the latter experiment fluorescent lipid probes have diffusion coefficients of approximately $D = 3 \times 10^{-9}$ cm^{2}sec^{-1}, indicating that the mobility of lipid-in-lipid is much greater than that of protein-in-lipid. In addition, heterogeneity can be found in the mobility of concanavalin A receptors, with some lectin–receptor complexes appearing almost immobile while others are apparently able to diffuse freely.

2. Ligand-Induced Redistribution of Cell Surface Components.

Mul-tivalent ligands such as antibodies and lectins labeled with fluorescent tags have been used in experiments on determining specific membrane protein and glycoprotein distributions. During such studies it has become apparent that these ligands are able to induce lateral movements and topographic rearrangements of ligand–receptor complexes on a variety of cell types. The inherent distribution of many cell surface receptors is essentially uniform or random over the entire membrane; however, binding of multivalent ligands can lead to redistribution of receptors as crosslinking of adjacent ligand–receptor complexes proceeds. Initially small ligand–receptor aggregates—"clusters"—are formed; these can further aggregate to larger "patches," and in certain situations patches can coalesce in an energy-dependent process to form a single polar "cap" (Figure 4). The patched or capped ligand–receptor complexes are often internalized by endocytosis at regions of "coalescence" of the ligand–receptor complexes, or they can be shed from the cell surface. The initial stages of the aggregation phenomenon may be similar to precipitation of antigens by multivalent antibody except that it occurs in the plane of the membrane. However, once the ligand–receptor aggregation occurs, its subsequent fate is determined by various factors including cell motility and transmembrane linkages, which are necessary for capping or endocytosis. In certain instances binding of a single ligand to the cell surface

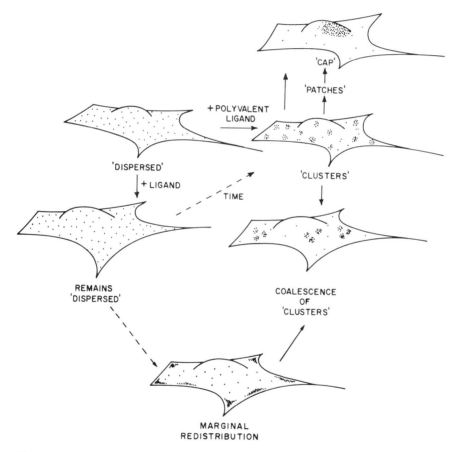

Figure 4. Alternate pathways of ligand-induced receptor redistribution on cell surfaces. After ligand binding, initially dispersed receptors can remain dispersed or undergo ligand-induced clustering.

is insufficient to induce redistribution of its specific receptor, but the addition of a second ligand (usually a second antibody capable of binding to the first ligand) may induce the redistribution. Although these findings suggest that ligand multivalence may be important for induction of receptor redistribution, it has been shown that in some cases even monovalent ligands such as Fab' antibodies are effective.

Several factors affect the rate and extent of ligand-induced redistribution of cell surface receptors, the most important being the nature of the ligand and receptor, the concentration of the ligand, and the number of receptors per cell, as well as the cell type. For example, the ligand lectin concanavalin A causes cap formation on normal mammalian lymphocytes, whereas binding of the same ligand to untransformed mammalian fibroblasts redistributes the receptors into discrete patches rather than a cap. However, treatment of both lymphocytes and fibroblasts with another ligand—a specific antibody to a common surface antigen—leads to capping on both cell types. There is also variation between cell types in the final location of the cap depending on the ligand used. For example, about 90 and 80% of surface immunoglobulin and concanavalin A-induced caps, respectively, were localized over the Golgi on splenic lymphocytes, whereas approximately 70% of Thy-1 and TL antigens capped by specific antibodies were opposite the Golgi on thymic lymphocytes. On fibroblasts, caps are usually located directly above the Golgi apparatus near the center of the cell.

Different receptors situated on discrete surface molecules can be redistributed independently on the appropriate ligands. For example, the ligand-induced redistribution of H2-D alloantigens on mouse lymphocytes is not accompanied by redistribution of H2-K alloantigens. In other situations, however, co-migration of antigens may occur, as is the case with HL-A histocompatibility antigens on human lymphocytes, which co-migrate with β-2 microglobulin. In this case co-migration may be due to the fact that the two receptors are carried either on the same molecule or on adjacent molecules that are closely associated; in other instances it may be due to the ability of the ligand to crosslink two discrete but adjacent receptors. For example, concanavalin A has discrete receptors on the surface of mouse lymphocytes, but this lectin can also bind surface immunoglobulin molecules via their carbohydrate chains. Low concentrations of concanavalin A cause redistribution of Con A receptors independent from surface immunoglobulins, but at higher concentrations (>25 $\mu g/ml$ Con A) co-migration occurs.

Cell surface lectin receptors have been shown to be more readily redistributed on certain cells, particularly transformed and tumor cells, whereas on other cell types, notably many untransformed cells, these receptors are relatively less mobile.

D. Topographic Control of Cell Surface Receptors

1. Nonrandom Distribution and Lateral Associations of Membrane Proteins. Although most surface receptors appear to be distributed randomly over the cell surface, certain studies have indicated that different cell surface receptors can have unique surface distributions and/or mobilities within the membrane. Nonrandom clustering of plasma membrane receptors and antigens has been observed in specialized membrane structures such as intercellular synaptic and neuromuscular junctions. The lateral mobility of these proteins is restricted because of lateral associations leading to aggregation of membrane components and eventually to a paracrystalline membrane structure. Cell junctions and synapses will be described in other chapters; it should be noted here that these structures share in common the property of developing from subunit components that form supramolecular aggregates in the membrane plane and also across to adjacent plasma membranes on other cells. Lateral associations between junctional subunits within the same cell membrane may be stabilized by disulfide bonds in addition to noncovalent bonds. Even though cell junctional complexes are embedded in a fluid lipid matrix, their mobility is limited because of their size and their attachments both within the cell and between adjacent cells. The enhanced stability of lateral associations is indicated by the finding that postsynaptic components remain associated even after removal of efferent presynaptic nerve membrane endings.

A somewhat different type of molecular segregation and regional specialization of membrane structure has been found in the distribution of surface receptors on mammalian spermatozoa. The distribution of surface anionic sites on the surface of sperm from different species is distinct and discontinuous, and the mobility of lectin receptors differs depending on the region of the sperm plasma membrane examined, with greater mobility found in the postacrosomal membrane region. In addition, certain antigens are localized preferentially to specific regions of the mammalian sperm head. Freeze-cleavage electron microscopy has revealed that in various mammalian spermatozoa the distribution of intramembranous particles in the acrosomal, postacrosomal, and tail regions is nonrandom. In the acrosome these particles are present in a paracrystalline array, which suggests a low rate of lateral mobility. This correlates with a low rate of redistribution of lectin receptors in the acrosomal region.

There are other examples indicating that controlling mechanisms must exist to govern cell surface dynamics and display of surface receptors, including the finding of nonrandom distributions of several neuronal surface antigens along chick neural cells, the segregation of certain antigens to either the presynaptic or axolemmal nerve membranes, as well as the finding that surface-immunoglobulin molecules on mouse lymphocytes appear to exist nonrandomly as interconnected networks.

In addition to hydrophobic lateral associations between integral membrane proteins mentioned above, other factors may be involved in determining segregation and restriction of mobility of membrane components. For example, the presence of different lipid phase states may drive proteins to aggregate if protein–protein interactions are favored over protein–lipid interactions in a given lipid phase. Also, if proteins are sequestered into fluid lipid domains, their dynamic display will be limited to these regions, and the converse would be true if some proteins preferentially associate with solid-phase lipids. Associations between oligosaccharides can also be a contributing force for stabilizing lateral associations. The association of components in the membrane plane can be considered a form of *cis*-control where events occurring at one side of the membrane or in the plane of the membrane control the mobility, display, and association of membrane components.

E. Transmembrane Control over Membrane Organization

In some membrane systems the display, topography, and dynamics of proteins and glycoproteins situated on one surface of the cell membrane are controlled through components on the opposite side of the membrane. This phenomenon is termed transmembrane control, since it requires transmembrane linkages between integral proteins and peripheral components. The peripheral components present on the external surface of cell membranes include proteins, glycoproteins, and glycosaminoglycans; and on the inner surface of the membrane they include structural proteins.

In the human erythrocyte membrane the lateral mobilities of the major integral glycoproteins are under restraint and unable to diffuse freely. This restricted mobility is due to linkages between the membrane-spanning glycoproteins and an inner-surface peripheral protein network composed of a fibrous protein—spectrin—and erythrocyte actin. During preparation of erythrocyte membrane ghosts some spectrin and actin are released, and the lateral mobility of the integral membrane proteins increases. This increased freedom of mobility of integral membrane proteins in erythrocyte ghosts may be restricted by controlling the state of spectrin aggregation. By sequestering antispectrin antibodies into lysed, resealed erythrocyte ghosts, the spectrin attached to the inner membrane surface can be aggregated, leading to concomitant aggregation of the integral transmembrane glycoproteins. The transmembrane glycoproteins are therefore probably linked to spectrin. This linkage is also inferred from the finding that aggregation of cell surface glycoproteins on erythrocyte ghosts with lectins at the outer surface is followed by aggregation of spectrin molecules on the inner surface.

1. Cytoskeletal Transmembrane Control. A more general transmembrane control mechanism common to many cell types is mediated via membrane-associated cytoskeletal assemblages such as microtubules and microfilaments. Microtubules have often been found in close association with the plasma membrane, but are also found in the cytoplasm and the nucleus. They are large, relatively rigid tubular structures composed predominantly of the protein tubulin. Cytoplasmic microtubules are not stable structures; they undergo rapid, reversible assembly and disassembly, depending on temperature, Ca^{2+} concentration, cyclic nucleotide concentration, pH, and pressure. Depolymerization of microtubules into subunit aggregates is caused by low temperature and high Ca^{2+} concentrations as well as by several drugs such as the alkaloids colchicine, colcemid, vinblastine sulfate, and vincristine.

Microfilaments are another important class of the membrane-associated cytoskeletal elements. They are thin, actin-containing polymers organized in "bundles" that penetrate into the cell from the inner surface of the plasma membrane, or "lattice" or "network" filamentous structures that are present throughout the cytoplasm. Microfilament assemblies can be disrupted by cyclic nucleotides or by mold metabolites called cytochalasins. It is thought that microfilaments perform musclelike functions in cells leading to cytoplasmic streaming, maintenance of cell shape, and locomotion, as well as movement or impedance of movement of plasma membrane components. The distribution and dynamics of surface receptors on several cell types seem to be under regulatory control by both microtubules and microfilaments.

The most documented example of cytoskeletal transmembrane control is in the immunoglobulin (Ig)-bearing bone-marrow-derived (B) lymphocyte. The binding of the multivalent ligand anti-lg to B lymphocytes causes redistribution of surface lg molecules to form clusters, patches, and eventually caps. A variety of drugs and environmental conditions can prevent capping in lymphocytes. Drugs that disrupt microfilament organization, such as cytochalasins, prevent cap formation to various degrees but not completely, whereas drugs that cause microtubule depolymerization, such as the alkaloids, have only little effect on cap formation. Since combinations of these drugs, cytochalasin B plus colchicine, almost completely block capping in lymphocytes and polymorphonuclear leukocytes, it is thought that both microfilaments and microtubules are involved in the capping process. The microfilament system may provide active contractile movement necessary to translocate the ligand–receptor clusters and patches, while the microtubules may serve as the skeletal structure necessary for the stabilization of contractile apparatus as well as proper orientation to ensure association of the aggregates to a cap at one end of the cell. In fact, a concept compatible with all drug effects suggests that microtubules and microfilaments play opposing but coordinated roles in the maintenance of surface receptor distribution. It proposes that microtubules serve to "anchor" receptors and restrict their lateral mobility within the membrane, while microfilaments are envisaged as also being linked to microtubules or to the same surface receptors, so that by microfilament contraction the receptors within the membrane may be redistributed.

Lymphocyte capping is dramatically inhibited by local anesthetics, which disrupt both microfilaments and microtubules. Local anesthetics are also capable of dissociating preformed caps and can modify the dynamics of other cell surface receptors and inhibit cell spreading, cell movement, adhesion, and fusion. The local anesthetics may cause microfilament disruption and microtubule depolymerization by increasing intracellular Ca^{2+} concentrations or by displacing it from calcium binding sites in the membrane. Modification in intracellular Ca^{2+} concentrations by introduction of calcium ionophores into cell membranes can indeed block capping on lymphocytes.

F. Transmembrane Architecture

In an attempt to synthesize the information described in the previous section, a scheme is presented in Figure 5. This representation is based on the fluid mosaic model of Singer and Nicolson with the addition of peripheral and membrane-associated components. On the extracellular surface of the membrane, glycosaminoglycans are shown to be associated with integral membrane glycoproteins, although certain parts of their structures may be anchored in the membrane directly.

In the plane of the membrane, integral proteins and glycoproteins (with their oligosaccharide portions protruding outward) are shown in asymmetric orientation, with some involved in lateral associations with other proteins and with peripheral components at the inner surface of the membrane. The membrane-associated cytoskeletal assemblies are shown in various types of associations. Parallel arrays of microfilaments are shown extending from the tip of a microvillus to which they are attached via α-actinin molecules into the cytoplasm where they may be structurally stabilized by association to other skeletal elements. Other arrays of microfilaments are shown running parallel and in close apposition to the cell membrane with occasional association to inner membrane peripheral components or directly to integral membrane components. Myosin molecules may crosslink adjacent microfilament arrays, and other, yer unidentified, molecules are illustrated as bridging various cytoskeletal elements and interconnecting microfilaments to microtubules. This scheme is compatible with the idea advanced by Edelman that the cytoskeletal system exerts modulatory control over the cell surface by existing

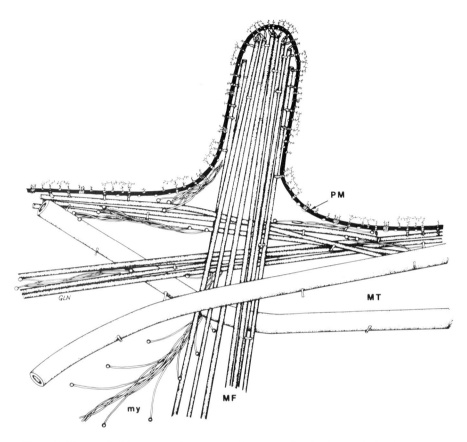

Figure 5. Hypothetical interactions between membrane-associated microtubule (MT) and micro-filament (MF) systems involved in transmembrane control over cell surface receptor mobility and distribution. This model envisages an opposite but coordinated role for the microfilaments (contractile) and microtubules (skeletal and directional) and suggests that they are linked to one another or to the same plasma membrane (PM) inner surface components. This linkage may occur through myosin molecules (my) or through cross-bridging molecules such as α-actinin. In addition, peripheral membrane components linked at the inner or outer plasma membrane surface may extend this control over specific membrane domains. (From G. L. Nicolson, G. Poste, and T. H. Ji, 1977, in *Dynamic Aspects of Cell Surface Organization*, Vol. 3 of *Cell Surface Reviews*, G. Poste and G. L. Nicolson, eds., pp. 1–73, North-Holland Publishing Co., Amsterdam.)

in "free" or "membrane-attached" equilibrium states so that at any one time certain classes of transmembrane-linked surface receptors are under cytoplasmic control. It is possible that only a few transmembrane linkage components control the distribution and mobility of a large number of cell surface receptors through peripheral interactions. This is illustrated in the form of glycosaminoglycan interactions with a variety of surface components in "membrane domains." This scheme is by no means complete, and much more information will have to be gathered to determine, for example, what molecules participate in transmembrane linkages and the control mechanisms of the assembly, disassembly, attachment, and cross-bridging of membrane-associated cytoskeletal elements. Present knowledge is sufficient to conclude that the plasma membrane is by no means just a simple boundary separating the cytoplasm from the exterior but a complex and dynamic structure containing a variety of physiologically vital enzymes and proteins that control not only surface phenomena but also a wide range of cellular activities.

SUGGESTED READING

Edelman, G. M. 1976. Surface modulation in cell recognition and cell growth. *Science* 192:218–26.

Edidin, M. 1974. Rotational and translational diffusion in membranes. *Ann. Rev. Biophys. Bioeng.* 3:179–201.

Nicolson, G. L. 1976. Transmembrane control of the receptors on normal and tumor cells. I. Cytoplasmic influence over cell surface components. *Biochim. Biophys. Acta* 457:57–108.

Nicolson, G. L. 1976. Transmembrane control of the receptors on normal and tumor cells. II. *Biochim. Biophys. Acta* 458:1–72.

Nicolson, G. L. 1979. Topographic display of cell surface components and their role in transmembrane signaling. *Curr. Top. Dev. Biol.* 3:305–38.

Nicolson, G. L., Poste, G., and Ji, T. H. 1977. The dynamics of cell membrane organization. In *Dynamic Aspects of Cell Surface Organization,* Vol. 3 of *Cell Surface Reviews,* G. Poste and G. L. Nicolson, eds., pp. 1–73. North-Holland Publishing Co., Amsterdam.

Quinn, P. J. 1976. *The Molecular Biology of Cell Membranes.* University Park Press, Baltimore.

Singer, S. J. 1974. The molecular organization of membranes. *Ann. Rev. Biochem.* 43:805–33.

Singer, S. J., and Nicolson, G. L. 1972. The fluid mosaic model of the structure of cell membranes. *Science* 175:720–31.

Steck, T. L. 1974. The organization of proteins in the human red blood cell membrane. A review. *J. Cell Biol.* 62:1–19.

Wallach, D. F. H. 1975. *Membrane Molecular Biology of Neoplastic Cells.* North-Holland Publishing Co., Amsterdam.

Wallach, D. F. H., and Winzler, R. J. 1974. *Evolving Strategies and Tactics in Membrane Research.* Springer-Verlag, New York.

2.2.   Cell Junctions[1]

Akhouri A. Sinha and Lazar M. Schwartz

In multicellular organisms, the epithelia covering the surface of the body and its cavities often develop intercellular junctions between the apposing plasma membranes of two or more adjacent cells. The junctional complexes are considered as local differentiation of plasma membranes. They have been observed in both invertebrates and vertebrates (20) and have been described in a variety of mammalian epithelia (2, 3, 5, 6, 12, 15). These complexes have also been studied in neoplastic tissues (6, 10, 18, 19).

While studying junctional complexes in epithelia of rat and guinea pig, Farquhar and Palade (2) concluded that these complexes function in cell-to-cell adhesion and affect permeability. They showed that the precise arrangement of junctions differs in epithelial cells of one organ to another and from one species to another. But the junctions were usually arranged as three successive components such as, zonula occludens (tight junction), zonula adherens (intermediate junction), and macula adherens (desmosome). Besides the above, other types of junctions have been described such as the gap junction (12, 17, 20), septate junction (23), spacing junction (5), and glial-axonal junction (7). These junctional complexes differ in their structure and function under experimental conditions (2, 13, 14) and have often led to additional classifications (1, 9, 20). However, developmental sequence of junction formation, junctional interdependence, and requirements for their *de novo* synthesis and degradations still remain to be elucidated.

Recently Staehelin and Hull (21) classified the junctional complexes into three broad categories: the tight junction, the adhering junction, and the gap junction. McNutt and Weinstein (12) discussed the problems associated with the terminologies and classifications of the junctions. Their study discussed junctions in epithelial, muscular, and connective tissues of vertebrates. They also reviewed different techniques, such as tracers, freeze-fracture and electron microscopy, which are often used in the study of junctions.

THE TIGHT JUNCTION

Farquhar and Palade (2) showed that the tight junction (zonula occludens) occurred along the lateral surfaces of adjacent epithelial cells lining the lumina

[1] This research was supported by Minneapolis Veterans Administration Medical Center.

155

of glands, their ducts, and the cavities of organs. The fusion of cell membranes often resulted in obliteration of the intercellular space. The junction occurs in anatomic situations where a sharp concentration gradient between a free lumen and bordering cells is required for a distinct separation between two compartments, such as blood–brain barrier (15), blood–testis barrier (4), nerve cells (7), smooth and cardiac muscles (3, 20), as well as absorptive and secretory surfaces. The freeze-fracture studies (5, 20) have shown that the number of sealing strands and the linear length of fused membranes vary from tissue to tissue. Such variations have been reported in normal tissues and tumors (12, 19, 20) (Figures 1, 2).

The tight junction functions as a diffusion barrier. It often occurs as a beltlike structure around the epithelial cells lining the cavities of organs and may be restricted in focal areas (12, 20). Although these junctions are essentially impermeable to compounds such as antibiotics and proteinous solutions, they do allow passage of compounds such as sugar, carbon dioxide, and ethyl alcohol (2, 15, 20). In freeze-fracture preparation, a beltlike meshwork of branched and anastomosing ridges on P (A) face and corresponding furrors on E (B) face of the plasma membranes can be seen. Recently Claude and Goodenough (1) have shown that the junction may be "leaky" compared to the degree of tightness in a variety of cells. For example, it is very tight in the urinary bladder of frog but very leaky in the mouse proximal convoluted tubules. In brief, the junction shows a direct structural and functional relationship. Recent studies show changes in tight junctions during mitotic activity of intestinal crypt cells (22), development of the junction in the thyroid gland of fetal rat (11), and heterogeneity of cell junctions in rat aortic endothelium (8).

THE ADHERING JUNCTIONS

Since the studies of Farquhar and Palade (2) on zonula or fascia adherens (also called intermediate junctions) and on macula adherens (also called desmosomes), classification as adhering type junctions has been used (6, 12, 20). In the adhering type junction the intercellular space is not occluded, but it is narrowed and often filled with less dense electron opaque material than the desmosome. The adjacent cytoplasm contains fine filaments. In general, zonula adherens is a beltlike junction immediately underneath the tight junction. It possesses an intercellular space (about 200 Å) occupied by amorphous homogeneous material over a distance of 0.2 to 0.5 μm (2, 20, 21). The junction is often found in the intercalated disc of cardiac muscle cells (4, 12).

The macula adherens or desmosome occurs either as a belt or spot junction. It has shown several variations in its arrangements, formation, and degrada-

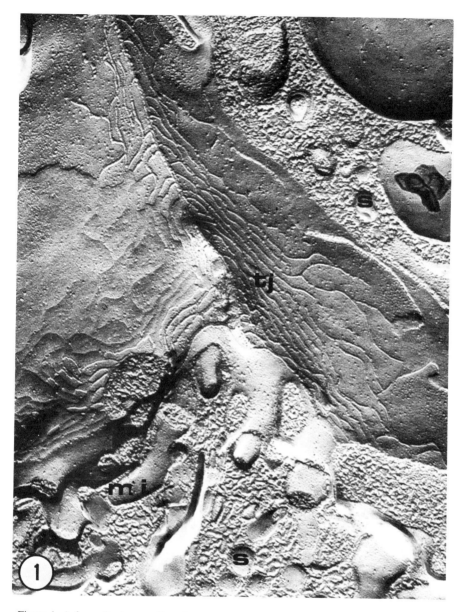

Figure 1. A freeze-fracture replica of a mouse prostate gland illustrates ridges and furrows of tight junctions (tj) between the plasma membranes of two adjacent epithelial cells, microvilli (mi), and secretory granules (s). (X64,350)

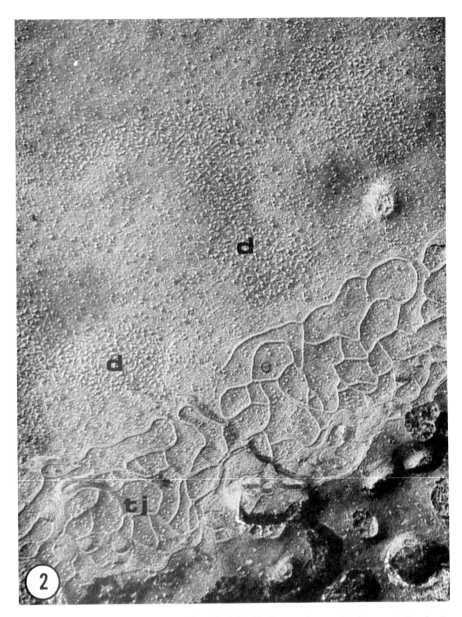

Figure 2. A freeze-fracture replica of epithelial cells from a human benign prostatic gland shows tight junctions (tj) and several desmosomes (d) with patches of packed particles. (X82,000)

tion (2, 14, 20). It is often found at surfaces under mechanical stress such as stratified squamous epithelium of the skin and in nearly all epithelial surfaces (12, 15, 20, 21). The spot desmosome forms buttonlike points of contact between the adjacent cells. Its intercellular space (about 250 Å) usually occupies dense material containing glycoprotein, but the inner side of each cell membrane possesses a plaque or plate of denser material for attachment of bundles of cytoplasmic fibrils (tonofibrils) (Figure 3). Tracers readily penetrate the intercellular space of desmosomes (12, 20). Freeze-fracture preparations have shown that the junction possesses patches of more or less closely packed particles of irregular size on the cell membranes (20) (Figure 2). Desmosomes play an important role in cell-to-cell adhesion (12). The junctions are readily denatured and separated by proteases or by removing calcium ions from the medium. Disruption of desmosomes frequently leads to the dissociation of the intercellular organization of tissues (13, 20). In brief, desmosomes enable a group of cells to function together as a structural unit.

The hemidesmosome is simply a half desmosome often occurring between an epithelial cell and the subjacent basal lamina (9). It serves as an anchoring site for the cells such as in the cervix and basal layer of the skin.

THE GAP JUNCTION

The gap junction (or nexus) is a small punctate structure which differs from other types of junctions in that it often includes an array of hexagonally arranged channels which permit direct two-way communication between apposing cells by means of ions and small molecules (6, 10, 12, 16, 17, 20). Revel and Karnovsky (17) demonstrated that the colloidal tracer, lanthanum hydroxide, penetrated extracellular space as well as in the gap region of the junction of mouse myocardium. The tracer impregnation and freeze-fracture studies are often needed to distinguish the gap junctions from the tight junctions. In gap junctions, the channels or conduits, which are hydrophilic, permit exchange of molecules up to 1000 daltons in molecular weight to pass between the cells. They allow passage of sugars, amino acids, nucleotides, vitamins, and regulatory molecules. In brief, the junction functions to facilitate intercellular and intercytoplasmic communication between cells to insure uniform metabolic response to circulating hormones or to nervous input (20).

Staehelin (20) described different types of gap junctions. Their variations were discussed by McNutt and Weinstein (12) and by Friend and Gilula (5). Each type of gap junction contains closely packed particles of equal size, which upon freeze-cleaving remain attached to one leaflet or the other (Figure 4).

In addition, the junctions function as points of low electrical resistance and transfer of electrical signals in excitable cells (12, 18, 20). The electrical

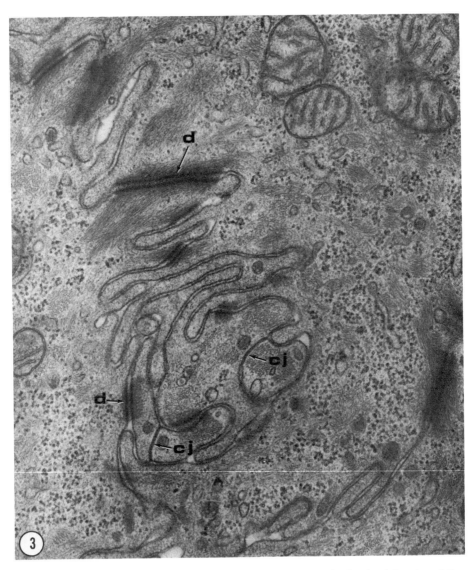

Figure 3. The micrograph illustrates desmosomes (d) and communicating (gap) junctions (cj) in an esophageal squamous epithelium. [×(estimated) 21,000] *(Courtesy: Dr. N. Simionescu)*

coupling, tracer, and metabolic coupling studies have shown that their main function is for intimate cell-to-cell communication. The junction is sensitive to calcium ions (10, 20). It also appears as a transient structure during embryogenesis of some fish, suggesting that it may play a role in differentiation. Malignant cells have fewer gap junctions than normal cells (12).

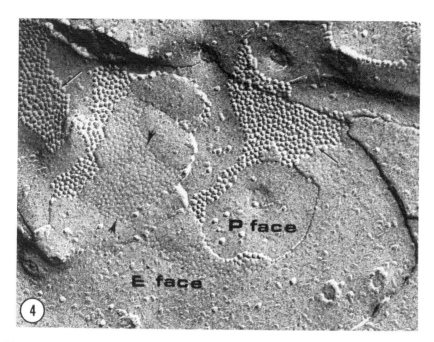

Figure 4. A freeze-fracture replica of an aortic endothelium showing the intramembrane organization of a communicating (gap) junction which appears as packed particles on the P face (arrows) and pits on the E face (arrowheads). (×160,000) (from M. Simionescu et al., *J. Cell Biol.* 1976. 68:710) *(Courtesy: Dr. N. Simionescu)*

CONCLUSION

The intercellular junctions have shown more variations in their structures and functions than had been previously recognized. Ultrastructure, tracer, and freeze fracture techniques continue to play a significant role in their study. Further research using experimental approaches should be able to define developmental and degradation sequences of junction formations and their functions in embryonic, adult, and cancerous tissues.

REFERENCES

1. Claude, P., and Goodenough, D. A. 1973. Fracture faces of zonulae occludentes from "tight" and "leaky" epithelia. *J. Cell Biol.* 38:390–400.
2. Farquhar, M. G., and Palade, G. E. 1963. Junctional complexes in various epithelia. *J. Cell Biol.* 17:375–412.
3. Fawcett, D. W. 1966. *The Cell, Its Organelles and Inclusion.* W. B. Saunders Co., Philadelphia, pp. 338–82.
4. Fawcett, D. W., Leak, L. V., and Heidger, P. M. 1970. Electron microscopic observations on the structural components of the blood-testis barrier. *J. Reprod. Fertil., Suppl.* 10:105–22.

5. Friend, D. S., and Gilula, N. B. 1972. Variations in tight and gap junctions in mammalian tissues. *J. Cell Biol.* 53:758–76.

6. Gilula, N. B. 1975. Junctional membranes in normal and neoplastic tissues. In: *Cellular Membranes and Tumor Behavior.* 28th Ann. Symp. on Fundamental Canc. Res. Williams and Wilkins Co., Baltimore, pp. 219–37.

7. Hirano, A., and Dembitzer, H. M. 1967. A structural analysis of the myelin sheath in the central nervous system. *J. Cell Biol.* 34:555–67.

8. Huttner, I., and Peters, H. 1978. Heterogeneity of cell junctions in rat aortic endothelium: A freeze-fracture study. *J. Ultrastruct. Res.* 64:303–08.

9. Kelly, D. E. 1966. Fine structure of desmosomes, hemidesmosomes and adepidermal globular layer in developing new epidermis. *J. Cell Biol.* 28:51–72.

10. Loewenstein, W. R. 1975. Intercellular communications in normal and neoplastic tissues. In: *Cellular Membranes and Tumor Cell Behavior.* 28th Ann. Symp. on Fundamental Canc. Res. Williams and Wilkins Co., Baltimore, pp. 239–48.

11. Luciano, L., Thiele, J., and Reale, E. 1979. Development of follicles and of occluding junctions between the follicular cells of the thyroid gland. *J. Ultrastruct. Res.* 66:164–81.

12. McNutt, N. S., and Weinstein, R. S. 1973. Membrane ultrastructure at mammalian intercellular junctions. *Prog. Biophys. Mol. Biol.* 26:45–101.

13. Muir, A. R. 1967. The effect of divalent cations on the ultrastructure of the perfused rat heart. *J. Anat.* 101:239–62.

14. Overton, J. 1973. Experimental manipulation of desmosome formation. *J. Cell Biol.* 56:636–46.

15. Pappas, G. D. 1973. Junctions between cells. *Hosp. Pract.* 8:39–46.

16. Raviola, E., and Gilula, N. B. 1973. Gap junctions between photoreceptor cells in the vertebrate retina. *Proc. Natl. Acad. Sci.* 70:1677–81.

17. Revel, J. P., and Karnovsky, M. J. 1967. Hexagonal array of subunits in intercellular junction of the mouse heart and liver. *J. Cell Biol.* 33:C7–C12.

18. Sheridan, J. D., Hammer-Wilson, M., Preus, D., and Johnson, R. G. 1978. Quantitative analysis of low-resistance junctions between cultured cells and correlation with gap-junctional areas. *J. Cell Biol.* 76:532–44.

19. Sinha, A. A., Bentley, M. D., and Blackard, C. E. 1977. Freeze-fracture observations on the membranes and junctions in human prostatic carcinoma and benign prostatic hypertrophy. *Cancer* 40:1182–88.

20. Staehelin, L. A. 1974. Structure and function of intercellular junctions. *Int. Rev. Cytol.* 39:191–283.

21. Staehelin, L. A., and Hull, B. E. 1978. Junctions between living cells. *Scientific Amer.* 238:140–52.

22. Tice, L. W., Carter, R. L., and Cahill, M. B. 1979. Changes in tight junctions of rat intestinal crypt cells associated with changes in their mitotic activity. *Tiss. Cell* 11:293–316.

23. Wood, R. L. 1959. Intercellular attachments in the epithelium of hydra as revealed by electron microscopy. *J. Biophys. Biochem. Cytol.* 6:343–52.

2.3. Myelin

Diethelm H. Boehme and Neville Marks

The previous two decades have witnessed substantial advances in our knowledge of myelin, especially in its formation from plasma membrane by accessory cells and in its chemical composition. This chapter will survey developments considered relevant for cell biologists; for other aspects the reader should consult recent monographs or reviews (see reference section). (Note: Numbered references refer to general references; an author, date system is used in citing selections from monographs.) Advances in myelin research have generally stemmed from introduction of new techniques by cell biologists and others in related disciplines, as summarized in Table 1. Among milestones that can be cited are the use of selected lipid stains, which led to the introduction of the term "myelin" by Virchow in 1834; light microscopic studies that demonstrated discontinuities in myelin; the use of physical techniques such as polarization microscopy and birefrigence in the 1930s, which provided evidence for periodicity within the myelin sheath; and the use of staining and fixation techniques with electron microscopy in the 1950s to show the existence of a lamellar structure (Table 1). More recently a combination of techniques, including that of freeze-fracture, have shown that myelin is an outgrowth and modification of the plasma membrane of the Schwann cell in the peripheral nervous system (PNS), as first indicated in the classic studies of Geren (1) and later shown by others to apply to the central nervous system (CNS) as well, except that the sheath in this case is formed from the oligodendrial membranes.

Taking advantage of the high lipid content and peculiar flotation properties, a number of groups have successfully isolated (compact) myelin and studied its properties in terms of its biochemical components. They established that the lamellae of peripheral and central myelin contain a number of unique components, notably proteins that are absent in other membranes. Research on myelin composition was accelerated by the finding that a basic protein extracted by acid can induce experimental demyelination when injected with Freund's adjuvant into suitable animals. This condition, known as experimental allergic encephalomyelitis (EAE), has similarities to demyelination seen in postvaccinal encephalomyelitis, and to a lesser extent in multiple sclerosis.

There has been considerable effort expended on determining the chemical

Table 1. Developments in Myelin Research.

YEAR	AUTHOR	COMMENT
1834	Virchow	Selective staining of myelin lipids.
1839	Schwann	Description of Schwann cells in PNS.
1878	Ranvier	Anatomical description of nodal regions—postulated role in nerve conduction.
1877	Schmidt-Lantermann	Description of discontinuities in myelin sheath.
1913	Göthlin	Birefringence of myelin observed.
1920 1941–1949	Lillie Tasaki Takenchi	Theory and evidence presented for saltatory conduction.
1935–1941	Schmidt (W. J.) Schmidt (F. O.) Firean	Application of polarization microscopy, X-ray diffraction. Evidence for paracrystalline structure of myelin with radial repeat units of 17 nm in PNS. Prediction of a concentric-lamellar structure.
1935	Davson Danielli	Bileaflet structure of membranes proposed.
1935–1949	Robertson Fernandez-Moran Sjostrand Peters Bunge Hirano	Application of electron microscopy techniques. Evidence for lamellar structure. Description of myelin formation in CNS involving oligodendrial membranes. Fine anatomy of paranodal regions described.
1954	Geren	Evidence that myelin sheath formed from Schwann cell plasma membrane in PNS.
1972	Singer and Nicolson	Molecular organization of membranes proposed. Fluid mosaic structure.
1975	Schnapp Mugnaini	Application of freeze-fracture techniques. Description of light junctions, intra-myelinic spaces.

This listing is merely a guide to some of the workers associated with major research developments. A full listing of the various participants can be found in reviews and recent monographs. Note that the first report of glial involvement in myelination occurred in the 1950s and largely stemmed from introduction of EM techniques.

structure of myelin basic protein, especially with respect to the peptide sequences responsible for inducing encephalitogenic reactions (for review, see ref. 2). Of particular interest are differences in protein composition between peripheral and central myelin described in detail below, with the presence in the PNS of a different basic protein (termed P_2) which can induce a peripheral demyelination with analogies to the Guillain-Barré-Strohl syndrome (20). The area of research where the least progress has been made is that of understanding the manner in which protein and lipid components are apposed within the membrane. This is consistent with the slow progress made in understanding the structure of all membranes.

CENTRAL AND PERIPHERAL MYELIN

Myelin, like other membranes, is best viewed in terms of the bileaflet model of Dawson and Danielli made as early as 1935, with modifications based on recent topographical studies largely with respect to protein components. The bileaflet consists of the sandwiching of a lipid bilayer (with hydrophobic tails apposed) between two protein monolayers; this creates a trilaminar structure. A number of deficiencies exist for this model because it does not adequately explain specialized membrane functions (cellular transport, secretion, pinocytosis) or account for the α-helical structure of membrane (globular) proteins. Singer and Nicolson (3) proposed that membranes have a mosaic pattern permitting movement of protein components, depending on functional requirements of the membranes (Figure 1). Physicochemical measurements (X-ray diffraction, spin label) continue to lend support to the bilayer theory, although the manner in which proteins are woven into the lipid framework has yet to be clarified.

Myelin is best defined as a composite structure consisting of lamellae formed from plasma membranes of accessory cells, with a unique composition with respect to arrangement and composition of lipids and proteins. Peripheral myelin and central myelin have many similarities in terms of gross morphology and mechanisms of formation, but differences arise in their chemical composition. In the PNS, the Schwann cells can myelinate only one nodal region, whereas in the CNS the oligodendrial cell can myelinate many axons (Figures 2 and 3). This is considered an important factor in pathology because damage to CNS myelin, unlike myelin of the PNS, may be beyond the reparative ability of a single glial cell. Figure 3 illustrates a number of other features concerning the fine anatomy of PNS and CNS myelin, which is described in more detail below. If it were possible to unfold the sheath as illustrated hypothetically, it would appear as a shovel-shaped area of about 300×800 μm for an axon of 3 μm diameter. Note the presence of a basal lamina with adhering collagen fibers, and the presence of a cell nucleus at one of the poles of the PNS internode.

Function of Myelin

The function of myelin has been the focus of many studies and appears to be related to its role as an insulator facilitating "saltatory conduction" (see

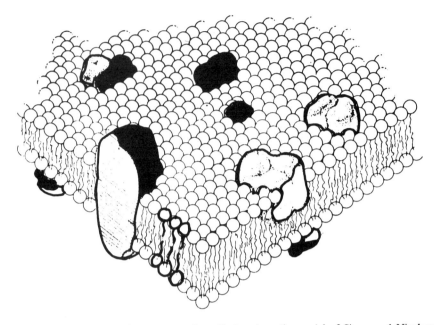

Figure 1. Illustration of the structure of myelin based on the model of Singer and Nicolson (1972). The model is itself a modification of the bileaflet structure originally proposed by Davson and Danielli (1935) and described in detail in the text. The bileaflet consists of hydrophilic ends of lipids (indicated by circles) on outer surfaces and hydrobolic fatty acid tails pointing inward. In the original model proteins were placed on outer surfaces; in the model shown proteins are embedded within the lipid matrix or extend through the membrane producing a dynamic structure yielding a mosaic-globular matrix.

monograph 4, Chapter 4). The electrical passivity of internodal myelin is in striking contrast to the demonstrable electrical responsiveness associated with the nodes of Ranvier, which are devoid of myelin, and which are regarded as essential for propagation of the action potential.

It is notable and worth repeating that myelinated fibers conduct pulses more efficiently than unmyelinated ones; it has been calculated, for example, that to maintain a speed of 25 m/sec at 20°C an unmyelinated axon of squid has to have a diameter of 500 μm compared to 12 μm of myelinated fiber of a frog.

FORMATION OF MYELIN

The advances in knowledge of myelin structure and mechanisms of formation have led to the introduction of terms absent in the older literature. In addition to node of Ranvier and Schmidt-Lantermann incisure and Schwann cell,

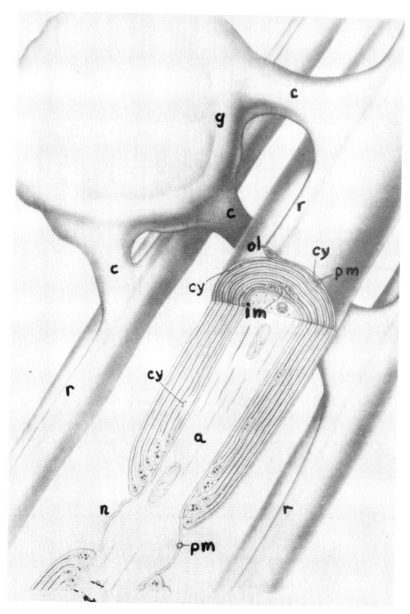

Figure 2. Diagram illustrating the multiple areas of myelination by a single oligodendrial cell of the CNS together with cross-sectional structure of the myelin sheath. Compare with the fine structure of the nodal region of the PNS in Figure 3. Note absence of basal lamina. Abbreviations: a, axon; n, node; pm, plasma membrane; im, inner mesaxon; cy, cytoplasm; ol, outer loop; r, ridge formed by outer loop; c, connection to oligodendrial cell body (g). [Figure reproduced by kind permission of Bunge et al. (4) with additional information from Raine (1977; see monograph 4, Chapter 1).]

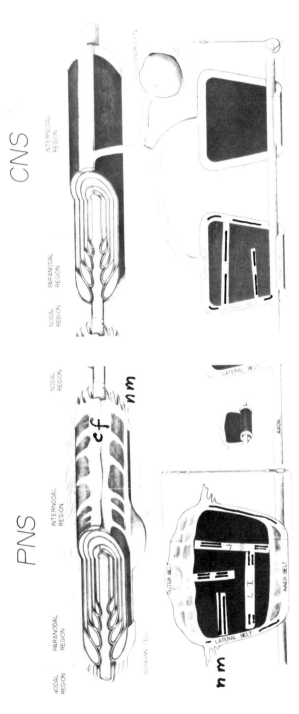

Figure 3. Diagram to demonstrate the distribution of cytoplasm in peripheral (left) and central (right) myelin sheaths. Note that cytoplasm is excluded from central regions to form compacted myelin (shaded). Longitudinal strips or circumferential ones (termed Schmidt-Lantermann clefts) are more frequent in the PNS. Myelin has been unwrapped from its axon to demonstrate the shape of an internodal region, and sizes of spaces are exaggerated. The localization of the "zona occludens" is within the clefts; they would appear as double strands except at points where they terminate to form tight junctions (see Figure 5). The outer turn of the Schwann cell sheath forms nodal microvilli (nm); also note that the outer wall of the Schwann cell tube is covered by a basal lamina with adhering collagen fibers (cf). Note the presence of the nucleus in the PNS. The dark areas represent compact myelin. The sizes of incisures in the unwrapped sheath are greatly exaggerated for purposes of illustration. The dark areas represent compact myelin and predominate with cytoplasm generally confined to the lateral belt. [Reproduced by kind permission of Mugnaini (12).]

dating from the last century, the newer terms are paranode, axoglial junction, the system of light junctions and zonula occludens, the intramyelinic (extracellular) spaces, major dense line, intraperiod line, transverse bands, or the intercellular septae that are characteristic of the paranodal or axoglial functions (Figures 8 and 9). A new nomenclature has been developed also to describe the major protein components, some of which are unique to myelin. Lipids present in myelin, on the other hand, were studied earlier and identified as present in most brain regions, especially white matter, and are not necessarily unique to myelin, except in terms of their ratios as compared to other brain regions (Table 2).

The myelin sheath is derived from an outgrowth of the plasma membrane of the Schwann cell, as shown in diagrammatic form in Figure 4. During ontogenesis, the axons, which penetrate developing tissue by means of an amoeboidlike growth cone, are accompanied by Schwann cells, which are ovoid at this stage and are derived from the neural crest: these cells then multiply and invade groups of growing axons, ultimately separating them into single axons. Schwann cells at this stage line themselves along the axis of the axon such that each cell myelinates only one segment; these segments are later known as the internodes and are separated by nodes of Ranvier. In thin (electron microscopy) sections, the Schwann cell is seen to become spindle-shaped with an elliptical nucleus, and is recognized by the characteristic presence of a basal lamina with adhering collagen fibers (Figure 3). Factors responsible for commencement of myelination of axons by Schwann cells are unknown although the diameter of the axon itself appears to be of special importance. In mammalian tissues, the Schwann cells invade the core of fiber bundles when they are between 0.2 and 0.5 μm in diameter, with the formation of the myelin spiral commencing when they reach 2 μm in diameter. Myelin formation on individual axons is initiated by Schwann cells present on the proximal end.

The process of myelination is best visualized in terms of the denuded axon lying in a furrow indenting the long axis of the Schwann cell, as shown in Figure 4. This furrow deepens, and its free edges extend toward each other with one sliding over the other when their tips come into apposition to form a mesaxon—a term introduced by analogy to the double membrane structure suspending the intestine (termed the mesentery). When consecutive turns of the mesaxon come into contact, the major dense line is formed by extrusion and compaction of the intervening cytoplasm; the intraperiod line consists of two adjacent Schwann cell membranes seen under high power electron microscopy as two thin lines (Figure 5). When unwrapped, the internodal myelin would appear as trapezoidal in shape with its shorter base attached to the axonal region (Figure 3). Thus when wrapped in a spiral manner, the lateral fold of the internode forms a helix as it approaches the

Table 2. Composition of CNS Myelin as Compared to Brain in Normals and Degenerating Myelin.

| | NORMAL MYELIN | | WHITE MATTER | | ABNORMAL HUMAN MYELIN | |
	HUMAN	BOVINE	HUMAN	BOVINE	MLD	SSPE
Total lipid (% dry wt.)	70	75.3	54.9	55.0	63.2	73.7
Total protein (% dry wt.)	30	24.7	39.0	39.5	ND	ND
Cholesterol	27.7	28.1	27.5	23.6	21.2	43.7**
Galactolipids	27.5	29.3	31.5	26.4	37.4	21.6
Cerebroside	22.7	24.0	23.7	19.8	9.0	18.8
Sulfatide	3.8	3.6	7.1	5.4	28.4*	2.8
Total phospholipid	43.1	43.0	45.9	46.3	36.1	36.6
Ethanolamine phospholipid	15.6	17.4	14.9	13.6	8.1	9.7
Lecithin	11.2	10.9	12.8	12.9	10.7	10.4
Sphingomyelin	7.9	7.1	7.7	11.4	7.1	8.8
Serine phospholipid	4.8	6.5	7.9	6.7	3.8	4.6
Monophosphoinositide	0.6	0.8	0.9	0.9	3.1	1.4
Plasmalogen	12.3	14.1	11.2	12.2	5.3	9.1

Data taken from Norton (1977, monograph 4) and Suzuki (1978, monograph 5). Values are expressed as % of total lipid except for total lipid and protein in the first section of the table. Totals for the two subgroups, galactolipids and phospholipids, are underlined. Note, with respect to galactolipids, the high concentration of cerebrosides (galactosylceramide) as compared to sulfatide, except in the disease metachromatic leukodystrophy (MLD) owing to absence of the enzyme arylsulfatase A, which hydrolyzes galactosylceramide sulfatide (*). In subacute sclerosing panencephalitis (SSPE) there are increased levels of cholesterol (**) and decreased levels of galactolipid.

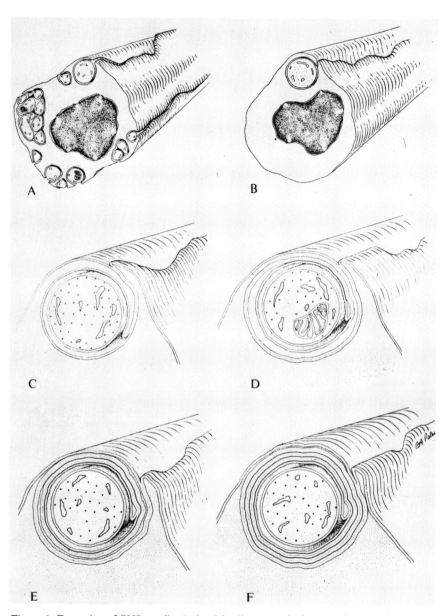

Figure 4. Formation of PNS myelin depicted in diagrammatic form to show a Schwann cell with bundles or single axons (A), an investment of a single axon around a designated axon (B), enveloping processes of the membrane to form a mesaxon (C), spiraling (D) with compaction and formation of major dense lines (E, F). For further details see text. [Reproduced by kind permission of Peters et al. (1976, monograph 1).] Formation of the CNS myelin is comparable except that processes are derived from oligodendrial cells.

171

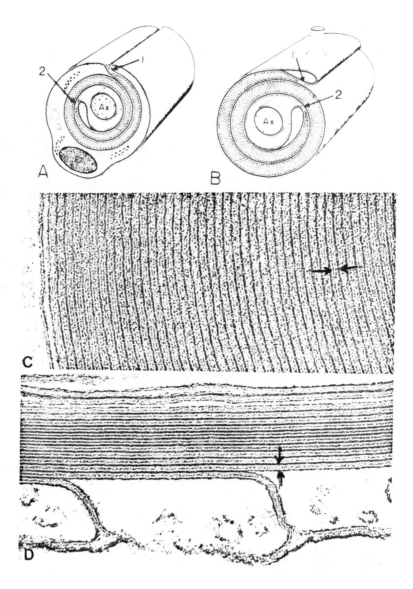

Figure 5. Illustration to demonstrate the presence of intramyelinic spaces in peripheral (A) and central (B) myelin. The space is indicated by cross-hatching and is greatly exaggerated for purposes of illustration. Note presence of tight junctions at the outer (1) and inner (2) mesaxons (Ax); the periaxonal space is white. Note paired dense lines between the major lines for peripheral (C) and central (D) sheaths (between arrows). ×200,000. [Reproduced by kind permission of Schnapp and Mugnaini (1978, monograph 5, Chapter 2).]

node. The transitional zone separating the internode from the node of Ranvier is referred to as the paranode and represents an axoglial junction. Usually when three to four turns of plasma membrane are present, the cytoplasm between them will be lost, and compact myelin will make an appearance; the only cytoplasm that persists is that present in a series of small helical pockets that form the Schmidt-Lantermann clefts (Figure 3).

Intramyelinic Spaces

The advent of freeze-fracture (or freeze-etching) has made a substantial contribution to our understanding of myelin fine structure. In this procedure, frozen tissue is cleaved under vacuum, leading to its fracture through the center of the lipid bilayer; cleavage along this plane generally results in the formation of two faces termed EF (exoplasmic face) and PF (protoplasmic face) (monograph 5, Chapter 2; ref. 12) (Figure 6). Replicas formed from freeze-fractured surfaces appear as particle-laden surfaces (representing membrane proteins) partially embedded in a lipid matrix that forms a homogeneous background (Figure 7). Such particles may be randomly distributed or assume an orderly arrangement at specialized regions such as the gap, tight, and septate junctions. Freeze-fracture studies of myelin show Schmidt-Lantermann clefts as channels located at different angles to the axis of the axon and communicating ultimately with the soma in the PNS, or the outer belt of cytoplasm in the CNS (Figure 3). This network combined with tight junctions of the specialized zones forms part of the zona occludens. According to Schnapp and Mugnaini (1978, monograph 5) the zona occludens forms a separate compartment consisting of the entire cytoplasm perimeter and its connecting incisures, with access limited by the presence of the tight junctions. These tight junctions occur at inner and outer mesaxons, between adjacent paranodal loops, and at cytoplasmic incisures. In freeze-fracture replicas the zona occludens appear as parallel strands visible on the P face and myelin; unlike other membranes there is no anastomosis of these channels (Figure 3). Myelin also contains an extracellular space between adjacent myelin lamellae extending from the periaxonal face through the spiral to the extracellular compartment (Figure 5). This structure is evident in conventional electron micrographs as a space separating the interperiod lines from the major dense one (in fresh frog peripheral nerve this space measures 15 Å and in central nerve 6 Å, but it may be larger when seen in fixed tissue) (Figure 5).

Significance of Intramyelinic Spaces

The significance of the zona occludens and other intramyelinic spaces may be related to metabolic processes that are essential for maintenance of myelin

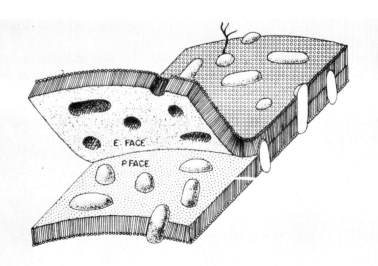

A. FREEZE–CLEAVED CENTRAL MYELIN

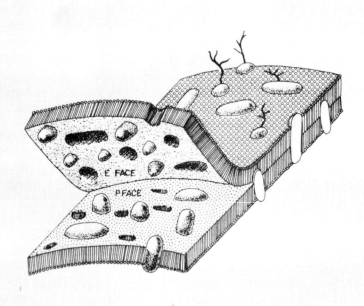

B. FREEZE–CLEAVED PERIPHERAL MYELIN

Figure 6. Diagram to illustrate fracture planes of central (A) and peripheral (B) myelin compact membranes. Generally in the central myelin, round and elongated particles seen on surfaces adhere to the P face, whereas in peripheral myelin many rounded particles adhere also to the E face. Compare with photograph in Figure 7, and with fracture planes in Figure 9. [Reproduced by kind permission of Mugnaini (12).]

integrity. Myelin was once held to be metabolically inert, but it has since been shown that the lipid and protein components are subject to breakdown and renewal. D'Monte et al. (7) were among the first to show active incorporation of labeled amino acids into myelin in vivo, with a resultant loss of radioactivity with time compatible with a half-life of about 20–40 days for the major protein components. Degradation and renewal of myelin sheath require access by enzymes and metabolites; it has been speculated that this could be facilitated by the channels that are evident in studies on the fine anatomy of myelin. In other tissues, the presence of tight or gap junctions prevents or retards access by large proteins such as peroxidase and ferritin. The structural significane of tight junctions in myelin is unknown, although it has been suggested that they play a biomechanical role in maintaining the spiral and thus restrict lateral diffusion of some myelin or possibly autoantigenic components. A thorough examination of the role of the zona occludens and related structures play during myelinogenesis and in metabolism of mature myelin may be instructive in determining the nature of pathologies linked to faulty myelin formation or its loss in pathology.

The Nodes of Ranvier

Since the nodes of Ranvier are a structural feature crucial to the phenomena of saltatory conduction, the fine anatomy of the axoglial junction has attracted considerable interest, especially because there are major differences between the CNS and PNS, summarized in Figure 8. Electron microscopy and freeze-fracture replicas show that the helix leaves an imprint on the adjoining axon not unlike that caused by embedding a screw into a soft surface. Thin sections show a scalloped appearance of the axolemma along with other special features, which include a reduction of the intercellular space between the glial cell membrane and axolemma to 30 Å and the presence of regular repeating septal units, known also as transverse bands, which because of the spiral indentation of the axolemma have a diagonal orientation to that of the long axis of the lateral (glial) belt. Also, the glial and axonal membranes are undulated in a regular manner such that the crests of the transverse bands coincide with the intercellular septae (Figures 7 and 9). As noted, PNS nodes are characterized by the presence of a basal lamina beneath which are finger-like extensions of Schwann cell cytoplasm in the form of microvilli separated by a space of 7–10 nm from the axon surface (monograph 9; Figure 8). Surface microvilli interdigitate with those of the adjacent paranode region. The nodal processes lie within a floccular substance containing sulfated mucopolysaccharides. Microvilli also contain microfilaments, and these together with the nodal substance undoubtedly play a role in the integrity and function of the nodal region.

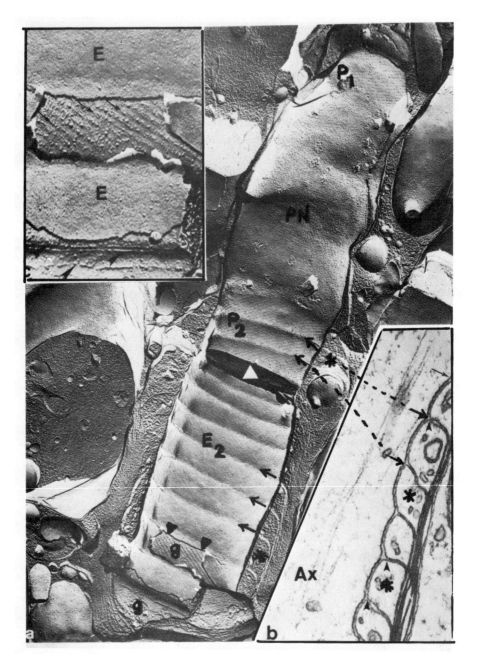

Figure 7

Passage of the Action Potential

The presence of a myelin sheath enables the action potential to be transmitted at higher conduction velocity by small fibers with a consequent saving in metabolic energy. This is of importance anatomically because it means that several nerve fibers can fit into a nerve bundle of a given diameter. The nodes of Ranvier in peripheral nerve (approximately 1 μm in diameter with a surface area of 50 μm^2) have been the object of many studies, culminating in those of Tasaki and Takeuchi (5), and Huxley and Stämpfli (6), who first demonstrated that excitability was localized at the nodes, while internodes played a purely passive role in conduction. If the electrical properties of node and internode are taken into account, then the Hodgkin-Huxley equation, which applies to the excitability mechanism for squid giant axon, can serve also to give a model for saltatory conduction (see monograph 4, Chapter 4). The patch of (axon) membrane at the node of Ranvier is a highly specialized area for the transport of the action potential, and has approximately 100 times the density of sodium channels as compared to small unmyelinated fibers (Cahalan, 1978, monograph 5), a figure based on quantitative assessments using toxins of marine origin which selectively block sodium channels. Thus with tetrodotoxin and saxitoxin, it has been estimated that there are 25–50 sites/μm^2 in unmyelinated frog or rabbit sciatic nerve as compared to 12,000 or more at the nodes of Ranvier. Application of the voltage clamp technique has proved to be exceptionally useful in studying permeability properties, since membrane potential is the controlling factor affecting the opening or closing of channels. The node of Ranvier is the target site for action by a large number of drugs and other agents because diffusion in the absence of the myelin barrier can readily occur. Such agents can be classified as conductance blockers or gating modifiers, and include tetraethyl-

Figure 7. Freeze-fracture of the CNS axoglial junction exposed on the P face at the end of the paranodal region (the axonal P face is depicted diagrammatically in Figures 6 and 9) of the node of Ranvier (PN) and its adjacent node (P$_2$) in contrast to the areas below the white triangle (E$_2$), which represent the E face of the paranodal axolemma. At the small black arrowheads in the lower portion of the figure, the fracture plane jumps across the intercellular space and communicates to the apposed glial membrane (g) at its P face, as shown in higher magnification in the upper left inset. Note that the axon surface is regularly indented by the lateral belt as it winds in a helical path around the axon, as shown in thin sections in the right-hand inset (b) between the arrows. Note presence of diagonally oriented components on P surfaces. In the inset (b) note that the paranodal loops (marked with an asterisk) correspond to those in freeze-fracture (*) with arrows showing adjacent loops in both photographs. Compare intercellular septae with those shown in Figure 9. Magnifications are b, 31,200; c, 60,000; and left-hand inset, 80,000. The thin section was fixed in ferrocyanide osmium. [Reproduced by kind permission of Schnapp and Mugnaini (1978, monograph 5, Chapter 2).]

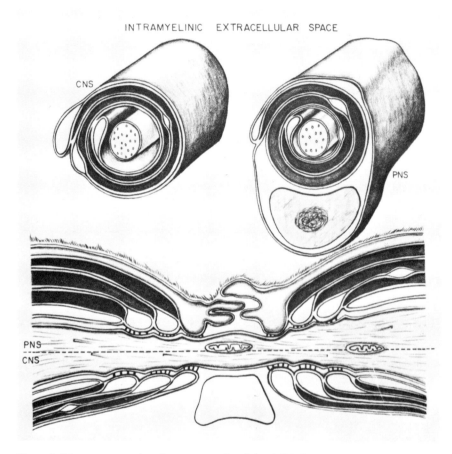

Figure 8. Diagram contrasting the structure of peripheral (PNS) and central (CNS) myelin at internodes (top) and paranodes (bottom). Note presence of microvillae and basal lamina in the PNS. The intramyelinic space is shown in exaggerated form in dark shading and compared with Figure 5 for presence of tight junctions. Note presence of transverse septae on paranodal loops and compare with model shown in Figure 9. [Reproduced by kind permission of Mugnaini (12).]

ammonium (TEA), local anesthetics, DDT, veratrine alkaloids, and a growing list of toxins derived from plant and animal sources.

Ionic Currents Across Myelin Membrane

The voltage clamp experiments of Hodgkin and Huxley on squid axon provided a framework for understanding the voltage-dependent changes in membrane potential with respect to sodium and potassium ions. Analysis of the ionic current across membranes indicated three components: an early *inward*

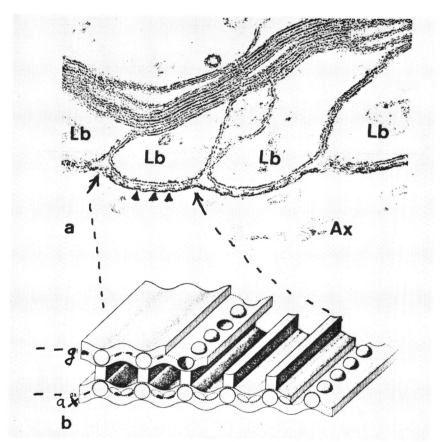

Figure 9. Thin section of the axoglial junction from a specimen fixed in potassium ferrocyanide–osmium with preservation of the trilaminar structure of the junctional regions. Note presence on paranodal loops of intercellular septae and their juxtaposition to the axolemma (loops indicated by arrows and septae by arrowheads in a). The lower portion of the figure (b) shows a tentative model of the junction and attempts to combine anatomical features seen in this section and freeze-fracture. Intercellular septae are depicted as transverse bands. The glial (g) and axonal (ax) membranes are undulated such that crests coincide with the intercellular septae, shown as transverse bands. The dashed line in the lower figure indicates fracture plane—only glial E face and axonal P face shown (see Figure 6). Abbreviations: Lb, lateral belt; Ax, axoplasm; g, glial surface; ax, axonal surface. ×240,000. Reproduced by kind permission of Schnapp and Mugnaini (1978, monograph 5, Chapter 2).

current carried by sodium responsible for the upward shift in the action potential, a *delayed current* carried by potassium ions responsible for repolarization, and a *leakage current* also involved in repolarization and restoration of the resting potential. The discovery of blocking agents for these different components (tetradotoxin eliminates the Na^+, and tetraethylammonium the

K^+) provided valuable tools for investigation of ionic channels present in membranes and at nodal points of myelinated sheaths. Hodgkin and Huxley in their original studies predicated the presence of reversible molecular changes in membranes associated with the opening and closing of ionic channels but did not have the equipment to detect the currents (now termed gating currents) associated with these movements. Apparatus has been designed that compensates for several components of the action potential noted above (linear capacitance, leakage components), enabling the detection of "asymmetric currents" associated with gating. An elegant description of the teasing out of single myelinated fibers from frog sciatic nerve bundles and the method of applying voltage clamps has been described by Cahalan (1978), and some of the technical difficulties are discussed by Moore (1978) (see monograph 5).

Axonal Variations

There has been interest in variations of axonal morphology and its functional significance, especially with respect to the pathological significance of internode–axonal ratios. It has been suggested that a value of 100–200 is optimal to maximize conduction velocity, but several examples exist where the ratio is less than 20, that is, fibers with closely spaced nodes of Ranvier (mesencephalic reticular formation, oculomotor nucleus). It has been shown that internode–axonal diameter ratios can vary along the course of a single fiber; they can be decreased in remyelinated axons of PNS and CNS fibers, and may be a distinguishing feature in such cases. Another variable of interest is the axon diameter as compared to the total diameter of the fiber, a ratio that is approximately 0.6 for most PNS myelinated fibers. It has been predicated that conduction velocity is maximal for a ratio of between 0.6 and 0.7. These geometrical considerations may have relevance to axonal function as demonstrated in acute pathological situations and accompanying demyelination (monograph 5, Chapters 5 and 9).

The fine anatomy of the node of Ranvier and the differences that exist between PNS and CNS are important in terms of the pathology and the subsequent effects on conduction velocity of the axonal fiber (Figure 8). Raminsky (1978, monograph 5) has calculated that average internodal conduction time is 20 μsec in normal rat fibers of internodal lengths 0.75–1.45 mm, but is greatly increased in demyelinated fibers, up to 10^3 μsec or longer. It has been demonstrated that blockage of conduction at one internode of a myelinated axon can severely hamper the function of the whole fiber. The insulating property of internodes is facilitated by the presence of exceptionally large numbers of lamellae. It has been estimated that a 15-μm-diameter (myelinated) fiber has a 4-μm-thick sheath consisting of up to 250 membranes.

Species Variation in the Rate of Myelination

The rate of deposition of myelin in different species and the changes that occur during development are of interest in terms of morphological and behavioral changes that ensue. Large grazing animals, for example, are born with a well-developed CNS and are capable of considerable motor coordination shortly after birth, in marked contrast to nest-building animals such as rats and mice, which are immature at birth and lack myelin. Myelination occurs at well-defined age periods in different species. In some, the rates of deposition are extremely high, with a 10–16-fold increase in total amount of myelin within 10 days after birth and with continued accumulation (albeit at lower rates) at periods well beyond those normally associated with maturation. Myelination follows a caudo-cranial gradient and appears to parallel the phylogenetic patterns associated with development of the CNS. Myelination occurs first in the PNS, next in the spinal cord, and finally in the CNS. Myelin from immature animals has a different lipid composition from that of adults, with a lower content of galactolipids and a higher content of phosphatidylcholine. (The ratio of these two lipids increases from $1:2$ at 15 days in the rat to $2:8$ at maturity.)

LIPID COMPOSITION

Myelin can be readily isolated from the CNS, and with more difficulty from the PNS, and its chemical composition studied. In white matter of mammalian brain, myelin represents up to 30% of total dry weight, and even in whole brain accounts for up to 20–25%, and more than 40% of total brain lipid (monograph 4, Chapter 5). A method similar in principle to that used by most laboratories for separating myelin (or more correctly compact myelin membranes free of axons) is summarized in Figure 10 (see monograph 7). Homogenization of brain in isotonic sucrose leads to formation of myelin vesicles of lower buoyant density compared to other intracellular organelles. As a result these structures can be separated by flotation over 0.85 M sucrose and subsequently purified further by submitting them to hypotonic media or water (to remove soluble contamination or entrapped particulates) and repurified on further sucrose gradients, or by use of $CsCl_2$ gradients (7). In the PNS, difficulties arise from the presence of collagen and connective tissue so that more drastic methods are required for homogenization. Although purified fragments of CNS and PNS myelin membrane have the lamellar structure generally associated with intact myelinated axons, the drastic procedures of isolation remove soluble components associated with the cytoplasmic inclusions such as those present in the Schmidt-Lantermann incisures, in the intramyelinic space, and at the paranodal regions. Purified membranes

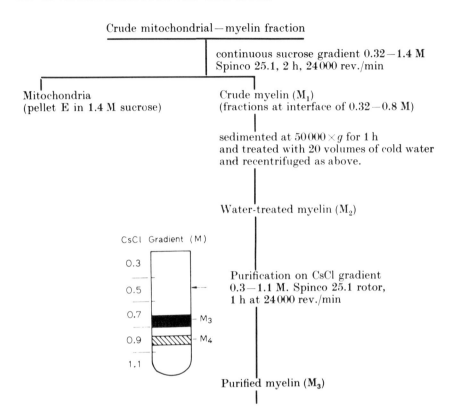

Figure 10. A scheme for the separation and purification of compact myelin fragments based on that of D'Monte, et al. (7). M_3 represents typical myelin figures seen under EM; M_4 represents small membrane vesicles that may represent an early form of myelin (see text). The crude mitochondrial fraction of brain is prepared by homogenizing whole brain tissue in 10 volumes of cold sucrose followed by centrifugation to remove debris and nuclei. This is followed by centrifugation (14,000g) to yield a pellet that contains myelin, synaptosomes, lysosomes, and mitochondria, frequently referred to in the literature as the P_2 fraction.

have a number of markers that can be used to establish their purity, including the nature of the protein components (see below) and the ratio of 2',2'-cyclic nucleotide-3'-phosphodiesterase to that of other enzymes such as proteinases or β-galactosidase (representing lysosomal contamination), 5'-nucleotidase (glial plasma membrane), and succinic dehydrogenase (mitochondria) (7) (monograph 4, Chapter 5). At one time, considerable significance was attached to the finding of light versus heavy fractions of myelin, but this can be partly accounted for by variations in fragmentation of the membrane during disruption, or by contamination from other cellular elements. It may represent a less "mature" form of myelin deficient in selected protein and lipid components, leading to different flotation properties (7).

Inferences concerning the composition of myelin made in early studies with crude preparations have largely been confirmed (8). Myelin contains 28% cholesterol, 29% galactolipid, and 46% phospholipid. A summary of the lipid/protein compositions is presented in Table 2. Progress in knowledge of lipids in myelin came about rapidly following the discovery that lipids can be extracted from fresh brain or purified myelin preparations by mixtures of chloroform–methanol (2:1 v/v), including lipids that are complexed with protein (proteolipids) (9). Extracts can be analyzed for lipids, proteins, or proteolipids, depending on the analytical procedures applied. If the extract if partitioned with water (approximately one-fifth of the volume), the upper phase contains gangliosides and water-soluble components. If myelin is dried prior to extraction, or treated with acid, all lipids (free or associated with protein) will be rendered soluble in a chloroform–methanol 2:1 solvent. In this way it can be shown that myelin from many species contains about 30% protein and 70% lipid.

The major classes of lipid found in whole brain are present also in myelin, with the exception of cardiolipid (a mitochondrial component). Data for the major classes of lipid are summarized in Table 2 and Figure 11. CNS preparations contain cholesterol, phospholipid, and galactolipid in a molar ratio of approximately 4:3:2, cholesterol constituting the largest proportion on a weight basis. Galactolipids (cerebrosides and sulfatide) have unsubstituted and α-hydroxy fatty acids, both of which can occur in the saturated and unsaturated forms, in contrast to sphingomyelin, which only has unsubstituted fatty acids. In the PNS, there is less galactosphingolipid and gangliosides and more sphingomyelin.

PROTEIN COMPOSITION

Fresh myelin is almost completely soluble in chloroform–methanol (2:1), indicating that most of the protein is complexed with lipids. By definition, proteins soluble in this organic solvent are classed as proteolipids; they were first discovered by Folch and Lees (9). Proteolipids are present in high concentration in CNS myelin, some four to five times higher in white than in gray, and relatively low in other organs. The second major protein(s) in myelin is basic in character and can be isolated readily by extraction of myelin with dilute acid (e.g., 0.1 N HCl). Other proteins, present as minor components of higher molecular weight, may include enzymes present in cytoplasmic inclusions associated with the myelin sheath. All of these proteins can be separated by electrophoresis on polyacrylamide gels, an experimental procedure suited for their detection and isolation (Figure 12). Solvent systems

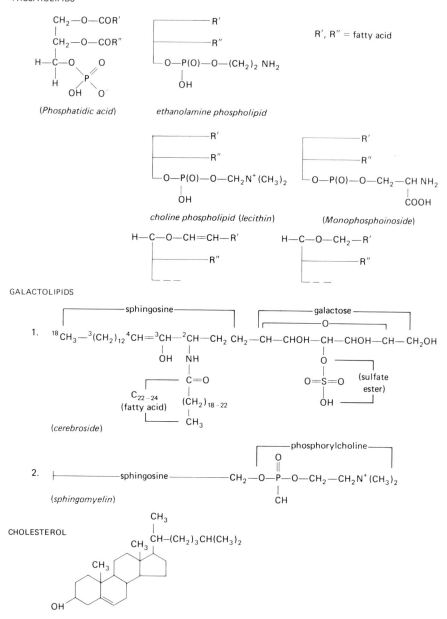

Figure 11. [For full structure of myelin lipids see Yatsu (1975, monograph 6, Chapter 3).] Phospholipids (phosphoglycerides or glycerophosphatides) have phosphatidic acid as their parent compound (*), noted as the three-pronged figure. For example, phosphatidic acid plus ethanolamine is known as ethanolamine phospholipid, plus choline as choline phospholipid or lecithin, plus inostol as monophosphoinosintrate. Fatty acids are ester-lined in positions 1 and 2 except in plasmalogens where in position 1 they are esterified in an α,β unsaturated ether linkage, which on hydrolysis yields a fatty aldehyde. Note that plasmalogens (**) are present in high concentration in myelin (see Table 2).

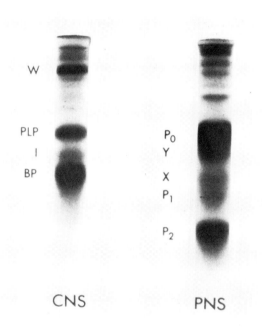

Figure 12. Separation of proteins on sodium dodecyl sulfate-acrylamide gels from CNS and PNS myelin. PLP denotes proteolipid protein (sometimes referred to as the "Folch-Lee's protein"); W refers to Wolfgram and is a high-molecular-weight acidic protein; BP refers to basic protein (one band in primates but two in rodents); I refers to an intermediate protein seen in extracts, which may represent a breakdown product of PLP. In the PNS, P_0 refers to the major glycoprotein, and P_1 and P_2 refer to basic proteins. P_2 is a component unique to peripheral myelin and can induce experimental allergic neuritis (EAN) when injected into animals with Fruend's adjuvant. P_1 is comparable in its properties to the major basic protein (BP) seen in the CNS. [Reproduced by kind permission of Braun and Brostoff (1977, monograph 4, Chapter 6).]

have been devised also for bulk separation of selected components (see monograph 4, Chapter 6). The major proteins of the CNS fall into three classes: acidic, often termed "Wolfgram" protein; proteolipid protein; and basic protein.

Basic Protein of Myelin

Basic protein is of particular interest since it can induce experimental allergic encephalomyelitis (EAE) when injected with an adjuvant into a susceptible animal species. Owing to its ease of isolation with dilute acids it is among the few proteins of the CNS that have been sequenced (Figure 13). In the

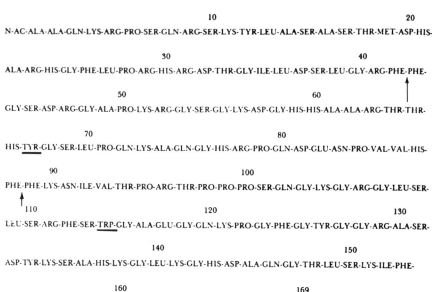

10   20
N-AC-ALA-ALA-GLN-LYS-ARG-PRO-SER-GLN-ARG-SER-LYS-TYR-LEU-ALA-SER-ALA-SER-THR-MET-ASP-HIS-

30   40
ALA-ARG-HIS-GLY-PHE-LEU-PRO-ARG-HIS-ARG-ASP-THR-GLY-ILE-LEU-ASP-SER-LEU-GLY-ARG-PHE-PHE-

50   60
GLY-SER-ASP-ARG-GLY-ALA-PRO-LYS-ARG-GLY-SER-GLY-LYS-ASP-GLY-HIS-HIS-ALA-ALA-ARG-THR-THR-

70   80
HIS-TYR-GLY-SER-LEU-PRO-GLN-LYS-ALA-GLN-GLY-HIS-ARG-PRO-GLN-ASP-GLU-ASN-PRO-VAL-VAL-HIS-

90   100
PHE-PHE-LYS-ASN-ILE-VAL-THR-PRO-ARG-THR-PRO-PRO-PRO-SER-GLN-GLY-LYS-GLY-ARG-GLY-LEU-SER-

110   120   130
LEU-SER-ARG-PHE-SER-TRP-GLY-ALA-GLU-GLY-GLN-LYS-PRO-GLY-PHE-GLY-TYR-GLY-GLY-ARG-ALA-SER-

140   150
ASP-TYR-LYS-SER-ALA-HIS-LYS-GLY-LEU-LYS-GLY-HIS-ASP-ALA-GLN-GLY-THR-LEU-SER-LYS-ILE-PHE-

160   169
LYS-LEU-GLY-GLY-ARG-ASP-SER-ARG-SER-GLY-SER-PRO-MET-ALA-ARG-ARG-COOH

Figure 13. Sequence of myelin basic protein. Note the presence of an N-acetyl alanine on the first position, the absence of cysteine, the presence of a triproline bridge at positions 97–100, and the presence of only one Trp at position 114. The points of cleavage by brain cathepsin D at the Phe-Phe bands are indicated by the arrows. The major encephalitogenic sequences are those surrounding Tyr in position 67 (underlined, active in rabbits) and Trp in position 114 (active in guinea pigs and rats). Arginine in position 106 can exist in mono- or dimethylated forms of myelin. Basic protein is found also to contain a small amount of phosphate present as phosphothreonine and phosphoserine (positions 33 and 54). The presence of methyl-acid phosphate groups can alter the physical properties of basic protein in vitro and may play a role in stabilization of the protein within the membrane.

CNS of rodents, electrophoresis on SDS-gels has revealed the presence of two basic protein components of slightly different composition, whereas in primates only one component exists, of approximately 18,000 daltons.

Basic protein has a number of unique chemical features, among which are the presence of an N-terminal protected group (N-acetyl-Ala), the absence of cysteine (no disulfide bridges), and a high percentage of basic amino acids (24%). Since most of the glutamic acid residues are amidated, the protein has a basic isoelectric point. Its actual localization in the myelin membrane (at the major periodal or intraperiodal lines), is still subject to doubt, but in view of its chemical properties it is likely to be (loosely) complexed with membrane lipids. Other chemical features of myelin basic protein of particular interest are the presence of a triproline bridge that may give this otherwise linear protein a turn or twist, the presence of methylated arginine in position

106 (monomethyl, and diamethylated), the presence of small amounts of phosphoserine and phosphothreonine (basic protein is a good acceptor for endogenous brain protein kinases) (monograph 7). As noted, myelin isolated from rats and mice contains two basic proteins, one of 18,000 and the other of 14,000 daltons. The smaller protein differs from the larger by having a deletion of 40 amino acid residues in the interior of the molecule. A considerable amount of effort has been expended on finding the sequences within basic protein that are responsible for inducing demyelination. There appear to be two major sites, one that contains Trp and is active in guinea pigs and one that contains Trp and is active in rabbits (Figure 13). Smaller peptide fragments can be isolated by enzymatic digestion and shown to be encephalitogenic in the appropriate species. Incubation with lysosomal cathepsin D of brain leads to cleavage of the Phe-Phe bands at position 42–43 and 88–89 of bovine myelin basic protein, with release of three peptides, two of which contain the Tyr and Trp sequences and are active in the appropriate donor (11).

Proteolipid

The term *proteolipid* was introduced by Folch and Lees (9) to describe a protein–lipid complex soluble in chloroform-methanol (2:1). A major protein conforming to these criteria exists in myelin, and has received the designation proteolipid protein or PLP (Figure 12). Unlike myelin basic protein, the N-terminal is a free α amino acid group (Gly), but to date the full sequence of this protein is unknown. Its unusual solubility characteristics and its probable interaction with lipids suggest an important role in the maintenance of the myelin matrix. In addition to PLP, myelin contains other components, including: a protein termed DM-20, which migrates below PLP in SDS-acrylamide gels; a glycoprotein that can be labeled with fucose, glucosamine, or N-acetylmannosamine; and an acidic protein designated Wolfgram of approximately 50,000 daltons. The high-molecular-weight regions of SDS-acrylamide gels contain a number of other minor components that may be derived from neurotubulin or filaments associated with cytoplasmic inclusions, especially those of the paranodal regions.

PNS Myelin

The protein profile of PNS-myelin on SDS-acrylamide gels is different from that of CNS myelin (Figure 12). Only the large basic P_1 (18,000 daltons) is common; the other bands, termed P_2 and P_0, are unique to the PNS. Protein P_0 is a glycoprotein and accounts for approximately half of total protein extracted from PNS myelin; sugars reported present include galactose and mannose, and this glycoprotein can be shown to incorporate fucose in vivo. The P_1 protein is comparable in most respects to the larger basic proteins of the CNS; in contrast P_2 does not have sequence homologies with other known proteins. Studies on P_2 have attracted interest, since its injection can lead to peripheral neuritis, a model disease with similarities to the Guillain-Barré syndrome. Partial sequences of this protein have been identified; unlike basic protein it is devoid of histidine, but has some cysteine, has only two prolines, and has a high percentage of hydrophobic residues, imparting a distinct conformational structure. PNS myelin is characterized by an absence of PLP and acidic proteins of the Wolfgram type (Figure 12).

Myelin Enzymes

The enzyme content of myelin is unknown, owing to the occurrence of contamination during isolation. Several enzymes have a higher specific activity in myelin membranes as compared to other CNS components and have been used as markers. These include a 2',3'-cyclic nucleotide, 3'-phosphohydrolase, a cholesterol ester hydrolase, and an aminopeptidase (Marks, 1972, monograph 7; monograph 4, Chapter 5). No function has been assigned to the first enzyme, since 2',3' or 2'-nucleotides are absent in the free nucleotide pools of tissues having this enzyme activity. Other enzymes reported present, and which may be derived from cytoplasmic pools, depending on the purity of the isolated myelin, include various proteolytic ones (arylamidases, neutral proteinases) and nonspecific esterases. The presence of cyclic nucleotide dependent and independent protein kinases is regarded as important in view of the properties of phosphorylated proteins in membranes. Basic protein is an excellent substrate for protein kinases, and coupled with phosphoprotein phosphatases, also present in myelin, may play a role in the metabolism of myelin. The presence of enzymes in myelin appears to warrant closer examination, especially as related to their role in turnover and alterations that occur in disease.

MYELIN LOSS AND PATHOLOGY

A large number of conditions result in the loss of myelin, with consequent alterations in function (Table 3). Demyelinating disease per se is a term generally restricted by pathologists to inflammatory conditions leading to a loss of myelin while sparing the axon. The most common example of this in man is multiple sclerosis (MS). A separate class of diseases concerns those that are hereditary and includes animal mutants that fail to develop sufficient myelin during maturation (monograph 4, Chapter 14). Also, a number of demyelinating states occur as a result of toxic effects of drugs or nutritional deficiencies, or they result from trauma such as edema and compression.

Table 3. Demyelinating Diseases.

HUMAN	ANIMAL
1. *"Demyelinative" Conditions* (See text for definition)	
MS and variants	Canine distemper
Acute disseminated encephalomyelitis	Visna
Acute disseminated leukoencephalopathy	Mouse hepatitis virus
Acute hemorrhage leukoencephalopathy	Theiler's virus
Progressive multifocal leukoencephalopathy	Goat leukoencephalopathy
Idiopathic polyneuritis	EAE
Diphtheric neuropathy	EAN (PNS)
	Marek's disease (PNS)
	Coonhound paralysis (PNS)
2. *Hereditary Metabolic Diseases*	
Metachromatic leukodystrophy	Jimpy (mutant) mice
Krabbe's disease	Canine Krabbe's disease
Adrenoleukodystrophy	Quaking (mutant) mice
Refsum's disease	Border disease
Spongy degeneration	Murine muscular dystrophy
PKU	
3. *Toxic Conditions* (myelinotoxic compounds)	
Hexachlorophen	Triethyltin
Hypoxia (CO)	
4. *Nutritional Disorders* (developmental defects)	
Vitamin B_{12} deficiency	
Central pontine myelinolysis	
Marchiafava-Bignami's disease	
5. *Physically Induced Conditions* (traumatic)	
Edema	
Compression	

Abbreviations are: EAE, experimental allergic encephalomyelitis; EAN, experimental allergic neuritis; MS, multiple sclerosis.
Table taken from the data of Raine (1977, monograph 4; 1978, monograph 5).

Multiple Sclerosis

The etiology of MS has commanded considerable attention because of its prevalence in man. There is evidence based largely on epidemiological findings suggesting an infective agent possibly of viral origin. Multiple sclerosis has some similarity also to slow virus diseases in respect to the long incubation period required, but unlike the latter, it is a multiepisodic disease characterized by periods of exacerbation and remission of symptoms. The disease is classified by neuropathologists as a demyelinative disorder and is associated with perivascular inflammation and development of plaques in the CNS. Although it has similarities to delayed hypersensitive disorders of immune origin, specific antibodies have not been detected in body fluids except for a generalized increase in IgG in the CSF. The CSF is reported to contain basic protein or its breakdown products, which can be detected by sensitive radioimmunoassay procedures and thus have value as a diagnostic procedure indicative of MS (13).

The principal strategies adopted for treatment of MS have been attempts to interfere with autoimmune phenomena, leading to trials with immunosuppressive drugs (cyclophosphamide, azathioprine, methotrexate) or antilymphocyte serum, or other diverse agents such as glucosteroids and ACTH.

Experimental Allergic Encephalomyelitis

In the 1930s, it was found that the postinoculation encephalomyelitis that frequently developed in human subjects following injection with Pasteur antirabies vaccine was attributable to the presence of contaminating brain tissue. Those observations led to the development of a laboratory model for demyelination diseases by injection of extracts of spinal cord or whole brain mixed with adjuvant into suitable donor animals. This disease, known as experimental allergic encephalomyelitis (EAE), is characterized by development of CNS lesions, paralysis, and frequently death of the animal (monograph 8).

The chief causative agent of EAE in brain and spinal cord extracts has been identified as basic protein of myelin. This protein, with a molecular weight of approximately 18,000 daltons, occurs as a single component in myelin of primates (see above). It is a single polypeptide chain lacking cysteine and is relatively constant in composition in different mammalian species. In the case of bovine material, it has been completely sequenced. The induction of myelin breakdown by basic protein represents only one variant of demyelination, since studies with myelinotoxic factors present in serum of patients with MS indicate the presence of other factors. It has been demonstrated that serum from MS patients can induce demyelination of cultured cerebellum and spinal cord fibers in vitro, and that it has antigenic properties against whole brain tissue extract, but not specifically against myelin basic protein (monograph 5, Chapter 7).

Inflammatory Conditions in the PNS

Considerably more information is available concerning the etiology of inflammatory conditions in the PNS generally referred to as the Landry-Guillain-Barré group of diseases, or idiopathic polyneuritis (Table 3). Diseases of this group generally follow virus infections, although specific causative agents have not been identified. As in the case of EAE, an in vitro model exists: injection of peripheral myelin or its purified P_2 component (see above) with an adjuvant leads to experimental allergic neuritis (EAN), resulting in loss of myelin from peripheral fibers. The P_2 protein present in peripheral nerve differs in structure from other basic proteins present in the PNS and CNS, and studies are in progress to determine its peptide sequence. The EAN model appears to be comparable to the CNS counterpart (EAE) in most respects except the nature of the antigen.

Immune Mechanisms in Some Demyelinating Diseases

Similarities between MS and myelin loss in experimental models (EAE, orga-notypic cultures) have led to the view that demyelination is an autoimmune, cell-mediated response with myelin components acting as antigens. In EAE the response can be shown to be mediated largely by T-cells, since the disease can be produced in naive animals by passive transfer (Marks and Rodnight, 1977, monograph 7). The fact that EAE has a genetic determinant (some animal strains are more highly sensitive) may have implications with respect to MS. It has been shown that MS is prevalent in individuals who have the histocompatability antigen HLA-Dw2 on the surface of the lymphocytes. Detailed morphological studies show that loss of myelin in EAE is attributable in part to phagocytosis by hematogenously derived blood cells (PMN, mono-cytes, macrophages). The mechanism responsible for penetration of the CNS by cells mounting an attack on myelin is unknown. There has been speculation that peripheral sensitization precedes the cloning of specific T-cells which then penetrate the CNS. Sensitization of cells by myelin basic protein in EAE may require accessory or humoral factors present in serum. Alterna-tively, the view has been expressed that invasion of the CNS by inflammatory (sensitized) cells in secondary to a localized etiological factor (possibly local accumulation of IgG itself) at putative lesion sites. In the case of organotypic cultures, one of the toxic factors present in serum has properties of a comple-ment-dependent CNS specific antibody (monograph 5, Chapters 6 and 7). Destruction of complement by heating alters some of the destructive proper-ties, since treated sera in culture give only transient swelling of myelin. In the case of new myelin formed in culture, there is an abnormal periodicity, suggesting that damage to oligodendroglial cells may be a primary factor.

Demyelination of the Peripheral Nervous System

Demyelination of the peripheral nervous system proceeds along three different lines: (1) Wallerian degeneration, (2) segmental demyelination, and (3) dying back atrophy.

Wallerian degeneration is the prototype of disintegration of the peripheral nerve secondary to transection of the nerve itself. Subsequently, the proximal end degenerates to the nearest node of Ranvier, whereas there is total degener-ation of the distal end. The process goes through a stage of swelling followed by granular disintegration of the neurofibrils, followed by eventual fragmentation of myelin, which is characterized by esterification of the cholesterol componen⁺. The prototype for this lesion would be trauma.

Segmental demyelination is a process in which damage occurs first to a Schwann cell followed by disintegration of myelin in a defined segment of nerve. The classical prototype for this is postdiphtheric or lead neuropathy. In Guillain-Barré-Strohl syndrome, (15) segmental demyelination is followed by Wallerian degeneration.

Dying back atrophy is a process in which axon and myelin degenerate from the periphery to the center without observing segmental boundaries. It is explained by a failure of the neuron to maintain the metabolic needs of the periphery. The first degenerative alterations are observed in the boutons terminaux of the peripheral sensory nerve ending. Many industrial toxins induce this type of atrophy.

In a separate category belongs the group of hypertrophic neuropathies in which hyperplasia of the Schwann cell is thought to be induced by a primary degeneration of myelin of unknown origin. Best known is the recessive inherited disease syndrome, first described by Charcot, Marie, and Tooth, in which loss of myelinated fibers is finally followed by a significant increase of the connective tissue sheath surrounding the nerve and degeneration of the posterior columns. A similar syndrome, which, however, may be followed by more extensive central demyelination, was described by Refsum (16) under the designation of heredopathia atactica polyneuritiformis. In the same category falls, although it is clinically dissimilar, a progressive neurological disorder attended by bilateral foot deformity, wasting in the distal muscles of all limbs, and sensory disorder, described by Déjérine and Sottas.

A variety of other disorders are described in which, however, the damage to myelin does not appear primary.

Remyelination

The glial cells play a role in remyelination, especially in relation to pathological processes. It will be recalled that in the CNS during development, there is a partitioning of axon bundles by Schwann cells leading to a 1:1 ratio for each internode (see Figure 1). The recognition of cells for each other and the possible role of chemotactic factors represent important areas of clinical research. Also, the timing of events leading to formation of a uniform spiral and compactation of glial cell plasma membranes is a factor in remyelination. This is illustrated by the use of regenerating axons from myelin-deficient (mouse) mutants, which become myelinated only when presented to normal Schwann cells. If, for example, normal axons are presented to mutant Schwann cells, they do not become fully myelinated. The influence of accessory cells is further demonstrated by the change from typical PNS to CNS myelin at transitional regions where peripheral fibers enter the brain or spinal cord (see Figure 8).

Human diseases associated with destruction of myelin are conveniently grouped in two categories, the first one encompassing demyelinating diseases sensu stricto, which may be defined as those in which breakdown of normally formed myelin is followed by fibrous gliosis. Charcot (14) pointed out that in these diseases the primary damage is to the myelin sheath, whereas the axon remains undisturbed for various lengths of time. Typically, among this group are: multiple sclerosis, acute disseminated encephalomyelitis, central pontine myelinolysis, and idiopathic polyneuritis.

MONOGRAPHS AND REVIEWS ON MYELIN STRUCTURE

1. Peters, A., Palay, S. L., and Webster, H. de F. 1976. *The Fine Structure of the Nervous System.* W. B. Saunders, Philadelphia, PA.
   Chapter 6—The cellular sheaths of neurons, pp. 181–230.
2. Davison, A. N., and Peters, A., eds. 1970. *Myelination.* Charles C Thomas, Springfield, Illinois.
   Chapter 1—Peters, A., and Vaughan, J. E. Morphology and development of the myelin sheath, pp. 1–79.
3. Korey, S. R. 1959. *The Biology of Myelin.* Hoeber-Harper, New York.
   Chapter 6—Tasaki, I. Physiologic properties of the myelin sheath and of the node of Ranvier, pp. 159–87.
4. Morell, P. 1977. *Myelin.* Plenum, New York.
   Chapter 1—Raine, C. S. Morphological aspects of myelin, pp. 1–41.
   Chapter 4—Boyart, R. B., and Ritchie, J. M. Physiological basis of conduction in myelinated fibres, pp. 117–57.
   Chapter 5—Norton, W. T. Isolation and characterization of myelin, pp. 161–90.
   Chapter 6—Braun, P. E., and Brostoff, S. W. Proteins of myelin, pp. 201–27.
   Chapter 9—Schaumberg, H. H., and Raine, C. S. The neurology of myelin diseases, pp. 325–49.
   Chapter 14—Hogan, E. L. Animal models of genetic disorders of myelin, pp. 489–515.
5. Waxman, S. G. 1978. *Physiology and Pathobiology of Axons.* Raven Press, New York.
   Chapter 1—Hirano, A., and Dembitzer, H. Morphology of normal central myelinated axons, p. 65.
   Chapter 2—Schnapp, B. S., and Mugnaini, E. Membrane architecture of myelinated fibres as seen by freeze fracture, p. 108.
   Chapter 3—Moore, J. W. On sodium conductance gates in nerve membranes, p. 145.
   Chapter 4—Cahalan, M. Voltage clamp studies on the node of Ranvier, p. 155.
   Chapter 5—Waxman, S. G. Variations in axonal morphology and their functional significance, p. 169.
   Chapter 6—Raine, C. S. Pathology of demyelination, p. 283.
   Chapter 7—Bornstein, M. B. Immunobiology of demyelination, p. 313.
   Chapter 8—Suzuki, K. Biochemistry of myelin disorders, p. 337.
   Chapter 9—Raminsky, M. Physiology of conduction in demyelinated axons, p. 361.
6. Cohen, M. M. 1975. *Biochemistry of Neural Disease.* Harper and Row, New York.
   Chapter 3—Yatsu, F. M. *Lipid Disorders of the Nervous System,* pp. 79–129.

7. Marks, N., and Rodnight, R. 1972–1978. *Research Methods in Neurochemistry,* Plenum Press, New York.
   Volume 1: Spoln, M. and Davison, A. N. Separation of myelin fragments from the CNS, pp. 33–42.
   Horrochs, L. A., and Sun, G. Y. Ethanolamine plasmalogen, pp. 223–31.
8. Kies, M. W., and Alvord, E. G. 1959. *Allergic Encephalomyelitis,* pp. 1–559. Charles C Thomas, Springfield, Illinois.
9. Landon, D. N., ed. *The Peripheral Nerve.* Chapman and Hall, London.

GENERAL REFERENCES

1. Geren, B. B. 1954. The formation from the Schwann cell surface of myelin in peripheral nerves of chick embryo. *Exp. Cell Res.* 7:558.
2. Hashim, G. 1979. Myelin basic protein: Structure, function and antigenic determinants. *Immunol. Rev.* 39.
3. Singer, S. J., and Nicolson, G. L. 1972. The fluid mosaic model of the structure of cell membranes. Cell membranes are viewed as two-dimensional solutions of oriental globular proteins and lipids. *Science* 175:720.
4. Bunge, M. B., Bunge, R. P., and Ris, H. 1961. Ultrastructural study of remyelination in an experimental lesion in adult cat spinal cord. *J. Biophys. Biochem. Cytol.* 10:67.
5. Tasaki, I., and Takeuchi, T. 1941. Der am Ranvierschen Knoten entstehende Aktionstrom und seine Bedeutung für die Errgungsleitung, *Pflügers Arch. Ges. Physiol.* 244:896.
6. Huxley, A. F., and Stämpfli, R. 1949. Evidence for saltatory conduction in peripheral myelinated nerve fibers. *J. Physiol. (London)* 108:315.
7. D'Monte, B., Mela, P., and Marks, N. 1971. Metabolic instability of myelin protein and proteolipid fractions. *Eur. J. Biochem.* 23:355.
8. Brante, G. 1949. Studies on lipids in the nervous system with special reference to quantitative chemical determinations and topical distribution. *Acta Physiol. Scand.* 18 *Suppl.* 63.
9. Folch, J., and Lees, M. 1951. Proteolipids, a new type of tissue lipoproteins, their isolation from brain. *J. Biol. Chem.* 191:807.
10. Antillio, L. A., Norton, W. T., and Terry, R. D. 1964. The preparation and some properties of purified myelin from the CNS. *J. Neurochem.* 11:17.
11. Benuck, M., Marks, N., and Hashim, G. 1975. Metabolic instability of myelin. Breakdown of basic protein induced by brain cathepsin D. *Eur. J. Biochem.* 52:615.
12. Mugnaini, E. 1978. Fine structure of myelin sheaths. *Proc. Eur. Soc. Neurochem.* I, V. Neuhoff, ed., pp. 3–31. Verlag Chemie. Weinheim, New York.
13. Cohen, S. R., Herndon, R. M., and McKhann, G. M. 1976. Radioimmunoassay of myelin basic protein in spinal fluid. An index of active demyelination. *N. Engl. J. Med.* 295:1455; see also in (1978) *Myelination and Demyelination,* J. Palo, ed., p. 513, Plenum, New York.
14. Charcot, J. M. 1877. *Lectures on the Diseases of the Nervous System,* G. Sigerson, trans., 1st series, lecture 6 (delivered 1868). The New Sydenham Society, London.
15. Guillain, G., Barré, J. A., and Strohl, A. 1916. Sur un syndrome de radiculo-névrite avec hyperalbuminose du liquide céphalo-rachidien sans réaction cellulaire: Remarques sur les caractères cliniques et graphiques des réflexes tendineuses. *Bull. Soc. Méd. Hôp. Paris* 40:1462–70.
16. Refsum, S. 1965. Heredopathia atactica polyneuritiformis: Familial syndrome not hitherto described. A contribution to the clinical study of hereditary diseases of the nervous system. *Acta Psychiat. Scand., Suppl.* 38.

2.4. Cell Motility

Byung H. Park

Active movement may be considered a fundamental characteristic of all living cells. It has been observed in a variety of cell activities: cytoplasmic streaming, phagocytosis, morphogenesis, cytokinesis, mitosis, and locomotion including chemotaxis.

Electron microscopy, the isolation and analysis of subcellular components, the immunofluorescent technique, and the use of antimitotic agents (e.g., vincristine) and cell surface active ligands (e.g., various lectins) are some of the key developments that have facilitated many of the important advances in our understanding of cell motility in its structural, biochemical, and functional aspects.

The earlier studies of contractile proteins, the chemical basis for the mechanical energy of muscle contraction, and subsequent elucidation of ultrastructure of muscle fiber have stimulated and led to studies of the morphological and biochemical basis for the motility of nonmuscle cells, including unicellular organisms as well as plant cells.

In recent years, proteins (e.g., actin and myosin) that closely resemble those of skeletal muscle have been identified in most of the eukaryotic cells, ranging from vertebrates to amoeba. Since these and other "contractile" protein molecules appear to be distributed universally in all cells, it is believed that the study of these specialized protein molecules may provide a general mechanism for active movement of all living cells, of which muscle contraction may be only a specialized example.

Identification of actin and myosin in nonmuscle cells led to the early assumption that like in muscle cells, these molecules are capable of transforming the chemical energy into mechanical energy; that is, movement of the cells. However, some major differences between muscle and nonmuscle cells are becoming apparent: (1) In muscles, the contractile proteins (actin and myosin) are arranged in an orderly array of interdigitating filaments that slide past one another as the muscle contracts; in contrast, the nonmuscle cell in general, lacks these orderly and permanent structures. (2) There are biochemical differences that may be of key importance for the basic biological functions of actin and myosin in nonmuscle cells. (3) Regulatory factors in the interactions of actins and myosins in nonmuscle cells may be different from those in muscle cells. (4) Nonmuscle actins and myosins are able to form in vitro supramolecular assemblies like those of muscle filaments, or those corresponding to the microfilament bundles or stress fibers. This indicates that actin may play a cytoskeletal, as well as a contractile, role in nonmuscle cells.

DESCRIPTION AND CLASSIFICATION OF CELL MOTILITY

The circumstances in which cells of higher animals are motile are many. During early embryonic development, there are mass movements of cells during gastrulation, the migration of the neurocrest cells and the outgrowth of nerve processes. In the adult, however, cell locomotion is confined primarily to cells such as leukocytes and macrophages. The cells of adult solid tissue do, however, retain "dormant" locomotory abilities, which presumably assist in wound repair. On the other hand, excessive degrees of cell motility are probably one aspect of neoplastic cells.

Cell motility is most commonly studied by use of tissue culture, which provides certain advantages: (1) cells can be observed free of obstruction and interference by the surrounding bodies, and (2) cell motility can be controlled by altering the conditions of the cell environment (i.e., culture media).

Active cell movements may be tentatively classified into two broad categories for descriptive purposes:

1. Movement confined to a part of or whole individual cells, which may or may not necessarily be accompanied by displacement of the cell.
   (a) Spreading
   (b) Ruffling
   (c) Blebbing
   (d) Cytoplasmic steaming
   (e) Movement of cell surface
   (f) Cytokinesis or cell division

2. Locomotion of cells (displacement of a cell from one site to another)
   (a) Displacement in mass (e.g., during gastrulation)
   (b) Migration of primordial cells during embryogenesis
   (c) Migration via body fluid or tissues (e.g., leukocytes or tumor metastasis)
   (d) Chemotaxis of leukocytes

It should be kept in mind that the above is just a list of descriptive terminologies. In reality, I believe, many combinations of movement occur at a given time.

Spreading

The mechanism by which cells propel themselves is not fully understood. Nevertheless, several important clues are provided by certain movement of the cell surface and of material adhering to it.

A spread fibroblast has a thick central area containing the nucleus and other cytoplasmic organelles, surrounded by a thin or marginal area, typically consisting of two or more elongated flattened projections that are called lamellae. These lamellae somehow exert traction against the substratum, and each one tends to pull the cell body outward in its own direction. If the force of opposing lamellae is of equal strength, the cell simply remains stretched between them, but if the lamellae on one side dominate, the cell is pulled in that direction. As the adhesions at the rear margin are detached, the movement is often characterized by sudden jumps. If all adhesions are broken, the cell simply rounds up. How does the cell margin exert its directional force and thus pull itself forward?

A good analogy to the situation in the spread fibroblast would be a tug of war with an elastic rope; the contractivity of the cells, tending to pull the margins inward, is balanced by the tractional forces of locomotion by which the margin pulls itself outward. The effects of these forces can be seen by culturing cells on a flexible substratum, such as a plasma clot and silicone fluid, which are deformed by tension imposed upon them.

By this method, it was found (as expected) that the cell margin pulls the substratum rearward (inward) as the cell moves forward (outward). This tractional force tends to lie near plasma clot fibers along the axis of cell movement, and this alignment can be seen in a polarized light.

Ruffling

Probably the most obvious feature of fibroblast locomotion, especially when viewed by time lapse cinemicrography, is the cell surface movement known as ruffling. Ruffling consists of the repeated formation and movements of long narrow thickened areas, usually at the cell margin. These thickened areas, or ruffles, appear as dark, wavy lines in phase contrast microscopy. They form the margin at intervals of 30–60 sec, and move inward across the cell surface for a few micrometers before disappearing.

Ruffling occurs principally along those parts of the cell margin that are advancing forward, giving the subjective impression that cells are somehow pulled along by the ruffling movements. Similarly, when cells move on flexible substrata, they can be seen to pull the substratum inward, primarily along the ruffling area of the cell margin; therefore, it is clear that ruffling movements are somehow linked to the traction of the cells.

By observing fibroblasts in an inside view, it was found that ruffles form by the upfolding of the cell margin. The upfolded region corresponds to the thickened area, and much of this apparent rearward "propagation" consists of gradual folding.

Because of the speed of the upfoldings, the ruffle is somewhat irregular and frequently jerky. The average speed of the folding is 2–3°/sec. The length of a ruffle varies from 2 to 10 μm and sometimes up to 20 μm. Pinocytosis is often observed with ruffling; large vesicles of medium appear to become engulfed along the ruffle upfoldings and are taken into the cell. These vesicles then move inward, eventually collecting around the nucleus, although they often burst and disappear after a few minutes.

The observation that ruffles form by marginal upfolding does little to explain the relation of ruffling to locomotion. In itself, ruffling upfolding entails a slight retreat of the margin rather than an advance. Meticulous statistical analysis of cell margin movement showed that the cell margin constantly wavers, sometimes extending and sometime retracting. It was found that the net movement is forward because the outward protrusions are of a longer average duration than retractions. It was also shown that ruffle upfolding is predominant during the withdrawal phase.

Blebbing

Blebs are almost hemispherical herniations of the cell surface, which bulges out rapidly, filling with cytoplasmic fluid. It is reported that blebs are loaded with ribosomes, whereas mitochondira, endoplasmic reticulum, and other particulates are excluded from blebs. One does not find any ribosomes in ruffles. Projections of the cell surface that are intermediate in shape between blebs and ruffles are often observed, an indication that ruffling activity may change gradually into blebbing activity. Ruffles may be changed directly into blebs by introducing hypertonic medium or cytochalasin, for example, but a bleb has never been observed to convert directly into a ruffle.

Blebs usually expand rapidly within 5–10 sec, reaching a diameter of 2–10 μm. They contract more slowly, over 20–60 sec, their surface gradually wrinkling as they retract. Blebs may be observed anywhere on the cell surface, often on the surface of other blebs, developing chains 20–30 μm in length. The most usual site of blebbing, however, is the cell margin, where blebbing activity frequently alternates with ruffling. As cells spread their margin, bleb ruffles gradually take over as the cells become more flattened. Intermediate forms between blebs and ruffles are often observed in such circumstances.

It is suggested that blebs are formed when hydrostatic pressure within the cell is momentarily released by extension of weak points in the cell surface. In strongly hypertonic culture medium, this pressure collapses within a few seconds, and further blebbing ceases until cells are returned to a normal medium. At 0.4 M, the survival is sufficient to stop blebbing completely; less inhibition is produced by less hypertonic media.

Since blebs erupt preferentially around the cell margin, this part of the surface must be the weakest part of the cell, and hence most susceptible to the expansion. This suggests that the normal outward extension of the margin is also produced by a localized release of a hydrostatic pressure. Indeed, if a pressure differential does exist across the cell membrane, it cannot fail to contribute energy to an extension of the cell surface.

Movement of the Cell Surface Membrane

The occurrence of surface movement such as ruffling and blebbing raises the question of how the membrane itself moves during locomotion. By placing various small particles on the cell surface and observing their motion by light microscopy, a highly consistent pattern of surface particle transport has been observed. Particles lying on the substratum, which are encountered by a moving cell, are often picked up by the advancing cell margin and transported rearward over the dorsal surface of the cell, eventually accumulating either in the vicinity of the nucleus or at the trailing margin of the cell. Some particles remain stuck to the substratum as the cells move over them.

Since pinocytosis and phagocytosis are common at the cell margin, and since phagocytized objects also accumulate around the nucleus, it is essential to distinguish this rearward transport of particles on the cell surface from transport within the cell. Fortunately we have several grounds for being certain that the transported particles actually remain on the cell's exterior. For one thing, such particles occasionally come to lie in profile, especially in elongated cells, and also can be viewed from the side. Electron micrographs of sections have clearly shown the transported particles outside the plasmalemma. This ability to transport attached particles appears to be virtually universal among actively moving tissue cells, at least in culture. Particle transport has not been observed on a variety of fibroblastic cells, outgoing nerve axons, epithelial cells, and even macrophages and leukocytes. Particle transport is a concomitant of cell locomotion, and particles are always transported in the direction opposite that of the locomotion.

As to the mechanism for the transport of particles, three possibilities exist: (1) the surface membrane remains stationary, and the particles are transferred from point to point over the surface; (2) parts of the surface membrane, which become attached to the external object, are induced to flow inward, carrying the particles within them, while the remainder of the membrane "circulates" forward around these points; or (3) the whole cell surface membrane flows continuously backward (i.e., centripetally) with membrane material being disassembled in the central areas and reassembled at the advancing margin.

Currently, available evidence seems to support most strongly the third possibility, namely, continuous membrane assembly and flow. To account for this theory, it has been estimated that the necessary rate of membrane assembly may be more than a tenth of the total surface membrane per minute. Of course, other cells might move more slowly, and the expected rate of turnover might be less. More direct evidence in favor of the membrane-flow theory comes from experiments using concanavalin A as a surface binding marker.

If the cell membrane is continuously being reassembled in this way, it is to be expected that any newly synthesized membrane component will appear at first at the cell margin and gradually spread inward from there. There are several instances in which this pattern of surface behavior has been observed.

Contact Inhibition

If two normal cells in the monolayer make contact by their oscillating ruffles, ruffling immediately ceases in the contact region. This phenomenon is termed "contact inhibition of motility," and may be a reason why normal cells in culture do not overgrow beyond monolayers. Electron microscopic observations of the interior of isolated ruffles show the presence of a disorganized filamentous network in the cytoplasm. However, within 20 sec after contact between two ruffles, fiber bundles appear immediately under the membranes where the two ruffles are opposed. The bundles appear to become more extended during the time of ruffle contact.

On the other hand, malignant cells behave quite differently. When two malignant cells make contact by their respective ruffles, ruffling does not stop, and no contact inhibition of motility occurs. Furthermore, during the time of the ruffle contact, there is no evidence that fiber bundles form inside the ruffles. It therefore appears that the ability to form such fiber bundles inside ruffles is associated with a contact inhibition of motility and that inability to form the bundles results in loss of contact inhibition, which is characteristic of tumor cells.

It has been suggested that when the ruffles of two normal cells make contact, interactions between surface membrane components on the two ruffles lead to the transmission of some kind of signal across the membrane at the junction. The "signal" then induces a local organization of filamentous material into fiber bundles immediatly under the contacting membranes. Because there is insufficient time for new protein synthesis to be involved in fiber bundle formations, the malignant cell is then either: (1) unable to transmit signals across its ruffled membrane to the neighboring ruffle; (2) incapable of responding to the signal by organizing the fiber bundles; or (3) capable of transmitting abnormal signals that inhibit the formation of the bundles. It was recently reported that when the ruffles of normal human and malignant chicken cells were made to contact, the malignant cells failed to show internal fiber bundles, whereas the normal cells developed demonstrable fiber bundles.

Locomotion, Migration, and Chemotaxis

The cells of most tissues appear to be capable of active locomotion and migration. Cultured fibroblasts, or freshly isolated neutrophils, monocytes, or even lymphocytes, can be observed under the light microscope and by use of time lapsed cinemicrography for their movement in vitro.

The cells flatten first, and start to move on solid substrata by the fractional forces exerted by the thin outer cell margin (lamella). Some cells exert much stronger forces than others. In connection with this attraction, the cell surface undergoes several types of motion including ruffling (the repetitive upfolding of the cell margin), blebbing (the repeated herniation of the surface membrane), and particle transport (the continuous rearward or centripetal flow of marker objects on the cell surface).

Particle transport seems to reflect the continuous rearward flow of the surface membrane of both the dorsal and ventral surfaces. This would require the rapid reassembling of membranes at the leading margin and disassembly of the membrane on a more central area of the cell surface. It is suggested that this membrane flow propels the cell forward in a manner analogous to a tractor tread, except that the membrane "tread" flows rearward on both outer surfaces, while moving forward within the cell. The forces pulling the membrane inward are possibly the same as those that cause ruffling and blebbing, and might be produced by actinlike cytoplasmic filaments.

When the cell moves from one place to another (translocation), we call this movement *locomotion*. The term *random locomotion* refers to locomotion in which the axis of the moving cell is not oriented in relation to any stimulus (i.e., the cell moves around randomly without any preferred direction). *Directional locomotion* refers to cell locomotion in which direction is determined by a substance in the environment. *Chemotaxis* is a form of directional locomotion in which the direction is determined by the chemical gradient of the environment. *Chemokinesis* refers to a cellular reaction by which the speed, the frequency and the magnitude of the turns change in response to a substance in the environment. Chemokinesis may change the velocity of cells moving at random.

STRUCTURAL AND MOLECULAR BASIS FOR CELL MOTILITY

Contractile Proteins in Muscle Cells

Skeletal muscles consist of bundles of long fibers usually 10–100 μm in diameter and 2–3 cm in length (sometimes 50 cm long). Each fiber can be considered as a single cell with up to 100–200 nuclei. The plasma membrane (plasmalemma) is called the "sarcolemma," the cytoplasm is the "sarcoplasm," and the mitochondria are "sarcosomes." The muscle cell contain myofibrils, which are organized bundles of proteins (actin and myosin).

The myofibrils show repeating cross striations (dense Z-lines) with a distance of 2.5 μm. The space between two Z-lines is defined as the sarcomere, and is the basic contractile unit of muscle cell.

In the center of the sarcomere there is an intensely birefringent band called A-or anisotropic band. From both ends of the A-band to the adjacent Z-lines, there are bands which lack birefringence and are called I- or isotropic bands. The M-lines are located in the center of the A-bands, and are usually visible only with the electron microscope. Transverse sections of the sarcomere show a remarkably regular array of thick filaments, 12–16 nm in diameter and about 1.5 μm long, packed in a hexagonal array. Thin filaments, only 8 nm in diameter and about 1.0 μm long, extend from the Z-line into both outer edges of the A-band with an overlap of about 0.3 μm. They are also arranged in hexagonal fashion and extend into the area of overlap with the thick filaments. Contracted muscles show an increased length of the overlap, which indicates a sliding movement of the thick and thin filaments into each other, resulting in a shortening of the sarcomere by about 0.9 μm.

The thick filaments consist mainly of myosin; the thin filaments mainly of actin. Tropomyosin and troponin are associated with actin, α-actin is found in the Z-line, and M-protein resides in the M-lines.

The myosin molecule has a long, slender configuration (about 160 $\times$ 2 nm), and is made up of two apparently identical heavy chains in the form of an α-helix, coiled around to form a double-stranded rope. The C-terminal ends of the two chains appear to form a single rod, while the N-terminal ends join with four other smaller subunits (molecular weight 16,000–21,000) to form a pair of "heads." A short treatment with trypsin cleaves the myosin molecules into two pieces: a light meromyosin (LMM), 90 nm long, from the tail end, and a heavy meromyosin (HMM) from the head. The latter can be further split, by a longer trypsin treatment, into one S2 fragment (molecular weight about 62,000 and 40 nm long), and two S1 fragments (molecular weight about 110,000). Each of the S1 fragments corresponds to one of the two heads in HMM.

A large number of the myosin molecules (about 300 myosin molecules,

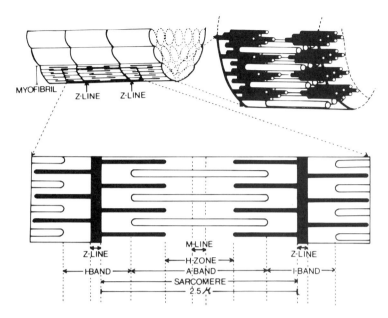

Figure 1. Schematic representation of a muscle fiber: Muscle fibers measure 10–100 microns in diameter and usually run the length of the muscle. They are comprised of many parallel, tubular elements called myofibrils, which have a diameter of 1 micron and consist of parallel thick (myosin) and thin (actin) filaments. In the two enlarged diagrams, myosin filaments are represented by thin black bars and actin filaments are the thicker white bars. The actin filaments are attached to thick, dense Z-lines which cross-striate the myofibril and divide it into units called sarcomeres. Other striations are caused by the overlapping of actin and myosin filaments and are called A-bands, I-bands, M-lines, and H-zones. The three-dimensional representation of a section of a myofibril makes evident the orderly arrangement of the actin filaments and the hexagonal array of the myosin filaments. The myosin filaments are 160 angstroms in diameter and lie a few hundred angstroms apart; thus approximately 200–300 myosin filaments are in the cross section of one myofibril. (Drawn by Penelope Kim)

or up to 30 rods) must be packed together to form a thick filament. In an electron micrograph, the heads of HMM appear to project from the thick filaments at intervals of 42 nm. Furthermore, these projected heads are not seen near the zone at the M-line, which suggests that the M-line represents the area of aggregated tail portions of myosin molecules. Another protein (the C-protein) also occurs in small amounts within the myosin filament.

When the thin filaments are dissolved in a low-ionic-strength medium containing ATP, they give rise to a soluble monomeric G-actin. Each G-actin monomer has a molecular weight of about 43,000 and contains about 374 amino acids, one molecule of bound ATP, and one Ca^{2+}. If 1 mM Mg^{2+} or 0.1 M KCl is added to this monomeric G-actin solution, a spontaneous transformation of G-actin into filaments similar to the thin filament of muscle occurs. This filamentous form of actin is called F-actin and is made up of 340–380 monomers of G-actin. In this reaction the ATP is hydrolyzed and the resulting ADP is bound to the F-actin filament as described below. This process is strikingly similar to the binding of nucleotides to microtubule subunits and to the contracting tail of bacterial phage.

Interactions of Actin and Myosin. Long before the ultrastructure of the myofibril became established, it was known that actin and myosin are responsible for the contraction of muscles. First, in 1929 ATP was recognized to be the energy source for muscle contraction. About ten years later it was shown that myosin preparation catalyzed the hydrolysis of ATP, and that a combination of actin and myosin (actomyosin) was required for Mg^{2+}-stimulated ATP hydrolysis (i.e., ATPase activity). The ATPase activity of myosin is located in the head part of the myosin molecule. The attachment of actin filaments to the heads of the myosin forms cross-bridges, which are required for induction of myosin ATPase activity. It is postulated that during contraction of muscle, the myosin heads are attached to the actin filaments. The hydrolysis of ATP, and consequently the liberation of free energy, is then utilized in some way to cause the thick and the thin filaments to be pulled past each other, resulting in the contraction of muscle fiber. The heads of myosin are then detached from actin as a consequence of the pulling, and reattached to a new location along the actin filaments. Repetition of this process is thought to cause the sliding motion of the filaments and contraction of muscle fibers.

Regulatory Proteins of Muscle Contraction. The endoplasmic reticulum of the muscle cells (sarcoplasmic reticulum) has a striking organization: it consists of interconnecting tubules that run longitudinally among the bundles of contractile fibers. At regular intervals, the tubules of the sarcoplasmic reticulum come in close contact with the enfolding of the outer cell membrane (the T-tubule system of the sarcolemma). The nerve impulses which travel along the plasmalemma reach the T-tubules. At the points of close contact, the nerve impulses are "somehow" transmitted to the sarcoplasmic reticulum, which contains a high concentration of Ca^{2+}. The arrival of nerve signals causes a sudden release of Ca^{2+} into the cytoplasm and myofibrils. The Ca^{2+} then binds to the "C-subunit" of troponin that is an oligomeric protein forming a regulatory complex with tropomyosin. In the absence of this regulatory complex the actin fibrils contract as long as the ATP is available. In the presence of the regulatory complex and in the absence of Ca^{2+}, however, the contraction and hydrolysis of ATP are blocked. Therefore, it is postulated that an elongated tropomyosin rod fits into the "grooves"

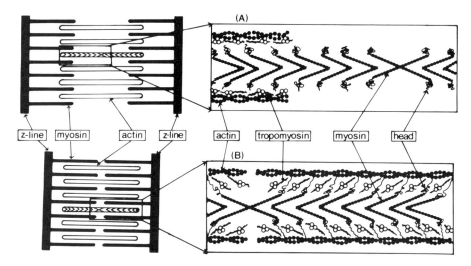

Figure 2. Schematic representation of a muscle fiber:

A. Resting muscle fiber: This enlarged representation of a relaxed muscle fiber illustrates the positions of the actin and myosin filaments, the heads of myosin molecules, and the troponin-tropomyosin complex when the concentration of calcium is $10^{-7}M$. The three-polypeptide troponin complex is represented by three adjoining circles: the three circles corresponding to TnT, TnI, and TnC. TnT is bound to the strand of tropomyosin and TnI is bound to the actin filament, thus inhibiting the heads of the myosin molecules from binding to the actin filament.

B. Contracting muscle fiber: With an increase in the calcium concentration caused by the stimulation of a muscle nerve fiber, calcium binds to TnC, causing the release of TnI from the actin filament. The tropomyosin molecule is then moved away from the actin filament, thus allowing the heads of the myosin to reach the active sites on the actin filament, which results in the sliding of the actin filaments toward the center of the sarcomere. (Drawn by Penelope Kim)

that are located between the actin and the heads of myosin. In resting muscle, the tropomyosin is bound to actin near the site where the SI portion of the myosin is to be bound. Consequently, the tropomyosin rod would block the cross-bridges between myosin and actin, and prevents actin from stimulating ATPase activity of myosin. Since one tropomyosin is about 41 nm long and contacts about seven actin subunits at one time, one troponin–tropomyosin complex would be able to control seven subunits of actin.

The troponin molecule (Tn) consists of three polypeptides (TnT, TnI, and TnC) that have masses of 18,000–37,000 daltons. The TnT binds tightly to tropomyosin about one-third of the way from the C-terminus to the N-terminus of the tropomyosin molecule. The TnI interacts with actin in the absence of Ca^{2+} and cooperates with the other two peptides to keep the tropomyosin in the proper position so that the ATPase activity of myosin is inhibited. The TnC binds Ca^{2+}, and in so doing removes the inhibition of ATPase activity and produces the contraction of myofibrils. X-ray diffraction and electron microscopy studies suggest that binding of Ca^{2+} to troponin moves the tropomyosin molecule away from SI fragments by an angle of about 20°. This movement might uncover the active site for myosin–ATP–actin interaction. The exact mechanism and the energy source for this movement have not been elucidated. Since binding of metals to a protein generally causes conformational changes in the protein molecules, it is tempting to speculate that Ca^{2+} binding may induce conformational changes in the TnC-peptides of troponin, which might be translated into the necessary energy for the movement of tropomyosin molecules.

Contractile Proteins (Cytoskeleton) in Nonmuscle Cells

Actin. Earlier studies of nonmuscle cells indicated that actin is a major component of all types of eukaryotic cells. Since 1974, actin has been purified from erythrocytes, macrophages, leukocytes and platelets, brain tissue, and cultured cells. Actin has also been purified from eggs and sperm and from the green algae amoeba.

These studies have revealed that all actins are similar in their physical and chemical properties. The nonmuscle actins have the same mobility on SDS-acrylamide gels as muscle actin, corresponding to a molecular weight of 42,000. They polymerize to form helical filaments identical in structure to those formed by muscle actin, as judged by electron microscopy. Mg^{2+} paracrystals, like those of muscle actin, have also been demonstrated in some cases. They are all able to activate Mg^{2+} ATPase.

Amino acid analysis and peptide mapping have indicated that actins from different sources are similar but not identical in structure. A partial amino acid sequence determination indicated that actins from the human heart muscle, platelets, brain, and skeletal muscle may differ by at least one amino acid, indicating that they are a product of different genes.

A variety of mammalian and avian cell lines and tissues each contain multiple actin species that differ in isoelectric points. One species (α-actin) is found primarily in differentiated striated muscle, and its synthesis is induced during myogenesis in culture. Most muscle cells have two other species predominately (β-actin and γ-actin). The γ-actin co-migrates with a chicken gizzard smooth muscle actin, and the β-actin has an isoelectric point intermediate between the other two. In the case of a rat skeletal muscle cell line, all three forms have been shown to contain N-methylhistidine.

Quantitative gel densitometry indicates that some 5–10% of the protein in nonmuscle cell is actin, yet actual recoveries of purified actin are typically 0.2% or less of total cell protein. Despite the small differences now being detected, it is clear that the basic structure of the actin molecule has been highly conserved throughout evolution.

A fraction with some properties resembling actin was isolated from *E. coli,* which contains the protein synthesis elongation factor called EF-Tu, a major *E. coli* protein. EF-Tu is similar to actin in size, solubility properties, and binding to DNAse. The amino acid compositions of EF-Tu and actins are sufficiently similar to suggest an evolutionary relationship. Monomeric (G) actin self-assembles into filamentous (F) actin at physiological ionic strength.

Myosin. Myosin has been found in most types of eukaryotic cells. The definitive characteristics of a myosin protein are ATPase activity stimulated by actin under physiological conditions and the ability to interact physically with actin. Most myosins have similar subunit structures (two heavy chains of identical molecular weight, plus two sizes of light chains) in a symmetric shape, are able to form bipolar thick filaments, and exhibit ATPase activity stimulated by EDTA in the presence of 0.6 M KCl.

Myosin has been purified and characterized from vertebrate brain and liver, macrophage, leukocyte, platelet, and several types of cultured cells. Invertebrate myosin has been isolated from echinoderm eggs and sperm, squid brain, and amoeba.

Quantitative gel densitometry and ATPase measurements suggest that myosin makes up 0.3–1.5% of the total protein in nonmuscle cells. In general, a large fraction (20–50%) of this can be recovered as purified myosin; for example, yields of 2–8 mg myosin/g total protein have been reported for several systems.

Most nonmuscle myosins closely resemble muscle myosins in structure and size according to their partition coefficient in column chromatography. Like muscle myosin, they contain two heavy chains, as judged by crosslinking experiments and physical properties. Estimated molecular weight of heavy chains ranges from 194,000 to 300,000. The mobilities of nonmuscle myosin are identical to that of muscle myosin. The high molecular weight of the myosin heavy chains makes it difficult to compare different myosins by standard peptide-mapping techniques. It is suggested that similar, but nonidentical, forms of myosin exist in nonmuscle cells, and that the variation is greater than that found among actins from different sources.

The light chains of nonmuscle myosin are similar to that of smooth muscle myosin. There are two sizes of light chains, 15,000 and 20,000 in molecular weight. A third small polypeptide was reported in brain myosin, which might be unique to nervous tissue or a tightly bound contaminant.

Nonmuscle myosins are capable of forming bipolar thick filaments in vitro, similar in structure, but usually shorter than those formed by striated muscle myosin. Vertebrate and invertebrate myosins form filaments at low ionic strength in the absence of bivalent cations. Although these filaments are typically about 0.3 μm in length, a larger filament (0.5–0.8 μm) has been reported for glial-cell myosin. Bivalent cations are not required for filament assembly by these myosins, but in certain cases they appear to affect the size or aggregation states of filaments, (e.g., aggregates up to 2.5 μm in length with 5–6 nm periodocity have been reported in purified *Physarum* myosin). Filaments up to 4 μm in length with 15 nm transverse banding have been reported. The crude myosin fraction from the amoeba *Proteus* yields filaments up to 1.5 μm in length with 14 nm transverse banding and two bare regions. A typical filament with 14 nm transverse banding is found in striated muscle myosin that has been freed of C-protein. The significance of these unusual structures is not clear; however, it is apparent that other components associated with myosin can affect filament assembly.

The enzymatic properties of the nonmuscle myosins generally resemble those of muscle myosin. The ATPase activity of the vertebrate and invertebrate myosins is activated by EDTA and to a similar but usually lesser extent by Ca^{2+}.

It is physiologically significant that myosin ATPase is activated at low ionic strength in the presence of Mg^{2+}: The ATPase activity of myosin alone is quite low under these conditions, but can be stimulated by the addition of actin by about tenfold in most vertebrate and invertebrate cells. In contrast, myosins from lower eukaryotic *Physarum* and *Dictyostellium* can be activated 20- to 40-fold by the addition of actin. On the other hand, myosin from macrophage and *Acanthamoeba* is not activated by actin except in the presence of a crude cofactor fraction.

In addition to its requirement for a cofactor, the myosin from an *Acanthamoeba* is unusual in its size and structure: a globular protein with a molecular weight of 180,000, containing one heavy chain (140,000) and two light chains (14,000 and 16,000). It cannot form filaments itself, but it does bind to actin filaments and cause them to aggregate. At the high KCl concentrations, the ATPase activity of an *Acanthamoeba* myosin is greatly stimulated by EDTA. In most cases, the only proteins sought in nonmuscle cells have been those expected by analogy with muscles. Therefore, the unusual aspect of this system leads to the speculation that other nonmuscle cells may also contain contractile elements different from those of muscle.

Control of Actin–Myosin Interactions. In striated muscles of verte-brates, our understanding of complex regulatory systems involving Ca^{2+} and proteins associated with the actin filament has been advanced greatly. For nonmuscle cells, however, the situation is not as clear. Current results indicate that both Ca^{2+} and actin-associated proteins are probably important in non-muscle systems, but the precise control mechanisms vary considerably among different types of cells.

Influenced by the well-established involvements of the Ca^{2+}-sensitive regula-tory proteins (tropomyosin–troponin) in striated muscle contraction, investigators have looked for tropomyosin and troponin-like proteins in nonmuscle cells. Tropomyosin-like proteins have been purified from human platelets, calf platelets, chicken brains, calf brains, calf pancreas, and mouse fibroblasts. All of these nonmuscle tropomyosins have a molecular weight of 30,000 in contrast to the 35,000 molecular weight of muscle tropomyosin. They form paracrystals with axial periodicity (banding) of about 34 nm, which is shorter than the 40 nm paracrystal periodicity of muscle tropomyosin, and appears to correspond to the length of molecules. The presence of tropomyosin in the cells does not necessarily establish the existence of a tropomyosin–troponin-like regulatory system. Troponin appears to be absent from mollusk muscle, and the Ca^{2+} control may be operated through a myosin-like molecule. Tropomyosin, on the other hand, is associated with the actin filaments in mollusk muscle, where it presumably serves another role, perhaps adding structural stability to actin filaments or a lowered threshold of interaction in the actin filament.

Filamins. Wang et al. in 1975 (33) reported the presence of a high-molecular-weight protein in smooth muscle, which they named filamin. Filamin, as extracted in soluble form, is a dimer of a polypeptide chain of molecular weight 250,000. It is chemically distinct from myosin, spectrin, and other common high-molecular-weight proteins, but may be the same as or similar to the actin-binding protein of macrophage reported by Stossel and Hartwig in 1975 (29) (see below).

Filamin is also present in a wide range of nonmuscle cells, as well as in smooth muscle, and can be detected by immunofluorescence. It is found on the stress fibers within cultured cells. Filamin is not found in striated muscle cells, which indicates that it is not required in actomyosin sliding mechanisms or in its control.

Pure filamin in aqueous buffered solution does not form a filamentous structure in a variety of conditions. Therefore, it is suggested that its presence on stress fibers in cells might result from its interaction with other filamentous components.

Immunofluorescence staining of myosin filament or tubulin in the same cell indicates that actin, myosin, and filamin are present in stress fibers of fibroblasts. Microtubules form a separate filamentous network as expected. In addition to the stress fiber, there is less well organized distribution of actin, myosin, and filamin in the body of the cells.

The distribution of the proteins in the cell ruffles, and in the region of cell–cell contact, showed that in these specialized regions of the cell periphery both actin and filamin are present, but myosin is greatly depleted or absent. While microtubules are found in these regions, they are few in number and are distributed and oriented irregularly.

The depletion of myosin from lesions of cell–cell contact is observed not only when relatively few contacts are made, but also when cells are in contact with other cells around much of their periphery.

Pure filamin and F-actin interact molecularly in solution to form fiber bundles and sheets. Further, filament and F-actin, but not myosin, are present in ruffles and in regions where cell–cell contact is made. Therefore, the formation of fiber bundles that occurs rapidly inside the ruffles after cell–cell contact has been made, may be due to a filamin–F-actin interaction in vivo. Nevertheless, this does not necessarily exclude other proteins that might be associated with the fiber bundles.

Actin Binding Protein (ABP).   Stossel and his colleagues have examined the contractile proteins of phagocytic cells. They have shown that actin and myosin are major components of contractile proteins in both monocytes and neutrophils. They have isolated and purified a high-molecular-weight protein called actin-binding protein (ABP), which cross-links F-actin filament bundles, and thus stoichiometrically induces the gelation of macrophage actin. The ABP is released from the membrane fraction into the soluble cytoplasm fraction during the particle ingestion by macrophages. The ABP constitutes about 1–1.2% of total protein in the cells, and has a molecular weight of about 270,000. It forms hollow coils of 12 nm diameter, does not have ATPase activity, and binds to macrophage actin but not to myosin. It cross-links F-actin into filamentous bundles, and causes gelation of actin in the absence of KCl or in the presence of EDTA.

Cofactors.   Stossel and coworkers have identified an unstable protein called "cofactor" in phagocytic cells. This factor stimulates the Mg^{2+}-ATPase activity of actomyosin in macrophages up to 22-fold. In the presence of Mg^{2+} and ATP, it increases the rate of contraction of gel derived from myosin-ABP combinations.

The cofactor has a molecular weight of about 70,000–90,000 and may be unique to the contractile proteins of phagocytic cells, together with ABP.

Desmin.   In addition to actin filaments and microtubules, the cytoplasm of many higher eukaryotic cells contains a third class of filaments, which are characteristically 100 Å in diameter when viewed in the electron microscope, and are consequently called 100 Å filaments. These filaments are present in such diverse cell types as fibroblasts, epithelial cells, skeletal muscle, cardiac muscle, smooth muscle, nerve cells, and endothelial cells. This class of filaments has recently attracted much experimental attention, but is still the least well understood of the three classes of cytoplasmic filaments.

One of the most characteristic morphologic features of the 100 Å filaments is their intimate association in a variety of cell types with desmosomes—hence the name desmin.

In the cytoplasm of smooth muscle cells, 100 Å filaments characteristically insert together with actin filaments into the Z-like dense bodies both within the cytoplasm and at the plasma membrane. Similarly, in the cytoplasm of skeletal and cardiac muscle cells, 100 Å filaments are frequently seen in close association with the Z-line and with intercalated discs in the area where the actin filaments of the terminal sarcomele insert into the plasma membrane. The close association into actin and 100 Å filament in the dense bodies and the Z-lines of smooth, cardiac, and skeletal muscle cells suggests that the major components of these filaments might interact at these cytoplasmic cell membrane sites.

To isolate and characterize the 100 Å filaments (desmin), Lazarides in 1976 (18) made use of the observation that in smooth muscle (chicken gizzard) 100 Å filaments are insoluble in salt concentrations that render the majority of actin, myosin, and tropomyosin soluble. The insoluble residue still contains a considerable amount of actin and a few high-molecular-weight proteins including a small amount of myosin, and is enriched in a new protein (desmin) that has an electrophoretic mobility corresponding to a molecular weight of about 50,000, a value that agrees closely with the molecular weight of the major components of the 100 Å filament obtained by other workers.

On the basis of strong association of actin to desmin and immunofluorescence localization of desmin, it is believed that in smooth, skeletal, and cardiac muscle, desmin filaments and/or their protein subunits may mediate the attachment of actin filament to specialized areas of plasma membranes. It is envisioned that desmin or desmin filaments function in the cytoplasm of a muscle cell as a matrix that connects individual myofibrils to one another and to a plasma membrane at Z-lines. Such an interconnecting matrix may provide tensile strength to the muscle and ensure that all of the myofibrils are mechanically integrated during the contraction and relaxation of muscles.

Spectrin. Spectrin is one of the extrinsic membrane proteins of red blood cells, and can be removed from red blood cell ghosts by simply immersing the membranes in low-ionic-strength buffers containing chelating agents. Marchesi and Steer extracted spectrin by use of ATP and β-mercaptoethanol based on the idea that spectrin might be an actin-like protein. The earlier preparation of spectrin was relatively crude, partly because of a technical problem, and partly because of the intrinsic properties of spectrin, that is, its extraordinary sensitivity to proteolytic degradation and its large size (molecular weight 225,000–250,000).

Although the spectrin polypeptides are easily extracted from red blood cell ghosts and are apparently soluble in distilled water, they have a remarkable capacity to aggregate in the presence of Ca^{2+} and other metals. Spectrin polymers bear some striking resemblances to the large-molecular-weight polypeptides of muscle myosin, which led to a hypothesis that spectrin may interact with actin or actinlike proteins in the red cells to form contractile apparatus for the membrane. Such a macromolecular complex may function in some way for the maintenance of the red cell shape. Further evidence for this assumption is provided by recent studies on the remarkable capacity of camel red blood cells to maintain their ellipsoid shape in the face of osmotic adversity. Such red cells have prominent spectrin polypeptides that are much more tightly bound to the cell membrane than in other species. The camel red cells change shape when the spectrin is removed.

Although many investigators suggested that spectrin polymers might function as actomyosin-like cytoskeleton in red cells, the first direct evidence for the association between spectrin and myosin was provided by the finding that antibodies directed against smooth muscle myosin cross-reacted with human spectrin. This indicates the immunologic identity of spectrin with myosin. The idea that spectrin and actin do form a complex on the inner surfaces of red cells is a most attractive one, and needs further experimental verification.

Microtubules

Microtubules were first described in 1954 as ultrastructural elements of "9 + 2" fibers in cilia. Since then, the advent of glutaraldehyde fixation has facilitated the recognition of this structure in a variety of animal and plant cells.

Each of the nine fibers consist of one complete 24-nm-diameter tubule (A-tubule) and one partial tubule of approximately the same diameter (B-subfiber) attached longitudinally to the A-tubule. These nine tubules form a cylinder (about 200 nm in diameter), with the A-tubule of each doublet toward the center so that the entire doublet is skewed by about 10° with respect to the cylindrical axoneme. At the two points diametrically opposite to those where the B-subfiber joins the A-tubule, arms are found attached to this tubule and directed toward the B-subfiber of the adjacent doublet.

The direction of the arms and the skewed nature of the doublets always appear clockwise when the cilium or flagellum is viewed from the base toward the tip. The arms consist of dynein, a protein with ATPase activity. They are responsible for movement of cilia and flagella. The paired dynein arms are disposed at 24-nm intervals along the A-tubule and generate motion through interaction with B-subfiber of the adjacent doublet via some ATP-specific cyclic interaction.

A sliding-filament mechanism appears to explain the ciliary movement;

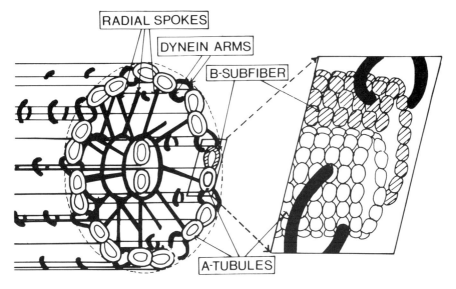

Figure 3. Schematic representation of a microtubule: Cross section of a microtubule reveals the "9 + 2" organization of the fibers. Nine doublets, each consisting of a cylindrical A-tubule and a partially cylindrical B-subfiber, are connected by dynein arms to form an axoneme. In the center of the axoneme are two singlet tubules which are connected to the nine outer tubules by radial spokes, which encompass the singlet microtubules. Both the dynein arms and the radial spokes are disposed at intervals of 24 nm along the A-tubules. Although not evident in the diagram on the left, the structure of the A-tubule and the B-subfiber is actually that of parallel tubulin filaments, which run along the axoneme. Thirteen and eleven filaments compose the A-tubule and the B-subfiber, respectively. The filaments are not aligned evenly along the axis of the doublet, rather they are displaced from each other by angles of 10 degrees, thus forming a helix with thirteen or eleven tubulin molecules in one turn of the helix. (Drawn by Penelope Kim)

when the linkage and spoke material are selectively disrupted by gentle tryptic digestion of demembranated sea urchin sperm axonemes, and ATP is then added, the sliding of individual doublets can be seen in dark-field microscopic examination as the axoneme is elongated to several times its original length.

The central pair consists of two singlet microtubules in the center of the axoneme and is connected to the outer fibers via radial spokes. Gill cilia beat in a direction perpendicular to a plane intersecting the central pair, and cilia sweep back counterclockwise, when viewed from above, in their recovery stroke after an effective power stroke. Thus, cilia can propagate a receiving stroke in either clockwise or counterclockwise directions and, therefore, this phenomenon is probably not a direct result of the constant enantiomorphic nature of the 9 + 2 pattern.

A stable microtubule of cilia is thought to be an integral part of the permanent motile structure, such as flagella. Labile microtubules are often found in the cytoplasm in which motion is taking place (e.g., in the pseudopodia of the amoeba). The mitotic spindle (another example of labile microtubules) consists of a series of microtubules that appear to function in the movement of chromosomes in a dividing cell. Microtubules are also found in the cleavage planes of plant cells during division.

Microtubules are found in the long axons of nerve cells and are believed to function in the fast transport of proteins and other materials from the cell body to the axons. Microtubules of unknown function are also found in many sensory cells. Recently, microtubules have been demonstrated throughout the cytoplasm of a variety of cells by use of an improved method. It is thought that motion in microtubular systems depends upon cooperation with other proteins. Thus, the arms of the microtubules of cilia catalyze the hydrolysis of ATP, and in this respect resemble the muscle myosin. Motion of cilia probably results from the sliding of the microtubule in a manner similar to that in muscles.

Microtubules are made of tubulins, mixed dimers (a and b) of two closely related subunits (molecular weight 60,000 each), together with smaller amounts of higher-molecular-weight proteins. The microtubule itself can be thought of as a series of parallel filaments formed by the end-to-end aggregation of tubulin molecules. Each tubulin dimer binds one molecule of guanosine triphosphate (GTP) strongly, and a second molecule more loosely. Although tubulin resembles actin in terms of the subunit size, there is little similarity between the two proteins in amino acid sequence.

It is commonly held that the labile microtubules of the cytoplasm are in a dynamic equilibrium with monomer or dimer units. Thus, the tubules can grow or be disassembled, depending upon metabolic conditions. GTP appears to be required for the microtubule assembly, and it is possible that the hydrolysis of this nucleotide triphosphate provides an essential step. Recent reports of phosphorylation of microtubular proteins suggests that the picture may be even more complex. Of special interest is the reaction of microtubules with colchicine. This compound is tightly bound to tubulin via its tropolone ring system. The striking result of this binding within living cells is the blocking of the assembly of labile microtubules including the mitotic spindles. Dividing cells, treated with colchicine, appears to be blocked at metaphase. This discovery has led to the widespread use of colchicine in inducing formation of tetraploid varieties of flowering plants. Similar effects upon microtubules are produced by antitumor agents such as Vincristine and Vinblastine.

Microtubule-Associate Proteins (MAPs).   When microtubules are purified by in vitro assembly and centrifugation, they carry with them a number of proteins called MAPs. These MAPs amount to between 5 and 20% of total proteins and form a set of bands corresponding to a high molecular weight on SDS gel analysis. MAPs were initially thought to be contaminants that somehow attached to assembled microtubules. However, indirect evidence accumulated by many laboratories indicates that the MAPs may play an important role in the assembly of microtubules. Furthermore, recent reports indicate that trace amounts of MAPs, not detectable on SDS gel analysis, can significantly affect microtubule assembly. It was suggested that the best criterion for purity of the isolated tubulin may be the absence of microtubule assembly even at the highest concentration of isolated tubulin.

Permanent Motile Structure in Nonmuscle Cells

Bacterial Flagella. The smallest organs of propulsion are the bacterial flagella, which are composed of only one kind of protein, flagellin. Flagellin molecules contain no cysteine or tryptophan and usually little phenylalanine, proline, or histidine. They have a high content of hydrophobic amino acid and contain one residue of the unusual ϵ-N-methyllysine. The subunits are arranged in a helix in which they also form 11 nearly longitudinal rows. A structural feature that cannot be explained by a simple helical stratum or subunit is the supercoil, with pitch about 2.3 μm. This feature appears to be essential for motility, since mutant bacteria with straight flagella are non-motile.

The supercoiled structure is presumed to be derived from a conformational difference, with altered dimension in the subunit of one longitudinal role. The individual flagella are too small to be seen with a light microscope, and it is difficult to obtain an electron micrograph of a functional flagellum. Since all of the flagellum subunits are identical, it might be possible to induce a cyclic contraction of one longitudinal role after another around the tubule, leading to the propagation of a helical wave. Despite the attractiveness of this idea, various experiments suggest that the flagellum is probably a rigid "propeller" that is rotated by a motor at the base. Some of the evidence comes from the observation that a bacterium linked artifically (by means of antibodies) to a flagellum of another bacterium can be rotated by a second bacterium.

Although it is impossible to see individual flagella on live bacteria, bundles of flagella can be viewed by dark-field light microscopy. Normal flagella appear to have a left-handed helical form, but curly flagella form a right-handed helix. Normal bacteria swim in straight lines, but periodically "tumble" before swimming in a new random direction. This behavior is part of the system of chemotaxis by which the organism moves toward a food supply. Curly mutants tumble continuously. It is suggested that when bacteria tumble, the flagella change from normal to curly. The pitch is reversed and shortened. A proposed mechanism for the change of pitch involves propagation of conformational change down additional roles of flagellin subunits.

Electron microscopy reveals a "hook" attached to a rod that passes through the cell wall and is in turn attached to a thin disc, the M-ring, embedded in the cytoplasmic membrane. The torque is thought to be generated between the M-ring and the S-ring, which is mounted on the cell wall. There is as yet no evidence for muscle-type proteins in the motor.

Cilia. The term cilia refers to eukaryotic flagella and most sperm tails. The ciliary axoneme is actually a complicated, isolated extension of the cytoplasm surrounded by a specialized continuation of the cell membrane. In contrast to the bacterial flagellum, where the long protein "wire" comprising the major portion of the organelle may be considered a passive structure, the axoneme in cilia produces the force to propel surrounding fluid or cause cell locomotion.

Cilia and sperm tails have the same axonemal elements (microtubules and thin appendages). Presence of the ciliary membrane allows the cell to control the axonemal environment in an exact way and influences ciliary movement and cell behavior. The formation of the wave, the direction of ciliary beat, and bend propagation along the axoneme appear to be controlled by the cells in some instances. All of these controls appear to be mediated by a common mechanism, membrane depolarization, followed by an increased Ca^{2+} concentration in cytoplasm. However, under normal conditions, cilia are continuously beating despite low concentrations of intracellular Ca^{2+}. We do not know how the Ca^{2+} alters beating of cilia.

PHYSIOLOGY AND PATHOLOGY OF CELL MOTILITY

Unicellular organisms such as the amoeba are not the only cells that can move around. In higher organisms including man, many types of cells are capable of migration, locomotion, and changing their shape. Obviously, the individual cells must have necessary mechanisms that enable them to do this. The nature of the machinery is not obvious in those cells that do not possess cilia or other appendages, as it is in skeletal muscle, which engages in locomotion or shape-altering movements. The subject is of much practical interest, since cell movement plays a crucial role in embryogenesis and other vital functions of cells. Furthermore, abnormality in cell motility may be a critical factor in certain disease conditions (see below).

When a single cell of certain tissue is isolated and placed in a culture medium, the cell can be seen to wander about over the bottom of the culture dish. Studying such movement has revealed that the moving cell thrusts the forward edge of its membrane ahead; as the thrust occurs, the advancing edge appears to flutter up and down. The undulating, advancing part of the membrane attaches itself to the substratum and apparently contracts to draw the cell body forward. The cell can readily change the direction of its travel by activating a different part of its perimeters; the side that has been moving forward becomes quiescent, and the newly activated side begins to flutter and extend itself, drawing the cell toward the new direction.

A related kind of movement is involed in the alteration of the shape of the cells that make up certain tissues. Usually a cell in a tissue remains in a fixed position in relation to its neighbors; nevertheless, it can change in shape by elongation or by a widening or narrowing of some part of its cell body, apparently through a process of contraction. When such a narrowing or elongation takes place, the tissue itself assumes a new configuration; a flat sheet, for example may be converted into a ball-like, hollow structure. This is the process that forms organs such as the lungs and the pancreas during the development of an embryo.

What kind of system could account for the cell's ability to elongate in the active movement? In strict biological terms, let's look at the basic features of the machinery for movements of an animal as a whole. Broadly speaking, this system has two principal components: the skeleton, which contributes rigidity to the shape of the animal and support of the body or its appendage; and the muscle, which provides the mechanical energy that moves the skeleton and thus the organism itself. Similarly, the individual cells possess analogous structures, which apparently account for the two very different types of movement discussed above—locomotion and change of shape, and also for a third kind of movement within the cell, the action of mitotic spindles in pulling the chromosomes apart when a cell divides.

The two basic components of the machinery for movement of cells are microtubules, which may be considered as a skeleton, and microfilaments, which may correspond to the myofibrils in muscle cells.

The Role of Actin and Myosin in Structure and Motility of Nonmuscle Cells

The contractile proteins (actin, myosin, and cofactor) from nonmuscle cells have been partially characterized. The actin from the nonmuscle cells is similar to muscle actin, although its amino acid sequence and some quantitative aspects of interaction with myosin are distinctive. Several features of its polymerization have also been found to be unusual. The myosin from *Acanthamoeba* is extraordinary among myosins in that its native form has a mass of less than 200,000 daltons. It is a soluble, globular protein, without a tail, consisting of a single heavy chain and two light chains. However, in its ATPase activity and ability to bind reversibly to actin filaments it is similar to muscle myosin. A third protein, termed cofactor, is required for actin to stimulate the Mg^{2+} ATPase activity of *Acanthamoeba* myosin, for example. The cofactor appears to be a protein composed of a single polypeptide chain with a mass of about 95,000 daltons. In addition to these identified contractile proteins, there may be associated proteins such as the actin-binding protein, as described above. Platelet myosin appears to be a large, symmetrical molecule, with a mass of about 500,000 daltons, comprised of two heavy chains and two sizes of light chains. The myosin constitutes only about 1% of platelet protein, but it can now be isolated in a highly purified form. Like muscle myosin, platelet myosin has a fibrous tail and a globular head. The light chains, which are associated with the head, have the actin-binding and ATPase activities. The tail of the platelet myosin is thought to be a broad-shaped α-helical coil about 150 nm long. Antibodies prepared against native human platelet myosins react with the tail, but not with the head, of the platelet myosin molecules. Further studies indicate that antibodies against cytoplasmic myosin may be species-specific. Serological analysis has established that human platelet myosin has antigenic specificities (and presumably amino acid sequences) different from human striated muscle myosin. The platelet myosin filaments are very small in comparison to the thick filaments formed from skeletal muscle myosin.

The most important common feature is the bipolar symmetry of the myosin filaments. The bipolar arrangement of myosin molecules is essential for sliding of actin filaments toward the center of the sarcomere in the striated muscle, and it may have a similar significance in nonmuscle cells. The second common feature is the packing of myosin molecules at 14.5-nm intervals in the core of the filaments. Intermolecular binding patterns in various myosin filaments are sufficiently similar to allow platelet myosin and smooth muscle myosin to copolymerize with skeletal muscle myosin. A final feature common to the different myosin filaments is the loose attachment of the head to the filament backbone. This flexibility is probably important for the efficient inter-action of myosin active site with actin filaments.

The variations in size of myosin filaments appear to reflect the functional requirements in each cell type. To generate large forces, striated muscles must have a large number of myosin cross-bridges interacting with each actin filament, hence large myosin filaments with hundreds of cross-bridges. In contrast, the force needed for cell movement is relatively small so that each force-generating unit can be small.

Keeping the myosin filaments relatively small, like the platelet myosin filaments, would at least have the advantage of increasing the diffusibility of these "motors" through the cytoplasm and maximizing the number of separated force-generating units formed from the available subunits.

Myosin filaments have not been regularly demonstrated in nonmuscle cells of vertebrates. There are three possible explanations for these observations: (1) myosin is not assembled into filaments within cells; (2) myosin filaments are present in vivo, but are destroyed during the preparation of cells for electron microscopy; (3) myosin filaments are present but not easily detected in electron micrographs of fixed, embedded cells. The filaments formed in vitro by vertebrate cytoplasmic myosin are short and thin. When the 10-nm-wide platelet myosin filaments are dehydrated during preparation for electron microscopy, they shrink laterally about 15%, thus being only 8–9 nm wide in embedded preparations. Consequently, these myosin filaments could be confused in situ with the 5–8-nm-wide actin filaments, which are much more numerous. Immunofluorescence studies using antibodies against platelet myosin showed that distribution of myosin inside the cell changed extensively during the cell cycle, with corresponding changes in actin distribution. This is particularly true for cytokinesis. Evidence exists for involvement of actin filaments in the contractile ring, and it may be that the contractile ring develops sufficient force to account for the furrowing. Myosin has also been identified in the cleavage furrow, which indicates that contractile protein develops the forces for its vital movement. However, demonstrating the presence of these contractile molecules in the spindle region of fixed cells does not prove that they are truly spindle components or that they are essential for active mitotic movements.

The Role of Contractile Proteins in Endocytosis

The term *phagocytosis* refers to the incorporation of relatively large, solid particles in the cells. The term *pinocytosis* literally means "drinking" and refers to the uptake of fluid. Both phagocytosis and pinocytosis require internalization of plasma membranes and are, therefore, called *endocytosis*. When the cells put out the digested or denatured material, that is called *exocytosis*. As Metchnikoff proposed some 80 years ago, phagocytic activity is an essential means for primitive cells like amoeba to obtain nutrition from the environment. Phagocytic activity appears to be the major function of neutrophils and monocytes in vertebrates and constitute a major component of the host defense system. However, many other cell types do retain phagocytic ability in varying degrees; for example, lymphocytes, fibroblasts, thyroid cells, and many other cells exhibit phagocytic activity under different conditions.

Observation of the ingestion process with the light microscope revealed that pseudopodia appeared at the point of cell–particle contact and flowed around the particle to enclose it. The pseudopodia were described as gelatinous. They were continuous with the peripheral hyaline ectoplasm of the cell, and refractile intracellular bodies appeared to be excluded from the pseudopodia. More recent studies utilizing transmission or scanning electron microscopy have shown that the pseudopodia become flattened as they flow about the particle, and they are composed of networks of interdigitating filaments. The concentration of filaments in the motile pseudopodia and the demonstration that some of these filaments are bound (HMM) indicate that the contractile proteins generate the mechanical forces for endocytosis.

It is speculated that the contact of an ingestible particle with the plasma-lemma could effect release of the actin binding protein (ABP) from the sites on the membrane. The activated or released ABP could initiate a cooperative interaction with G-actin and myosin + cofactor to effect localized gelation of the cytosol. Contraction of the cytoplasmic gel attached to the plasma membrane would create the flat, narrow hyaline pseudopods that embrace the particle. The crosslinking of actin filaments permits myosin to produce net movements of actin filaments without elaborate mechanical arrangements or restriction on the polarity on the actin filaments. It is believed that an explanation for localized, reversible assembly of actin filaments is as vital to the ingestion process as is a mechanism for the movement of these filaments.

The Role of Contractile Proteins in Membrane Function

Cell movement, change in cell shape, and intracellular translocation of vesicles have been assumed to be related to membrane-associated microtubules and/or microfilaments; additional examples are cilia and flagella action, amoeboid movement, endocytosis and exocytosis, secretion of neurotransmitters, and cytokinesis. A further example is the recently recognized phenomenon of movements of intrinsic membrane protein that are certainly affected by agents thought to be specific proteins of microtubules and microfilaments. It may be that the cytoskeletal elements of the cell play a role in transmitting signals from the cell surface to the nucleus. For example, the effects of mitogenic lectins that act on the cell surface may stimulate mitosis via microtubules and/or microfilaments.

Morphological observations indicate that microfilaments are actins, because of their interaction with muscle HMM, and their underlying and close proximity to the plasma membrane of many cells. The general localization of microfilaments under the plasma membrane is greatly enhanced at regions where a phagocytic vesicle is being formed, and one can observe a change in orientation with, for example, filaments that normally lie parallel to a surface assuming an orientation perpendicular to that surface. Immediately upon formation of phagocytic vesicles, the surrounding microfilaments are lost, so that the filament–membrane association, if real, must be capable of rapid dissociation. Morphological data are limited by the resolution of the microscope and the uncertainties of the preparative methods; microscopy alone cannot prove the attachment of contractile proteins to membranes.

Co-isolation of membranes and microfilaments indicates that highly purified plasma membranes from almost any mammalian or amoeboid cell contain a large concentration of associated microfilaments. These can be observed by electron miscroscopy and can be detected by gel electrophoresis. In several instances, the filaments have been further characterized by decoration with HMM and by their removal under conditions that polymerized actin filaments.

Actin, myosin, and/or related proteins have been detected in membrane preparations that, at least without special treatment, contain no discernible filaments. Actin can be isolated in and isolated from rat brain synaptic membranes and human erythrocytes. These observations demonstrate "motility proteins" in close association with, or as an integral part of, membranes. The erythrocyte, although containing actin, seems not to contain myosin. Instead, it contains spectrin, which may be considered a myosin-like protein. The cytoplasmic surface of the erythrocyte is coated with an amorphous layer (largely spectrin) that seems to assume a fibrous character only after the actin component of the membrane is induced to form a microfilament by the addition of heavy meromyosin.

A number of ligands will induce patching of membrane receptors followed by capping at one pole of the cell. Patching is independent of cell metabolism and occurs at low temperatures, whereas capping is metabolically dependent. Both patching and capping phenomena are modulated by colchicine and cytochalasin B. In B lymphocytes, microtubules are few and difficult to localize but it is believed that the capping region of the plasma membrane may be the site for microtubule polymerization. It is most likely that a complex interaction may take place between microfilaments, microtubules, and intrinsic membrane proteins at these sites.

The Role of Contractile Proteins in Cell Locomotion

Knowledge of the involvement of myosin and actin in the active movement of nonmuscle cells is fragmentary, but can be summarized as follows:

1. Nonmuscle myosins have ATPase activity, which by itself is low under physiologic conditions, but which can be activated by actin filaments. This reaction in muscle systems has been studied in great detail, which indicates that a cyclic reaction of myosin with ATP and actin generates the contractile forces. Since it is possible to substitute muscle actin for nonmuscle actin in the study of steady-state kinetics, it may be assumed that the molecular details of the reaction may be similar in muscle and nonmuscle cells. An important difference is that some nonmuscle myosins required the presence

of an activator, called cofactor, for the cyclic interaction with actin and ATP.

2. Cytoplasmic myosin can crosslink actin filaments. Most of the cytoplasmic myosin forms bipolar filaments so that when they bind in actin filaments at either end, the complex would have the same physical relation as the muscle sarcomere. This structural similarity indicates that the molecular basis for the force-generating structure may be the same in both nonmuscle cells and muscle cells.

3. Myosin has now been identified at the cytokinetic contractile ring, which indicates further evidence for direct involvement of contractile protein in cell movement.

4. Myosin is required for contraction of reconstituted motile proteins in vitro. More extensive enzymatic studies and localization of myosin at the ultrastructural level will be needed in addition to continued work with model motile systems in vitro.

SUMMARY AND PERSPECTIVES

Knowledge of the widespread presence of actin and myosin and other contractile proteins in nonmuscle cells and the recent advances in our understanding of muscle contraction have set a new stage for our investigation into the role of contractile proteins in the functions of cells at the molecular level.

Ultrastructural studies have shown that the organization of the contractile machinery in the nonmuscle cell is in a dynamic state, varying according to the temporal needs of the cell. Further studies will better elucidate the precise location and organization of specific contractile proteins in cells, which will be crucial for understanding how these contractile proteins function to produce cell motility.

The biochemical basis of cell motility or cell shape determination is far from complete. It is desirable to complete the systematic identification and purification of each component of cytoskeletal proteins, and reconstitute them in vitro into functional supramolecular assemblies. This process has begun for the actomyosin contractile system. Where actin has been purified to homogeneity, the purification procedure has always involved selective methods that depend on its ability to interact with myosin or its ability to polymerize, and yields of actin have been generally low. Mammalian and avian cells are now known to contain multiple species of actin, and it is necessary to separate these species and examine them for functional differences. Other unsolved questions regarding actin include the role of bound nucleotides, the anchoring of actin to the membrane, regulation of the G-actin–F-actin equilibrium, and control of the formation of higher-order supramolecular assemblies. Furthermore, it will be important to determine the total number of actin genes and the transcriptional and translational control of the synthesis of various actin species. The same types of questions pertain to nonmuscle myosins; they deal with the nature and stoichiometry of the myosin subunits, the role of the light chains, the occurrence and significance of multiple species of myosin, the role of bipolar filaments for force transduction, and the role of phosphorylation.

Although actin, myosin, and, in some cases, tropomyosin have been found in nonmuscle cells, many other related proteins have undoubtedly escaped detection. The identification of these unknown components would be facilitated by the study of mutants, and the "experiment of nature" (i.e., the patients with unusual diseases).

Progress in understanding the biochemistry of contractility has been impeded by the lack of specific assays for the purification of individual contractile elements. Assays that measure properties, such as the extent of actin activation of myosin ATPase, viscosity, and sedimentation rate, should be adapted for purifying proteins that affect the actin–myosin or actin–actin interaction. Quantitative electron microscopy can be utilized to assay for factors that affect the formation of specific supramolecular assemblies.

Although there is strong suggestive evidence for the involvement of actin and myosin in several nonmuscle contractile processes, the fundamental role of actin or myosin has yet to be demonstrated directly. Nevertheless, a uniform and consistent picture is beginning to emerge. It appears that the various forms of cell movement, including the healing of wounds, in the migration of embryonic cells, the migration of certain cells in adult organisms, cell division, mitosis, the shaping of cells, locomotion, and transmembrane control of cell function, are all produced by a common mechanism—the system of contractile filaments. Elucidation of the exact mechanism by which these contractile proteins interact and delineate the control mechanism will surely provide us with a new insight into the workings of living cells.

ACKNOWLEDGMENT

In response to editorial guidelines, only selected references have been listed. Consequently, proper recognition and credit have not been given in detail to the original works contributed by many investigators, for which omission the author expresses his apology.

Preparation of this review and some of the work from the author's laboratory were supported in part by grants from the National Institute of Health, grant #HL-19628-02, BRS grant #RR 05493; the Periodontal Disease Research Center, grant #DE04898, N.I.H. grant #CA-24215; and the National Dairy Counsel, #2767.

REFERENCES (Selected)

1. Abercrombie, M. 1961. The basis of the locomotory behaviour of fibroblasts. *Exp. Cell Res.* 8s:188–98.
2. Abercrombie, M., Heaysman, J. E. M., and Pergram, S. M. 1970. The locomotion of fibroblasts in culture. I. Movement of the leading edge. *Exp. Cell Res.* 59:393–98.
3. Abercrombie, M., Heaysman, J. E. M., Pergram, S. M. 1970. The locomotion of fibroblasts in culture. II. Ruffling. *Exp. Cell Res.* 60:437–44.
4. Altman, P. L., and Katz, D. D., eds. 1977. *Biological Handbooks. I. Cell Biology*, pp. 34–58. Fed. Am. Soc. Exp. Biol., Bethesda, Maryland.
5. Boxer, L. A., Hedley-Whyte, E. T., and Stossel, T. P. 1974. Neutrophil actin dysfunction and abnormal neutrophil behavior. *N. Engl. J. Med.* 291:1093–99.
6. Bray, D. 1977. Actin and myosin in neurones: A first review. *Biochemistry* 59:1–6.
7. Clark, M., et al. 1977. Non-muscle contractile proteins: The role of actin and myosin in cell motility and shape determination. *Ann. Rev. Biochem.* 46:797–822.
8. Curtis, A. G. S. 1967. *The Cell Surface: Its Molecular Role in Morphogenesis*. Academic Press, New York.
9. Edelman, G. M. 1976. Surface modulation in cell recognition and cell growth. *Science* 192:218–26.
10. Eliasson, R., Mossberg, B., Camner, P., and Afzelius, B. A. 1977. The immotilecilia syndrome. A congential ciliary abnormality as an etiologic factor in chronic airway infections and male sterility. *N. Engl. J. Med.* 297:1–6.
11. Goldman, R. D. 1975. The use of heavy meromyosin binding as an ultrastructural cytochemical method for locating and determining the possible functions of actin-like microfilaments in non-muscle cells. *J. Histochem. Cytochem.* 23:529–42.
12. Goldman, R., Pollard, T., and Rosenbaum, J., eds. 1976. *Cell Motility*. Book A, B, C, p. 1373. Cold Spring Harbor Laboratory.
13. Harris, A. 1969. Initiation and propagation of the ruffle in fibroblast locomotion. *J. Cell. Biol.* 43:165a–66a.
14. Heaysman, J. E. M., and Pergram, S. M. 1973. Early contacts between normal fibroblasts and mouse sarcoma cells. *Exp. Cell Res.* 78:479–81.
15. Heaysman, J. E. M., and Pergram, S. M. 1973. Early contacts between fibroblasts. An ultrastructural study. *Exp. Cell Res.* 78:71–78.
16. Ingram, V. M. 1969. A side view of moving fibroblasts. *Nature* 222:641–44.
17. Lazarides, E., and Hubbard, B. D. 1976. Immunological characterization of the subunit of the 100 Å filaments from muscle cells. *Proc. Natl. Acad. Sci.* 73:4344–48.
18. Marchesi, V. T., and Futhmayer, H. 1976. The red cell membrane. *Ann. Rev. Biochem.* 45:667–98.
19. Owen, M., Auger, J., Barber, B. H., Edwards, A. J., Walsh, F. S., and Crumpton, M. J. 1978. Actin may be present on the lymphocyte surface. *Proc. Natl. Acad. Sci.* 75:4481–88.
20. Park, B. H., Dolen, J., and Snyder, B. 1977. Defective chemotactic migration of polymorphonuclear leukocytes in patients with Pelger-Huet Anomaly. *Proc. Soc. Exp. Biol. Med.* 155:51–54.
21. Pollard, T. D. and Weihing, R. R. 1974. Actin and myosin and cell movement. *CRC Crit. Rev. Biochem.* 2:1–65.
22. Porter, K. R. 1966. Cytoplasmic microtubules and their function. In *CIBA Foundation Symposium—Principles of Biomolecular Organization*, G. E. W. Wolsteholme and M. O'Connor, eds., pp. 308–45. Churchill, London.
23. Salisbury, J. L., and Floyd, G. L. 1978. Calcium-induced contraction of the rhizoplast of a quadriflagellate green algae. *Science* 202:975–77.

24. Snyder, J., and McIntosh, J. R. 1976. Biochemistry and physiology of microtubules. *Ann. Rev. Biochem.* 45:699.

25. Soifer, D. ed., 1975. The biology of cytoplasmic tubules. *Ann. N.Y. Acad. Sci.* 253:1–848.

26. Squire, J. M. 1975. Muscle filament structure and muscle contraction. *Ann. Rev. Biophys. Bioeng.* 4:137–63.

27. Stephens, R. E., and Edds, K. T. 1977. Microtubules: Structure, chemistry and function. *Phys. Rev.* 50:709–77.

28. Stossel, T. P., and Hartwig, J. H. 1975. Interactions between actin, myosin and actin binding protein from rabbit alveolar macrophages. *J. Biol. Chem.* 250:5706–12.

29. Stossel, T. P., et al. 1976. Interactions of actin, myosin and a new actin-binding protein of rabbit pulmonary macrophages. II. Role in cytoplasmic movement and phagocytosis. *J. Cell Biol.* 68:602–12.

30. Sundqvist, K. G., and Ehrnst, A. 1976. Cytoskeletal control of surface membrane mobility. *Nature* 264:226–31.

31. Taylor, E. W. 1972. Chemistry of muscle contraction. *Ann. Rev. Biochem.* 41:577–616.

32. Wang, K., Ash, J. F., and Singer, S. J. 1975. Filamin, a new high-molecular weight protein found in smooth muscle and non-muscle cells. *Proc. Natl. Acad. Sci.* 72:4483–86.

2.5. Cell-Cell Interactions

Fritz Sieber

In this chapter the term "cell–cell interaction" will be reserved for processes that take place when cells are either in direct contact with each other or only very short distances apart. It will accordingly include events that might involve the short-range exchange of soluble material, but not interactions via circulating humoral factors. Because an adequate coverage of the vast literature on cell–cell interactions is far beyond the scope of this chapter, only a few selected references will be listed at the beginning of sections. Most references are comprehensive reviews that will not only direct the reader to the pertinent original literature but also acquaint him with aspects of cell–cell interactions that are not discussed in this review.

Communications between two neighboring cells can be effected by different means: (1) Cells may interact directly via specific surface molecules. (2) The membrane can transduce a signal it received on its outer surface via a second messenger (e.g., an elevation of cellular cyclic adenosine monophosphate or a change in the intracellular concentration of an ion). (3) The communication may be mediated by the extracellular matrix. (4) Cytoplasmic molecules may be exchanged via vesicles or across specialized junctions.

Cell–cell interactions have been implicated or actually demonstrated to occur in a number of biological events such as fertilization, morphogenetic movements during embryogenesis, embryonic induction, tissue organization and maintenance, metabolic cooperation (electric coupling), wound healing and regeneration in the adult organism, stimulation of T lymphocytes by macrophages, destruction of target cells by cytotoxic lymphocytes, maturation of bone marrow cells, invasion by microorganisms, and metastasis and tissue invasion by tumor cells. Some of these phenomena are rather complex and probably result from the interplay of proliferation, differentiation, movement, recognition, and adhesion.

CELLULAR INTERACTIONS AND CELL MOVEMENT

Contact Guidance (1, 4, 6, 10, 11)

Cell movement is difficult to study in an intact organism. However, the few systems that are amenable to experimentation have produced evidence that during embryogenesis certain cells (e.g., neural crest cells) reach their proper locations within the developing embryo after migration over rather long and surprisingly precise paths. It is possible that these cells follow chemical gradients (chemotaxis), but guidance by other cells or substrates (extracellular matrix) is equally probable.

Contact guidance can be simulated in vitro by the use of nonuniform substrates such as palladium gradients, grooved glass plates, glass fibers, or plasma clots whose surface has been treated with a brush or whose fibrin mesh has been reoriented in a nonuniform way. Under these conditions cells follow the metal gradient, become elongated, and align themselves parallel to the linearly oriented substrate, and also preferentially move parallel to the substrate orientation. Experiments with fibroblasts growing on glass fibers of different diameters suggest that cells adhere to nonuniform surfaces in a way that minimizes exposure to curvatures which could interfere with the formation of linear bundles of microfilaments attached to focal contacts.

Contact Inhibition of Movement (1, 6, 11)

The term "contact inhibition" (of movement) was coined by Abercrombie and Heaysman in 1954 and refers to the inability of nontransformed fibroblasts to migrate over each other's surfaces. The radial outgrowth of explants, the arrangement of cells in parallel arrays, and the formation of monolayers are thought to be related to this typical social behavior of nontransformed cells.

Contact inhibition of movement is usually quantified by determination of the degree of nuclear overlap: Assuming a random distribution of the cells in the culture dish, the statistical frequency of nuclear overlaps can be calculated for any given nuclear size and cell density. The ratio between the experimentally determined and calculated number of nuclear overlaps is then used as a measure for contact inhibiton of movement. The ratio (or index) is typically in the neighborhood of 0.1 for normal fibroblasts and around 0.5 for transformed cells.

Abercrombie and Heaysman also studied contact inhibition in mixed cultures. Embryonic chick and neonatal mouse fibroblasts turned out to be mutually contact-inhibited, suggesting that contact inhibition of movement is not (or at least not always) species-specific. When, however, sarcoma cells (an invasive cancer cell strain) were mixed with normal fibroblasts, no contact inhibition between these two cell types was noted. In contrast, epithelial cells were capable of stopping sarcoma cells.

During the past two decades, contact inhibition of movement has been extensively studied by time-lapse cinemicrography yielding more detailed information about the chain of events taking place when two moving cells collide: After two cells have made contact, protrusive activity stops in the area of contact, the ruffling membrane of the leading edge is locally paralyzed (contact paralysis), movement in the original direction ceases, and the cells contract slightly and establish a firm adhesion. Ruffling may eventually resume in a different area of the cell surface not facing another cell, and the two cells may break apart and move away from each other. At a later stage of migration, a new ruffling membrane can be formed in the area that had previously undergone contact paralysis, indicating that contact inhibition of movement is both a local and a transient phenomenon. Collision of a migrating cell with an inanimate obstacle takes a markedly different course: The ruffling membrane is generally not paralyzed, and the cell does not contract, even in cases when the cell is forced to stop and eventually change its direction of movement.

The underlying mechanism of contact inhibition of movement is still not known. Some authors have tried to explain contact inhibition of movement in terms of differential adhesions between cells and between cells and substrate. Others reject this hypothesis because it cannot readily explain the coordinate withdrawal of filopodia in the growth cone of migrating nerve cells after only one of them has made contact with another nerve cell (but not with a fibroblast). Alternative explanations include the formation of specialized junctions between filopodia followed by an exchange of cytoplasmic material or a local change of membrane permeability.

Associative Movement (1)

Associative movement (or "contact promotion") becomes evident when solid–substrate locomotion fails either because cell–substrate adhesion is very weak in comparison to cell–cell adhesion or because cells are grown in suspension. After initial contacts have been made, cells are forced closer together, thus giving rise to (often multilayered) aggregates. Associative movement might be a driving force in sorting-out of mixed populations of embryonic cells.

CELLULAR INTERACTIONS AND GROWTH

Density-Dependent Inhibition of Growth (8)

Cells growing in a culture vessel containing an adequate supply of nutrients gradually slow down their growth rate and eventually stop dividing. The final cell density is characteristic for a particular cell strain when grown under a defined set of culture conditions. The saturation density is considerably higher for transformed cells than for their nontransformed counterparts.

Density-dependent inhibition of growth has been restored in transformed cells after incubations with dibutyryl cyclic AMP or monovalent concanavalin A. Confluent monolayers of nontransformed cells escape density-dependent inhibition of growth and go through another round of division after brief incubation with proteolytic or glycolytic enzymes, addition of fresh serum and addition of purified peptide growth factors or colchicine, or after an increase of the pH of the culture medium. Density-dependent inhibition of growth does not seem to be simply a matter of depletion of the medium or accumulation of growth inhibitors. Fresh cells seeded at low density into "spent" medium grow to the same saturation density as in fresh medium. Local depletion of the medium or local accumulations of growth inhibitors (change of the microenvironment) have also been proposed as possible causes of density-dependent inhibition of growth. Proof of these two hypotheses has not been possible to date. A more recent hypothesis suggests that changes of the intracellular pH (which is in part affected by the anion permeability of the plasma membrane) play a crucial role. The observation that some nontransformed cells can induce density-dependent inhibition of growth in transformed cells prompted the speculation that the transformed cells which are capable of receiving the growth-inhibition signal have lost the capability to emit or transmit the signal. Whether cell–cell contact is required to bring about density-dependent inhibition of growth is still debated.

CELLULAR INTERACTIONS AND DIFFERENTIATION

Embryonic Induction (2, 4)

In the developing embryo, certain tissues require the close apposition of another tissue (inducer) in order to differentiate normally. The phenomenon has been studied for over 50 years, yet its molecular mechanism is still poorly understood. Transplantation experiments have shown that embryonic induction is neither species-specific nor strictly tissue-specific. Even dead tissue can be an effective inducer. Purified extracts from various tissues as well as a number of substances taken from the laboratory shelf have been shown to induce differentiation. Among the substances that can cause differentiation are nucleic acids, proteins, carbohydrates, fatty acids, vitamins, and steroids. Even mechanical trauma can induce differentiation.

So-called transfilter experiments were designed to study the transmission of the inductive signal. In a transfilter experiment, the two interacting tissues are separated by a thin porous membrane. Induction across such a filter membrane was first interpreted as evidence for the transmission of a soluble factor by free diffusion. Electron micrographs, however, showed that the filters had been penetrated by long cellular processes. More recent experiments, carried out with filters of narrowly defined pore size, indicate that transfilter induction can take place as long as the pore diameter is not less than approximately 0.15 μ, the smallest pore readily permeable to cell processes. Closer examination of filters and intact tissues revealed that processes of the two interacting tissues are less than 10 nm apart, with no noticeable accumulation of matrix material between two opposite surfaces. It is still not known whether specialized junctions are established between interacting cell processes, or whether the tissues communicate via specific cell surface molecules.

INTERCELLULAR ADHESION

The capability of cells to recognize each other and to form selective aggregates with isotypic or heterotypic cells is of central importance for morphogenesis, tissue organization and maintenence, immunological interactions, and tumor metastasis. Intercellular adhesion is a complex process that includes a recognition step as well as probably several adhesion steps. Because there is no direct and universally accepted way of measuring adhesion, "adhesion" or "adhesiveness" is used in a strictly operational sense. It is defined by the assay employed and the particular aspect of the adhesive process it focuses on.

Experimental Systems (2, 4, 5, 10, 11)

There are a few experimental systems (e.g., fertilization of echinoid eggs, mating of the unicellular green algae *Chlamydromonas,* aggregation of the cellular slime mold *Dictyostelium discoideum*) in which intercellular adhesion can be conveniently studied under almost physiological conditions. In these systems, aggregation occurs naturally, single cells are formed spontaneously, and the cells do not have to be prepared by destruction of an intact piece of tissue. In addition, *Dictyostelium* strains have been isolated that carry mutations affecting various stages of the aggregation process.

The most popular specimens for research on intercellular adhesion, however, have been single cells isolated from intact sponge or vertebrate (embryonic or more recently also adult) tissue. Dissociation is usually achieved by mechanical shear, high pH, metal ion chelators, proteolytic or glycolytic enzymes, or a combination of several of the above. Although the resulting single cells may look perfectly viable as judged by the usual criteria for viability (e.g., exclusion of trypan blue), one has to consider the possibility that their surfaces and perhaps even their metabolic processes have been traumatized in a way that affects their adhesive behavior.

Measurement of Intercellular Adhesion (5, 11)

At first glance it might seem most logical to quantify adhesiveness by measuring the force (or, more accurately, the work) required to pull two adherent cells apart. Such measurements have actually been performed, leading to the widespread belief that tumor cells are less adhesive than normal cells. However, the results obtained were inconclusive because the tension applied to cell pairs often ruptured the plasma membrane while the area of cell–cell contact stayed intact. Most laboratories therefore base their estimates of intercellular adhesiveness on reaggregation experiments. Assays designed to yield information about the earliest phases of the adhesive process measure the time-dependent formation of aggregates or the disappearance of single cells in cell suspensions. The collection of single cells by preformed aggregates or the adherence of single cells to preformed monolayers (determination of adhesion *rates*) can also be measured. Insight into the adhesive behavior of cells has also been gained by analyzing the relative positions of cells within mixed aggregates after "sorting-out" has taken place. This approach is, however, limited to cells that are capable of moving within an aggregate. The method also focuses on the later stages of the adhesion process because sorting-out usually takes a few days to be completed.

Adhesive Specificity (3–5)

When single cells derived from dissociated tissue reaggregate, they do not just form random conglomerates of cells. They often aggregate preferentially with cells of the same type and organize themselves in a manner similar to the tissue from which they had been isolated. Sponge cells, for example, can reconsitute functioning sponges. Initially, mixtures of embryonic cells may aggregate indiscriminately, but the cells often sort out at a later stage. Most of the time they sort according to cell type, but species specificity has also been reported. One explanation of the initially unspecific aggregation of embryonic cells is that their recognition mechanism has been temporarily impaired by the isolation procedure. Several theories have been put forward to explain sorting-out. The theories assume qualitative or quantitative adhesive differences or a sorting-out on thermodynamical grounds without involvement of any specific cell surface molecules.

Molecular Mechanism of Intercellular Adhesion (4, 5, 7, 9, 11)

Hypotheses for the molecular mechanism of intercellular adhesion can be grouped into two broad categories: The first one attributes intercellular adhesion to physicochemical interactions such as the formation of hydrogen bonds between oligosaccharide chains on neighboring cell surfaces, Ca^{2+}-bridges between anionic groups, or the combined effects of London–Van der Waals forces and repulsive electrostatic forces. The second model postulates complementary molecules on the cell surface which combine like antigens and antibodies in a "lock-and-key"–like fashion, or macromolecular factors ligating specific cell surface binding sites. Variations of the lock-and-key model assume cell surface molecules that are activated by limited proteolysis and cell surface glycosyl transferases interacting with oligosaccharides on opposite cell surfaces. The "enzyme–substrate" theory is attractive from two points of view: (1) It easily explains adhesive specificity because glycosyl transferases are highly apecific with respect to both sugar donor and sugar acceptor. (2) The model can also explain modifications of the adhesive behavior of a cell: When a glycosyl transferase exerts its catalytic function, another sugar residue is added to the oligosaccharide chain on the opposite cell surface, which then might (or might not) combine with another transferase in order to establish another (stronger, weaker, or equal) intercellular bond. Experimental data lend support to several of the above hypotheses, suggesting that different mechanisms might be at work in different tissues and at different stages of the adhesive process.

Isolation and Characterization of Adhesive Molecules (4, 5, 9)

Soluble or membrane-bound activities affecting (stimulating or inhibiting) cell–cell adhesion have been partially purified from slime molds, sponges, and embryonic and adult vertebrate tissues. The amounts of purified material, however, have been too small to allow a rigorous physicochemical characterization. In marine sponges—to choose one arbitrary example—adhesion seems to be mediated by species-specific aggregation factors linking species-specific aggregation receptors (baseplates) on the surface of opposite cells. The isolated aggregation factor is usually firmly associated with high-molecular-weight particles and displays a "sunburst" or an elongated filamentous configuration on electron micrographs. Aggregation of sponge cells requires Ca^{2+}, but in contrast to aggregation of cells derived from higher organisms, it is independent of elevated temperatures, metabolic energy, and protein synthesis. Even fixed cells or agarose beads derivatized with purified baseplates aggregate in a species-specific manner.

In *Dictyostelium discoideum,* so-called type A contact sites are responsible for tip-to-tip aggregation, whereas type B contact sites mediate side-by-side aggregation. Because antibody labeling experiments indicate that A sites are present on the entire cell surface, one has to consider the possibility of spatial control of adhesive activity.

Antibodies directed against a cell-adhesive molecule derived from embryonic neural retina cells prevent cell–cell adhesion, whereas antibodies or lectins interacting with other membrane sites do not interfere. This observation lends strong support to the view that only a small fraction of the total cell surface participates in the (early) adhesive events.

Indications that carbohydrates are involved in the adhesive process have been numerous: Both aggregation factors and aggregation receptors have been reported to contain substantial amounts of carbohydrate. Furthermore, sugars can act as hapten inhibitors of factor-mediated aggregation, and cells can recognize and selectively bind to certain insolubilized sugars. Interestingly, a sialyl transferase activity has been demonstrated in sponge aggregation factor which sialylates the aggregation receptor.

Recently methods have been developed to select tumor cells with altered invasive and metastasizing properties. Such cells adhere differently under conditions in vitro and show different lectin binding patterns. Physicochemical methods, however, failed to reveal any major changes of cell surface components. It is conceivable that the change is too subtle or affects too small a fraction of the surface to be detected by current techniques.

REFERENCES

1. Abercrombie, M., 1967. Contact inhibition: The phenomenon and its biological implications. *Natl. Cancer Inst. Monogr.* 26:249–77.
2. Brinkley, B. R., and Porter, K. R., eds. 1977. *International Cell Biology 1976–1977*, pp. 31–100. Rockefeller University Press, New York.
3. Gottlieb, D. I., Rock, K., and Glaser, L. 1976. A gradient of adhesive specificity in developing avian retina. *Proc. Natl. Acad. Sci. U.S.A.* 73:410–14.
4. Lash, J. W., and Burger, M. M., eds. 1977. *Cell and Tissue Interactions*. Raven Press, New York.
5. Marchase, R. B., Vosbeck, K., and Roth, S. 1976. Intercellular adhesive specificity. *Biochim. Biophys. Acta* 457:385–416.
6. Porter, R., and Fitzsimons, D. W., eds. 1973. *Locomotion of Tissue Cells.* Ciba Foundation Symposium 14 (new series). Elsevier–Excerpta Medica–North-Holland; Amsterdam, London, New York.
7. Roseman, S. 1970. The synthesis of complex carbohydrates by multiglycosyltransferase systems and their potential function in intercellular adhesion. *Chem. Phy. Lipids* 5:270–97.
8. Rubin, H. 1974. Regulation of growth in animal cells. In *Membrane Transformations in Neoplasia*, J. Schultz and R. E. Block, eds., pp. 173–91. Academic Press, New York and London.
9. Rutishauser, U., Thiery, J.-P., Brackenbury, R., Sela, B.-A., and Edelman, G. M. 1976. Mechanisms of adhesion among cells from neural tissues of the chick embryo. *Proc. Natl. Acad. Sci. U.S.A.* 73:577–81.
10. Townes, P. L., and Holtfreter, J. 1955. Directed movements and selective adhesion of embryonic amphibian cells. *J. Exp. Zool.* 128:53–120.
11. Trinkaus, J. P. 1969. *Cells into Organs. The Forces That Shape the Embryo.* Prentice-Hall, Englewood Cliffs, New Jersey.

2.6. On the Phenomenon of Cell Transformation

Miguel M. Azar and James J. O'Leary

The growth of normal cells is modulated by a series of well-correlated biological reactions. One property common to the growth of normal diploid cells is the phenomenon of contact inhibition, which is the density- or population-dependent inhibition of proliferation. Transformation is generally defined by the development of new growth characteristics and by the loss of contact inhibition when cells are cultured in vitro.

It is evident that control of normal cell growth and proliferation is exerted primarily at the level of the cell membrane. Membrane interactions between cells and with various biochemical agents control the activity of the various enzymes that participate in cell growth, including adenylate cyclase, guanylate cyclase, the enzymes for glucose transport, and enzymes controlling the levels of calcium and magnesium ions. In turn, the changes in these systems induced by membrane interaction affect the cell nucleus and other cytoplasmic systems. The control systems are further influenced by feedback from the nucleus and cytoplasm, or the cell membrane.

Cell transformation is characterized by profound alterations in these controlling systems. Originally, transformation was correlated with viral infection, but now a wide variety of transforming agents, including chemical carcinogens, are recognized. Chemicals, physical agents, or tumorigenic viruses act on the genetic center of the cell, altering the genetic information of the control systems or cell membrane in such a way that there is loss of the regulation of cell proliferation. Table 1 summarizes some of the characteristics of typical transformed cells as opposed to normal cells. A particular transformed cell line may not possess all of these characteristics, but there are exceptions. Many of the alterations in Table 1 are probably secondary to other effects. For example, changes in glycolysis are probably secondary to metabolic stress induced by uncontrolled proliferation.

In what follows, we will discuss three subjects of primary interest in relation to growth regulation of normal cells and changes observed in the transformed state: serum growth factors, cell surface enzymes and carbohydrates, and the role of cyclic AMP. The aforementioned are perhaps the most important

Table 1. Some Characteristics of Normal and Transformed Cells.

NORMAL CELLS	TRANSFORMED CELLS
Requirement for growth factors	Decreased requirement for growth factors
Division stops at monolayer stage	Continue to proliferate as multilayers
Contact inhibition operative	Contact inhibition nonoperative
Normal cell adhesiveness	Decreased cell adhesiveness
Normal deformability	Increased deformability
Normal agglutinability by lectins	Increased agglutinability by lectins
Normal membrane turnover	Altered membrane turnover
Normal membrane composition	Altered membrane composition
Normal tRNA	Abnormal tRNA
Normal aerobic glycolysis	Increased aerobic glycolysis

and certainly the best studied of the control systems involved in cell transformation.

SERUM GROWTH FACTORS

The growth of mammalian cells in culture is promoted by or may require the addition of blood serum from the same or another species. Many serum factors responsible for this effect have been postulated. For example, a highly purified low-molecular-weight protein that promotes the growth of cells in culture, but cannot replace serum completely and does not increase the slow growth observed at low serum concentration has been demonstrated. For 3T3 cells (a line of normal mouse fibroblasts), at least four serum growth factors have been isolated. Two of these are heat-stable and two are heat-labile.

Some of the growth factors in serum are low-molecular-weight nutrients found either as free compounds or bound to proteins. For example, limitations of arginine, glutamine, histidine, isoleucine, lysine, phenylalanine, tryptophan, tyrosine, or valine are associated with growth arrest. Addition of the missing amino acid is usually followed by initiation of DNA synthesis after 15 hours. The other types of growth factors belong to several categories in terms of function. These include factors that serve as nutrient carriers, factors that stimulate the uptake of nutrients, factors that affect the levels of cyclic AMP modulated by membrane interaction, factors that influence cell migration and movement, and miscellaneous factors whose exact effects are not known. The action of all of these serum factors appears to be mediated by the cell membrane. Even the critical nutrients must be transported into the cell to exert their effects. With cell transformation, the requirement for growth factors is changed (in most cases by alteration of the cell membrane), and the need for some growth factors is eliminated.

CELL SURFACE ENZYMES AND CARBOHYDRATES

Cell surface enzymes and carbohydrates play a crucial role in the recognition of both distal and local signals for cell growth. Some of these substances are specific receptors for hormones, mitogens, and other agents that can stimulate or suppress cell growth. Proteolytic and hydrolytic enzymes present on the cell surface act in a different fashion. These enzymes are present on the cell surface of transformed cells in an increased amount. They can be activated by other proteases, insulin, and serum factors in a cascade similar to the complement or blood coagulation system. The result of this process is altered agglutinability, motility, and, when activated by protease treatment of normal 3T3 cells, loss of contact inhibition.

Because of the increased amount of proteases on transformed cells, protease inhibitors can be used to inhibit their growth. The use of these inhibitors reduced the saturation density and agglutinability of transformed cells, but fails to arrest the cell in the G_1 or resting phase of the cell cycle. The simple inhibition of cell surface proteases, therefore, is unable to correct the intrinsic nuclear defect of the transformed cell.

Some of the more significant findings with respect to proteolytic and hydrolytic enzymes on transformed cell surfaces are summarized as follows:

1. Elevated peptidase and cathepsin levels in the interstitial fluid of transformed cells.
2. Elevated glycosidase activity in extracts of solid tumors.
3. Production of a fibrinolysin inhibitor by tumor-bearing animals.
4. Inhibition of growth of transformed cells by protease inhibitors.
5. Higher membrane turnover in transformed cells.
6. Stimulation of growth or release from growth control of normal cells upon treatment with a large series of proteolytic enzymes.

However, the specific role of proteases in growth regulation is still open to question for the following reasons: First, many protease inhibitors have multiple effects on cells, including the profound inhibition of protein synthesis. Second, clones of transformed cells have been isolated with "normal" levels of plasminogen activator, a protease that was characteristically thought to be elevated with transformation. Third, there are certain proteases that have significant effects on the cell surface yet fail to be mitogenic.

Alterations in the cell surface carbohydrates of transformed cells involve both glycoproteins and glycolipids. They vary from tumor to tumor as well as in different transformed cells derived from a single cell line. Some of these changes are as follows:

1. The membranes of transformed cells yield glycoproteins of higher molecular weight.
2. Changes in glycoproteins are both qualitative and quantitative. Glycoproteins present in some normal cells are not detected in their transformed variants. The LETS protein or fibronectin is one example. Some proteins are less and others more glycosylated, suggesting an abnormal activity of glycosyl transferases in transformed cells.
3. The sialic acid content of transformed cells is decreased and may lessen the net negative charge on the cell surface.
4. The total amount of gangliosides is decreased. The ratios between various ganglioside species are altered. Hematoside is decreased while lactosyl ceramide is increased. Gangliosides that are present in cryptic form are unmasked. In DNA and RNA virus-transformed cells, gangliosides are markedly decreased in comaprison to contact-inhibited parent cell lines. Hematoside and lactosyl ceramide vary the same in the period of growth as in the period of confluence. Hematoside catalyzes an early step in the synthesis of the oligosaccharide chain of gangliosides.
5. A ceramide trihexoside (Gal-Gal-Glc-Cer) that is normally synthesized during the early G_1 phase of the cell cycle is decreased in transformed cells.

In addition to these membrane enzymes and carbohydrates, a large number of other membrane markers such as histocompatibility antigens may show altered expression in the transformed state, but these changes are generally nonspecific. It should also be noted that many transformed cell lines develop surface markers detectable by antibody that are not found on normal cells and may be unique to that transformed cell line. The exact function of these tumor-specific transplantation antigens is not known but, for virally transformed cells, may represent expression of the viral genome of the surface of the transformed cell. The significance of these antigens in host reactions to the transformed cell is beyond the scope of this discussion.

CYCLIC AMP

There are probably several intracellular mediators of membrane signals. The most important and best characterized is cyclic 3',5'-adenosine monophosphate (cyclic AMP). Cyclic AMP levels act as a chemical switch that regulates enzyme activity and the rates of protein synthesis. Because of this regulatory activity and its disposition within the cell membrane, cyclic AMP fulfills the requirement of a "second messenger" for membrane-initiated events.

Cyclic AMP affects overall cell activity in several ways. In general, its levels vary during cell growth, and there is a definite operational relationship between these levels and the phase of the cell cycle. Contact-inhibited cells are arrested in early G_1 (G_0) and have high levels of cyclic AMP; therefore, G_1 is a probable point of action of cyclic AMP. Also, a block point at G_2 suggests an effect at the middle of the G_1 phase. The mechanism by which cyclic AMP influences DNA and protein synthesis is more likely related to phosphorylation. Perhaps after cell-to-cell contact and cell division, normal cells modulate the organization of the plasma membrane, then transport rates are inhibited, cyclic AMP levels become elevated, and cell proliferation gets under control. In transformed cells this elevation of cyclic AMP is not seen. However, during growth, both normal cells and transformed cells show increased levels of cyclic AMP. The level of cyclic AMP increases as the normal cell ceases to grow at confluency. Transformed cells at confluency, have low levels of cyclic AMP. Temperature-sensitive transformed cells, which grow normally at one temperature but lose contact inhibition at another temperature, show increased cyclic AMP levels at nonpermissive or restrictive temperature and decreased levels at permissive temperature.

Contact inhibition in some transformed cells may be restored by treatment with cyclic AMP analogs or inhibitors or phosphodiesterase, but rapid growth resumes after removal of these agents. Membrane changes are essential in triggering the growth mechanism. Cyclic AMP changes are associated with surface membrane alterations but do not necessarily represent a direct result of such alterations. Cyclic AMP mediates the smooth conveyance of the signal to the cell machinery that synthesizes proteins. Factors that act at the membrane are referred to as "pleiotropic activators." Cyclic AMP is a pleiotropic mediator that carries that signal as a messenger to the cytoplasm and nucleus. Levels of cyclic AMP are decreased by chemical carcinogens, X-ray, oncogenic viruses, or spontaneous selection, and its decrease accounts for some of the abnormal properties of transformed cells.

Adenylate cyclase catalyzes the formation of cyclic AMP from adenosine triphosphate; this reaction requires Mg^{2+} or Mn^{2+}. Adenylate cyclase activity in transformed or malignant cells is low, a phenomenon that might be due to loss of hormone responsiveness. There is a relationship between transformation and decreased specific activity of adenyl cyclase. Because membrane-associated adenyl cyclase may also be detected in the cytosol of transformed cells, it has been suggested that the shift from the membrane site to the interior of the cell interferes with regulatory mechanisms and facilitates malignant transformation.

It is possible that a membrane-associated protein is normally produced following cell-to-cell contact and mitosis. This protein would be affected by an abnormal or defective gene product responsible for its production during the transformed state. This membrane component could be an actin-like protein, or an enzyme such as adenylate or guanylate cyclase, a transport enzyme complex, or an intrinsic membrane protein, perhaps related to intramembrane-ous particles.

Other cyclic nucleotides are important in the regulation of the cell cycle. The levels of cyclic AMP/cyclic GMP vary in an inverse proportion during growth. Cyclic GMP may also have a role in cell regulation. It is beyond the scope of this chapter to review this specific aspect of cell growth. The reader is therefore alerted to the many current papers dealing with this subject.

REFERENCES

1. Holley, R. W. 1974. Serum factors and growth control. In *Control of Proliferation in Animal Cells,* C. Clarkson and R. Baserga, eds., pp. 13–18. Cold Spring Harbor Laboratory, New York.

2. Edidin, M., and Weiss, A. 1974. Restruction of antigen mobility in the plasma membranes of some cultured fibroblasts. In *Control of Proliferation in Animal Cells,* C. Clarkson and R. Baserga, eds., pp. 213–19. Cold Spring Harbor Laboratory, New York.

3. Talmadge, K. W., Noonan, K. D., and Burger, M. M. 1974. The transformed cell surface: An analysis of the increased lectin agglutinability and the concept of growth control by surface proteases. In *Control of Proliferation in Animal Cells,* C. Clarkson and R. Baserga, eds., pp. 313–25. Cold Spring Harbor Laboratory, New York.

4. Pasten, I., Anderson, W. B., Carchman, R. A., Willingham, M. C., Russell, T. R., and Johnson, G. S. 1974. Cyclic AMP and malignant transformation. In *Control of Proliferation in Animal Cells,* C. Clarkson and R. Baserga, eds., pp. 563–70. Cold Spring Harbor Laboratory, New York.

5. Pastan, I. H., Johnson, G. S., and Anderson, W. B. 1975. Role of nucleotides in growth control. *Annu. Rev. Biochem.* 44:493–522.

6. Pastan, I., and Johnson, G. S. 1974. Cyclic Amp and the transformation of fibroblasts. In *Advances in Cancer Research,* G. Klein, S. Weinhouse, and A. Haddow, eds., pp. 303–29. Academic Press, New York.

7. Willingham, M. C., Johnson, G. S., and Pastan, I. 1972. Control of DNA synthesis and mitosis in 3T3 cells by cyclic AMP. *Biochem. Biophys. Res. Commun.* 48:743–48.

8. Hollenberg, M. D., and Cuatrecasas, P. 1973. Epidermal growth factor: Receptors in human fibroblasts and modulation of action by cholera toxin. *Proc. Natl. Acad. Sci. U.S.A.* 70:2964–68.

9. Scott, R. F., and Furcht, L. T. 1976. Membrane pathology of normal and malignant cells. *Hum. Pathol.* 7:519–32.

2.7. Bacterial Cell Envelope

Lazar M. Schwartz

The cell envelope of microorganisms may be represented by several simple models despite the considerable species variety and variations induced by mutations. Before we proceed, several terms require definition: *Cell membrane* refers to the structural layer enclosing the bacterial cytoplasm. *Cell wall* refers to the layers outside the cell membrane. *Cell envelope* refers to all the layers separating the cell cytoplasm from the environment. *Periplasma* refers to the space between the inner and outer membranes. *Outer membrane* refers to an additional structural layer seen in Gram-negative bacteria. *Protoplast* refers to a cell that has been stripped of its wall, leaving only the cell membrane. (See Figure 1 for a schematic representation of the cell envelope.)

CELL MEMBRANE

The cell membranes of bacteria resemble in many aspects the cell membranes of eukaryotes. Basically there is a lipid bilayer, protein and carbohydrates. The small amounts of RNA and DNA detected are contaminants. Although the Gram (+) bacteria are regarded as more complex than the Gram (−) species, the membrane of the latter shows greater complexity.

Isolation of the cytoplasmic membrane has been facilitated by removal of the cell wall, resulting in naked cells, called protoplasts. By freeze-etching techniques the membrane can be split along a median hydrophobic zone

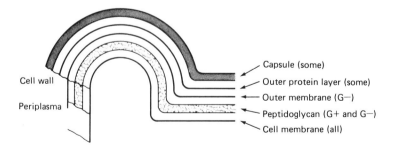

Figure 1. Schematic representation of bacterial cell envelope.

similar to that of eukaryotic cell membranes. Globular structures referred to in eukaryotes as plasma membrane particles (PMP) are abundant. They are located in the inner half of the lipid bilayer. This asymmetric distribution reflects the increased number of proteins expressed on the cytoplasmic aspect of the membrane. They are thought to function in transport or act as specific permeases. Aggregation, network formation, or clustering of PMP is frequently observed. Their displacement is correlated to changes in the fluidity of the membrane dependent on the transitions of membrane lipids from a crystalline phase to a more geliform state.

Cell Membrane Composition

The cell membrane of *Mycoplasma,* a microorganism that has no other cell coats, shows the following composition:

Protein	50–59%
Lipid	32–40%
Carbohydrates	0.2–0.5%
DNA	1%
RNA	2–5%

Gram-negative and Gram-positive bacteria show similar cell membrane composition. Generally they show an average composition of

Protein	62%
Lipid	30%
Hexosamine	0.7%
Nonamino carbohydrate	1.3%
RNA	0.6%
DNA	0.1%

Cell Membrane Lipids

Most of the bacteria (e.g., *E. coli*) can synthesize their own lipid, but some bacteria cannot. For example, *M. Laidlawii* does not synthesize unsaturated fatty acids (UFA), which should be added to the medium for the growth of this bacterium. Other strains require both UFA and saturated fatty acids (SFA) and may or may not require cholesterol. Incorporated sterols from the medium account for up to 10% of the total membrane lipid, but there is no reciprocal relationship between the incorporation of sterols and the amount and composition of the fatty acids. Only sterols with a 3-β-hydroxyl group and a relatively planar nucleus are taken up. The *E. coli* UFA auxotrophs require that about 20% of the total fatty acids in the medium be of this type. UFA are required for the maintainance of membrane fluidity and functional integrity. Whereas for growth at 37°C *E. coli* requires 15–20% UFA, the required amount decreases to 11% at 45°C and increases to 30–32% at 27°C. The native *E. coli* membrane, however, contains up to 50% UFA, the excess membrane fluidity apparently being required for survival at sudden changes in temperature.

E. coli is able to control the composition of the membrane so as to maintain a constant fluidity despite the temperature of growth. The mechanism for doing so is called homeoviscous adaption, and involves controlling the level of synthesis of UFA. The mechanism has distinct limits, however.

Bacterial membranes contain many unusual lipids including acid esters of phosphatidyl glycerol, a variety of glycosyl diglycerides, and unusual fatty acids such as cyclopropane fatty acids and high-molecular-weight fatty acids.

Phase Transition

The membrane phospholipids are heterogenous, some with areas of hexagonal, close, and ordered packing (gel) and others with random, less-ordered packing (liquid, fluid). The change from one physical state to another has been called order–disorder transition or phase transition (Figure 2). It depends on temperature. The midpoint and ranges of transition depend on both the polar head group and the fatty acid composition of the phospholipid. The region of the lipid bilayer close to the polar head is less mobile than that in the interior. The position of the ethylenic bond within the membrane determines the depth at which organization may become less ordered. Changes in the proportions of UFA to SFA in the lipid molecules or increase in their heterogeneity alters the transitions.

The phase transitions lead to the simultaneous existence of fluid and solid

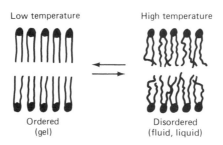

Low temperature   High temperature

Ordered   Disordered
(gel)   (fluid, liquid)

Figure 2. Arrangement of the fatty acyl chains in a liquid bilayer at temperatures below or above the extremes of the lipid phase transition. Polar head groups represented as solid spheres (Ref. 1).

domains, which impart structure to the system and permit concentration of selected metabolites in local regions and separation or juxtaposition of dissimilar or related biological functions. Examples of those functions are the release of enzyme complexes from the membrane, chemotactic activity, permease induction, maintainance of cell integrity, or just providing a fluid environment for the activity of certain enzymes.

Proteins of the Inner Membrane

The inner membrane functions as the osmotic barrier of the cell and as a site for anabolic functions. The proteins of the inner membrane comprise most of the enzymes involved in lipid biosynthesis, the cytochromes and other proteins involved in processes of oxidative phosphorylation, and proteins acting as carriers in membrane transport. The peptidoglycan synthesizing enzymes and adenosine hydrolyzing enzymes are located on the outside aspect of the inner membrane. The interactions of membrane proteins and lipids involve multiple aspects: (1) activation of membrane protein by lipids; (2) immobilization of the lipids bound by protein and the reverse; and (3) influencing the temperature dependence of at least some functional proteins.

The exact location of some membrane proteins varies with the bacterium under consideration. For example, in G (+) bacteria ATPase is part of the inner membrane. In *S. faecalis* it is linked to the membrane by another protein called nectin, and its activity is influenced by still another membrane protein which can be inactivated by dicyclohexylcarbodiimide. In *E. coli,* ATPase is located in the periplasmic space at the inner aspect of the outer membrane. The location varies in smooth and rough variants of the same strain. In smooth variants it remains in the periplasmic space, but in rough strains it is partially associated with lipopolysaccharides and located at the cell surface.

CELL WALL

The cell wall of bacteria consists of a layer of peptidoglycan that determines its shape and rigidity. The peptidoglycan may be complexed with other molecules such as teichoic acids or lipoproteins or be covered by an additional layer called the outer coat or outer membrane, consisting of lipopolysaccharide, phospholipid, and protein (Figure 1). Many species with or without the outer coat are encapsulated. The capsule consists of polysaccharide.

Peptidoglycan

Peptidoglycan is a complex polysaccharide consisting of a glycan portion with linear but alternating N-acetylglucosamine and N-acetylmuramic acid residues in a β-1,4 linkage, and a peptide moiety linked through its N terminal to the carboxyl group of muramic acid, with alternating L- and D-amino acids. The cross-linking bridges between the peptide units are characteristic of the microorganism under consideration. The schematic organization of the peptidoglycans is depicted in Figure 3. The sites of linkage in the various units of peptidoglycan are shown in Figure 4.

The amount of peptidoglycan present varies with the species. In some species it forms an electron-dense layer; in others it is thin and barely discernible. Some marine bacteria lack a discernible peptidoglycan layer. The average chain length of the molecule varies between 10 and 65 disaccharide units. Isolated peptidoglycan structures are called murein sacculi.

Peptidoglycan is the structural layer that maintains the shape of all bacteria. Changes in shape from sphere to rod resulting from growth in different culture conditions are associated with changes in number and homogeneity of the disaccharide units of peptidoglycan. The peptidoglycan of Gram-negative bacteria probably exists as a monolayer. That of Gram-positive bacteria appears thicker with a multilayered structure. Species variation in the glycan moiety consists in the extent of O-acetylation at position 6 and the number of muramic acid residues that are not substituted with peptides. The peptide portion of the peptidoglycan comprises four amino acid residues with considerable variation of the amino acid sequence. Other species variations consist in binding of polymeric structures or proteins to the peptidoglycan.

Synthesis of the peptidoglycan begins in the cytoplasm from which the molecule is transferred at the cell surface, followed by polymerization. Local controlled hydrolysis of the molecule may create sites for addition of the

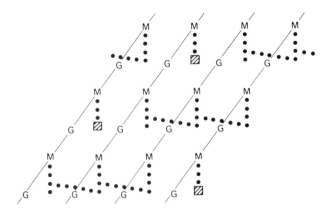

Figure 3. Schematic representation of peptidoglycan (based on Ref. 3). G: N-acetylglucosamine. M: N-acetylmuramic acid. Dots: Peptide moieties linking the peptidoglycan molecules.

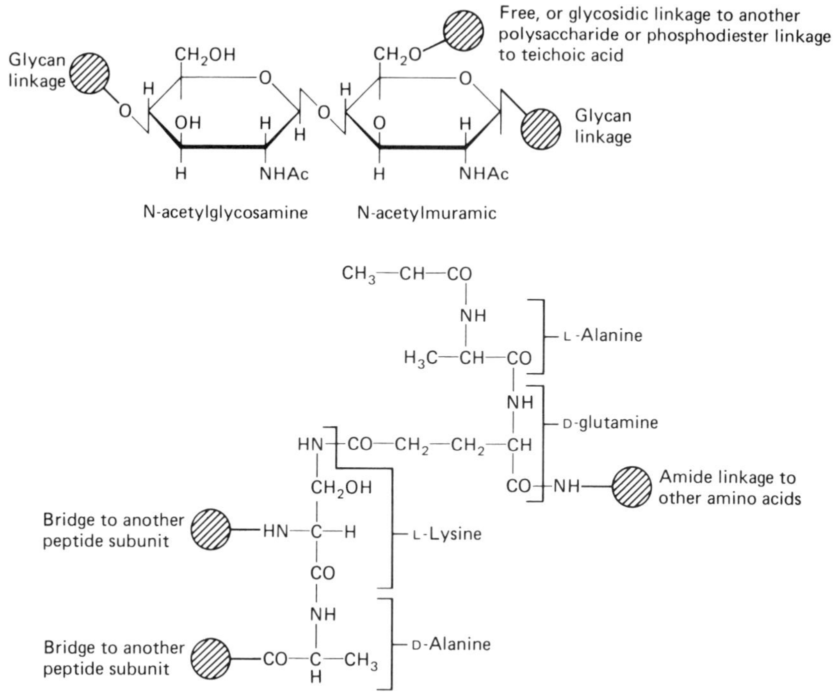

Figure 4. The peptidoglycan unit and sites of linkage.

incoming precursors. Many antibiotics (e.g., penicillin) act by interfering with the transfer through the membrane and cross-linking of the molecules.

Teichoic Acids

In addition to peptidoglycan many G (+) bacteria show teichoic acids. These are polyolphosphate polymers covalently bound via a phosphate–diester bond to the hydroxyl group of position 6 of the muramic acid. Binding of teichoic acid may involve up to 50% of the existing peptidoglycan. The synthesis of both compounds occurs simultaneously, and incorporation of one into another is apparently random. Many cells contain multiple homopolymers of teichoic acid which can be substituted by nigerose or kojibiose.

Teichoic acids are hydrophilic molecules intimately associated with glycolipids on the outer side of the cell membrane. Although the mechanism is not completely clarified, teichoic acids function in the regulation of ionic composition in the membrane, essential for the integrity of cation-dependent enzymes. This particularly applies to the capture of Mg^{2+} ion from the environment and its transfer for membrane-bound enzyme activity. Mutants lacking teichoic acids are viable, however.

Phages show specific selectivity for different carbohydrate portions of teichoic acids, which may thus be regarded as specific phage attachment sites.

Peptidoglycan–Lipoprotein Complex

In some G (−) bacteria the peptidoglycan is bound also to the outer coat via a lipoprotein molecule composed of 57 amino acid residues. The linkage occurs through the protein moiety. The covalently linked lipid component is phospholipid, which serves to anchor the outer membrane to the peptidoglycan layer. The lipoprotein is first synthesized free in the periplasma and then is bound by the peptidoglycan. The role of this complex is to provide an inelastic foundation to the whole cell envelope.

OUTER MEMBRANE

The outer membrane is a feature of G (−) bacteria. Basically it also consists of a hexagonal, closely packed lipid and protein bilayer similar to that of other membranes. However, the phospholipids and proteins in this bilayer are qualitatively different from those of the inner membrane. Characteristic of the outer membrane is the presence of a variable amount of lipopolysaccharides whose lipid moieties participate in the formation of the membrane continuum, while the oligosaccharide moieties are associated with the inside or outside surfaces of this bilayer.

The only known enzymatic activity of the outer membrane is associated with lipid degradation, and apparently they are not essential for the maintenance of cell integrity. They act as a molecular sieve excluding a number of substances from reaching the more inner parts of the cell wall. Variations in the proportions of UFA and SFA are also dependent on the culture medium and affect the permeability of the outer membrane. The protein component is, however, not affected by changes in the culture medium.

Lipopolysaccharide

The lipopolysaccharide (LPS) molecule represents a polymer of about three LPS basic units with a sedimentation coefficient of 3.5 to 4.1 and a molecular weight of 10,000 to 29,000 daltons. The LPS molecule shows a highly polar polysaccharide region and a large nonpolar lipid region. The amphipathic character allows for strong interactions with phospholipids through its lipid region and protrusion of the hydrophilic polysaccharide region on the inside and the outside of the outer membrane.

LPS is synthesized on the cell membrane proper, and subsequently is extruded to form the outer membrane. However, it remains connected to the peptidoglycan, leaving a space, 0.44 Å wide, called the periplasmic zone. The extruded portion exchanges continuously with newly synthesized material.

LPS comprises three components. First, there is a lipid moiety, called lipid A (Figure 5), consisting of a glucosaminyl-glucosamine disaccharide fully substituted by esterified and amide-linked fatty acids and by phosphate. The glucosamine residues are linked by a 1–6 glucosidic bond. The fatty acids (HM, FA) are bound to the free hydroxyl groups of the diglucosamine residues. Three such diglucosamine units are linked by 1–4 pyrophosphate bridges in forming the polymer.

The second component of LPS is known as the core region or R-core, and can be subdivided into:

1. An inner core region linked to the disaccharide and containing: three molecules of an eight-carbon sugar acid, 3-deoxy-D-mannooctulosonic acid, commonly called 2-keto-3-deoxyoctonate, abbreviated KDO; two molecules of a seven-carbon sugar; L-glycero-D-mannoheptose, abbreviated Hep; and phosphate and phosphorylethanolamine.
2. An outer core region for linkage of the O-antigen, with two molecules of glucose; two molecules of galactose; and one molecule of N-acetyl glucosamine.

The structure of the lipid A and of the R-core is constant for a given genus of bacteria. The number of sugars in the R-core may increase to eight or nine, allowing the distinction of several chemotypes, the simplest of which seems that of *S. typhimurium* with only five sugars. Other sugars, both common and rare, may also be found.

The third component is the O-antigen region, a surface polysaccharide

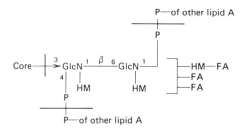

Figure 5. Structure of lipid A of lipopolysaccharide molecule of the outer coat of Gram-negative bacteria. GlcN = glucosamine; HM = 3-D(−) hydroxymyristic acid; FA = lauric acid, palmitic acid, and myristic acid.

chain that exhibits extreme variability and provides the basis for serologic classification. The O-antigen protects the outer membrane by limiting the interactions with antibodies and complement at some distance from the membrane. R strains devoid partially or totally of O-antigen show increased susceptibility to damage.

The O-antigen has a relatively simple structure comprised of repeating oligosaccharide units. The component sugars are hexoses, deoxyhexoses, and dideoxyhexoses with or without ester-linked acetyl groups and arranged in linear or branched forms. This forms the basis for separation into major serological groups and minor subgroups.

The major phospholipid present is phosphatidyl ethanolamine (PE), but it may be substituted by other synthetic or natural phospholipids. There is however the requirement that the entire glycerophosphate backbone be present. The phospholipid molecules interdigitate between molecules of LPS (about 5–10 PE molecules for each LPS molecule). Both LPS and phospholipid form the mosaic structure of the cell surface of Gram-negative bacteria. It is likely that variations in the concentrations of both molecules exert an allosteric effect on the wall-associated enzymes.

The phage specificity of G (−) bacteria is determined by the terminal sugars present in the LPS molecule. The phage receptor sites contain both lipoprotein and LPS.

BACTERIAL CAPSULE

Capsules are more or less defined slime layers present on the exterior of the specialized cell wall in both Gram-positive and Gram-negative bacteria. They consist of heteropolysaccharides. The general structure is that of a repeating tetrasaccharide unit with three linearly arranged sugars and a branched substituted glucoside (Figure 6). Often but not always the branched glucoside is an uronic acid which confers a polyanionic character to the entire molecule.

The sugar residues may vary with the strain of bacteria, some of which show further substitution by O-acetyl groups or unidentified compounds. Functionally the capsule protects the cell by blocking the access to the wall. Phagocytes cannot attach the capsulated bacteria. Hence virulent strains (e.g.,

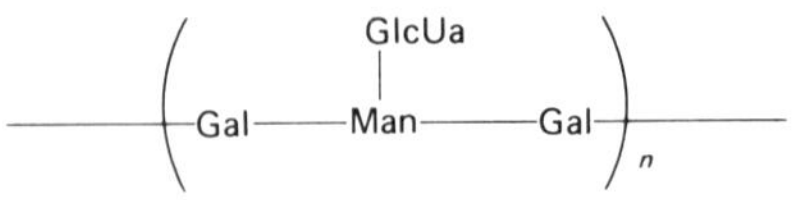

$$\left(\!\!\begin{array}{c} \text{GlcUa} \\ | \\ \text{Gal}\!-\!\!-\!\!\text{Man}\!-\!\!-\!\!\text{Gal} \end{array}\!\!\right)_{\!n}$$

Figure 6. The repeating tetrasaccharide unit of capsular polysaccharide.

Pneumococcus) have a capsule, whereas avirulent strains do not. The capsule may also serve as a site of attachment of capsule-specific phages.

In a few species of *Salmonella, Citrobacter,* and *E. coli* the capsular material is known as the Vi antigen, which is a polymer of partly acetylated N-acetyl-D-galactosaminuric acid. The capsular polysaccharides of streptococci, termed soluble specific substances (SSS), exist in many antigenic forms, allowing the serotypic distinction of these microorganisms.

REFERENCES

1. Schleifer, K. H., and Kandler, O. 1972. Peptidoglycan types of bacterial cell walls and their taxonomic implications. *Bacteriol. Rev.* 36:407.
2. Costerton, J. W., Ingram, J. M., and Cheng, K. J. 1974. Structure and function of the cell envelope of Gram negative bacteria. *Bacteriol. Rev.* 38:87.
3. Cronan, J. E., Jr., and Gelman, E. P. 1975. Physical properties of membrane lipids. Biological relevance and regulation. *Bacteriol. Rev.* 39:232.
4. Henning, U. 1975. Determination of cell shape in bacteria. *Ann. Rev. Microbiol.* 29:45.
5. Salton, M. R. J., and Owen, P. 1976. Bacterial membrane structure. *Ann. Rev. Microbiol.* 30:451.
6. DiRienzo, J. M., Nakamura, K., and Inouye, M. 1978. The outer membrane protein of Gram negative bacteria: Biosynthesis, assembly and function. *Ann. Rev. Biochem.* 47:481.

2.8. Mesosomes

Lazar M. Schwartz

Mesosomes are invaginations of the plasma membranes of bacteria. In G (+) species they appear as saclike vesicular structures; in G (−) species they have a multiply branched tubular structure and are inconspicuous and difficult to identify. Internal membranes resembling mesosomes have also been described in some *Mycobacteria* and fungal myceliums. The number of mesosomes per cell varies slightly with different strains, but there seems to be a negative correlation between their number in a given cell and their degree of structural complexity. In contrast to that, they vary widely in terms of size, shape, and intracellular location. Variations in shape in the same strain are explained by changes in the physiological state of the cell at the time of the experiment.

The ultrastructural appearance of the mesosomes varies with the technics used. Generally, they show a body with a saccular or tubular structure and a neck that communicates with the external medium by pores in the membrane at the origin of the invagination. The sac seems continuous with the plasma membrane. Within the sac there is an internal membrane attached to one or two specific points of the sac. In G (+) bacteria the internal membrane is most commonly seen as vesicles, but lamellar, tubular, or whorled structures can also be seen. These forms may represent sequential stages in the development of mesosomes or the influences of the external ionic strength or divalent cation concentration. The interior of the mesosome is extracytoplasmic, but the cytoplasm has access to the inner regions of the overall structure through the infoldings of the sac. In hypertonic media, mesosomes can evaginate in the periplasmic space. In bacteria in the exponential growth phase the mesosomes are located at sites of the membrane where the dividing septa will develop. This location is not exclusive. Mesosomes may be found at other membrane sites, and similar structures were also described in the nucleus. (See Figures 1–3.)

The composition of mesosomes is compared to that of the plasma membrane in Table 1. The usually lower protein:lipid ratio is due to the lower protein content rather than to the increased lipid of mesosomal membranes. They also contain material with the properties of teichoic acid. The specific activity of mesosomal enzymes is lower than that of plasma membrane enzymes, although somewhat higher in Gram-positive than in Gram-negative bacteria.

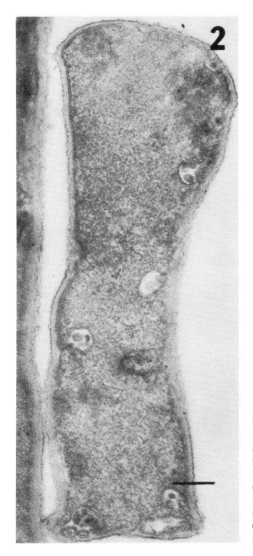

Figure 1. Micrograph of a thin section of *Bacterionema matruchotii* fixed with glutaraldehyde and OsO_4 and stained with uranyl acetate and lead. Pocket-like invaginations of the plasma membrane which contain profiles of vesicles are readily apparent. The trilamellar track of the plasma membrane is very distinct. Bar represents 0.25 um. Reproduced with permission from ref. 1.

Mesosomes of *M. lysodeikticus* also contain an autolytic enzyme that acts under specific conditions on the peptidoglycan layer.

CELLULAR ROLE OF MESOSOMES

The specific cellular role of mesosomes is still unknown although there are several hypotheses.

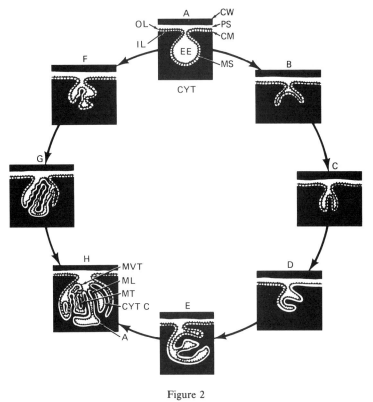

Figure 2

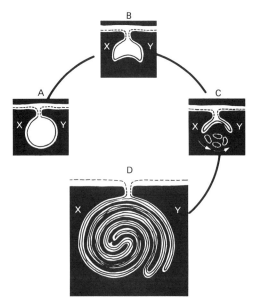

Figure 3

Table 1. Chemical Composition of Mesosomal (M) and Peripheral (P) Membranes of Selected Gram-Positive Bacteria (from Ref. 1).

	MEMBRANE	CHEMICAL COMPOSITION (% DRY WT.)				
		PROTEIN	LIPID	CARBO-HYDRATE	RNA	PROTEIN TO LIPID RATIO
B. licheniformis	M	44	17	ND	2–10	2.6
	P	43–49	18–25	ND	13–15	1.9–2.7
S. aureus	M	41	34	4	8	1.2
	P	56	25	4	15	2.2
M. lysodeikticus	M	30–40	26.1	20	ND	1.0–1.4
	P	42–50	26.4	4.7	ND	1.6–2.9

Figures 2 and 3. Diagrammatic representations of possible models of mesosome formation. Figure 2 illustrates a wide variety of mesosome-like forms seen in both Gram-positive and Gram-negative bacteria but primarily in Gram-positive cells. A through C are simple structures, all of which are proposed to be derived from the initial invagination of the plasma membrane to form the sac (A). Collapsing of the spherical sac could result in the forms shown in B and C. D–H and E–H illustrate two of many possible ways in which complex vesiculotubular and lamellar forms could arise by secondary invaginations of the initial sac membrane. Sidedness of plasma membrane is maintained in all structures regardless of complexity. CW = cell wall, PS = periplasmic space, CM = cytoplasmic membrane, OL = outer leaflet of plasma membrane (indicated by dark particles), IL = inner leaflet, CYT = cytoplasm, EE = external environment. Plasma membrane including sac is indicated by hash marks; newly synthesized membrane at sites of secondary invaginations are unmarked (D–H and E–H). MVT = mesosome vesiculotubules, ML = mesosome lamella, MT = mesosome tubule, CYT C = cytoplasmic channel (formed by secondary invagination of sac so that cytoplasmic components are potentially compartmented by these membranes even though the system is not completely closed), A = proposed site of attachment of chromosome (DNA) to mesosomal sac. Figure 3 shows a possible mode of formation of complex, multilamellar whorls observed in such cells as E. coli O111$_a$. Panels A through C show forms similar to those in Figure 2, representing the development of a flattened saccule from the spherical mesosomal sac. X and Y represent end points of saccule and potential sites of extension (growth) of intracellular membranes. For simplification, the diagram illustrates major extension at X by sequence of arrows and vesicles, although some extension is shown at Y also as indicated in panel C. Panel D shows a complex multilamellar structure formed primarily by the growth and infolding of the flattened saccule upon itself by the extension of X to X' and Y to Y'. Such a structure represents a closed system maintaining a distinct outside (light gray) and inside (darker). The potential for concentrating and/or compartmenting constituents of the external milieu and of the cytoplasm through the formation of complex channels separated by membranes that retain original asymmetric topography (sidedness) is an important feature of this model. (Reproduced with permission from John W. Greenawalt and Theresa L. Whiteside, Mesosomes: Membranous bacterial organelles, Bacteriol. Rev. 39:405, 1975.)

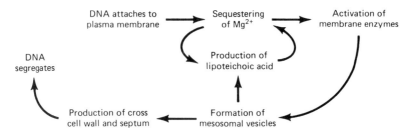

Figure 4. Relationship between mesosomes and cell growth (3).

1. Mesosomes may be involved in electron transport and oxidoreduction processes. The evidence for this supposition is lacking. Indeed, mesosomes are deficient in many of the required components of oxidoreduction such as succinic dehydrogenase, NADH oxidase, $NADH_2$ dehydrogenase, ATPase, and cytochromes.

2. They may play a role in the replication and apportionment of bacterial DNA. This is based on the observation that the nucleoid comes into contact with the mesosomal sac and that after replication of DNA the mesosomes divide. Subsequently, each of the segregating parts pulls with it the daughter nucleoid. The separation process is brought about by the production of new plasma membrane and formation of the septum. Although the role of the cell membrane in the replication of bacteria is recognized, the exact mechanism remains debatable. The uncertainty applies also to the mesosomes.

3. Mesosomes may play a role in the cell wall remodeling. Elongation of the cell wall occurs by splitting of the crosslinkages of the mesosomes to the plasma membrane with subsequent displacement of the crosslinks. In this hypothesis mesosomes are attached to critical points for new wall formation.

4. There is the belief that in Gram-positive microorganisms, all the lipoteichoic acid is produced in the mesosomes. Since lipoteichoic acids are related to Mg^{2+} movements in and out of the membrane, Huff, Cole, and Theodore propose the integrating scheme of Figure 4.

On the other hand, Mindich and Dales deny any role of mesosomes in the growth of the plasma membrane.

REFERENCES

1. Greenawalt, J. W., and Whiteside, T. L. 1975. *Bacteriol. Rev.* 39:405.
2. Rogers, H. J. 1970. *Bacteriol. Rev.* 34:194.
3. Huff, E., Cole, R. M., and Theodore, T. S. 1974. *J. Bacteriol.* 120:273.
4. Mindich, L., and Dales, S. 1972. *J. Cell Biol.* 55:32.

2.9. Sporulation

Lazar M. Schwartz

Sporulation is a process whereby under conditions unfavorable for growth, certain bacteria (e.g., genus *Bacillus, Clostridium, Myxococcus,* etc.) undergo a sequence of changes in morphology and physiology resulting in a multicoated structure, the spore, which becomes resistant to the adverse effects of the environment and is metabolically dormant. One cell generally gives rise to one spore, which according to the species may be located terminally, subterminally, or centrally. Spores of this type are called endospores. Sporulation begins immediately following the end of exponential growth in cultures or after transfer of the growing cells in a medium incapable of supporting growth. After the first stage of sporulation has been initiated, it may proceed in a nutrient-free medium, a process termed endotrophic sporulation.

MORPHOLOGY AND COMPOSITION OF A RIPE SPORE

The typical endospores are oblate spheroids usually with axes of 0.5 nm and 1.5 nm. The spore comprises several layers enclosing a portion of the bacterial cytoplasm containing nucleic acids, protein synthesizing machinery, and enzymes and substrates for the generation of chemical energy.

In several species the spore appears separated from the cyptoplasm of the bacterium by a membranelike structure called exosporium (Figure 1). At least in some of the bacteria studied the exosporium is not formed from preexisting membranes. The exosporium contains low levels of the enzymes usually associated with the bacterial membranes, suggesting that it may facilitate the redistribution of these components during the sporulation process. Crystalline protein inclusions (parasporal proteins) can be located in the space separating the exosporium from the body of the spore or outside the exosporium. The parasporal protein comprises a heterogenous population of small polypeptides with larger protein subunits detected in several species. There is evidence indicating that parasporal proteins result from overproduction of spore coat proteins.

The most external coat contains three distinct layers (Figure 1):

1. An external cross-patched layer (CP) composed of parallel stacked flattened rods forming uniform patches 60–90 nm in length. The CP layer

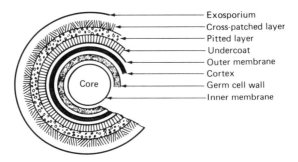

Figure 1. Diagramatic representation of the spore coats.

varies with the species and the conditions of spore formation. It is deficient in sulfite-containing spores, in spores produced in agar and in some inclusions forming species.

2. A pitted layer (P) containing rows of pits or holes, 6–7 nm in diameter.
3. An undercoat with no distinctive architecture and varying in thickness along the circumference of the undercoat.

About 90% by weight of the spore coat consists of proteins comprising the common amino acids and varying amounts of amino sugars and phosphate. These proteins contain three to five times more half cystine residues and an unusually high content of glycine in comparison with the cell wall. In some mutants the outer coat is deficient or nonexistent. The latter forms are called bald spores.

The inner coat consists of (Figure 1):

1. An outer membrane separating the undercoat and the cortex.
2. The cortex, a layer of mucopeptides similar to those of the cell walls, comprising also a number of lytic enzymes. In some species the proteins contain diaminopimelic acid instead of lysine.
3. Germ cell wall, an intermediate layer beneath the cortex.
4. The inner membrane, an equivalent of the plasma membrane of the bacterial cell.

The core is the central soluble portion of the spore. It contains a constant amount of double-stranded DNA, usually half of that characteristic for the vegetative form of the species. The core RNA is two to seven times higher than the DNA content, and all RNA classes are represented. The amino acid and free nucleotide pools are much lower. The core contains a large number of enzymes whose levels appear similar to those of vegetative cells in the early stages of spore formation. Some enzymes are, however, absent or at very low levels. In some species the tricarboxylic acid cycle enzymes and cytochromes are absent.

The core contains picolinic acid as high as 15% spore dry weight. Picolinic acid is absent from the vegetative cells. In the spore the picolinic acid does not have any metabolic role and is chelated with Ca^{2+} and Mn^{2+} ions.

STAGES IN SPORULATION

The events leading to the initiation of sporulation are not known. The two prevailing hypotheses are as follows:

1. Initiation of sporulation occurs by relief of a suppression mechanism similar to that operative in induced enzymes.

2. Sporulation occurs during a unique period of the cell cycle and represents a constant probability per unit time. A metabolic shift-down due to depletion of particular nutrients at times when the chromosome replicates, facilitates the initiation of sporulation. In some species methionine starvation or the presence of methionine antagonists are the initiating events. Methionine starvation effects are related to insufficient production of spermidine, a repressor of sporulation. Methionine is a precursor of spermidine.

Sporulation develops in seven stages (Figure 2):

Stage I (1.4 hours). The bacterial DNA is condensed along the main axis of the cell, forming a long filament.

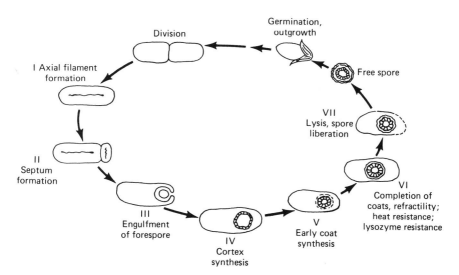

Figure 2. Life cycle of a sporulating bacillus. In this schematic representation the vegetative cell wall has been omitted for clarity; The outermost layer shown is the vegetative cell cytoplasmic membrane. (Reproduced with permission from Ref. 3.)

Stage II (0.9 hour). The cell membrane invaginates, pinching off part of the nuclear material. A transverse septum thus forms which separates the cell into two unequal protoplasts, each apparently containing one genome equivalent of DNA material. The smaller protoplast is called the forespore.

Stage III (1.8 hours). The forespore is engulfed by growth of the larger protoplast membrane around it. The forespore has now two membranes which are oriented inside out in comparison with other membranes and preclude active transport of molecules into the developing spore.

Stage IV (1.6 hours). The spore wall synthesis proceeds by deposition of cell wall–like peptidoglycan. Both the forespore and the mother cell presumably contribute mucopeptides to this process.

Stage V (2 hours). Protein is deposited in the outer coat, Ca^{2+} and dipicolinic acid start to accumulate. The spore becomes refractile and resistant to octanol.

Stage VI. This stage is ill defined and represents the ripening of the spore with completion of the coats. The spore gains resistance to chloroform, heat, and lysozyme digestion.

Stage VII. The cell wall is lysed, and the spore is released in free form. It may survive in this form for years.

PROTEIN SYNTHESIS AND TURNOVER DURING SPORULATION

In sporulation induced by starvation there is an extensive protein turnover related to production of new proteins, some of which appear different, at least by immunoelectrophoresis. The rate of protein synthesis may increase two to ten times, and recycling of the parent protein may be as high as 18% per hour. The nature and the capacity of the protein synthesizing machinery seem similar in both the vegetative cell and the spore. The turnover would provide the developing spore with means of eliminating unnecessary enzymes and with the amino acids required for synthesizing sporulation enzymes. Some of the proteins of the vegetative cell are retained intact in the core and represent many protein species, including that in the ribosomes. Chloramphenicol added at various stages of sporulation inhibits the further development of the forespore.

The coat proteins are unique to the spore. Some compositional differences were already mentioned. The amount of coat protein per spore amounts to 1.6×10^{-13}, with the undercoat and P layer comprising 80% of the total coat protein. Synthesis occurs at a constant rate during sporulation, and synthesis and assembly into the coat seem to occur concomitantly.

The formation of the parasporal protein occurs in stages II and III, and its production may delay the development of the spore. There is some evidence that the parasporal proteins differ in some respect from the coat proteins. In *C. perfringens* the parasporal protein has toxin properties.

GERMINATION AND OUTGROWTH

Germination and outgrowth occur upon transfer in an appropriate medium and by various chemical or physical treatments such as sublethal heating for short periods, protein hydrolysates, some divalent cations, exposure to thiol reagents, or exposure to strong oxidizing agents. Most effective in this respect is the presence of L-alanine on the medium. Once initiated, the germination is irreversible. It occurs in sequential steps, suggesting a preprogrammed process.

The outer coat fractures, the cortex breaks under the influence of lytic enzymes, and dipicolinic acid, Ca^{2+}, mucopeptides, and other compounds are released from the germinating cell. The ATP level, which in the spore state was very low, increases rapidly within the first 3 min, followed by a second increase between 5 and 15 min later. RNA and protein synthesis also occur early. Within 20 min nucleic acid precursors begin to form, followed at 60 min by DNA synthesis, which marks the beginning of the vegetative phase.

REFERENCES

1. Aronson, A. I., and Fitz-James, P. 1976. Structure and morphogenesis of the bacterial spore coat. *Bacteriol. Rev.* 40:360.
2. Barker, L., Gould, G. W., and Wolf, L., eds. 1971. *Spore Research.* Academic Press, New York.
3. Kornberg, A., Spudich, J. A., Nelson, D. L., and Deutscher, M. P. 1968. Origin of proteins in sporulation. *Annu. Rev. Biochem.* 37:51.
4. Markham, R., Bancroft, J. B., Davies, D. R., Hopwood, D. A., and Horne, R. W., eds. 1973. *The Generation of Subcellular Structures.* American Elsevier, New York.
5. Sadoff, H. L. 1973. Comparative aspects of morphogenesis in three prokaryotic bacteria. *Annu. Rev. Microbiol.,* 27:133.

2.10. Cell Wall of Yeasts

Lazar M. Schwartz

The cell envelope of yeasts comprises the plasma membrane and the cell wall proper separated by an irregular intervening region celled periplasmic space and containing a number of enzymes. Invaginations of the plasma membrane and irregularities of the inner aspect of the wall allow variations in the volume of the periplasmic space depending on the cell environment. The cell wall measures 100–200 nm in thickness and is fairly rigid. In *Saccharomyces* species the wall contains about 29% glucan, 31% mannan, 13% protein, 8.5% lipid, and 3% inorganic matter. The porportions vary with the yeast strain, age of the cells, and growth conditions. The wall contains three main protein complexes: glucan–protein, mannan–protein I, and glucomannan–protein II. Other components of the wall include phosphorylated compounds such as peptidophosphomannan and phosphomannan. In fungi the wall contains chitin instead of glucan. In yeasts chitin is present in wall scars at sites where budding has taken place (bud scars). The cell wall except for the bud scars can be lysed by a polysaccharide-splitting enzyme from the gut juice of the snail *Helix pomatia*.

GLUCAN

The glucan layer provides the network for the structure of the cell wall. There are two components: a main internal component, in which the glucan has a crystalline structure forming a fibrillar layer, and an outer amorphous region. Both are glucose polymers, differing only in their mode of attachment. The fibrillar layer has predominantly β-1$\rightarrow$3 linked glucose units with some in β-1$\rightarrow$6 linkages. The amorphous layer shows predominantly β-1$\rightarrow$6 linked glucose units with side chains in β-1$\rightarrow$3 linkages.

The synthesis of crystalline glucan occurs initially in a soluble form which subsequently aggregates, forming a concentration gradient around the cell. Glucan secretion is not sensitive to inhibitors of protein synthesis.

MANNAN

The mannan layer is located at the external surface and is probably enmeshed with the glucan of deeper layers. The different arrangements of these components account for the antigenic characteristics of different genera and strains of yeasts.

Mannan consists of an α-1→6 linked mannose polysaccharide backbone to which are attached α-1→2 and α-1→3 mono-, di-, and trimannosyl branches. The molecule also contains phosphomannosyl residues and N-acetyl glucosamine. It is linked to protein via N-glycosidic linkages from N-acetyl glucosamine to asparagine and via O-glucosidic linkages from mannose to serine and threonine. The schematic structure of mannan is shown in Figure 1. The polysaccharide chains attached to serine and threonine residues are shorter than those attached to asparagine. The ratios between the mono-, di-, and trimannosyl branches vary from species to species and with the age of the culture. The peptidophosphomannan is part of the cell wall, while the phosphomannan forms the outermost layer. In other yeast species such as *Cladosporium wernickii* or *Candida albicans* the phosphorylated sugar may comprise phosphomannan, phosphogalactan, or phosphogalactomannan.

Mannan peptide synthesis apparently occurs in the cytoplasm of some membranes or vesicles, from which the complex is transported to the plasmalemma and excreted to the outside. In contradistinction to glucan, the formation of the mannan wall matrix is sensitive to inhibitors of protein synthesis because mannan is transported only in a protein complexed form.

CHITIN

Chitin is a linear polymer of N-acetyl glucosamine, found mainly in the bud scars of yeast wall. Budding occurs first by formation of a disk, called primary septum, which is comprised primarily of chitin. Plasma membrane and cell wall material deposit on both sides of the primary septum, forming the secondary septa and completing the enclosure between mother and daugh-

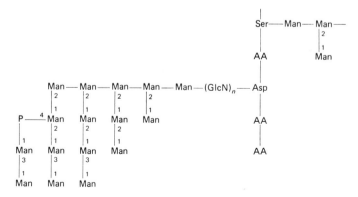

Figure 1. Schematic structure of mannan. AA: amino acid other than Ser or Asp.

ter cell. Separation of the daughter cell follows. The bud scar represents the area of the mother cell wall that retains the septum portion. Once there, it remains for the life of the cell. The structure of chitin is shown in Figure 2.

The synthesis and incorporation of chitin requires a chitin synthetase modulating system that includes three components:

1. Zymogen precursor, bound to particulate material and uniformly distributed in the plasma membrane. The precursor probably contains chitin synthetase enzyme in the inactive form.
2. Activating factor, probably a protease, which activates the zymogen at the site of future budding. What factors determine the selection of the segment of the wall where budding is to occur are not known. The activating factor is probably enclosed in vacuoles or vesicles. It has been suggested that coalescence of the vesicle with the plasma membrane is responsible for the activation of specific areas.
3. An inhibitor of the chitin synthetase system, a small protein that would interact allosterically with the activating factor. The inhibitor would inactivate protease that has spilled into the cytoplasm. Chitin synthesis is arrested.

OTHER CHARACTERISTICS OF THE CELL WALL OF YEASTS

The polysaccharide chains in the wall do not seem extensively bonded together, but their content of glucosamine and protein may play a role in the insolubility of the wall. The proteins are linked to polysaccharides in ester linkages and have a functional role in maintaining the morphology of the wall. Once incorporated into the wall, glucose and glucosamine are metabolically inert, suggesting little turnover of the hexosyl residues of the cell wall. Variation in the phosphomannan–protein complex determines the degree of cell aggregation. A nitrogenous component of the wall seems critical in this respect. When its rate of synthesis is insufficient to maintain a certain concentration in the cell wall, flocculation does not occur. Some yeasts grow at the surface, forming a head (top yeasts), whereas others form a sludge at the bottom of the vessel (bottom yeasts). The mechanism of aggregation is

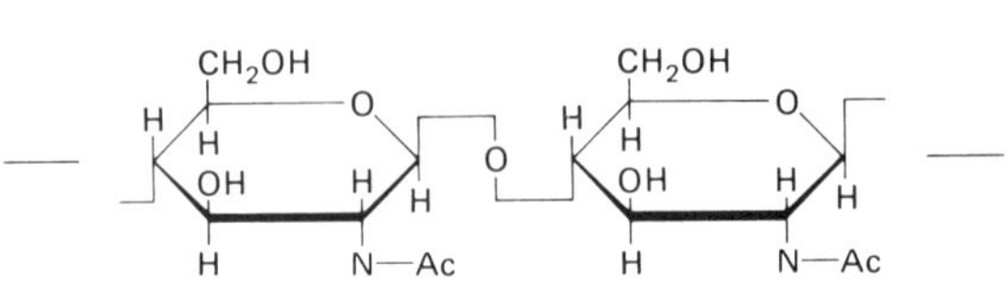

Figure 2. The structure of chitin.

not known. It was suggested that it involves cross-bridging by calcium ions between phosphomannan–proteins of adjacent walls.

Many of the mural and extracellular yeast enzymes are glycoproteins. They play a role in modifying constituents of the medium to forms more accessible to the organism. They are relatively stable to enzymatic proteolysis, elevated temperature, and a wide range of pH, probably owing to their glycan content. Of these enzymes, invertase is one of the best known. Invertase comprises three variants. The major species, called glycoinvertase, is a glycoprotein located in the periplasmic space, which contains 50% mannosyl and 3% glucosaminyl residues. It was suggested that the enzyme is maintained in this location by surrounding rigid S–S containing structures. The minor species is located within the plasma membrane. It is a protein of 135,000-dalton molecular weight. Both forms have the same antigenic determinants. The third form of invertase is intracellular.

Other surface enzymes include acid phosphatase, catalase, proteases, and mannase, to name only a few. Some are characteristic of the strain under consideration (e.g., melibiase in *S. carlbergensis* or glucamylase in *S. diastia*). Some of them are involved in the budding process and the final shape of the bud.

The cell wall also contains glycoproteins with no known enzymatic activities. They may serve as recognition molecules for various functions such as mating between like cells or the flocculation process.

REFERENCES

1. Necas, O. 1971. Cell wall synthesis in yeast protoplasts. *Bacteriol. Rev.* 35:149.
2. Gander, J. E. 1974. Fungal cell wall glycoproteins and peptidopolysaccharides. *Annu. Rev. Microbiol.* 28:103.
3. Cabib, E. 1975. Molecular aspects of yeast morphogenesis. *Annu. Rev. Microbiol.* 29:191.

SECTION 3
CELL RECEPTORS

MORLEY D. HOLLENBERG, SECTION
EDITOR

3.1. Receptors, Acceptors, and Other Cell Surface Markers: An Overview

Morley D. Hollenberg

The idea that the biological response of cells to a variety of endogenous or foreign ligands (e.g., hormones, drugs) is mediated via a specialized membrane-localized "receptor substance" or "receptor" can be traced directly back to the work of Langley (12), Ehrlich (6), and Clark (3, 4). The "receptor" concept has been enormously productive in analyzing, from a pharmacologic point of view, the action of many compounds. So successful has been this approach, that today, the receptor molecules that early investigators may have only vaguely conceptualized are being detected as discrete molecular entities by a variety of techniques (e.g., as stained bands subsequent to gel electrophoresis, or protein peaks, subsequent to chromatographic separation). Reference can now be made to a number of comprehensive reviews and treatises dealing both with the details of the methodologies involved and with a large amount of information about many neurotransmitters and hormones (1, 2, 5, 7, 9–11, 13, 14, 17, 18). In addition to the increasing sophistication with which investigators have been able to analyze concentration–effect relationships for both agonist (i.e., compounds that cause a response) and antagonist (i.e., compounds that oppose the action of agonists) agents, there have been major advances in the understanding of the molecular biology of receptors. There have been many exciting discoveries since about 1965, consequent to the development of reliable techniques to measure the binding of radioactive ligand probes to specific cellular receptors.

It is most important to point out, however, that the notion of a cellular receptor is inextricably linked to the biological responsiveness of a system of interest. Thus, the distinction of receptor from nonreceptor interactions in binding studies [a problem that can present considerable difficulties (9)] can be seen to depend largely on an interpretation of the binding data in the context of a background of observed concentration–response data for a variety of ligands similar to the one of particular interest. The use of a number of other criteria in the interpretation of ligand binding data, having to do with appropriate ligand affinities, saturability, reversibility, stereochemical specificity, and appropriate tissue distribution, can often serve to distinguish "specific" (i.e., receptor-related) from "nonspecific" binding. It is now evident that, in addition to cell surface binding sites representing "true" receptor-related pharmacologic recognition sites, there may be other highly selective binding sites (e.g., for catecholamines) that are unrelated to known pharmacologic receptors.

It is also becoming increasingly evident that, aside from "true" receptors and from other chemically specific nonreceptor binding sites, there are also membrane recognition sites ("acceptors") that, in addition to the familiar ion or metabolite transport sites, have to do with the communication of chemical information from the cell exterior to the cytoplasm.

The term "receptor" may, therefore require a more restricted and precise definition. In pharmacologic terms, the membrane receptor for agents such as neurotransmitters can be thought of as a macromolecule (probably an oligomer) that has the dual function of both recognizing a ligand of interest in a chemically specific manner (recognition function) and causing an immediate perturbation of membrane function (i.e., the action function) that in some manner leads to a biological response. This recognition–action function of a receptor may be distinguished from a membrane "acceptor" site that may function solely as a recognition molecule for the selective cellular uptake of certain serum-borne constituents.

An example of a cellular "acceptor" can be seen in the function of transcobalamin-II (TC II) (16), a protein that serves as a transport agent for cobalamin in the circulation and subsequently delivers cobalamin to the cell interior (15). In the case of cobalamin, the TC II–cobalamin complex can bind to a specific cellular acceptor site, leading to the translocation of the complex and the subsequent intracellular release of cobalamin for further metabolic processes. In this instance, cobalamin can be thought of as the pharmacologic agent active at an intracellular (enzyme) receptor; the membrane constituent that recognizes the TC II–cobalamin complex, in a highly specific manner (e.g., the TC II–cobalamin complex, but neither free TC II nor free cobalamin binds to the acceptor site), clearly functions in a manner different from the one envisioned for neurotransmitter receptors and may, therefore, be termed an "acceptor." The cellular binding site for low-density lipoprotein (LDL) (8) can be thought of in similar terms, wherein the feedback regulator, cholesterol, is the pharmacologically active ligand in the cell interior subsequent to internalization via the LDL acceptor. Importantly, for acceptors as well as receptors, it is to be expected that a strict chemical specificity will be observed along with other criteria that are consistent with a reversible, high-affinity recognition function. In the context of the above discussion, steroid hormone receptors, which reside in the cytoplasm, can be seen to play a role separate from either that of the recognition–action function of the neurotransmitter receptor or that of the passive translocation function of the TC II–cobalamin or LDL acceptor.

In the chapters that follow, attention will first be given to the development of the receptor concept (Chapter 3.2) and to receptors for a variety of pharmacologically active agents such as acetylcholine, catecholamines, histamine, polypeptides, and steroids (Chapters 3.3 to 3.7). These receptors are known to be involved in a wide spectrum of cellular responses. Attention will then be given to those membrane-localized constituents involved in the immune response (surface immunoglobulins and histocompatability complex molecules: Chapters 3.8 and 3.9). These surface-localized components can be seen in many ways to function in a manner analogous to receptors for hormones. Finally, consideration will be given to cell recognition sites for viruses, to the process whereby cell surface interactions lead to aggregation, and to the appearance, upon cell de-differentation, of cell antigens that may play some role either in tumorigenesis or in fetal development (Chapters 3.10 to 3.12). In keeping with the objectives of this book, overviews of the areas of interest will be given, with reference made to more extensive treatises on the individual subjects.

REFERENCES

1. Birdsall, N. H. M., and Hulme, E. C. 1976. Biochemical studies on muscarinic acetylcholine receptors. *J. Neurochem.* 27:7–16.
2. Blecher, M., Vol. Ed. 1976. *Methods in Receptor Research; Methods in Molecular Biology,* Vol. 9, Parts I and II. A. I. Larkin and J. A. Last, ser. eds. Marcel Dekker, New York.
3. Clark, A. J. 1926a. The reaction between acetylcholine and muscle cells. *J. Physiol. (London)* 61:530–46.
4. Clark, A. J. 1926b. The antagonism of acetylcholine by atropine. *J. Physiol. (London)* 61:547–56.
5. Cuatrecasas, P., and Hollenberg, M. D. 1976. Membrane receptors and hormone action. *Adv. Protein Chem.* 30:251–451.
6. Ehrlich, P. 1908. On partial functions of the cell. Nobel lecture, in *The Collected Papers of P. Ehrlich,* Vol. III, p. 183, F. Himmelweit, M. Marquardt, and H. Dale, eds. Pergamon Press, New York, 1956.
7. Ginsberg, B. H. 1977. The insulin receptor: Properties and regulation. In *Biochemical Actions of Hormones,* Vol. IV, G. Litwack, ed., pp. 313–49. Academic Press, New York.
8. Goldstein, J. L., and Brown, M. S. 1975. Hyperlipidemia in coronary artery disease: A biochemical genetic approach. *J. Lab. Clin. Med.* 85:15–28.
9. Hollenberg, M. D., and Cuatrecasas, P. 1978a. Distinction of receptor from non-receptor interactions in binding studies: Historical and practical perspectives. In *The Receptors, a Treatise,* Vol. 1, R. D. O'Brien, ed. Plenum Press, New York.
10. Hollenberg, M. D., and Cuatrecasas, P. 1978b. Membrane receptors and hormone action: Recent developments. *Prog. Neuropsychopharmacol.* 2:287–302.
11. Kahn, C. R. 1976. Membrane receptors for hormones and neurotransmitters. *J. Cell Biol.* 70:261–86.

12. Langley, J. N. 1906. On nerve endings and on special excitable substances. *Proc. R. Soc. B* 78:170–94.

13. Lefkowitz, R. J. 1975. Identification of adenylate cyclase coupled beta-adrenergic receptors with radiolabeled beta-adrenergic antagonists. *Biochem. Pharmacol.* 24:1651–58.

14. Lefkowitz, R. 1978. Identification and regulation of alpha and beta-adrenergic receptors. *Fed. Proc.* 37:123–29.

15. Mahoney, M. S., and Rosenberg, L. E. 1975. Inborn errors of cobalamin metabolism. In *Cobalamin Biochemistry and Pathophysiology.* B. M. Babior, ed., pp. 369–402. John Wiley & Sons, New York.

16. Nexø, E. 1978. Transcobalamin I and other human R-Binders: Purification, structural, spectral and physiologic studies. *Scand. J. Haematol.* 20:221–236.

17. Roth, J. 1973. Peptide hormone binding to receptors: A review of direct studies *in vitro. Metabolism* 22:1059–73.

18. Yamamura, H., Enna, S., and Kuhar, M. 1978. *Neurotransmitter Receptor Binding.* Raven Press, New York.

3.2. Pharmacological Receptors

John J. Mieyal

A. INTRODUCTION

In his forward to the monograph *Drug Receptors* (1), Rang proposed a broad definition of the term "drug" to include any relatively small molecule (e.g., endogenous neurotransmitters such as acetylcholine and norepinephrine, hormones such as insulin and glucagon, and synthetic drugs such as the antihistamines diphenhydramine and metiamide) that reacts with a specific site on a macromolecule and thereby modifies the macromolecule so as to alter its functional properties and elicit a physiological response. The specific macromolecular complex, usually localized to cellular membranes, that binds the "drug" and initiates the development of the physiological response is called a *receptor*. This terminology evolved from the studies begun about a century ago by Langley (2, 3), who coined the term "receptive substance" and introduced the concepts of the law of mass action to the interpretation of drug action at the molecular level (see below). In other chapters in this section, specific details are given concerning the receptors for various hormones and neurotransmitters that have been investigated extensively. This chapter is devoted to a general discussion of drug–receptor interactions.

The sequence of molecular events described above occurs when a drug reaches its site of action. The magnitude of the physiological response or drug action is dependent upon the concentration of free drug at the target tissue which contains the specific receptors for that drug. Various factors may affect the amount of drug that ultimately reaches that receptor locale. These factors include the dose or total quantity of drug administered, the route of administration, the extent to which the drug is bound to plasma proteins (especially albumin), the rate and extent of biotransformation of the drug into metabolites with altered efficacy, and the extent of redistribution of the drug to tissues separate from the target organ. Thus, a sufficient dose of the drug must be given in order to satisfy the various competing phenomena and still deliver the appropriate amount to the site of action in order that the desired response be achieved. Thorough accounts of how each of these competing factors may limit the concentration of drug available at the target tissue have been presented elsewhere (4, 5). The purpose of this chapter is to focus on drug–receptor interactions and consider how they are related to the physiological responses.

B. DRUG–RECEPTOR THEORIES

It has been observed generally that there is a systematic relationship between the effective concentration of a drug and the magnitude of the response it elicits. The interpretation of this dose–response relationship was formulated most simply in terms of the mass law by Clark (6) in the 1920s. He postulated that the observed biological effect resulted from complex formation between drug molecules and their receptors, and that the magnitude of the response was directly proportioned to the number of receptors occupied by the drug molecules. Thus, the maximum response would correspond to 100% occupation. These concepts are represented by the following equation:

$$D + R \underset{k_{-1}}{\overset{k_1}{\rightleftharpoons}} DR \rightarrow \rightarrow \rightarrow \text{Response} \tag{1}$$

where D refers to the concentration of free drug, R is concentration of free receptor, and DR is concentration of the drug–receptor complex. Then, if the physiological change or response is designated Δ, this *occupancy theory* is most simply expressed as $\Delta = \text{const.} (DR)$, and the maximum response is given by $\Delta_{max} = \text{const.} (R_{TOT})$, where "const." is a proportionality constant. Since the total receptor concentration $R_{TOT} = R + DR$, the following equation is the equilibrium expression for the drug–receptor complex:

$$K_D = \frac{k_{-1}}{k_1} = \frac{(R_{TOT} - DR)\,(D)}{(DR)} \tag{2}$$

where K_D is the dissociation constant for the drug–receptor complex. From the equations above, it can be shown that $\Delta/\Delta_{max} = (DR)/(R_{TOT})$ and:

$$\Delta = \frac{\Delta_{max}\,(D)}{K_D + (D)} \tag{3}$$

In the usual situation, the concentration of drug at its site of action is much greater than (R_{TOT}), so that it may be assumed for equation (3) that little of the total amount of drug is complexed, that is, that $(D) \equiv (D_{TOT})$. This simplification allows the data for the dependence of biological effect on administered drug concentration to be treated according to equation (3) and expressed graphically as shown in Figure 1.

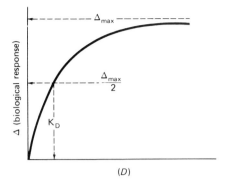

Figure 1. Dose response relationship, rectangular hyperbolic form (see text)

The molecular interpretation of Figure 1 is that as the concentration of drug is increased, more and more receptor sites are occupied by drug until full occupation is achieved, which corresponds to the maximum biological response (depicted by the asymptote, Δ_{max}). It follows from equation (3) that the value for the concentration of drug at which the half-maximal efffect ($\Delta_{max}/2$) is obtained corresponds to K_D (Figure 1). This relationship between $\Delta_{max}/2$ and K_D is fundamental to the occupancy theory, and it is true only if all events subsequent to drug–receptor complex formation that ultimately generate the physiological effect are intimately coupled, so that the fractional response of any one of the events is equivalent to the fractional occupancy of the receptor. (Exceptions to this situation are discussed below.)

Representations of dose–response data are often more convenient in formats other than that of Figure 1. For example, a linear relationship may be obtained by inverting equation (3):

$$\frac{1}{\Delta} = \frac{K_D}{\Delta_{max}} \cdot \frac{1}{D} + \frac{1}{\Delta_{max}} \tag{4}$$

Figure 2 displays the double-reciprocal plot and shows how K_D and Δ_{max} are so obtained.

Another way to represent the dose–response data, which is used in pharmachological studies where the dose range is extensive, is to convert to a logarithmic scale. Rearrangement of equation (3) and conversion to logarithms yields the following expression:

$$\log \left(\frac{\Delta}{\Delta_{max} - \Delta} \right) = -\log D + \log K_D \tag{5}$$

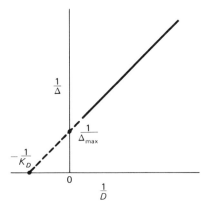

Figure 2. Dose response relationship, double reciprocal plot (see text)

A plot of log $(\Delta/\Delta_{max} - \Delta)$ versus $-\log D$ yields a straight line whose slope is unity; when $\Delta = \Delta_{max}/2$, log $(\Delta/\Delta_{max} - \Delta) = 0$, and log $D = \log K_D$ (Figure 3). Equation (5) and Figure 3 are analogous to the Hill equation and Hill plot, respectively, which are used to assess the degree of cooperativity in drug–receptor interactions, the only difference being the inclusion of the Hill coefficient n in the expression; that is, $-n \log D$ (see further discussion of cooperativity, below).

In many cases, an extrapolated value of Δ_{max} is not easily obtained so that the data may be represented in the format of Figure 3. It has therefore become common practice to simply present semilogarithmic plots of Δ versus $-\log D$. The typical so-called log dose–response (LDR) curve is sigmoid in shape (Figure 4).

Throughout the foregoing discussion, the term "drug" was used to describe

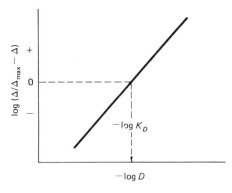

Figure 3. Log fractional response vs log dose (Hill plot).

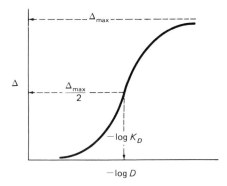

Figure 4. Typical log dose response curve.

an agent that elicits some physiological response such as change in muscle tension, change in ion fluxes, change in blood pressure, and so forth. A more specific term for such an agent is *agonist*. On the other hand, an agent that diminishes the effectiveness of an agonist without producing an effect itself is called an *antagonist*. The latter type of agents may be further classified as competitive or noncompetitive. If the inhibition caused by a particular concentration of antagonist can be overcome by increasing the concentration of the agonist, ultimately approaching the same maximal effect, the antagonist is competitive. This situation is illustrated by Figure 5, curve B, where the presence of the competitive antagonist shifts the LDR curve for the agonist to the right; the apparent K_D for the agonist is now given by $(1 + I/K_I) \cdot K_D$, where I is the concentration of the antagonist and K_I is the dissociation constant for the antagonist–receptor complex. This type of inhibition is generally interpreted to mean that the antagonist reversibly binds directly to the

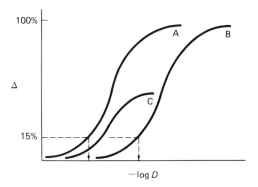

Figure 5. A: agonist alone. B: agonist + competitive antagonist. C: agonist + noncompetitive antagonist. Log dose response relationships showing effects of antagonists.

agonist receptor site, but it can also result from reversible or irreversible interaction of the antagonist at some other site as long as such interaction alters the affinity of the receptor for the agonist without affecting the maximum response potential. Noncompetitive antagonism is insurmountable by increasing agonist concentration (Figure 5, curve C). In effect the antagonist removes some of the receptors from action, but does not alter the affinity for agonist of those remaining functional. This result may occur from irreversible binding of antagonist at any site to prevent binding of agonist to receptor (or even destruction of receptor sites); or it could occur by reversible or irreversible interaction of antagonist with any component of the system so as to prevent the development of the physiological response after agonist–receptor complex formation. Besides these situations, there are also examples of mixed-type antagonism in which both the affinity and maximal response to the agonist are affected.

It is not always possible to develop complete LDR curves such as those shown in Figure 5. For example, the agonist may not be soluble enough, or it may elicit toxic effects at the higher doses necessary to determine whether or not a maximal response can be reattained in the presence of an antagonist. In such cases, a different approach is necessary to determine whether or not the antagonism is competitive in nature. This can be done by using a null method with regard to the drug effect (i.e., by determining the doses of agonist necessary to achieve the same submaximal response in the presence and absence of antagonist). This is illustrated on Figure 5 (curves A and B) for a response corresponding to 15% of maximum. This method of matching effects can be carried out for several different antagonist concentrations in order to determine the nature of the inhibition. A convenient mathematical relationship was derived by Schild and Arunlakshana (7), which pertains to the situation of competitive antagonism. As noted above, the apparent K_D for the drug in the presence of competitive antagonist (inhibitor) is given by $(1 + I/K_I) \cdot K_D$. Substituting this expression into equation (3), above, one obtains equation (6), which describes the response of the system in the presence of the antagonist:

$$\Delta = \frac{\Delta_{max} (D)'}{K_D(1 + I/K_I) + (D)'} \tag{6}$$

In the situation where the same response is achieved in the presence of antagonist as in its absence, the right-hand sides of equations (3) and (6) may be set equal, and the following expression is derived:

$$\frac{(D)'}{(D)} - 1 = I/K_I \tag{7}$$

Reconverting equation (7) to logarithmic format yields the so-called Schild equation (8):

$$\log\left[\frac{D'}{D} - 1\right] = \log I - \log K_I \tag{8}$$

where D'/D is the ratio of the concentrations of agonist in the presence (D') and absence (D) of antagonist that yield the same response, I is the concentration of antagonist, and K_I is the dissociation constant for the antagonist–receptor complex. Figure 6 illustrates the use of the Schild equation to characterize competitive antagonism. Thus, an antagonist is competitive if the slope of a plot of log (dose ratio − 1) versus log (antagonist) is equal to unity. The dissociation constant for the antagonist is obtained directly as the x-intercept; that is, it corresponds to that concentration of antagonist such that double the dose of agonist is necessary to achieve the same effect as in the absence of antagonist. It is a prerequisite for the application of this method of data treatment that the antagonist have no agonist activity. A corollary to the Schild equation, which may be used in a diagnostic fashion, is that a specific competitive antagonist should cause the same degree of antagonism in a certain dose irrespective of the agonist used, provided that all of the agonists act on the same receptor.

It is evident from the description of competitive antagonism above that binding of a drug to the receptor is not a sufficient condition for generation of a response; otherwise pure antagonism could not occur. It is generally thought that the combination of an agonist with its receptor activates the

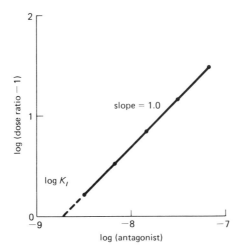

Figure 6. Plotting procedure to demonstrate competitive antagonism (Schild plot)

response network by causing a specific conformational change in the macro-molecular environment surrounding the receptor site; it must be presumed that the binding of a pure antagonist either does not generate such a change, or that the change elicited is inappropriate. It is certainly conceivable that agents exist that could generate a change whose magnitude lay between the extremes of full response and zero response. Such agents are called *partial agonists*. The recognition that even within a congeneric group of drugs some of the agents were only partial agonists or antagonists marked the departure from strict adherence to the occupancy theory of drug action. It was shown, however, that such behavior could still be reconciled with the law of mass action if a minor modification were incorporated into equation (3). (See equation (9) below.) In proposals separately reported by Ariens (8) and Stephenson (9), the concept was developed that for a chemical compound to manifest biological activity it is necessary not only that it have affinity for the receptor, but also another property, called intrinsic activity by Ariens and efficacy by Stephenson. This latter property is what was alluded to above, namely, the ability to activate the responding system. The mathematical expression for this theory is given as follows:

$$\Delta = \frac{\epsilon \cdot R_{\text{TOT}} \, (D)}{K_D + (D)} \tag{9}$$

where ϵ is the efficacy constant unique to each drug. According to Ariens, the value of ϵ can vary from 1 (in the case of a full agonist, i.e., $\epsilon \cdot R_{\text{TOT}} \equiv \Delta_{\text{max}}$ of equation (3)) to 0 (in the case of a competitive antagonist). Stephenson further suggested that when the value of ϵ is sufficiently high, it may happen that the overall response is limited by the responding system itself so that a fraction of receptors may not be occupied even though the maximum response has been achieved. This latter idea is the concept of *spare receptors.* It should be emphasized that the adjective "spare" may be misleading. Although some of the receptors might be unoccupied at maximal effect, they could not be destroyed or otherwise removed because they still participate (according to the mass law) in governing the fraction of receptors that are occupied, and the effect is directly related to that fraction. In other words, the total number of receptors could not be diminished without affecting the dose–response relationship. Since formation of drug–receptor complexes is a bimolecular reaction, the diminution of receptors would lower the absolute number of drug–receptor complexes at a given drug concentration and thereby lower the magnitude of the response; the net effect would be a shift of the LDR curve to the right.

An apparently quite different theory of drug action was formulated by Paton and Rang (10), who postulated that the biological effect is proportional not to the number of occupied receptors but to the total number of encounters of the drug with its receptor per unit time. According to this *rate theory,* agonists display high dissociation rates, partial agonists intermediate dissociation rates, and antagonists low dissociation rates. Although this theory seems to be quite far afield of the others, its mathematical formalism is nevertheless analogous to them because the rate of dissociation is proportional to the concentration of drug–receptor complexes. At equilibrium, the rate of association is equal to the rate of dissociation, and the following equation holds for the rate theory:

$$A = \frac{k_2 \ (D)}{K_D + (D)} \tag{10}$$

where A is the rate of association of the drug-receptor complex, and k_2 is the dissociation rate constant.

In all of the models of drug action described above, the drug molecules were assumed to bind to identical, independent receptor sites; occupation of the receptor by an agonist would activate it, and the activation would cease when the drug dissociated. There are many examples of drugs that do behave in that fashion and give dose–response curves that mimic Figure 1 (i.e., hyperbolic) and Figure 3 (i.e., slope =1). There are several examples, however, where the dose–response relationship for certain agents displays *cooperativity.* This behavior is manifested by a distinctly sigmoid curve (for positive cooperativity) when the data are plotted according to Figure 1, rather than the usual rectangular hyperbola; the Hill plot of the data (Figure 3) yields a slope > 1 (for positive cooperativity). Several molecular interpretations of this behavior may be offered. For example, binding of drug molecules to some of the receptors might induce an increase in the affinity for drug of the remaining unoccupied receptors; or the occupation of a sufficient number of the receptors might induce a change in the efficiency of the response system by "recruiting" more than a stoichiometric number of responding units. Negative cooperativity (Hill coefficient $n < 1$) would be interpreted conversely.

With the cooperative interaction of oxygen with hemoglobin as a physical model, numerous mathematical models have been developed to explain the phenomenon of cooperativity (11). The principal current model is the so-called *two-state theory,* and this concept has been applied to the interpretation of cooperative drug action as well (12, 13). In the simplest expression of the theory, the macromolecular receptor complex is assumed to exist in two conformational states that are in reversible equilibrium (T $\rightleftharpoons$ R). In the resting state T the receptor would display a high affinitiy for antagonists but little affinity for agonists. In the active state R (which initiates the response), the receptor would bind agonists preferentially and thus be stabilized by them. The cooperative excitation process would then consist of the displacement of the $T \rightleftharpoons R$ equilibrium in favor of the active state R by agonists. When the Hill format is used for the analysis of a cooperative interaction, the plot should show three separate linear segments if a sufficiently broad range of drug concentrations were used (Figure 7); that is, the slope at the midsection manifests the degree of cooperativity (Hill coefficient, n), but the slopes at the extremes revert to 1.0. The projections on Figure 7 show how values for the affinity of agonist for the resting state (K_T) and the activated state of the receptor (K_R) may be estimated.

In contrast to the two-state theory, other concepts of cooperative drug–receptor interactions are based upon the assumption that all interactions between drug and receptor occur with equal affinity, but the responding system (or effector units) can be coupled to drug–receptor occupancy in a cooperative fashion (14, 15). For example, Biltonen (15) has described "domains" of receptor–effector pairs that could be activated such that the binding of a single "drug" to any receptor in the domain would activate all the effector units contained within that domain.

All of the above considerations were developed with the understanding that there exists a fixed stoichiometric relationship (1:1) between receptor and responding system (or effector unit). An alternative model has recently been suggested by Cuatrecasas and coworkers (16) and by DeHaën (17), which has been termed the *mobile receptor hypothesis.*

The impetus for development of this theory was the realization that a single type of responding system, namely, the adenylate cyclase enzyme, interacts with a variety of different agonists (catecholamines, prostaglandins, glucagon, ACTH, etc.), but the response to multiple agonists generally is not

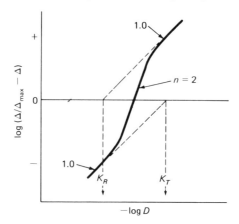

Figure 7. Hill plot illustrating positive cooperativity.

additive. Hence a model was developed that would embody the concept of a competition among different agonist receptors for the same effector. According to this theory all receptor units would contain a common effector combining region, but different agonist combining regions. In essence, this model allows for the dissociation of the receptors from the effector units such that there exists an equilibrium between free receptors and receptor–effector complexes within the membrane (i.e., $R + E \overset{K_1}{\rightleftharpoons} RE$). Thus, there are two ways that an activated responding system may be assembled in the presence of a particular "drug" (agonist); namely $D + R \overset{K_2}{\rightleftharpoons} DR$ and $DR + E \overset{K_3}{\rightleftharpoons} DRE$ or $D + RE \overset{K_4}{\rightleftharpoons} DRE$. According to the mobile receptor hypothesis, the affinity of the receptor for the effector is greater when the receptor is occupied by "drug," i.e., $K_3 > K_1$. From the appropriate expressions for the various equilibrium constants, it can be shown that:

$$K_4 = \frac{DRE}{D \cdot RE} = \frac{DR}{D \cdot R} \cdot \frac{DRE}{DR \cdot E} \cdot \frac{R \cdot E}{RE} = K_2 \cdot K_3/K_1$$

Therefore, $K_4 > K_2$. It follows from this relationship that as long as there are a significant number of receptors uncomplexed to effector units within the membrane, then there must be at least two species of binding sites of different affinity for drug even though there is only a single type of receptor (see additional discussion under Section D, below).

Perhaps the most compelling evidence that receptor and effector units are separate entities (i.e., products of separate genes) comes from studies of the β-adrenergic receptors of mutant forms of S49 lymphoma cells (18). Two unique mutants have been described. In one (AC^-) the adenylate cyclase activity seems to be lacking, while the agonist receptors appear normal; in the other (UNC), both agonist binding and basal adenylate cyclase activity are present, but the agonists do not activate the cyclase enzyme. This latter case seems most intriguing, because of its implications with regard to sorting out the various theories of agonist–receptor–effector coupling.

C. STRUCTURE–ACTIVITY RELATIONSHIPS AND RECEPTOR CLASSIFICATION

A corollary to the theoretical concept of the existence of drug receptors has been the assumption that structurally specific drugs should present a high degree of molecular complementarity toward the sites at which they act. Accordingly, studies have been carried out in which systematic modifications have been made in specific molecular features of a drug considered prototypic for eliciting a particular biological response. The resultant structural analogs form a congeneric series of drugs whose differences in efficacy have been used as clues to the physicochemical nature of the receptor site.

Analogs that differ in stereochemical configuration or that are fixed in specific conformations have been used to visualize the three-dimensional makeup of receptors. Through the elucidation of such structure–activity relationships (SAR), information has been gleaned concerning the types of interactions important in stabilizing the drug–receptor complex, and this remains a valuable approach to the development of drugs that are highly selective in action (i.e., side effects are minimized). The binding force that holds a drug in combination with its receptor is usually the concerted composite of multiple noncovalent interactions including ionic bonds, hydrogen bonds, hydrophobic interactions, and dipole-induced dipole attractions. An apparent paradox in the understanding of drug action is the notion that an antagonist may fit more easily into a receptor binding pocket and form a stronger interaction than the agonist. The good and tight fit, however, does not generate a response. On the other hand, the agonist that may have to force its way into the binding site (induced fit) may thereby cause the change in conformation necessary to activate the responding network. In the following paragraphs, examples are given of how structural data have been used to classify receptors and predict their molecular constitution for several different groups of pharmacological agents.

Ahlquist's original classification in 1948 (19) of α- and β-receptors for adrenergic drugs relied upon the differential action of analogs of epinephrine (adrenaline) on the contractility of smooth muscle; excitatory drugs were said to act at α-receptors, inhibitory drugs at β-receptors. Since that time, α- and β-adrenergic agents have been shown to mediate many biological effects, and their receptors are expected to be ubiquitously distributed in the body (see also Chapter 3.4). The classification has been confirmed also via demonstration of the selective inhibition of the drug-induced α and β effects by specific antagonists. Thus, phenylephrine is the prototype agonist, and phentolamine the antagonist of the α-receptor; isoproterenol is the prototype agonist and propranolol the antagonist of the β-receptor. It seems that the amino group in the adrenergic drugs is of particular importance for the intrinsic activity on α-receptors, whereas the phenolic hydroxyl groups of the catechol ring may be the structural characteristic of intrinsic activity on β-receptors (20). Epinephrine, which possesses both characteristics, has both α- and β-adrenergic properties.

Cholinergic drugs (which mimic or block the action of acetylcholine) have been classified in a similar fashion. In this case, the receptors have been named *muscarinic* or *nicotinic* after the differential cholinomimetic action of muscarine and nicotine. The corresponding specific antagonists are atropine and tubocurarine, respectively. It has been suggested that the two receptors may recognize or induce the favorable binding of two different conformations of acetylcholine in which the N-atom to ester O-atom distances are different (21). (See also Chapter 3.3.)

More recently, the story of multiple receptors for histamine has been more clearly defined. Some of the effects of histamine such as bronchoconstriction and contraction of the gut are readily antagonized by the familiar antihistamines like diphenhydramine which are considered to involve H_1 receptors. Histamine-induced gastric secretion, on the other hand, is not effectively blocked by the well-known antihistamines, but it is inhibited by the newly developed histamine antagonists which are considered to act at H_2 receptors (22). The molecular structures of the H_1 antagonists all contain an ethylamine moiety (like the side chain of histamine) which is somehow linked to one or more aromatic rings; none of them contain the imidazole moiety like histamine. In contrast, all of the H_2 antagonists contain an imidazole moiety as well as an ethylamine moiety, but these two structural features are separated by several intervening atoms in those molecules unlike histamine itself, in which imidazole is directly linked to the ethylamine side chain. (See also, Chapter 3.5).

Knowledge of the biological effects (relief of pain and production of euphoria) of substances extracted from the opium poppy extends back at least to several centuries B.C., but a thorough understanding of the mechanisms of action of morphinelike analgesic agents is still evolving, and a major advance has been made within the last few years. A wide variety of drugs either derived from natural opiates or synthesized have been observed to display most of the characteristics of opiate action. On casual observation there is seemingly no structural basis for the similarity in their actions, but three-dimensional analysis of their preferred or fixed conformations and the stereo-specificity of their effects have indicated that all of them include or can simulate a piperidine ring (23). In 1975 the first publication appeared of the chemical structures of naturally occurring peptides extracted from mammalian brain that have been demonstrated to mimic the actions of morphine. These peptides, called enkephalins ("from brain") or endorphins ("endogenous morphines"), appear to be derived from the larger polypeptide β-lipotropin. Studies of the localization and physiological function of the endogenous narcotics constitute an intensive area of current research in many laboratories (24).

D. LOCALIZATION AND ISOLATION OF RECEPTORS

All of the considerations of drug receptors in the preceding sections of this chapter are hypothetical, based either on the mathematical interpretation of dose–response relationships or on the molecular interpretation of structure–

activity relationships. The reality of receptors can be established, however, only when they are localized and isolated and their physicochemical properties determined directly by the techniques described in the chapters of Section 1 of this volume. Successful localization of particular receptors within tissues, or the isolation and purification of these receptors, requires that the distinction be made between specific and so-called nonspecific binding of agonists or antagonists of the receptor of interest. There are certain basic assumptions commensurate with the practical realization of this distinction. For example, it is assumed that the "drug" binds to its receptor with a higher affinity than to other nonreceptor portions of the membrane. Also, it is expected that the absolute number of receptor sites is much smaller than the total number of binding sites for the drug. Thus, receptor sites are characterized by high affinity and low capacity, whereas nonspecific binding is low affinity and high capacity. The validity of these assumptions has been confirmed generally from studies of the soluble steroid hormone receptors, which preceded investigations of the perhaps more difficult problem of identifying membrane-bound receptors.

A general experimental approach to the characterization of specific binding has evolved. According to this procedure, a radioactive stereospecific ligand of the receptor is added to the preparation, and the excess unbound ligand is removed by washing, ultrafiltration, molecular sieving, charcoal absorption, or some other technique for separating the free ligand from the tissue or tissue homogenate or subcellular fraction containing the receptors. The amount of radioactivity that remains associated with the preparation is the measure of *total binding* of the ligand. In a second step, the above procedure is repeated but a large excess (usually 1000-fold) of *non*radioactive ligand is added along with the same concentration of the radioactive form; on a statistical basis it is assumed that essentially all of the limited number of high-affinity specific sites will be occupied by nonradioactive ligand, whereas the amount of radioactivity associated with the low-affinity sites (which are still not "saturated" by the total concentration of ligand added) is not much affected. Thus, the second experiment yields the measure of *nonspecific binding*. The difference in radioactivity between steps one and two is the measure of *specific binding* for that particular concentration of radioactive ligand. This process is then carried out for a range of concentrations of radioactive ligand, and the data are analyzed according to the Scatchard rearrangement of the mass law equation:

$$\frac{(DR)}{(D)} = -\frac{1}{K_D} \cdot (DR) + \frac{R_{TOT}}{K_D} \tag{11}$$

where *(DR)* is the concentration of drug–receptor complex determined from the amount of specifically bound radioactivity, *(D)* is the concentration of unbound drug determined from the difference between total radioactivity added and specifically bound radioactivity, K_D is the dissociation constant for the complex, and R_{TOT} is the total number of receptors. Figure 8 is a typical Scatchard plot and shows how the values of K_D and R_{TOT} are obtained.

A single straight-line plot like Figure 8 is obtained as long as there is only a single population of noninteracting receptors involved. A curvilinear Scatchard plot may be interpreted in several ways. It may indicate that there is interaction among the receptor sites of a single population of receptors (i.e., cooperativity), in which case it could be analyzed according to Figure 7. On the other hand, it may indicate multiple populations of receptors whose individual K_D and R_{TOT} values may be derived separately (25). A special interpretation of the latter case was developed earlier (Section B) with respect to the mobile receptor hypothesis whereby identical receptors would display different affinities for drug depending on whether they were "free" or associated with the effector system (16).

The direct measurement of the K_D for a drug–receptor interaction by the experimental approach outlined above permits a direct test of the occupancy theory of drug action. For an in vitro test system where factors such as absorption and metabolism of the drug are minimized, the concentration of drug that elicits half-maximal response should be equivalent to K_D if the occupancy theory is valid. In some cases a good agreement has been noted, in others not. In the former situation the response must be intimately linked to receptor occupation as discussed earlier. The latter situation may arise because the ultimate response may be linked through several intervening steps to the drug–receptor complex, and one of these steps may be limiting. For example, it is known that most of the actions of the β-adrenergic agent isoproterenol are mediated via the second messenger cyclic AMP. The sequence of events may entail: (a) combination of isoproterenol with receptor,

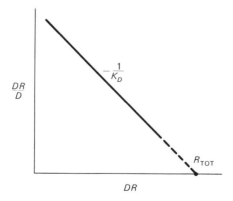

Figure 8. Scatchard plot characterizing drug receptor affinity and number of receptors.

(b) receptor conformational change which mediates activation of the adenyl cyclase enzyme, (c) production of c-AMP, (d) activation of a protein kinase by c-AMP, (e) phosphorylation of a specific protein by the protein kinase, and (f) ultimate response (e.g., change in membrane permeability). If the overall response were governed by the amount of protein kinase activated by c-AMP, then the correspondence between initial receptor occupation and ultimate response would be dependent upon the amount of c-AMP produced per receptor occupied and upon the K_M of the protein kinase for c-AMP. Therefore, it is conceivable that 10% occupation of receptors, for example, may produce enough c-AMP to fully activate the protein kinase and thereby give rise to the maximum response. Hence the K_D for isoproterenol measured directly would be much larger than the concentration of isoproterenol necessary to elicit the half-maximal response. There are several other interpretations for such a lack of correspondence between K_D and K_{ACT}. In addition to the interactions among agonists, receptors, and effectors, there may be additional modulator substances such as guanine nucleotides or divalent metal ions which can alter the coupling between receptor occupancy and response. According to the concept of receptor–effector domains (15) which was described above, the presence of guanine nucleotide may activate the β-adrenergic sensitive network so that a single drug–receptor complex would elicit responses from all of the adenylate cyclase effector units within the membrane domain. Alternatively, the mobile receptor concept (16, 17) could be extended to include the idea that a single drug–receptor complex might migrate and interact with many effector units, transforming them from the inactive to the active state. This notion would require that the time constant for the relaxation of the activated effector unit to the inactive form be slow relative to the rate of dissociation of the drug–receptor complex from the effector unit and relative to the time constant for the physiological response. A theoretical treatment of such slow conformational transitions has been presented by Neet and coworkers (26).

A caution with regard to the isolation of "receptors" is that specific binding of a drug is only a necessary condition for receptor identification, it is not the sufficient condition. Once a receptor has been separated from its responding system, it is difficult to prove that it is indeed a receptor and not simply a binding protein. Nevertheless, the current thrust of experimentation is toward isolation, purification, and reconstitution of the separate components necessary for complete agonist-sensitive responding systems including receptors, coupling factors, and effectors. (See further discussion with regard to individual types of receptors in later chapters in this section.)

The remarkable discovery of the endogenous morphinelike peptides after a period of curiosity of more than 5000 years causes one to question whether the term "drug receptor" may in all cases be a misnomer, simply reflecting our ignorance at this point in time of the endogenous agents for which that receptor was evolved.

REFERENCES

1. Rang, H. P., ed. 1973. *Drug Receptors.* University Park Press, Baltimore.
2. Langley, J. N. 1878. *J. Physiol.* 1:339.
3. Langley, J. N. 1905. *J. Physiol.* 33:374.
4. La Du, B. N., Mandel, H. G., and Way, E. L., eds. 1971. *Fundamentals of Drug Metabolism and Drug Disposition.* The Williams & Wilkins Co., Baltimore.
5. Goldstein, A., Aronow, L., and Kalman, S. M., 1974. *Principles of Drug Action,* 2nd ed. John Wiley & Sons, New York.
6. Clark, A. J. 1933. *The Mode of Action of Drugs on Cells.* E. Arnold & Co., London.
7. Arunlakshana, O., and Schild, H. O. 1959. *Br. J. Pharmacol.* 14:48.
8. Ariëns, E. J. 1954. *Arch. Int. Pharmacodyn.* 99:32.
9. Stephenson, R. P. 1956. *Br. J. Pharmacol.* 11:379.
10. Paton, W. D. M., and Rang, H. P. 1966. *Adv. Drug Res.* 3:57.
11. Edelstein, S. J. 1975. *Annu. Rev. Biochem.* 44:209.
12. Changeux, J. P., and Podleski, T. R. 1968. *Proc. Nat. Acad. Sci. U.S.A.* 59:944.
13. Colquhoun, D. 1973. In *Drug Receptors,* H. P. Rang, ed., p. 149. University Park Press, Baltimore.
14. Levitzki, A., Segel, L. A., and Steer, M. L. 1975. *J. Mol. Biol.* 91:125.
15. Biltonen, R. L. 1977. *Fed. Proc.* 36:2112.
16. Jacobs, S., and Cuatrecasas, P. 1976. *Biochim. Biophys. Acta* 433:482.
17. De Haën, C. 1976. *J. Theor. Biol.* 58:383.
18. Maguire, M. E., Ross, E. M., and Gilman, A. C. 1977. *Adv. Cyclic Nucleotide Res.* 8:1.
19. Ahlquist, R. P. 1948. *Am. J. Physiol.* 153:586.
20. Ariëns, E. J. 1966. *Adv. Drug Res.* 3:235.
21. Weinstein, H., Apfelderfer, B. Z., Cohen, S., Maayani, S., and Sokolovsky, M. 1973. In *Conformation of Biological Molecules and Polymers,* E. D. Bergmann and B. Pullman, eds., p. 531. Academic Press, New York.
22. Black, J. W., Duncan, W. A. M., Durant, C. J., Ganellin, C. R., and Parsons, E. M. 1972. *Nature (London)* 236:385.
23. Martin, W. R. 1967. *Pharmacol. Rev.* 19:463.
24. Snyder, S. H. *Chem. Eng. News,* Nov. 28, 1977, p. 26.
25. Klotz, I. M., and Hunston, D. L. 1971. *Biochemistry* 10:3065.
26. Ainslie, G. R., Jr., Shill, J. P., and Neet, K. E. 1972. *J. Biol. Chem.* 247:7088.

ADDITIONAL READING

Featherstone, R. M., ed. 1973. *A Guide to Molecular Pharmacology–Toxicology,* Parts I, II. Marcel Dekker, Inc., New York.
Roberts, G. K. C., ed. 1977. *Drug Action at the Molecular Level.* University Park Press, Baltimore.
Birnbaumer, L., Pohl, S. L., and Kaumann, A. J. 1974. Receptors and acceptors: A necessary distinction in hormone binding studies. *Adv. Cyclic Nucleotide Res.* 4:240.
Waud, D. R., 1968. *Pharmacol. Rev.* 20:49.

3.3. Cholinergic Receptors

Michiko Okamoto

The concept of chemical mediation for nerve impulse transmission to the effector sites in the autonomic nervous system opened a new path to understanding the mechanism of the drug receptor interactions that occur in this system.

While the idea that epinephrine might be a possible neurochemical mediator in sympathetic neuro-effector junctions was advanced at first by Elliot (32) and Langley (63), the neurochemical mediator theory for the parasympathetic nervous system was initiated by an observation that greatly impressed Dixon (24): namely, that of the correspondence between the pharmacologic effects of the alkaloid muscarine and the response to vagal nerve stimulation in intact animals. He concluded from his experimental data that "excitation of a nerve induces the local liberation of hormone which causes specific activity by a combination with some constituents of the end-organ, muscle or gland." Accordingly, an experiment of Loewi (66) on frog heart provided a historic work and presented the first convincing evidence of the chemical (i.e., acetylcholine, Ach) transmitter theory of information transfer across synapses.

Historically, the development of experimental approaches for characterizing Ach receptors significantly reflects the extraordinary advance of modern scientific knowledge and technology. Initially, methods of investigating Ach receptors were indirect and were dominated by the pharmacologic approach. This approach draws inferences about a receptor from the biologic responses produced by drugs. The study of structure–activity relationships (SAR), utilized originally by Hunt and Taveau (43), and later by Dale (23), has been a powerful pharmacological tool in characterizing cholinergic systems. A suitable biologic effect of a drug is chosen for study. The molecular structure of a prototype drug which elicits the characteristic effect is then modified systematically. Substituents are added or subtracted at various positions and in different steric configurations. By testing the numbers of a series and observing how biologic potency is affected by each molecular modification, one may ultimately draw conclusions about the precise mode of combinations of a drug with its receptor's surface. Nevertheless, the effects of the alkaloids muscarine and nicotine on cholinergic junctions, which provided the basis for Dale's classical differentiation of receptor types, are still accurate for both the peripheral and central nervous systems. Accordingly, by convention, the cholinoreceptive sites are classified into two types, muscarinic and nicotinic (Table 1). Furthermore, the experimental evidence indicates that the "nicotinic" receptors of autonomic ganglia and skeletal muscle are not completely identical because they respond differently to certain stimulating and blocking agents, as can be seen in Table 1. Some evidence suggests as well that the muscarinic receptors of smooth muscle may also be separable into more than one type (13). Furthermore, the situation at autonomic ganglia is complicated by the fact that the ganglion cells also have a secondary component of muscarinic receptors. The cholinergic receptors on various neurons of the CNS are also either nicotinic or muscarinic; the former predominate on the Renshaw cells of the spinal cord, whereas most of those at cortical and subcortical sites are muscarinic.

From a three-dimensional molecular model and systematic structure–action relationship studies, Welsh and Taub (103, 104) have mapped the cholinoreceptor site in the calm heart (Figure 1) and have drawn certain conclusions about its nature. The fact that a cationic group was necessary for the drug molecule in producing the response, indicated the presence of a complementary anionic group on the receptor surface. The molecular model revealed that the nitrogen atom, bearing its methyl groups as substituents, was free to rotate with relation to the carbon chain. The decrease in pharmacologic activity caused by removal of methyl groups on the cationic "head" and substitution of ethyl groups, suggested further that the anionic site on the receptor was embedded in a cavity that would just accommodate two methyl groups. Because one of the three symmetrically placed methyls must point away from the receptor surface, and because free rotation makes all three methyls equivalent, removing one or changing it to ethyl has little effect. It is assumed that the two essential methyl groups help to stabilize the Ach receptor complex through van der Waals forces, and that any larger substituents, not fitting properly into the cavity, seriously hinder the tight fit of the rest of the molecule to its complementary site. It is likely that the carbon atoms of the main chain lie in close approximation to a flat portion of the receptor surface, contributing further van der Waals attraction to the overall binding. The carbonyl oxygen action might well participate in hydrogen bond formation with an appropriate receptor group (e.g., the –NH of a peptide bond), thus further stabilizing the interaction. These deductions were fairly consistent in a variety of SAR studies utilizing other experimental cholinoreceptive preparations (cf. Waser, 101).

The broad deductions from SAR data have been refined considerably

Table 1. Cholinoreceptive Sites and Their Selective Agonists and Antagonists.

CHOLINERGIC NEURONS	I POSTGANGLIONIC PARASYMPATHETIC	II AUTONOMIC PREGANGLIONIC	III SOMATIC MOTOR	IV CNS
Type of receptor	Muscarinic	Muscarinic Nicotinic I	Nicotinic II	Muscarinic Nicotinic
Receptor location	Autonomic effector cell	Autonomic ganglionic cell	Striated muscle	CNS neurons
Cholinomimetic agent	Muscarinic	DMPP	PTMA	Muscarine carbachol
Cholinergic blocking agent	Atropine	C_6 d-TC	C_{10} d-TC	Atropine d-TC

C_6—hexamethonium; C_{10}—decamethonium; d-TC—d-tubocurarine; DMPP—dimethylphenylpiperazinium; PTMA—phenyltrimethylammonium.

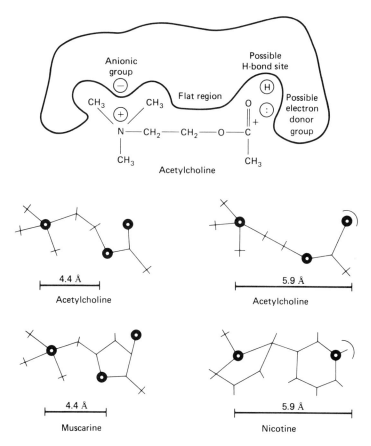

Figure 1. Molecular structures of Ach and its congeners muscarine and nicotine: postulated interaction with a receptor (see text).

through X-ray crystallographic studies on crystals of Ach and its congeners (18–20) and by measurements on scale models of the molecules (4). Acetylcholine is relatively flexible and capable of assuming various molecular conformations. Congeners containing a ring system, like nicotine and muscarine, have much more rigid structures, permitting the prediction of which atoms and distances are critical for the given receptor interactions (Figure 1).

In addition to a cationic nitrogen center, there is a group 5.9 Å distant that can act as an acceptor for hydrogen bond for a nicotinic receptor. In Ach and some of its congeners this is the carbonyl oxygen, but in nicotine it is the pyridine nitrogen. In the muscarinic series the hydrogen acceptor is an oxygen atom at 4.4 Å from the center of positive charge. This is the steric oxygen in Ach and the ring oxygen in muscarine. In addition, a methyl group corresponding to the acetyl methyl in Ach and the ring methyl in muscarine strongly reinforces the molecular interaction.

The SAR study of nicotinic blocking action of certain polymethylene bismethonium compounds further revealed that the molecular conformational requirements for ganglionic and for skeletal neuromuscular junctional receptors are considerably different. This has been demonstrated by Paton and Zimis (78, 79), for example, by comparing the potency of polymethylene bismethonium compounds for producing transmission block at cervical or synaptic ganglia and at the tibialis neuromuscular junction in cats in vivo. Two distinct optima were found, one at the carbon chain length of 5 to 6 for ganglionic blockade, another at the chain length of 10 for neuromuscular blockade. It is apparent therefore, that despite the stimulation of both ganglionic and skeletal muscle end-plate receptors by the release of Ach from nerve endings, these receptors are not identical. Thus, it is assumed that there is a configuration complementary to that of Ach present in both receptors. The necessity of the second cationic group for blocking action indicates the presence of a second anionic site on the receptor surface, lying outside the acetylcholine combining region. Both anionic sites are presumed to be embedded in cavities capable of accommodating a nitrogen head with two methyl groups. The essential difference between the ganglionic and muscle end-plate receptors is, therefore, presumed to be in the distance between these anionic sites. Additionally, it is interesting to note that the covalent modification of the Ach receptor, namely, reduction of at least one S–S group, also alters the pharmacologic specificity of the Ach receptor (45). The response to the monoquaternary agonists (Ach, carbachol, butyltrimethylammonium) is decreased (45), and the response to the bisquaternary antagonist (decamethonium) is increased (48); hexamethonium, normally a blocker, acts as an agonist in the reduced-state receptor (47). Furthermore, these effects of reduction are fully reversed by addition of oxidizing agents. This reversal is blocked by prior treatment by an alkylating agent such as N-ethylmaleimide (45). In the absence of prior reduction of Ach receptor, quaternary ammonium derivatives of maleimide such as 4-(N-maleimido) benzyltrimethyl ammonium act reversibly as competitive inhibitors and, therefore, they have been used for affinity labeling of the reduced receptor. It has been calculated that the distance between the quaternary ammonium head to the reactive maleimide double bond is about 1 nm, suggesting a similar distance in the Ach binding site between the negative binding site for quaternary ammonium group to at least one of the SH groups (47, 48) in the nicotinic receptor.

The studies on agonists and antagonists have suggested that the receptor binding site in the active state (reduced state) assumes a molecular conformation slightly shorter than in the inactive state (nonreduced state) (48).

EXPERIMENTAL APPROACHES IN CHARACTERIZING Ach RECEPTORS ON CELLS AND TISSUES

Significant progress has been made in recent years in the molecular description of the Ach receptor interaction (cf. 17, 25, 56, 62). Because the information available for nicotinic receptors is more extensive, much of this chapter is devoted to a discussion of the nicotinic receptor. All approaches to the Ach receptor are contingent upon the response of cells to Ach and on the modification of the produced response. The binding properties of the Ach and the congeners to the receptor are characterized by the extent of response that is produced as a function of their concentration. The occupation of binding sites is determined by the Langmuir absorption isotherm; that is, it is equivalent to the Michaelis-Menten equation. The response to agonists is assumed to increase with increasing occupation. If the response were linearly proportional to occupation, then the equilibrium dissociation constant for an agonist–Ach receptor complex would be equal to the concentration of agonist that produces a half-maximal response. The latter value is termed the apparent dissociation constant (K_{app}) although, in reality, the relationship between the measured response and the extent of occupation is governed by a more complex relationship. Generally the dose–response curve is also more complex and does not obey the expected hyperbolic Langmuir equation but rather assumes an S-shape with an initial upward concavity and a Hill coefficient greater than one (16, 40, 46, 90). On the other hand, the experiments on binding of the agonists to membranes and to solubilized Ach receptors have shown that these phenomena assume a typical hyperbolic function with a Hill coefficient equal to one. It has been suggested that this discrepancy is due to cooperative interactions (cooperative model) among subunits of oligomeric Ach receptors (46) and/or among subunits in the extended membrane lattice (15). An alternative is that two or more independent binding sites must be occupied to produce a primary response (noncooperative model) (22, 90).

The primary physiological cell response to Ach is an increase in the permeability of the receptive membrane to Na^+ and K^+ (1–3), which results in the depolarization of the membrane. In general, the permeability changes are not measured directly in experiments but rather indirectly through electrophysiological monitoring of the cell responses (i.e., by voltage, current, and conductance). The conductance changes are by no means simple functions of the permeability changes; however, under usual conditions, there are approximate proportionalities in their magnitude of changes (for further details, see Refs. 4–12).

It has been calculated that there is an electric field of approximately 105 V/cm² generated through Ach receptors in a membrane. In contrast to the action potential generating system, the conductance change at the Ach receptor is not usually dependent on the resting membrane potential; however, as the membrane potential changes from zero to positive values, the conductance changes produced by the agonists approach zero (1, 3). Furthermore, the fact that the end-plate potential decays more rapidly in more positive membrane potential suggests that the active conformation of the Ach receptor is thermodynamically less favored in the more positive membrane potentials (17, 18). It has been estimated (10) in frog neuromuscular junction that the "elementary" response to Ach at Ach receptor produces ionic conductance changes of approximately 100 pmho and duration of 1 msec during which there is a net transfer of approximately 5×10^4 monovalent ions. Interestingly, acetylcholine esterase appears to have no role in determining the duration of this "elementary" response, and it functions in limiting an Ach molecule from combining with Ach receptor (10).

Localization and Quantitation of Ach in the Cell

Because the Ach receptor comprises a fraction of the total cell structure, a highly specific technique is required to identify and quantitate it. For example, the high-affinity labeling technique has been utilized for electroplax of *Electrophorus* (49, 50). The labeling is accomplished by initially treating the cell with a reducing agent, such as dithiothreitol, and then alkylating it with (^{3}H) 4-(N-maleimido) benzyltrimethyl-ammonium. The nonreceptor labeling is measured by repeating the same procedure after protecting the true Ach receptor from labeling by adding a cholinergic ligand or an affinity oxidizing agent. The difference between these two values designates the specific Ach receptor labeling. It has been estimated that 10 to 20 pmol of labeled sites are designated as the quantity of Ach receptor per gram net weight of cell. Additionally, electron microscopic determination estimated that about 30% of the area of the innervated surface of the electroplax is synaptic structure, and, therefore, 2000 to 3000 sites/μM^2 of synaptic membrane are occupied by Ach receptors (50). During the peak of receptor membrane activation in electroplax, as much as 100 mA of inward Na^+ current passes per square centimeter of membrane area (92), or 2×10^{17} Na^+ ions/sec in a typical 35 mg cell. Since it is estimated that there are approximately 2×10^{11} Ach receptors in a 35 mg cell, there are on the order of 10^6 cations transported across the receptor membrane per second per site, producing conductance of 1 pmho per site (51). The value for ion transport is estimated to require a channel mechanism for translocation of ions rather than simple diffusion processes (51). Also, the value for ionic conductance is approximately one-half of the value reported by Katz and Miledi at frog neuromuscular junction (59).

The venom of elapid and hydrophid snakes contains polypeptide α-neuro toxins which are specific for the Ach receptors in neuroskeletal muscle junction and in electroplax (cf. 64). These toxins are curarelike, neuromuscular blockers, long-acting, and demonstrated to act at the postsynaptic membrane. The extent of binding of radioactive toxin was found to be correlated with the extent of electrophysiologically monitored response (2, 81). Autoradiographic techniques illustrated that at low concentration the toxin (e.g., α-bungarotoxin) binds predominately at the end-plate region of normal skeletal muscle; a major portion of this binding which occurs at Ach receptors is inhibited by the presence of d-tubocurarine (1, 7, 74, 84). The binding of the toxin increases after denervation with an increase in sensitivity to Ach (7, 38, 74). Interestingly, an increase in the binding of the toxin has been demonstrated to correlate also to the development of a depolarizing response to applied Ach in cultured differentiating myogenic cells (65, 69).

The density of the toxin binding at the surface of the mature mammalian neuroskeletal muscle junction has been estimated to be about $12,000/\mu M^2$ (33, 84), and about 30,000 sites/μM^2 in *Electrophorus* electroplax synaptic membrane (11), values which are considerably higher than the estimates obtained by the affinity labeling.

EXPERIMENTAL APPROACHES IN CHARACTERIZING Ach RECEPTORS ON MEMBRANE FRAGMENTS

Isolation of Ach Receptors

The Ach receptors reside in the synaptic membrane; therefore, the isolation of subcellular membrane fractions that are rich in synaptic membrane is the first step in Ach receptor purification. *Torpedo* and *Electrophorus* electric organs are known to be excellent and abundant sources of nicotinic Ach receptors.

A sucrose density gradient technique has been most successful in isolating Ach receptor–rich membrane fragments and even in dissociating them from the membrane-bound Ach esterase fragments (26). With this method, 75 pmol Ach receptor/mg protein was obtained by affinity labeling estimation (52) in *Electrophorus*. On the other hand, a higher yield has been reported from the fraction isolated from *Torpedo marmorata,* which was found to contain 2000 pmol toxin binding sites/mg protein (21).

Binding of Cholinergic Agents

In order to characterize the Ach receptor in membrane fragments the dissociation constants of the binding of small ligands to cholinoreceptive sites in these fragments have been determined by several methods. These include competition with another small labeled ligand (97), equilibrium dialysis (98), and retardation of the rate of toxin binding (92) (Table 2). A similar dissociation constant K and K_{app} have been obtained by the competition and retardation methods in intact cells and from ion conduction changes in vesicles in *Electrophorus* (57, 102). However, the values for K vary considerably when they are determined by equilibrium dialysis (27, 29) exposing multiple binding sites. Furthermore, for example, the α-toxin binding sites and decamethonium binding sites appear to be heterogeneous and do not exactly approximate each other. It has been shown in membranes from *Electrophorus* that approximately 65% of decamethonium nonspecific binding sites can be blocked by α-bungarotoxin while the remaining 35% were assumed to be the true Ach receptive sites (58). Furthermore, only half of the α-toxin of *Naja naja* in *Electrophorus* can be blocked by decamethonium (65).

Affinity Labeling

As described previously, a portion of the total labeling is dependent on the amount of reduced Ach receptors after treatment with a reducing agent such as DDT. The rate of specific affinity alkylation, such as with (^{3}H)-4-(N-maleimido) benzyltrimethyl ammonium, is also shown to be slowed by cholinergic agonists and blockers, including toxin, and is blocked by affinity reoxidation (51, 53, 55) in the receptor-rich membrane fragments. Also, as with intact electroplax, the specific labeling has been found to be associated with a polypeptide component of approximately 40,000 molecular weight (55).

Permeability Control in Membrane Vesicles

A vesicular membrane fraction has been prepared from *Electrophorus* electric tissues by homogenizing and sedimenting them by the discontinuous sucrose gradient method, which can be used to measure cationic permeability across the membrane. The efflux of $^{22}Na^+$ from preloaded vesicles is faster in the presence of cholinergic agonists. Furthermore, these effects are blocked by competitive cholinergic antagonists and toxins (57). The values for K_{app} obtained from the agonists and the antagonists determined by dose–response curves in this preparation are found close to the values obtained electrophysiologically in intact electroplax (58). The average conductance increase per Ach receptor site in the vesicular preparation is estimated to be 10^{-15} mho (58), which is three to five times smaller than that estimated in intact cells (51, 59). Apparently, only a small fraction of the receptors present in the vesicle preparation contribute to the permeability response.

Table 2. Dissociation Constants (μM) for Cholinergic Ligands.

	ACH	CARBACHOL	NICOTINE	C_{10}	d-TC	REF.
Equilibrium dialysis:						
Torpedo membrane	0.0008		0.2	0.13	0.04	27, 28
	0.068			0.59	1.0	
				8		
Torpedo solubilized membrane	0.0014					30
Electrophorus membrane	0.22		0.06	55	6.4	75
	2.3			0.0025	0.08	29
				0.055	40	
				2.5		
				100		
Competitive binding with C_{10}:						
Torpedo membrane				0.7	0.2	102
Electrophorus membrane		40		1.3	0.2	57
Retarding toxin binding:						
Torpedo membrane	0.008	0.5	0.8		5	102
		5			5	35
Torpedo solubilized membrane		50				35
Electrophorus membrane		22		0.8	0.17	102
Dose–response:						
Electrophorus electroplax	3	30		1.2	0.16	16, 40, 47

EXPERIMENTAL APPROACHES IN CHARACTERIZING Ach RECEPTORS ON SOLUBILIZED MEMBRANE

It has been shown that the Ach receptor can be solubilized and extracted from membrane by nonionic surfactants or bile salt solutions. This also can be done under conditions in which the Ach receptors are complexed with labeled α-toxin (7, 65, 69, 73, 74, 89), or affinity-labeled (52, 55) prior to the solubilization of the receptor. The NaCl 50–100 mM buffered solution is centrifuged, and a receptor-rich supernatant is obtained. It is interesting to note that preextraction of membrane, initially with 1 M NaCl, removes most of the Ach esterase (95) but not the Ach receptors (52, 65), and thus both the receptor and the esterase can be differentially extracted.

The extracted Ach receptor is purified using primarily an affinity chromatographic technique. The electric tissue of *Electrophorus* was found to contain approximately 65 pmol toxin binding sites/g tissue (76, 88), and a similar number of sites was identified by specific affinity labeling (52). *Torpedo* electric tissue contains 10^{-5}-fold more Ach receptor/g than *Electrophorus* tissue (21, 85, 94). The specific activities obtained for purified Ach receptor indicate $1–2 \times 10^5$ daltons per site and contains two or more molecular weight classes of polypeptides. A polypeptide of approximately 40,000 daltons is consistently present. This bond is labeled consistently by affinity labeling (52). Similarly, in intact electroplax (91) and in membrane fragments (55), the specifically labeled component appears to be a polypeptide of 40,000 daltons. Other characteristics have shown this bond to contain all or part of the Ach binding site (52, 91). The origin of the other polypeptide bonds is not certain. If they are indeed subunits of Ach receptor, associated with 40,000-daltons polypeptide, then a molecular weight of 90,000 to 140,000 g of protein per Ach binding site would be expected. On the other hand, the toxin binding components of *Electrophorus* or *Torpedo* membrane, extracted in mild nonionic detergent (61, 68, 88) and purified (8), or extracted in bile salt solution (68), have been shown to have a much larger molecular weight, approximately 3×10^5. The state of this Ach receptor aggregation in the membrane is not well-defined; however, a molecular weight of 3×10^5 has been shown to correlate with the dimensions of particles seen by freeze-etching of membrane from *Torpedo* (96).

RECONSTITUTION OF MEMBRANE

Proof that a purified preparation of receptor is complete and functional can be provided by reconstituting the receptor fraction into known lipid membrane constituents and by demonstrating Na^+ and K^+ permeability characteristics. Purified receptor from *Electrophorus* and from *Torpedo* has been incorporated into phospholipid vesicles (86, 87). The reconstituting method, for example, involves suspending purified receptor in cholate with phospholipid and dialyzing the cholate out slowly. Later the phospholipid vesicles that incorporated receptors are separated from the rest by a flotation technique in a sucrose density gradient. The reports are not consistent in demonstrating cation permeability characteristics (70, 86).

IMMUNOLOGICAL METHODS

Antisera against purified Ach receptor from *Electrophorus* have been produced in rabbits (83, 96). These antisera were found to precipitate all toxin binding activity in crude extracts of *Torpedo* membrane and of embryonic chick muscle (96). It is clinically interesting that the immunized rabbits develop a muscle paralysis that resembles human myasthenia gravis (82, 83).

THE MUSCARINIC Ach RECEPTORS

With the same research approach, considerable progress has been made in characterizing the muscarinic receptors (cf. 10). In contrast to the advances made for nicotinic receptors, research in isolating and characterizing the Ach receptors has been slow, owing to the delay in identifying which tissues are rich in muscarinic receptor sources.

As assayed by binding studies, the caudate nucleus, the longitudinal smooth muscle of the ileum, and possibly cerebral cortex are relatively rich sources of muscarinic receptor (102).

Following the initial demonstration by Paton and Rang (80), the presence of high-affinity binding sites for reversible muscarinic antagonists in smooth muscle and brain has been confirmed, and the studies have been further extended. The antagonists that have been studied include atropine, N-methylatropine, quinuclidinylbenzilate, benzetimide, and propylbenzylcholine (cf. 10). The binding of low concentrations (10^{-11}–10^{-6} M) of these radiolabeled antagonists to brain and smooth muscle subcellular fractions has been demonstrated utilizing a variety of techniques such as that described in the nicotinic receptors (5, 6, 14, 93, 100). Binding of ^{3}H-antagonists can be displaced by pharmacologically effective concentrates of drugs that are known to be selective muscarinic agonists and antagonists but not by nicotinic drugs, including anticholinesterases, indicating the selectivity of the site.

As has been the case for the nicotinic receptors, the criteria for specific binding for the muscarinic receptor have also been fulfilled pharmacologically by specificity of antagonists and saturability (cf. 10). It has also been shown in crude synaptosome preparations from the rat cortex that the levels of binding at saturation are the same for all ^{3}H-antagonists and are in the order of 1.6–2.2 nmol/g protein (9). Furthermore, it is interesting to note that the antagonist binding site in a variety of tissues as diverse as smooth muscle, parotid gland, and brain show almost identical affinity constants (6, 9, 105, 106). Furthermore, these affinity constants correlate closely to the values obtained from the classical pharmacological agonist–antagonist response studies such as in smooth muscle (80) and ion fluxes (13).

The binding to the muscarinic agonists has been likewise determined in brain subcellular fractions (9) and in smooth muscle (14, 99, 106, 107), either directly or by displacement of a labeled antagonist by an agonist. The results of these experiments have shown (cf. 10) that the agonist binding is complex and cannot be described by a single affinity constant, and that there are again generally two types of binding sites, namely, high- and low-affinity binding sites. Low concentrations of three potent radiolabeled agonists, Ach, oxotremorine, and methylfurmethide (3, 106), bind to the high-affinity sites exclusively. It was found that the high-affinity component represents approximately 30% of the total sites, and the values of affinity constants for K_{high} and K_{low} were found to be 1.2×10^7 M^{-1} and 1.2×10^5 M^{-1}, respectively. The complex agonist binding properties of the muscarinic receptors are mirrored in the variety of pharmacological and biochemical dose–response relationships that are characteristically produced by the muscarinic agonists and blocked by the muscarinic antagonists. The complex agonist dose–response curves might be interpreted as the presence of heterogeneous receptors. The experimental evidence supporting this interpretation is from the work of Burgen and Spero (13), who have examined the patencies of a series of muscarinic agonists in producing ileum smooth muscle contraction and K$^+$ efflux, and suggested that these two responses might be mediated by two distinct receptor populations. However, the two responses were shown to produce identical affinity constants for a number of reversible antagonists.

There has been some evidence that influx of extracellular Ca^{2+} is an important factor for production of the muscarinic-linked responses. Responses such as smooth muscle contraction (13), protein secretion from pancreatic acinar cells (42), and smooth muscle cell depolarization (12) are inhibited by the removal of extracellular calcium or stimulated by calcium ionophores. The elevation of cyclic guanosine monophosphate (cGMP) levels was also shown to be Ca^{2+}-dependent (60). On the other hand, muscarinic responses such as K$^+$ efflux from ileum smooth muscle are relatively insensitive to calcium concentration (13). Another biochemical response, the agonist-stimulated breakdown and consequent resynthesis of phosphatidylinositol, is also known to be relatively Ca^{2+}-independent (44, 71). Phosphatidylinositol breakdown is postulated to be one of the most closely linked response-associated activations of muscarinic receptor (72).

The muscarinic receptor has proved to be most vulnerable to solubilization, and the binding activity is destroyed by a wide range of nonionic and ionic detergents (34). Solubilization of the muscarinic receptor with retention of the binding activity has been reported with the use of digitonin (5). Although it is difficult to solubilize the muscarinic receptor and retain binding activity, it is possible to solubilize membrane fragments which are pretreated with radiolabeled antagonists. Analysis by SDS gel electrophoresis further shows that the labeling occurred at the protein band of approximately 87,000 molecular weight (10).

REFERENCES

1. Albuquerque, E. X., Barnard, E. A., Chiu, T. H., Lapa, A. J., Dolly, J. O., Jansson, S. E., Daly, J., and Witkop, B. 1973. *Proc. Natl. Acad. Sci. U.S.A.* 70:949.
2. Albuquerque, E. X., Barnard, E. A., Jansson, S. E., and Wieckowski, J. 1973. *Life Sci.* 12:545.
3. Bebbington, A., Brimblecome, R. W., and Shakeshaft, D. 1966. *Br. J. Pharmacol.* 26:56.
4. Beers, W. H., and Reich, E. 1970. *Nature* 228:917.
5. Beld, A. J., and Ariens, E. J. 1974. *Eur. J. Pharmacol.* 25:203.
6. Beld, A. J., Van den Hoven, S., Wouterse, A. C., and Zegers, M. A. P. 1975. *Eur. J. Pharmacol.* 30:360.
7. Berg, D. K., Kelly, R. B., Sargent, P. B., Williamson, P., and Hall, Z. W. 1972. *Proc. Natl. Acad. Sci. U.S.A.* 69:147.
8. Biesecker, G. 1973. *Biochemistry (Washington)* 12:4403.
9. Birdsall, N. J. M., Burgen, A. S. V., Hiley, C. R., and Hulme, E. C. 1976. *J. Supramol. Struct.* 4:367.
10. Birdsall, N. J. M., and Hulme, E. 1976. *J. Neurochem.* 27:7.
11. Bourgeois, J. P., Ryter, A., Menez, A., Fromageot, P., Bouguet, P., and Changeux, J. P. 1972. *F.E.B.S. Lett.* 25:127.
12. Brading, A., Bulbring, A., and Tomita, T. 1969. *J. Physiol. London* 200:637.
13. Burgen, A. S. V., and Spero, L. 1968. *Br. J. Pharmacol.* 34:99.
14. Burgen, A. S. V., Hiley, C. R., and Young, J. M. 1974. *Br. J. Pharmacol.* 51:279.
15. Changeux, J. P., Thiery, J., Tung, Y., and Kittel, C. 1967. *Proc. Natl. Acad. Sci. U.S.A.* 57:335.
16. Changeux, J. P., and Podelaki, T. R. 1968. *Proc. Natl. Acad. Sci. U.S.A.* 59:944.
17. Waser, P. G. 1975. *Cholinergic Mechanisms.* Raven Press, New York.
18. Chothia, C., and Pauling, P. 1968. *Nature* 219:1156.
19. Chothia, C., and Pauling, P. 1969. *Nature* 223:919.
20. Chothia, C., and Pauling, P. 1970. *Proc. Natl. Acad. Sci. U.S.A.* 65:477.
21. Cohen, J. B., Weber, M., Huchet, M., and Changeux, J. P. 1972. *F.E.B.S. Lett.* 26:43.
22. Colquhoun, D. 1973. In *Drug Receptors,* H. P. Rang, ed., p. 149. Macmillan, London.
23. Dale, H. H. 1914. *J. Pharmacol. Exp. Ther.* 6:147.
24. Dixon, W. E. 1907. *Med. Maz.* 16:454.
25. Rang, H. P. 1973. *Drug Receptors.* University Park Press, Baltimore.
26. Duguid, J. R., and Raftery, M. A. 1973. *Arch. Biochem. Biophys.* 159:512.
27. Eldefrawi, M. E., Britten, A. G., and Eldefrawi, A. T. 1971. *Science* 173:338.
28. Eldefrawi, M. E., Eldefrawi, A. T., and O'Brien, R. D. 1971. *Proc. Natl. Acad. Sci. U.S.A.* 68:1047.

29. Eldefrawi, M. E., Eldefrawi, A. T., Gilman, L. P., and O'Brien, R. D. 1971. *Mol. Pharmacol.* 7:420.
30. Eldefrawi, M. E., Eldefrawi, A. T., Seifert, S., and O'Brien, R. D. 1972. *Arch. Biochem. Biophys.* 150:210.
31. Eldefrawi, M. E., and Eldefrawi, A. T. 1973. *Arch. Biochem. Biophys.* 159:362.
32. Elliot, T. R. 1905. *J. Physiol.* 32:401.
33. Fambrough, D. M., and Hartzell, H. C. 1972. *Science* 176:189.
34. Fewtrell, C. M. N., and Rang, H. P. 1971. *Br. J. Pharmacol.* 43:417.
35. Franklin, G. I., and Potter, L. T. 1972. *F.E.B.S. Lett.* 28:101.
36. Goldman, D. E. 1943. *J. Gen. Physiol.* 27:37.
37. Harrington, L. 1973. *J. Gen. Physiol.* 62:58.
38. Hartzell, H. C., and Fambrough, D. M. 1972. *J. Gen. Physiol.* 60:248.
39. Hazelbauer, G. L., and Changeux, J. P. 1974. *Proc. Natl. Acad. Sci. U.S.A.* 71:1479.
40. Higman, H. G., Podelaki, T. R., and Bartels, E. 1963. *Biochim. Biophys. Acta* 75:187.
41. Hodgkin, A. A., and Katz, B. 1949. *J. Physiol. London* 108:37.
42. Hokin, M. R. 1968. *Arch. Biochem. Biophys.* 124:280.
43. Hunt, R., and Taveau, R. De M. 1906. *J. Pharmacol. Exp. Therap.* 1:303.
44. Jones, L. M., and Michell, R. H. 1975. *Biochem. J.* 148:479.
45. Karlin, A., and Bartels, E. 1966. *Biochim. Biophys. Acta* 126:525.
46. Karlin, A. 1967. *J. Theor. Biol.* 16:306.
47. Karlin, A., and Winnik, M. 1968. *Proc. Natl. Acad. Sci. U.S.A.* 60:668.
48. Karlin, A. 1969. *J. Gen. Physiol.* 54:2453.
49. Karlin, A., Prives, J., Deal, W., and Winnik, M. 1970. In *Molecular Properties of Drug Receptors,* R. Porter and M. O'Connor, eds., pp. 247–59. J. & A. Churchill, London.
50. Karlin, A., Prives, J., Deal, W., and Winnik, M. 1971. *J. Mol. Biol.* 61:175.
51. Karlin, A. 1973. *Fed. Proc.* 32:1847.
52. Karlin, A., and Cowburn, D. A. 1973. *Proc. Natl. Acad. Sci. U.S.A.* 70:3636.
53. Karlin, A., Cowburn, D. A., and Reiter, M. 1973. In *Drug Receptors,* H. P. Rang, ed., pp. 193–208. Macmillan, London.
54. Karlin, A. 1974. *Life Sci.* 14:1385.
55. Karlin, A., and Cowburn, D. A. 1974. *Neurochemistry of Cholinergic Receptors,* E. De Robertis and J. Schacht, eds., p. 37. Raven Press, New York.
56. Karlin, A. 1976. In *Methods in Receptor Research,* Part 1, Chapter 1, B. Blecker, ed. Marcel Dekker, Inc., New York.
57. Kasai, M., and Changeux, J. P. 1971. *J. Membr. Biol.* 6:1.
58. Kasai, M., and Changeux, J. P. 1971. *J. Membr. Biol.* 6:58.
59. Katz, B., and Miledi, R. 1972. *J. Physiol. London* 224:665.
60. Kebabian, J. W., Steiner, A. L., and Greengard, P. 1975. *J. Pharmacol. Exp. Ther.* 193:474.
61. Klett, R. P., Fulpiur, B. W., Cooper, D., Smith, M., Reich, E., and Possani, D. 1973. *J. Biol. Chem.* 248:6841.
62. Koelle, G. B. 1975. In *The Pharmacological Basis of Therapeutics,* 5th ed., Section IV, L. S. Goodman and A. Gilman, eds. Macmillan, New York
63. Langley, J. N. 1906. *Proc. Roy. Soc. B.*78:170.
64. Lee, C. Y. 1972. *Ann. Rev. Pharmacol.* 12:265.
65. Lindstrom, J., and Patrick, J. 1974. In *Synaptic Transmission and Neuronal Interaction,* M. V. L. Bennett, ed. Raven Press, New York.
66. Loewi, O. 1921. *Pflugers Arch. Gesamte Physiol.* 189:239.
67. Martin, A. R. 1955. *J. Physiol. London* 130:114.
68. Meunier, J. C., Olsen, R. W., and Changeux, J. P. 1972. *F.E.B.S. Lett.* 24:63.

69. Meunier, J. C., Olsen, R. W., Menez, A., Fromageot, P., Boguet, P., and Changeux, J. P. 1972. *Biochemistry (Washington)* 11:1200.
70. Michaelson, D., Vandlen, R., Bode, J., Moody, T., Schmidt, J., and Raftery, M. A. 1974. *Arch. Biochem. Biophys.* 165:796.
71. Michell, R. H. 1975. *Biochim. Biophys. Acta* 415:81.
72. Michell, R. H., Jones, L. M., and Jefferji, S. S. 1976. In *Stimulus-Secretion Coupling in the Gastrointestinal Tract,* R. M. Case and H. Goerbel, eds., p. 89. MIT Press, Cambridge, Massachusetts.
73. Miledi, R., Molinoff, P., and Potter, L. T. 1971. *Nature* 229:554.
74. Miledi, R., and Potter, L. T. 1971. *Nature* 233:599.
75. Moody, T., Schmidt, J., and Raftery, M. A. 1973. *Biochem. Biophys. Res. Commun.* 53:761.
76. Olsen, R., Meunier, L. C., and Changeux, J. P. 1972. *F.E.B.S. Lett.* 28:96.
77. Paterson, B., and Prives, J. 1973. *J. Cell Biol.* 59:241.
78. Paton, W. D. M., and Zaimis, E. J. 1949. *Br. J. Pharmacol.* 4:381.
79. Paton, W. D. M., and Zaimis, E. J. 1952. *Pharmacol. Rev.* 4:219.
80. Paton, W. D. M., and Rang, H. P. 1965. *Proc. Res. Soc.* 163B:1.
81. Patrick J., Heineman, S. F., Lindstrom, J., Schubert, D., and Steinbach, J. H. 1972. *Proc. Natl. Acad. Sci. U.S.A.* 69:2762.
82. Patrick J., and Lindstrom, J. 1973. *Science* 180:871.
83. Patrick J., Lindstrom, J., Culp, B., and McMillan, J. 1973. *Proc. Natl. Acad. Sci. U.S.A.* 70:3334.
84. Porter, C. W., Chiu, T. H., Wieckowski, J., and Barnard, E. A. 1973. *Nature New Biol.* 241:3.
85. Potter, L. T. 1973. In *Drug Receptors,* H. P. Rang, ed., pp. 295–310. Macmillan, London.
86. Racker, E. 1972. *J. Biol. Chem.* 247:8198.
87. Racker, E. 1973. *Biochem. Biophys. Res. Commun.* 55:224.
88. Raftery, M. A., Schmidt, J., Clark, D. G., and Wolcott, R. G. 1971. *Biochem. Biophys. Res. Commun.* 45:1622.
89. Raftery, M. A., Schmidt, J., and Clark, D. G. 1972. *Arch. Biochem. Biophys.* 152:882.
90. Rang, H. P., 1971. *Nature* 231:91.
91. Reiter, M. J., Cowburn, D. A., Prives, J. M., and Karlin A. 1972. *Proc. Natl. Acad. Sci. U.S.A.* 69:1168.
92. Ruiz-Manresa, F., and Grundfest, H. 1971. *J. Gen. Physiol.* 57:71.
93. Schleifer, L. S., and Eldefrawi, M. E. 1974. *Neuropharmacology* 13:415.
94. Schmidt, J., and Raftery, M. A. 1973. *Biochemistry (Washington)* 12:852.
95. Silman, H. I., and Karlin A. 1967. *Proc. Natl. Acad. Sci. U.S.A.* 58:1664.
96. Sugiyama, H., Benda, P., Meunier, J. C., and Changeux, J. P. 1973. *F.E.B.S. Lett.* 35:124.
97. Takeuchi, A., and Takeuchi, N. 1960. *J. Physiol. London* 154:52.
98. Takeuchi, N. 1963. *J. Physiol. London* 167:128.
99. Taylor, I. K., Cuthbert, A. W., and Young, J. M. 1975. *Eur. J. Pharmacol.* 31:319.
100. Terenius, L. 1974. *Acta. Pharmacol. Toxicol.* 34:88.
101. Waser, P. G. 1961. *Pharmacol. Rev.* 13:465.
102. Weber, M., and Changeux, J. P. 1974. *Mol. Pharmacol.* 10:1.
103. Welsh, J. H., and Taub, R. 1950. *J. Pharmacol. Exp. Ther.* 99:334.
104. Welsh, J. H., and Taub, R. 1951. *J. Pharmacol. Exp. Ther.* 103:62.
105. Yamamura, H. I., and Snyder, S. H. 1974a. *Proc. Natl. Acad. Sci. U.S.A.* 71:1725.
106. Yamamura, H. I., and Snyder, S. H. 1974b. *Mol. Pharmacol.* 10:861.
107. Young, J. M. 1975. *F.E.B.S. Lett.* 46:354.

3.4. Adrenergic Receptors

Michiko Okamoto

Dale's (24) classic paper described blocking by certain ergot alkaloids, of the pressor response to sympathetic nerve stimulation and injected epinephrine, whereas the depressor response to epinephrine injection was not blocked. These early observations led other investigators to suspect the existence of more than one type of adrenergic receptor. Two major types (α and β) of receptors for catecholamines have been identified through extensive drug structure–activity relationship (SAR) studies, and the orders of potency of various agonists and antagonists have been determined (1, 2). Ahlquist studied the relative efficacy of norepinephrine, epinephrine, isoproterenol, and other α-methyl derivatives of epinephrine and norepinephrine in producing a variety of catecholamine-dependent pharmacologic responses, such as vasoconstriction and vasodilatation of various muscular beds, heart rate and its contractile force, and the effects on the intestine and the uterus. A more recent development with selective blockers for each type of adrenergic receptors not only supported the conclusion that the adrenergic receptors can be classified into two major types, but also served in characterizing these receptors directly with specific binding techniques. A few of the general references related to the adrenergic receptors will be listed (3, 6, 12, 37).

The present classification of adrenergic receptors (30, 34) is generally based on (a) the relative potency of a series of adrenergic agonists for eliciting the specific response and (b) the potency of an antagonist for blocking the response to a given agonist. Furchgott (30) gave a more general definition of a α and β receptors based on these criteria (Table 1):

α-Receptors: An α-receptor is one that mediates a response pharmacologically characterized by: (1) a relative potency series in which norepinephrine $>$ epinephrine $>$ phenylephrine $>>$ isoproterenol, and (2) a susceptibility to specific blockers at low concentrations (phentolamine, dibenamine, or phenoxybenzamine).

β-Receptors: A β-receptor is one that mediates a response pharmacologically characterized by: (1) a relative potency series in which isoproterenol $>$ epinephrine $>$ norepinephrine $>$ phenylephrine, and (2) a susceptibility to specific blockers (either propranolol or pronethalol at relatively low concentrations). More recent extensive applications of SAR studies reveal that α-

Table 1.   Adrenergic Receptor Responses (for more extensive coverage see 40).

EFFECTOR ORGANS	RECEPTOR TYPE α	RECEPTOR TYPE β	RESPONSES
Heart		β_1	↑ heart rate ↑ contractility ↑ automaticity ↑ conduction velocity
Blood vessels	α		constriction
		β_2	dilatation
Lung Bronchial muscle		β_2	relaxation
Stomach	α		sphincter constriction
		β	motility and tone
Intestine	α		sphincter constriction; ↓ motility and tone through Auerbach's plexus
Spleen	α		constriction
		β	relaxation
		β	↓ motility and tone
Urinary bladder	α		contraction
		β	relaxation
Eye	α		radial muscle constriction
		β	ciliary muscle relaxation
Skin	α		pilomotor muscle constriction sweat gland (palms of hand, etc.) secretion
Liver		β_2	glycogen synthesis
Fat cells		β_1	lipolysis
Salivary gland	α		K^+ and water secretion
		β	amylase secretion

and β-receptors can be further classified into several subgroups, or, possibly, that within the α- and β-receptor groups each receptor organ has sufficiently different selectivity of its own to enable development of selective agonists and antagonists to each of the clinically important adrenergic receptor organs. For example, the development of selective agonists and antagonists to cardiac β-receptors that do not affect bronchial smooth muscle β-receptors and vice versa is of significant importance in medicine. Receptors specific for dopamine also have been identified.

Of all the catecholamine receptors, the β-adrenergic receptors have been studied in the most detail, probably because the initial biochemical response induced by the binding of agonist to the β-receptor has been identified as the activation of the enzyme adenylate cyclase. The enzyme catalyzes the production from adenosine 5' triphosphate (ATP) to cyclic adenosine 3'-5' monophosphate (cAMP), which in turn serves as a "second messenger." The concept of cAMP as a second messenger arose originally from the studies of Sutherland and his colleagues (76), and it constitutes a milestone in hormone research.

Generally, the β-receptors are thought to be coupled with the enzyme adenylate cyclase which utilizes intracellular ATP as a substrate. The relationship between the β-receptor and adenylate cyclase appears to be similar to the relationships between many of the polypeptide hormones such as glucagon, ACTH, secretin, and so on, and the enzyme adenylate cyclase (23). In a number of cell types (e.g., fat cells and liver cells), the β-receptors as well as the receptors to polypeptide hormones have been found to be coupled to the enzyme adenylate cyclase. The second messenger cAMP then triggers a series of biochemical reactions typical of the cell, usually starting with an activation of the enzyme protein kinase (82). It has been postulated that β-adrenergic neurons facilitate adenylate cyclase production through this process. Then, the enzyme is coupled with β-receptor at the postsynaptic membrane. The generated cAMP appears next to stimulate protein kinase, which in turn phosphorylates important endogenous substrate proteins; this process leads to a typical β-adrenergic physiologic effect (40). However, some β-adrenergic responses are not necessarily coupled with the adenylate cyclase system. For example, it has been shown that β-adrenergic cell activity in turkey erythrocytes is independent of the adenylate cyclase system (the cell response cannot be mimicked by cAMP or dibutyryl cAMP) but is dependent on the calcium ion efflux. This ion efflux and, hence, the cell response can be induced by β-receptor agonists and can be blocked by β-antagonists (74). Recently, it was also shown in the turkey erythrocyte ghost (20) that a specific GTPase activity is coupled to the β-receptor. This enzymatic activity may be involved in the regulatory control of the β-receptor–dependent adenylate cyclase (see later section).

Significant progress has also been made in the elucidation of the biochemical responses coupled to α-receptors. It has been demonstrated that the primary event occurring upon occupation of the α-agonist is the influx of calcium ion, which in turn functions as the second messenger (70). Furthermore, the specific calcium ionophore A23187, when incorporated into this membrane, can substitute for the α-adrenergic ligand and bypass the receptor-dependent mechanism (71). (See later section.)

A summary of the biochemical signals elicited initially by the different catecholamine receptors is given in Table 2.

Table 2. The Primary Response by Catecholamine Receptor Activation.

RECEPTORS	PRIMARY RESPONSE	REFERENCE
α-Receptors	(1) Ca^{2+} influx	11, 70, 71
	(2) K^+ efflux	11, 32, 33, 70, 71
	(3) phosphate incorporation to phosphatidylinositol	58
β-Receptor	(1) adenylate cyclase activation	63, 76
	(2) Ca^{2+} efflux	73
	(3) specific GTPase activation	20
Dopamine receptor	(1) specific adenylate cyclase activation	21, 35

DIRECT APPROACHES IN CHARACTERIZING CATECHOLAMINE RECEPTORS

One of the direct approaches in characterizing receptors is to study binding properties utilizing specific ligands. There are two general approaches: (1) measurement of ligand binding using radioactive high-specific-activity ligands or fluorescent ligands for determining both the quantity of receptors and their affinity to the receptor ligands; (2) use of the irreversible affinity labels utilizing receptor-specific agonists or antagonists.

Until recently, progress in this area of identification and direct study of adrenergic receptors has lagged behind that of cholinergic receptors because of the lack of ligands with high selective affinity and high radioactive specificity. Furthermore, enriched adrenergic receptor sources comparable to electroplax, a cholinergic receptor source, are not available thus far. Accordingly, the quantity of β-receptors available is in the picomoles per milligram range, whereas in the electric organ of the electric fishes, the amount of nicotinic receptor is in the nanomoles per milligram range.

The discovery of direct adenylate cyclase coupling to β-adrenergic receptor activity has allowed the study of these receptors by monitoring the biochemistry of adenylate cyclase under tightly controlled laboratory conditions. Cell or membrane suspensions can be studied by measuring the rate of cAMP formation resulting from the selective β-receptor activation and/or deactivation. It has been found that the β-receptor exhibits stereoselectivity to ligands, and only the l-form or $(-)$-stereoisomer of both agonists and antagonists is capable of activating or inhibiting adenylate cyclase. Furthermore, the molecular structural similarity between agonists and antagonists for the β-receptor suggests that the two types of ligands compete for the same receptive site (78). Accordingly, the kinetic studies of inhibition of epinephrine-dependent adenylate cyclase activity by propranolol in turkey erythrocytes have shown that both ligands are competing for the same sites (44). A serious limitation in studying the β-receptor by the measurement of adenylate cyclase activity, or any other metabolic process, is that the receptor–agonist or antagonist interaction cannot be analyzed directly. A direct measurement of catecholamine and β-adrenergic receptor interactions must involve studies of the binding characteristics of the receptor.

Binding Studies of β-Ligands to the β-Receptor

The binding of ^{3}H-catecholamines to the β-adrenergic receptors in a variety of tissues has been reported (13, 25, 27, 41–44, 53, 68, 77). A careful examination of these binding experiments revealed (21, 48, 49) that the ligand specificity determined therein does not necessarily agree with the ligand specificity as defined by their capacity to activate catecholamine-dependent adenylate cyclase in these systems (13, 22, 25, 43, 44, 49). One source of discrepancy has been the binding of catecholamine to nonreceptor catecholamine–binding proteins, (possibly catecholamine o-methyl transferase), which are probably present in greater amounts than the specific β-adrenergic receptors. Thus, the reported number of receptors per cell, and the structural specificities required for a β-ligand, are frequently not correlated to those required by the β-adrenergic receptor itself. In an attempt to overcome this difficulty, many different ligands have been explored. Most of these are potent β-adrenergic antagonists. Levitzki et al. (48) and Atlas et al. (7) used (^{3}H)($\pm$)propranolol, Lefkowitz et al. (^{3}H)($-$)alprenolol (45), and Aurbach et al., ^{125}I-hydroxybenzylpindolol (9). However, the same precaution should apply when one uses these antagonists as ligands. β-Adrenergic antagonists may also bind to other nonreceptor sites in addition to the true β-receptors. When carefully examined, however, the properties of these nonreceptor binding sites are generally distinct and separable from those of the β-receptors. Also, a recently developed method of competitive receptor binding displacement assay can be employed for the determination of β-receptors. This method is based on the principle that the concentration of a competing ligand that inhibits the bound radioligand to the receptor for 50% (EC_{50}) is directly proportional to the affinity constant of the competing ligand to the receptor. Although the value (EC_{50}) obtained by this method is not necessarily equivalent to the true affinity constant which is determined directly by agonist and antagonist for the β-receptor (the experimental conditions are the determining factors; the essential variables are the radioligand concentration, the affinity constant of radioligand, and the concentration of receptor site), the true affinity constant can be calculated from EC_{50} values by certain sets of equations (60, 64).

Thus, Maguire et al. (52) found, in cultured glioma cells, $^{125}I(\pm)$ hydroxybenzylpindolol bound to two distinct sets of sites, one set having properties expected of the β-adrenergic receptors, the other having identical affinity but without stereospecificity and with different kinetic characteristics. $^3H(\pm)$propranolol has also been shown to bind to a variety of nonreceptor sites. However, Levitzki et al. (48) and Atlas et al. (7) have studied $(^3H)(\pm)$propranolol binding to turkey erythrocyte ghosts and its displacement by nonradioactive ligands. They were able to characterize true β-adrenergic receptors. It has been found that: (1) binding of propranolol and catecholamines can be specific for the stereoisomers; (2) the dissociation constant for propranolol binding and the constant obtained from the adenylate cyclase inhibition assay by propranolol were identical (2.5×10^{-9} M); (3) ^3H-propranolol is displaced only by β-agonists; (4) all binding phenomena are rapid (less than 1 min) and reversible.

$^3H(-)$alprenolol, as a ligand for identifying β-adrenergic receptors has the advantages of being pure stereoisomer and being available in high specific radioactivity. Most important, the nonspecific binding with this agent is relatively low. It has been generally agreed that these blockers can only be displaced from the receptor by $(-)$ catecholamines and not by $(+)$ catecholamines. Furthermore, compounds that do not affect the β-receptor–dependent adenylate cyclase do not displace the antagonists from their binding site, although they can compete effectively with catecholamine binding. Using ^3H-propranolol, Levitzki et al. (48) have calculated that the mature turkey erythrocyte possesses 600–1000 β-receptors per cell (approximately 20 receptors/μm^2) as compared to 91,000 catecholamine binding sites that were orginally assumed to be the β-receptors (13, 27, 41–44, 53, 77). Binding studies utilizing these specific β-receptor antagonists were extended to cover mammalian tissues, including heart (4), pineal (36, 85), brain (4), human leukocytes (84), and cultured glioma cells (52). Receptor-bound drug was quantitated by several methods, including equilibrium dialysis (7, 48), microcentrifugation (4, 9, 45, 56), and vacuum filtration techniques (4, 52, 84). Good results and the lowest amounts of nonspecific binding were reported using the vacuum filtration method through glass fiber filters (46).

The binding characteristics determined by these three agents are comparable (4, 16, 17, 36, 45, 52, 64). "Specific" binding determined by each of these ligands displayed all the characteristics of affinity, specificity, and stereospecificity that were expected of true β-adrenergic receptor binding. Furthermore, careful correlative studies of binding and adenylate cyclase activation produced by each of these agents (8, 9, 36, 64) supported the notion that adenylate cyclase activity is indeed coupled to β-adrenergic receptors. The data were also consistent with the notion that β-adrenergic agonists and antagonists competed for an identical set of receptor binding sites (56).

Affinity Labeling of the β-Receptor

Affinity labeling of the β-receptor has been developed recently using a reversible β-blocker to which the reactive bromoacetyl radical is attached (8). The compound N-(2-hydroxy-3-naphthoxypropyl)-N'-bromoacetyl-ethylenediamine (NHNP-NBE) has been shown to inhibit the epinephrine-dependent adenylate cyclase activity irreversibly without affecting the fluoride-dependent activity in turkey erythrocyte membrane fragments (8). Furthermore, this affinity labeling reaction can be prevented by propranolol and l-epinephrine. The compound not only irreversibly inhibits the cell activities produced by the β-receptor stimulation, but also, proportionally the ^{3}H-propranolol binding to the β-receptor (8). The β-receptor affinity labeling helps to establish whether the hormone receptor and the enzyme activity resides on separate polypeptide chains.

Furthermore, this method is useful in tagging β-receptors in solubilized cell preparations. Since the adenylate cyclase from the erythrocytes has been known to lose its hormone sensitivities in response to both catecholamine and polypeptide, the direct monitoring of β-receptor by affinity labeling or a reversible ligand possessing high affinity becomes essential for characterization of the receptors.

This compound can be displaced from the β-receptor only by ($-$)-epinephrine or ($-$)-propranolol but not by the ($+$)-isomers. Using this compound, Atlas and her colleagues (54) have shown the localization of the β-receptors in various tissues of the mouse, such as Purkinje cells in the cerebellum, the spinal cord, and kidney, and so on. This approach and the technique can be extremely useful for the study of the properties of receptors of any type and, in particular, for the localization and mapping of specific receptors in heterogeneous tissues such as the brain, liver, and kidney.

β-Receptor Monitoring in a Solubilized Preparation

Theoretically, radioactive β-blockers can be used to monitor β-receptors in the solubilized state. Caron and Lefkowitz (19) have reported using ^{3}H-alprenolol and the equilibrium dialysis method to monitor β-receptors in the solubilized state. Success of the equilibrium dialysis method, however, depends on whether the concentration of receptors used is in the range of the dissociation constant toward the ligand (49). Furthermore, compounds such as ^{125}I-iodohydroxy-benzylpindolol, possessing very high affinity to the β-receptor, are extremely useful for monitoring β-receptors in the solubilized state.

ADENYLATE CYCLASE ACTIVATION BY β-RECEPTOR AGONIST

The occupation of β-receptor by β-agonist and the consequent production of cAMP as the second messenger is the first step, which in turn triggers the cell responses. The degree of adenylate cyclase activation and hence of cAMP production, however, is governed not only by the binding of a β-agonist to the β-receptor but also by many other regulatory ligands such as GTP (14, 60, 69) and Ca^{2+} (73, 74).

The Role of GTP and GppNHp in β-Receptor Activity

Rodbell and his colleagues have shown that GTP and its analogs such as Gpp(CH2)p and guanylylimidooliphosphate (GppNHp) play an important role in the activation of adenylate cyclase by glucagon (51, 62, 67). They have suggested that GTP acts synergistically with the hormone in activating the enzyme. GTP analogs were also found to produce an effect on the adenylate cyclase activation by β-agonists in nucleated erythrocytes such as frog (69), turkey (14, 50), and pigeon erythrocytes (60). A detailed kinetic analysis using GppNHp (26, 50) found that the role of the catecholamine is to facilitate the activation of enzyme by the guanyl nucleotide according to the following scheme:

$$RE + G \leftrightarrows REG$$

$$REG + H \rightleftharpoons KREG \overset{k}{\rightarrow} HRE''G$$

where R is the receptor; E, the enzyme; G, the guanyl nucleotide effector; and H, the hormone. The binding processes are fast and reversible, and the rate of conversion of inactive form of the enzyme to its active state E occurs with a rate constant of $k = 0.7$ min^{-1}. The active form of the enzyme system is very stable and remains stable even after the removal of the hormone and the excess GppNHp. This stable state of the enzyme can be converted back to the low-activity form in the presence of the hormone and ATP (50). Apparently, the hormone or ATP, alone, cannot induce the deactivation of the enzyme. The deactivation process requires the coordinated actions of these two ligands. Structural specificity of these activation and deactivation processes to the β-agonist and antagonist has also been studied (50). Whether GppNHp effects on the membrane reflect the direct role of GTP itself has to be investigated in future studies.

One interesting aspect of this active state E″ of enzyme coupled to the β-blockers to the receptor, is that the properties of the β-receptors, determined by the binding affinity of the β-blockers to the receptor, remain the same while the enzyme is in its active E″ state (49, 72).

The Role of Ca^{2+}

Calcium is also known to modulate the activity of hormone-dependent adenylate cyclase. The β-receptor–dependent adenylate cyclase from turkey erythrocytes in the membrane (74) and in the whole cell preparation is inhibited by Ca^{2+}. The mechanism of this Ca^{2+} inhibition was studied in detail on the membrane preparation (74). The Ca^{2+} was found to interact with the specific Ca^{2+} regulatory sites on the adenylate cyclase moiety, and to affect the allosteric properties of the enzyme. Thus Ca^{2+} affects V_{max} of the enzyme activity without altering the affinity of the β-receptor to the agonists (74) or antagonists (49) and with no effect on the kinetic parameters of the cyclase system to Mg^{2+} or ATP (74). A solubulized and partially purified adenylate cyclase in erythrocytes was found to retain its Ca^{2+} sensitivity. In cardiac tissue, on the other hand, Ca^{2+} was shown to inhibit adenylate cyclase by competing with Mg^{2+} at the Mg^{2+} allosteric site (26). Calcium has also been known to function as the second messenger of α-receptor action (11, 70, 71).

REGULATION OF β-ADRENERGIC RECEPTORS

The development of the laboratory technique for directly probing membrane receptors led to the discovery that the concentration of a ligand can regulate the binding properties of the receptors on the target cell (66). Using ^{3}H-alprenolol, Lefkowitz and his colleagues showed that prolonged exposure of frog erythrocytes to a β-adrenergic catecholamine in vivo (56) or in vitro (55) produced a 50–70% decrease in the number of alprenolol binding sites without a change in affinity of the receptor to the β-antagonist. The order of effectiveness of this action was isoproterenol > epinephrine > norepinephrine. The β-antagonist propranolol blocks this action produced by the β-agonists but does not decrease the total number of receptor sites. This regulatory process may account for the physiological phenomenon of functional desensitization (tachyphylaxis or tolerance) of the target tissue in vivo and in vitro, which is frequently seen by repeated exposure to the β-agonists. A similar regulatory phenomenon was observed by Axelrod and his colleagues on the β-receptors of the rat pineal gland (36). When these receptors were stimulated physiologically in vivo by keeping the animals in the dark, or pharmacologically, activating the β-receptor by injecting l-isoproterenol, a rapid fall in the number of ^{3}H-alprenolol binding sites was found. A 70% reduction in the number of receptor sites occurred within 2 hours after the treatment, and the effect was completely reversible within 4 hours. On the other hand, decreasing sympathetic activity by exposing the rats to light resulted in an increase of the number of β-receptors as measured by ^{3}H-alprenolol binding. Furthermore, it was found that the number of the β-receptors on the pineal gland varied with circadian rhythm and was inversely related to the cycle of neurotransmitter release (64). This mechanism may provide an efficient regulator of receptor response, especially when the maximal physiologic response can be achieved by the cell by occupying only a small fraction of the total number of receptors. In the presence of a large "receptor reserve" [e.g., as postulated for muscarinic cholinergic receptors (5, 28, 29, 57, 75, 81) or for histamine receptors (10)], a decrease in the number of available active receptors should not cause a decrease in the potential "maximal response," but should result in a shift of the dose–response curve to higher agonist concentrations.

α-RECEPTORS

In contrast to the well-documented β-receptors, characterization of α-receptors has been lagging. Despite extensive SAR studies in determining the molecular structural conformation necessary for α-agonists (61, 83), the structural correlation between α-agonist and α-antagonists is not clear; in contrast, β-antagonists have been described as having many structural features in common with β-agonists.

According to Pulman et al. (61), two intermolecular distances of an α-agonist such as norepinephrine are important for the binding of a molecule to the α-receptor conformation. One is a distance D from the cationic center N to the center of the aromatic ring, equal to 5.1–5.2 Å, and the other, a distance H from the cationic N^+ to the plane of the aromatic ring equaling 1.2–1.4 Å. Clonidine, a potent central α-agonist, has been found to fulfill the structural requirements (83).

The initial biochemical signal(s) consequent to α-receptor occupation are much less well defined than with the β-receptors. The widely studied (cf. 70) rat parotid gland secretory cell system possesses three classes of receptors, namely, β-adrenergic, α-adrenergic, and cholinergic muscarinic receptors. Stimulation of the β-adrenergic receptor results in the formation of cAMP, which in turn controls the enzyme-rich gland secretion. On the other hand, in response to the stimulation of the α-receptors and the muscarinic receptors, calcium was found to serve as second messenger, which, in turn, leads to K^+ release and water secretion. Calcium entry appears to be the primary response that occurs with the α-receptor activation in this event. Selinger et al. (71) have demonstrated that A23187, the ionophore for divalent cations, is capable of mimicking the α-adrenergic response in the presence of Ca^{2+} and causes K^+ and water secretion in rat parotid gland slices (71). The activated α-receptor apparently fulfills the function of an ionophore by releasing Ca^{2+} into the cell, whereas the activation of the β-receptor leads to the stimulation of adenylate cyclase. The influx of Ca^{2+} then produces the efflux of K^+ and water by some unknown mechanism. The action of an α-adrenergic agonist is, therefore, dependent on the presence of extracellular Ca^{2+} (71). Whether the activation of α-receptor always involves Ca^{2+} as a second messenger remains to be studied. On the other hand, Oron et al. (58) have shown that incorporation of inorganic ^{32}P into phosphatidylinositol is induced by α-adrenergic stimulation in slices of the parotid gland. This biochemical event is shown to be independent of Ca^{2+} and unrelated to K^+ efflux and water secretion. Calcium-independent activation and phospholipid effect have also been observed in the same preparation of the parotid gland (58) by the stimulation of muscarinic receptors. These observations tend to support Selinger's (71) assertion that the phospholipid effect and Ca^{2+}-dependent K^+ release are two different biochemical responses to α-receptor stimulation.

In comparison with binding studies performed with β-receptor probes, the evaluation of the binding of agonist and antagonist probes and α-receptors is in a relatively embryonic state. Nonetheless, remarkable success has been achieved using radioactively labeled clonidine and WB-41D1, a benzodioxan-derived α-antagonist (31, 79), to label α-adrenergic receptors in brain membranes. Interestingly, ^3H-labeled epinephrine and norepinephrine can be used successfully to label α-adrenergic receptors in brain (80), whereas the use of these ligands in other tissues has failed to label adrenergic receptors (discussed above). Importantly, the agonist and antagonist probes appear to differ in their binding to receptors, as has been previously observed for the binding of opiate drugs to receptors. A peripheral tissue, ^3H-labeled dihydroergotamine, has been used to label α-receptors (summarized by 47).

INTERCONVERSION OF α- AND β-RECEPTORS

Reports in the literature have suggested that the α-receptors and the β-receptors are two allosteric configurations of the same receptor. The experiments (38, 39, 58) were performed on frog heart, in which the stimulation of cardiac rate and contractility by catecholamines have characteristic β-adrenergic responses at warm temperatures 25–37°C) and α-adrenergic responses at low temperatures (5–15°C). Caron and Lefkowitz (18) examined this hypothesis by studying adenylate cyclase responses over a wide range of temperatures in various preparations, and concluded that the only adrenergic blockers that had temperature effects on enzyme activity were the β-type. Caron and Lefkowitz (18) have pointed out, however, that the receptor conversion studies were done in vivo, while their adenylate cyclase studies were done on isolated membrane fractions.

A GENETIC APPROACH TO THE β-RECEPTOR–CYCLASE SYSTEM

A most promising approach for the study of the β-receptor, stemming from the initial observations of Tomkins and his coworkers (15), uses cultured cells (S49 lymphoma) for the selection of specific variants. The genetic variants isolated can potentially lack individual components of the receptor–cyclase system (i.e., recognition site, catalytic site, and a regulatory purine nucleotide binding site). As summarized by Gilman and coworkers (65), considerable progress with this approach has been made.

REFERENCES

1. Ahlquist, R. P. 1948. *Am. J. Physiol.* 153:586.
2. Ahlquist, R. P. 1967. *Ann. N.Y. Acad. Sci.* 139:549.
3. Ahlquist, R. P. 1976. *Am. Heart J.* 92:661.
4. Alexanderm, R. W., Davis, J. N., and Lefkowitz, R. J. 1975. *Nature* 258:437.
5. Ariens, E. J. 1964. *Mol. Pharmacol.,* Vol. 1. Academic Press, New York.
6. Ariens, E. J., and Beld, A. J., 1977. *Biochem. Pharmacol.* 26:913.
7. Atlas, D., Steer, M. L., and Levitzki, A. 1974. *Proc. Natl. Acad. Sci.* 71:4246.
8. Atlas, D., and Levitzki, A. 1976. *Biochem. Biophys. Res. Commun.* 69:397.
9. Aurbach, G. D., Fedak, S. A., Woodward, C. J., Polmer, J. S., Hauser, D., and Troxler, F. 1974. *Science* 186:1223.
10. Batzri, S., Selinger, A., Schramm, M., and Robinovitch, R. 1973. *J. Biol. Chem.* 248:361.
11. Batzri, S., Selinger, Z., Schramm, M., and Robinovitch, R. 1975. *J. Biol. Chem.* 248:356.
12. Berthelsen, S., and Pettinger, W. A. 1977. *Life Sci.* 21:595.
13. Bilezikian, J. P., and Aurbach, G. D. 1973. *J. Biol. Chem.* 248:5577.
14. Bilezikian, J. P., and Aurbach, G. D. 1974. *J. Biol. Chem.* 249:157.
15. Bourne, H. R. Coffino, P., and Tomkins, G. M. 1975. *Science* 187:750.
16. Brown, E. M., Hauser, D., Troxler, F., and Aurbach, G. D. 1976. *J. Biol. Chem.* 251:1232.
17. Brown, E. M., Rodbard, D., Fedak, S. A., Woodward, C. J., and Aurbach, G. D. 1976. *J. Biol. Chem.* 251:1239.
18. Caron, M. G., and Lefkowitz, R. J. 1974. *Nature* 249:258.
19. Caron, M. G., and Lefkowitz, R. J. 1976. *Biochem. Biophys. Res. Commun.* 68:315.
20. Cassel, D., and Selinger, Z. 1976. *Biochim. Biophys. Acta* 452:538.
21. Clement-Comer, Y. C., Kebabian, J. W., Petzold, G. L., and Greengard, P. 1974. *Proc. Natl. Acad. Sci.* 71:1113.
22. Cuatrecasas, P., Tell, G. P. E., Sica, V., Parkh, I., and Chang, K. J. 1973. *Nature* 247:92.
23. Cuatrecasas, P. 1974. *Ann. Rev. Biochem.* 43:169.
24. Dale, H. H. 1906. *J. Physiol.* 34:163.
25. DePlazas, S. F., and De Robertis, E. 1972. *Biochim. Biophys. Acta* 266:246.
26. Drummond, G. E., and Duncan, L. 1970. *J. Biol. Chem.* 245:976.
27. Dunnick, J. K., and Marinett, G. V. 1971. *Biochim. Acta* 249:79.
28. Furchgott, R. F. 1966. In *Advances in Drug Research,* C. Harper and A. B. Simmonds, eds. Academic Press, London.
29. Furchgott, R. F., and Bursztyn, P. 1966. *Ann. N.Y. Acad. Sci.* 144:882.
30. Furchgott, R. F. 1972. In *Handbook of Experimental Pharmacology,* XXXIII, H. Blaschko and E. Muscholl, eds., p. 283. Springer-Verglag, Berlin.
31. Greenberg, D. A., U'Prichard, D. C., and Snyder, S. N. 1976. *Life Sci.* 19:69.
32. Haylett, D. G., and Jenkinson, D. H. 1972. *J. Physiol. London* 225:721.
33. Haylett, D. G., and Jenkinson, D. H. 1972. *J. Physiol. London* 225:752.
34. Jenkinson, D. H. 1973. *Br. Med. Bull.* 29:142.
35. Kebabian, J. W., Petzold, G. L., and Greengard, P. 1972. *Proc. Natl. Acad. Sci.* 63:2145.
36. Kebabian, J. W., Zatz, M., Romero, J. A., and Axelrod, J. 1975. *Proc. Natl. Acad. Sci.* 72:3735.

37. Koelle, G. B. 1975. In *The Pharmacological Basis of Therapeutics,* 5th ed., Section IV, L. S. Goodman and A. Gilman eds. Macmillan, New York.

38. Kunos, G., and Szentivanyi, M. 1968. *Nature* 217:1077.

39. Kunos, G., Yong, M. S., and Nickersen, M. 1973. *Nature* 241:119.

40. Langan, T. A. 1973. In *Advances in Cyclic Nucleotide Research,* Vol. 3, P. Greengard and A. Robison, eds., p. 99. Raven Press, New York.

41. Lefkowitz, R. J., and Haber, E. 1971. *Proc. Natl. Acad. Sci.* 68:1773.

42. Lefkowitz, R. J., Haber, E., and O'Hara, D. 1972. *Proc. Natl. Acad. Sci.* 69:2828.

43. Lefkowitz, R. J., O'Hara, D., and Warshaw, J. 1973. *Nature New Biol.* 244:79.

44. Lefkowitz, R. J., Sharp, G., and Haber, E. 1973. *J. Biol. Chem.* 248:342.

45. Lefkowitz, R. J., Mukherjee, C., Coverstone, M., and Carlon, M. G. 1974. *Biochem. Biophys. Res. Commun.* 60:703.

46. Lefkowitz, R. J. 1976. *Life Sci.* 18:461.

47. Lefkowitz, R. J. 1978. *Fed. Proc.* 37:123.

48. Levitzki, A., Atlas, D., and Steer, M. L. 1974. *Proc. Natl. Acad. Sci.* 71:2773.

49. Levitzki, A., Sevilla, N., Atlas, D., and Steer, M. L. 1975. *J. Mol. Biol.* 97:35.

50. Levitzki, A., Sevilla, N., and Steer, M. L. 1976. *J. Supramol. Struct.* 4:405.

51. Lin, M. C., Salomon, Y., Rendell, M., and Rodbell, M. 1975. *J. Biol. Chem.* 250:4246.

52. Maguire, M. E., Wiklund, R. A., Anderson, H. J., and Gilman, A. G. 1976. *J. Biol. Chem.* 251:1221.

53. Marinetti, G. V., Ray, T. K., and Tomasi, V. 1969. *Biochem. Biophys. Res. Commun.* 36:185.

54. Melamed, E., Lahav, M., and Atlas, D. 1976. *Nature* 261:420.

55. Mickey, J., Tate, R., and Lefkowitz, R. J. 1975. *J. Biol. Chem.* 250:5727.

56. Mukherjee, C., Caron, M. G., and Lefkowitz, R. J. 1975. *Proc. Natl. Acad. Sci.* 72:1945.

57. Nickersen, M. 1956. *Nature* 178:697.

58. Oron, Y., Lowe, M., and Selinger, Z. 1975. *Mol. Pharmacol.* 11:79.

59. Perkins, J. P., *Adv. Cyclic Nucleotide Res.* 3:1, and references therein.

60. Pfeuffer, T., and Helmreich, E. J. M. 1975. *J. Biol. Chem.* 250:867.

61. Pulman, B., Coubeils, J. L., Courriere, P. H., and Gervois, J. P. 1972. *J. Med. Chem.* 15:17.

62. Rendell, M., Salomon, Y., Lin, M. C., Rodbell, M., and Berman, M. 1975. *J. Biol. Chem.* 250:4253.

63. Robison, G. A., Butcher, R. W., and Sutherland, E. W. 1968. *Ann. Rev. Biochem.* 37:149.

64. Romero, J. A., Zatz, M., Kebabian, J. W., and Axelrod, J. 1975. *Nature* 258:435.

65. Ross, E. M., Maguire, M. E., Sturgill, T. W., Biltdnen, R. L., and Gilman, A. G. 1977. *J. Biol. Chem.* 252:5761.

66. Ruff, M. 1976. *Nature* 259:265.

67. Salomon, Y., Lin, M. C., Londons, C., Rendell, M., and Rodbell, M. 1975. *J. Biol. Chem.* 250:4239.

68. Schramm, M., Feinstein, H., Naim, E., Lang, M., and Lasser, M. 1972. *Proc. Natl. Acad. Sci.* 69:523.

69. Schramm, R., and Rodbell, M. 1975. *J. Biol. Chem.* 250:2232.

70. Schramm, M., and Selinger, Z. 1975. *J. Cyclic Nucleotide Res.* 1:181.

71. Selinger, Z., Eimerl, S., and Schramm, M. 1974. *Proc. Natl. Acad. Sci.* 71:128.

72. Spiegel, A. M., Brown, E. M., Fedak, S. A., Woodward, C. J., and Aurbach, G. J. 1976. *J. Cyclic Nucleotide Res.* 2:47.

73. Steer, M. L., and Levitzki, A. 1975. *Arch. Biochem. Biophys.* 167:371.

74. Steer, M. L., and Levitzki, A. 1975. *J. Biol. Chem.* 250:2080.

75. Stephenson, R. P. 1956. *Br. J. Pharmacol.* 11:379.

76. Sutherland, E. W., Oye, I., and Butcher, R. W. 1965. *Recent Prog. Horm. Res.* 21:623.
77. Tomasi, V., Loretz, S., Ray, T. K., Dunnick, J., and Marinetti, G. V. 1970. *Biochim. Biophys. Acta* 211:31.
78. Triggle, D. J. 1972. *Ann. Rev. Pharmacol.* 12:185.
79. U'Prichard, D. C., Greenberg, D. A., and Snyder, S. N. 1977. *Mol. Pharmacol.* 13:454.
80. U'Prichard, D. C., and Snyder, S. N. 1977. *Life Sci.* 20:527.
81. Van Rossum, J. M. 1966. *Adv. Drug Res.* 3:189.
82. Walsh, D. A., Perkins, J. D., and Krebs, E. G. 1968. *J. Biol. Chem.* 243:3763.
83. Wermuth, W. G., Schwartz, J., Leclerc, G., Garnier, J. P., and Rouot, B. 1973. *Clin. Ther.* 1:115.
84. Williams, L. T., Snyderman, R., and Lefkowitz, R. J. 1976. *J. Clin. Invest.* 57:149.
85. Zatz, M., Kebabian, J. W., Romero, J. A., Lefkowitz, R. J., and Axelrod, J. 1976. *J. Pharmacol. Exp. Ther.* 196:714.

3.5. Histamine Receptors

Henry Brezenoff

Histamine, or 5-(2-aminoethyl)-imidazole (Figure 1), is present in varying amounts in virtually all animal tissues. It is synthesized in vivo by decarboxylation of the amino acid histidine, a reaction catalyzed by a specific histidine decarboxylase. The major tissue depot for histamine is in the mast cells, where it is localized in the cytoplasmic granules, associated with a heparin–protein complex. This pool of histamine has a slow turnover and is biologically inactive until released in response to such factors as allergic reaction, injury, or certain drugs. A pool of non–mast cell histamine also exists in certain tissues, notably the gastric mucosa and the brain. This pool has a rapid turnover and may play a more active and tonic role in physiological function. In this regard, there is convincing evidence that histamine is important for the secretion of gastric acid, and there is a growing body of evidence implicating histamine as a neurotransmitter in the central nervous system. An extensive review of histamine and its metabolism recently has been presented by Maśliński (12).

It is now evident that histamine interacts with two distinct populations of receptors. The existence of more than one type of receptor was suspected for some time, based on the observations that the classical antihistamines (e.g., diphenhydramine, mepyramine) antagonized contraction of guinea pig ileum and bronchial smooth muscle by histamine but had no effect on histamine-induced stimulation of gastric acid secretion or relaxation of rat uterus. The term H1 was suggested for those receptors blocked by low concentrations of antihistamines such as mepyramine (1). Several years later a new chemical compound, burimamide (3), was developed which antagonized the effects of histamine on gastric acid and rat uterus without inhibiting the effects mediated through H1-receptors. The term H2 was coined for those receptors inhibited by burimamide. Subsequently, two more specific H2-receptor antagonists, metiamide and cimetidine, have been developed (8, 13).

Histamine obviously interacts with both H1- and H2-receptors. Modification of the histamine structure has led to some understanding of the requirements for its pharmacological activity. Both the imidazole nucleus and the 2-aminoethyl side chain are important. Converting the side-chain nitrogen to a secondary or tertiary amine does not result in any loss of biological

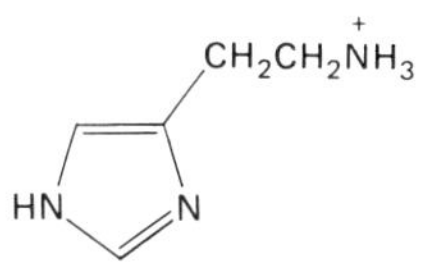

$$\overset{\text{CH}_2\text{CH}_2\overset{+}{\text{N}}\text{H}_3}{\underset{\text{HN}\diagdown\text{N}}{\diagup}}$$

Figure 1. Histamine (monocation).

activity. Most other modifications, however, markedly alter or reduce its pharmacological properties. For example, 2-methylhistamine is a relatively selective H1-receptor agonist, while 4-methylhistamine shows a high degree of specificity for H2-receptors, and 3-methylhistamine is inactive (3).

PHARMACOLOGICAL PROPERTIES

Histamine exerts an effect on a wide variety of biological tissues, although the nature of the response shows considerable variation between animal species. Some of the more notable actions of this amine are described in the following sections.

Nonvascular Smooth Muscle

The effect of histamine on smooth muscle varies with different species and even with different muscles in the same species. For the most part, however, the usual response is contraction, an effect mediated through activation of H1-receptors. The contraction is caused by a histamine-induced increase in the intracellular concentration of free calcium ions. Certain muscles, such as the bronchioles and intestine of the guinea pig, respond vigorously to very low concentrations of histamine. Guinea pig ileum has long been used in the bioassay of this amine. In contrast, some smooth muscle is relaxed by histamine, as, for example, the rat uterus and the lower bronchioles of the sheep. These relaxant effects are exerted through activation of H2-receptors (3, 9). In general, activation of H1-receptors in smooth muscle causes contraction, while H2-receptor activation results in relaxation.

Vascular System

The actions of histamines on the cardiovascular system recently have been reviewed by Owen (14). In most species (e.g., cat, dog, man) administration of histamine in doses as low as 10^{-10} mole/kg is followed by a rapid dose-related fall in blood pressure. The hypotensive effect of the lower doses is abolished by the classical H1-receptor antagonists. Depressor responses elicited by the higher doses, however, are refractory to these drugs, and only a partial inhibition is observed (10). The H2-receptor antagonists by themselves are without significant effect on the hypotensive response; yet when they are administered in conjunction with a maximum blocking dose of an H1-antagonist, a further inhibition ensues (4). Thus, both receptor types in some species mediate a hypotensive response to histamine, although the H1-receptors appear to play the dominant role at low doses.

On the other hand, the rabbit responds to histamine with a biphasic change in blood pressure, although only an increase may be seen with high doses. The fall in pressure is prevented by H2-receptor antagonists, while the pressor response is blocked by the H1-antagonists (5). In the rabbit, therefore, the two receptor types mediate opposing vascular effects.

The decreases in blood pressure are related in large measure to the effects of histamine on the microcirculation. Terminal arterioles are dilated, causing a fall in peripheral resistance. In addition, the epithelial cells of the postcapillary venules appear to contract, causing separation of the cells and an increase in vascular permeability. The latter effect results in a leakage of plasma protein and fluid from the circulation.

Histamine also directly affects the larger vessels, but the direction of this response also is species-dependent. It is predominantly arterial constriction in rodents and cats, but dilation in the dog and man. In rabbits, activation of H1-receptors produces vasoconstriction, while H2-receptors mediate vasodilation.

Heart

Histamine causes an increase in both the force and rate of contraction of the heart. The mechanism involved in this response was unclear for some time because of two major factors. In the first place, the cardiac effects are refractory to the classical H1-receptor antagonists (the only type available at that time). Second, histamine causes the release of catecholamines from chromaffin cells, which could indirectly affect the heart. That the positive chronotropic and inotropic responses to histamine are not mediated by liberated catecholamines has been amply demonstrated by observations that they are not enhanced by cocaine or diminished by reserpine or β-adrenergic blocking agents.

In recent years it has been shown that the cardiac effects of histamine can be mimicked by 4-methylhistamine and blocked by burimamide. Mepyramine and other H1-receptor antagonists can partially prevent these responses; however, this inhibition appears to be noncompetitive in nature. Thus, the increased force and rate of cardiac contraction evoked by histamine is mediated largely through activation of H2-receptors. The effects of histamine on the heart have been reviewed by Verma and McNeill (18).

Gastric Acid Secretion

Discovery of the H2-receptor blocking agents has greatly advanced our knowledge of the physiological role of histamine in the secretion of gastric acid. Histamine is among the most potent stimulants of such secretion, yet its action is almost totally resistant to inhibition by the classical antihistamines. Indeed, this disparity was one of the key factors that led to the concept of two distinct populations of receptors for histamine.

It is now well established that secretion of gastric acid by histamine is mediated through H2-receptors (3). Not only do the H2-receptor antagonists inhibit the stimulatory effects of histamine and 4-methylhistamine, but they also decrease the basal and food-stimulated release of gastric acid. Furthermore, the secretory response to acetylcholine, gastrin, and pentagastrin appears to be preceded by the release of histamine and is also inhibited by burimamide (7, 15). Thus, it appears that histamine, acting on H2-receptors in the gastric mucosa, may be the final common mediator for the secretion of gastric acid.

Role of Cyclic Nucleotides

Histamine activates adenyl cyclase and increases the levels of cyclic adenosine monophosphate in several tissues, notably gastric mucosa, heart, and brain (13, 15, 18). Although this response resembles that to epinephrine, the histamine-induced increase in cyclic AMP is not inhibited by β-adrenergic receptor antagonists such as propranolol. In the gastric mucosa and heart, activation of adenyl cyclase by histamine is competitively inhibited by burimamide. H1-receptor antagonists cause only a partial and noncompetitive block of this response, suggesting that the increase in cyclic AMP is mediated through H2-receptors. In the brain, however, there is some indication that interaction of histamine with either H1- or H2-receptors can lead to activation of adenyl cyclase and increased tissue levels of cyclic AMP (2).

In the gastric mucosa the increased levels of cyclic nucleotide are accompanied by an increased release of gastric acid. Other chemical stimulants of gastric acid secretion, such as pentagastrin and acetylcholine, release histamine and also result in activation of adenyl cyclase and increased levels of cyclic AMP. These effects are blocked by burimamide. On the other hand, while cyclic AMP itself can induce gastric acid secretion, this effect is not blocked by burimamide and is not accompanied by histamine release (7, 15). This and other evidence suggests that cyclic AMP is involved in the sequence of events between activation of H2-receptors and the pharmacological response to histamine.

STRUCTURAL FEATURES OF HISTAMINE ANTAGONISTS

Imidazoles can exist in several tautomeric forms (Figure 2), depending on their pK_a and the pH of the medium (4, 5 for review). It is likely that the ability of histamine to interact with the two distinct populations of receptors is related to its ability to adopt the preferred conformation at the receptor site. At physiological pH histamine exists almost exclusively as the monocation; the ring is uncharged, while the terminal nitrogen is protonated. Classical considerations can lead to the assumption that the receptor therefore contains a localized negative charge that forms an ionic bond with the onium cation. Recent data (6), however, suggest that the charge distribution is dispersed over the entire histamine molecular skeleton rather than being localized at the terminal nitrogen atom. If this is correct, then the receptor could be considered as having a region of negativity so that powerful coulombic forces attract the histamine monocation to the site but receptor specificity is determined by other forces.

Although changes in receptor specificity can be accomplished with only slight modification of the histamine molecule, marked structural differences are apparent between the H1- and H2-receptor antagonists (Figure 3). Drugs that block the H1 receptor in general are substituted aminoethyl derivatives or contain an aminoethyl fragment within a ring structure. They possess a side chain that is positively charged (usually at an ammonium group) at physiological pH, yet they tend to be lipophilic owing to the presence of an aryl ring. The ring structure does not need to be an imidazole. Since

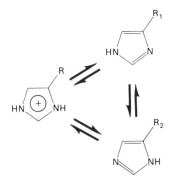

Figure 2. Tautomeric forms of an imidazole nucleus with a side chain. R_1 = electron withdrawing group; R_2 = electron releasing group.

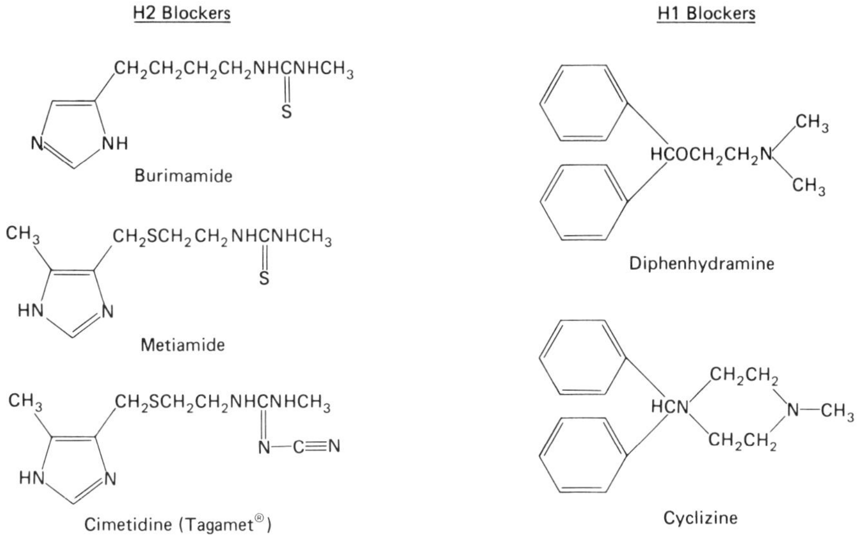

H2 Blockers   H1 Blockers

CH$_2$CH$_2$CH$_2$CH$_2$NHCNHCH$_3$
‖
S

Burimamide

Diphenhydramine

HCOCH$_2$CH$_2$N
CH$_3$
CH$_3$

CH$_3$ CH$_2$SCH$_2$CH$_2$NHCNHCH$_3$
‖
S

HN   N

Metiamide

CH$_3$ CH$_2$SCH$_2$CH$_2$NHCNHCH$_3$
|
N—C≡N

HN   N

Cimetidine (Tagamet®)

HCN
CH$_2$CH$_2$
N—CH$_3$
CH$_2$CH$_2$

Cyclizine

Figure 3. Structures of H2 and H1 blockers.

the side chain is protonated, as is the aminoethyl chain of histamine, it is likely that electrostatic forces are involved in the binding of the antihistamine to the H1 receptor. Ionic bonding probably is not a major determinant of receptor affinity, however, since antihistaminic activity is not correlated with the pK_a, and quaternization usually is associated with a decreased pharmacological effect. On the other hand, it is generally thought that the aryl groups are major participants in the drug–receptor interaction, possibly through hydrophobic binding.

The H2-receptor antagonists more closely resemble histamine in that they are hydrophilic and consist of an imidazole nucleus with a side chain in the 5-position. The side chain is polar but differs from the aminoethyl group of histamine by being longer and uncharged, and possessing a thiourea or cyanoguanidine moiety. These latter groups are important in that they affect the pK_a of the imidazole ring and are thought to thus maintain the ring in the tautomeric form for affinity with the H2-receptor (3, 4).

REFERENCES

1. Ash, A. S. F. and Schild, H. O. 1966. Receptors mediating some actions of histamine. *Br. J. Pharmacol. Chemother.* 27:427–39.
2. Baudry, M., Martres, M. P., and Schwartz, J. C. 1975. *Nature* 253:362–64.
3. Black, J. W., Duncan, W. A. M., Durant, C. G., Ganellin, C. R., and Parsons, E. M. 1972. Definition and antagonism of histamine H2-receptors. *Nature* 236:385–90.

4. Black, J. W., Owen, D. A. A., and Parsons, M. E. 1975. An analysis of the depressor responses to histamine in the cat and dog: Involvement of both H1- and H2-receptors. *Br. J. Pharmacol.* 54:319–24.

5. Brimblecombe, R. W., Owen, D. A. A., and Parsons, M. E. 1974. The cardiovascular effects of histamine in laboratory animals. *Agents Actions* 4:191–92.

6. Chand, N., and Eyre, P. 1975. Classification and biological distribution of histamine receptor sub-types. *Agents Actions* 5:277–94.

7. Dousa, T. P., and Code, C. F. 1974. Effect of histamine and its methyl derivatives on cyclic AMP metabolism in gastric mucosa and its blockade by an H2-receptor antagonist. *J. Clin. Invest.* 53:334–37.

8. Durant, G. F., Emmet, J. C., Ganellin, C. R., Miles, P. D., Parsons, M. E., Prain, H. D., and White, G. R. 1977. Cyanoguanidine–thiourea equivalence in the development of the histamine H2-receptor antagonist, cimetidine. *J. Med. Chem.* 20:901–6.

9. Eyre, P. 1973. Histamine H2-receptors in the sheep bronchus and cat trachea: The action of burimamide. *Br. J. Pharmacol.* 48:321–321.

10. Folkow, B., Haeger, K., and Kahlson, G. 1948. Observations on reactive hyperemia as related to histamine on drugs antagonising vasodilation induced by histamine and on vasodilation properties of adenosinetriphosphate. *Acta Physiol. Scand.* 15:264–78.

11. Ganellin, C. R., Durant, G. J., and Emmett, J. C. 1976. Some chemical aspects of histamine H2-receptor antagonists. *Fed. Proc.* 35:1924–30.

12. Maśliński, C. 1975. Histamine and its metabolism in mammals. *Agents Actions* 5:89–225.

13. McNeill, J. H., and Verma, S. C. 1974. Blockage by burimamide of the effects of histamine and histamine analogs on cardiac contractility, phosphorylase activation and cyclic adenosine monophosphate. *J. Pharmacol. Exp. Ther.* 188:180–81.

14. Owen, D. A. A. 1977. Histamine receptors in the cardiovascular system. *Gen. Pharmacol.* 8:141–56.

15. Rangachari, P. K. 1975. Histamine release by gastric stimulants. *Nature* 253:53–55.

16. Richards, W. G., and Wallis, J. 1976. Charge distribution of histamine monocation in its "essential" conformation. *J. Med. Chem.* 19:1250–52.

17. Symposium (Goth, A., chairman). 1976. Histamine H2-receptor antagonists. *Fed. Proc.* 35:1923–52.

18. Verma, S. C., and McNeill, J. H., 1976. Cardiac histamine receptors and cyclic AMP. *Life Sci.* 19:1797–1802.

3.6. Polypeptide Hormone Receptors

Morley D. Hollenberg

Receptors for polypeptide hormones, like receptors for a variety of nonpeptide hormones and neurotransmitters, are localized in the plasma membrane of responsive cells. Advances in our understanding of these receptors have come from two main lines of endeavor. The first approach concerns the study of the action of polypeptide analogues; the second direction concerns the measurement of the binding of polypeptides to specific membrane recognition sites. The enormous strides in synthetic peptide chemistry have permitted the preparation of hormone analogues (e.g., for oxytocin and vasopressin) with which receptor "complementarity" can be probed (49, 50). Structure–activity relationships can be evaluated, and the receptor binding regions of such polypeptides can thereby be deduced. This approach has proved useful not only for the neurohypophysial hormones, but for a variety of peptides including adrenocorticotrophic hormone (ACTH), the angiotensins, and, of late, the enkephalins. The strength of this synthetic approach lies in the ability to distinguish distinct receptors on the basis of bioassay alone. Thus the receptor for oxytocin can be distinguished from the one for vasopressin; the adrenal receptor for angiotensin II can be distinguished from the receptor in the vasculature (51), and the receptors for enkephalins can be seen to be heterogeneous (36). In the case of polypeptides as large as insulin, where the total chemical synthesis of analogues is impractical, a wealth of biological information can be obtained by using chemically and enzymatically prepared derivatives. The data obtained with modified insulins, taken together with the crystallographic structure of insulin, have served to define a receptor binding region of the molecule (41). With polypeptide hormones, as with other active agents, the biological data obtained with analogues of known biological activity provide the essential background for the complete evaluation of receptor characteristics by ligand binding methods.

Over the past decade or so, the study of the binding of a variety of polypeptide hormones to putative membrane receptors has met with considerable success. There are by now a number of comprehensive reviews that summarize the techniques used and the kind of progress that has been made, and the kinds of concerns and pitfalls inherent in such studies as well (1, 8, 18, 28, 29, 33, 44). The success with the study of peptide hormone receptors rests in large part on (1) the development of techniques for radioimmunoassay and (2) the development of a pharmacologic approach to the evaluation of binding studies, elegantly typified by early studies on the muscarinic receptor for acetylcholine (39). The key to work with polypeptides resides in the ability to prepare radioactive derivatives of very high specific activity (usually by the introduction of ^{125}I or ^{131}I) that retain full biological activity. The binding of the radioactive probes to specific membrane binding sites can then be measured (in a manner analogous to the binding of similarly prepared derivatives to antibodies), and can be reasonably assumed to reflect the binding of the parent compound at the receptor site. The ability of a variety of polypeptide analogues to compete for the binding of the labeled compound is then measured, and the relative binding affinities can be correlated with the known relative biological potencies of the analogues in a variety of test systems. When sufficient data are collected, it is usually possible to determine whether or not the binding site measured truly reflects the receptor recognition site involved in the biological response (28). This general approach has been used for an enlarging number of polypeptides, as indicated in the reviews referenced above. In the sections that follow, the methods that have succeeded in the past will be briefly summarized to indicate the kind of information that can be readily obtained from ligand binding studies.

CHARACTERIZATION OF RECEPTORS BY LIGAND BINDING STUDIES

Preparation of Radioactive Ligand Derivatives and Measurement of Binding

It is possible to generalize somewhat on the properties of hormone–receptor interactions. For most peptide hormones, the affinities are remarkably high, with dissociation constants usually less than 10^{-8} M. In addition, the receptors found on any given cell are present in vanishingly small numbers, usually less than 10^5 per cell. Because of the high affinities and small numbers of receptors present on responsive cells, ligand binding studies necessitate the use of radioactively labeled compounds of very high specific activity (e.g., 1000–3000 Ci/mmole). To achieve sufficiently radioactive derivatives, peptides are usually substituted with ^{125}I or ^{131}I to the extent of one atom of iodine per peptide molecule. Polypeptides are particularly attractive compounds for such studies, since it is frequently possible to introduce the iodine atom at a position that is not critical for the biological activity of the peptide of interest. As discussed elsewhere (8), there are a variety of methods for the preparation of highly radioactive peptide derivatives.

It is most important to point out, however, that the radioactive peptide derivative must be evaluated for its biological activity. Ideally, the derivative should be fully biologically active, as has been established for insulin molecules substituted to the extent of one iodine atom per molecule. In contrast, the substitution of iodine into the tyrosine residue of oxytocin or vasopressin abolishes biological activity. If it can be established that the substituted polypeptide derivative is fully active, it can be logically assumed that the binding of the derivative reflects the binding of the unlabeled compound to the receptor recognition site.

Most measurements of ligand–receptor interactions are done under equilibrium conditions. Aliquots of the cell, membrane, or soluble receptor preparation of interest are incubated with increasing concentrations of radioactive ligand both in the absence and in the presence of an amount of unlabeled ligand (100–1000-fold excess) sufficient to saturate all of the high-affinity binding sites. The preparation is allowed to equilibrate (usually 30–60 min at 24°C), and the receptor-bound radioactivity is then rapidly separated from the free ligand in the supernatant (e.g., cells or membranes are rapidly collected and washed on Millipore filters, or cultured cell monolayers are rapidly rinsed free of supernatant). It is usually the case that even in the presence of a large excess of unlabeled ligand, an appreciable amount of radioactivity is still bound to the membrane or cell preparation. The amount of bound radioactivity for which the unlabeled parent compound cannot compete is assumed to represent "nonspecific" or "nonreceptor" binding. The "specific" binding, usually reported in receptor studies, represents the total binding minus the "nonspecific" binding. With the use of the above experimental paradigm, a binding isotherm for the ligand of interest can be obtained, as indicated for insulin in Figure 1 (upper). The concentration of radioactive ligand at which binding is half-maximal provides an estimate of the equilibrium dissociation constant. Alternatively, the binding data can be analyzed mathematically in a variety of ways to yield the affinity constant and maximum binding capacity (e.g., see discussion in Ref. 42).

As an alternative to measuring the entire binding isotherm with radioactively labeled ligand, it is possible to determine binding-competition curves using a constant amount of radioactive ligand and increasing amounts of unlabeled parent ligand or ligand analogues (Figure 1, lower). Such binding competition curves are analogous to those used for radioimmunoassay, where the binding agent is an antibody rather than a receptor. For receptor binding, it is expected that the relative order of potency of analogues to compete for binding will reflect the relative biological potency of the analogues in a variety of test systems. For insulin, the binding data have agreed remarkably

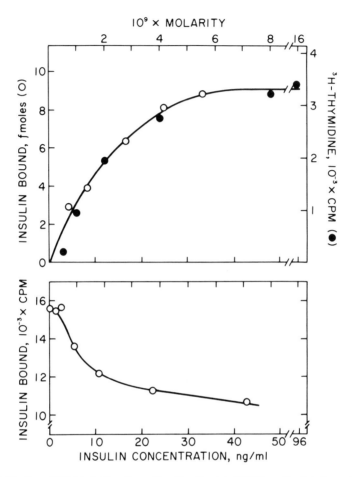

Figure 1. Binding of ^{125}I-labeled insulin and insulin-stimulated DNA synthesis in lens cell mono-layers. *Upper:* Binding of ^{125}I-labeled insulin (sp act, 640,000 cpm/ng or 3800 cpm/fmol), mea-sured on replicate monolayers (72 μg of protein or about 72,000 cells), is corrected for the amount of radioactivity bound in the presence of 2000 ng/ml unlabeled insulin and is expressed as femtomoles bound per monolayer. Incorporation of ^{3}H-thymidine (1 μCi/ml) into similar triplicate monolayers was measured during a 1-hr period begun 23 hr after the addition of 0.015 ng/ml of EGF–URO and varying amounts of insulin in a total volume of 1 ml. The points represent the mean incorporation per monolayer and are corrected for the incorporation observed in the presence of EGF–URO alone (4200 ± 400 cpm); the thymidine incorporation in the absence of added polypeptides was 3800 ± 200 cpm. *Lower:* Binding competition by increasing amounts of unlabeled single-component insulin was measured in the presence of ^{125}I-labeled insulin (5 ng/ml; sp act, 694,000 cpm/ng or 4100 cpm/fmol) in a total volume of 470 μl. The points represent the average counts bound per monolayer (78 μg of protein or about 78,000 cells). Data from Hollenberg (1975) (27).

well with observed biological data, as studied in detail by Gliemann and coworkers (21). The use of peptide analogues for binding competition experiments thus provides essential information to establish the "receptor" nature of the observed binding.

In addition to equilibrium data, measurements of the rates of binding (both on- and off-rates) provide useful information concerning the receptor ligand interaction. In the case of insulin, a half-life of the receptor ligand complex of approximately 16 min can be observed at 24°C; at higher temperatures, the half-life is much shorter. The rate of formation of the receptor–ligand complex can be analyzed in terms of a simple bimolecular reaction, so as to yield an on-rate constant. The quotient of the off-rate (k_{-1}) and on-rate (k_1) constants can be used to calculate the equilibrium constant: $K_D = k_{-1}/k_1$. In general, remarkably good agreement has been observed between the dissociation constant determined from equilibrium binding measurements and the constant calculated from the rate constants. Particularly illustrative analyses of the rates of formation and dissociation of the insulin–receptor complex have been provided by Pollet et al. (40) and by DeLean and Rodbard (11).

PROBING RECEPTOR STRUCTURE WITH ENZYMES AND LECTINS

The use of enzyme and lectin probes has served to complement measurements of ligand binding, thus adding considerably to the accepted models of receptor structures. The ligand recognition site of a number of receptors (e.g., for insulin) has been found to be remarkably sensitive to proteolytic enzymes. Such data not only indicate the protein nature of the receptors, but suggest that the ligand recognition sites are located in a relatively exposed portion of the plasma membrane. In addition to the exposed sites for ligand recognition, it is evident from experiments with phospholipases that a certain portion of the recognition sites may not be exposed to the external environment, but may be masked by membrane lipids. Other data with enzymes that hydrolyze glycosidic bonds (e.g., neuraminidase, β-galactosidase) suggest that sugar residues may play a role not only in the coupling of receptor occupation to cellular activation, but also in the specific recognition of the ligand. For example, neuraminidase abolishes the action of insulin on adipocytes without affecting insulin binding, whereas the simultaneous treatment of adipocytes with neuraminidase and β-galactosidase markedly affects insulin binding. The use of enzyme probes for the study of receptor structure has been well documented in studies with the insulin receptor (5).

Studies with plant lectins further suggest that peptide hormone receptors are glycoproteins. Not only can lectins such as concanavalin A (Con A) and wheat germ agglutinin (WGA) block the binding of polypeptides such as insulin and epidermal growth factor–urogastrone to receptors, but the lectins themselves can be observed to cause hormonelike effects. For example, both Con A and WGA have insulinlike effects in fat cells. In addition to serving as probes of receptor structure, the lectins have proved useful, as insolubilized derivatives, for the isolation of receptors by affinity chromatographic techniques.

SOLUBILIZATION AND ISOLATION OF RECEPTORS

Certain peptide hormone receptors (e.g., for insulin) are able to retain the ligand recognition property subsequent to solubilization with nonionic detergents like Triton X-100, whereas some receptors (e.g., for epidermal growth factor–urogastrone) lose the ligand recognition property upon solubilization. In the soluble state, the receptor for insulin is amenable to analysis by a variety of physicochemical methods, including velocity sedimentation, column chromatography, isoelectric focusing, and gel electrophoresis. In the majority of the studies with insulin receptor, use has been made of the receptor's insulin binding property to detect the presence of receptor (e.g., in sucrose gradients or subsequent to chromatography). Only recently has sufficient receptor been isolated to detect the receptor by more conventional means (32).

Based on the data so far accumulated for the insulin receptor, the recognition macromolecule appears to be a glycoprotein, with a subunit apparent molecular weight of 135,000, as estimated from SDS–acrylamide gel electrophoresis. In nonionic detergent solutions (Triton X-100), the receptor behaves as a larger molecule (apparent stokes radius about 72 Å) with an estimated molecular weight of 300,000 (4). Recent work indicates that even in nonionic detergents the receptor may be able to dissociate into subunits of smaller size (about 40 Å; Refs. 19 and 38.) It is likely that the properties of the insulin receptor will not prove too dissimilar from the characteristics of receptors for other polypeptide hormones.

In the event that solubilization abolishes the ligand recognition property, other approaches are necessary for receptor characterization. Polypeptides provide the advantage that a variety of covalent coupling methods may be used to "affinity-label" the receptor prior to solubilization. For the polypeptide epidermal growth factor–urogastrone (EGF–URO), both photoaffinity labeling (9) and affinity crosslinking with glutaraldehyde (45) have succeeded in identifying a specific recognition macromolecule. On gel electrophoresis, the recognition site exhibits an apparent molecular weight of about 200,000. As with the insulin receptor, there is evidence that the EGF–URO receptor is a glycoprotein (2, 26, 45), and that it may possess an oligomeric structure in the membrane (45). In the future, it is anticipated that the techniques outlined above will yield a considerable amount of detailed information concerning the molecular structure of a large number of polypeptide hormone receptors. As indicated above, a large amount of information is already available, as summarized extensively in a number of reviews (1, 8, 18, 33) and outlined in Table 1.

RECEPTORS, ACCEPTORS, AND THE ACTION OF POLYPEPTIDE HORMONES

As indicated in the introductory chapter of this section (3.1), the term receptor can be regarded in a restricted sense to mean that membrane-localized macromolecule that both recognizes the polypeptide hormone in a specific manner and then causes a membrane perturbation leading to a biological response. It is as yet not certain whether or not the "recognition function" and "action function" reside in the same macromolecule, or whether the receptor exists as an oligomeric structure, only part of which functions as a recognition site. According to this model, it is the receptor that is the cellular activating species, once triggered by the binding of the specific hormone. This mechanism is to be contrasted with the function of a specific acceptor, such as the transcobalamin-II (TC-II) acceptor or the low-density lipoprotein (LDL) acceptor that serve as specialized transport systems to transfer the active agents [cobalamin, attached to TC-II (37) or cholesterol, bound to LDL (25)] from the cell exterior to the cytoplasm.

Despite the above model of the receptor, and despite the now incontrovertible evidence that the cell membrane constitutes the primary site of action for many polypeptide hormones, it is still reasonable to ask: Does the cell surface constitute the only site of action for polypeptide hormones? Recent ligand binding studies with radioactively labeled polypeptides are directing a close look at this question. It is now evident from a number of studies

Table 1. Properties of Polypeptide Hormone Receptors.

RECEPTOR	PROBABLE COMPOSITION	MOLECULAR WEIGHT	SIZE OF SUBUNIT	REFERENCES
Epidermal growth factor–urogastrone	Glycoprotein	190,000	100,000	9, 45
Gonadotropin	Glycoprotein	194,000	90,000	15
Glucagon	Lipoprotein	190,000	90,000	20, 35
Insulin	Glycoprotein	300,000	135,000	5, 17, 19,
			75,000	32
Prolactin	Protein	220,000	220,000	47
Thyroid-stimulating hormone (TSH)	Glycoprotein	280,000	166,000	48
			75,000	
			24,000	

that, subsequent to the binding of a radioactively labeled polypeptide at the receptor site, ligand internalization can occur. In the case of mouse EGF–URO, the disappearance in intact cells of available receptor sites (apparent "down-regulation") observed consequent to the binding of ligand is associated with the appearance in the medium (at 37°C) of ligand degradation products (2). It appears that the EGF–URO receptor complex once formed undergoes pinocytosis and liposomal degradation. As alluded to above, such a mechanism is thought to liberate cobalamin into the cell interior from the TCII–cobalamin complex and cholesterol from the LDL–cholesterol complex. It is, therefore, not unreasonable to hypothesize that a degradation fragment of EGF–URO released in the cell interior subsequent to receptor binding and internalization may play a role in the well-known mitogenic action of this polypeptide. Since it is the rule, rather than the exception, that at least some proportion of an active ligand present in the external medium can be found in the cellular cytoplasm, the proof or disproof of the above hypothesis may be much more difficult than it was to establish the cell surface as the primary point of hormone action. Even in the case of well-controlled studies with polypeptide–agarose derivatives, it could be argued that a portion of the peptide might be cleaved at the cell surface so as to permit selective internalization without the release of appreciable ligand into the medium. The detection of nuclear binding sites for insulin that appear to be distinct from the membrane-localized insulin binding sites (22–24) bears directly on the potential role of internalized insulin fragments.

The above arguments are not to be construed as opposing the main tenet that has developed, implicating membrane-localized reactions in the action of perhaps the majority of neurotransmitters and polypeptide hormones. Indeed one might predict that all agents bringing about rapid (i.e., seconds to minutes) cellular events (e.g., membrane depolarization, stimulation of glucose transport, activation of adenylate cyclase, and modulation of cyclic AMP–dependent processes) would act solely at the plasma membrane. In this context, the process of ligand internalization and liposomal degradation may prove to be an important aspect of receptor regulation per se that is linked to but separate from the "action function" of the receptor as envisioned by the mobile receptor paradigm (see Chapter 3.2). The observations that anti-insulin receptor antibodies exhibit insulinlike actions in isolated adipocytes (16, 31, 34) argue convincingly, if not unequivocally, in favor of a membrane-localized site of action for insulin. On the other hand, it is important not to rule out the possibility that ligand internalization may play a role for agents causing a relatively slow (hours to days) cellular response (e.g., cell division or nerve cell differentiation). In this regard, insulin, which can cause both rapid (glucose transport; antilypolysis) and delayed (fibroblast growth) cellular effects might be found possibly to act either at the cell surface or via internalization, depending on the cell type affected. Presumably, further studies will clarify the role of receptor internalization (and shedding) in the action of a variety of hormones.

RECEPTOR COOPERATIVITY AND HORMONE ACTION

It is often the case that an analysis of ligand binding data [e.g., by the method of Scatchard (46)] suggests either the presence of ligand–receptor cooperativity or the presence of more than one ligand binding site. While there are a number of possible factors that can result in nonlinear Scatchard plots of the data (discussed at some length in Refs. 42 and 43), recent discussions in the literature have favored a negative cooperativity model for the interaction of a number of hormones with specific receptors. The interpretations rest on two principal kinds of data: (1) equilibrium binding data yielding Scatchard plots that are concave up, and (2) a kinetic analysis of ligand receptor dissociation kinetics done in either the absence or the presence of an excess of unlabeled ligand.

It should be noted at the outset that the interpretation of both kinds of data is fraught with difficulty. First, even if the equilibrium binding data are interpreted in terms of multiple binding sites, it is often very difficult to establish the ligand specificity of each binding site according to the criteria outlined above and discussed elsewhere (28). Furthermore, the occurrence of anomalous dissociation kinetics in nonreceptor preparations such as talc (7) indicates that the unequivocal analysis of similar data in biological systems may prove difficult. As originally demonstrated, the talc-binding data for insulin can be seen to be of a nonreceptor character, distinct from data obtained in membrane preparations.

The most extensively documented data supporting a negative cooperativity model came from work with insulin (12–14), based primarily on an assay measuring the accelerated dissociation rate of ^{125}I-insulin from cultured IM-9 lymphocytes and from mouse liver membranes, caused by unlabeled insulin and by a variety of insulin analogues. It has been concluded that the insulin molecule possesses a receptor binding region as well as a distinct region responsible for causing an increased insulin receptor dissociation rate. Despite these detailed studies with insulin analogues, which are consistent with an agonist-mediated acceleration of the dissociation of previously bound hormone, an alternative careful kinetic analysis of insulin binding to either unsaturated or partially saturated receptor preparations reveals no difference in the intrinsic receptor affinity constant for insulin (40). It is evident that different methods of kinetic analysis yield apparently conflicting results. The kinetic experiments of both DeMeyts and coworkers and Pollet et al. have been recently reevaluated by DeLean and Rodbard (11). It should be apparent from the above discussion that, in the absence of evidence at least as extensive as that obtained by DeMeyts and coworkers for insulin, the simple demonstration that a ligand enhances its own dissociation rate is insufficient to confirm or disprove receptor cooperativity.

A consideration of insulin action, in terms of the mobile or floating receptor hypotheses (6, 10, 30), predicts that insulin binding by a single receptor macromolecule could readily exhibit multiple affinities, as well as negative cooperativity (30). Recent work suggests that whereas the soluble insulin receptor insolated by affinity chromatography does not exhibit negative cooperativity (38), other membrane-localized constituents can interact with the insulin receptor so as to increase the receptor's apparent molecular size and confer upon the receptor the complicated equilibrium binding kinetics observed either in membrane preparations or in crude soluble receptor preparations.

Thus, while the receptor binding of insulin may indeed exhibit cooperativity, as suggested by DeMeyts and coworkers, a model akin to the mobile receptor paradigm wherein receptor–effector interactions lead to alterations in ligand affinity is suggested, rather than a model comprising site–site interactions between receptors, as was originally proposed (13). Future work should provide data to distinguish between the models not only for insulin, but also for other polypeptide hormones for which cooperative receptor interactions are suspected. It should be noted that the role of receptor cooperativity in terms of biological response is readily accommodated by the mobile receptor model.

NEW DIRECTIONS

Studies of receptors for polypeptide hormones are at a new threshold. Up to the present time, major efforts have been directed to the development of methods for the reliable detection of the ligand recognition site and to the characterization of the receptor's ligand specificity. As indicated above, considerable success has been achieved, such that the physicochemical parameters of an ever increasing number of polypeptide hormone receptors are now being determined. The challenge now is to elucidate further the membrane-localized mechanisms that are involved in hormone action. Attention must be directed to the study of other membrane-localized constituents with which the receptor interacts, and to the factors that affect the receptors themselves (e.g., membrane turnover, hormonal regulation). Additionally, attempts must be made to determine if the purified receptors per se possess ligand-modulated enzymatic activity that may account for the "action function" alluded to above. It is apparent that, although we have been able to gain a reasonable "first look" at receptor structure and function, new approaches will be necessary to elucidate further the complex series of reactions that lead from receptor occupation to cellular activation. It is hoped that this chapter may serve as a small stimulus toward the solution of this intriguing problem.

REFERENCES

1. Blecher, M., vol. ed. 1976. *Methods in Receptor Research; Methods in Molecular Biology,* A. I. Laskin and J. A. Last, ser. eds., Vol. 9, Parts I and II. Marcel Dekker, New York.
2. Carpenter, G., and Cohen, S. 1976. ^{125}I-labeled human epidermal growth factor. Binding internalization and degradation in human fibroblasts. *J. Cell Biol.* 71:159–71.
3. Carpenter, G., and Cohen, S. (1977). Influence of lectins on the binding of ^{125}I-labeled EGF to human fibroblasts. *Biochem. Biophys. Res. Commun.* 79:545.
4. Cuatrecasas, P. 1972. Properties of the insulin receptor isolated from liver and fat cell membranes. *J. Biol. Chem.* 247:1980–91.
5. Cuatrecasas, P. 1973. Insulin receptor of liver and fat cell membranes. *Fed. Proc.* 32:1838–46.
6. Cuatrecasas, P. 1974. Membrane receptors. *Annu. Rev. Biochem.* 43:169–214.
7. Cuatrecasas, P., and Hollenberg, M. D. 1975. Binding of insulin and other hormones to non-receptor materials: Saturability, specificity and apparent "negative cooperativity." *Biochem. Biophys. Res. Commun.* 62:31–41.
8. Cuatrecasas, P., and Hollenberg, M. D. 1976. Membrane receptors and hormone action. *Adv. Protein Chem.* 30:251–451.
9. Das, M., Miyakawa, T., Fox, C. F., Pruss, R. M., Aharonov, A., and Herschman, H. R. 1977. Specific radiolabeling of a cell surface receptor for epidermal growth factor. *Proc. Natl. Acad. Sci. U.S.A.* 74:2790–94.
10. DeHaen, C. 1976. The non-stoichiometric floating receptor model for hormone-sensitive adenylate cyclase. *J. Theor. Biol.* 58:383–400.
11. DeLean, A., and Rodbard, D. 1978. Kinetics of cooperative binding. In *The Receptors, a Comprehensive Treatise,* R. D. O'Brien, ed. Vol. 1, pp. 143–192. Plenum Press, New York.
12. DeMeyts, P. 1976. Insulin and growth hormone receptors in human cultured lymphocytes and peripheral blood monocytes. In *Methods in Molecular Biology,* A. J. Laskin and J. A. Last, eds., Vol. 9, *Methods in Receptor Research,* M. Blecker, vol. ed., Part I, pp. 301–83. Marcel Dekker, New York.
13. DeMeyts, P., Bianco, A. R., and Roth, J. 1976. Site–site interactions among insulin receptors. Characterization of the negative cooperativity. *J. Biol. Chem.* 251:1877–88.
14. DeMeyts, R., Roth, J., Neville, D. M., Jr., Gavin, J. R., III, and Lesniak, M. A. 1973. Insulin interactions with its receptors: Experimental evidence for negative cooperativity. *Biochem. Biophys. Res. Commun.* 54:154–61.
15. Dufau, M. L., Ryan, D., Baukal, A., and Catt, K. J. 1975. Gonadotropin receptors: Solubilization and purification by affinity chromatography. *J. Biol. Chem.* 250:4822–24.
16. Flier, J. J., Kahn, C. R., Jarrett, D. B. and Roth, J. 1976. Characterization of antibodies to the insulin receptor. *J. Clin. Invest.* 58:1442–49.
17. Gavin, J. R., III, Buell, D. N., and Roth, J. 1972. Water-soluble insulin receptors from human lymphocytes. *Science (Washington, D.C.)* 178:168–69.
18. Ginsberg, B. H. 1977. The insulin receptor: Properties and regulation. In *Biochemical Actions of Hormones,* Vol. IV, G. Litwack, ed., pp. 313–49. Academic Press, New York.
19. Ginsberg, B. H., Kahn, C. R., Roth, J., and DeMeyts, P. 1976. Insulin-induced dissociation of its receptor into subunits: Possible molecular concomitant of negative cooperativity. *Biochem. Biophys. Res. Commun.* 73:1068–74.

20. Giorgio, N. A., Johnson, C. B., and Blecher, M. 1974. Hormone receptors. III. Properties of glucagon-binding proteins isolated from liver plasma membranes. *J. Biol. Chem.* 249:428–37.

21. Gliemann, J., and Gammeltoft, S. 1974. The biological activity and the binding affinity of modified insulin determined on isolated rat fat cells. *Diabetologia* 10:105–13.

22. Goldfine, I. D., and Smith, G. J. 1976. Binding of insulin to isolated nuclei. *Proc. Natl. Acad. Sci. U.S.A.* 73:1427–31.

23. Goldfine, I. D., Smith, G. J., Wong, K. Y., and Jones, A. L. 1977a. Cellular uptake and nuclear binding of insulin in human cultured lymphocytes: Evidence for potential intracellular sites of insulin action. *Proc. Natl. Acad. Sci. U.S.A.* 74:1368–72.

24. Goldfine, I. D., Vigneri, R., Cohen, D., Plaim, N. B., and Kahn, C. R. 1977b. Intracellular binding sites for insulin are immunologically distinct from those on the plasma membrane. *Nature* 269:698–700.

25. Goldstein, J. L., and Brown, M. S. 1975. Hyperlipidemia in coronary artery disease: A biochemical genetic approach. *J. Lab. Clin. Med.* 85:15–28.

26. Hock, R. A., and Hollenberg, M. D. 1977. Characteristics of the epidermal growth factor/ urogastrone receptor of human placenta. *Clin. Res.* 25:665A.

27. Hollenberg, M. D. 1975. Receptors for insulin and epidermal growth factor: Relation to synthesis of DNA in cultured rabbit lens epithelium. *Arch. Biochem. Biophys.* 171:371–77.

28. Hollenberg, M. D., and Cuatrecasas, P. 1978a. Distinction of receptor from non-receptor interactions in binding studies: Historical and practical perspectives. In *The Receptors, a Comprehensive Treatise,* Vol. 1, R. D. O'Brien, ed. Vol. 1, pp. 193–214. Plenum Press, New York.

29. Hollenberg, M. D., and Cuatrecasas, P. 1978b. Membrane receptors and hormone action: Recent developments. *Progr. Neuropsychopharmacol.* 2:287–302.

30. Jacobs, S., and Cuatrecasas, P. 1976. The mobile receptor hypothesis and "cooperativity" of hormone binding application to insulin. *Biochem. Biophys. Acta* 433:482–95.

31. Jacobs, S., and Cuatrecasas, P. 1978. Insulin-like activity of antibodies to purified insulin receptor. *Science* (in press).

32. Jacobs, S., Shechter, Y., Bissel, K., and Cuatrecasas, P. 1977. Purification and properties of insulin receptor from rat liver membranes. *Biochem. Biophys. Res. Commun.* 77:981.

33. Kahn, C. R. 1976. Membrane receptors for hormones and neurotransmitters. *J. Cell Biol.* 70:261–86.

34. Kahn, C. R., Baird, K., Flier, J. S., and Jarrett, D. B. 1976. Effect of anti insulin receptor antibodies on isolated adipocytes. *Diabetes* 25 (*Suppl* 1):322.

35. Klein, I., Fletcher, M. A., and Levey, G. S. 1973. Evidence for a dissociable glucagon binding site in a solubilized preparation of myocardial adenylate cyclase. *J. Biol. Chem.* 248:5552–54.

36. Lord, J. A., Waterfield, A. A., Hughes, J., and Kosterlitz, H. W. 1977. Endogenous opioid peptides: Multiple agonists and receptors. *Nature* 267:495–99.

37. Mahoney, M. S., and Rosenberg, L. E. 1975. Inborn errors of cobalamin metabolism. In *Cobalamin Biochemistry and Pathophysiology,* B. M. Babior, ed., pp. 369–402. John Wiley & Sons, New York.

38. Maturo, J. M., III, and Hollenberg, M. D. 1978. Insulin receptor: Interaction with non-receptor glycoprotein from liver cell membranes. *Proc. Natl. Acad. Sci. U.S.A.* 75:3070–3074.

39. Paton, W. D. M., and Rang, H. P. 1965. The uptake of atropine and related drugs by intestinal smooth muscle of the guinea pig in relation to acetylcholine receptors. *Proc. R. Soc. B* 163:1–44.

40. Pollet, R. J., Standaert, M. L., and Haase, B. A. 1977. Insulin binding to the human

lymphocyte receptor. Evaluation of the negative cooperativity model. *J. Biol. Chem.* 252:5828–34.

41. Pullen, R. A., Lindsay, D. G., Wood, S. P., Tickle, I. J., Blundell, T. L., Wollmer, A., Krail, G., Brandenberg, D., Zahn, H., Gliemann, J., and Gammeltoft, S. 1976. Receptor-binding region of insulin. *Nature* 259:369–373.

42. Rodbard, D. 1973. Mathematics of hormone–receptor interactions I. Basic principles. In *Receptors for Reproductive Hormones,* B. W. O'Malley and A. R. Means, eds., pp. 289–326. Plenum Press, New York.

43. Rodbard, D., and Bertino, R. E. 1973. Theory of radioimmunoassays and hormone–receptor interactions: II Simulation of antibody divalency, cooperativity and allosteric effects. In *Receptors for Reproductive Hormones,* B. W. O'Malley and A. R. Means, eds. pp. 327–41. Plenum Press, New York.

44. Roth, J. 1973. Peptide hormone binding to receptors: A review of direct studies in vitro. *Metabolism* 22:1059–73.

45. Sahyoun, N., Hock, R. A., and Hollenberg, M. D. 1978. Insulin and epidermal growth factor–urogastrone: Affinity crosslinking to specific binding sites in rat liver membranes. *Proc. Natl. Acad. Sci. U.S.A.* 75:1675–79.

46. Scatchard, G. 1949. The attractions of proteins for small molecules and ions. *Ann. N.Y. Acad. Sci.* 51:660–72.

47. Shiu, R. P. C., and Friesen, H. G. 1974. Solubilization and purification of a prolactin receptor from the rabbit mammary gland. *J. Biol. Chem.* 249:7902–11.

48. Tate, R. L., Holmes, J. M., Kohn, L. D., and Winand, R. 1975. Characteristics of a solubilized thyrotropin receptor from bovine thyroid plasma membranes. *J. Biol. Chem.* 250:6527–35.

49. Walter, R. 1976. Conformation–activity studies of peptide hormones. Excerpta Medica Int. Congr. Ser. No. 403. *Endocrinol. Proc. V Int. Congr. Endocrinol.,* Hamburg, July 18–24, Vol. 2, V. H. T. James, ed., pp. 553–60. Excerpta Medica, Amsterdam.

50. Walter, R. 1977. Identification of sites in oxytocin involved in uterine receptor recognition and activation. *Fed. Proc.* 36:1872–78.

51. Williams, G. H., McDonnell, L. M., Raux, M. C., and Hollenberg, N. K. 1974. Evidence for different angiotensin II receptors in rat adrenal glomerulosa and rabbit vascular smooth muscle cells. *Circ. Res.* 34:384–90.

3.7. Steroid Receptors and Mechanisms of Steroid Hormone Action*

Kenneth S. McCarty, Jr., and Kenneth S. McCarty, Sr.

A knowledge of steroid receptor theory is essential to form a basis for progress in the understanding of the molecular biology of hormone response. Even though it has been presumed for many years that steroid-induced changes in morphology and functional activities in target cells represent some form of regulation of the synthesis of specific proteins, the task of establishing an exact mechanism still remains a major goal (1).

Steroid hormone action is restricted to those cells that contain appropriate receptor proteins. In contrast to membrane-bound receptors involved in polypeptide hormone action (2), the major steroid hormone receptors are localized in the cytoplasm and nucleus (3). Further, the polypeptide hormone receptors demonstrate a high degree of specificity for a single polypeptide (e.g., insulin receptor), whereas the steroid receptor protein may demonstrate either high specificity (e.g., estradiol receptor) or a wide range of specificities (e.g., progesterone receptor). A single cell often contains receptor proteins for more than one steroid hormone.

An important characteristic of cytoplasmic steroid hormone receptors is their wide fluctuation in intracellular concentration. Specific steroid receptor protein concentrations frequently show dependence on other hormone action. To the extent that it has been tested, steroid receptor binding activity appears to be cell cycle–dependent.

MECHANISMS OF STEROID HORMONE ACTION

Although the model for hormone action was proposed in the early 1960s (4) and remains much the same today, it is becoming increasingly clear that most, if not all, steroid hormone action depends on its translocation to the

* Supported by NOI-CB-63996-34 and NOI-CB-84223 from the National Cancer Institute.

nucleus and its interaction with some specific nucleoproteins in the chromatin. A summary of these concepts is presented in Figure 1 to emphasize the following points: (a) steroids, possibly because of their lipophilic nature, are not impeded by cell membranes; (b) target tissues contain a high affinity ($K_d \simeq 10^{-9}$ to 10^{-12} M) receptor protein with a limited number of molecules per cell (5 to 16,000); (c) free receptor is found predominantly in the cytoplasm in the absence of steroids; (d) the steroid–receptor complex undergoes a temperature-dependent alteration in its physical properties prior to, or simultaneously with, its translocation to the nucleus; (e) once the steroid–receptor complex enters the nucleus, it binds with DNA and specific chromosomal proteins, altering the pattern of gene expression and inducing the transcription of specific mRNAs. Molecular hybridization, with mRNA–cDNA probes, provides an approach to identify those RNA transcripts that result from complex protein–protein and protein–DNA steroid receptor associations. One product of such studies is the demonstration of progesterone induction of ovalbumin and ovomucoid in the chick oviduct. Improvements in in vitro

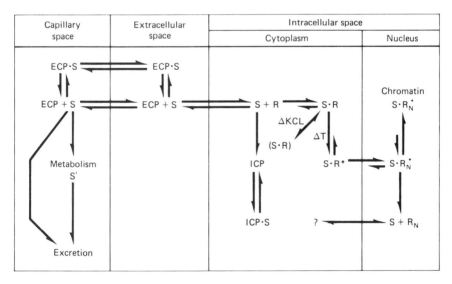

Figure 1. Interrelationship of steroid receptor proteins in the capillary, extracellular, intracellular cytoplasmic, and nuclear spaces. Extracellular proteins (ECP), metabolism (S′), and excretion all influence the availability of steroids (S) for the target cell. Intracellular proteins (ICP) compete for steroid binding with the specific cytoplasmic receptor (R) at many levels. Although the 8S [(S·R)] is an important marker for the identification of the steroid receptor complex, there is no evidence that it is an obligatory intermediate in vivo. The steroid receptor undergoes a critical temperature-dependent (ΔT) modification (S·R⁰) required for its translocation to the nucleus (SR$_N$⁰) and binding to chromatin. Little is known concerning the release of the nuclear receptor (R$_N$) or the free steroid.

translation of specific mRNAs are needed to provide conclusive evidence that steroid hormone–induced mRNA transcripts truly represent information for specific proteins.

TRANSPORT AND AVAILABILITY OF STEROIDS FOR INTERACTION WITH TARGET CELLS

Passive Diffusion Versus Facilitated Transport

The entry of steroids into cells appears to be nonspecific and is currently ill-defined (3). Present dogma suggests that, because of their nonionic-lipophilic nature, steroids diffuse and reflux freely in nontarget cells. In target cells, at least one essential role of the intracellular binding proteins is the maintenance of a steroid concentration gradient across the cell membrane.

The possibility of some form of facilitated transport should not be lightly dismissed. On the basis of comparisons of steroid entry versus concentration, Baulieu (5) suggests both a saturability and a hormone specificity for entrance, using as examples estrogenic versus nonestrogenic hormones. This observation is consistant with Milgrom's studies (6), in which certain sulfhydryl blocking agents inhibit steroid entry into uterine cells. Unfortunately the presence of large numbers of low-affinity steroid-binding proteins does not provide ideal conditions for rigorous interpretation of equilibrium data. An alternative explanation is to postulate that small differences in steroid structure might exert significant effects on plasma membrane permeability, relieving any necessity of invoking active transport mechanisms. Finally, the fact that Peck et al. (7) were unable to repeat the experiments of Milgrom suggest a need for more experimental study.

In contrast to complex polypeptide hormones whose information content resides in their amino acid sequences, the low-molecular-weight steroids ($\simeq$ 300) appear to require noncovalent interactions with specific proteins whose functions provide: (a) extracellular transport, (b) intracellular concentration, (c) translocation from the cytoplasm to the nucleus, and (d) specific recognition of chromosomal proteins. Because of the critical role of both the intracellular and extracellular proteins, we will briefly discuss some of their properties.

Extracellular Steroid-Binding Proteins

The extracellular concentration of steroids available for entry into target cells is in the range of 10^{-6} to 10^{-10}M, of which 90% appears to be protein-bound (8). If steroid entry is determined principally by passive diffusion, then both the extracellular and intracellular binding proteins influence the intracellular steroid concentration.

At least two factors must be considered as determinants: (a) quantity and nature of both specific and nonspecific nonreceptor binding proteins and (b) steroid metabolic clearance rates.

The specific properties of plasma proteins that bind 90% of the circulating steroids are less well defined than the cytoplasmic receptors (8). Some of the extracellular proteins and a few of their properties are included in Table 1. Reversible binding of steroids to protein has been studied more widely with serum albumin than any other protein. Because of its high concentration ($\approx$4% of total plasma) albumin remains as a candidate for hormone binding despite its low specificity and comparatively low binding affinity. Some selectivity is apparent in that the steroid affinity of albumin is inversely related to the number of polar groups in the steroid molecule.

All the well-characterized high-affinity nonreceptor binding proteins are α or β glycoproteins (Table 1). Probably the best-characterized of these is transcortin or corticosteroid-binding globulin (CBG). Other proteins include progesterone-binding globulins (PBG), α_1-acid glycoprotein (AAG), and testosterone-estrogen-binding α-fetoprotein (TeBG).

As an example of a high-affinity serum protein, the binding globulin for progesterone (PBG) demonstrates a capacity to bind significant amounts of steroid. PBG appears to be a polydispersed glycoprotein, with a pI of 2.8, and a molecular weight average of about 88,000. The carbohydrate content of this protein is usually high and contains sialic acid, hexosamine, and fucose.

Unfortunately, only a few studies have concentrated on these extracellular steroid-binding proteins. Progress in this area has been limited owing to a lack of adequate techniques for their purification. Significant progress has been seen utilizing sulfopropyl Sephadex (SP) chromatography, affinity chromatography, and the use of estradiol derivatives covalently coupled to polyethylene oxide.

The specific function of each of these proteins remains to be elucidated, since they are not generally accepted as essential for transport. The serum steroid-binding proteins influence steroid excretion and metabolic conversions by buffering wide fluctuations in serum levels. These proteins may further influence delivery of the steroids to the target cells owing to altered affinity resulting from metabolic changes associated with increased tissue demand.

Effect of Intracellular Steroid Metabolism

As soon as a steroid enters the cytoplasm of its target cell, it forms a functionally active complex with the receptor protein (characterized by both high affinity and ligand specificity). This does not exclude the possibility that the steroid may be loosely bound at some time to endoplasmic reticulum and/ or the inner surface of the plasma membrane. Since steroid hydroxylation

Table 1. Some Physicochemical Properties of Serum Steroid-Binding Proteins.

PROTEIN	$S_{20,w}$	M.W.	(CHO)	f/f_0	pI	MOBILITY (GLOBULIN)	STEROID BOUND (COMPETING EFFICIENCY)
Albumin	4S	69,000	(0%)	1	—	—	Nonspecific; progesterone >11β OH progesterone > testosterone
Transcortin (cortico-steroid-binding globulin)(CBG)	3.8S	46,000–51,000	(24%)	1.4	—	α	21-carbon type; $K_d \simeq 10^{-8}$ M
Progesterone-binding protein (PBG)	4.5S	200,000 (SDS) 88,000 (VC)	(60–70%)	1.7	2.8	α	100% Progesterone; 40% testosterone; 0% estradiol; 0% cortisol; $K_d \simeq 10^{-10}$ M
Orosomucoid α1-acid glycoprotein protein (AAG)	—	48,000 (SDS) 37,000 (VC)	(42%)	—	—	α1	Progesterone >> testosterone; 9×10^{-5} M progesterone; 1×10^{-4} M cortisol
Testosterone-estrogen-binding globulin (α-fetoprotein)(TEBG)	—	50,000	(32%)	—	5.6	α	$K_d \simeq 1 \times 10^{-9}$ M testosterone
Sex steroid-binding globulin (SSBG)	—	—	—	—	—	β	Requires 17β-OH-group 19-carbon type; ↑ estradiol-17β; $K_d \simeq 10^{-9}$ M
Vitamin D plasma-binding protein	3,8S	53,000	—	1.22	—	α1	Vitamin D_3

Table 2.   Procedures for Receptor Analysis.

METHOD	RATIONALE
Charcoal	Method rapid, reproducible, and inexpensive. Charcoal used to absorb free steroid. Sensitivity .001 → .8 nM. Problem: Charcoal may differentially strip nonsteroid and steroid-binding components. Difficult to interpret when competing multiple-binding components are present.
Hydroxylapatite	All known steroid receptors bind. Since elevated salts do not interfere, can be used for nuclear receptors. Problem: Some nonspecific binding, high background binding.
DEAE filter	Used for glucocorticoid receptor absorption binding. Advantage for dilute solutions. Major drawback: Absorption of free steroids, resulting in high background.
Protamine precipitation	Useful for both bound and free receptors, good for first steps in purification. Stabilizes receptor protein against proteolytic activity. Disadvantage: Nonspecific binding proteins may precipitate with receptor fraction.
Gel filtration	Gentle technique, gives good fractionation, dependent on salt concentration. Disadvantage: Technically difficult for multiple assays. Requires higher protein concentrations and should be performed in parallel with several varying concentrations of competing steroid.
Gel electrophoresis	Elegant test, gives good fractionation. Problem: Stripping and co-electrophoresis of labeled steroids; pH. Works well with progesterone receptor; its use for estrogen receptor requires further development.
Affinity labeling	Use of 4-mercuri-17β-estradiol to form a pseudocovalent bond with –SH of receptors. Problem: Complexity of assay and fractionation of product.
Immobilized antibody	Antiserum to estrogen receptor is immobilized to vinylidene fluoride film. Competition of tritiated estradiol binding with the binding protein. Stable 2 months. Problem: Interpretation of complex binding kinetics with multiple equilibrium constants.
Sucrose gradients	Excellent for identification of receptor and separation of specific from nonspecific binding proteins. Problem: Quantitation complicated by lack of equilibrium conditions during centrifugation; time and equipment required.

and metabolism may occur on the endoplasmic reticulum, such binding is likely to result in steroid modification and provide a modulation of available steroid for receptor binding and translocation.

The metabolism of testosterone to dihydrotestosterone (Figure 2) appears to be a critical determinant in its hormonal activity. In some cells only dihydrotestosterone is recognized by the receptor protein. This serves to emphasize the fact that this androgen receptor is highly specific in the recognition of the shape of the A ring structure. The enzyme 5α-reductase, present in most male accessory sexual glands, provides intracellular dihydrotestosterone in cells containing dihydrotestosterone receptor. The specificity of the recogni-

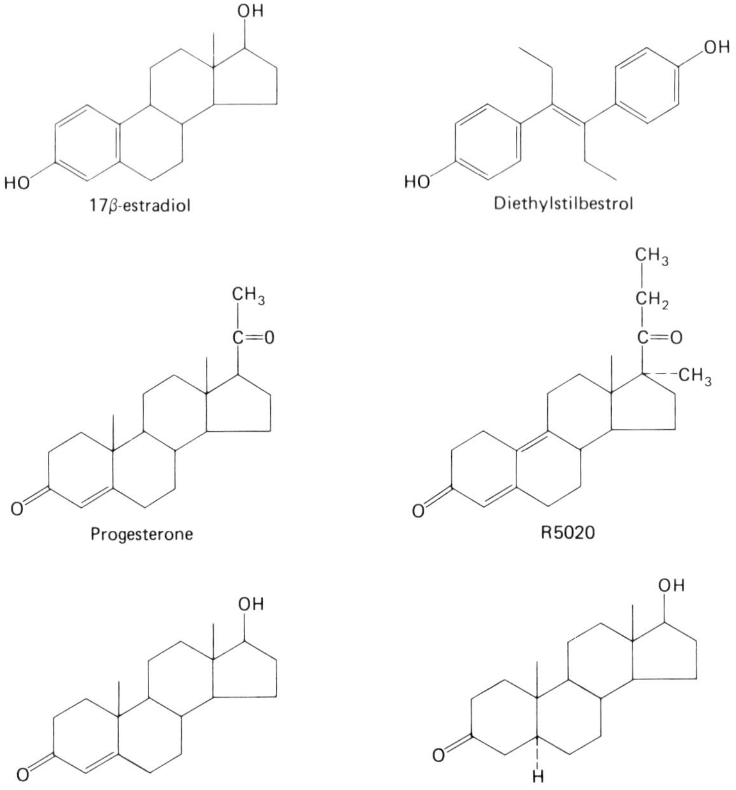

Figure 2. Structures of selected steroid hormones.

tion of this androgen is particularly evident by the fact that testosterone itself is the active androgen in muscle cells. The existence of distinct and specific dihydrotestosterone and testosterone receptors in different tissues (e.g., prostate vs. levator ani muscle) is implied.

The net effect of intracellular steroid metabolism is determined by the recognition of the metabolites by the cytoplasmic steroid receptor protein. That striking differences occur in the recognition of testosterone metabolites should not be permitted to overshadow other less dramatic effects of metabolism that may also prove to be important factors in the modulation of hormone activity. One may consider, for example, the potential importance of the metabolism of estrogens. The hormone normally secreted by the ovary is 17β-estradiol, whereas both estrone and estriol are largely products of extraovarian metabolism. The receptor-binding affinity of estradiol is 10^{-9}M; estrone, 10^{-8}M; and estriol, 2×10^{-8}M. These observations taken together suggest that the metabolic conversion of 17β-estradiol to estrone and/or estriol would influence its biologic activity. Although there is little to suggest the necessity of metabolic conversions for the specific binding and biologic activity of most steroids, the significance of the effects of metabolism has not been thoroughly investigated.

CYTOPLASMIC RECEPTOR PROTEINS

The accumulation of steroid hormones in their respective target cells is for the most part due to the presence of specific high-affinity steroid receptor proteins in the cytoplasm. After binding, the steroid–protein complex undergoes a temperature-dependent conformational change and is then translocated to the nucleus to bind to DNA and specific nuclear chromosomal proteins. Within 2 min, RNA transcription is initiated, and within 2 hr a four-to tenfold increase of specific messenger RNAs (mRNA) can be detected.

Some Physicochemical Characteristics of the Steroid Receptor

The physical properties of the receptor should at all times be considered in terms of: (a) its binding affinity (K_a or $1/K_d$); (b) the number of molecules or binding sites per cell; (c) its steroid specificity; (d) its tissue specificity; (e) evidence of a quantitative correlation with an identifiable biologic response; and (f) a saturable phenomenon in which the steroid receptors represent a finite number of binding sites.

Scatchard analyses of steroid receptor binding show that in addition to the specific binding of a limited number of cytoplasmic protein receptors (5 to 16,000 receptors/cell; K_d, 2 to 10×10^{-10}M), some intracellular nonspecific binding proteins are almost always in evidence (K_d, 10^{-5} to 10^{-6}M). The low-capacity specific steroid receptor is easily distinguished from nonspecific steroid-binding proteins both by its sedimentation properties and by competitive binding with compounds of similar receptor affinity and specificity (e.g., diethylstilbestrol for estradiol, etc.). It has become apparent that, for positive identification of receptor content, competition analysis using specific steroid analogs in conjunction with sucrose density gradients, or equivalent physical techniques, are essential to differentiate specific receptor from nonspecific low-affinity binding proteins.

The property of molecular self-association of steroid–receptor complexes represents a convenient means of identification of the receptor moiety. The low-salt sucrose density gradient still assumes a primary role in receptor analysis, in both receptor characterization and its fractionation. In fact, it must be conceded that much of the early work contributing to our present knowledge of the steroid receptor would not have been accomplished without this technique.

The aggregate form of the receptor protein for most steroids has an apparent molecular weight average of >200,000 daltons. Because of its unusual size in this aggregated state, the receptor complex may be separated from other low-molecular-weight extracellular and intracellular steroid-binding proteins. It should be noted that most steroid receptors form complexes ≃ 6–8S in low salt. Dissociation of the receptor to ≃ 4S in high salt occurs, reducing the apparent molecular weight average from >200,000 to ≃ 130,000 daltons. All forms of the receptor have unusually high Stokes radii.

Steroid receptors appear to share a number of general molecular properties: (1) alteration in sedimentation constant with changes in ionic strength, (2) protamine sulfate precipitability, and (3) a temperature-dependent activation. At ionic strength above 0.15 M KCl the receptor–steroid complex sediments at 4S. Because of its high degree of asymmetry, the assignment of an exact molecular weight to either the hormone receptor or its subunits should be viewed with caution. For progesterone receptors, sedimentation analysis of the dimer in high salt suggests a value of ≃ 90,000 daltons, whereas by SDS gel electrophoresis a value of >227,000 daltons is obtained. The monomer is composed of two nonidentical subunits when dissociated in 5 M urea. The monomer binds two steroid molecules, one for each of the A and B subunits. The molecular weight determinations of the urea-dissociated subunits give sedimentation molecular weight values of ~ 65,000 for each. The fact that these two subunits are dissimlar is emphasized by SDS–acrylamide gel electrophoresis, which yields values of 110,000 for the A subunit and 117,000 for the B subunit. The principal physical properties of the receptors and their subunits do not appear to be altered significantly during their purification, so that their identity may be confirmed throughout their purification by following their hormone-binding kinetics. In low salt (ionic strength below 0.15 M), the receptor proteins aggregate to form a tetramer with molecular weights greater than 200,000. This aggregation to an 8S tetramer is a unique characteristic of the receptor proteins, quite distinct from other binding proteins and reversible by altering the ionic milieu. Two points should be emphasized: (1) only 8S and not higher aggregates are observed, and (2) only 4S and not temperature-activated 5.4S molecules are capable of aggregation to the 8S form.

Of the steroid receptors that have been analyzed, most appear to represent acidic proteins with pI of 4 to 6. The physicochemical similarities of the cytoplasmic receptors cited above have been shown for receptor complexes for estrogen, progesterone, dexamethasone, 5α-dihydrotestosterone, and aldosterone (Table 3). Electron microscopy has been performed on negatively stained purified progesterone receptor preparations, revealing cigar-shaped

Table 3. Some Physicochemical Properties of Cytoplasmic Steroid Receptors.

RECEPTORS FOR	$S_{20,W}$	M.W.	f/f_0	pI	STEROID BOUND BY COMPETITON ANALYSIS
Estrogen	4S 8S	$S_{20,w}$ 110,000 SDS 200,000	1.5	5.8	100% Estradiol-17β 10% Estrone, estriol, 0% progesterone
Progesterone	6–8S	$S_{20,w}$ 86,000–99,000 SDS 102,000–357,000 225,000 A, 110,000 B, 117,000	1.74	(4–4.5)	100% Progesterone 40% Pregnanedione-5α 20% Deoxycorticosterone 3% Testosterone 1% Estradiol-17β 1% Cortisol
Glucocorticoids	6–8S	200,000	1.35		Dexamethasone ≃ Cortisol
5α-Dihydrotestosterone	8S	290,000	1.96	5.8	DHT > estradiol
Testosterone	7.9S	270,000	1.98	4.8	Testosterone 100%, DHT 15%
Aldosterone	8.5S	—	—	—	Aldosterone > Desoxycorticosterone > prednisone ≃ cortisol > progesterone
1,25 Dihydroxy-cholecalciferol	3.5–3.7S	—	—	—	1 α hydroxyl and 25 hydroxyl group required for binding
Vitamin A	2S	14,000–14,500	—	—	Trans retinols > Cis retinols

dimeric molecules. The frictional coefficients (f/f_0) suggest that the receptors for estrogen and 5α-dihydrotestosterone are also oblate ellipsoidal structures.

Fractionation of Steroid Receptors

Three major obstacles exist in the purification of steroid receptors: (1) the receptor represents an unstable protein present in extremely low concentrations, even in the induced state (10 to 100,000 molecules/cell); (2) the steroid receptor has an unusually high capacity to associate with other proteins and/or intracellular organelles; and (3) its identification is at present exclusively dependent on the demonstration of specific binding of a radioactively labeled steroid of high specific activity. [Antibody to estrophilin has been prepared by Jensen's laboratory (9).] In most cases the steroid specificity is not absolute, with the steroid capable of binding other proteins. It should be emphasized that, at all steps in its purification, the receptor must conform as closely as possible to the criteria stated previously.

Affinity chromatography appears at this time to offer one of the most practical solutions for receptor purification. Three modifications have been used:

1. Affinity immobilization of the steroid by linkage of a steroid hemisuccinate used as a spacer, which has proved most efficacious in the purification of estrogen receptor and progesterone receptor.
2. Affinity by immobilization of anti-receptor antibodies, which has been successful in partially purifying the estrogen receptor (9).
3. Phase separation using a liquid–liquid affinity labeled phase.

In the third method, a steroid or steroid derivative is coupled to polyethylene oxide (molecular weight, 6000 daltons) and a two-phase partitioning system using this polyethylene oxide–steroid couple and dextran T80 is used to partition the steroid-binding proteins. This system results in the receptor proteins being almost completely partitioned with the steroid-linked polyethylene oxide. The technique is rapid, and the yields appear to be good. The enzyme oxosteroid isomerase, which demonstrates a high affinity for estradiol, has been isolated using this method.

CYTOPLASM-TO-NUCLEUS TRANSLOCATION OF STEROID RECEPTORS

The imaginative and pioneering work of Mueller and coworkers (10) helped to direct attention to the critical link between steroid hormone action and gene expression. These early observations ultimately resulted in the development of cell-free systems to study the nuclear-binding and mRNA synthesis-inducing properties of the estrogen–receptor complex. Workers in many laboratories, including King et al. (11), Maurer and Chalkley (12), and Teng and Hamilton (13), have shown that the receptor has a high affinity for nucleochromatin. Many refinements in techniques, including those described by Spelsberg and Cox (14), Yamamoto and Alberts (15), and O'Malley et al (16), have extended these concepts. Since the studies of Jensen in the early 1960s, it has repeatedly been shown that, once formed, the estrogen–receptor complex is concentrated in the nucleus. It became apparent that the properties of the receptor–steroid complex differ from those of the free receptor. On sedimentation in sucrose density gradients, the nuclear receptor appears as a 5 to 5.4S moiety versus the 4 to 4.6S and 8S components observed for the cytoplasmic receptor–steroid complexes. Although this change in sedimentation is frequently ascribed to allosterism, the justification for this judgment is not firm, and more information about the steroid binding site is needed.

The uptake of steroid into the nucleus of target cells is rapid, usually requiring less than 30 to 45 min. The presence of the hormone appears to impart a capacity to the receptor to bind specific nuclear proteins, which may be viewed as a two-step mechanism. The hormone in the cytoplasm binds the free receptor with a high affinity in the first step of the reaction. The second step results in a temperature-dependent activation and translocation of the receptor–steroid complex. This two-step mechanism would provide both facilitated transport through the nuclear membrane and the necessary specificity for binding specific chromatin sites as well. It is reasonably well established that the nuclear translocation process is temperature-dependent (20°C), although it may take place very slowly at 4°C. Jensen was one of the first to suggest that this transformation of the receptor is an essential step in steroid hormone action (17). The temperature-dependent step involves transformation from a cytoplasmic 4S or 8S component to a 5 to 5.4S component that can be transported to the nucleus.

The translocation of the steroid receptor from the cytoplasm to the nucleus can be shown to be intimately related to the biologic response to these hormones. Feherty et al. (18) have demonstrated the preferential cytoplasmic localization of the receptor when the hormone concentration is low and the nuclear concentration of the receptor in case of high hormone levels. There is an increase in the cytoplasmic estrogen receptor during the first phase of the menstrual cycle and a profound decrease after ovulation.

EVIDENCE OF STEROID RECEPTOR ACTIVITY

There are two central concepts concerning steroid receptor proteins that deserve emphasis: (1) that steroid hormone response is dependent on the concentration of circulating steroid, representing a gradation in response; and (2) that the activation or repression of the synthesis of the hormone receptor or a second hormone receptor or peptide as a manifestation of the response to a given steroid hormone, occurs as a marker of cellular differentiation.

The experiments of Ruh et al. (19) and those of Sarff and Gorski (20) both show a positive correlation of estradiol concentration and total intracellular estrogen receptors. This is particularly important because Anderson et al. (21) have suggested that the only rate-limiting factor in steroid response is the amount of total steroid receptor. A number of experiments from Tomkins' laboratory (22) using HTC cells in culture suggest that the glucocorticoid system is similar.

As a result of estrogen administration, new estradiol receptor proteins are synthesized, with a cytoplasmic turnover time of 5 days. Evidence that estradiol-mediated induction of its own receptor represents de novo protein synthesis has been given by cycloheximide inhibition studies. Estradiol is also a positive effector in the induction of other steroid receptors. Thus the intracellular quantity of progesterone receptor is stimulated by estradiol. In addition to steroid receptor induction, estradiol elevates the pituitary levels of prolactin and the levels of prolactin receptors in the mammary gland. An example of a negative steroid effect is illustrated in the repression of the activity of the estradiol receptor by progesterone.

MODELS OF STEROID HORMONE ACTION

The essential features describing steroid hormone action (passive diffusion, cytoplasmic receptor, and nuclear translocation) have been retained with little deviation from the two-step model proposed over 10 years ago. The early model lacked the details of molecular structure of the receptor protein and its interaction with chromatin. It has become clear now that the mechanism is more complex than predicted, requiring specific protein–protein interactions as well as specific DNA–protein interactions.

Current dogma suggests that a nuclear component, presumed to be chromatin, is responsible for accumulation of the steroid–receptor complex by specific binding interactions. This concept has led to a number of studies that demonstrate that the estrogen–receptor complex interacts directly with chromosomal proteins, some of which are basic and some acidic (23, 24).

The activated steroid receptor is depicted as a dimer composed of two different subunits, although these components have been partially purified and characterized only for the progesterone receptor. The B subunit appears to retain a high specificity binding affinity for acidic chromosomal proteins (AP$_3$) obtained from chick oviduct. In contrast, the A subunit binds DNA only, without specificity or recognition of chromosomal proteins.

O'Malley concludes from the progesterone studies (25) that the binding potential of the progesterone receptor is fulfilled only when both A and B subunits interact with both DNA and chromosomal proteins, respectively.

Until further purification of other steroid receptors (estrogen, cortisol, etc.) has been achieved, generalizations should be made with caution.

The molecular basis of steroid hormone action is based on the following observations:

1. The steroid is concentrated in the target cell as a consequence of its binding to the cytoplasmic receptor.

2. The translocation of the steroid from the cytoplasm to the nucleus represents at least one function of the receptor in its activated configuration.

3. Within the nucleus, the steroid–receptor complex is dependent on the recognition of specific acceptor sites in order to fulfill its role in transcriptional control. This recognition is complex in that it involves both DNA and protein. The binding to DNA at this time does not appear to be specific and has been shown to be nonsaturable. In addition, the steroid–receptor complex preferentially binds euchromatin and not heterochromatin.

4. The steroid hormone demonstrates a capacity to bind tissue-specific and cell-specific acidic chromosomal proteins such as the AP_3 protein. In the case of progesterone, the B subunit appears to bind the AP_3 protein, and the A subunit appears to interact with free DNA.

5. Polymerase II activity is induced with an increase in the synthesis of hnRNA and specific mRNA.

6. Continued interaction of steroid–receptor/receptor–acceptor chromatin is required for continued stimulation of transcriptional activity.

7. Feedback regulation of receptor synthesis occurs, both positive and negative, depending on the specific steroid and target cell.

In considering chromatin–steroid–acceptor site dependency on the cell cycle it is helpful to realize that chromatin exists in one of three configurations:

1. *Inactive*—heterochromatin or solenoidal structure in which the nucleosomes are tightly compacted, and the acceptor sites are inaccessible. In late G1 phase of the cell cycle, H1 is phosphorylated to release the constraints imposed by the solenoidal structure.

2. *Permissive*—euchromatin or extended nucleosome configuration. This form of euchromatin would appear to be the result of phosphorylation. The steroid–receptor complex binds nonspecifically and may induce acetylation of histones H_3, H_4, and H_{2a}, and H_{2b} and single-stranded DNA.

3. *Active*—euchromatin or half nucleosome complex. This form may then allow the completion of the specific recognition of the steroid–receptor complex protein and allow polymerase activity to be initiated.

This model is also useful in explaining a number of other observations. For example, this proposal explains how an activated 5.4S is able to recognize, with a high degree of precision, a limited region of the DNA. The precision of the multistage model and the ultimate specificity require the recognition of a single strand of DNA (nucleosome-open structure) and protein located near, but external to, nucleosomal DNA. This provides both single-stranded DNA and specific AP_3-type proteins.

This model will also dictate the uniqueness of the mRNA products limited to a specific tissue and cell type. The enzymes of acetylation and possibly also methylation are cell-specific. Perhaps the DNA strand separation is at the promotor initiator region. The model also explains how a gradation in response would be commensurate with steroid hormone concentration.

The multiple hormone receptor induction by a single steroid is readily explained by the model. Acetylation may provide the permissive state required for transcription of other mRNAs in the synthesis of different steroid receptor proteins (e.g., estradiol induction of progesterone receptor proteins).

These general observations appear to apply to all steroid hormones studied to date including mineralocorticoids, glucocorticoids, androgens, estrogens, 1,25 dihydroxycholecalciferol, and progestins. While differences exist between the pattern of response and requirements for metabolism, considerable similarity is retained among the various steroid classes (26).

A number of important questions as yet remain unanswered, particularly with respect to possible mechanisms of steroid transport, membrane steroid binding sites, characterization of the regulation of chromatin binding, and events involved in the induction of chromatin by steroids from a permissive to an active state, as well as the fate of the steroid after receptor–acceptor chromatin binding.

REFERENCES

1. Yamamoto, K. R., and Alberts, B. M. 1976. Steroid receptors: Elements for modulation of eukaryotic transcription. *Annu. Rev. Biochem.* 45:721–46.
2. Tager, H. S., and Steiner, D. F. 1974. Peptide hormones. *Annu. Rev. Biochem.* 43:509–38.
3. Mainwaring, W. I. P. 1975. Steroid hormone receptors: A survey. *Vitam. Horm.* 33:223–45.
4. Jensen, E. V., and Jacobson, H. I. 1962. Basic guides to the mechanism of estrogen action. *Recent Prog. Horm. Res.* 18:387–414.
5. Baulieu, E. E. 1975. Some aspects of the mechanism of action of steroid hormones. *Mol. Cell. Biochem.* 7:157–74.
6. Milgrom, E., Atger, M., and Baulieu, E. E. 1973. Studies on estrogen entry into uterine cells and on estradiol–receptor complex attachment to the nucleus: Is the entry of estrogen into uterine cells a protein mediated process? *Biochim. Biophys. Acta* 320:267–83.
7. Peck, E. J., Jr., Burgner, J., and Clark, J. H. 1973. Estrophilic binding sites of the uterus: Relation to uptake and retention of estradiol in vitro. *Biochemistry* 12:4596–603.
8. Westphal, U. 1971. Steroid–protein interactions. In *Monographs on Endocrinology*, Vol. 4. Springer-Verlag, New York.
9. Greene, G. L., Closs, L., Fleming, H., Desombre, E., and Jensen, E. V. 1977. Antibodies

to estrogen receptors. Immunochemical similarity of estrophilin from various mammalian species. *Proc. Natl. Acad. Sci.* 74:3681–85.

10. Mueller, G. C. 1953. Incorporation of glycine-2-C^{14} into protein by surviving uteri from α-estradiol treated rats. *J. Biol. Chem.* 204:77–90.

11. King, R. J. B., Gordon, J., and Steggles, A. W. 1969. The properties of a nuclear acidic protein fraction that binds (6,7-^{3}H) oestradiol-17β. *Biochem. J.* 114:649–57.

12. Maurer, H. R., and Chalkley, G. R. 1967. Some properties of a nuclear binding site of estradiol. *J. Mol. Biol.* 27:431–41.

13. Teng, C.-S., and Hamilton, T. H. 1969. Role of chromatin in estrogen action in the uterus. II. Hormone-induced synthesis of nonhistone acidic proteins which restore histone-inhibited DNA-dependent RNA synthesis. *Proc. Natl. Acad. Sci. U.S.A.* 63:465–72.

14. Spelsberg, T. C., and Cox, R. F. 1976. Effects of estrogen and progesterone on transcription, chromatin and ovalbumin gene expression in the chick oviduct. *Biochim. Biophys. Acta* 435:376–90.

15. Yamamoto, K. R., and Alberts, B. 1974. On the specificity of the binding of the estradiol receptor protein to deoxyribonucleic acid. *J. Biol. Chem.* 249:7076–86.

16. O'Malley, B. W., Toft, D. O., and Sherman, M. R. 1970. Progesterone-binding components of chick oviduct. II. Nuclear components. *J. Biol. Chem.* 246:1117–22.

17. Jensen, E. V., Suzuki, T., Kawashima, T., Stumpf, W. E., Jungblut, P. W., and De Sombre, E. R. 1968. A two step mechanism for the interaction of estradiol with rat uterus. *Proc. Natl. Acad. Sci. U.S.A.* 59:632–38.

18. Feherty, P., Robertson, D. M., Waynforth, H. B., and Kellie, A. E. 1970. Changes in the concentration of high-affinity oestradiol receptors in rat uterine supernatant preparations during the oestrus cycle, pseudopregnancy, pregnancy, maturation and after ovariectomy. *Biochem. J.* 120:837–44.

19. Ruh, T. S., Katzenellenbogen, B. S., Katzenellenbogen, J. A., and Gorski, J. 1973. Estrone interaction with the rat uterus: In vitro response and nuclear uptake. *Endocrinology* 92:125–34.

20. Sarff, M., and Gorski, J. 1971. Control of estrogen binding protein concentration under basal conditions and after estrogen administration. *Biochemistry* 10:2557–63.

21. Anderson, J. N., Peck, E. J., Jr., and Clark, J. H. 1975. Estrogen-induced uterine responses and growth: Relationship to estrogen receptor binding by uterine nuclei. *Endocrinology* 96:160–63.

22. Tomkins, G. M. 1970. Regulation of specific protein synthesis in eucaryotic cells. *Cold Spring Harbor Symp. Quant. Biol.* 35:635–40.

23. Spelsberg, T. C., and Cox, R. F. 1976. Effects of estrogen and progesterone on transcription, chromatin and ovalbumin gene expression in the chick oviduct. *Biochim. Biophys. Acta* 435:376–90.

24. Shimke, R. T., McKnight, S. G., Shapiro, D. J., Sullivan, D., and Palacios, R. 1975. Hormonal regulation of ovalbumin synthesis in the chick oviduct. *Recent Prog. Horm. Res.* 31:175–211.

25. Rosen, J. M., Woo, S. L. C., Holder, J. W., Means, A. R., and O'Malley, B. W. 1975. Preparation and preliminary characterization of purified ovalbumin mRNA from the hen oviduct. *Biochemistry* 14:69–78.

26. O'Malley, B., and Birnbaumer, L., eds. 1978. *Receptors and Hormone Action*, Vol II. Academic Press, New York.

3.8. Lymphocyte Surface Immunoglobulin

Connie Clark

The immune system is comprised of thymic-dependent (T) and thymic-independent (B) lymphocytes, macrophage, and a variety of circulating and cell- or tissue-fixed molecules whose combined function is to maintain the integrity of the host. The primary focus of this chapter is one aspect of the immune system, the presentation of current concepts of B lymphocytes expressing surface immunoglobulins (sIg). In addition, the following topics will be considered: (1) the relationship of sIg to antigen-specific receptors on T cells; (2) chemical characteristics of an Ig molecule as they relate to its ability to interact with antigen; (3) current postulates regarding the genetic basis for generation of antibody diversity; (4) an examination of ontogenetic development and the interrelations of lymphocytes bearing different Ig classes on their surface; (5) the role of sIg in events that culminate in B cell activation.

Extensive heterogeneity exists within the population broadly defined as surface immunoglobulin bearing. Subpopulations can be delineated on the basis of sIg class and subclass expressed, whether or not they exhibit Fc receptors, and by the presence or absence of receptors for the C3b or C3d components of complement. The extent of overlap among these subpopulations has not been rigorously defined and may vary from species to species. References that provide more detailed treatment of these areas are listed at the end of the chapter.

ANTIGEN-SPECIFIC T CELL RECEPTORS

T as well as B lymphocytes express specific antigen-recognition units which are membrane-associated and derived from endogenous synthesis. While the B lymphocyte receptor is known to be immunoglobulin, the molecular nature of the T cell receptor has not been defined. Some similarity exists between B and T cell receptors for antigen as shown by Wigzell and coworkers (1, 2). Anti-idiotypic antibodies raised against T cell receptors cross-reacted completely with relevant idiotypic receptors on B lymphocytes; further, it was suggested that idiotypic T cell receptors were coded for by genes linked to the heavy chain immunoglobulin genes.

Stem cells give rise to both T (thymic-dependent) and B (bursal-dependent) lymphocytes; thus, selective suppression of the genetic repertoire occurs during the maturational processes which lead to formation of the B and T cell lines. The resulting, divergent populations can be categorized with respect to unique membrane structures as well as functional capacities. However, some attributes appear to be conserved and are expressed by subpopulations within each cell line. The heterogeneity of the T cell population is also considerable; functional activity (cytotoxic, suppressor, amplifier, helper) and membrane markers ($Lyt^{1,2,3+}$, Lyt^{1+}, $Lyt^{2,3+}$, Ia^{+}, Fc receptor^{+}, histamine receptor^{+}) serve to delineate various subpopulations. Although several postulates have been presented to explain the generation of antibody diversity at the B cell level, what hypotheses are tenable to account for the generation of T cell diversity? Questions that might be considered are: Are immunological capacities relegated to genetically restricted subpopulations programmed to function only as cytotoxic, suppressor, amplifier, or helper cells? Are the antigen-specific receptors expressed by these various T cell subpopulations as diverse in nature as the Ig receptors on B cells? What mechanisms dictate the preferential interaction of specific helper T cells with B lymphocytes bearing Ig molecules of different allotypes?

NATURE OF THE IMMUNOGLOBULIN MOLECULE

No evidence currently exists to support the notion that endogenously synthesized membrane immunoglobulin occurs other than in a monomeric form, although the predominant form in serum may be pentameric (IgM). Indeed, the question of whether distinct or interdependent biosynthetic pathways exist for secreted, as opposed to membrane-associated, Ig has not been resolved. Since sIg exists in the monomeric form, we can use IgG as a model to relate its structural characteristics to its ability to interact specifically with antigen.

The IgG molecule is comprised of two identical heavy (H) and two identical light (L) chains. On the basis of amino acid similarities of IgG molecules, the H and L chains can be divided into homology units of approximately 110 residues in length (Figure 1). These homology units are referred to as variable (V) or constant (C) regions. The H chain exhibits four homology units (V_H, C_H1, C_H2, C_H3), whereas the L chain expresses two (V_L, C_L). Within the variable regions (V_H, V_L) it is apparent that areas of extensive diversity (hypervariable regions) occur; this includes residue variation as well as sequence deletions or insertions. X-ray crystallographic analysis indicates that at least five of the seven hypervariable regions (three in the L chain

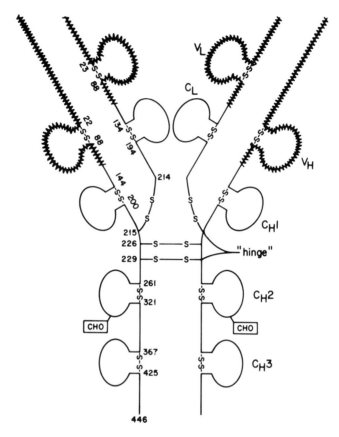

Figure. 1. Diagrammatic representation of an immunoglobulin molecule. Domains are each comprised of about 110 amino acid residues and contain a 60-residue S-bonded loop. Domains with invariant sequences are represented by smooth lines (C_L, C_H1, C_H2, C_H3), whereas those with variable sequences are shown by jagged lines (V_L, V_H). Numbered positions refer to cysteinyl residues that form S-S bonds. (Based on G. M. Edelman, *Biochemistry* 9:3197, 1970.) The Fc region encompasses the C_H2 and C_H3 domains, while the F(ab')$_2$ region includes the remainder the the molecule.

and four in the H chain) probably constitute the walls (framework determinants) of the antigen-binding crevice. These hypervariable regions reflect the genetic basis for the diversity of antigen-binding sites that constitute the repertoire of the host and raise questions with regard to the mechanisms for generating diversity.

GENERATION OF ANTIBODY DIVERSITY

Two major postulates have been proposed to explain the basis of the diversity exhibited by antibody molecules. The *somatic theories* hold that diversity of antibody genes arises in each individual during the course of development, probably as a result of hypermutation events that occur during antigen-independent differentiation. *Germ-line theories,* on the other hand, are based on the concept that genetic diversity exists prior to somatic differentiation. Instead of viewing these or other theories such as the *multispecificity* and *combinatorial* hypotheses, as being completely exclusive models, antibody diversity may, in fact, result from a combination of these mechanisms, one or more of which may predominate at a particular stage of B cell maturation or differentiation.

Clearly, the phenotypic capacities exhibited by pre-B cells, by virgin immunocompetent B cells, and by memory B cells, for example, reflect the operation of poorly understood regulatory events that permit expression or cause suppression of genetic information dictating the immunological function exhibited. Such regulatory signals may arise endogeneously as an integral part of cellular differentiation processes, exogenously from microenvironmental stimuli, or from a combination of both. Although the complexity of events is considerable, delineation of the nature of these regulatory stimuli and the processes that they induce is essential to our understanding of antigen–cell and cell–cell interactions in the immune response.

ONTOGENY OF THE B LYMPHOCYTE LINE

Prenatal development of murine B cells occurs first in fetal liver and spleen, whereas the major postnatal sites are bone marrow and, to a lesser extent, the spleen. The earliest B lymphocytes (pre-B cells) contain cytoplasmic IgM (cIgM), while those that follow bear surface IgM (sIgM). sIgM+ cells undergo transition and give rise to sIgD+, sIgG+, and sIgA+ populations. The precise interrelationships of these populations is not completely clear; sIgG+ cells arise from sIgM+ lymphocytes, but whether sIgA-bearing populations are derived from sIgG+, sIgM+, or both, has not been rigorously established in mammals. It is of interest to note recent evidence that indicates that sIgE-bearing cells arise independently of the sIgM+ cell line, and apparently cooperate with a distinct subpopulation of T cells in the production of an IgE antibody response.

The well-documented occurrence of simultaneous synthesis of two different Ig classes (e.g., IgM–IgD or IgM–IgG) by a single B lymphocyte, the detection of J-chain synthesis in IgG+ cells, and data supporting the concept that sIgM+ cells give rise to lymphocytes bearing sIg of other classes provide compelling evidence that B lymphocytes are not restricted with respect to Ig class. The advantage of simultaneous integration of all C_H genes early in the ontogeny of B cells is that isotype expression would involve regulatory events centered only on differential gene activation or repression while variable region specificity is maintained.

Since Ig class heterogeneity develops in germ-free as well as in congenitally athymic mice, it might be argued that neither exposure to antigen nor T lymphocytes exert an influence on or direct the development of Ig heterogeneity. On the other hand, studies by Pierce and Klinman (3) indicate that the class of Ig produced by individual clonal precursors may depend on interaction of I-region gene products expressed on T-helper cells and the responding B cells.

IMMUNOGLOBULIN RECEPTORS AND B CELL ACTIVATION

Monomeric IgM molecules are integral glycoproteins of the B lymphocyte plasma membrane, the Fab portions being exposed at the cell surface while the Fc region is immersed in the lipid bilayer. Modulation of sIg using anti-Ig antisera has been employed as a model that is assumed to simulate the interaction of antigen with specific sIg receptors. The fact that use of anti-Ig antisera does not activate B cells has given rise to two main hypotheses to account for events that do culminate in triggering of B cells. The *two-signal theory* (4) states that antigen interaction with specific Ig receptors constitutes a tolerogenic signal; activation requires the delivery of a second signal, supplied by T-helper cells if it is a thymic-dependent antigen or by properties that are intrinsic to thymic-independent antigen molecules. The *self–nonself discrimination theory* (5, 6) suggests that T but not B cells become tolerant to self-antigens—that is, B-cell tolerance is defined as a change from a resting to a tolerant state as a consequence of signal delivery by a thymic-dependent antigen. According to this concept, proof of an induced state of tolerance in B cells would be to activate B cells from a tolerant animal using a polyclonal B cell activator (PBA) and fail to detect induction of antibody to the specific tolerogen. It was in fact observed that PBA did induce tolerogen-specific antibody production by tolerant B lymphocytes.

The immunological maturational state of the animals (neonatal or fetal vs. adult) studied is critical. For example, if the effect of modulation with anti-μ antisera is compared using adult as opposed to newly formed sIgM+ lymphocytes, evidence suggests the signal is interpreted very differently. The adult sIgM+ population readily regenerated sIgM, whereas immature cells were rendered functionally inactive; thus, immature cells would be especially susceptible to inactivation, and development of tolerance to "self" antigens would be assured. Clearly, the mechanisms that are operative in cells at different stages of the maturation process may differ markedly.

REFERENCES

1. Binz, H., and Wigzell, H. 1975. Shared idiotypic determinants on B and T lymphocytes reactive against the same antigenic determinants. I. Demonstration of similar or identical idiotypes on IgG molecules and T-cell receptors with specificity for the same alloantigens. *J. Exp. Med.* 142:197.

2. Binz, H., Wigzell, H., and Bazin, H. 1976. T-cell idiotypes are linked to immunoglobulin heavy chain genes. *Nature* 269:639.
3. Pierce, S. K., and Klinman, N. R. 1975. The allogenic bisection of carrier-specific enhancement of monoclonal B-cell responses. *J. Exp. Med.* 142:1165.
4. Bretscher, P., and Cohn, M. 1970. A theory of self–nonself discrimination. *Science* 169:1042.
5. Gronowicz, E., and Coutinho, A. 1975. Hapten-induced B cell paralysis. II. Evidence for trivial mechanisms of tolerance. *Eur. J. Immunol.* 5:413.
6. Moller, G., Gronowicz, E., Persson, U., Coutinho, A., Moller, E., Hammarstrom, L., and Smith, E. 1976. Spleen cells from animals tolerant to a thymus-dependent antigen can be activated by lipopolysaccharide to synthesize antibodies against the tolerogen. *J. Exp. Med.* 143:1429.

SUGGESTED READING

7. *Cold Spring Harbor Symp. Quant. Biol.* (1977). XLI, Parts 1 and 2.
8. Warner, N. L. 1974. Membrane immunoglobulins and antigen receptors on B and T lymphocytes, *Adv. Immunol.* 19:67.
9. Lymphocyte immunoglobulin: Synthesis and surface representation. *Transplant. Rev.* 4:1973. Munksgaard, Copenhagen.
10. Davies, D. R., Padlan, E. A., and Segal, D. M. 1975. Three-dimensional structure of immunoglobulins. *Ann. Rev. Biochem.* 44:639.
11. Williamson, A. R. 1976. The biological origin of antibody diversity. *Ann. Rev. Biochem.* 45:467.
12. Melchers, F., vonBoehmer, H., and Phillips, R. A. 1975. Organ distribution and ontogeny of immunoglobulin-synthesizing and of mitogen-sensitive cells. *Transplant. Rev.* 25:26.
13. Schreiner, G. F., and Unanue, E. R. 1976. Membrane and cytoplasmic changes in B lymphocytes induced by ligand–surface immunoglobulin interaction. *Adv. Immunol.* 24:38.
14. Niederhuber, J. E., and Frelinger, J. A. 1976. Expression of Ia antigens on T and B cells and their relationship to immune-response functions. *Transplant. Rev.* 30:101.
15. Herzenberg, L. A., Okumura, K., and Metzler, C. M. 1975. Regulation of immunoglobulin and antibody production by allotype suppressor T cells in mice. *Transplant. Rev.* 27:57.

3.9. Cell Membrane Receptors of the Major Histocompatibility Complex (Human) with Brief Reference to Analogous Murine Receptors

Elias Cohen

The cell membrane constituents determined by the major histocompatibility gene complex (MHC) of the human are of central biological importance. They are involved in the control of transplantation reactions, immune responsiveness, and resistance to oncogenic viruses, as well as susceptibility to infectious and autoimmune diseases. The MHC-determined cellular antigens (receptors) are important for cell interaction and differentiation and occur in all species of higher organisms (Chordata) studied to date (1). The human MHC is homologous to that of other mammals, that is, composed of series of many closely linked genes (2) assigned to chromosome 6, by family studies and by genetic analysis with somatic cell hybrids. The MHC determines more than just the highly polymorphic system of antigens on human leukocytes and platelets, originally designated the HL-A system (HL-A = human leukocyte locus A). When first described, the original serologically defined specificities of the HL-A system were described as two separate series (first or LA and second or Four), corresponding to two linked loci with multiple alleles (3,4).

The WHO (World Health Organization) IUIS (International Union of Immunological Societies) Terminology Committee nomenclature for factors of the HL-A system designated the *genetic region* that includes those interrelated loci as *HLA* (5). The current scheme is HLA (for region or system) and A,B,C,D, etc., as symbols for loci. W(w) indicates a provisional specificity, subject to further studies. The arabic numbers 1, 2, etc., refer to specificities for each locus. The gene loci that control complement components C2, C4, and C3, proactivator (GBG, Bf, etc.) (8), as well as the Chido and Rodgers erythrocyte blood groups, are considered to be assigned to HLA.

The findings of the 7th International Histocompatibility Workshop, as presented in October 1977, list the latest nomenclature of the factors of the HLA system, as shown in Table 1, prepared by the WHO committee on

Table 1. Nomenclature for Factors of the HLA System—1977

LOCUS A	PREVIOUS	LOCUS B	PREVIOUS	LOCUS C	PREVIOUS
A1		B5		CW1	
A2		B7		CW2	
A3		B8		CW3	
A9		B12		CW4	
A10		B13		CW5	
A11		B14		*CW6*	T7
A25(10)	AW25	*B15*	BW15		
A26(10)	AW26	*B17*	BW17		
A28		B18		LOCUS D	PREVIOUS
A29		B27			
AW19		*B37*	BW37	DW1	
AW23(9)		*B40*	BW40	DW2	
AW24(9)		BW16		DW3	
AW30		BW21		DW4	
AW31		BW22		DW5	
AW32		BW35		DW6	
AW33		BW38(16)		*DW7*	LD107
AW34		BW39(16)		*DW8*	LD108
AW36		BW41		*DW9*	TB9,OH
AW43		BW42		*DW10*	LD16
		BW44(12)	B12(not TT*)	*DW11*	LD17
		BW45(12)	TT*		
		BW46	HS,SIN2		PREVIOUS
LOCUS B	PREVIOUS	*BW47*	407*,MO66,	LOCUS DR	(WORKSHOP)
			CAS,BW40C		
BW4	W4,4a	*BW48*	KSO,JA,BW40.3	*DRW1*	WIA1,Te6
BW6	W6,4b	*BW49*(21)	BW21.1,SL-ET	*DRW2*	WIA2,Te4
		BW50(21)	BW21.2,ET*	*DRW3*	WIA3,Te5
		BW51(5)	B5.1	*DRW4*	WIA4,Te1.1
		BW52(5)	B5.2	*DRW5*	WIA5,Te5.2
		BW53	HR	*DRW6*	WIA6,Te10
		BW54(22)	BW22j,SAP1,SN1,J1	*DRW7*	WIA7,Te3

Designations are assigned by WHO Committee on leukocyte nomenclature. New designations are italicized. The broad specificities are shown in parentheses following particular splits (such listing is optional).
NOTE: A newer (1980) HLA nomenclature is available in Terasaki, P.I. (1980). Histocompatibility testing 1980. Univ. California Los Angeles, Tissue Typing Lab., Los Angeles, California.

leukocyte (lymphocyte) nomenclature. The antigens designated are categorized as serologically detectable (SD), and those detected by mixed lymphocyte culture (MLC) are also designated as lymphocyte-defined (LD). The locus D determined cellular antigens were solely LD in nature, but a new category and locus, DR, includes SD antigens. It has been evident that some human leukocyte (lymphocyte) specificities existed that were determined by the HLA loci-bearing chromosomes, but distinct from the HLA loci A, B, C, and D, respectively. Terasaki's group (6) has described five B–cell specificities (vs. T cell lymphocyte) that occur in Caucasians, blacks, and Japanese. Furthermore, a close relationship, appears to exist between HLA-DW and the B-lymphocyte antigenic specificities (7). Human B lymphocytes have at least one B–cell alloantigenic system that is not located on chromosome C6 (24, 25). However, Johnson, Ward, and Amos (26) have presented evidence of six B–cell alloantigenic groups and additional evidence of a second B–cell locus that maps to the right of the HLA-B locus. A new 1980 nomenclature is available (44).

The HLA gene product–antigens (receptors) are present on virtually all nucleated cells studied. This suggests an important role in the biology of the organism. The HLA molecules are located on the external cell membrane, as shown by labeling studies as well as serologic methods. In both the murine and human systems, the MHC cell membrane products (antigens) are glycoproteins of approximately 45,000 daltons, tightly incorporated into the matrix of the plasma membrane. These glycoproteins are noncovalently associated with an 11,600-dalton protein, the beta 2-microglobulin. The ratio of association is a 1:1 ratio, considered specific. See Chapter 11 of Snell, Dausset, and Nathenson (4) for details of the biochemical and structural properties of murine and human MHC antigens; also, the recent paper on biochemistry of the human MHC, by Fuks et al. (36).

The question of biological significance is this: Are they (the HLA glycoproteins) ligands, or are they receptors? For instance, it is known that membrane-localized glycoproteins function as receptors for hormones such as insulin, so as to convey the insulin signal to the cell interior. A possibility to be considered is that the HLA glycoproteins may serve either to convey a hormonal signal or to modulate the signal conveyed by a hormone receptor that may be situated next to the HLA glycoprotein. Alternatively, the HLA glycoprotein may serve as an external cellular signal (i.e., the ligand) that could find its specific receptor on the surface or other cells. It may be of more than passing interest in this respect that in the mouse there appears to be an association between H-2 haplotypes and the steady state levels of cyclic adenosine monophosphate (cAMP) in liver tissue (37). Indeed, a receptor and/or effector role for the MHC molecules is suggested by the phenomenon of "MHC restriction," wherein killer T-cells are observed to attack only those target cells sharing an H-2 locus with the killer cell host (38).

Shared antigens of human leukocytes and erythrocytes are known (3); that is, Bg(a) erythrocyte antigen is HLA-B7, Bg(b) is HLA-BW17, and Bg(c) is HLA-A28. It is known that murine H-2 histocompatibility antigens also occur on erythrocytes.

Antigens specific to granulocytes, as well as some HLA antigens, are present on those cells, particularly neutrophils. The granulocyte antigen system and detection of their alloantibodies in humans have been described by Lalezari and Radel (9).

The exact time that the HLA antigens appear on fetal tissue is not defined, but multiparous females are the primary source of reagent sera (10). The study of the natural history of human HLA gene products (cellular membrane antigens) and murine H-2 gene products seem to go hand in hand. For example, it has been observed that murine H-2 and human HLA antigens are absent from the spermatogonia of impuberal mice or men, although the T antigen is present. This is true for H-2 in the embryonic cells of teratomas (35). A variety of antigen deduction techniques exist (45).

Anthropologic studies have been enhanced by the detection of cell membrane receptors (antigens) of the HLA complex. Organ transplantation (skin and kidney) (11, 12) and bone marrow grafts (see 4) have been facilitated by HLA typing, crossmatching, and selection of best donor–recipient pairs. In blood transfusion, the use of HLA antigen typing and matching has made platelet and granulocyte transfusions more effective. Graft versus host hazards of bone marrow grafts and the role of anti-HLA, as well as anti-non-HLA antibodies in neonatal thrombocytopenia and leukoneutropenia are summarized in the recent text of Snell et al. (4). Graft versus host disease (GVHD) may be a more probable risk than a hemolytic transfusion reaction due to erythrocyte blood group incompatibility for the patient who has congenital immunodeficiency or who is on a course of immunosuppressive drug therapy. Blood or blood products contain immunocompetent lymphocytes capable of proliferating in responses to foreign tissues. This revelation has required the irradiation of blood or blood products with a gamma source prior to issue for transfusion (14). A recent symposium report (15) describes GVDH.

Paradoxically, recent work has demonstrated clearly that the greater the number of transfusions prior to kidney allograft, the better the transplant prognosis (13). A prospective study with transfused Rhesus monkeys revealed a fourfold increase in mean survival time compared with the nontransfused controls, as reported by Dr. J. J. van Rood in the March 5, 1977 issue of *Lancet,* pp. 506–9.

The human or murine lymphocyte has been the main point of reference, since it is in daily use for determination of individual HLA (human) or H-2 murine histocompatibility types. No quantitative report is available as to the number of HLA sites on human B versus T lymphocytes or of H-2 antigens on murine subpopulations of lymphocytes (4). The methodology of harvest and the identification of lymphocyte subpopulations have been the focus of many investigators. Recent reviews (16, 17) discuss isolation and identification as well as immunobiological function and use in therapy (18, 19). The origin of lymphocytes and the lymphatic system, as well as the isolation of subpopulations, have been reviewed by Marchalonis (20). There is still a need for innovative approaches to the identification of lymphocyte subpopulations. Recently such identification was accomplished by the differential binding of various strains of bacteria (21). Other groups have used invertebrate blood agglutinins for identification and/or subsequent isolation of human lymphocyte subpopulations (22, 23).

The complexity of the structure and specificity of the lymphocyte cell membrane receptor (antigens) and antibodies was recently summarized in the report of Malley, Goodman, and Wofsy (27). Work is described on lymphocyte receptors and their functions in murine and canine, as well as human, species. It is possible that many useful biological reagents exist for detection of as yet unknown cellular membrane receptors of human and other species. Such feasibilities were examined in a symposium on biomedical perspectives of agglutinins of invertebrate and plant origins (28). The specificity of some lectins, as limulin, has been utilized to absorb proteins, as ceruloplasmin, to lectin–agarose columns (29).

No review of HLA and relevant non-HLA cellular membrane antigens would be complete without a discussion of the role of histocompatibility genes and disease. The HLA gene products and their association with human diseases were reviewed by Mittal (30). Certain genes in the HLA region are proposed to control specific interactions of distinct cell types necessary for activation of immunocompetent cells (31). A combination of factors, such as the amount of microbe–host cell membrane antigenic similarity, immune responsiveness, genetically determined "susceptibility," and other external and internal environmental factors might finally determine the overall suceptibility of a host to a particular disease.

Convenient tables of reported HLA antigens in nonmalignant and malignant diseases are currently available (3, 4, 32). One review, on histocompatibility antigens associations with disease, focuses on allergy (33). Another focuses on malignancy (34).

The closest association that has been discovered between an HLA antigen and a disease is between HLA-B27 and ankylosing spondylitis (AS). Ankylosing spondylitis has provided an excellent human model for study, since HLA-B27 occurs in 85–95% of normal individuals.

During the early part of the last decade, HLA and histocompatibility experts concentrated on the practical applications of the MCH system in transplantation. It is now clear that the chromosomal area (on C6) that contains the MHC is important in pathophysiology and probably in the immune response in general (4). Murine MHC H-2 studies support that view (4). The HLA antigens serve as markers to help the differentiation of certain heterogeneous clinical entities and the reclassification of diseases that were often clinically associated. Rheumatology has benefited the most from this new diagnostic and/or prognostic tool—HLA typing.

Snell, Dausset, and Nathenson (4) have taken in account the serologic, genetic, and biochemical knowledge of the vertebrate MHC, as a single main system, dominating all other systems in many species. Despite extreme polymorphism, the human system does have structural similarities with comparable systems in all mammals studied, but primarily based on murine and human comparison. Any hypothesis about the origin of the MHC must account for the marked complexity at the species and individual level. Yet, such a hypothesis would have to account for its remarkable persistence during phylogenic diversification.

REFERENCES

1. Gotze, D., ed., with contributions by E. Albert, H. Balner, N. Cohen, N. H. Collins, C. S. David, M. E. Dorf, W. R. Duncan, A. F. Geczy, D. Gotze, I. W. Streilein, H. M. Vriesendorp, and A. L. de Weck. 1977. *The Major Histocompatibility System in Man and Animals,* pp. 1–340. Springer-Verlag, New York.
2. Ceppellini, R., and van Rood, J. J. 1974. The HL-A system, I. Genetics and molecular biology. *Semin. Hematol.* 11:233–51.
3. Cohen, E. 1977. Leukocyte and platelet immunohematology. In *Blood Bank Technology,* 2nd ed., L. M. Schwartz and W. Miles, eds., Chapter 8, pp. 79–86. Williams and Wilkins, Baltimore, Maryland.
4. Snell, G. D., Dausset, J., and Nathenson, S. 1976. *Histocompatibility,* pp. 1–40. Academic Press, New York.
5. WHO-IUIS Terminology Committee. 1976. Nomenclature for factors of the HL-A system. *Transplant. Proc.* 8:109–14.
6. Saito, S., Terasaki, P. I., and Park, M. S. 1977. B-lymphocyte antigens in three racial groups. *Transplant. Proc.* 9:1697–1700.
7. Park, M. S., Terasaki, P. I., Saito, S., and Opelz, G. 1977. Relation between HLA-DW and the B-lymphocyte specificities. *Scand. J. Immunol.* 6:413–18.
8. Moller, G., ed. 1976. Biology of complement and complement receptors. *Transplant. Rev.* 32:1–167. Munksgaard, Copenhagen.
9. Lalezari, P., and Radel, E. 1974. Neutrophil specific antigens: Immunology and clinical significance. *Semin. Hematol.* 11:281–90.
10. Rodey, G. E. 1976. History and nomenclature of the HLA system. *HLA Typing,* Chapter 1, pp. 1–13. American Association of Blood Banks, Washington, D.C.
11. Dausset, J., Rapaport, F. T., Ivanyi, P., and Columbani, J. 1965. Tissue alloantigens and transplantation. H. Balner, F. L. Cleton, and J. G. Eernisse, eds., In *Histocompatibility Testing,* pp. 63–72. Munksgaard, Copenhagen.
12. Van Rood, J. J., Van Leeuwen, A., Schippers, A. M. J., Vooys, W. H., Fredricks, E., Balner, H., and Eernisse, J. G. 1965. Leukocyte groups, the normal lymphocyte transfer and homograft sensitivity. In *Histocompatibility Testing,* H. Balner, F. L. Cleton, and J. G Eernisse, eds., pp. 37–50. Munksgaard, Copenhagen.

13. Van Hooff, J. P., Kalff, M. W., van Poelgeest, A. E., Perslin, G. G., and van Rood, J. J. 1976. Blood transfusions and kidney transplantation. *Transplantation* 22:306–7.
14. Hansen, J. J., Mayer, K., and Harris, J. 1977. Personal communication.
15. Thomas, E. 1976. Marrow transplantation for acute leukemia. In *Human Bone Marrow Transplantation.* pp. 19–28, Chapter 3. American Association of Blood Banks, Washington, D.C.
16. Natvig, J. B., Perlmann, P., and Wigzell, H., eds. 1976. *Lymphocytes: Isolation, Fractionation and Characterization,* pp. 1–184. University Park Press, Baltimore, Maryland.
17. Boyum, A. 1977. Separation of lymphocytes, lymphocyte subgroups and monocytes: A review. *Lymphology* 10:71–76.
18. Hogman, Claes, F., Lindahl-Kressling, K., and Wigzell, H. 1977. *Blood Leukocytes: Function and Use in Therapy,* pp. 1–88. Almquest & Wiksell Inter, Stockholm.
19. Golub, E. S. 1977. *The Cellular Basis of the Immune Response,* an approach to immunobiology, pp. 1–278. Sinauer Assoc. Inc., Sunderland, Massachusetts.
20. Marchalonis, J. J., ed. 1977. *Lymphocyte, Structure and Function,* Immunology Series 5, pp. 1–369. Marcel Dekker, New York.
21. Teodorescu, M., Mayer, E. P., and Dray, S. 1977. Identification of five human lymphocyte subpopulations by their differential binding to various strains of bacteria. *Cell. Immunol.* 29:353–62.
22. Cohen, E., Minowada, J., Pliss, M., Pliss, L., and Blumenson, L. E. 1976. Differentiation of human leukemic from normal lymphocytes by *Limulus* serum agglutination. *Vox Sang.* 31:117–23.
23. Wernet, P., and Baron, D. 1977. A new typing method for human Ia alloantigen by standard workshop cytotoxicity after rapid "one-step" B cell separation on *Helix pomatia-agglutinin* (HpA). Sepharose columns. *Tissue Antigens* 10:235.
24. Mann, D. L., Strober, W., Katz, S. I., Hsia, S., and Amos, D. B. 1976. Br and Wh, B cell antigens in gluton sensitive enteropathy and dermatitis herpetiforms. In *The Role of Products of the Histocompatibility Complex in Immune Responses,* p. 56. Academic Press, New York.
25. Legrand, L., and Dausset, J. 1975. A second lymphocyte system (Ly-Li). In *Histocompatibility Testing,* F. Kissmeyer-Nielsen, ed., p. 665. Munksgaard, Copenhagen.
26. Johnson, A. H., Ward, F. E., and Amos, D. B. 1977. B-Lymphocyte antigens, *Scand. J. Immunol.* 6:403–8.
27. Malley, A., Goodman, J. W., and Wofsy, L. 1977. Sixteenth Midwinter Conference of Immunologists Structure and specificity: Antibodies and receptors. *Clin. Immunol. Immunopathol.* 8:353–65.
28. Cohen, E., ed. 1974. Biomedical perspectives of agglutinins of invertebrate and plant origins. *Ann. N.Y. Acad. Sci.* 234:1–412.
29. Spivak, J. L., Small, D., and Hollenberg, M. D. 1977. Erythropoietin: Isolation by affinity chromatography with lectin-agarose derivatives. *Proc. Natl. Acad. Sci.,* 74:4633–35.
30. Mittal, K. K. 1977. Possible mechanisms for association of HLA antigens and disease. In *HLA and Malignancy,* G. P. Murphy, E. Cohen, J. E. Fitzpatrick, and D. Pressman, eds., pp. 39–51. A. R. Liss Inc., New York.
31. Katz, D. H., and Benacerrof, B. 1975. The function and interrelationships of T-cell receptors, Ir genes and other histocompatibility gene products. *Transplant. Rev.* 22:175–95.
32. Dausset, J., and Svejgaard, A. eds. 1977. *HLA and Disease,* pp. 1–316. Munksgaard, Copenhagen.
33. de Weck, A., and Blumenthol, M. N. 1977. HLA and allergy. *Monographs in Allergy,* Vol. 11, pp. 1–123. S. Karger, Basel.

34. Murphy, G. P., Cohen, E., Fitzpatrick, J. E., and Pressman, D., eds. 1977. *HLA and Malignancy*, pp. 1–248. A. R. Liss Inc., New York.
35. Artzt, K., and Jacob, F. 1974. Absence of serologically detectable H-2 on primitive teratocarcinoma cells in culture. *Transplantation* 17:632–34.
36. Fuks, A., Kaufman, J. F., Orr, H. T., Parham, P., Robb, R. R., Terhorst, C., and Strominger, J. L. 1977. Structural aspects of the products of the human major histocompatibility complex. *Transplant. Proc.* 9:1685–89.
37. Muerelo, D., and Edidin, M. 1975. Association of mouse liver adenosine 3'5'. Cyclic monophosphate (cyclic AMP) levels with histocompatability-2 genotype. *Proc. Natl. Acad. Sci. U.S.A.* 72:2644–48.
38. Howard, J. C. 1978. H-2 restriction, the thymus and the immune response. *Nature* 272:11–13.
39. Bodmer, W. F. 1978. The HLA system: Introduction *Brit. Med. Bull.* 34:213–216.
40. Joysey, V. C. and Wolf, E. 1978. HLA-A, -B and -C antigens, their serology and crossreaction. *Brit. Med. Bull.* 34:217–222.
41. Bradley, B. A. and Festenstein, H. 1978. Cellular typing. *Brit. Med. Bull.* 34:223–232.
42. Bodmer, J. G. 1978. Ia antigens. Definition of the HLA-DRw Specificities. *Brit. Med. Bull.* 34:223–240.
43. Kemple, K. and Bluestone, R. 1977. The histocompatibility complex and rheumatic diseases. *Med. Clin. N. Amer.* 61:331–345.
44. Terasaki, P. I. 1980. Histocompatibility testing 1980, UCLA, Tissue Typing Lab, Los Angeles, CA.
45. Dick, H. H., and Kissmeyer-Nielsen, F., Eds., 1980, Histocompatibility Techniques, Elsevier-North Holland Biomedical Press, Amsterdam, Netherlands 1–212.

3.10. Cell Agglutination: The Red Cell as a Model

Robert J. Bowman

In this chapter the major feature of cell agglutination will be reviewed. The red cell will be used as the model for cell agglutination, since it has been most thoroughly studied. The chemical and physical principles will be emphasized so that the reader will be left with a framework to use to place the available literature in perspective. A comprehensive list of references will be omitted. Instead, a list of selected references that will lead the reader to the most appropriate literature is included.

HEMAGGLUTINATION

Hemagglutination or red cell agglutination is an important topic in biology for a variety of reasons. For example, knowledge of the factors involved in agglutination provides important information about the cell surface. This information is important in defining some of the basic chemical and physical properties of the cell, and it also finds direct application in research and clinical laboratories. (The blood bank laboratory is an obvious example where donor red cell compatibility with a recipient is measured by agglutination tests.)

Hemagglutination may be divided into two stages although it should be realized that the first stage does not necessarily need to be complete before the second stage begins. The first stage may be referred to as sensitization and is characterized by antibodies binding to antigens at the surface of cells. The second stage is the agglutination or "clumping" of the sensitized cells.

Stage 1. Sensitization

The study of the primary reaction between antibody and red cell antigen yields a considerable amount of data concerning the red cell. One of the important applications has been to estimate the number of antigenic sites and equilibrium constants of various antibody–antigen reactions. For quantitative purposes, the reaction between red cell antigen and antibody may be represented as:

$$Ag + Ab \underset{k_d}{\overset{k_a}{\rightleftharpoons}} AgAb$$

Ag, Ab, and AgAb represent the antigen, antibody, and antigen–antibody complex, respectively. The constants k_a and k_a and k_d and association and dissociation rate constants, respectively. At equilibrium, when the rates of the forward and reverse reactions are equal:

$$k_a (Ag) (Ab) = k_d (AgAb)$$

and:

$$\frac{(AgAb)}{(Ag) (Ab)} = \frac{k_a}{k_d} = K$$

where K is the equilibrium constant. The term (Ag) in this equation needs clarification. It refers to the "concentration" of antigen in the suspension. But this is not a concentration in the usual sense, in which this component would be dissolved in solution. The antigenic sites present on the red cell are not independent molecular species in solution but are kinetically restricted to the red cell surface. Thus, this equilibrium condition, shown above, describes a situation analogous to adsorption of chemicals from solution onto a solid phase per unit volume of suspension. (Similar comments apply to the (AgAb) term).

To determine K one needs a method of separating and quantitating bound and free antibody. One technique is to use antibody labeled with radioactive iodine. Iodinated antibody bound to red cells and free in the supernatant can be separated and measured in a gamma counter. Several manipulations of the equations to obtain K are possible. For example, at equilibrium one can apply a "Scatchard" analysis (see Chapter 1.9), and with antibody excess

$$(AgAb)/(Ab) = K(Ag)_i - K(AgAb)$$

where $(Ag)_i$ represents the initial "concentration" of sites. Note that a plot of the left-hand side of this equation (bound/free) versus the (AgAb) (bound) yields a straight line with slope K and intercept $(Ag)_i$ (a measure of the total number of sites available). Another method to determine K is to make independent measurements of the k_a and k_d. The ratio k_a/k_d then determines

K. Table 1 lists some representative examples of *K* for various blood group antibodies. Note that *K* is of the order of 1×10^8 liters/mole.

It is useful to consider the implications of these equilibrium constants. To do so one can ask what fraction of antibody is free when antigen and antibody are mixed in equimolar amounts. Under these conditions one can show that if $K = 1 \times 10^8$ liters/mole, then at equilibrium the fraction of antibody (or antigen) that is uncombined is only 0.0001 or 0.01%.

The analysis of antigen–antibody reactions used above allows quantitation of the number of antigenic sites on the red cell surface. The reader also probably will have noted that when labeled antibody and antigen are mixed in equal amounts or with labeled antibody in excess, virtually all of the antigenic sites are occupied. Thus, the maximum labeled antibody bound may provide a reasonable estimate of the number of antigenic sites. An additional refinement of this approach is to use the Scatchard plot of the data developed above and extrapolate data to give an estimate of the number of antigenic sites $(Ag)_i$. Table 2 gives some selected estimates of the number of antigenic sites for several red cell antigens. Note that the number vaires markedly from a few thousand to over one million sites per red cell. [Other methods of quantitation of red cell antigen exist and have been reviewed by Rosenfield (4).]

A common observation in the study of the primary reaction between antigen and antibody is variability in *K*. The variability may be reflected in the Scatchard plot by curvilinear plots rather than straight lines and is most likely due to heterogeneity in antibody (see Ref. 3). (Heterogeneity could also be present in the structures of the antigens or in structures surrounding the antigens which might alter antibody binding.) Variations in antibody structure would not be surprising, however, when one considers that the usual humoral immune response results in formation of a variety of proteins (the response is not monoclonal). Thus in measurements of *K* what is actually determined is an "average" value, but these average values are sufficiently accurate for some interpretations to be made.

In the formulation used above, the antibody is assumed to be univalent

Table 1. Equilibrium Constants.

ANTIBODY SPECIFICITY	CLASS	EQUILIBRIUM CONSTANT (LITERS/MOLE)
anti-Kell	IgG	$1.0–3.0 \times 10^{10}$
anti-Rh$_0$	IgG	$0.8–1.8 \times 10^8$
anti-A	IgG	$0.6–13.0 \times 10^8$
*anti-L	IgG	3×10^9

* This is an ovine antibody directed against an ovine antigen.

Table 2.   Number of Antigenic Sites per Cell.

ANTIGEN	NUMBER OF SITES
Kell	3,500–6,000
Rh_o	23,000–50,000
A	200,000–1,200,000
L (sheep cells)	1,200–1,800

and to combine with only one antigenic site. The validity of this assumption can be tested using whole immunoglobulin molecules and F_{ab} units of appropriate specificity. By determining the equilibrium constant for the intact antibody molecules (which are divalent) and comparing it to the equilibrium constant for F_{ab} units (which are univalent), one can obtain evidence for the valency of binding of the whole divalent molecule. For IgG anti-D the K is about the same as that for F_{ab} anti-D units, suggesting that only one valence of the IgG anti-D molecule is used in binding at each antigenic site. For IgG anti-A the K for F_{ab} units was found to be more than 100-fold less than that for the complete bivalent IgG. This observation is interpreted to mean that both binding sites on the IgG anti-A molecule are involved in binding the antibody to the red cell A antigens. Similar considerations apply to IgM antibodies. IgM anti-D and anti-B are believed to bind by two sites. (See Ref. 2 for additional discussion.)

Stage 2. Agglutination

In discussing red cell agglutination a potential semantic problem exists in defining what is meant by agglutination as opposed to terms like aggregation and rouleaux formation.

For purposes of this discussion, agglutination is a special case of aggregation, but with an important added feature (specificity!). Aggregation means "clumping" of red cells and includes the phenomenon called rouleaux formation where red cells line up like a stack of coins. Therefore, agglutination means antibody-induced aggregation. Agglutination is specific in that red cells lacking the appropriate antigen will not agglutinate. Elsewhere the reader will encounter different definitions of these terms and the distinction made here is probably nonsignificant; it is important to realize that forces that modify the tendency of red cells to aggregate also modify the tendency to agglutinate. In the following discussion the forces between cells promoting aggregation and agglutination will be briefly outlined (for an excellent and more extensive review, see Ref. 1).

While space does not permit an extensive discussion, the reader is forewarned that quantitation of aggregation and agglutination is a significant problem and occasionally a source of confusion. If different methods are measuring the same process, then the results would be expected to be similar although not necessarily directly comparable. Quantitive comparisons must take into acount the conditions under which the measurements are made. Microscopic observations have the advantage of being direct, but tend to be tedious and are limited to low cell concentrations and static (zero flow) conditions. Some other less direct techniques utilize rheologic properties of cell suspensions (red cell aggregation at low flow rates increases apparent viscosity, light transmission, and scattering; aggregate formation increases transmission and decreases scattering) and differing flow properties of cell aggregates varying in size (aggregates can be decanted, lysed, and measured photometrically from a flowing cell suspension in continuous-flow methods).

FORCES OF AGGREGATION

Aggregation of red cells results from bridging between red cells by macromolecules which are adsorbed to the cell surface. (The reader should anticipate that antibody molecules also can form bridges between cells.) Macromolecular adsorption and bridging can be considered a force favoring aggregation. Forces favoring disaggregation include mechanical mixing or shearing. Other forces may also exist, but this discussion will be limited to macromolecular bridging forces, mechanical shearing forces, and electrostatic forces.

Macromolecular Bridging Forces

Macromolecules may be adsorbed to the red cell surface. The efficiency with which adsorbed molecules produce aggregation depends on the strength of the bonds that bind these molecules to the red cell and hence the red cells to each other. Plasma proteins (negatively charged at physiological pH) and dextrans are adsorbed to a lesser extent than are positively charged macromolecules like polybrene. Dextrans are probably bound by weaker bonds like van der Waals forces or hydrogen bonds, whereas positively charged molecules are bound by stronger ionic bonds. Antibodies bound by several bonds at the binding site, can be expected to produce more efficient aggregation, in this case agglutination.

Mechanical Forces

The effect of mechanical forces on red cell aggregation can be complex. For example, in dilute flowing cell suspensions the flow rate of the suspension may increase the likelihood of collision between cells so that macromolecular bridging can occur. However, increasing flow rates still further can cause disaggregation by mechanically deforming the aggregates (this would especially be expected when rouleaux formation is induced in a relatively low concentration of weakly aggregating macromolecules). In the simple case of a suspension in a test tube, gravitational forces (centrifugation) can be used to enhance aggregation, and unless the cells are held together by relatively strong bridging forces, the aggregate can be broken up by shaking.

Electrical Forces

The surface of the red cell is negatively charged primarily because of the presence of N-acetylneuraminic acid (sialic acid). The presence of these charged groups at the surface of a red cell in contact with an ionic medium will influence the distribution of ions about that red cell. Ions of opposite (positive) charge will be attracted toward the charged surface, and ions with similar (negative) charge will be repelled. These electrical forces are counteracted in part by random thermal motions of the ions (diffusion), which tend to make the distribution of positive and negative ions uniform. The result is that the excess concentration of positive ions about a red cell falls off rapidly as one moves away from the negatively charged surface. The charge on the surface is then partly screened by the positive ions, but when the cell is placed in an electric field, it will still migrate as a negatively charged particle. As the cell migrates, it carries with it some water and ions enclosed in a slipping plane at which the surface potential is referred to as the "zeta potential." By measuring the mobility of the red cell in an electric field one can calculate the zeta potential, and it in turn can be used for estimating repulsive forces between red cells that are aggregated. As red cells approach one another, these repulsive forces increase exponentially and can overcome macromolecular bridging forces. Thus, electrical forces act to disaggregate or prevent the formation of red cell aggregates. (See Ref. 5 for a review of the electrokinetic behavior of red cells.)

It is useful to consider the net force of aggregation as the result of the forces of macromolecular bridging, mechanical forces, and electrical forces. Thus,

$$F_A = F_B - F_M - F_E$$

where F_A represents the resultant force of aggregation. The specific result under a given set of circumstances then will depend on the intrinsic properties of the red cell and the environment of the red cell.

AGGLUTINATION

When red cells are aggregated or agglutinated, they must approach one another closely enough that the macromolecules can produce bridges between the cells. For example, the intercellular distance in rouleaux induced by fibrinogen has been estimated at an average of 25 nm, whereas the fibrinogen molecule is about 30–40 nm in length, which is adequate to bridge the average gap between the red cells. The distance between binding sites in an IgG molecule may be taken as about 15 nm, whereas that of an IgM molecule is approximately 40 nm. Clearly then it should not be surprising that, in general, IgM antibodies produce more marked agglutination than IgG antibodies. In fact, if the bridging forces are unable to overcome electrostatic (and other disaggregating) forces that may exist at separations of 15 nm, then agglutination will not occur with some IgG antibodies. A secondary antibody can then be used to produce bridges between the bound primary antibodies and thus produce agglutination. The secondary antibody then allows one to detect the presence of the primary antibody by agglutination. The antibody-induced aggregation is specific. From the above discussion it should be clear that if sufficient nonspecific bridging forces exist in a suspension (but not enough to produce observable aggregation) and a specific antibody is added, the resultant bridging forces may be adequate to produce agglutination (if the cells have the appropriate antigen). Thus, specific agglutination can be modified by the forces of aggregation. The bridging forces due to antibody then represent a special case of the bridging forces produced by other macromolecules. The "unique" feature of antibody-induced bridging forces is the specificity of the antibody for red cell antigens. In summary, antibodies cause agglutination by specific macromolecular bridging forces (see Ref. 10 for experimental verification).

BIBLIOGRAPHY

Reviews

1. Chien, S. 1975. Biophysical behavior of red cells in suspensions. In *The Red Blood Cell,* Vol. II, D. MacN. Surgenor, ed., pp. 1031–33. Academic Press, New York.
2. Hughes-Jones, N. C. 1972. The attachment of IgG molecules on the red cell surface. *Haematologia* 6:269–74.
3. Hughes-Jones, N. C. 1975. Red-cell antigens, antibodies and their interaction. *Clin. Haematol.* 4:29–43.
4. Rosenfield, R. E. 1976. Quantitation of erythrocytic antigens. In *A Seminar on Performance Evaluation,* pp. 93–114. American Association of Blood Banks, Washington, D.C.
5. Seaman, G. V. F. 1975. Electrokinetic behavior of red cells. In *The Red Blood Cell,* Vol. II, D. MacN. Surgenor, ed., pp. 1135–229. Academic Press, New York.

Papers

6. Economidou, J., Hughes-Jones, N. C., and Gardner, B. 1967. The functional activities of IgG and IgM anti-A and anti-B. *Immunology* 13:227–34.
7. Holburn, A. M., Cartron, J. P., Economidou, J., Gardner, B., and Hughes-Jones, N. C. 1971. Observations on the reactions between D-positive red cells and (^{125}I) IgM anti-D molecules and subunits. *Immunology* 21:499–507.
8. Hughes-Jones, N. D., and Gardner, B. 1971. The Kell system—studied with radioactively-labeled anti-K. *Vox Sang.* 21:154–58.
9. Lauf, P. K., and Sun, W. W. 1976. Binding characteristics of M and L isoantibodies to high and low potassium sheep red cells. *J. Membr. Biol.* 28:351–72.
10. Romano, E. L., and Mollison, P. L. 1973. Mechanism of red cell agglutination by IgG antibodies. *Vox Sang.* 25:28–31.

3.11. Oncofetal Antigens

Thomas S. Chen

Oncofetal antigens (OFA) are defined as fetal proteins elaborated by malignant tissues in large amounts, and by normal adult tissues in minute quantities. Among the various OFA, alpha-fetoprotein (AFP) and carcinoembryonic antigen (CEA) are well delineated.

The origin of OFA is not known. The most commonly held view is that OFA arise from gene derepression. Fetal genes active during ontogenesis are repressed during adult life. They become activated by a yet undescribed mechanism during malignant transformation. Other hypotheses such as a viral origin are not excluded.

ALPHA-FETOPROTEIN

Physiochemical Properties

Fetal, adult, and tumor AFP are identical glycoproteins containing 4% carbohydrate. The molecular weight on SDS–gel electrophoresis is 70,000 daltons with a sediment coefficient between 4.5 and 5.5S and an alpha-1-globulin mobility. AFP is comprised of three branched polysaccharide units and one polypeptide chain. Hexose, hexosamine, and sialic acid occur in the ratio of 2.2:1.2:0.9 by weight. After cyanogen bromide cleavage, seven major polypeptide units are recognized on SDS–gel electrophoresis with molecular weights of 23,000, 12,000, 9,000, 8,000, 6,500, 4,000, and 3,500 daltons. The smallest unit represents the C-terminal peptide with valine present but no homoserine. Although they are physiochemically similar, there is no homology between AFP and albumin. The glycine and isoleucine contents of albumin are one-half and one-third those of AFP, while the serine and threonine in AFP are 50% higher than in albumin. At least three types of human, and two types of rat AFP are identified on gel electrophoresis. Synergic immunization with AFP does not lead to antibody production. The tolerance is probably a low-zone type maintained by T cells.

Formation

Fetal human AFP (half life 3.5–4.0 days) is produced by the liver, yolk sac, thymus, and gastrointestinal tract. It reaches a maximal serum concentration of 3.0 μg/ml during the third month of gestation and drops linearly as birth approaches. AFP declines rapidly in the first 2 weeks of life. By the second year of life, the normal adult level of 1–40 ng/ml is maintained.

The rate of AFP formation is an inherent characteristic of certain tumor cell lines. Clones of rat hepatoma cells produce AFP at high rates and albumin at low rates. Other clones show the reverse. Other properties of hepatoma cells such as chromosome complement and growth rate also affect the capacity to produce AFP. In general, fast-growing aneuploid tumors produce more AFP than slow-growing hepatomas. AFP synthesis depends on hepatocyte proliferation, a relationship not observed for albumin. Hepatocarcinogens such as N-2-fluroenylacetamide increase AFP production by fetal hepatocytes only when DNA synthesis is stimulated. Mitosis per se is not required. Hormones (e.g., glucocorticoids and epinephrine) that block hepatocyte regeneration decrease AFP production.

Function

The physiological role of AFP is not known. Speculation centers on four observations. First, serum level of AFP is high, while that of albumin is low during fetal life. The similarities in solubility, molecular weight, isoelectric point, and electrophoretic properties suggest that AFP is a fetal analogue of albumin. There is, however, no definitive evidence that AFP is involved in transport functions. Second, rat AFP can bind estrogen avidly, with $K_d = 10^{-9}–10^{-10}$M for estrone > estradiol > estriol. An estimated 20–30% of rat fetal serum and 90% of amniotic fluid AFP contain bound estrogens. In humans, less than 2% of AFP binds estrogen. The receptor function of AFP may protect the fetus against maternal estrogen. Third, intracellular AFP may regulate cell growth by its interaction with estrogen and very low-density lipoprotein (VLDL). Estradiol stimulates the production of VLDL, whereas VLDL inhibits DNA synthesis in fetal hepatocytes. AFP, by binding intracellular estradiol, prevents the stimulatory effect on VLDL synthesis. The net effect is a secondary increase of DNA synthesis. A fourth hypothesis implicates AFP in immunoregulation during pregnancy. In vitro AFP exerts immunosuppressive action on humoral antibody responses, and in cell-mediated reactions such as mitogen-induced lymphocyte transformation and mixed lymphocyte reaction. Receptors for AFP have been identified on the surface of a subset of mouse T lymphocytes. AFP may help maintain the fetus as an allograft in a genetically incompatible womb.

Clinical Aspects

AFP serves as a valuable biochemical marker for primary hepatocellular carcinoma and gonadal teratoblastoma. Some 70–80% of the patients in the

United States and 70–95% of patients in other countries with primary hepato-cellular carcinoma display sustained and high serum concentrations of AFP (usually greater than 500 ng/ml). Levels do not correlate with tumor size, histology, or growth. In a third of the patients with gonadal teratoblastoma, similar high levels of AFP are seen. In 10% of cases with metastatic liver carcinoma, 5% of gastrointestinal carcinoma, and 20–30% of acute and chronic hepatitis serum AFP is low (50–500 ng/ml). Other conditions showing elevated AFP include anencephaly, other neuroectodermal defects, ataxia telangectasia, Indian childhood cirrhosis, and congenital tyrosinemia.

CARCINOEMBRYONIC ANTIGEN

Physiochemical Properties

Unlike AFP, CEA is not a homogeneous molecule. Characterization depends on the source of material and the isolation procedure. The CEA derived from human metastatic colonic carcinoma is a perchloric-acid-soluble glyco-protein. It is insoluble in alcohol but remains heat-stable. The molecular weight by SDS–gel electrophoresis is 200,000 ± 20,000 daltons. It has a sedimentation coefficient of 7–8S and a β-mobility on agar electrophoresis. Isoelectric focusing reveals heterogenous electrically charged groups, with points between 3.5 and 4.5. CEA contains 42–77% carbohydrate and 30–46% protein. The amino acids glutamine, asparagine, serine, and threonine account for 40% of the protein portion. Methionine is absent. The N-terminal amino acid is lysine, but the C-terminal amino acid has not been identified. N-acetyl glucosamine constitutes 50%, galactose 21–27%, mannose 13–20%, and fucose 13–20% of the carbohydrate moiety. In contrast, N-acetyl galac-tosamine is absent or low. The sialic acid content, 1–11%, varies considerably between preparations, and probably accounts for the charge heterogeneity. The CEA molecule begins with a N-acetyl glucosamine side chain joined to the aspartate moiety. This grouping represents the tumor-specific antigenic site of CEA. Antigenic differences exist between CEA extracts from fetal tissue, primary colonic tumor, and its metastasis. Isomeric species of CEA, such as CEA-S, have been identified.

Normal Biology

CEA is localized in the glycocalyx layer of normal, inflamed, and malignant mucosa of entodermally derived organs. It is not an integral structural compo-nent of the plasma membrane. Rather, CEA represents a secretory product of cells.

The biological role of CEA is not known. Little information is available about the metabolism of CEA. Following injection of radioactive labeled CEA into rats, 70% disappears within the first hour and accumulates in the liver. By 24 hours, 95% of the administered material is excreted into the urine. The liver represents a major site of catabolism.

Clinical Aspects

Normal persons show no detectable serum CEA by radioimmunoassay (< 1 ng/ml). The value of 2.5 ng/ml differentiates benign from malignant disorders. Elevations occur in neoplasms of the colon (80–95% of cases), lung (70%), breast (60%), pancreas, and other sites. Benign and hyperplastic lesions usually exhibit lower concentrations than malignant tumors. High values (> 25 ng/ml) suggest hepatic metastases. Benign conditions in which serum CEA is < 2.5 ng/ml and the positive rate exceeds 30% include: emphysema, pneumonitis, alcoholism, acute and chronic liver diseases, chronic renal failure, renal transplants, and the smoking habit. CEA determination is most useful when employed serially to monitor cancer surgery or chemotherapy.

REFERENCES

Hirai, H., and Alpert, E., eds. 1975. Carcinofetal proteins: Biology and chemistry. *Ann. N.Y. Acad. Sci.* 259:1–452.

Tomasi, T. B., Jr. 1977. Structure and function of alpha-fetoprotein. *Annu. Rev. Med.* 28:453–65.

3.12. Lymphocyte Differentiation

James J. O'Leary and Miguel M. Azar

The term "lymphocyte" is used to designate a morphologically distinct set of cells present in most higher organisms. Functionally all lymphocytes appear to be involved in immune function or are precursors of immunologic effector cells. They are primarily located in the blood, bone marrow, spleen, thymus, and lymphatic system. In the fetus they are also found in the liver and yolk sac. As has been demonstrated, lymphocytes are a general class of cells with functionally and genetically distinct subpopulations in the same sense that granulocytes are composed of several cell types and their precursors.

DEFINITION OF MAJOR LYMPHOCYTE SUBPOPULATIONS

In the peripheral blood two major classes of lymphocytes are clearly defined, and a third major subpopulation may exist. The two defined cell types are designated T and B cells. The third population we will refer to as "null" cells for this discussion, although this term may not be entirely adequate.

In humans, T cells are operationally defined as lymphocytes that bear receptors which bind sheep red blood cells. The binding results in rosettes with a T lymphocyte surrounded by red cells, referred to as E-rosettes. The exact significance of this receptor is unknown, but it is a general property of all but the most primitive cells in this series. The origin of the designation T cell lies in the fact that the differentiation of these cells is intimately related to thymic function.

B lymphocytes are operationally defined by the presence of readily detectable surface immunoglobulin which is tightly bound and not passively acquired. This immunoglobulin represents B cell receptors for antigen. Again all but the most primitive B cell precursors possess this property.

The existence of a third major lymphocyte population is the subject of current investigation. These cells do not form E-rosettes in man and do not bear surface immunoglobulin. There is also evidence that they are not simply T or B cell precursors, which also lack these properties.

T LYMPHOCYTE DIFFERENTIATION

The differentiation of the T cell population is the best studied, primarily because T cells possess surface antigens whose expression is a function of maturation (5). In most higher organisms the development of T cells is intimately related to the presence of the thymus. Neonatally thymectomized and congenitally athymic animals do not develop mature T cells and are immunologically incompetent with respect to most antigens. T cell differentiation can be induced by thymus grafts placed in special millipore chambers that do not allow the passage of cells and by various polypeptide preparations discussed below. Neonatally thymectomized animals treated with doses of irradiation lethal to the remaining lymphocytes and transplanted with bone marrow cells from a genetically identical donor can be induced to produce competent T cells in a similar fashion. This is one line of evidence that the earliest cells committed to T lymphocyte differentiation arise from a stem cell in the bone marrow of the adult. While these pre-T cells can differentiate in the absence of a thymus, in the intact animal the thymus is the primary site for the next stages of differentiation (4).

In the thymus, the pre-T cells develop a variety of surface determinants. The pre-T cells give rise to a population of what we will call T0 cells (3), which express these determinants. The T0 lymphocyte is the first to form E-rosettes. A serological species-specific antigen, and in the mouse strain-specific antigen, develops, which is characteristic of T cells at later stages of development. In the mouse, which we will use as a model for T cell differentiation, the T specific antigens are called θ or Thy. A number of other important markers become serologically detectable on the T0 cell. The antigens of the major histocompatibility complex (H-2 in the mouse) are detectable at low concentration. Again in the mouse, the Lyt antigens appear. We will consider three Lyt antigens (Lyt 1, 2, or 3) in this discussion, and all are expressed at this stage. In many mice strains, the TL antigen is found on the T0 lymphocyte. This is a genetically heterogenous system, whose gene products are only expressed within the thymus of normal animals. TL stands for thymus-limited antigen. In addition there are a few other antigens expressed on the thymocytes, as, for example, GIX (5).

The T0 lymphocytes are relatively large, rapidly dividing, and short-lived. They are sensitive to high doses of hydrocortisone in vivo and of relatively low density with respect to other lymphocytes (20). Functionally, the T0 and the pre-T cell can be stimulated to proliferate by the mitogens concanavalin A and especially phytohemagglutinin (PHA), as are more mature T cells. Interestingly, the ability to react to allogeneic cells (mixed lymphocyte interaction) precedes PHA responsiveness in ontogenic development. The T0 cells are primarily located in the cortical areas of the thymus, and only about

5% of the thymocytes in the cortex survive to leave the thymus and reach maturity. The high mitotic rate and apparent wastage of cortical thymocytes is one aspect of some clonal selection theories for the development of specific antigen-responsive lymphocytes (5). The properties of T0 cells are enumerated in Table 1.

The next stage of T cell maturation (refer to Figure 1) can occur both in the thymus and in blood and peripheral lymphoid organs. In the mouse the lymphocytes lose the TL marker and show increased expression of H-2. Specific anti-thymocyte sera in other species are no longer cytotoxic. These cells, which we will designate T1 cells (again see 3), are short-lived and do not recirculate; that is, tagged cells injected at one location do not reappear at other locations. The T1 cells are still sensitive to high doses of hydrocortisone and are immunologically "virgin"; that is, the differentiation is not dependent on antigen exposure. They also have a high rate of division and are probably the primary cell population in the PHA response of periphal blood lymphocytes.

The differentiation of T1 from T0 cells seems to require the presence of a thymic factor(s). The T1 cell remains Lyt 1, 2, and 3 positive. Further differentiation requires antigen exposure or thymic factor(s) or perhaps both. There are two possibilities for further differentiation. The T1 cell can become either a "memory" cell or precursor, which we will call a T2 cell, or develop into an immunologic "effector" T cell, as shown in Figure 1. Huber et al. (10) designate both the effector and memory T lymphocyte T2 cells, whereas, Araneo et al. (1) call only the small precursor and memory cell T2. The T2 cell as designated in Figure 1 and Table 1 may be either Lyt 1 positive or Lyt 2, 3 positive, as are the effector cells. At this time T2 cells that are positive for all three Lyt antigens or negative for all three have not been found. T2 cells are resistant to hydrocortisone and are long-lived. The relative life spans of T1 and T2 are illustrated by the fact that T1 cells are not detectable within 2 weeks of adult thymectomy, but T2 cells persist for many months. T2 cells recirculate and are found in greater numbers in blood and lymph nodes than in spleen and thymus. The long life span of T2 cells points to the role of memory cells in the secondary immune response. Since T2 cells and effector cells possess similar patterns of Lyt antigen expression, it can be postulated that these memory cells are functionally restricted; that is, repeated antigen challenge causes a cell of this type to differentiate into a specific effector cell, rather than all classes of effectors (1).

The ultimate differentiation of T cells is into immunologic effector cells. There are at least four functional classes of effector lymphocytes: cytotoxic, helper, suppressor, and delayed hypersensitivity. The cytotoxic T cell is capable of direct cell-mediated lysis of H-2 nonidentical lymphocytes in the mouse, as well as other types of nonidentical cells and tumor cells. The helper cell

Table 1. T Cell Properties.

	PRE-T	T0	T1	T2	EFFECTOR CELLS			
					HELPER	SUPRESSOR	CYTOTOXIC	DELAYED HYPERSENSITIVITY
Antigens								
θ or Thy*	-	+	+	+	+	+	+	+
Lyt*	-	1, 2, 3	1, 2, 3	1, 2, 3	1	2, 3	2, 3	1
H-2*	-	+	++	++	++	++	++	++
Ia*	-	?	?	+/-	++	++	?	-
Hydrocortisone sensitivity	+	++	+	-	-	-	-	-
Size	Large	Large	Large	Small	Small	Small	Small	
Recirculation	-	-	-	+	+	+	+	+
Sensitivity to thymic factors	+	+	+	-	-	-	-	-
Primary location	Bone marrow	Thymus	Thymus lymph nodes	Liv. & spleen	Liv. & spleen	Liv. & spleen	Liv. & spleen	Lymph nodes
Memory	-	-	-	+**	+**	+**	+**	+**
Lifetime	Short (days)	Short (days)	Short (days & wks.)	Long (wks. & mos.)	Short***	Short***	Short***	Short***
*Mitogen response****								
PHA	++	++	+	+	+	+	+	+
ConA	+	+	+	+	+	+	+	+
PWM	-	-	-	-	-	-	-	-
LPS	-	-	-	-	-	-	-	-

* Mouse antigens.

** Question as to whether T₂ and effector are distinct subsets. (See text discussion.)

*** Dependent on antigen.

**** PHA, phytohemagglutinin; ConA, concanavalin A; PWM, pokeweed mitogen; LPS, bacterial lipopolysaccharide.

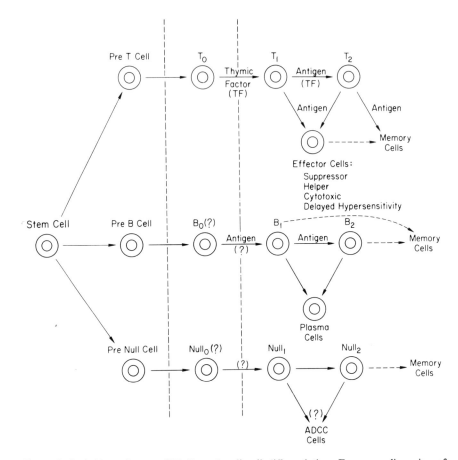

Figure 1. Probable pathways of T, B, and null cell differentiation. For some discussion of problems in lymphocyte terminology see Bach et al. (3). Question marks on arrows indicate lack of evidence for a specific differentiating agent. Question marks after the cell type indicate uncertainty of existence of the cell type. Null cells are here presumed to be precursors of ADCC cells. The null memory cell indicates the possibility that null cell populations specific for a particular immunoglobulin Fc type may persist as "memory" cells. Dotted lines indicate questions of deviation of memory cells.

is necessary, along with a macrophage factor, for the differentiation of mature B cells into plasma cells in response to antigens (considered under the heading "B Cell Differentiation"). This cell type also amplifies the cytotoxic response and is implicated in the development of the mixed lymphocyte interaction and graft versus host reactions. The suppressor T cells have a negative effect on the magnitude of B cell responses, mixed lymphocyte responses, and graft versus host reaction. Both suppressor and helper activities are antigen-specific, although there is some nonspecific helper and suppressor activity generated in their interactions with B cell populations. Curiously, both the specific and nonspecific helper functions may be mediated by soluble factors. (Specific helper activity is discussed in more detail with B lymphocyte differentiation.) The final type of effector mediates the antigen-specific inflammatory response of classical delayed hypersensitivity. Evidence that these functions are mediated by separate subpopulations is the fact that cytotoxic and suppressor cells are only Lyt 2, 3 positive and helper and cytotoxic cells only Lyt 1 positive. It is interesting that the cytotoxic and delayed hypersensitivity cell populations show this evidence of differential maturation, since both cells are active in two forms of cell-mediated immunity (11). With some difficulty a product of the H-2 region in the mouse, which is normally easily detected on B cells, can be found on effector T cells. This is the Ia antigen (for a review of the H-2 and I complex see Ref. 16). Helper and suppressor T lymphocytes are slightly Ia positive, while delayed hypersensitivity cells are not, again showing that the functions are divided among different subpopulations. A summary of these properties is presented in Table 1.

We have already alluded to the fact that thymic function can be replaced by thymic factors (TF) and thymic implants in millipore chambers. It would appear that despite the fact that T0 cells seem to mature from pre-T cells normally only in the thymus, extrathymic maturation can occur under the influence of a soluble factor(s) from the thymus. A number of factors have been isolated from various animal sources, and some have been purified and chemically characterized. All possess the ability to convert pre-T bone marrow precursors to θ positive cells in the mouse. In addition, they can induce TL expression in some peripheral blood lymphocytes, induce maturation of T1 and T2 cells, and reconstitute the ability to generate effector cells in an athymic animal. Interestingly, the principal sources of these isolates have been calf thymus and pig blood, but the functional assays have primarily utilized the mouse, illustrating a common phylogenetic background.

The TFs are all polypeptides, but these preparations show striking variability in composition. A. L. Goldstein's thymosin, which has been used to treat some human T-cell–deficient patients, has a molecular weight of 12,000 and a blocked N terminus. Trainin's THF (thymic humonal factor) has a molecular weight of about 3000. G. Goldstien's thymopoetin has two fractions, I and II, of molecular weight about 7000 and serine at the N-terminus. The thymopoetins were initially assayed by their ability to produce a delayed neuromuscular blockade, as a model for myasthenia gravis. J. F. Bach's TF from pig blood has a molecular weight of about 1000 and a blocked N-terminus.

It is difficult to say whether or not these putative hormones are all fractions of the same molecule with a critical active site, but they all function reasonably well in T-cell induction. Recently, it has been found that substances, such as insulin, theophylline, PGE_2, and dibutyryl c-AMP (cyclic AMP), elevating intracellular c-AMP, also induce T cell markers in a fashion similar to the TFs. This has been taken as evidence that TFs are true hormones acting by a "second messenger." However, thymosin and Bach's TF do not increase c-AMP in vitro, and serum from both normal and thymectomized animals possesses a factor that does increase c-AMP in lymphocytes. Astaldi et al. (2), argue that the TFs are indirectly hormones in that they produce a second compound in vivo that specifically elevates c-AMP in T-cell precursors. G. Goldstein, furthermore, has isolated a compound called UBIP (ubiquitin) that induces the maturation of T cells and is not restricted in distribution to the thymus. But both UBIP and agents that simply elevate c-AMP not only cause T cell maturation but also induce B cell maturation, unlike the TFs, which only affect the T differentiation. Whatever the mechanism of TF action on the T precusor cells, therefore, there is little doubt that they represent a real mode of thymic influence. (For a review of this area see Ref. 4.)

B CELL DIFFERENTIATION

B cell maturation, unlike T cell maturation, with the exception of the Bursa of Fabricius in fowl, does not appear to be under the control of an organ analogous to the thymus. As in T cell differentiation, there is assumed to be an uncommitted stem cell precursor. Again there is evidence that the stem cell is in the bone marrow where further maturation takes place. Unlike the T cell series, B cells have not been found to have a variety of specific markers, and there has not been observed a specific B inducer comparable to the TFs. This is unfortunate, since precise understanding of B differentiation will certainly lead to a better understanding of antibody diversity.

The initial stage of differentiation from an uncommitted stem cell to a committed pre-B cell appears to involve a cell lacking in detectable immunoglobulin. About 50% of the lymphocytes in mouse bone marrow lack either T or B markers. These cells can be isolated and will migrate to the spleen of a syngeneic host; within 20 hours one-half develop surface immunoglobulin (SIg) (15). Further evidence for the bone marrow as the site of B cell maturation comes from the observation that the SIg distribution of marrow B cells is considerably more heterogenous than in the lymph nodes or spleen. The next stage is characterized by the appearance of detectable IgM within the cytoplasm. These cells rapidly take up ^{3}H-thymidine in vivo, indicating a high rate of cell division. The label does not appear in cells with SIgM for about 24 hours. These developing cells are probably the same as the B1 cell or "virgin" precursor cell found by density gradient studies (12). These B1 cells do not recirculate and are (in man) of two types on the basis of the SIg: cells with only IgM and cells with both IgM and IgD. The SIg produced on B cells are the antigen-specific receptors. Cells that have only IgM and some of the cells with IgM and IgD are the precursors of IgM-producing plasma cells in the unprimed animal. The other IgM- and IgD-bearing B1 cells are the unprimed precursors of IgG-producing plasma cells (6).

Some of the B1 cells are converted, after interaction with antigen, into long-lived cells which we will term B2 cells. These cells are B "memory" cells, which confer long-term responsiveness. Recent data have shown that there are two populations of memory cells in rats. One consists of large cells rapidly turning over, which persist only for weeks and carry IgM receptors. They probably represent IgM memory cells. The second population of memory cells are small, with a low rate of turnover, persist for months, and carry IgG_{2a}. These may be the IgG memory cells (19). IgG_1-bearing lymphocytes have also been shown in man to become IgG_1-producing plasma cells in secondary immune responses. In the bone marrow the majority of the SIg cells are of the B1 type, and in the spleen the majority belong to the B2 type.

In addition to SIg, some B cells carry receptors for the activated third component of complement (C3′). Ontogenically, in the mouse, cells with SIg appear first. C3′ plus SIg lymphocytes do not appear for at least 2 weeks (8). In adult bone marrow that is reconstituted after irradiation, there is a similar time lag. The exact significance of the C3′ receptor remains to be elucidated, but it may be involved in amplifying antigen recognition or providing a second signal to the B cell. B cells show some variation in their expression of Ia antigens. Most B1 and B2 cells are Ia-positive, but a few Ia-negative cell precursors are found. The Ia-negative cells and the IgM plasma cell producers are apparently identical. It has been speculated that the expression of Ia may reflect coding for a switch mechanism that allows IgM-to-IgG conversion in the production of the plasma cells resulting from antigenic stimulation (14).

The basic concept, then, is that B1 and B2 cells have antigen-specific immunoglobulin cell surface receptors. Each B cell probably carries only one or at least a very limited number of specific receptors. It is interesting that perinatal B cells are much more easily stripped of SIg receptors and fail to regenerate them as adult cells do. This may be one mechanism for the development of self-tolerance in fetal life. The final stage in differentiation of B cells is the production of plasma cells. As we have mentioned, the triggering of a particular B cell clone bearing a specific antigen receptor may require the presence of a T helper cell which is also antigen-specific, and a macrophage factor. There are also so-called T independent antigens, which can stimulate a B cell clone directly without the need for a helper cell (17). The helper cell seems to serve some function in antigen presentation to the Ig receptors of the B cell. This function may be to modify the antigen to facilitate binding by surface immunoglobulin of B cells. Plasma cells carry H-2 antigens and a specific plasma cell antigen on their surfaces (21). They are morphologically distinct from the lymphocyte and function as factories for the specific immunoglobulin determined by the parent B cell. The properties of B cells discussed here are summarized in Table 2. Young plasma cells are still capable of several rounds of cell division.

NULL LYMPHOCYTE DIFFERENTIATION

We will conclude this chapter by briefly outlining the third possible pathway of lymphocyte differentiation (see Figure 1 and Table 3). There exists in peripheral blood a population of lymphocytes that do not form E-rosettes, have no bound surface immunoglobulin, lack specific T lymphocyte antigens, and have no C3' receptors (19). These cells, which we will call null cells, are apparently different from the B cell precursors of bone marrow, although some investigators feel that these cells represent a subpopulation of B cells with little SIg or possibly some form of pre-T cell. These lymphocytes, as well as some B cells and a small population of activated T-cells, possess Fc receptors, which bind the constant regions of some subclasses of IgG. The Fc receptor is usually detected by the ability to bind aggregated immunoglobulin. The numbers of lymphocytes of all types that are found to have Fc receptors are a function of the precise methodology of this assay. In addition, other cell types (e.g., macrophages) also have Fc receptors (7).

The function of the Fc receptor on lymphocytes is related to a type of cell-mediated cytotoxicity. If a target cell (e.g., tumor cell or lymphocyte) is coated with an appropriate immunoglobulin, the population bearing Fc receptors is able to effect direct cell-mediated lysis, probably through binding of the receptor to the constant region of the coating immunoglobulin. The null cell population is the major cell type involved in this antibody-dependent cell-mediated cytotoxicity (ADCC) (7, 9, 13). Selective removal of cells bearing C3' receptors and SIg, as well as treatment with antithymocyte (anti-T cell) sera, enhances the ADCC activity (18). Recent work has shown that the null cell population has rapidly renewed and slowly renewed subpopulations, similar to T and B cell populations (14). The possible scheme for null cell differentiation shown in Figure 1 is based more on the possible similarities to T and B cell differentiation than on hard evidence. It should be emphasized that the work in this area is too recent to prove that null cells are a distinct population, but it seems highly likely. The properties of null cells are summarized in Table 3. The question marks indicate the degree of uncertainty at the time of this writing.

Table 2. B Cell Properties.

	PRE-B	B0	B1	B2	PLASMA CELL
Surface immunoglobulins					
IgG	−	−	−	−	+*
IgD	−	−	+	+	?
IgM	−	−	+	+	+
Cytosol immunoglobulins					
IgG	−	−	?	?	+*
IgD	−	−	?	?	−?
IgM	−	+	+	+	+
Ia	−	−	+/−**	+	−
Plasma cell antigen	−	−	−	−	+
Fc receptor	−	+/−	+/−	+/−	−
C'3 receptor	−	−	?	+/−	−
Mitogen responses					
LPS	?	?	+	+	−
PWM	?	?	+	+	−
Lifetime	Short (days)	Short (days)	Intermediate (days–mos.)	Long (mos.)	Short (days)
Memory	−	−	+/−***	+	−
Sheep red cell rosettes	−	−	−	−	−
Size	Large	Large	Large	Small	Variable

* Secretory immunoglobulins.
** Ia (mouse) may not be present on cells capable of producing only IgM.
*** Large B₁ cell may be IgM memory cell.

389

Table 3. Null Cell Properties.

	PRE-NULL	NULL1	NULL2	NULL3
Surface immuno-globulins	−	−	−	−
C_3' receptor	−	−	−	?
Fc receptor	−	+	+	+
θ, Thy	−	−	−	−
Sheep red cell or rosette	−	−	−	−
Lifetime	Short	Short	Short	Long
Recirculation	−	−	−	+
Antigen specificity*	−	−	−	−
Mitogen response	?	?	?	?
ADCC	−	−	?	+**

* Only the sensitizing antibody is antigen-specific.
** May or may not be a function of a subset of B cells as well as null cells.

CONCLUSION

The three lines of lymphocyte differentiation discussed here have some similarities. Each has populations with rapid and slow turnover, and all three are important in the expression of full immunocompetency. More striking are the differences in functional properties, membrane determinants and receptors, and cellular interactions. It is hoped that this brief outline will aid the student and scientist alike in attaining a better grasp of this heterogenous entity we so glibly call the lymphocyte.

REFERENCES

1. Araneo, B. A., Marrack, P., and Kappler, J. W. 1977. Functional heterogenicity among the T-derived lymphocytes of the mouse: VII. Conversion of T1 cells to T2 cells by antigen. *J. Immunol.* 119:765–71.
2. Astaldi, A., Astaldi, G. C. B., Wiljermans, P., Groenewould, M., Schellekens, P. Th. A., and Eijsvoogel, V. P. 1977. Thymosin induced serum factor inducing cyclic GMP. *J. Immunol.* 119:1106–8.
3. Bach, J-F., Cantor, H., Roelants, G., and Stutman, O. 1975. T cell subsets: Terminology problems. In *The Biological Activity of the Thymic Hormones,* D. W. Bekkum, ed., pp. 159–68. Kookyer Science Publ., Rotterdam.
4. Bach, J-F., and Carnaud, C. 1976. Thymic factors. *Prog. Allergy* 21:342–408.
5. Cantor, H., and Weissman, I. 1976. Development and function of subpopulations of thymocytes and T lymphocytes. *Prog. Allergy* 20:1–64.
6. Coffman, R. L., and Cohn, M. 1977. The class of surface immunoglobulin on virgin and memory B lymphocytes. *J. Immunol.* 118:1806–15.
7. Dickler, H. B. 1976. Lymphocyte receptors for immunoglobulin. *Adv. Immunol.* 24:167–214.

8. Gelfand, M. C., Elfenbein, G. J., Frank, M. M., and Paul, W. E. 1974. Ontegeny of B lymphocytes: II. Relative rates of appearance of lymphocytes bearing surface immunoglobulins and complement receptors. *J. Exp. Med.* 139:1125–41.

9. Horowitz, D. H., and Garrett, M. A. 1977. Distinctive functional properties of human blood L lymphocytes: A comparison of T lymphocytes, B lymphocytes, and monocytes. *J. Immunol.* 118:1712–21.

10. Huber, B., Cantor, H., Shen, F. W., and Boyse, E. A. 1976a. Independent differentiative pathways of Ly 1 and Ly 2, 3 subclasses of T cells: Experimental production of mice deprived of selected T cell subclasses. *J. Exp. Med.* 114:1128–33.

11. Huber, B., Devinsky, O., Gershon, R. K., and Cantor, H. 1976b. Cell-mediated immunity: Delayed-type hypersensitivity and cytotoxicity responses are mediated by different T-cell subclasses. *J. Exp. Med.* 143:1534–39.

12. Owen, J. J. T., Wright, D. E., Habu, S., Raff, M. C., and Cooper, M. D. 1977. Studies on the generation of B lymphocytes in fetal liver and bone marrow. *J. Immunol.* 118:2067–72.

13. Pape, G. R., Troye, M., and Perlman, P. 1977. Characterization of cytolytic effector cells in peripheral blood of healthy individuals and cancer patients: I. Surface markers and K cell activity after separation of B cells and lymphocytes with Fc receptors by column fractionation. *J. Immunol.* 118:1919–24.

14. Press, J. L., Klinman, N. R., and McDevitt, H. O. 1976. Expression of Ia antigens on hapten-specific B cells: I. Delineation of B-cell subpopulations. *J. Exp. Med.* 144:414–27.

15. Ryser, J-E., and Vassali, P. 1974. Mouse bone marrow lymphocytes and their differentiation. *J. Immunol.* 113:719–28.

16. Schreffler, D. C., and David, C. S. 1975. The H-2 major histocompatibility complex and the I immune response region: Genetic variation, function, and organisation. *Adv. Immunol.* 20:125–95.

17. Schreiner, G. F., and Unanue, E. R. 1976. Membrane and cytoplasmic changes in B lymphocytes induced by ligand-surface immunoglobulin interaction. *Adv. Immunol.* 24:38–165.

18. Stobo, J. D., Rosenthal, A. S., and Paul, W. E. 1973. Functional heterogeneity of murine lymphoid cells: V. Lymphocyte lacking detectable surface or immunoglobulin determinants. *J. Exp. Med.* 138:71–88.

19. Strober, S. 1976. Maturation of B lymphocytes in rats: III. Two subpopulations of memory B-cells in the thoracic duct lymph differ by size, turnover rate, and surface immunoglobulin. *J. Immunol.* 117:1288–94.

20. Stutman, O. 1977. Two main features of T-cell development: Thymus traffic and post-thymic maturation. In *Contemporary Topics in Immunobiology,* Vol. 7, O. Stutman, pp. 1–46.

21. Takahashi, T., Old, L. J., and Boyse, E. A. 1970. Surface alloantigens of plasma cells. *J. Exp. Med.* 131:1325–41.

SECTION 4
TRANSPORT, SECRETION, AND STORAGE

KHALIL AHMED, SECTION EDITOR

4.1. Membrane Transport of Water

Khalil Ahmed and Said A. Goueli

GENERAL CONSIDERATIONS

Water constitutes a preponderant fraction of all living systems. Because of its characteristic properties, it is the most suitable solvent to sustain living matter. Study of cell water is essential in determining intracellular changes in composition and cell viability. Clearly, regulation of its content is of fundamental importance in the maintenance of homeostasis.

Water is capable of acting as a solvent for ionic, polar, and apolar solutes. The interaction of water with various solutes is referred to as hydration. The hydration of macromolecules accompanies the formation of a variety of cagelike structures by water. Thus, it appears that water may have quite different properties at interfaces and surfaces from those usually associated with it in bulk phase. Evidence of ordered water around macromolecules is being derived from several physical (e.g., nuclear magnetic resonance) and chemical (e.g., exchange of H by D) probes. However, determination of the state of water in tissues and membranes remains a challenging problem. Studies utilizing muscle and nerve fibers have strongly indicated differences in state between intracellular and extracellular water. Marked changes have been noted in the state of intracellular water as a result of biological activity in muscle and nerve preparations.

Because water must cross biological membranes, its interaction with these structures is of particular interest. It appears that either a net decrease in the icelike structure or a net increase in the ordering of water within biological membranes may occur. Depending on the size of the channel in the membrane, either of the two changes may have important consequences. For a larger channel, a decrease in icelike structure within it will result in increased flexibility and decreased barrier resistance to its passage. For a very small channel (e.g., one that admits only single molecules of water), the structure will simulate the situation of water dissolved in the barrier if interaction of individual water molecules approximates those in bulk water. If the attractive forces between water and the membrane are either much greater or, in the case of hydrophobic materials, much less, the barrier in all likelihood will be largely impermeable to water. If water becomes organized about either ionic and polar groups at the surface of the channel or at nonpolar, hydrophobic surfaces, the increased icelike structure of the water within the channels may profoundly affect the penetrability of the barrier to water; either cause of an increased structure of water within small aqueous channels may obstruct the passage of water, but possibilities for different effects may exist. The increased organization of water molecules that surround ionic groups arises from the interaction of the dipoles of water molecules with charged groups. The attractive force between the membrane and neighboring water molecules would be responsible for the icelike state of water in the membrane in this situation. At nonpolar surfaces, on the other hand, the lack of interaction of water with the nonpolar surface or groups results in increased water structure. Thus both conditions may result in a more icelike water in the membrane, but the frictional resistance between water and the membrane will be high in the former situation and may be low in the latter. The latter situation may give rise to molecular slippage at the interface between the liquid and the membrane.

TRANSFER OF WATER

Transfer of water across a membrane appears to be passive rather than active, osmosis being the most common process by which this is accomplished. Cells respond to the tonicity of the medium in which they are suspended, and accordingly their volume can vary. Derivation of mathematical equations describing this process is based on the assumptions that (1) cell membranes are semipermeable, (2) cells tend to achieve osmotic equilibrium, and (3) intracellular solutes are capable of reducing the chemical potential of intracellular water.

The chemical potential of water (μ_w) is defined as the free energy per mole of water. The chemical potential difference between two locations is a measure of the "driving force" for the movement of that component. Thus, the bigger the chemical potential difference $\mu_w^A - \mu_w^B$, the faster the spontaneous change takes place—in this case, the larger the flux of water from region A to region B.

The chemical potential of water is represented by the sum of the various components into which it can be analyzed:

$$\mu_w = \mu_w^* + RT \ln a_w + \bar{V}_w P + Z_w FE$$

where μ_w^* is the standard chemical potential of pure water at atmospheric pressure and the temperature of the system under consideration; R is the gas constant; T is the absolute temperature; a_w is the activity of water, $\bar{V}$ is the partial molal volume of water, P is the hydrostatic pressure in excess of atmospheric pressure, Z_w is the number of charges on water molecules, F is the Faraday, E is the electrical potential, and $a_w = \gamma_w C_w$.

The activity coefficient (γ_w) of water is usually less than unity for a solution because the thermodynamically effective concentration (a_w), or activity of a species such as water in this case, is generally less than its actual concentration.

Since we are dealing with nondissociable water molecules (i.e., $Z_w = 0$), the electrical term does not contribute to its chemical potential. If we consider that the concentration (or mole fraction of water) becomes less when the water molecules are displaced by those of the solute, then the presence of solutes in an aqueous solution tends to decrease the activity of water (a_w). As the water activity decreases, the chemical potential will decrease. It is also known that the presence of solutes can lead to an osmotic pressure (π) in the solution. An increase in the concentration of solutes raises the osmotic pressure, indicating that (π) and a_w change in opposite directions. This is represented by the following equation:

$$RT \ln a_w = -\overline{V}_w \pi$$

As the solutes are added, a_w decreases from its value of unity for pure solvent, $\ln a_w$ is, therefore, negative, and π is positive.

In general, the greater the concentration of solutes, the more negative $\ln a_w$ becomes, and the larger is the osmotic pressure. The activity of pure water is unity, while in general a_w equals $\gamma_w N_w$, where N_w is its mole fraction.

$$N_w = \frac{n_w}{n_w + \sum_j n_j} = 1 - \frac{\sum_j n_j}{n_w + \sum_j n_j}$$

where n_w is the number of moles of water, n_j is the number of moles of solute j, and the summation $\sum_j$, is the overall solutes in the system being studied. If $n_w \gg \sum_j n_j$, then we approach the case of an ideal solution.

$$\ln a_w \simeq \ln N_w = \ln \left(1 - \frac{\sum_j n_j}{n_w + \sum_j n_j} \right)$$

$$\simeq - \frac{\sum_j n_j}{n_w + \sum_j n_j} \simeq - \frac{\sum_j n_j}{n_w}$$

In the absence of solutes ($\Sigma n_j = 0$), ln a_w is zero, and a_w is unity, while the presence of solutes decreases the activity of water from the value of one for pure water.

Since $RT \ln a_w = \overline{V}_w \pi$, it follows that:

$$\pi_s \simeq -\frac{RT}{\overline{V}_w} \left(-\frac{\sum\limits_j n_j}{n_w} \right) = RT \sum_j \frac{n_j}{\overline{V}_w n_w} = RT \sum_j C_j$$

where $\overline{V}_w n_w$ is the total volume of water in the system, $n_j / \overline{V}_w n_w$ is the number of moles of species j in that volume, and therefore the concentration of species j is (C_j), and the summations are over all solutions. This equation describes what is called the Van't Hoff relation, but its use is justified only for dilute ideal solutions. The Van't Hoff relation for a dilution of real solutes can be represented by $\pi_s = RT \sum\limits_j \gamma_j C_j$.

Since we are not dealing with ideal solutions,

$$\pi_s = \phi RT C_j$$

where ϕ is the molal osmotic coefficient, and C_j is the molal concentration of species j.

It is apparent from these equations (for a compartment that is capable of expansion) that water will move across the membrane in accordance with its chemical potential (osmotic flow). This is followed by transfer of electrolytes to maintain electroneutrality and Donnan distribution of ions on each side of the membrane to reach a new equilibrium. If forces such as an electrogenic ion pump are operative, then water flow may also occur by electroosmosis, that is, as a solvent of charged particles (e.g., ions) across a membrane with fixed charges.

INTRACELLULAR ELECTROLYTES

The bulk of the intracellular electrolytes consists of Na^+, K^+, and Cl^-. A variety of studies indicate that there may be intracellular gradients of cations so that their concentration and activities may vary in different compartments. Some cations may also be bound to proteins. Likewise, the concentration of cations in some intracellular organelles may be different from that in the bulk of the cell water. It is also apparent that the intracellular concentration of electrolytes ($Na_i + K_i$) may be considerably higher than the extracellular ($Na_o + K_o$), and yet be at a steady state. This is clear because the concentration of internal electrolytes measured by selective microelectrodes was different from that determined chemically. This indicates that the cations either are being bound by cell constituents (i.e., proteins) or are compartmentalized (i.e., owing to some intracellular structural barriers such as nuclear or mitochondrial membranes). This binding accounts for 70–80% of cellular Na^+ in muscle and a significant amount of K^+ in the kidney. In general, this binding leads to an overestimation of the intracellular osmotic pressure; that is, the apparent (computed) intracellular concentration of cations is not a real estimate of the true value. In this context, the vapor-equilibration method indicated that a portion of the cell water was not available as solvent. This method distinguishes between the bound water and free active water molecules in the cell. Water may be bound to cellular proteins, or intracellular barriers may change the physical and/or chemical state of water molecules close to macromolecules, resulting in apparent physical compartmentalization. The absence of hydrostatic pressure across the erythrocyte membrane, which can withstand a pressure gradient to about 1.4 atm, has also been shown to give inaccurate values for water. Consequently, the computed solute concentration on the basis of analytically determined total cell water may represent underestimated values.

OSMOTICALLY INDUCED TRANSPORT OF WATER

It has long been known that when cells or tissues are subjected to conditions that result in an impaired supply of metabolic energy (e.g., anaerobiosis, cold, uncoupling agents), they tend to swell. Reversal of these conditions causes extrusion of water from the cells. Obviously blocking of metabolic energy causes a net passive flux of water and small electrolytes (according to their electrochemical gradients) across the semipermeable membrane. Accordingly, Na^+ and Cl^- will enter the cell, and K^+ will leak out of it. Owing to the presence of nondiffusible anions in the cell water, bulk electrolytes flow into the cells to satisfy the Donnan equilibrium. This results in the cells swelling until a new steady state is achieved. With the availability of metabolic energy, cells extrude Na^+ and accumulate K^+ through the mechanism of a Na^+–K^+ pump. The transport of these cations proceeds against their respective electrochemical gradients while Cl^- moves passively. As a result of this transport, water is extruded from the cells as an isotonic solution of electrolytes (osmotic flux). This implies that the steady-state volume of cells is controlled by a leak-and-pump mechanism. This situation is illustrated by the following equations. A permeable substrate (S) is extruded by both active and passive mechanisms with flow rate constants p and l, respectively; and a nonpermeable substrate (A) is also present intracellularly; then:

$$(A)_i + (S)_i = (S)_o$$

at osmotic equilibrium,

$$l((S)_o - (S)_i) = p(S)_i$$

But at equilibrium $\Delta S = 0$; then:

$$(A)_i = \frac{p(S)_o}{(l+p)} = \frac{1}{1 + (l/p)}(S)_o$$

Since $(A)_i$ is related to the cell volume V by $(A)_i = A/V$.

Then:

$$(A) = \frac{V}{1 + (l/p)}(S)_o$$

and

$$V = \frac{(A)}{(S)_o} \cdot (1 + l/p)$$

Thus, any factors that increase the leak and/or inhibit the pump will result in cellular swelling, and, conversely, if the leak is inhibited and the pump is activated, the cells will shrink. Theoretically, complete inhibition of the pump should bring out conditions approaching Donnan distribution between the cellular and extracellular compartments. This model did not take into consideration that a cation exchange mechanism across the membrane is operative. However, studies of tissue swelling carried out at 0°C reveal deviations from this possibility.

EVALUATION OF THE LEAK-AND-PUMP HYPOTHESIS

Studies carried out on the effects of ouabain on the transport of water and electrolytes in a variety of cells have drawn attention to the inadequacies of the leak-and-pump hypothesis as the sole mechanism of cellular volume control. Ouabain, which is a specific inhibitor of the pump, would be expected to cause extensive cellular swelling according to the above hypothesis. However, when cells were previously loaded with Na^+, Cl^-, and water at 0°C, ouabain did not prevent extrusion of water as an isotonic salt solution from the cells, even though the pump was inhibited. This ouabain concentration (0.3 mM), which was 500 times higher than the K_i for the inhibition of the (Na^+-K^+)-ATPase, inhibited Na^+-dependent accumulation of α-methylglucose (which is related to the Na^+ pump operation), and also inhibited the accumulation of K^+ and the O_2 uptake related to the operation of the Na^+ pump.

In the same vein, presence or absence of Ca^{2+}, which markedly influences the membrane leakiness, did not significantly alter the steady-state level of tissue water. A marked extrusion of water can also be observed in the absence of external K^+. These observations may be reconciled by invoking two processes to be involved in the control of water transport. First, it may be associated with the ouabain-sensitive $Na^+–K^+$ pump where a stoichiometric $1:1$ relationship of transport in the opposite direction would produce only small movement of water and anions. Second, an ouabain-insensitive system capable of extruding NaCl (as a practically isotonic solution) without coupling to K^+ transport could produce considerable fluxes of water. Both of these processes are dependent on metabolic energy. The ouabain-insensitive process seems to be particularly affected by changes in external Ca^{2+} and pH. The effects of ouabain and external Ca^{2+} are markedly pH-dependent so that significant swelling is produced at pH 8 whereas no change is observed between pH 6.2 and 7.4 (pH effects on cellular swelling are complex and cannot be dealt with adequately in the present discussion). It may also be noted that the ouabain-insensitive system of transport operates in addition to the leak-and-pump system. It does not show specificity for monovalent cations, and does not appear to operate in all mammalian cells. The dependence on Ca^{2+} and ATP, and demonstration of the phenomenon of superprecipitation, suggest it to be a mechanochemical process. These characteristics are very similar to those described for the actomyosin system, which is also Ca^{2+}- and ATP-dependent.

CURRENT HYPOTHESES

As described above, electrolytes extrusion from the cell may proceed by two distinct pathways, both of which depend on metabolic energy for their protection. In the first case the transport of Na^+ and K^+ takes place against their electrochemical gradients, the system shows specificity for Na^+ but not K^+, it can carry out $Na^+–K^+$ exchange, and it is specifically inhibited by cardiac glycosides. $Na^+–K^+$-ATPase appears to be the enzymic mechanism of the operation of this pump. The second pathway of electrolyte transport is ouabain-insensitive, and does not require coupling with K^+. It shows no specificity for Na^+, but requires metabolic energy. The electrolytes extruded by either of the two mechanisms may enter the cell by the "leak" down their electrochemical gradient. Of the various hypotheses put forward to explain the mechanism of ouabain-insensitive Na^+ and water extrusion, the so-called mechanochemical hypothesis seems to be the most satisfactory at the present time. This hypothesis is based on the involvement of Ca^{2+} and ATP with the membrane. A variety of data has shown that Ca^{2+} and ATP influence the physical properties of the cell membrane. These may be mediated via a Ca^{2+}-activated ATPase present in the membrane. This ATPase has properties similar to those of actomyosin ATPase, and may directly influence membrane permeability to water.

SUGGESTED READING

Dick, D. A. T. 1966. *Cell Water.* Butterworth, Washington, D.C.

Fogg, C. E., ed. 1965. *Symposia of the Society for Experimental Biology,* Number XIX, The state and movement of water in living organisms. Academic Press, New York.

Kleinzeller, A. 1972. Cellular transport of water. In *Metabolic Transport,* L. E. Hokin, ed. Academic Press, New York.

Klotz, I. M. 1970. Water: Its fitness as a molecular environment. In *Membranes and Ion Transport,* E. E. Bittar, ed. Wiley-Interscience, London.

Nobel, P. S. 1974. *Water—Introduction to Biophysical Plant Physiology.* Freeman & Co., San Francisco. 488 pp.

Stein, W. D. 1967. *The Movement of Molecules Across Cell Membranes.* Academic Press, New York.

Whipple, H. E., ed. 1965. *Ann. N.Y. Acad. Sci.* 125:249–772.

4.2. Electrolyte Transport (Monovalent Ions)

Khalil Ahmed and Said A. Goueli

GENERAL CONSIDERATIONS OF MODES OF TRANSPORT

The internal milieu of all cells is protected by the plasma membrane, which acts as a barrier between the internal and external environment of the cell. Obviously, besides internal demands, the structural nature and functions of the membrane will regulate the movement of materials across it. This process may take place by one or a combination of the following modes: (1) simple or passive diffusion, (2) active transport, and (3) facilitated or mediated diffusion.

Simple or Passive Diffusion

The passive movement of solutes and ions across the membrane obeys Fick's first law. It is thus dependent on the concentration gradient of the solute which will determine the rate and direction of movement. For transfer of charged ions, however, the electrical potential across the membrane, in addition to the concentration gradient, will influence the passive permeability. To understand these factors which regulate passive transport, we will consider the mathematical treatment as follows.

The mean velocity of species j moving across the plane $(\overline{V}_j)$ times the number of those molecules per unit volume which can move (C_j) equals the flux of that species (J_j):

$$J_j = \overline{V}_j C_j$$

Also, the average velocity $\dfrac{J_j}{C_j}$, equals the mobility of species j, u_j, times the force on j that causes it to move $\dfrac{-\partial u_j}{\partial x}$, where the driving force is represented by the negative gradient of the chemical potential of species j; that is:

$$J_j = \overline{V}_j C_j = u_j \left(\frac{-\partial u_j}{\partial x} \right) \cdot C_j$$

which means the greater the mobility of that species j, the larger its velocity is response to a given force.

For a charged particle moving across biological membranes, the appropriate expression is:

$$u_j = u_j^* + RT \ln a_j + Z_j FE + \overline{V}_j P$$

where u_j^* is the chemical potential of species j for a suitable reference state when the activity of species j is unity which will be canceled when two conditions for species j are compared. Both have the dimensions of energy per mole of the substance (i.e., joules/mole or cal/mole). The term a_j is the activity of species j, which is related to its concentration by means of the activity coefficient, γ_j (i.e., $a_j = \gamma_j C_j$). Activity coefficient γ_j usually is less than unity unless it is a very dilute solution; therefore, the greater the activity of species j (loosely speaking, the higher its concentration), the larger will be its chemical potential. The value of $RT \ln a_j$ is expressed in energy per mole, where R is the gas constant (1.987 cal/deg K mole = 8.3143 joules/mole-deg K). The quantity T is the absolute temperature $(273 + °C)$; Z_j is an integer representing the charge number of species j; F is a constant known as the Faraday = 96,487 coulombs/mole or 96,487 joules/mole-volt = 23,060 cal/mole-volt; and E is the electrical potential. For a nonelectrolyte or water $(Z_w = 0)$, the electrical term does not contribute to its chemical potential. The term $Z_j FE$ is called the electrochemical potential; and $\overline{V}_j$ is the volume per mole, (i.e., the partial molal volume of species $j = 18$ cm^3/mole for water), P is the pressure, and $\overline{V}_j P$ has units of energy per mole.

Because the term $\overline{V}_j P$ makes a relatively small contribution to the Δu_j of an ion, it will be canceled from now on. The activity term $(RT \ln a_j)$ leads to Fick's first law; the pressure term $(\overline{V}_j P)$ accounts for Darcy's law and Poiseuille's law; the electrical term $(Z_j FE)$ yields Ohm's law. In each case flux is found experimentally to be directly proportional to the appropriate driving force. For one-dimensional cases, u_j must be differentiated with respect to x, $\partial u_j / \partial x$ (under isothermal conditions where T is constant).

$$\frac{\partial u_j}{\partial x} = RT d\text{-}\ln a_j/\partial x + Z_j F \partial E/\partial x$$

where

$$\partial \ln a_j/\partial x = \frac{1}{a_j} \partial a_j/\partial x = \frac{1}{\gamma_j C_j} \partial \gamma_j C_j/\partial x$$

$$J_j = -\frac{u_j RT}{\gamma_j} \cdot \frac{\partial \gamma_j C_j}{\partial x} - u_j C_j Z_j F \frac{\partial E}{\partial x}$$

So, J_j is made up of two components of driving forces: the gradient in activity and electrical potential.

For simplicity, we can consider γ_j to be constant. In the absence of electrical potential gradients ($\partial E/\partial x = 0$), and for neutral solutes ($Z_j = 0$),

$$J_j = -u_j RT \, (\partial C_j/\partial x)$$

Again, this is represented as Fick's first law $(J_j = -D_j \, \partial C_j/\partial x)$ where $u_j RT$ replaces the diffusion coefficient D_j. This shows the dependency of D on the temperature T, since $D_j = u_j RT$. This means that Fick's first law is a special case of the general flux relation, where the pressure and the electrical effects are ignored. Also, it shows that for neutral substances or nonelectrolytes the only driving force considered when Fick's first law is being considered is the concentration gradient.

In contrast to neutral solute, the flux of an ion also depends on electrical driving force $\partial E/\partial x$ in addition to its concentration gradient $\partial C_j/\partial x$. If charged particles diffuse toward regions of lower concentration, an electrical potential difference is created. This electrical potential difference is referred to as a "diffusion potential." If a cationic species has a higher mobility (u_j) than the anionic ones, the more mobile cations will move faster than their oppositely charged anions, resulting in a charge separation. This will set up an electrical potential gradient leading to a diffusion potential. The flux of a cation (J^+) equals that of the anion (J^-) across the same membrane for the neutrality principle, and C^+ equals C^-, which is represented as C; then:

$$-u^+ RT \frac{\partial C}{\partial x} - u^+ CF \frac{\partial E}{\partial x} = -u^- RT \frac{\partial C}{\partial x} + u^- CF \frac{\partial E}{\partial x}$$

where the plus sign on the right side occurs because the monovalent anion considered in this case carries a negative charge ($Z^- = -1$). Then the electrical potential gradient is expressed as

$$\frac{\partial E}{\partial x} = \left(\frac{u^- - u^+}{u^- + u^+}\right) \cdot \frac{RT}{FC} \cdot \frac{\partial C}{\partial x}$$

This equation indicates that $\partial E/\partial x \neq 0$ when the mobility of the cation u^+ differs from that of the anion u^-, and there is a concentration gradient. When this happens, the electrical field created will be in the direction that speeds up the slower ion and slows down the faster ion to preserve electrical neutrality.

In a steady state condition, where E and C remain constant with time, and going along the X axis from region I to region II of that membrane, we find the following:

$$\int_I^{II} (\partial E/\partial x)\, dx = \int_I^{II} dE = E^{II} - E^I$$

for steady state and

$$\int_I^{II} (1/c)(\partial c/\partial x)\, dx = \int_I^{II} dc/c = \ln\,(c^{II}/c^I)$$

that is,

$$E^{II} - E^I = \left(\frac{u^- - u^+}{u^+ + u^-}\right) \cdot \frac{RT}{F} \ln \frac{c^{II}}{c^I}$$

$$= 59.2 \left(\frac{u^- - u^+}{u^+ + u^-}\right) \cdot \log \frac{c^{II}}{c^I} \text{ mV at } 25°C$$

For membranes, solute concentration will be replaced by K_jC_j where K_j is the partition coefficient of species j in that membrane versus the solution where the cell is placed. Also, we will assume that the electrical potential (E) varies linearly with distance across the membrane; that is, $\partial E/\partial x$ is a constant $= E_M/\Delta x$ where E_M is the electrical potential difference across the membrane $(E^i - E^o)$, where E^i is inside and E^o is outside electrical potential. We need to assume also, as before, that γ_j, the activity coefficient of species j, is constant across the membrane. Then:

$$u_jK_jC_jZ_jF\frac{E_M}{\Delta x} + J_j = -u_jRTK_j\frac{\partial C_j}{\partial x}$$

that is:

$$\frac{Z_jFE_M}{RT\Delta x} \cdot dx = -\frac{K_jdC_j}{\left(K_jC_j + \dfrac{J_j\Delta x}{u_jZ_jFE_M}\right)}$$

For a steady state $\partial C_j/\partial t = 0$ while $\partial C_j/\partial x \neq 0$ because the flux is constant along the membrane. For simplicity, we can consider the mobility u_j of each species to be constant within the membrane. Because of the thickness of the membrane (Δx), Z_j, F, and E_M are all constant. The quantity $(J_j\Delta x/u_jZ_jFE_M)$ becomes a constant. Integrating the last equation from outside of the membrane to the inside we get the following:

$$J_j = J_j^{\text{in}} - J_j^{\text{out}} = \left(\frac{K_j u_j Z_j F E_M}{\Delta x}\right)\left(\frac{1}{e^{Z_i F E_M/RT} - 1}\right)(C_j^o - C_j^i e^{Z_j F E_M/RT})$$

Where J_j^{in} is the influx of species j, J_j^{out} is its efflux, and their difference is the net flux.

The last equation shows that the passive flux of some charged species j depends on its internal and external concentrations and on the electrical potential difference across the membrane.

For most cell membranes, E_M is negative (i.e., the inside of the cell is at a lower electrical potential than is the outside). The sign of J_j depends on the value of C_j^o relative to that of $C_j^i \cdot e^{Z_j F E_M/RT}$, since the product of the terms in the first parenthesis on the right side of the equation is always positive.

When C_j^o is $> C_j^i$, then $e^{Z_i FE_M/RT}$ in the expression in the last parenthesis in the above equation is positive, and a net inward flux of species j occurs ($J_j > 0$). This is similar to the case $(J_j = P_j(C_j^o - C_j^i))$ where P_j is the permeability coefficient of species j, where the electrical effect was absent for neutral solutes. This means that for neutral solutes, $C_j^o > C_j^i$ is adequate to describe the inward movement of species j.

However, knowledge of the concentration difference alone is not sufficient to predict the magnitude or even the direction of the flux of ions; therefore, we must consider the electrical potential difference between the two regions.

Goldman developed an equation that deals with the above discussion and gives the diffusion potential existing across the membrane. For ionic flux consisting of K^+, Na^+, and Cl^-, the cation flux should equal the anionic flux.

$$J_K + J_{Na} - J_{Cl} = 0$$

Introducing the permeability coefficient, $P_j = D_j K_j/\Delta x$; and we know that $J = -D_j \partial C_j/\partial x$, $D_j = u_j RT$, and $K_j u_j RT/\Delta x = K_j D_j/\Delta x$. So, the unknown mobility of species j in a given membrane, the unknown thickness of the membrane, and the partition coefficient for the solute can be replaced by one parameter that describes the permeability properties of that solute crossing that particular membrane.

Then from the last equation, $J_K + J_{Na} - J_{Cl} = 0$ and

$$P_K\left(\frac{1}{e^{FE_M/RT} - 1}\right)(C_K^o - C_K^i e^{FE_M/RT}) + P_{Na}\left(\frac{1}{e^{FE_M/RT} - 1}\right)(C_{Na}^o - C_{Na}^i e^{FE_M/RT})$$

$$+ P_{Cl}\left(\frac{1}{e^{-FE_M/RT} - 1}\right)(C_{Cl}^o - C_{Cl}^i e^{-FE_M/RT}) = 0$$

where Z_K and $Z_{Na} = 1$ and $Z_{Cl} = -1$, and if $\dfrac{1}{e^{FE_M/RT} - 1}$ is canceled from each of the terms for the three net fluxes. Then:

$$P_K C_K^o - P_K C_K^i e^{FE_M/RT} + P_{Na} C_{Na}^o - P_{Na} C_{Na}^i e^{FE_M/RT}$$
$$- P_{Cl} C_{Cl}^o e^{FE_M/RT} + P_{Cl} C_{Cl}^i = 0$$

Then:

$$E_M = \frac{RT}{F} \ln \frac{(P_K \cdot C_K^o + P_{Na} \cdot C_{Na}^o + P_{Cl} \cdot C_{Cl}^i)}{(P_K \cdot C_K^i + P_{Na} \cdot C_{Na}^i + P_{Cl} \cdot C_{Cl}^o)}$$

The last equation is known as Goldman-Hodgkin-Katz equation. Here we assumed independent passive movements of K^+, Na^+, and Cl^- across the membrane, in which $\partial E/\partial x$, γ_j, J_j, and u_j are all constant. Thus this equation gives the electrical potential difference arising from the different tendencies of K^+, Na^+, and Cl^- to diffuse across a membrane to regions of lower chemical potential. The inclusion of divalent and trivalent ions in the derivation of an expression for E_M complicates the calculation considerably; the fluxes of such ions may be rather small because of their small mobility, which makes the last equation adequate for describing the membrane potential. In cases where there are immobile charges inside the cell, the movement of mobile charges will be controlled by the Donnan potential. The Donnan potential is the electrical potential difference associated with immobile or fixed charges in some region adjacent to an aqueous phase containing small mobile ions. The region containing the immobile charges is called the Donnan phase. These charges may be contributed by carboxyl groups in the case of the plant cell wall or due to proteins, DNA, or RNA inside the cells, where there are many carboxyl and phosphate groups from which protons can dissociate, leaving the macromolecules with a net negative charge. Donnan potential thus can be calculated assuming constancy of the chemical potential.

The equilibrium distribution of any ion from the Donnan phase to the aqueous phase extending away from the barrier must satisfy the Nernst potential (E_{N_j}) for that particular ion.

$$E_{N_j} = E^{II} - E^I = (RT/Z_j F) \ln (a_j^I/a_j^{II})$$

The tendency of the mobile ions to diffuse away owing to thermal agitation causes a slight charge separation and thus sets up an electrical potential difference between the Donnan phase and the bulk of the adjacent solution. Assuming a monovalent cation diffusing away from a monovalent immobile barrier, we describe it as

$$E^{II} - E^{I} = (u^{-} - u^{+})/(u^{+} + u^{-}) \cdot (RT/F) \ln (C^{II}/C^{I})$$

Fixed anions have zero mobility $(u^{-} = 0)$; then:

$$E^{II} - E^{I} = -(RT/F) \ln (C^{II}/C^{I})$$

which is simply the Nernst potential for monovalent cations:

$$E^{II} - E^{I} = (RT/F) \ln (C^{I}/C^{II})$$

Thus the Donnan potential can be regarded as a type of diffusion potential occurring as the mobile ions tend to diffuse away from the charges of opposite sign, which remain fixed with the Donnan phase.

Active Transport

Active transport requires three different aspects to describe it, namely, supply of energy, movement, and increase in chemical potential. Active transport is known to involve an energetically uphill movement. Removal of energy such as by using metabolic disruption techniques is the most effective approach to distinguish between active and passive transport. The passive process also can have a rather high temperature coefficient, Q_{10}, if there is an appreciable energy barrier; that is, it will have a marked temperature dependence. Thus, a marked enhancement of solute flux caused by increasing the temperature does not necessarily indicate that active transport is involved. The most reliable way to decide whether there is active or passive transport is to use the Ussing-Teorell equation. In active transport, the initial movement of net charge across the membrane leads to a fairly rapid charging or discharging of the membrane capacitance. So the initial drop in potential across the membrane (ΔE) is much larger in active transport, an effect due to the large net charge (Q) enclosed initially within the cell compared to its capacitance (C):

$$\Delta E = Q/C$$

By determining the influx of an ion and its efflux independently, we may use the Ussing-Teorell equation:

$$\frac{J_{j}^{in}}{J_{j}^{out}} = \frac{C_{j}^{o}}{C_{j}^{i} \cdot e^{Z_{j}FE_{M}/RT}}$$

This relationship is only valid for ions moving passively without interacting with other substances that may also be moving across the membrane. The

Ussing-Teorell equation can thus be used to determine whether the observed influxes and effluxes are passive (i.e., responses to the chemical potentials of the ions on the two sides of the membrane), or whether additional factors such as interactions between species or active transport are involved. In other words, if active transport is involved, then the actual J_j^{in} would be the passive unidirectional flux predicted by the Ussing-Teorell equation plus the influx due to active transport.

From the Ussing-Teorell equation: if we take the logarithms of both sides and multiply by RT,

$$RT\ln\frac{J_j^{in}}{J_j^{out}} = RT\ln\frac{C_j^o}{C_j^i} - Z_jFE_M$$
$$= RT\ln a_j^o + Z_jFE_M^o - RT\ln a_j^i - Z_jFE^i$$
$$= u_j^o - u_j^i$$

A difference in chemical potential of species j across a membrane would cause the flux ratio of the passive fluxes to differ from unity. When $u_j^i = u_j^o$, the electrical potential difference across the membrane is the Nernst potential, E_{N_j}. Thus, E_M equals E_{N_j} for species j, J_j^{in} equals J_j^{out}, and no net passive flux of that ion is expected across the membrane, nor is any energy expended in moving the ion from one side of the membrane to the other. This means that any deviation from the above equation indicates active transport (i.e., energy requirement), or that such ions are not moving independently (i.e., interdependent movement, which is described by irreversible thermodynamics). These equations are satisfactory for explaining the movement of ionic species but are unable to explain the selectivity or competition between those species.

Actual experimental observations in different cells have also shown that the flux of a solute across the cell membrane tends to saturate with increasing concentration after a linear phase up to a certain concentration gradient. In other words, Fick's first law would be applicable only at relatively lower concentrations. Many similar substances show widely different rates of passive movement across the cell membrane, again a deviation from simple passive diffusion. Because passive and active transport could not explain this competition between different substances, the third type of transport (facilitated diffusion) will be discussed in the following section.

Facilitated Diffusion

Competition studies showed that certain solutes are bound to, or associated with, a particular carrier, and there is a competition of similar ions for a carrier binding site. There is a specific carrier to transport K^+ and Na^+, one for Mg^{2+} and Mn^{2+}, one for Ca^{2+} and Sr^{2+}, another for Cl^-, I^-, and Br^-, and so on.

The uptake or influx of ions into the cell is described by the following Michaelis-Menten equation:

$$J_j^{in} = \frac{J_j^{in} \max \cdot C_j^o}{K_j + C_j^o}$$

This means that the influx is dependent on the external concentration of the ion, C_j^o, and also on the affinity of the carrier for that species, j, and the external concentration for half-maximal influx, where $K_j \cdot J_{max}^{in}$ is the maximum influx under infinite external concentration of that species j. A lower K_j means a higher affinity of the carrier for that species; that is, that species j will be efficiently bound even when its external concentration is relatively low, a condition that is observed for active transport. The last equation can describe active transport without the metabolic energy requirement. For a solute to diffuse across the membrane only requires that it be transported by a carrier. This passive entry of a solute mediated by a carrier is termed facilitated diffusion. Some molecules are transported faster than is predicted from their structure or when compared with analogous substances; that is, they are facilitated in diffusing across the membrane. In addition, the net charge is still toward lower chemical potentials, and hence would be in the same direction as ordinary diffusion. Such a facilitation of entry by carriers may also be regarded as a special means of lowering the activation energy needed for the solute to cross the energy barrier represented by the membrane, a situation exactly analogous to enzymatic effects on substrate conversion to products.

Facilitated diffusion has the following characteristics:

1. Net flux is toward lower chemical potentials, whereas active transport is in the energetically uphill direction and can employ the same carriers as facilitated diffusion.
2. Movement in facilitated diffusion is more rapid than expected for ordinary diffusion.
3. The carriers exhibit a high degree of selectivity.
4. Carriers in facilitated diffusion become saturated when the external concentration is raised sufficiently.
5. Competitors, such as those with analogous molecular structure to the species j, can impede diffusion of that species j.

Exchange diffusion describes an increase in both J_j^{in} and J_j^{out} in the undirectional fluxes by a carrier over the values predicted for ordinary diffusion.

In such a case the molecules are interacting with the carrier, and the Ussing-Teorell equation would not be obeyed, since it presupposes that there are no interactions with other substances.

Passive fluxes J_j^{in} are proportional to the external concentration C_j^o for neutral solutes. For ions, it depends on internal and external concentrations C_j^i and C_j^o in addition to the electrical potential difference across the membrane. But this proportionality applies only over the range of external concentrations for which the permeability coefficient is essentially independent of concentration, and the membrane potential must not change in the case of charged solutes. However, the active influx or the facilitated diffusion shows saturation effects at higher concentration, as shown by the Michaelis-Menten equation. Also facilitated diffusion and active transport show both a high degree of selectivity and the competition phenomenon, whereas ordinary diffusion does not.

Passive Permeability

From the foregoing, it is clear that a cell's ionic balance is determined by a combination of passive and active movements of ions. It is likely that the sodium pump operates at a finite rate. So the question arises whether or not there are constraints on upper limits of passive permeability. It appears that fixed positive charges, lipids, and Ca^{2+} are involved in determining membrane permeability. Changes in pH and ionic strength that cause significant alterations in cation permeability can be related to alterations in density of fixed positive charges of the membrane. Metabolic inhibitors (iodoacetate, fluoride, and lead) act synergistically with calcium to increase permeability of K^+. It appears that metabolic inhibitors produce this effect by interfering with the efficient pumping of Ca^{2+}, which is necessary to maintain it at low intracellular levels. Agents that react with membrane sulfhydryl groups (e.g., para-chloromercuribenzene sulfonate) influence the permeability of cations, a situation reversed by cysteine.

A number of cyclic antibiotics are also known to influence the permeability of selective cations. For example, valinomycin stimulates the permeability of K^+ across the membrane but not that of Na^+. It appears that the cyclic antibiotic possesses a hydrophobic outer shell (which facilitates its incorporation into the membrane) and an inner hydrophilic region that allows K^+ but not Na^+ to pass through. Likewise, "ionophores" for other cations are known.

GENERAL PROPERTIES OF THE SODIUM PUMP

With a few exceptions (such as the genetic variant in sheep which have low K^+ in erythrocytes) most mammalian cells have high internal K^+ and low Na^+, a situation maintained in the face of the exact opposite extracellular monovalent cation composition. If the metabolic machinery of the cell were impaired, and this electrochemical gradient were not maintained, K^+ would leak out and Na^+ and water would enter the cell, causing it to swell with eventual total loss of function. As mentioned earlier, in normal cells Na^+ and Cl^- are constantly leaking in and K^+ leaking out. However, in metabolically active cells there is a continuously operating pump that transports Na^+ outward and K^+ inward across the cell membrane. Activity of this Na^+–K^+ pump is regulated by both the internal Na^+ and external K^+, and in most cells that have been rigorously examined, it appears that the movements of Na^+ and K^+ are coupled. The pump shows asymmetry with respect to the actions of Na^+ and K^+; that is, Na^+ acts on the pump internally while K^+ acts on it externally. An important feature of this pump is the process known as "exchange diffusion" whereby external Na^+ (or K^+) can exchange for internal Na^+ (or K^+), a process independent of the electrochemical gradient. The existence of this activity was taken as prima facie evidence for a "carrier" mechanism residing within the membrane. The Na^+–K^+ pump is specifically inhibited by cardiac glycosides (digoxin, digitoxin, strophanthin-G, etc.). It is also inhibited by inhibitors of cellular metabolism, particularly those that impair the production of ATP. The effect on the pump in this case is, of course, indirect (i.e., the lack of availability of energy to drive the pump). Cardiac glycosides (and some other drugs) inhibit the pump without having an effect on cellular energy metabolism.

Nature of Cellular Energy for Transport

A variety of high-energy compounds have been tested as possible sources of energy for the pump system. The techniques include, for example, internal perfusion of nerve, reversible hemolysis of erythrocytes, and so on. In all these experiments it was found that ATP was the most effective compound (compared with other phosphate compounds) in energizing the Na^+–K^+ pump. In utilizing ATP energy for transport, the pump may actually consume an estimated amount as great as 30% of the total cellular ATP. (The mechanism by which this may take place is described in Chapter 4.4.) Female rats injected with ethionine show a drastic reduction in the levels of their liver cell ATP, accompanied by loss of intracellular K^+ with a concomitant rise of Na^+. As mentioned above, anoxia and inhibitors of ATP synthesis will produce similar changes in vitro. Thus, there is little doubt about ATP being the source of energy for the pump. Current estimates suggest that 2–3 Na^+ (and 2 K^+) are transported per high-energy phosphate bond split from ATP.

Reactions of the Na⁺–K⁺ Pump

At least five modes of ion movements can be characterized as mediated by the Na^+–K^+ pump. A crucial test of these pump-linked activities is their sensitivity to the cardiac glycoside ouabain.

Normal Operation of the Pump.   In this mode linked Na^+ and K^+ exchange occurs at the expense of ATP. Studies with red cells and squid axon have shown that 3 Na^+ are exchanged for 2 K^+ per ATP utilized. The unequal amounts of Na^+ and K^+ transported in opposite directions should make the pump "electrogenic." This has been confirmed in nerve and muscle cells. It should also be noted that under certain circumstances a variable coupling ratio between Na^+ and K^+ has been observed.

Reversal of the Na⁺–K⁺ Pump.   If transport of Na^+ out coupled with K^+ into the cell expends ATP, then a reverse process should result in the synthesis of ATP. This has been achieved in studies of transport in red blood cells. By maintaining concentration gradients of Na^+ and K^+ higher than normal and an ATP/(ADP + P) ratio lower than normal, the Na^+–K^+ pump is made to run backward and synthesize ATP. This process is ouabain-sensitive.

Exchange Diffusion of Na⁺ (Na⁺–Na⁺ Exchange).   Experiments with red cells, partially poisoned giant axons, and frog muscle have shown that when these cells are incubated in K^+-free, high Na^+-containing media, they carry out an exchange of intracellular Na^+ with extracellular Na^+. That this is mediated through the Na^+–K^+ pump is indicated by its sensitivity to ouabain and other kinetic characteristics. The process does not utilize ATP, although it shows a requirement for ADP.

Exchange Diffusion of K⁺ (K⁺–K⁺) Exchange.   The presence of K^+–K^+ exchange has been demonstrated in red cells and can take place in the absence of Na^+–K^+ exchange without expenditure of ATP energy, although the presence of ATP (without hydrolysis) seems to be a requirement for this exchange. Unlike Na^+–Na^+ exchange, ADP is not required, but the presence of inorganic phosphate seems essential. It has been estimated that about 20–25% of K^+ entering the cell follow this mode.

Uncoupled Movement of Na⁺.   In red cells, under certain experimental conditions, ouabain-sensitive efflux of Na^+ not accompanied by Na^+ or K^+ movement inward can be demonstrated. This efflux of Na^+ is mediated by the carrier mechanism and involves breakdown of ATP during its operation.

Other Types of Ion Movements

Certain unidirectional fluxes of Na^+ and K^+ may occur but do not depend on the operation of the Na^+–K^+ pump. These fluxes are ouabain-insensitive.

Na^+ sites in the Na^+–K^+ pump appear to be specific for Na^+, which cannot be replaced by any other cation. On the other hand, K^+ sites do not exhibit such a specificity, and K^+ can be replaced by Tl^+, Rb^+, NH_4^+, Cs^+, and Li^+. These cations thus can accumulate in the cell and their intracellular concentration (if they are present as contaminants) would depend on factors such as rate of their uptake and leakiness.

Interaction of Na^+ and K^+ with the Pump

It appears that Na^+ and K^+ interact with the Na^+–K^+ pump in a random fashion. Several models have proposed a sequential or consecutive interaction of cations with the pump. However, other studies indicate that the cations (Na^+ and K^+) interact with the pump in a "simultaneous fashion." Current studies on the mechanism of the pump have not yielded conclusive results to determine a final scheme for the operation of the pump. Whereas certain kinetic studies of the pump favor the simultaneous interaction of cations with the pump, experiments with transport Na^+–K^+–ATPase have yielded results that favor the sequential interaction. (This aspect is discussed further in Chapter 4.4.)

Inhibition of the Na^+–K^+ Pump by Cardiac Glycosides

The number of glycoside binding sites, rapidity of binding, and tightness of binding (reversibility) vary from tissue to tissue. The tissues that have a very active pump (e.g., nerve cells) compared with those with low pump activity (e.g., erythrocytes) have a larger number of binding sites. The tissues that bind ouabain reversibly also show apparent competition between ouabain and K^+. In general, K^+ antagonizes the binding of glycosides, whereas Na^+ promotes it.

Functions of the Na^+–K^+ Pump

It was stated earlier that the Na^+–K^+ pump may have the fundamental function of maintaining high K^+ and low Na^+ levels in the cell. Its role in controlling cell volume has already been discussed. It also has a function in controlling the rates of metabolism of several macromolecules and enzyme reactions. Further, the pump provides the mechanism for generating a potential difference across the membrane. Yet another important role of the Na^+–K^+ pump is in the control of movement of divalent cations (e.g., Ca^{2+}) across the membrane. The active movement of Na^+ and K^+ also provides energy for the transport of nonelectrolytes such as carbohydrates and amino acids. As discussed earlier, some 30% of the cell ATP is used up by the pump.

It can, therefore, provide a mechanism for generation of ADP and P_i in the cell. The responsiveness of the pump to a variety of drugs and hormones may thus result in alterations in cellular metabolism. The calorigenic effect of certain hormones and chemicals may also be mediated through activation or even induction of synthesis of new pump molecules.

SUGGESTED READING

Baker, P. F. 1972. In *Metabolic Pathways,* Vol. VI, *Metabolic Transport,* L. E. Hokin, ed., pp. 243–68. Academic Press, New York.

Edelman, I. S. 1974. In *Drugs and Transport Processes,* B. A. Callingham, ed., pp. 101–10. MacMillan, London.

Glynn, I. M., and Karlish, S. J. D. 1975. *Ann. Rev. Physiol.* 37:13–55.

Judah, J. D., and Ahmed, K. 1964. *Biol. Rev.* 39:160–93.

Kernan, R. P. 1965. *Cell K.* Butterworth, Washington, D.C.

Kotyk, A., and Janacek, K. 1970. *Cell Membrane Transport.* Plenum Press, New York.

Soutter, L. P., and Judah, J. D. 1972. In *Transport and Accumulation in Biological Systems,* E. J. Harris, ed., pp. 347–68. Butterworth, London.

Stein, W. D. 1967. *The Movement of Molecules Across Cell Membranes.* Academic Press, New York.

Ussing, H. H., Erlij, D., and Lassen, U. 1974. *Ann. Rev. Physiol.* 36:17–49.

Whittam, R., and Wheeler, K. P. 1970. *Ann. Rev. Physiol.* 32:21–60.

4.3. Intracellular Calcium Regulation and Transport Leading to Calcium Control of Physiological Processes

James L. Matthews, Carole J. VanderWiel, and Roy V. Talmage

Calcium plays a major regulatory function in all living organisms. So important is its intracellular function that it can be said that any agent regulating the entrance of calcium into cells is itself a major regulator of cellular metabolism. Calcium, as an ion or in an active state, exerts stimulatory or inhibitory effects on most metabolic processes, and through these processes it can bring about specific physiological changes in many tissues. Its ionic concentration is closely regulated intracellularly (10^{-7}M) and extracellularly (10^{-3}M); the activities of calcium are so specific and its influence is so related to slight changes in its concentration that an elaborate system of modulating substances and binding processes has necessarily evolved to achieve its regulation both within the cell and extracellularly. In spite of these close controls, calcium must be transported through cells and moved through extracellular fluids.

Calcium intake may be received from oral ingestion in unregulated and varying amounts. In vertebrates, particularly mammals, most body calcium is stored in bone. Large amounts may be required in localized areas for deposition into bone, while other areas of bone may be releasing it into extracellular fluid. Both the effect of calcium on metabolic activities and its gross physiological functions require cellular activity. Therefore, if we are ultimately to understand its role, the entrance of calcium into cells, its control, storage, and excretion by the cell, and its mode of transcellular movement must be learned. The treatise to follow is our present understanding of how calcium controls the cell and how the cell controls calcium.

CELL CALCIUM

The primary characteristic of interest for calcium is its affinity for forming complexes with organic compounds, particularly proteins. As calcium atoms are added, protein molecular conformation changes, causing the protein to change its function. For example, the addition of the proper number of calcium atoms to a protein may turn an inert molecule into an active enzyme. It is this characteristic of calcium that requires the cell to closely regulate the intracellular ionic concentration of the element. This concentration, in most cells, is about 10^{-7}M, but rises to at least 10^{-6}M in muscle cells when contraction occurs. Calcium concentrations (ionic) on the order of 10^{-5}M cause cell death. Additional nonionic calcium in the cytosol may bring the total calcium content of the typical cell to above 10^{-3}M. In many bone cells and in damaged or unhealthy cells, total calcium content may be much higher. Calcium is distributed throughout the cell as follows:

Calcium in the Cytosol

There is not an even distribution of calcium within the cytoplasm, as several specific organelles (intracellular compartments) possess remarkably high calcium-accumulating capacities, notably the mitochondria and microsomal fraction. Recently, Rose and Loewenstein (24) used the calcium ion–sensitive luminescent protein acqueorin to follow the distribution of calcium in the cytoplasm following a local iontophoretic injection. They found that diffusion throughout the cell was not total; rather, local constraints limited the calcium spread to small regions. These constraints were found to be due primarily to the presence of calcium-accumulating organelles in the injected regions, preventing an overall increase in free calcium ion concentration in the cytosol. As a result, they hypothesized that because of selective ion accumulation, the cell calcium could be effectively compartmentalized, making it possible for variations in local concentrations of calcium ions to serve as discrete signals within the cell.

Calcium not only influences the stiffness of matrices, but also influences the sol–gel phase of protoplasm. Gels such as calcium pectate, calcium casein, blood clots, and protoplasm are stiffened or coagulated by calcium. Eggs of *Chaetopterus* and amoeba cytoplasm have been used to demonstrate the direct influence of calcium on protoplasmic viscosity. Calcium has a diphasic action on sol–gel stiffness; low concentrations cause a decrease in viscosity, whereas larger amounts elicit stiffening. Excessively high levels may inhibit the "coagulation" reaction (13).

Calcium on the Plasma Membrane

Sodium and potassium ion fluxes across cell membranes have been recognized as the principal current carriers in the cell membrane. However, calcium ion fluxes across the membrane and calcium incorporation into the membrane offer major constraints to passage of these other ions (4). Because the calcium–membrane structures are metastable, modification of the calcium distribution significantly alters the constraints to ion flow. Propagation of nerve action potentials, for example, is characterized by a marked transfer of sodium ions across the membrane, due largely to the change in membrane stability (calcium–membrane complex) resulting from an applied stimulus (electrical or neurochemical) (1). Calcium directly affects the permeability of cell membranes. Calcium presumably binds to the head groups of membrane phospholipid molecules, stabilizing the membrane influencing the passage of water, sodium, potassium, and calcium itself. In the latter case, high extracellular Ca^{2+} reduces calcium permeability, and, conversely, low intracellular calcium raises calcium permeability. A major portion of cellular calcium is on the cell membrane.

Two major features of the calcium atom may help explain why its distribution in membranes and other structures may be unique: (1) the ionic radius of nonhydrated calcium and sodium is .95 Å, the radius of magnesium is very small (.65 Å), and that of potassium is large (1.35 Å); (2) X-ray diffraction studies show Mg^{2+} has a coordination number of 6, and Ca^{2+} a number of 7–8. Of great importance is the length of the coordination bonds. Whereas Mg^{2+} bonds are of equal length, making a regular octahedron, coordination bond length and angle vary widely in the calcium atom. Thus, Ca^{2+} can interact in a variety of geometric forms with countless different substances, especially proteins. Magnesium, on the contrary, has a limited capacity for cross-reacting, because of its regularity. Additionally, it should be noted that oxygen atoms, rather than nitrogen, and so on, almost exclusively coordinate the Ca^{2+}, such that the presence of N_2 in a coordination site excludes Ca^{2+} (32, 7).

It is proposed that Ca^{2+} may regulate the interaction of some proteins with their membrane-binding sites, affecting enzymatic functions induced by the complex. Possibly Ca^{2+} influences the membrane structure and function by affecting lipid–lipid, protein–lipid, and protein–protein interaction. This becomes apparent when one studies the more recent models of membrane structure as described by Singer (28).

Calcium and Cell-to-Cell Junctions

The permeability of cell-to-cell junctions is also markedly influenced by calcium (17); the junction permeability illustrated with dyes and other means falls when Ca^{2+} at a junction rises above 5×10^{-5}M to 8×10^{-5}M (24). The protective effect of calcium on membranes is well established, and its influence on holding cells together is also widely demonstrated. As early as 1894, Ringer and Sainsburg (23) recognized that the presence of trace amounts of lime salts served to maintain tissue integrity in solutions. A classic example of this was reported in 1900 by Herbst (14), who described sea urchin eggs pulling apart when calcium was removed. More recent work clearly implicates calcium as an integral part of cell junctions. The incorporation of calcium into membranes not only affects their adherence and permeability, but may, in fact, effect a configurational change in membranes.

Calcium Extrusion from Cells

It is apparent that if cell calcium ion concentrations are low with respect to their surrounding media, an electrochemical gradient exists, which allows calcium to diffuse passively into the cell, but requires metabolic energy for calcium extrusion. Schatzman (27) has reported that the protein responsible for calcium extrusion is an integral part of the inner membrane surface, and its action is dependent upon the presence of ATP and magnesium. The ATP is hydrolyzed in the presence of calcium ion, being a true Ca–Mg–ATPase system (illustrated in the insert in Figure 1). Although the precise

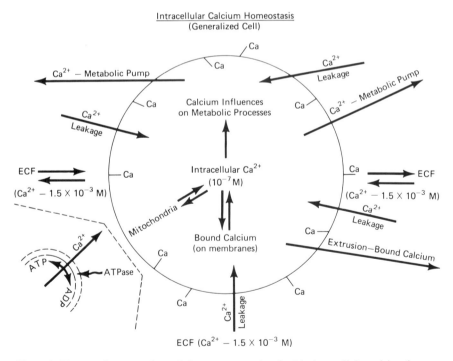

Figure 1. Diagram demonstrating cellular components involved in intracellular calcium homeostasis.

energetics of calcium transport is not established, it is postulated that a conformational change in the membrane proteins following calcium binding on the inner side moves the calcium sufficiently to traverse the hydrophobic parts, attaching it to a low-affinity configuration in the external site.

A second system has been described for calcium ejection from cells of nerve tissue. In this system, a carrier is present in the membrane that exchanges Na^+ for Ca^{2+}. This exchange capability is not surprising when one realizes that the atomic radii variances of length and angle of the two elements are very similar. The transport functions by exchanging one Ca^{2+} ion for three Na^+ ions of the extracellular fluid. This is an electrogenic "pump," as the Na^+ gradient provides the majority of the energy for the pump, although some ATP is needed at the inner membrane surface (2).

Calcium and Mitochondria

One organelle associated with rapid intracellular calcium transport, and one that has received extensive experimental attention, is the mitochondrion (reviewed in Refs. 8 and 16). Calcium incorporation into a mitochondrion occurs against a concentration gradient and is an energy-limited process, dependent upon either electron transport or hydrolysis of ATP. In both types of transport, calcium loading is inhibited by uncouplers of oxidative phosphorylation. Again, the precise mechanism of transport is not fully understood, but Malmstrom and Carafoli (18) suggest that the energy may be responsible for a membrane potential, which may be the driving force for the calcium movement. Clearly, the presence of inorganic phosphate increases the amount of calcium that may be incorporated, owing to the precipitation of the mitochondrial calcium with the phosphate.

Whether significant amounts of calcium are bound directly to mitochondrial membranes has not been established, but studies using pyroantimonate fixation methods employed in the presence of P_i do not produce granules; instead, a pattern forms within the mitochondrion that follows the precise topography of the inner mitochondrial membrane. If one compares the surface area of these membranes with that of the cell membrane, the tremendous capacity of mitochondria in this role is impressive, amounting to 40 m^2/g protein. Carafoli calculates that mitochondria may incorporate 200–300 μmoles Ca^{2+}/g tissue if P_i is present. Whether calcium ion is held within mitochondria without interaction with phosphate ion is being investigated. It is apparent that uncouplers can effect release of calcium from mitochondria as can ionophores, sodium ion, and ruthenium red. Physiologic release can be achieved by cyclic AMP and prostaglandins and is likely influenced by hormones such as PTH and calcitonin. Thus, mitochondria have the capacity to load but, equally important, to unload calcium, providing an intracellular sink.

This function is to maintain an ionic concentration of approximately 10^{-7}M in the cytosol by removing excess amounts during physiologic activities that involve transient rises in cytosolic calcium levels, such as occur in muscle contraction, secretory processes, hormonal responses, calcium transport across epithelia, and so forth. Several authors have suggested that this calcium-sequestrating function of mitochondria may serve an additional function, namely, to provide a means of storing calcium and phosphate in cells prior to the initiative events of matrix mineralization in bone, teeth, and cartilage. Although no direct contribution of mitochondrial content into matrix vesicles of normal mineralizing tissue has been established, several workers have found cells in premineralizing zones of cartilage, antler bone, shells, and so on, to possess mitochondria with an abundance of calcium-phosphate deposits. These workers find fewer deposits in these cells following onset of matrix mineralization, suggesting that the mitochondrial stores find their way into the matrix crystals, possibly contributing to the nucleator itself.

Although mitochondria can unload calcium and phosphate in physiologic conditions, perturbations of the unloading process can lead to excess accumulations. Traumas produced by X-radiation, chemical injury, carbon tetrachloride, and high calcium, and those caused by excesses of dihydrocholecalciferol, bacterial, or viral insult, and so forth, can result in cell calcification, with the mitochondria serving as the first sites of crystal formation.

Calcium and Intracellular Membranes

Numerous internal membranes have been shown to interact with calcium, in addition to the plasma membrane and the mitochondrial system already discussed. The endoplasmic reticulum (19), microsomal fractions (33), and the more intensely studied sarcoplasmic reticulum of striated muscle (11) all bind calcium. This sarcoplasmic reticulum (SR), found surrounding groups of contractile filaments in muscle cells, controls the cytoplasmic calcium ion concentration via an active transport process involving membrane-associated ATPase. Three classes of calcium-binding sites are located on the ATPase molecule, and their different binding affinities and Ca^{2+} sensitivities correlate with regulation of the active membrane pump (15). This system is responsible for modulating the contractile activities by regulating the level of cytosolic calcium ion. Figure 2 shows the SR membranes and filament-related calcium in a contracting muscle. The tissue was fixed in a potassium–pyroantimonate–aldehyde fixation in order to enhance the visualization of aggregated calcium.

Calcium and Intracellular Fibrils, Proteins, and Filaments

Calcium ions also bind selectively to certain sites on cell fibrils. Possibly the best known of these are the filamentous proteins of muscle cells. Calcium

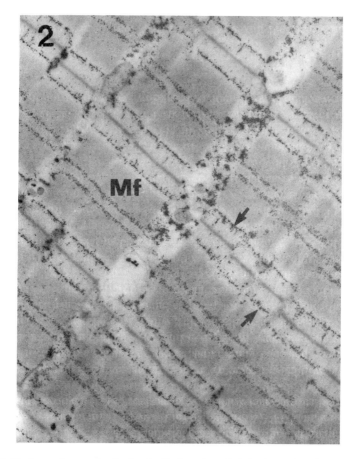

Figure 2. Electron micrograph of a longitudinal section of skeletal muscle. The sarcoplasm is filled with closely packed myofibrils (Mf), and the interstice between these myofibrils is occupied by mitochondria, sarcoplasmic reticulum, and glycogen granules. The arrows indicate an electron-dense pyroantimonate precipitate, which is considered to show localization of calcium. ×12,500.

binds to myosin, actin, and troponin. Troponin (Tn) consists of three subunits: TnC, TnT, and TnI. In this complex, contractile activation involves calcium binding to TnC, resulting in induction of movement of the protein tropomyosin owing to protein–protein interation between the troponin complex and the actin-and-tropomyosin complex. Other sites and proteins with calcium-binding properties are postulated. In contraction, as with many physiologic events involving calcium binding, it is apparent that the calcium binding elicits a specific response. Thus, binding to intracellular structures represents more than simple storage of an element; indeed, it becomes the signal initiating event of a sequence of cell activities. In the case of muscle, this coupling of calcium release from SR to select binding on filament acceptor sites and the consequent contractile response is called "excitation-contraction coupling." This subject was recently reviewed in a symposium edited by Carafoli (6).

Microfilaments are not limited to muscle tissue; some are found in most cells. These filaments function in a variety of cell processes, including organ morphogenesis, cytokinesis, cell motility, ion transport, cell-inclusion movement, and so forth. Interestingly, histochemical and immuno-specific techniques have shown these filaments to be comparable, if not identical, to certain muscle proteins, including those that have select calcium-binding affinities. It is postulated that the activation of these filaments might also be calcium-coupled.

Microtubules, which are also ubiquitous in cells, serve as components of cell stroma and mitotic spindles and are found in cilia and flagella and in association with secretory granules. Calcium apparently plays a signal role for activation of microtubule protein, but the exact mechanism is not known. It has been suggested that calcium enhances organization of tubule subunits. Goodman et al. (12) have proposed that microtubules are activated by calcium following phosphorylation of the tubulin, initiated by a cyclic AMP–dependent protein kinase. Kinases with this property have been found in several tissues, including the adrenal and the pancreas. In fact, the presence of microtubules, calcium, and cyclic AMP appears to be a common feature of most secretory tissues.

Control of Intracellular Ionic Calcium Concentrations

From the above discussion, it is obvious that the cell must have specific systems for ensuring a proper ionic calcium level. The primary control of the level apparently resides in the mitochondria. However, because calcium diffuses passively into cells, methods must be available to expel the ion, to tie it up in an inactive state, or to excrete it as a complex. For a simple diagram of intracellular calcium control, refer back to Figure 1.

TRANSCELLULAR CALCIUM TRANSPORT

It is well recognized that there are cell layers across which calcium must be rapidly transported (i.e., gut epithelial cells, kidney cells, mammary glands, and the placental barrier). The intracellular calcium levels of these cells are significantly lower than that in their bathing fluids, so calcium enters the cell via passive diffusion. Transcellular movement becomes a problem of moving the calcium that entered the cell out through at least one surface of the cell against a concentration gradient.

Transcellular calcium movement through gut epithelium serves to illustrate the extent of our knowledge of this problem. Calcium transport in the gut could traverse two pathways: (1) Calcium could potentially pass through the tight junctions between adjacent epithelial cells. (This junction has been found to be leaky, and elements such as lanthanum have been observed in these clefts.) Movement by this method must be down a calcium-diffusion gradient. (2) Calcium could pass through the epithelial cells. The second option seems to be the more significant pathway, as it can occur against a transcellular gradient.

Calcium absorption is stimulated by vitamin D and its metabolites, vitamin D taking several hours to enhance absorption, while 1,25-$(OH)_2D_3$ enhances absorption more rapidly. This suggests that vitamin D first influences a cell metabolic event that facilitates transcellular calcium movement (9). Even this most active vitamin D metabolite involves a few hours' delay in absorption. Vitamin D and its metabolites behave as steroids and selectively concentrate in the nuclei of the transporting cells. It is now established that some transcriptional event takes place, with the result that proteins are synthesized within the target cells. At least two proteins are produced in gut epithelial cells in response to vitamin D. One of them is the "calcium-binding protein" (CaBP), described by Wasserman and Taylor (31). This protein is vitamin D–dependent and is secreted by goblet cells forming a calyx over gut cell microvilli. The role this protein plays in transcellular movement is unknown. The second vitamin D–dependent protein formed is an actin-like substance that may serve as a cell calcium acceptor in the terminal web region of the cell. Cell organelles are separated from the luminal plasma membrane by filaments of the terminal web. Figure 3 is an electron micrograph of gut epithelial cells showing the junctional complex uniting the cells at their apical borders, a narrow intercellular space, and the terminal web filaments extending into the microvilli.

Recently, vesicles derived from the Golgi complex have been described in gut absorptive cells. These vesicles contain a lipoprotein that binds calcium. The *hypothesized* route is that calcium enters at the microvillus membrane and complexes with actin-like filaments of the terminal web. It dissociates from these filaments to enter vesicles for movement to the lateral cell membrane, where calcium is released into the intercellular channel following fusion of the vesicles' membrane with the plasma membrane. Such a method for calcium movement reduces the danger of high intracellular ionic calcium levels and the heavy requirement for energy needed to extrude calcium via an ATPase system. Whether or not the system postulated for gut applies to other transporting epithelia is not known.

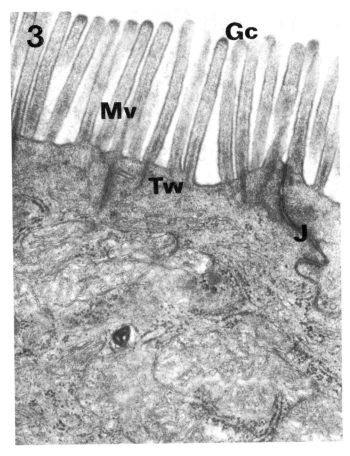

Figure 3. Electron micrograph of a longitudinal section of the apical part of an intestinal epithelial columnar cell and its microvilli (Mv). At the lumen surface, a thin cloud of electron-dense material, the glycocalyx (Gc), surrounds the microvilli. The microvilli contain filaments which are extensions of the filaments of the terminal web (Tw). The junction (J) between two cells is seen at the right of the figure. ×25,000

CALCIUM MOVEMENT INTO BONE

Transport of calcium between bone and ECF or vice versa presents a unique problem. Bone surface is covered with a single layer of cells (the osteoblasts or "bone-lining cells") that are closely approximated and are somewhat inter-digitated along their lateral borders. This is diagrammatically illustrated in area C of Figure 4. No junctional complexes are present, however, and studies using tracers such as horseradish peroxidase (a protein of 50,000 molecular weight) have clearly shown that these tracers can leave the blood vessels and enter the bone fluid by passing between the lining cells. It is possible

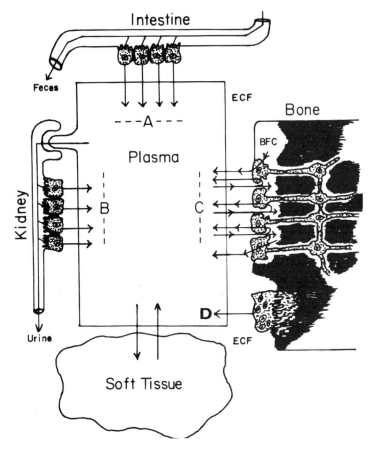

Figure 4. Diagram demonstrating the sites of control of plasma calcium concentrations: (A) Intestinal absorption of calcium. (B) Renal excretion and reabsorption of calcium. (C) Calcium fluxes into and out of bone fluid. (D) Osteoclastic bone resorption.

that bone mineral stores may diffuse out into the surrounding ECF because of the intercellular clefts. However, since the ECF is believed to be supersaturated relative to bone fluid, net diffusion should be only in one direction, that is, into bone (21). Also, considerable data from animals prelabeled with isotopic calcium and phosphate have shown that the plasma ratio of labeled Ca/P_i following bone mineral mobilization with PTH and other substances does not reflect a diffusion of molar amounts of apatite Ca and P_i. Similarly, the separation of the hypophosphatemic and hypocalcemic response of animals to calcitonin also argues against a simple equilibrium and diffusion between bone fluid and ECF. However, diffusion between these two compartments must play a significant role. The question yet to be fully answered is: "Can outward diffusion of calcium between lining cells occur under physiological conditions, or does outward flux of calcium occur only *through* these lining cells?" Certainly calcium can enter bone fluid via the intercellular route, as suggested by the influx arrows in area C of Figure 4. If such transcellular calcium efflux occurs, the precise mechanism for its extrusion through the plasma membrane against a concentration gradient is not known. Could a system such as that discussed for gut epithelium exist also in bone cells? Or could a sodium channel mechanism, as found in nerve cells, or the Ca/ Mg ATP of erythrocyte membranes be involved? As these lining cells change cell shape and arrangement markedly following hormonal stimulus, credence for a functional bone cell membrane has been established. However, the relationship of this "membrane" to transcellular movement of calcium is not yet established. A possible schema for the exchange of ions between bone fluid and ECF has been presented by Talmage (29).

GENERAL PHYSIOLOGICAL EFFECTS OF CALCIUM

From the preceding brief citation of cell structures that have precise mechanisms for binding, transporting, or storing calcium, and the knowledge of the function of the structures involved, calcium coupling seems to be a general cell-trigger mechanism. It is clear that the provision for compartmentalization of calcium atoms within cells and the mechanisms for regulation of calcium fluxes between the inside of cells and their exterior milieu permit a system whereby redistribution of calcium between these compartments can be used to activate or control most of the basic physiologic processes, including irritability, contractility, conductivity, secretion, reproduction, and integration. Only the briefest review can be given here. For a general discussion of the influence of calcium on intercellular metabolism, a review by Talmage et al. (30) is recommended. For a more technical review of ion interactions intracellularly, the review by Rasmussen et al. (22) is suggested.

Excitation-Contraction Coupling

Excitation-contraction coupling has been described in all muscle types (skeletal, cardiac, and smooth). A discussion of calcium and troponin has already been given. Needless to say, calcium release into the cytosol and its coupling with muscle proteins is basic to the contractile process. For a general review, a paper by Murray and Weber (20) is recommended.

Excitation-Conduction Coupling

Calcium-excitation-conduction coupling has been demonstrated in nerve tissue. In this case, it is postulated that calcium enters the neuron following membrane permeability changes initiated by the propagated membrane depolarization. Calcium then is believed to enhance the probability that the synaptic vesicles will stick to the membrane and discharge. The role of calcium ions in neural processes has been reviewed by Rubin (25).

Excitation-Secretion Coupling

The clear establishment of the need for calcium in the "release" of vesicular materials within various nerve cells led Douglas (10) to postulate the presently accepted concept of excitation-secretion coupling. It has been presumed that the secretory product is invested in a membrane vesicle prior to secretion and that calcium in some way influences the fusion of the vesicle to the secretory face of the cell, resulting in expulsion of secretory product. The mechanism is not fully understood and may vary in different cell types. It is possible that calcium modifies the surface of the vesicle or a site on the plasma membrane that causes a fusion between the two units. Calcium could change the electrostatic properties of the vesicle, reducing expulsion from the plasma membrane. However, this would not explain the blocking actions of other divalent cations such as magnesium. Another hypothesis is that calcium causes a configurational change in the microfilament–microtubular system providing for the translocation and extrusion of granules. The extrusion process may be related to the calcium activation of ATPase situated on the membranes of many secretory granules. Secretory-granule-associated calcium may represent intracellular stores that are released following receptor site activation by a secretogogue. In this respect, it has been suggested that cyclic AMP may be effective in secretory mechanisms by enhancing the mobilization of calcium from stores, such as mitochondria, or by increasing the rate of entry of calcium into the cell, although this has not been clearly established in secretory cells. (See Ref. 25, 26.)

Stimulus-Secretion Coupling

In addition to enhancement of secretion of vesicle-bound materials, data now support the concept that calcium may couple secretion of other, nonvesicular materials such as glucose and vitamin D metabolites. The secretion of these substances is more closely related to the rates of synthesis of the product; so the term "stimulus-synthesis coupling" might be a better term than "secretion coupling."

Enzymatic-Activation Coupling

The intracellular ionic calcium concentration determines the activity of most if not all enzymes. The calcium concentration for optimal enzyme activity is characteristic of the enzyme. Therefore, changes in intracellular calcium concentrations may shift the activity of enzymes, suppressing some while stimulating others. Calcium can be considered a second messenger, and any agent that influences calcium entry into cells may, through calcium, influence cell metabolism. The list of enzymes studied that are sensitive to discrete changes in calcium concentration is constantly growing. The enzymes involved include those that regulate energy production by activating glycogenolysis, by affecting electron transport, and many others, as recently reviewed by Rasmussen et al. (22).

Other Systems

Other special systems await elucidation. Among these recently considered are excitation of visual cells (5). In that very specialized organ the eye, light stimulation compared to dark adaption results in marked alteration of calcium within the end element of the retinal rods of the frog retina. In this case, an action potential results from the calcium translocation, the opposite of events in peripheral nerve excitation-conduction coupling. Discrete loci for calcium are found in several other cell types, including platelets. The granules in these cells may be changed in the presence of serotonin and are affected by aspirin and ADP levels. Calcium localization in activated lymphocytes and in histamine-stimulated parietal cells is also established. Its role in other special sense organs and in other tissues and cell types is presently under investigation.

EXTRACELLULAR CALCIUM HOMEOSTASIS

This chapter has dealt with problems of intracellular calcium control and function. However, intracellular calcium is influenced by extracellular concentrations. Therefore, a brief review of the control of plasma calcium concentrations will conclude this review (illustrated in Figure 4).

Ionic calcium concentrations in extracellular fluid are closely maintained at 1.5×10^{-3}M. In plasma, almost an equal amount is bound to proteins. The primary necessity for this close regulation appears to be the health of cell membranes, most obvious in nervous and muscular tissue. There are three primary calcium-regulating hormones: 1,25-dihydroxycholecalciferol ($1,25(OH)_2D_3$), parathyroid hormone (PTH), and calcitonin (CT). Many other hormones and agents can influence the control of plasma calcium levels indirectly, but their effects are compensated for by changes in the activity of one of the three listed hormones. Calcium control is a coordination of hormones at multiple sites as diagrammed in Figure 4. The hormone $1,25(OH)_2D_3$ can be considered the basic conditioning hormone; PTH is the most sensitive to minor fluctuations in calcium; the function of CT is still not clearly understood, but it is thought to prevent temporary hypercalcemia (a rare occurrence) and to aid in storage of calcium.

The active metabolite $1,25(OH)_2D_3$ increases intestinal absorption of calcium and acts on most bone cells (areas A, C, and D in Figure 4). In case C, its conditioning action appears necessary for the more rapid action of PTH. Its primary role in extracellular calcium homeostasis appears to be to regulate the supply of calcium entering extracellular fluid. The basic action of the metabolite may be to increase membrane permeability to calcium.

Parathyroid hormone is the primary regulator of the level of calcium in plasma and the extracellular fluid (ECF). Its secretion is controlled by a negative feedback with plasma ionic calcium concentrations. Because the parathyroid gland responds rapidly to small changes in ionic calcium, and because the action of the hormone is rapid, all actions of PTH can be considered to be related to the task of extracellular calcium control. PTH acts on the kidney to increase tubular reabsorption of calcium and to decrease tubular reabsorption of phosphate (area B in Figure 4). It also increases renal hydroxylation of vitamin D_3 to the $1,25(OH)_2D_3$ metabolite, thereby stimulating the actions of this metabolite in gut and bone. In bone, PTH also has at least two functions. It acts on bone lining cells and associated osteocytes to regulate calcium fluxes into and out of bone (area C in Figure 4). The exact mechanism by which this is accomplished is not completely understood, but it is believed that this is the most important action of PTH in setting plasma calcium concentrations. The other action of PTH in bone is to increase the rate of bone turnover (area D in Figure 4). This action will temporarily provide calcium through bone resorptive mechanisms. If a sufficient dietary source of calcium is not available, the bone resorptive action of PTH will eventually provide the primary source of calcium for plasma.

Calcitonin is a hormone whose function is still not clearly delineated. Its secretion can be stimulated by raising plasma calcium concentrations. However, in mammals the primary effort required is to keep plasma calcium levels from falling. Therefore, in both normal and pathological situations, the role of CT as an antihypercalcemic agent appears minor. Recent studies suggest that its secretion is related to digestive processes and that a role for this hormone is to store calcium in a labile form during the intestinal calcium absorptive phase (in area C in Figure 4). Unfortunately, this concept has not yet been established, and some investigators consider calcitonin to be a vestigial hormone, at least in humans.

Addendum. Since this report was prepared, research in the control of intracellular calcium and the control by calcium of cell metabolism has received an impetus by identification of and studies on the calcium binding protein, calmodulin. It is suggested that interested readers refer to the report by W. Y. Cheung, "Calmodulin plays a pivotal role in cellular regulation," *Science* 207:19, 1980 and to the published symposium on Calcium Pumps, A. N. Martonosi, Chairman, in *Federation Proceedings* **39**:2401–2441, 1980.

REFERENCES

1. Baker, P. F. 1972. *Prog. Biophys. Mol. Biol.* 24:177.
2. Baker, P. F. 1976. In *Calcium in Biological Systems,* C. J. Duncan, ed., p. 67. Cambridge University Press, Cambridge.
3. Borle, A. B. 1967. *Clin. Orthop. Res.* 52:267.
4. Brink, F. 1954. *Pharm. Rev.* 6:243–95.
5. Brown, J. E., and Blinks, J. R. 1974. *J. Gen. Physiol.* 64:643.
6. Carafoli, E. 1975. In *Calcium Transport and Secretion,* E. Carafoli, ed. Elsevier/North Holland, Amsterdam.
7. Carafoli, E 1977. In *Living Systems as Energy Converters,* R. Buvet et al., eds., p. 153. Elsevier/North Holland, Amsterdam.
8. Carafoli, E., Crompton, K., Malmstrom, K., Sigel, E., Salzmann, M., Chiesi, M., and Affolter, H. 1977. In *Biochemistry of Membrane Transport,* G. Simenza and E. Carafoli, eds. Springer-Verlag, Heidelberg.
9. DeLuca, H. F. 1976. In *Handbook of Physiology,* G. D. Aurbach, ed., Sec. 7, Endocrinology, Vol. VII, p. 265. Williams and Wilkins, Baltimore.
10. Douglas, W. W. 1974. *Biochem. Soc. Symp.* 39:1–28.
11. Ebashi, S., and Endo, M. 1968. *Prog. Biophys.* 18:125.
12. Goodman, D. B. P., Rasmussen, H., and Guthrow, C. E. 1970. *Proc. Natl. Acad. Sci.* 67:652.
13. Heilbrunn, L. V. 1930. In *An Outline of General Physiology,* 3rd ed., p. 530. W. B. Saunders Co., Philadelphia.
14. Herbst, B. 1900. *Arch. Entwicklungsmech.* 9:424.
15. Ikemoto, N. 1976. In *Calcium Transport in Contraction and Secretion,* E. Carafoli, ed., p. 289. North Holland, Amsterdam.
16. Lehninger, A. L. 1970. *Biochem. J.* 119:129.
17. Lowenstein, W. R. 1966. *Ann. N. Y. Acad. Sci.* 137:708.
18. Malmstrom, K., and Carafoli, E. 1975. *Arch. Biochem. Biophys.* 171:418.
19. Meisde, L., Rubin-Altschul, B., and Machado, R. D. 1970. *J. Biol. Chem.* 245:1883.
20. Murray, J. M., and Weber, A. 1974. *Sci. Am.* 230:581.
21. Neuman, W. F., and Neuman, M. W. 1958. In *The Chemical Dynamics of Bone Mineral.* University of Chicago Press, Chicago.
22. Rasmussen, H., Goodman, D., Friedmann, N., Allen, J., and Kurokawa, K. 1976. In *Handbook of Physiology,* R. Greep and E. Astwood, eds., p. 225. Williams and Wilkins, Baltimore.
23. Ringer, S., and Sainsburg, G. 1894. *J. Physiol.* 16:1.
24. Rose, B., and Lowenstein, W. R. 1975. *Science* 190:1204–6.
25. Rubin, R. P. 1970. *Pharm. Rev.* 22:389–428.
26. Rubin, R. P. 1974. In *Calcium and the Secretory Process,* p. 89. Plenum Press, New York.
27. Schatzmann, H. J. 1976. In *Calcium Transport in Contraction and Secretion,* E. Carafoli, ed., pp. 45–52. North Holland, Amsterdam.
28. Singer, S. J. 1972. *Science* 175:720.
29. Talmage, R. V. 1970. *Am. J. Anat.* 129:467.
30. Talmage, R. V., Cooper, C., and Park, H. 1970. In *Vitamins and Hormones,* Vol. 28, p. 103. Academic Press, New York.
31. Wasserman, R. H., and Taylor, A. N. 1966. *Science* 152:791–93.
32. Williams, R. J. P. 1976. In *Calcium in Biological Systems,* G. J. Duncan, ed. Cambridge University Press, Cambridge.
33. Yoshida, H., Kadota, K., and Fujisawa, H. 1966. *Nature* 212:291.

4.4. Na⁺, K⁺-ATPase

Khalil Ahmed

During the past 20 or so years considerable progress has been made in establishing the biochemical basis of cation transport across the cell membrane. The discovery by Skou in 1957 of an ATPase in crab nerve microsomal preparation led the way for these studies. This ATPase system requires the combined action of Na^+ and K^+ for maximal activity, and a large body of research now suggests that this enzyme system represents the biochemical basis of the Na^+ and K^+ pump. This ATPase, localized in the cell membrane, is referred to as "Na^+,K^+–ATPase" or "transport ATPase."

Na⁺,K⁺-ATPase AND THE Na⁺ PUMP

That Na^+,K^+–ATPase represents the enzymic basis of the Na^+ pump is suggested by a large number of observations, some of which can be summarized as follows:

1. The enzyme is localized in the membrane.
2. Its maximal activity is achieved in the presence of Mg^{2+} + Na^+ + K^+ when Na^+ and K^+ are present at concentrations that support maximal rates of transport in the intact cell.
3. ATP is utilized as the substrate.
4. Asymmetry is shown toward Na^+ and K^+. The former acts from the inside, while K^+ acts from the outside of the membrane.
5. The enzyme is inhibited by cardiac glycosides, which are specific inhibitors of the sodium pump. Both the ATPase and the pump show similar sensitivity to cardiac glycosides and other inhibitors of transport.
6. The action of cardiac glycosides also demonstrates asymmetry (i.e., it acts from the outside of the membrane).
7. ATP acts from the inside surface of the membrane.
8. Cells with low K^+, as in the LK variety of sheep erythrocyte, contain low Na^+,K^+–ATPase in the membrane.
9. The rate of operation of ATPase is commensurate with that of the pump.

10. An ATP-dependent, ouabain-inhibitable Na^+ transport has been demonstrated in vesicles reconstituted from purified Na^+,K^+–ATPase preparations.

GENERAL PROPERTIES OF Na^+,K^+–ATPase

The overall ATPase reaction requires Mg^{2+} as an essential divalent cation. Of the various nucleoside triphosphates, ATP is the most effective, and only a small activity is observed in the presence of CTP, UTP, GTP, and ITP. Both ADP and P_i, which are products of ATP hydrolysis, inhibit the enzyme activity, so that the linearity of the ATPase reaction is generally lost when about 10% of the ATP is hydrolyzed. In the presence of Mg^{2+} and Na^+, and the absence of K^+, a small amount of ATPase activity is observed which is insensitive to ouabain. This activity is not a part of the Na^+,K^+–ATPase and is largely eliminated during purification of the enzyme. Working with partially purified preparations, however, this activity must be subtracted from the total activity observed in the presence of $Mg^{2+} + Na^+ +K^+$ to calculate the Na^+,K^+-dependent activity. The optimal ratio of Na^+ and K^+ is about $10:1$ (e.g., 100 mM Na^+ to 10 mM K^+), whereas for Mg^{2+} and ATP, it is $1:1$. At higher concentrations of ATP, substrate inhibition is observed. Divalent cations other than Mg^{2+} tend to inhibit the reaction when added with Mg^{2+}, or substitute very poorly for Mg^{2+}. The various ligands appear to interact with the enzyme system in a random fashion; that is, no specific order of binding is necessary for the operation of the enzyme. The requirement for Na^+ is specific in that other monovalent cations do not substitute for it; however, several other monovalent cations, including NH_4^+, Li^+, Rb^+, Cs^+, or Tl^+, can substitute for K^+ with varying degrees of efficacy in the ATPase reaction in vitro.

Associated with the Na^+,K^+–ATPase preparations is the K^+-dependent phosphatase. This activity is inhibited by Na^+ or ATP, and can utilize a number of substrates such as p-nitrophenyl phosphate and acyl phosphates. This activity appears to be an integral part of the Na^+,K^+–ATPase system for several reasons: (1) its kinetics are commensurate with those of the ATPase; (2) the activity is inhibited by cardiac glycosides; (3) inactivation of ATPase results in loss of K^+–phosphatase activity. The K^+-dependent phosphatase appears to represent the terminal phosphatase activity involving K^+ (see also later in this chapter).

A variety of drugs and chemicals inhibit the activity of the enzyme. Cardiac glycosides are highly specific inhibitors of the sodium pump and are equally effective toward Na^+,K^+–ATPase. This inhibition is an important criterion to establish a given ATPase activity as being related to Na^+,K^+–ATPase. A variety of antibiotics, antihistamines, fatty acids, mercaptans, piperazine derivatives, and sulfhydryl blocking agents such as n-ethylamaleimide (NEM) block the activity of Na$^+$,K$^+$–ATPase.

PURIFICATION AND SUBUNIT COMPOSITION

Na$^+$,K$^+$–ATPase is a lipoprotein in nature and is deeply embedded in the membrane. Hence, its purification has been tedious. For most tissues, a microsomal preparation is a convenient starting material; Na$^+$,K$^+$–ATPase in this fraction is derived from membranes that sediment along with microsomes. Two main approaches to its purification have been used. In the first case, use is made of an ionic detergent such as sodium dodecyl sulfate or deoxycholate, which can remove extraneous membrane proteins, leaving behind a fairly purified enzyme preparation, which can then be subjected to density gradient centrifugation to effect additional purification. These procedures have been successful with a variety of tissues as the source of enzyme. In the second case, all the membrane proteins are solubilized by using a nonionic detergent such as Lubrol WX, and the enzyme is then fractionally precipitated out by the usual techniques. An important factor in achieving success in either of the above approaches is to use a highly active tissue source of the enzyme, for example, outer renal medulla, the electric organ of the electric eel *(Electrophorus electricus)*, or the rectal salt gland of the spiny dogfish shark. In some of these preparations a treatment of the starting microsomal preparation with a solution of NaI of fairly high concentration has also been utilized. Based on the method of calculation, these enzyme preparations appear to be 65 to 95% pure.

The purified Na$^+$,K$^+$–ATPase, when subjected to SDS–polyacrylamide gel electrophoresis, yields two polypeptides. The larger one has a molecular weight of 84,000 to 139,000, whereas the smaller one (a glycoprotein) has a molecular weight in the range of 35,000 to 57,000. The exact molar ratio of the two subunits in the enzyme is not settled upon, and estimates range from 1:2, to 1:1, to 2:1 (the estimated molecular weight of the Na$^+$,K$^+$–ATPase is of the order of 250,000).

The larger polypeptide undergoes phosphorylation (in the presence of Mg^{2+} + Na$^+$ + ATP), but the function of the glycoprotein subunit is not clear (see also later).

As stated earlier, the purified enzyme contains lipids which appear to be essential for its activity. Different lipids have been shown to cause activation of the "delipidated" enzyme preparations. However, the divergence of results in this area may reflect inadequate removal of all the bound lipids, and/or irreversible denaturation of the enzyme protein during procedures employed for delipidation of the enzyme. Among the various lipids that have been shown to reactivate (or stimulate) the activity of delipidated Na$^+$,K$^+$–ATPase preparations are cholesterol, phosphatidylserine, phosphatidylcholine, diphos-phatidylglycerol, or phosphatidyl-inositol. Several investigators have found phosphatidyl serine to be the activating lipid, although it seems that any acidic lipid may serve the function. A high sulfatide content has also been reported in some preparations. The precise role of phospholipids in the operation of the Na^+,K^+–ATPase is not clear. It is speculated that they may provide a lipid matrix for the enzyme, or hydrophobic regions, or alter the negative charge, or even be part of the active center providing ion specificity.

OPERATION OF Na^+,K^+–ATPase

The mechanism of operation of Na^+,K^+–ATPase is not fully established, although much information on the subject has been gained during the past 18 years. If this enzyme system is part of the sodium pump, a precise knowledge of the ATPase reaction would be central to an understanding of the pump mechanism.

It appears that Na^+,K^+–ATPase undergoes sequential phosphorylation and dephosphorylation during its interaction with Na^+ and K^+, respectively. In the presence of $Mg^{2+} + Na^+$, γ-^{32}P-ATP transfers ^{32}P to the enzyme (in the large polypeptide). The phosphoenzyme (E-P) formed exists in two conformations (i.e., E_1-P and E_2-P). Mg^{2+} tends to promote E_1-P $\rightarrow$ E_2-P transition. These two forms of the phosphoenzyme are chemically identical. The phosphate is primarily on the β-aspartyl residue. The E_1-P form of the enzyme can react with ADP to cause its breakdown, whereas the E_2-P form reacts with K^+ to yield $E_2 + P_i$. With the conversion of E_2 to E_1, the whole cycle is restarted. The promotion of E_2 to E_1 is mediated by ATP, Na^+, or solvents which tend to remove H_2O from the active center. The foregoing reactions can be summarized as follows:

$$E + ATP \xrightleftharpoons{Mg^{2+} + Na^+} E_1\text{-}P$$

$$E_1\text{-}P \xrightleftharpoons{Mg^{2+}} E_2\text{-}P$$

$$E_2\text{-}P \xrightleftharpoons{K^+ + H_2O} E_2 + P_i$$

$$E_2 \rightleftharpoons E_1$$

The K^+-dependent phosphatase activity (discovered by Judah, Ahmed, and McLean), for example, toward p-nitrophenyl phosphate (or other acyl phosphates), appears to reflect the terminal K^+-dependent phosphoenzyme in the above reactions. Besides this K^+-dependent partial reaction, Na^+-dependent ADP–ATP exchange, and $Mg^{2+} + K^+$–dependent $P_i \rightleftharpoons HOH$ exchange have also been reported. It should be pointed out that although a large body of evidence supports the foregoing reaction schemes in the ATPase operation, this view is by no means accepted by all the investigators. For details of other schemes, the reviews cited in the suggested reading should be consulted.

The Na$^+$,K$^+$-ATPase theoretically should be reversible. The reversibility of the various individual steps is indicated by the partial reactions, such as ADP–ATP exchange, exchange of ^{18}O between P$_i$ and H–^{18}O–H, and P$_i$–ATP exchange. By using ^{32}P and appropriate ionic conditions, Na$^+$,K$^+$–ATPase was shown to yield ^{32}P-labeled ATP due to synthesis.

CATION-ACTIVATION SITES AND ROLE OF WATER

Both Na$^+$ and K$^+$ are needed for the activation of Na$^+$,K$^+$–ATPase. Kinetic analyses of Na$^+$ and K$^+$ binding sites have been carried out. These kinetics have been expressed as allosteric models with changing affinities for various cations. A larger number of investigators have favored the multiple-site models with distinct sites for Na$^+$ and K$^+$ with a certain amount of interdependence between them. This interpretation is suggested by the sigmoidal nature of the cation activation curves, and the competitive relationship between Na$^+$ and K$^+$.

It appears that 2 to 3 Na$^+$ are required for the activation of the ATPase. Kinetic analysis of the overall reaction has suggested these multiple Na$^+$ activation sites to be equivalent. Under certain conditions, it appears that the activating Na$^+$ may be of a nonequivalent nature. This possibility, however, needs to be further analyzed. It may be noted that the kinetic analyses do not distinguish between equivalent and nonequivalent site models. Likewise, two activation sites for K$^+$ have been reported. These sites may be nonequivalent; however, the same reservation as the above applies to the nature of these sites.

Among the various factors that may influence cation activation sites (e.g., lipids, pH, temperature) can be included solvent water (as opposed to substrate) playing a modulating role in the Na$^+$ and K$^+$ interaction with the ATPase. A number of studies have utilized different solvents (e.g., deuterated water, ^{2}H$_2$O, dimethylsulfoxide, alcohol, acetone, etc.). Some of these solvents inhibit the Na$^+$-dependent phosphoenzyme formation (e.g., ^{2}H$_2$O, dimethylsufoxide) while stimulating the K$^+$-dependent phosphatase activity. On the other hand, solvents such as acetone stimulate the Na$^+$-dependent phosphoenzyme formation while inhibiting the K$^+$-dependent phosphatase step. The role of water, from these studies, may be interpreted in terms of controlling the hydrophobicity–hydrophilicity at the active center of the ATPase. Removal of H$_2$O from the active center seems to be necessary for Na$^+$-activation of phosphoenzyme formation (and promotion of the E$_1$-P form of the phosphoenzyme). The increased hydrophobicity (due to removal of H_2O) would then tend to stabilize the phosphoenzyme and prevent its spontaneous breakdown. The interaction of K^+, on the other hand, is favored by H_2O, suggesting that the breakdown of K to E_2-P may occur in a hydrophilic region of the active center where E_2-P is hydrolyzed. Stimulation of this step by ^2H_2O and dimethylsulfoxide suggests that H_2O would tend to favor the shift of the E_1-P to the E_2-P form. This interpretation also offers an explanation for the increased affinity of K^+ for the ATPase at reduced temperatures if one considers that the enzyme complex favors the E_2 conformation at lower temperatures owing to an increase in bound H_2O and/or stronger H bondings, whereas at higher temperatures the opposite may be the case (i.e., the E_1 conformation is favored).

Solvent studies have further supported the role of phosphoenzyme in the overall reaction scheme of the ATPase, and have also provided clear evidence for a random mechanism of action of various ligands in the operation of the ATPase.

ACTION OF DRUGS ON Na$^+$,K$^+$–ATPase

Numerous chemicals and drugs have been found to inhibit the Na$^+$,K$^+$–ATPase. They may inhibit the enzyme activity by acting at one or more of the partial reactions of the ATPase. Many drugs have been suggested to produce their in vivo pharmacological effects via an influence on the ATPase (e.g., the action of mercurial diuretics). A number of membrane-active compounds (such as antihistamines, chlorpromazine, quinidines) inhibit the enzyme activity to varying degrees. Sulfhydryl blocking agents such as n-ethylmaleimide or p-chloromercuribenzoate inhibit the enzyme.

However, the most specific inhibitors of Na$^+$,K$^+$–ATPase are the cardiac glycosides. Much current work suggests that Na$^+$,K$^+$–ATPase may be the receptor (or very closely associated with it) for the pharmacological effect of cardiac glycosides in vivo. Inhibition of the ATPase by cardiac glycosides (and the sodium pump) may underlie the positive inotropic effect produced by these drugs, presumably via Ca^{2+} uptake, which may coincide with Na$^+$ uptake. The precise mechanism of these actions is not clear. It may be noted that the cardiac glycosides appear to influence the K$^+$-mediated steps more than the Na$^+$-mediated steps in the ATPase reaction.

The action of cardiac glycosides in vivo is antagonized by K$^+$. The in vitro interaction of cardiac glycosides and Na$^+$,K$^+$–ATPase is very complex and is grossly modulated by various ligands and solvents. The interaction is, in general, fairly slow, and is promoted by Mg^{2+} + Na$^+$ + ATP, whereas K$^+$ decreases the rates of association and dissociation. Binding is also stimulated in the presence of $Mg^{2+} + P_i$; however, in this case Na^+ or K^+ decreases the rate of association but does not influence the rate of dissociation. The available data tend to support the view that cardiac glycoside inhibition of Na^+,K^+–ATPase is likely due to an allosteric modulation of the enzyme in the presence of the drug.

A variety of hormones influence the biosynthesis of the enzyme (although they generally do not affect the ATPase in the in vitro assay experiments). Some examples of this are the influence of the adrenal gland on kidney Na^+,K^+–ATPase, and the control of prostatic enzyme by androgen. Since almost 30% of the cellular energy is utilized by the Na^+,K^+–ATPase system, it has been suggested that thermogenesis may be controlled via the synthesis of new pump molecules. Particularly noteworthy is the evidence that thyroid hormones may induce new molecules of Na^+,K^+–ATPase (in kidney) as a mechanism of their calorigenic effect.

CONCLUDING COMMENTS

From the brief account of Na^+,K^+–ATPase given here, it should be clear that although much is known of the reaction scheme of ATPase, a great deal more remains to be learned to arrive at a final mechanism of Na^+ and K^+ transport as it relates to Na^+,K^+–ATPase. A major step forward would be the complete purification and sequencing of the ATPase molecule and analysis of the ligand interactions with it.

A point that needs resolution concerns the simultaneous versus consecutive interaction of cations with the pump. The scheme of the operation of ATPase is based on a consecutive interaction of Na^+ and K^+. On the other hand, it appears that Na^+ and K^+ react with the pump simultaneously. The data in support of the operation of the ATPase are very strong. These apparently divergent observations might be reconciled if it were possible to discover a specific mechanism by which the sequential interaction could mimic the responses expected of a simultaneous interaction. One of the proposed models that may account for some of these observations is the "half-of-the-sites-reactive" model, in which the enzyme is believed to be a tetramer composed of two dimers. One of the subunits of a dimer would exist with high affinity for Na^+, while the other would have high affinity for K^+. Oscillation between these two subunits would effect the translocation of Na^+ and K^+. Thus, despite an apparently independent sequential response of the phosphoenzyme toward these cations, it would appear that the two sites exist simultaneously. For such a case, one-half of the enzyme should bind ~P (i.e., formation of phosphoenzyme), while the other half should bind ATP at the same time; some evidence for this has been documented.

SUGGESTED READING

Albers, R. W. 1967. *Annu. Rev. Biochem.* 36:275.

Askari, A., ed. 1974. Symposium on Na$^+$,K$^+$–ATPase, New York, November, 1973. *Ann. N. Y. Acad. Sci.,* Vol. 242.

Bonting, S. L. 1970. In *Membranes and Ion Transport,* Vol. I, E. E. Bittar, ed., pp. 257–364. Wiley-Interscience, New York.

Edelman, I. S. 1975. *Med. Clin. North Am.* 59:605–14.

*Foster, D., and Ahmed, K. 1976. *Biochim. Biophys. Acta* 429:258–73.

*Foster, D., and Ahmed, K. 1977. *Mol. Pharmacol.* 13:142–49.

Glynn, I. M., and Karlish, S. J. D. 1975. *Annu. Rev. Physiol.* 37:13–55.

Hokin, E., and Dahl, J. L. 1972. In *Metabolic Pathways,* Vol. VI, *Metabolic Transport,* L. E. Hokin, ed., pp. 270–315. Academic Press, New York.

Judah, J. D., and Ahmed, K. 1964. *Biol. Rev.* 39:160–93.

Mitchell, P. 1967. *Adv. Enzymol.* 29:33–87.

*Mordh, S., and Post, R. L. 1977. *J. Biol. Chem.* 252:633–38.

Post, R. L., Kume, S., and Rogers, F. N. 1973. In *Mechanisms in Bioenergetics,* G. F. Azzone, L. Ernster, S. Rapa, E. Quagliariello, and N. Silipranti, eds., pp. 203–18. Academic Press, New York.

Schwartz, A., Lindenmayer, G. E., and Allen, J. C. 1975. *Pharmacol. Rev.* 27:3–134.

Skou, J. C. 1975. *Q. Rev. Biophys.* 7:401–34.

Tonomura, Y. 1972. *Muscle Proteins, Muscle Contractions, and Cation Transport.* University Park Press, Baltimore, Maryland.

---

* These individual references have been listed only because they do not appear in any of the review articles cited above.

4.5. Carbohydrate Transport

Lazar M. Schwartz, Said A. Goueli, and Khalil Ahmed

GENERAL CONSIDERATIONS

As discussed in an earlier chapter, carbohydrate transport across cell membranes can occur by a number of mechanisms, including passive diffusion, facilitated diffusion, active transport, and group translocation. The process of *passive diffusion* would follow Fick's first law (i.e., the steady-state rate of diffusion would be strictly proportional to the concentration difference within reasonable limits of concentration). The solute movement would thus occur down the concentration gradient, and at equilibrium the concentrations of the solute on each side of the membrane would be the same. Presumably no interaction occurs between the solute and the membrane components, and there would be no stereospecific selection of solutes, nor would structural analogs compete with each other for movement across the membrane. The process of *facilitated diffusion* differs from the above in that a presumed short-lived reversible complex with a membrane "carrier" is invoked. This view is based on the observations that the movement of solutes is more rapid than accounted for by passive diffusion, and the process shows saturability and stereospecificity (e.g., D-glucose transport occurs more rapidly than that of L-glucose). Neither passive diffusion nor facilitated diffusion, however, requires metabolic energy to transport solutes. This is the major difference between these modes of transport and *active transport,* which requires a constant supply of metabolic energy to carry out transport of solute against a concentration gradient. The coupling of metabolic energy to the process of transport may take a number of forms, depending upon the system in question. The fourth type of transport, *group translocation,* differs from active transport in that the transported molecule may undergo a chemical change during the process of translocation.

MOVEMENT OF SUGAR ACROSS BACTERIAL CELL MEMBRANES

Given the variety of microorganisms, diversity of requirements for sources of energy, and the spontaneous or experimentally induced mutations, the subject of transport across bacterial cell membranes is very complex. A definition of each system would require knowledge of the bacterial cell involved and the sugar being transported, as well as the composition of the growth media utilized. Thus, some bacteria may transport sugar exclusively by the process of group translocation, whereas others may use a combination of facilitated diffusion and active transport or facilitated diffusion alone. It may be noted that bacterial transport can be differentiated into two broad categories. The first is *constitutive,* in which the components of the system are present at high levels and do not increase in amount with changing concentrations of substrate. The second is *inducible,* in which the components of the system are present at a basal level and correspondingly increase in amount with elevated concentrations of substrate. In general, glucose transport belongs to the first category, while several other transport systems besides glucose belong to the latter category.

Studies at the subcellular level have led to the recognition of solute-binding transporting proteins (permeases). A phosphotransferase system (PTS) in which phosphoenol pyruvate (PEP) is the phosphoryl donor for the formation of many sugar phosphates has also been implicated in sugar transport.

Phosphotransferase System

Studies of this group translocation have been carried out with both Gram-negative (e.g., *E. coli* and *S. typhimurium*) and Gram-positive (e.g., *S. aureus*) organisms. During the process of transport across the membrane, sugar molecules are phosphorylated by the phosphotransferase system. It appears that phosphorylation of a given sugar requires four proteins, two of which show no specificity, whereas the other two are sugar-specific. Among the latter one or both, sugar-specific proteins may be membrane-bound.

Enzymes. The two soluble proteins involved in nonspecific phosphorylation are termed enzyme I and HPr; these two enzymes are coupled in the reactions involved in the transfer of P from PEP. The phosphorylated HPr (P ~ Hpr) then can act as a phosphoryl donor in the presence of two membrane-bound sugar-specific enzymes (termed IIA and IIB) or a soluble sugar-specific enzyme (or factor) termed III.

The coupled operation of these enzymes is depicted below:

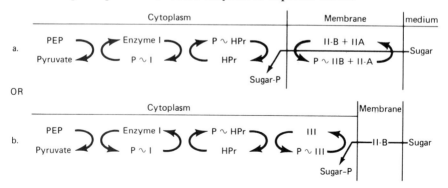

Properties of PTS Enzymes. The enzyme I has been partially purified. It is inactivated by sulfhydryl reagents. Its phosphoryl form has also been isolated, and it appears that the phospho group is attached to a histidine residue in the protein. The transfer reaction requires Mg^{2+}.

The HPr, which is a phosphate-carrier protein, has been purified to homogeneity from the various organisms mentioned above. It has a molecular weight of 9300–9700, lacks organic phosphate or carbohydrate, and has the usual amino acids except Cys, Tyr, and Trp. Each protein molecule contains histidine residues, one of which incorporates P in the N-1 position in the imidazole ring. Mg^{2+} is not required for the formation of P $\sim$ HPr, which is considerably labile, and thus may be regarded as a high-energy compound. Among the sugar-specific proteins, a few are constitutive to the cells, while others are inducible. Pairs of these proteins with sugar-specificity have been described, and some of them have been purified. For example, the constitutive proteins specific for glucose in *E. coli* are IIA and IIB. The latter protein makes its appearance when the IIA complex is heated with deoxycholate and then subjected to polyacrylamide gel electrophoresis, which indicates its molecular weight to be 36,000. Another pair of proteins isolated from *E. coli* and specific for glucose appear to be in the soluble fraction (designated as factor III), as well as in membrane-bound form (with properties different from those of IIB described above). Factor III proteins isolated from different microorganisms and possessing different sugar-specificity possess different molecular weights. The molecular weight of factor III proteins has been shown to vary, depending on the nature of the microorganisms and sugar-specificity.

Although the phosphotransferase system is responsible for the group translocation of a variety of sugars, the system does not occur in all bacteria (e.g., it appears to be absent in *P. aeruginosa*). Likewise, even though some cases of cation-dependent sugar transport have been described, this mode does not seem to be of universal importance in microorganisms.

Permease Systems

A number of genetically linked membrane proteins are known that may either simply bind sugars or may additionally be involved in their transport. The proteins are referred to as permeases. For example, in certain strains of *E. coli,* sugar permeases such as D-galactose permease, methylgalactoside permease, lactose permease, and so on, have been described. Kinetically, the methylthiogalactoside permease system would be considered to transport the sugar by facilitated diffusion with superimposed active transport. The latter is blocked by metabolic inhibitors such as azide and dinitrophenol.

Obviously, the permease system offers an immense variety of such proteins because of the possibility of their induction in response to a given substrate. To a certain extent, the physiological significance of the feasibility of a large variety of proteins with no role in transporting a normal substrate remains unclear. Nonetheless, some of the examples encountered (e.g., methylgalactoside permease or galactose permease) can produce very substantial concentration gradients.

Studies Using Bacterial Membrane Vesicles

Membrane vesicles (e.g., from *E. coli*) have proved to be extremely useful in studying various types of transport across bacterial membranes and the nature of energy transduction for this process. By utilizing ^{14}C-labeled glucose and ^{32}P in a double-label experiment, the phosphotransferase system described above was shown to provide one such mechanism. However, active uptake of some other sugars (e.g., galactose, arabinose) did not involve ATP, but rather appeared to be coupled to a membrane respiratory chain. Electrons derived from D-lactate oxidation to pyruvate (flavin-linked dehydrogenase) or some other source are passed to oxygen via a membrane bound respiratory chain, and the respiratory energy is utilized for transport. A large number of respiration-dependent transport systems in isolated bacterial membrane vesicles have been described. Although a few examples are known in which the solute-specific permeases appear to be part of the electron chain, a number of other experimental observations indicate that solute transport may not be directly coupled with electron transport, but may be an indirect consequence of electron transport. In particular, the major objections to direct electron transport coupling to solute transport are: (1) the discrepancy between rates of oxidation of D-lactate compound with solute transport; (2) the lack of quantitative conversion of D-lactate to pyruvate; (3) transport under anaerobic conditions; and (4) the effect of uncouplers of oxidative phosphorylation (e.g., dinitrophenol), which influence the transport but not respiration.

A very attractive hypothesis, commonly known as the chemiosmotic model, has been proposed by Mitchell to explain the coupling mechanism. According to this hypothesis, solute translocation is coupled to net proton translocation by a proton-coupled porter system. These systems depend on the stoichiometry and proticity of the overall translocation reaction at given values of electric and chemical components of the total proton motive force (Δp), as follows:

$$\Delta p = \Delta \psi - Z\Delta \mathrm{pH}$$

where $\Delta \psi$ is transmembrane electrical potential difference, $\Delta \mathrm{pH}$ is transmembrane pH difference, and Z is 2.303 RT/F. Despite the attractiveness of the above hypothesis, some inconsistent observations remain, and further studies are needed to resolve them in a unified mechanism.

CARBOHYDRATE TRANSPORT IN ANIMAL CELLS

The presence of mechanisms that are responsible for concentrating D-glucose uphill across mammalian epithelia has long been recognized. It is now realized that carbohydrate transport in animal cells can occur by facilitated diffusion or by active transport systems. The general characteristics of facilitated diffusion as well as active transport were described in a previous chapter (see Chapter 4.2).

The facilitated diffusion systems can be divided into two types:

1. Insulin-independent. Included in this category are the following systems: red blood cells, tumor cells, blood–brain and brain–cerebrospinal fluid barriers, placenta, and liver and some other tissues.
2. Insulin-dependent. Among these systems are included: skeletal muscle, cardiac muscle, adipose tissue, and so on.

The active transport systems are represented by epithelia such as those of intestine and kidney.

Facilitated Diffusion

Insulin-Independent Systems

Red Blood Cells. A number of fixed-site hypotheses were advanced to account for the kinetics of sugar uptake in erythrocytes. In these hypotheses, the existence in the membrane of carrier with sugar-binding capability and with access to both interfaces was postulated. This model gave way to the "mobile carrier" model after the demonstration of the "counterflow or countertransport phenomenon" in erythrocytes. This model, known as Widdas' model, with some additional refinement, is capable of accounting for most of the observations on kinetics of sugar transport in erythrocytes. It is schematically represented as follows:

$$
\begin{array}{c|c|c}
 & \text{Membrane} & \\
\hline
\text{Outside} & & \text{Inside} \\
\hline
S_1 & C_1S_1 \rightleftharpoons C_2S_2 & S_2 \\
 & \updownarrow \qquad \updownarrow & \\
 & C_1 \rightleftharpoons C_2 &
\end{array}
$$

In the above scheme, C_1 and C_2 are the forms of carrier that occur with binding of S (sugar) from the outside (S_1) for transport to the inside (S_2).

To accomodate for some of the quantitative differences observed experimentally and using the Widdas model, Lieb and Stein have proposed a tetramer model of the "carrier" in the membrane [see review by LeFevre (4)].

The sugar transport in erythrocytes shows a high degree of stereoselectivity. An interesting point, which strengthens the Widdas model, is that despite the wide range of the apparent K_m values for a number of sugars, the observed V_{max} is essentially the same for all of them. The existing information does not yield any strict structural characteristics for the apparent affinity of a given sugar. However, D-glucose and 2-deoxy-glucose show the highest affinity, followed by aldoses, whereas ketoses show a very low affinity. Based on such observations and others on the comparative transfer of various methyl-substituted aldoses, it has been suggested that the aldopyranose ring conformation may favor interaction with membrane "carrier." A large number of chemicals have been shown to inhibit the erythrocyte sugar transport system. Inhibition by sulfhydryl blocking agents such as NEM suggests the involvement of sulfhydryl groups in transport. Phloretin (the aglycone of phlorizin) is an inhibitor of erythrocyte transport though it is relatively inactive toward kidney glucose transport (which is inhibited strongly by phlorizin).

Tumor Cells. The characteristics of glucose transport and inhibitor sensitivity are essentially the same as those for erythrocytes, suggesting the operation of mobile carrier.

Blood–Brain and Blood–Cerebrospinal Fluid Barriers. Some characteristics of blood–brain transfer are similar to erythrocyte transport. It appears that low-affinity carrier may be involved in the transfer of sugar across the blood–brain barrier. Similarly, transfer across cerebrospinal fluid shows the various characteristics of facilitated diffusion.

Placenta. The fetal blood glucose levels are always lower than the mother's. Transfer of glucose follows saturation kinetics. Other similarities to the erythrocyte transport system have also been documented.

Liver and Other Tissues. Uptake of D-glucose in liver takes place at a rate that is some one hundred times greater than that of L-glucose. This uptake is inhibited by phlorizin. Protozoa and a number of other tissues seem to possess mobile carrier sugar transport mechanisms.

Insulin-Dependent Systems

Insulin stimulation elicited in a number of systems seems to result primarily in a quantitative rather than qualitative change in sugar uptake. Earlier studies using rat diaphragm implicated the membrane (rather than the hexokinase step) in the insulin-mediated enhancement of glucose uptake.

Skeletal Muscle. Earlier studies established glucose uptake in muscle tissue and its stimulation by insulin. The effect of insulin is apparent with a number of sugars such as D-glucose, D-galactose, D-mannose, and so on, but not with sugars such as D-fructose, L-sorbose, D-arabinose, and so on. The broad variation in stereospecificity is thus similar to that observed with insulin-independent tissues. The insulin effect is noted very rapidly in experimental tissue models such as rat diaphragm, and is blocked by a number of metabolic inhibitors (e.g., NaCN, DNP) and by sulfhydryl blocking agents such as NEM and iodoacetate.

Electrically stimulated muscle also shows an increased sugar uptake analogous to insulin action. Na^+ in the medium partially influences the uptake of glucose in diaphragm; however, its presence is not essential for the uptake process.

Cardiac Muscle. The transport system in cardiac muscle is considerably more rapid than in the skeletal muscle. Insulin, at very low concentrations, stimulates this uptake. Electrical activity also produces similar effects on sugar uptake by cardiac muscle.

Adipose Tissue. Cells separated from adipose tissue respond to insulin by showing increased sugar uptake. This action is primarily mediated by a decrease in K_m of the substrate without a change in V_{max}. At low concentrations, a number of agents (some of which can even cause disruption of the membrane) such as phospholipase A, chelators, PCMB, iodoacetate, and a host of other inhibitors accelerate sugar uptake in adipose cells. This stimulation is additive to that of insulin.

Active Transport Systems

It has long been appreciated that sugar transport by mechanisms other than those described above takes place in a number of cells where there is need for sugar movement against a concentration gradient. This ability for uphill transport is observed, for example, in intestinal and kidney epithelia.

Intestinal Epithelium. Numerous investigators using preparations of isolated gut segments have shown movement of sugar (glucose, galactose) from the mucosal to the serosal side, building up an opposing gradient. This process follows Michaelis-Menten kinetics as shown by active transport studies with glucose, galactose, and 3-O-methylglucose. Similarly, studies carried out with isolated hamster gut villi or isolated intestinal epithelial cells of rat and rabbit have corroborated the accumulation of sugars in those cells by the same process. Glucose inhibits the transport of 3-O-methylglucose, suggesting a common transport system for these sugars. Structural specificity studies for active sugar transport indicate the requirement of a hydroxyl group at position 2 in the D-glucopyranose ring in which carbon-5 is linked to carbon-6. These requirements, however, are not strictly met. Although certain structural changes from the above are not tolerated, others are to varying degrees (e.g.,

L-glucose and 6-deoxyglucose are transported, whereas 6-O-methylglucose is not). It has been suggested that sugar forms a "hydrogen bond" with the transport recognition site in the membrane at the C_6 position. However, such bonding involvement of carbon positions 1, 2, 3, and 4 is also indicated by studies employing analogs and structural isomers of glucose.

Active sugar transport is inhibited by anoxia or by common poisons of respiratory activity. A number of heavy metal ions at low concentrations also inhibit, and agents such as arsenite or molybdate inhibit glucose transport in rat gut. Phlorizin is a particularly potent inhibitor of sugar transport, acting in an apparently competitive manner. On the other hand, phloretin is essentially inactive. It has been suggested that the glucoside structure may only be involved in the recognition of the sugar transport sites through an interaction with the carrier, and a subsequent release of phloretin (by action of tissue β-glucosidase).

An important facet of active sugar transport relates to the Na^+ requirement in the medium. The involvement of Na^+ is in an energy-independent and substrate-specific uptake step at the brush-border surface. Cations such as K^+, Li^+, Mg^{2+}, NH_4^+, choline$^+$, and so forth, all fail to support active transport of sugar, and indeed inhibit the Na^+-dependent uptake. Ouabain, a specific inhibitor of the sodium pump, when placed at the serosal side (thereby blocking cation transport) also inhibits the sugar pump at the mucosal side. Na^+ appears to act by greatly reducing the K_m of sugar without altering the V_{max}. The actual operation of the Na^+-dependent sugar uptake is greatly supported by the natural gradients for both Na^+ and K^+. Further, it appears that Na^+ may alter the affinity of different sugars to a varying degree. The sugars that are not actively transported do not show a significant decrease in the K_m in the presence of Na^+.

The above mechanisms are further supported by the correlation of "short circuit current" in rabbit ileum sheets involving co-transport of Na^+ and sugar. Based on measurements of transmucosal potential difference (PD) in rat gut everted sacs, it appears that active sugar transport produces a significant and rapid increase in positivity (decrease in negativity) of the serosal side, whereas sugar metabolism tends to reduce it. Up to 25 mM glucose markedly increases the PD, whereas fructose lowers it. At higher sugar concentrations, the diminishing PD showed a constant ΔPD, the magnitude of which in turn correlated with the Na^+ up to 50 mM. Double reciprocal plots of ΔPD versus sugar concentration at varying Na^+ gave linear plots so that an apparent constant V_{max} is observed; however, increasing Na^+ greatly enhances the apparent affinity for the sugar. A ternary sugar–carrier–Na^+ complex may be visualized, which is in accord with the observation that not only does Na^+ enhance the affinity of the sugar, but also the sugar itself greatly decreases the K_m for Na^+.

Kidney Epithelium.   In mammals total glucose resorption takes place in the proximal convoluted tubules but none in the distal tubules. The transit time for the filtration and reabsorption of glucose is calculated to be about 10 sec. A carrier mechanism has been postulated to account for reabsorption. The kinetics show a reasonable fit to the Michaelis-Menten–type analysis.

Kidney cortex slices have been shown to accumulate sugars (e.g., galactose, glucose, and a number of others) in a Na^+-dependent manner. A large component of the efflux is Na^+-independent. Unlike intestinal transport, Na^+ in kidney increases the V_{max} rather than K_m. The difference compared to the intestinal system also relates to selection by the kidney of some sugars that are not transported in intestine, and poor uptake of others that are transported in intestine. The hydroxyl group on C_1 does not seem to be essential, since α-methyl-D-glucoside is readily transported. However, the C_2 hydroxyl seems to be essential for sugar–carrier–Na^+ interaction. The C_6 hydroxyl enhances accumulation, whereas C_3 hydroxyl appears to be required for active sugar transport.

Despite some sharing of L-glucose transport through the D-glucose or carrier system, the kidney seems to have the capability of handling L-glucose differently from D-glucose. Unlike D-glucose, which is reabsorbed from the tubules, L-glucose is actively secreted from the cells into the lumen of the perfused tubule.

The renal sugar uptake is relatively insensitive to metabolic inhibitors such as DNP or DNC in vivo. However, in vitro (e.g., in work with kidney cortex slices) DNC is shown to block sugar uptake. Cardiac glycosides (which are inhibitors of the alkali metal cation transport pump) cause a reduction in sugar transport in kidney both in vivo (resorption studies) and in vitro (cortex slices). Phlorizin is a potent inhibitor of glucose transport in kidney, and acts specifically from the luminal side.

GENERAL CONCLUDING REMARKS

In intestinal and kidney epithelia Na^+-dependent active sugar uptake is not directly linked to energy-yielding metabolic processes. There is sufficient evidence to support the gradient hypothesis developed by Crane to provide for the energy requirement of the active transport process. According to this hypothesis, part of the energy for active transport of organic solutes is supplied by Na^+ concentration difference on the two sides of the membrane. External high Na^+ tends to move this cation into the cell, and the nonelectrolyte solute is transported inward via the coupled transport system. Na^+ is then pumped out of the cell by the cation transport system. The cellular energy is thus devoted to maintenance of low intracellular Na^+ concentration. On the other hand, the hypothesis proposed by Mitchell (the chemiosmotic hypothesis) has attempted to link the metabolic energy to osmotic work. In this regard, it is entirely dependent on electrolyte movements and development of potential differences across the membrane, whereas the gradient hypothesis is completely independent of them. The proposal that proton motive force (6) drives some chemiosmotic processes tends to bring the above two hypotheses somewhat closer. Recently, some progress has been made toward obtaining reconstituted transport systems from brush border membrane, and it is hoped that future studies in such purified systems would lead to a definitive understanding of the mechanism underlying carrier-mediated active transport.

SUGGESTED READING

1. Crane, R. K. 1977. The gradient hypothesis and other models of carrier mediated active transport. *Rev. Physiol. Biochem. Pharmacol.* 78:101–59.
2. Kaback, H. R. 1974. Transport studies in bacterial membrane vesicles. *Science* 186:882–92.
3. Kotyk, A., and Janácek, K. 1970. *Cell Membrane Transport. Principles and Techniques.* Plenum Press, New York and London.
4. LeFevre, P. G. 1972. Transport of carbohydrates by animal cells. In *Metabolic Pathways,* Vol. VI, *Metabolic Transport,* L. E. Hokin, ed., pp. 385–454. Academic Press, New York.
5. Mitchell, P. 1970. Reversible coupling between transport and chemical reactions. In *Membranes and Ion Transport,* Vol. I, E. E. Bittar, ed., pp. 192–256. Wiley-Interscience, London.
6. Mitchell, P. 1973. Performance and conservation of osmotic work by proton-coupled solute porter systems. *Bioenergetics* 4:63–91.
7. Roseman, S. 1972. Carbohydrate transport in bacterial cells. In *Metabolic Pathways,* Vol. VI, *Metabolic Transport,* L. E. Hokin, ed., pp. 41–89. Academic Press, New York.
8. Schultz, S. G., and Curran, P. F. 1970. Coupled transport of sodium and organic solutes. *Physiol. Rev.* 50:637–718.
9. Whittam, R., and Wheeler, K. P. 1970. Transport across cell membranes. *Annu. Rev. Physiol.* 32:21–60.

4.6. Transport of Amino Acids

Lazar M. Schwartz, Khalil Ahmed, and Said A. Goueli

The subject of amino acid transport is very extensive, and only a brief summary is presented here. Owing to the relatively large number of natural amino acids that may be transported across biological membranes, it is obvious that several transport systems are likely to exist. These systems can, however, be divided into a number of groups, depending upon the chemical nature of the various amino acids (e.g., neutral amino acids, acidic or basic amino acids, and aromatic amino acids). In the bacterial systems, a number of amino acid binding proteins have been isolated; the concept that they may be involved in the transport of amino acids is at present based on circumstantial evidence. Although carrier-mediated transport of amino acids in mammalian cells is widely observed, there is no agreement on the nature of the carrier. At present, it cannot be stated whether or not the so-called amino acid binding proteins play a role in the transport of amino acids into mammalian cells.

The general considerations pertaining to the various modes of nonelectrolyte transport, discussed under carbohydrate transport (see Chapter 4.5), are equally applicable to amino acid transport.

AMINO ACID TRANSPORT IN BACTERIA

Bacteria possess the ability to produce amino acids intracellularly and store them in fairly high concentrations. The intracellular concentration of these acids has often been referred to as the amino acid pool. The nature of the amino acid pools in bacteria is likely to vary with the composition of the growth medium and other growth conditions. In general, it appears that the Gram-positive bacteria contain some ten times higher content of free amino acids when compared with that in the Gram-negative bacteria. The latter also tend to lose their amino acid content more readily than the Gram-positive bacteria (e.g., on washing at lower temperatures). The cells, however, regain the amino acids when re-incubated at 37°C.

The study of rates of uptake of various amino acids in bacteria can be undertaken provided that the cells are previously treated with an inhibitor of protein synthesis such as chloramphenicol or cycloheximide. Under these conditions, the uptake of amino acids can be very rapid (e.g., leucine reaches near-saturation levels in *E. coli-K12* within 1–2 min). The initial rates and the steady-state levels of different amino acids vary in a given organism; likewise, these characteristics will further alter with the type of bacterial system under investigation.

A number of transport systems in different strains of bacteria have been recognized. Some of them are distinct for single amino acids, whereas others can transport groups of amino acids. For detailed description of these systems, the reviews listed in the references are highly recommended. Some of the transport systems are as follows: (1) A transport system for glycine, alanine, and serine has been recognized. The uptake of these amino acids is blocked by α-aminoisobutyric acid, which is also actively accumulated by several organisms. (2) A transport system for valine, leucine, and isoleucine has been recognized for most microorganisms, although some bacteria have additional specific systems for one or two of these amino acids. Different strains of *E. coli* have yielded a binding protein referred to as LIV binding-protein, which has a molecular weight of 36,000. (3) The transport of phenylalanine, tyrosine, and tryptophan is shared by a single system in several microorganisms. This system is also referred to as the aromatic permease system. (4) The two basic amino acids lysine and arginine share a common transport system in many bacteria; however, the presence of individual systems for these amino acids in other cells has been indicated. (5) Glutamic and aspartic acids utilize a common transport system in a variety of microorganisms. (6) Besides the above shared transport systems, individual systems exist for the transport of a number of other amino acids, including proline, histidine, and methionine.

In all the above cases, a number of common kinetic properties are encountered for the transport of the various amino acids. For example, in general a broad temperature range (35–55°C) is encountered for near-optimal accumulation of amino acids in bacteria. The optimal pH range is also very broad, giving similar rates between pH 6 and 8 (e.g., in the case of isoleucine uptake in *E. coli-K12* cells). An even higher optimal pH has been observed in some other cases (e.g., lysine accumulation in *S. faecalis*). The transport follows saturation kinetics and can be described by Michaelis-Menten kinetics. However, double reciprocal plots may yield biphasic plots which may indicate that the entry of a given amino acid may be through a specific (high affinity, low K_m) system as well as a nonspecific (low affinity, high K_m) system. Uptake of histidine in *Salmonella typhimurium* follows these kinetics, indicating that histidine transport occurs via a specific system and in addition via the aromatic permease system with considerably lower affinity.

The possible role of binding proteins in transport of amino acids into microorganisms is speculated on largely from indirect evidence such as the presence of binding proteins in bacterial envelope, parallel kinetics of binding and transport, and the conversion of mutants from binding-protein negative to positive with reversion to the transporting form. The considerations regarding the source of energy for this transport function are similar to those discussed under carbohydrate transport in bacteria (see Chapter 4.5).

AMINO ACIDS TRANSPORT IN ANIMAL CELLS

General Considerations

The ability of animal cells to concentrate amino acids was first described by Van Slyke and Meyer about 65 years ago. It now appears that animal cells transport amino acids through a number of systems which show a considerable overlap of substrate affinity and possess the characteristics of carrier-mediated transport systems. The active amino acid uptake in mammalian cells, in general, follows saturation kinetics, and can be expressed by the Michaelis-Menten relation, although the estimates of K_m and maximal flux velocity may not be entirely reliable. Amino acid transport is characterized by several general properties. Different amino acids influence the transport of each other. This can be observed even when an unlabeled amino acid is added to a medium containing an isotopic form of the same amino acid. Different amino acids may stimulate or inhibit the uptake of a given amino acid. The inhibition (*cis* inhibition) is generally of an apparently competitive nature and is quite commonly observed. The *cis* stimulation of certain amino acids is observed in the presence of other amino acids. The amino acid transport is also characterized by *trans* stimulation or counterflow, in which case the presence of an amino acid on the *trans* side of the membrane results in enhanced uptake of the same amino acid present on the *cis* side of the membrane. A fourth property sometimes observed is referred to as *trans* inhibition, in which the presence of a given amino acid on the *trans* side inhibits the uptake of another amino acid present on the *cis* side.

Transport Systems

As mentioned earlier, various transport systems do not strictly discriminate between amino acids, and a given amino acid may be transported by more than one apparently independent system. Christensen has postulated three major amino acid transport systems in mammalian cells. These are referred to as systems A (alanine preferring), ASC (alanine, serine, cysteine–preferring), and L (leucine–preferring). Each of these systems has overlapping affinities.

System A prefers amino acids with short polar or linear side chains, including alanine, proline, serine, glycine methionine, α-amino-isobutyric acid and cycloleucine. It requires Na^+ for transport of these amino acids, and is present in most cells except erythrocytes and reticulocytes. The ability of this system to transport α-(methyl amino) isobutyric acid distinguishes it from the ASC and L systems. The ASC system also varies from the A system in that it shows a restricted range of specificity and is considerably sensitive to pH changes. As in the case of the A system, the ASC system is also strictly dependent on Na^+ for transport. This system is present in most cells. System L shows a preference for leucine, isoleucine, phenylalanine, methionine, valine, and cycloleucine. This system is distinguished from the other two by its ability to transport 2-aminobicyclo–(2,2,2)–heptane-2-carboxylate (BCH), which is not transported by the other systems, and in addition, its lack of Na^+-dependence for transport. Overlap in these systems is typified by the example of methionine, which is transported by the A system in a Na^+-dependent manner, but also by the L system in a Na^+-independent manner. The L system is also widely distributed, and can carry out active exchange of amino acids demonstrating *trans* stimulation.

Besides the aforementioned amino acid transport systems, a general system for cationic amino acids (Ly^+ system) exists in cells of higher animals and is involved in the transport of lysine and arginine. At high Na^+ levels, the affinity of neutral amino acids tends to increase for this system. However, this system can be distinguished by using the artificial amino acid 4-amino-1-guanyl-piperidine-4-carboxylic acid (GPA). The systems for anionic amino acids do not seem to be as widely distributed as the aforementioned systems. An example of the Ly^+ system is the transport of glutamate in brain tissue slices.

Source of Energy

It is well established that active transport of amino acids in animal cells takes place as judged by the criteria that (1) it occurs against the electrochemical potential gradient of the amino acid being transported, and (2) it is dependent on metabolic energy.

The coupling of energy for amino acid transport in mammalian cells, however, seems to be of an indirect nature (i.e., ATP is not directly utilized for this purpose). The clue to the question of energy utilization for this purpose is given by the observation that active uptake of many amino acids in the various animal tissues examined requires Na^+.

Currently, considerable support has accumulated for the gradient hypothesis proposed by Crane. According to this hypothesis, the energy for transport of solutes is derived from the inwardly directed gradient of Na^+. A detailed discussion of this aspect is provided in the reviews by Crane (2) and Heinz (4).

Regulation of Amino Acid Transport

The accumulation of amino acids is influenced by a large number of stimuli including environmental conditions, substances that induce proliferation, and steroid hormones. In general, it appears that these stimuli predominantly influence the Na^+-dependent A system described earlier. It is not clear at present what, if any, physiologically significant purpose is served by such stimulative effects of these substances on the uptake of amino acids in animal cells, since optimal protein systhesis appears to continue at considerably lower levels of amino acid than are usually maintained intracellularly.

A number of peptide hormones stimulate the Na^+-dependent amino acid transport in cells, including insulin, growth hormone, thyroid stimulating hormone (TSH), follicle stimulating hormone (FSH), and glucagon. Insulin effects have been determined from studies of uptake in diaphragm muscle cells. Growth hormone influences the transport in kidney and muscle cells (except heart muscle), whereas glucagon has been shown to influence uptake in liver tissue. TSH and FSH act primarily in their target organs.

Catecholamines (e.g., epinephrine, isoproterenol) have been shown to stimulate the Na^+-dependent amino acid transport (system A) in a number of tissues (such as liver, jejunal mucosa) but also to inhibit it in certain other tissues (such as isolated fat cells, diaphragm, and exocrine gland tissues).

Variable effects of thyroid hormones in different tissues have been observed. It appears that T_3 is more effective than T_4 in stimulating amino acid uptake. Likewise, glucocorticoids enhance amino acid uptake in certain tissues (liver, cultured fibroblasts, leukemic myeloblasts), but depress it in certain other tissues (rat thymocytes, rat muscle, human leukemic lymphocytes, etc). With respect to the sex steroids, estrogens and androgens when administered in vivo result in stimulation of amino acid transport in the respective target tissues. These steroids appear to produce their primary effect on transport system A. In general, the addition of these steroids in vitro to preparations of target tissues does not elicit a definitive response with respect to amino acid transport. The effects produced in vivo relate to the protein synthesizing activity (occurring after a certain lag period) in the target organs of castrated animals given the appropriate sex steroid, and do not necessarily relate to the primary physiological effects by which these hormone trigger the multitude of activities in target cells.

Further advances in the field of membrane solute transport, its regulation, and mechanisms of energy utilization will be forthcoming with the current interest in studying the membrane function in purified reconstituted systems.

SUGGESTED READING

1. Christensen, H. N. 1975. *Biological Transport,* 2nd ed. W. A. Benjamin, Reading, Massachusetts.
2. Crane, R. K. 1977. *Rev. Physiol. Biochem. Pharmacol.* 78:101–59.
3. Guidotti, G. G., Borghetti, A. F., and Guzzola, G. C. 1978. *Biochim. Biophys. Acta* 515:329–66.
4. Heinz, E. 1972. In *Metabolic Pathways,* Vol. VI, *Metabolic Transport,* L. E. Hokin, ed., pp. 455–501. Academic Press, New York.
5. Oxender, D. L 1972. In *Metabolic Pathways,* Vol. VI, *Metabolic Transport,* L. E. Hokin ed., pp. 133–85. Academic Press, New York.
6. Spaziani, E. 1975. *Pharmacol. Rev.* 27:207–86.

4.7. The Golgi Apparatus

Becca Fleischer and Sidney Fleischer

STRUCTURE

The Golgi apparatus is a membranous structure present in most mammalian and plant cells. It is one of the oldest known organelles, first described by Camillo Golgi (1) in 1898 in Purkinje cells of the cerebellum. After impregnation of neuronal cells with an osmic acid–rubidium bichromate mixture followed by treatment with silver nitrate, an "internal reticular apparatus" appeared as a network of darkly stained fibrils, visible throughout the cytoplasm using light microscopy. Similar, though sometimes more compact, areas capable of impregnation with salts of heavy metals were found subsequently in nearly all cell types studied (Figure 1). This structure has come to be known as the Golgi apparatus or complex.

For many years, the existence of this organelle was actively debated, but the issue was finally settled in the early 1950s when electron microscopy was applied to the study of subcellular structure. By means of electron microscopy, the structure of the organelle was redefined by Dalton and Felix (2) as consisting of three parts: (1) a stacked series of flattened, membrane-bound cisternae; (2) small vesicles peripheral to the ends of the cisternae, also referred to as "transitional vesicles"; and (3) large secretory vesicles often clustered near one face of the stacked cisternae (Figure 2). More recently, freeze-fracture studies on unfixed cells have confirmed this form of the organelles in a variety of both plant and animal cells (Figure 3).

The Golgi apparatus often shows a marked polarity both in structure and in cytochemical staining (3). This has led to one side being designated the immature, forming, proximal or *cis* face, and the opposite side the mature, secreting, distal or *trans* face. In secreting cells, the polarity of the structure is obvious, whereas in others such as the hepatocyte, this is not necessarily the case, and special staining procedures have been used to visualize the polarity.

FUNCTION

Even in the early days of its recognition as a distinct cell organelle, the Golgi apparatus was linked to the synthetic and secretory capacity of the

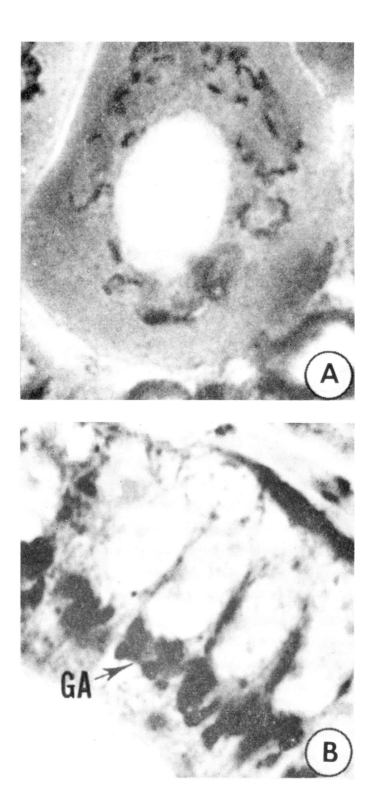

cell. Palade and co-workers studied the acinar cells of the pancreas which synthesize and secrete digestive enzymes eventually used in the intestine. The organization of the cytoplasmic organelles of these cells reflects their secretory function (Figure 4). Their rough endoplasmic reticulum and Golgi are highly developed. The digestive enzymes are found in membrane-bound granules clustered near the plasma membrane facing the lumen of the duct into which the enzymes are released. By injecting radioactive leucine into animals and following the time course of the appearance of labeled proteins in the various components of the cells, both by autoradiography of the intact cells and by direct measurement in isolated cell fractions (Figure 5), Palade and his co-workers showed that newly formed proteins move from the rough endoplasmic reticulum where they are synthesized, through the Golgi apparatus, to the zymogen granules, where they are stored. The zymogen granules finally discharge their contents by fusion of their limiting membrane with the plasma membrane facing the lumen of the duct. They concluded that the Golgi packages proteins for export (4).

In addition to simple proteins, Golgi of mammalian cells is involved in the secretion of mucopolysaccharides (5), glycoproteins (6), and lipoproteins (7). In some types of algae, cell wall components containing protein and cellulose fibers have been shown to be assembled in the Golgi apparatus and transported to the plasma membrane where the cell wall is completed (8). In some algae and in higher plants, however, the plasma membrane appears to be the locus of cellulose synthesis.

Many secreted proteins are glycoproteins; that is, they contain a variety of carbohydrates attached covalently to a functional side group of the peptide backbone of the polymer. Studies on the incorporation of radioactive sugars into glycoproteins, in both isolated cell fractions and intact cells, have shown that during secretion different sugars are added to the protein at different points in the secretory pathway. For example, galactose, fucose, and sialic acid are incorporated first in the Golgi apparatus, whereas mannose appears first in the rough endoplasmic reticulum. N-Acetylglucosamine is incorporated initially in both. In fact, the site of glycosylation is related to the structure of the glycoprotein. This is illustrated in Figure 6, which shows the structure of a typical secreted glycoprotein. "Core" sugars, that is, sugars close to the protein backbone such as N-acetylglucosamine and mannose, are attached in the rough endoplasmic reticulum (Site 1) very close to the time the secreted protein is being synthesized by polysomes attached to the

Figure 1. Golgi apparatus stained for light microscopy with heavy metal impregnation. (A) Ganglion cell with perinuclear distribution of the Golgi apparatus. (B) Epithelial cell with apical distribution of the Golgi apparatus; GA, Golgi apparatus. (From H. W. Beams and R. G. Kessel, *Int. Rev. Cytol.* 23:209–76, 1965, courtesy of the authors and Academic Press.)

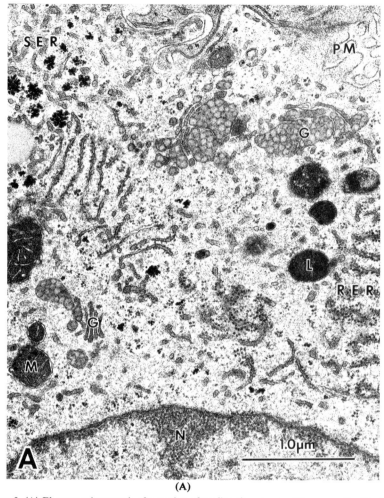

(A)

Figure 2. (A) Electron micrograph of a section of rat liver hepatocyte. The organelles illustrated are: N, nucleus; G, Golgi apparatus; M, mitochondria; RER, rough endoplasmic reticulum; SER, smooth endoplasmic reticulum; L, lysosomes; PM, plasma membrane. (B) The Golgi apparatus in rat liver. Characteristic features are (1) three or four stacks of flattened cisternae; (2) peripheral vesicles or anastomizing tubules; and (3) large secretory vesicles.

membrane. Core sugars appear to be first assembled stepwise on a carrier lipid, which in mammalian systems is dolichol pyrophosphate, and then transferred as a unit to the polypeptide backbone via an N-glycosidic bond between the first N-acetylglucosamine residue of the oligosaccharide chain and an asparagine residue of the polypeptide chain (9). The outer mannose units

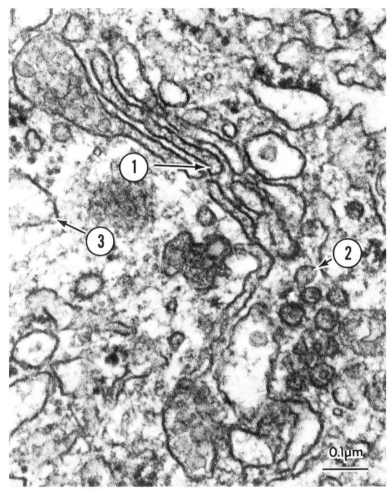

Figure 2. (B)

(Site 2) are believed to be added stepwise via dolichol phosphate mannose in both rough and smooth endoplasmic reticulum. The more terminal (Site 3) sugars such as N-acetylglucosamine, galactose, sialic acid, and fucose (when present) are added by a different mechanism. They are attached stepwise directly to the nonreducing end of the carbohydrate side chain of the incomplete glycoprotein by the action of specific glycosyltransferases using nucleotide sugars as donors (10). Site 3 sugars of secreted proteins appear to be added exclusively in the Golgi apparatus.

Other modifications of glycoproteins may occur during passage through the Golgi apparatus. Golgi membranes contain an α-D-mannosidase which

Figure 3. The Golgi apparatus of the alga *Micrasterias denticulata* illustrating the typical structural features as revealed in an unfixed, freeze-etched sample. (From L. A. Staehelin and O. Kiermayer, Membrane differentiation in the Golgi complex of *Micrasterias denticulata Breb.* visualized by freeze-etching, *J. Cell Sci.* 7:787–92, 1970, Cambridge University Press.)

differs from cytosolic or lysosomal mannosidases (11). This enzyme may be involved in modifying secreted glycoproteins by removing particular mannose groups. The Golgi apparatus of lactating mammary gland contains a kinase that phosphorylates casein, the major protein of milk, using ATP as substrate (12).

The Golgi apparatus may be implicated in the biosynthesis of another class of glycoproteins, the proteoglycans (mucopolysaccharides) (13). These substances, together with collagen and elastin, form the "ground substance" or intercellular glue present in most tissues. They consist of a protein core to which are linked many chains of disaccharide repeating units. The repeating units commonly consist of an acetylated amino sugar and a uronic acid, and are often sulfated. The disaccharide polymer chains are attached to the protein backbone via three neutral sugar residues (Figure 7).

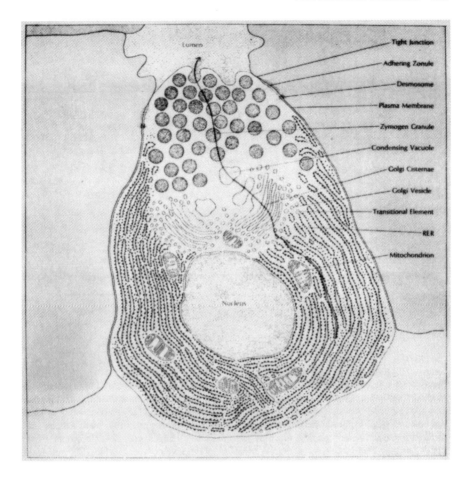

Figure 4. Diagrammatic representation of an acinar cell of the pancreas illustrating the polar arrangement of intracellular organelles. The arrow shows the intracellular pathway of secreted proteins from rough endoplasmic reticulum, through the Golgi, condensing vacuoles, and zymogen granules, and finally to the lumen of the glandular tract. (Drawings by B. Tagawa from J. D. Jamieson, Membranes and secretion, *Hosp. Prac.* 8 (No. 12), and from *Cell Membranes: Biochemistry, Cell Biology & Pathology,* G. Weissmann and R. Claiborne, eds., HP Publishing Co., New York, 1975.)

The exact subcellular site(s) of synthesis of proteoglycans is not known. Addition of galactose and xylose to the protein appears to be greatest in RER of chondrocytes, whereas polymerization of the disaccharide occurs in both RER and smooth microsomes. Sulfation is highest in smooth microsomes (13), which are at least partly derived from the Golgi. The antibiotic X537A inhibits the incorporation of both glucosamine and sulfate into proteo-

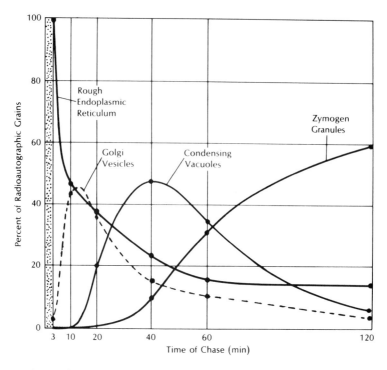

Figure 5. Change of radioactivity, as measured by radioautographic grains, of different membranous compartments of pancreatic acinar cells with time after a 3-min pulse of radioactive leucine followed by a chase of nonradioactive leucine. The kinetics of labeling of the various compartments can be best explained by a wave of labeled protein, newly synthesized in the rough ER, passing through the Golgi to condensing vacuoles and finally to zymogen granules. (Drawings by B. Tagawa from J. D. Jamieson, Membranes and secretion, *Hosp. Pract.* 8 (No. 12), and from *Cell Membranes: Biochemistry, Cell Biology & Pathology,* G. Weissmann and R. Claiborne, eds., HP Publishing Co., New York, 1975.)

glycans and also causes swelling of the Golgi apparatus of cultured smooth muscle cells (14), but the mechanism of this action is not clear.

ISOLATION

In order to isolate organelles for biochemical study, cells of the tissue are first broken by mechanical means to form a homogenate. During homogenization procedures normally used to isolate particulate cell organelles from mammalian tissues, membranous organelles such as endoplasmic reticulum, Golgi, and plasma membranes are often disrupted into vesicles or "microsomes." The cellular origin of smooth-surfaced microsomes is difficult to define by morphological means. In order to evaluate the purity of any isolated organelle,

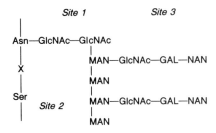

Figure 6. Carbohydrate side-chain of a typical serum glycoprotein secreted by liver. N-Acetylglucosamine (GlcNAc) and mannose (MAN) in the form of an oligosaccharide are attached first to an asparagine residue of the protein via a dolichol pyrophosphate oligosaccharide intermediate in the rough endoplasmic reticulum (Site 1). Additional mannose residues are added via dolichol phosphate mannose as the mannose donor, as the glycoprotein travels from the rough to the smooth endoplasmic reticulum (Site 2). The more terminal sugars such as N-acetylglucosamine, galactose (GAL), and sialic acid (NAN), are added stepwise in the Golgi apparatus (Site 3) via glycosyltransferases which use nucleotide sugars as sugar donors (10).

therefore, one must be able to define the amount of contamination present from other organelles or vesicles derived from them by some means other than morphology alone. This is most often done by using "marker" enzymes, that is, enzymes localized ideally in only one subcellular organelle.

The first isolation of Golgi was carried out in the 1950s by Schneider and Kuff using rat epididymis, a tissue rich in Golgi and relatively poor in smooth endoplasmic reticulum. The work was extended by Kuff and Dalton, who found that they could obtain a fraction recognizable in the electron microscope as Golgi by homogenizing the tissue in 50% sucrose followed by ultracentrifugal flotation in a sucrose step-gradient (15). The purity of the preparation, however, could not be estimated owing to lack of knowledge of the biochemical properties of the Golgi and many of the other organelles in this tissue.

Mollenhauer, Morré, and their co-workers isolated morphologically identifiable Golgi apparatus using glutaraldehyde as a stabilizing agent in the ho-

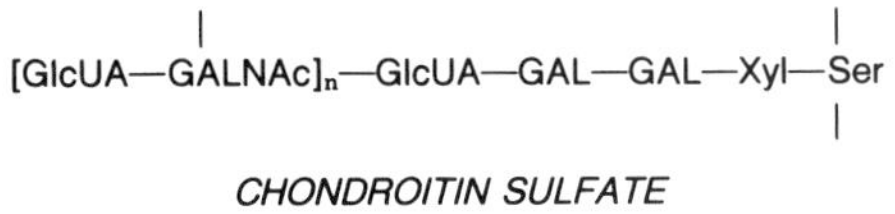

$$SO_4$$
$$| \qquad \qquad \qquad \qquad \qquad |$$
$$[GlcUA{-}GALNAc]_n{-}GlcUA{-}GAL{-}GAL{-}Xyl{-}Ser$$
$$|$$

CHONDROITIN SULFATE

Figure 7. A typical carbohydrate sequence of a proteoglycan, chondroitin sulfate. The linkage region of carbohydrate to protein begins with xylose (Xyl) O-glycosidically linked to a serine residue of a protein followed by two galactose units and a glucuronic acid (GlcUA). The rest of the chain consists of repeating disaccharide units of glucuronic acid and N-acetylgalactosamine (GALNAc) sulfate.

mogenizing medium (16). This work yielded the first studies of the Golgi apparatus by negative staining, that is, drying down the entire structure in the presence of phosphotungstic acid on the specimen grid and viewing the membranes directly in the electron microscope by negative contrast. In addition to flattened sacs, a large array of anastomizing tubules extending from the periphery of the plates was found. Because artifacts can be produced by this treatment, these results must be viewed with caution. However, electron microscopic studies carried out by Claude on serial sections of rat liver reveal tubular extensions of smooth endoplasmic reticulum connecting with Golgi fenestrated plates and solid Golgi sacs (17). Thus, in some tissues at least, the small "vesicles" often seen associated with the periphery of the Golgi stacks may actually be tubular in nature.

A significant advance in the problem of isolating and defining the properties of the Golgi apparatus came in 1969 when a unique biochemical property of the Golgi-rich fractions isolated from bovine liver was identified (18). Galactosyltransferase is the enzyme responsible for galactose incorporation into glycoproteins (equation 1). This enzyme also utilized free N-acetylglucosamine as a substrate (equation 2).

$$\text{UDP-Gal} + \text{Protein-GlcNAc} \xrightarrow[\text{Mn}^{2+}]{\substack{\text{galactosyl}\\\text{transferase}}} \text{UDP} + \text{Protein-GlcNAc-Gal} \quad (1)$$

$$\text{UDP-}^{14}\text{C-Gal} + \text{GlcNAc} \xrightarrow[\text{Mn}^{2+}]{\substack{\text{galactosyl}\\\text{transferase}}} \text{UDP} + {}^{14}\text{C-Lactosamine} \quad (2)$$

Using the reaction shown in equation (2) and measuring the amount of radioactive disaccharide formed, a subfraction of bovine liver microsomes highly enriched in galactosyltransferase activity and poor in enzymes characteristic of other cellular organelles of liver was isolated. The fraction consisted of sacs with attached tubules, and reacted heavily with osmium tetroxide, a property characteristic of Golgi. Since then, the procedure has been modified to give good yields of the galactosyltransferase activity from rat liver (19). The isolation procedure is based on gentle homogenization of the tissue directly in a medium containing phosphate buffer and a high sucrose concentration followed by a single flotation in a sucrose step-gradient. If the fraction is fixed with glutaraldehyde directly from the gradient, largely intact, purified Golgi apparatus is obtained (Figure 8). The method has also been applied successfully to other tissues such as kidney.

A different procedure for isolating the Golgi apparatus from rat liver was developed independently by Morré and co-workers (20). In this method, the tissue is homogenized in isotonic sucrose in the presence of 5 mM Mg^{2+}

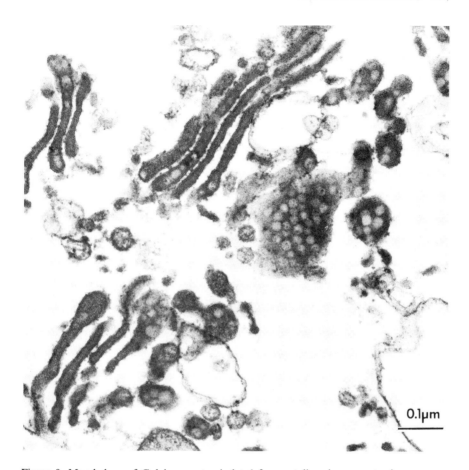

Figure 8. Morphology of Golgi apparatus isolated from rat liver homogenates in a sucrose step-gradient illustrating that the characteristic three-dimensional structure of the Golgi has been retained in the isolation. Compare with rat liver Golgi in situ (Figure 2).

to stabilize the Golgi apparatus. The Golgi as well as other large cell organelles is sedimented at a low g-force. The upper portion of the pellet is further fractionated on a sucrose step-gradient containing 5 mM Mg^{2+} to yield a Golgi preparation morphologically identifiable and rich in galactosyltransferase activity. It was shown to be enriched in N-acetylglucosaminyl and sialyltransferase activities as well.

Another approach to isolating the Golgi from liver is that of Ehrenreich et al. (21), who administered ethyl alcohol to rats to induce the formation of large amounts of very-low-density lipoprotein particles in liver. The particles are secreted by the Golgi and act to modify the density of the Golgi apparatus. A microsomal fraction is first prepared from the liver homogenate and then subfractionated on a sucrose step-gradient. The Golgi vesicles containing very-low-density lipoprotein particles are easily separated from most endoplasmic reticulum vesicles.

BIOCHEMICAL CHARACTERIZATION

In the secretory process, the Golgi apparatus mediates the transfer of diverse secretory products from the endoplasmic reticulum (ER) to the plasma membrane and eventually to the exterior of the cell. In this process the membranes of the Golgi interact with both the ER and the plasma membrane. The isolation of the Golgi from rat liver has made possible extensive studies on the chemistry and enzymology of the Golgi membrane in comparison with both purified endoplasmic reticulum and plasma membranes.

PROTEINS

Membranes consist of insoluble complexes of lipids and proteins. Comparison of the proteins present in isolated membranes is possible if the components are first dissociated and the proteins separated by electrophoresis in polyacrylamide gels containing dissociating agents. Commonly used dissociating agents are sodium dodecyl sulfate or mixtures of phenol, acetic acid, and urea. Extensive comparison of the protein patterns of plasma membranes, rough and smooth microsomes, and Golgi vesicles have been carried out for beef liver, rat liver, and rat kidneys, using both types of separation. Complex mixtures of proteins were found for all membrane types studied. Within a single cell type, the Golgi differs from both endoplasmic reticulum and plasma membranes. Key differences persist even after the contents of the isolated Golgi vesicles are largely removed or when the ribosomes are separated from "rough" ER membranes. In addition, Golgi from different cell types are distinct in their membrane protein profiles. Membranes isolated from secretory granules of pancreas have a protein composition that is distinct from, and much simpler than, Golgi membranes or plasma membranes from the same cell. Thus the secretory granule membrane is distinct from both the membrane from which it is derived and the membrane with which it fuses during the secretion process.

LIPIDS

Comparisons of the lipid content and composition of the Golgi apparatus with other membranous organelles has been carried out in detail in only a few mammalian tissues. Tables 1 and 2 summarize the results found for

Table 1. Lipid Content of Golgi Apparatus Compared with Other Organelles of Rat Tissues.

	LIVER[a]					KIDNEY[a]				TESTIS[b]	
	MITO	RER	GOLGI	GOLGI MEMBRANES	PM	MITO	RER	GOLGI	PM	MICROSOMES	GOLGI
Total Lipid	0.202	0.425	1.01	1.17	0.994	0.286	0.587	0.859	1.32	0.63	1.26
% NL	13.4	13.6	33.3	29.3	32.4	14.0	19.8	18.9	24.0	14.5	39.4
% GL	—	—	—	—	—	10.8	13.0	17.1	11.0	1.7[c]	2.3[c]
% Su	—	—	—	—	—	5.6	3.7	13.6	4.2	—	—
Cholesterol	0.003	0.014	0.071	0.078	0.128	0.008	0.053	0.071	0.119	0.030	.090
Ubiquinone	1.3	ND	4.7	6.2	0.18	2.3	0.2	1.1	0.1	—	—

All values expressed as mg/mg protein except for ubiquinone (coenzyme Q), which is in μg/mg protein. Golgi membranes were prepared by disruption of the liver Golgi apparatus using a Parr bomb. Total lipid is the sum of the neutral lipid, phospholipid, and glycolipid values. % NL is (neutral lipid/total lipid) $\times$ 100. % Su is (sulfatide/total lipid) $\times$ 100. % GL is (glycolipid/total lipid) $\times$ 100. ND, not detected. Dashes indicate values not determined. The ubiquinone value in plasma membrane can be accounted for by contamination of the fraction with mitochondria. Abbreviations: Mito, mitochondria; RER, rough endoplasmic reticulum; PM, plasma membrane. [a] Data of Zambrano, Fleischer, and Fleischer (22). [b] Data of Keenan, Nyquist and Mollenhauer (23). [c] The major glycolipid in rat testes is a sulfated galactosyldiglyceride (24).

Table 2. Phospholipid Composition of Rat Subcellular Fractions.

PHOSPHO-LIPID	LIVER[a]					KIDNEY[a]			TESTIS[b]	
	MITO-CHONDRIA	ROUGH MICRO-SOMES	GOLGI COMPLEX	GOLGI MEMBRANE	PLASMA MEMBRANE	PLASMA MEMBRANES	GOLGI COMPLEX	ROUGH MICRO-SOMES	GOLGI	TOTAL MICRO-SOMES
Origin	0.9	0.9	1.0	0.8	0.9	1.5	1.1	1.1	—	—
PE	34.6	21.8	23.5	19.6	23.3	31.4	23.1	22.4	21.5	26.0
PC	40.3	58.4	54.0	49.6	39.3	33.2	52.1	37.9	56.8	53.0
Sph	0.5	2.5	7.8	7.6	16.0	16.6	6.7	19.5	7.0	6.7
DPG	17.8	1.1	1.0	1.2	1.0	0.0	0.0	0.0	0.0	0.0
PI	4.6	10.1	8.6	12.6	7.7	1.7	7.1	1.7	9.0	7.0
PS	0.7	2.9	3.0	5.6	9.0	10.0	5.4	11.0	3.1	4.4
LPE	0.6	1.1	0.3	1.6	1.3	0.5	0.3	1.6	1.1	0.9
LPC	ND	0.5	0.4	1.4	1.0	4.5	3.6	4.0	1.4	1.3
PA	ND	0.8	0.4	0.4	0.5	0.6	0.7	0.7	—	—

All values expressed as % of total phospholipid phosphorus. Phospholipid abbreviations are: PE, phosphatidylethanolamine; PC, phosphatidylcholine; Sph, sphingomyelin; DPG, diphosphatidylglycerol; PI, phosphatidylinositol; PS, phosphatidylserine; LPE, lysophosphatidylethanolamine; LPC, lysophosphatidylcholine; PA, phosphatidic acid. The values for the kidney fractions were corrected for a small amount of mitochondrial contamination. [a] Data of Zambrano, Fleischer, and Fleischer (22). [b] Data of Keenan, Nyquist, and Mollenhauer (23).

rat liver (22), kidney (22), and testes (23). Golgi differs both from endoplasmic reticulum and from plasma membrane in its lipids. Unlike most other cytoplasmic organelles, it has a high content of neutral lipid, mainly cholesterol. In this property Golgi resembles the plasma membrane. It also has a high level of ubiquinone, a lipid oxidation–reduction component originally discovered in mitochondria. Removal of most of the contents of the Golgi cisternae by disruption of the preparation using N_2 decompression does not remove the ubiquinone, an indication that it is a membrane component. Its role in Golgi metabolism is not known.

Liver Golgi closely resembles ER in its phospholipid composition except for its content of sphingomyelin, which appears to be intermediate between that of ER and plasma membrane. This is not true for kidney Golgi, however, whose phospholipids resemble liver Golgi more than other membranes from kidney. Kidney is rich in sulfatide, a sulfated galactosylceramide. This lipid is practically absent in liver. As we will discuss in the next section, Golgi in kidney is involved in the synthesis of sulfatide, and indeed is very rich in this glycolipid. In testis, however, the major glycolipid is a sulfated monogalactosyldiglyceride (24). Its distribution among the subcellular fractions in testis has not been described, but it appears to be present in the germinal cells of the testes and in mature sperm in a number of species. Sulfation of monogalactosyldiglyceride also appears to take place in the Golgi apparatus of testis.

ENZYMES

"Marker" Enzymes Glycosyltransferases

Careful enzymatic studies on purified subcellular fractions of liver have shown that Golgi apparatus is enzymatically distinct from both endoplasmic reticulum and plasma membranes (Figure 9). Liver Golgi differs from plasma membrane in its low ATP'ase, 5'-nucleotidase (AMP'ase) and UDP-Gal hydrolase activities, and from endoplasmic reticulum in its low glucose-6-phosphatase. Rotenone-insensitive NADH-cytochrome c reductase activity, an enzyme characteristic of endoplasmic reticulum of many cell types, is low in rat liver Golgi but is high in Golgi from beef liver. Thiamine pyrophosphatase activity, useful as a histochemical marker for Golgi apparatus in many tissues, is not useful as a marker enzyme for isolated Golgi membrane from liver, since both isolated endoplasmic reticulum and plasma membranes have about the same level of activity as the Golgi.

UDP-Gal:GlcNAc galactosyltransferase and CMP-NAN:desialylated glycoprotein sialyltransferase activities, enzymes involved in the terminal glycosylation of secreted glycoproteins, are characteristic enzymes of the Golgi,

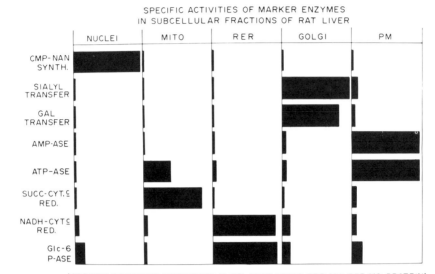

SPECIFIC ACTIVITIES OF MARKER ENZYMES
IN SUBCELLULAR FRACTIONS OF RAT LIVER

(SPECIFIC ACTIVITIES EXPRESSED IN RELATIVE UNITS PER MIN PER MG. PROTEIN)

Figure 9. Distribution of some marker enzymes in isolated and purified subcellular fractions of rat liver. The Golgi shows high levels of galactosyl- and sialyltransferase activities, which are very low in other fractions. It can be distinguished from nuclei by its low cytidine monophosphate sialic acid synthetase activity, and from plasma membranes by its low 5'-nucleotidase and ATPase activities. It also lacks succinate cytochrome c reductase of mitochondria and is low in rotenone-insensitive NADH-cytochrome c reductase and glucose-6-phosphatase activities characteristic of endoplasmic reticulum. The purity of the Golgi is 80–90% as judged by the presence of activities of the marker enzymes for other organelles.

and appear to be localized predominantly in the Golgi apparatus in mammalian liver and kidney. Galactosyltransferase has been studied in a wide variety of mammalian tissues including pancreas, testes, lung, and adrenal medulla, and shown to be localized predominantly in the Golgi. Galactosyltransferase is not a marker for Golgi membranes in all tissues, however. Lactose synthetase, for example, occurs as a soluble protein in milk and is a complex between galactosyltransferase (Protein A) and α-lactalbumin (Protein B). A soluble form has also been described at low levels in human serum and at high levels in embryonic chicken brain.

Galactosyltransferase of Golgi is a membrane-bound enzyme that can be released from the membrane by treatment with nonionic detergents such as Triton X-100 (25, 26). The solubilized enzyme binds Triton X-100 and aggregates if detergent is removed, indicating that it is an intrinsic membrane protein (26).

Enzymes of Lipid Biosynthesis

Liver Golgi is involved in the secretion of serum lipoproteins which contain lecithin, sphingomyelin, and triglycerides as well as other lipids. Stein and Stein (27) showed, using autoradiography, that in vivo glycerol and palmitic acid are incorporated first into rough and smooth endoplasmic reticulum in rat liver and later appear in the Golgi apparatus. Studies with isolated rat liver fractions also indicate that these lipids are not synthesized in the Golgi apparatus but in the endoplasmic reticulum (Table 3). Bovine liver is similar except that the acylation of lysolecithin to form lecithin is present in bovine liver Golgi. Other lipid-synthesizing steps that are present in endoplasmic reticulum of liver but are absent in Golgi include the formation of CDP-diglycerides, palmityl CoA, phosphatidylinositol, and phosphatidylserine, and the conversion of phosphatidylserine to phosphatidylinositol. Since the Golgi membrane contains these phospholipids, they must be transported there from the endoplasmic reticulum, the major site of their synthesis.

Glycosphingolipids are another major class of lipids found in mammalian cells. The level varies from very high in tissues such as brain, to moderate in kidney, to very low in liver. Like the glycoproteins, the glycosphingolipids are formed by the stepwise addition of carbohydrates mediated by specific glycosyltransferases (10) (Figure 10). Glycolipids are generally not secreted but remain in the cell as membrane components. Isolated subcellular fractions of kidney have been studied for their ability to synthesize glycosphingolipids.

Table 3. Relative Specific Activities of Lipid Synthesizing Enzymes in Golgi Apparatus from Rat Liver.

	MICROSOMES		GOLGI	PM
Formation of lecithin	Smooth	Rough		
CDP-choline + diglyceride	100	64	9.6	6.1
Acyl-CoA + lysolecithin	100	48	5.6	—
N-Methylation	100	149	5.3	10.0
Formation of triglycerides				
Acyl-CoA + diglyceride	100	186	3.4	—
Formation of sphingomyelin				
CDP-choline + ceramide	100	110	4.1	9.9
% Contamination with smooth microsomes	—	—	8	9

The relative specific activity is expressed as the specific activity of that fraction divided by the specific activity of that enzyme in smooth microsomes × 100. [From Fleischer, Zambrano, and Fleischer (28).]

GLYCOLIPID BIOSYNTHESIS

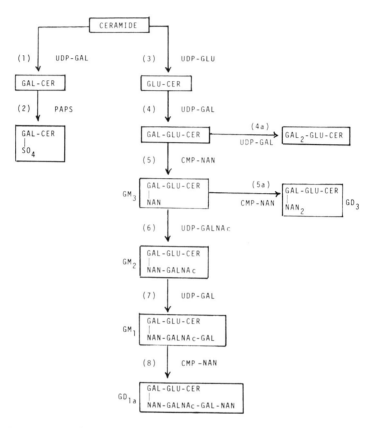

Figure 10. Two possible pathways in the biosynthesis of cerebrosides, sulfatide, and gangliosides. Abbreviations: CER, ceramide; GAL, galactose; GLU, glucose; NAN, N-acetylneuraminic acid (sialic acid); GALNAc, N-acetylgalactosamine; PAPS, 3'-phosphoadenosine-5'-phosphosulfate. Each step, 1–8, is probably catalyzed by a distinct glycosyltransferase.

The results (Figure 11) show that the Golgi apparatus is involved in the modification of glycolipids as well as glycoproteins. The initial glycosylation of ceramide to form galactosylceramide, enzyme 1, does not appear to be exclusively due to a Golgi enzyme but to one that is present in all of the fractions. Similarly, myelin, a plasma-membrane-derived structure in brain, has been demonstrated to have a relatively high level of this enzyme.

As illustrated in Figure 11, kidney Golgi carries out the sulfation of galactosylceramide to form sulfatide (enzyme 2). Studies on the incorporation of

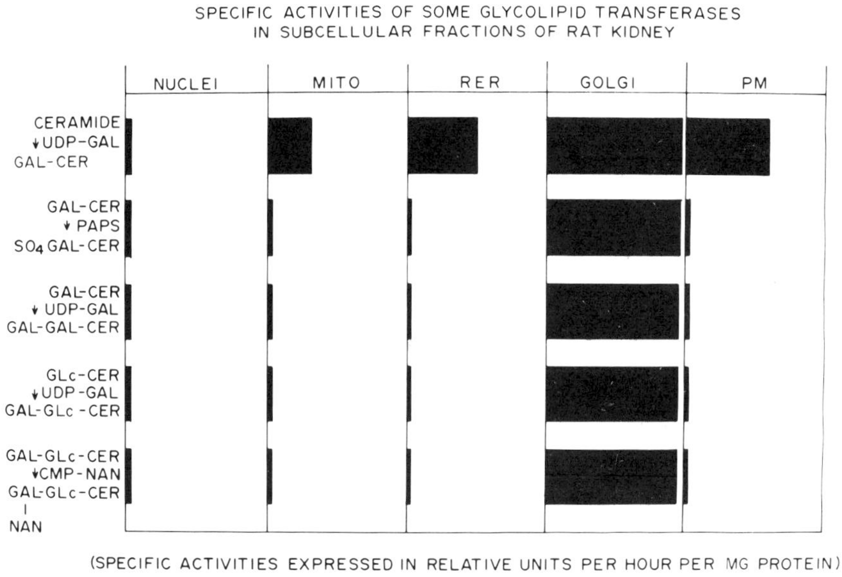

SPECIFIC ACTIVITIES OF SOME GLYCOLIPID TRANSFERASES
IN SUBCELLULAR FRACTIONS OF RAT KIDNEY

(SPECIFIC ACTIVITIES EXPRESSED IN RELATIVE UNITS PER HOUR PER MG PROTEIN)

Figure 11. Distribution of some glycolipid glycosyltransferase activities in isolated and purified subcellular fractions of rat kidney. They correspond to enzymes 1, 2, 4, and 5 of Figure 10. Enzymes 2, 4, 5 and the formation of digalactosylceramide (enzyme 4a) are localized predominantly in the Golgi. Data of B. Fleischer, *J. Supramol. Struct.* 7:79–89, 1977. Enzymes 6, 7, and 8 have been shown to also be localized predominantly in Golgi in rat liver. (T. W. Keenan, D. J. Morré, and S. Basu, *J. Biol. Chem.* 249:310–15, 1974.)

radioactive sulfate into kidney sulfatides in vivo have shown that the sulfatide in Golgi is labeled before that in plasma membrane (Figure 12). The pattern of labeling is consistent with a precursor–product relationship between sulfatide of the Golgi and that of the plasma membrane, and is the first direct evidence for the synthesis of a plasma membrane component by the Golgi apparatus (28).

Golgi in kidney is also the main locus of galactosyltransferases which convert glycosylceramide to lactosylceramide or to digalactosylglucosylceramide. These activities are not present in liver Golgi, and are therefore distinct from protein galactosyltransferase. UDP-Gal : ceramide galactosyltransferase (enzyme 1, Figure 10) also is very low in liver, as is enzyme 4, the enzyme that forms lactosylceramide. This may explain why liver as a tissue is very low in all glycolipids. The sialyltransferase that forms sialyllactosylceramide (hematoside) from lactosylceramide (enzyme 5) is present in both kidney and liver Golgi, although the specific activity is much higher in kidney Golgi. Enzymes 6, 7, and 8 are also primarily localized in liver Golgi as compared to endoplasmic reticulum and plasma membranes.

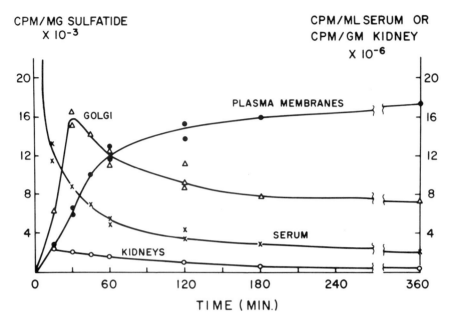

Figure 12. Rate of appearance of radioactive sulfatide in isolated Golgi apparatus and plasma membrane fractions from rat kidney after intravenous injection of the rats with ^{35}S-sulfate at zero time. The values for serum and kidney are total counts. The Golgi and plasma membrane values are counts found in the glycolipid fraction prepared from the membranes and represent radioactive sulfatide. The time course of labeling is consistent with a precursor–product relationship between sulfatide of the Golgi apparatus and that of the plasma membrane.

OTHER MODIFICATIONS OF SECRETION PRODUCTS

The Golgi apparatus is involved in the secretion of simple proteins as well as glycoproteins. A well-studied example is the secretion of serum albumin by the Golgi apparatus of liver cells. After pulse-labeling with ^{14}C-leucine, radioactive serum albumin appears first in the rough endoplasmic reticulum of liver, then in the smooth endoplasmic reticulum, and finally in the Golgi apparatus (Figure 13). Release of radioactive albumin into the blood begins 15 min after injection of the label and continues steadily for 55 min, concurrent with its decline in the Golgi.

Within the cisternae of the RER, albumin exists in a precursor form, or proalbumin, consisting of albumin with an extension of five or six amino acids on its N-terminal end. During its passage through the smooth endoplasmic reticulum and the Golgi, the extension is cleaved so that the protein secreted is entirely in the albumin form (29) (Table 4).

A precursor form of proalbumin, called preproalbumin, has also been de-

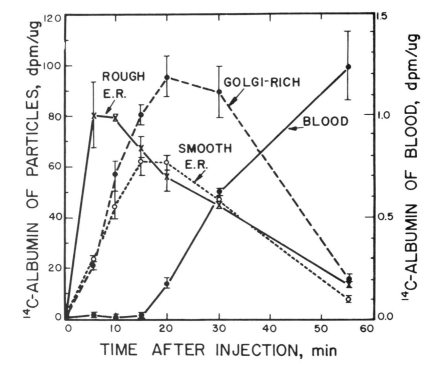

Figure 13. Appearance of newly synthesized serum albumin in cell fractions of rat liver after intravenous injection of ^{14}C-leucine. E.R., endoplasmic reticulum. Serum albumin was isolated from each cell fraction using a specific antiserum and the specific radioactivity of the purified albumin determined. Albumin, synthesized in rough endoplasmic reticulum, appears later in the smooth microsome and Golgi fractions with peak times of 16 and 22 min, respectively. Release of radioactive albumin into the blood begins after a lag of 15 min and proceeds steadily, concurrently with the decline in the Golgi. These results indicate the pathway of albumin secretion in the hepatocyte to be from the rough ER to the smooth ER to the Golgi to the blood. (Data from T. Peters, Jr., B. Fleischer, and S. Fleischer, *J. Biol. Chem.* 246:239–44, 1971.)

scribed (30). It is formed when mRNA for albumin is translated without the presence of membrane-bound polysomes and contains a 2500-dalton polypeptide extension on the N-terminal end of the albumin molecule. These findings can be explained by the "signal hypothesis" of Blöbel and Sabatini (31). Secreted proteins may carry, on their N-terminal end, a polypeptide that causes attachment of the nascent chain, and the polysome synthesizing it, to the endoplasmic reticulum membrane. This "signal peptide" then penetrates the membrane, and, during translation of the remainder of the mRNA, the completed protein moves through the membrane into the cisternae of the RER. During the secretion process, the signal peptide is cleaved off,

Table 4.   The Ratio of Proalbumin to Albumin in Subcellular Fractions of Rat Liver.

SUBCELLULAR FRACTION	PROALBUMIN (%)	ALBUMIN (%)	PROALBUMIN ——————— ALBUMIN
Rough endoplasmic reticulum	95	5	19
Smooth endoplasmic reticulum	51	49	1.0
Golgi apparatus	33	67	0.5
Supernatant fraction[a]	0	100	0.0

[a] Albumin in the supernatant fraction is derived mainly from blood in the liver used to obtain the subcellular fractions. [From studies of K. Edwards, B. Fleischer, H. Dryburgh, S. Fleischer, and G. Schreiber (29).]

probably in the RER, and additional specific cleavages may occur before the protein is finally discharged. These cleavages may occur during the passage of the protein from the endoplasmic reticulum to the Golgi apparatus or in the Golgi apparatus before release of the secreted protein. A number of secreted proteins in addition to albumin have now been shown to be synthesized initially in a larger form and to undergo post-translation cleavage during the secretion progress, including insulin, glucagon, parathyroid hormone, immunoglobulin light chain, and trypsinogen. Not all secreted proteins undergo this type of post-translational modification, however; so cleavage is not a prerequisite for the secretion step.

ROLE OF GOLGI IN THE BIOSYNTHESIS OF OTHER CELL ORGANELLES

Lysosomes

Primary lysosomes are intracellular granules or membrane-limited vesicles filled with acid hydrolases of various types. They contain a stored form of these enzymes and fuse with plasma-membrane-derived endocytotic or pinocytotic vesicles to form secondary lysosomes which carry on intracellular digestion. Primary lysosomes are clearly analogous to the zymogen granules of secretory cells and are present ubiquitously in mammalian cells and many plant cells as well. In certain cell types, there is good evidence that primary lysosomes are formed via the Golgi apparatus by mechanisms analogous to those described previously for pancreas secretory granules. In spermatids the Golgi is involved in the formation of proacrosome granules which fuse to form the acrosome, a caplike structure at the head of the mature spermatozoan. The acrosome contains acid hydrolases and functions during penetration of the oocyte membrane by the sperm. Another example is the polymorphonuclear leukocyte, a phagocytic blood cell that contains two types of hydrolytic granules, azurophils and specific granules. The azurophils are a special type of primary lysosome containing acid hydrolases as well as peroxidase, whereas the specific granules contain alkaline phosphatase. Both types of granules are formed via the same Golgi apparatus, at different times and from different sides of the same Golgi stack (32). By histochemical staining for acid phosphatases, a specialized region of smooth membranes between the endoplasmic reticulum and the Golgi apparatus, termed GERL (33), has been implicated in the formation of lysosomes in some cells.

Plasma Membrane Glycoproteins and Glycolipids

Most of the glycoproteins of the plasma membrane are located on the external surface of the cell. The distribution of glycolipids in plasma membranes has not been defined. Carbohydrates on the cell surface in the form of glycolipids and glycoproteins have considerable biological importance as immunological determinants, cell recognition and adhesion sites, viral receptors, and possibly hormone receptors, as well. There is considerable circumstantial evidence that the Golgi is involved in the biosynthesis of these membrane components, although glycosylations of glycoproteins at the cell surface may also occur (34) (see, however, Ref. 35). Radioactive fucose, incorporated initially into glycoproteins in the Golgi apparatus, is found later in the plasma membrane (36). Specific plasma membrane components such as acetylcholine receptors in developing embryonic myotubes have recently been shown cytochemically to be present in the Golgi apparatus and to be on the pathway of transport of newly synthesized receptors into the plasma membrane (37). 5'-Nucleotidase (38) and adenyl cyclase (39), characteristic enzymes of liver plasma membranes, have also been shown cytochemically to be present in liver Golgi membranes although there are no data as yet on the possible precursor relationship of the Golgi enzymes with the plasma membrane enzymes. Topologically, 5'-nucleotidase is present on the cisternal side of the secretory vesicle membrane while adenyl cyclase is on the cytoplasmic side. This is the correct orientation for transfer to the plasma membrane after fusion, as 5'-nucleotidase is on the outside of the plasma membrane while adenyl cyclase is on the cytoplasmic side. The mechanism of transport is presumably the fusion of secretory Golgi membranes with the plasma membrane during exocytosis. This process must be regulated in a number of as yet unknown ways because it occurs at specific parts of the plasma membrane in most cells, and because there is no general mixing of the membrane components of the Golgi with the plasma membrane (i.e., both retain their unique chemical and enzymatic characteristics). The fusion step is known to require energy and calcium ions. It is possible that Golgi membranes, after fusion with the plasma membrane, are recycled back into the cell in the form of pinocytotic vesicles.

ACKNOWLEDGMENTS

The authors thank Mr. Akitsugu Saito for the electron micrographs from our laboratory used in this paper. The work was supported in part by Grants AM 14632 and AM 17223 of the U.S. Public Health Service.

REFERENCES

General Reviews:

Beams, H. W., and Kessel, R. G. 1968. The Golgi apparatus: Structure and function. *Int. Rev. Cytol.* 23:209–76.
Whaley, W. G. 1975. *The Golgi Apparatus,* Cell Biology Monographs, Vol. 2. Springer-Verlag, New York.
Palade, G. 1975. Intracellular aspects of the process of protein synthesis. *Science* 189:347–58.

Specific References:

1. Golgi, C. 1903. *Opera Omnia,* Vol. 2, pp. 643–76. Ulrico Hoepli, Milano.
2. Dalton, A. J., and Felix, M. D. 1953. *Am. J. Anat.* 92:277–305.
3. Friend, D. A. 1969. *J. Cell Biol.* 41:269–79.
4. Jamieson, J. D., and Palade, G. E. 1967. *J. Cell Biol.* 34:577–96, 597–615.
5. Neutra, M., and LeBlond, C. P. 1966. *J. Cell Biol.* 30:119–36.
6. Schachter, J., Jabbal, I., Hudgin, R. L., Pinteric, L., McGuire, E. J., and Roseman, S. 1970. *J. Biol. Chem.* 245:1090–1100.
7. Mahley, R. W., Hamilton, R. L., and LeQuire, V. S. 1969. *J. Lipid Res.* 10:433–39.
8. Brown, R. M., Jr. and Willison, J. H. M. 1974. In *International Cell Biology 1976–1977,* B. R. Brinkley and K. R. Porter, eds., pp. 267–83. Rockefeller University Press, New York.
9. Waechter, C. J., and Lennarz, W. J. 1976. *Annu. Rev. Biochem.* 45:95–112.
10. Roseman, S. 1970. *Chem. Phys. Lipids* 5:270–97.
11. Tulsiani, D. R. P., Opheim, J. D., and Touster, O. 1977. *J. Biol. Chem.* 252:3227–33.
12. Bingham, E. W., and Farrell, H. M., Jr. 1974. *J. Biol. Chem.* 249:3647–51.
13. Horwitz, A. L., and Dorfman, A. 1968. *J. Cell Biol.* 38:358–68.
14. Somlyo, A. P., Garfield, R. E., Chacko, S., and Somlyo, A. V. 1975. *J. Cell Biol.* 66:425–43.
15. Kuff, E. L., and Dalton, A. J. 1959. In *Subcellular Particles,* T. Hayashi, ed., pp. 114–27. Ronald Press, New York.
16. Mollenhauer, H. H., Morré, D. J., and Bergmann, L. 1967. *Anat. Rec.* 158:313–18.
17. Claude, A. 1970. *J. Cell Biol.* 47:745–66.
18. Fleischer, B., Fleischer, S., and Ozawa, H. 1969. *J. Cell Biol.* 43:59–79.
19. Fleischer, B. 1974. *Methods Enzymol.* 31:180–91.
20. Morré, D. J., Hamilton, R. L., Mollenhauer, H. H., Mahley, R. W., Cunningham, W. P., Cheetham, R. D., and LeQuire, V. S. 1970. *J. Cell Biol.* 44:484–91.

21. Ehrenreich, J. H., Bergeron, J. J. M., Siekevitz, P., and Palade, G. E. 1973. *J. Cell Biol.* 59:45–72.
22. Zambrano, F., Fleischer, S., and Fleischer, B. 1975. *Biochim Biophys. Acta* 350:357–69.
23. Keenan, T. W., Nyquist, S. E., and Mollenhauer, H. H. 1972. *Biochim. Biophys. Acta* 270:433–43.
24. Kornblatt, M. J., Knapp, A., Levine, M., Schachter, H., and Murray, R. K. 1974. *Can. J. Biochem.* 52:689–97.
25. Smith, C. A., and Brew, K. 1977. *J. Biol. Chem.* 252:7294–99.
26. Fleischer, B., and Smigel, M. 1978. *J. Biol. Chem.* 252:1632–38.
27. Stein, O., and Stein, Y. 1967. *J. Cell Biol.* 33:319–39.
28. Fleischer, B., Zambrano, F., and Fleischer, S. 1974. *J. Supramol. Struct.* 2:737–50.
29. Edwards, K., Fleischer, B., Dryburgh, H., Fleischer, S., and Schreiber, G. 1976. *Biochem. Biophys. Res. Commun.* 72:310–18.
30. Strauss, A. W., Donohue, A. M., Bennett, C. D., Rodkey, J. A., and Alberts, A. W. 1977. *Proc. Natl. Acad. Sci. U.S.A.* 74:1358–62.
31. Blöbel, G. 1977. In *International Cell Biology, 1976–1977,* B. R. Brinkley and K. R. Porter, eds., pp. 318–25. Rockefeller University Press, New York.
32. Bainton, D. F., Nichols, B. A., and Farquar, M. G. 1976. In *Lysosomes in Biology and Pathology,* J. T. Dingle and R. T. Dean, eds., Vol. 5, pp. 3–32. North-Holland, Amsterdam.
33. Novikoff, A. B. 1976. *Proc. Natl. Acad. Sci.* 73:2781–87.
34. Shur, B. D., and Roth, S. 1975. *Biochim. Biophys. Acta* 415:473–512.
35. Deppert, W., Werchau, J., and Walter, G. 1974. *Proc. Natl. Acad. Sci. U.S.A.* 71:3068–72.
36. Bennett, G., LeBlond, C. P., and Haddad, A. 1974. *J. Cell Biol.* 60:258–84.
37. Fambrough, D., and Devreotes, P. N. 1978. *J. Cell Biol.* 76:237–44.
38. Farquhar, M. G., Bergeron, J. J. M., and Palade, G. 1974. *J. Cell Biol.* 60:8–25.
39. Cheng, H., and Farquar, M. G. 1976. *J. Cell Biol.* 70:671–84.

4.8. Secretory Granules

Michael J. Wilson

Secretory granules are membrane-bound vesicles in which secretory material is accumulated, condensed, and stored prior to export from the secretory cell. This material may include simple fluids such as water or dilute salt solutions, low-molecular-weight molecules such as the catecholamines, peptides, proteins, or macromolecular complexes, or, as in plant cells, preformed subunits for the cell wall. Secretory granules are formed in association with the Golgi apparatus and are found in the cytoplasm between the Golgi region and the plasma membrane.

The synthesis, intracellular transport, and storage of exportable proteins have been studied in a variety of secretory cell model systems including those of the pancrease, salivary gland, liver, thyroid follicular cells, odontoblasts, and others. The general schema established concerning these intracellular events includes: (1) synthesis of the secretory proteins on polyribosomes attached to endoplasmic reticulum (ER) and vectoral transfer of the proteins to the cisternae of the rough endoplasmic reticulum (RER), (2) movement of secretory proteins through the RER to smooth-surfaced transitional regions and to the Golgi complex culminating in packaging in secretory granules, and (3) postsynthetic modifications of the secretory proteins during intracellular transport leading to granule formation. (See Figure 1.)

SECRETORY GRANULE FORMATION

Although generalizations of molecular events in the secretory process have often been inferred from the most extensively studied model of the exocrine pancreatic cell, variations in individual steps have been reported and will be noted in the following discussion. In the guinea pig pancreas, the genesis of secretory granules occurs in close proximity to the trans (exit) side of the Golgi membranes and is marked by the formation of condensing vacuoles. Pulse labeling of secretory proteins with radioactive amino acids suggests that these proteins pass from RER to the transitional elements of the ER; at this site small vesicles are formed that carry the seceretory proteins to the condensing vacuoles. At present, some uncertainty exists concerning the mechanism of passage of secretory material through these vesicles to the

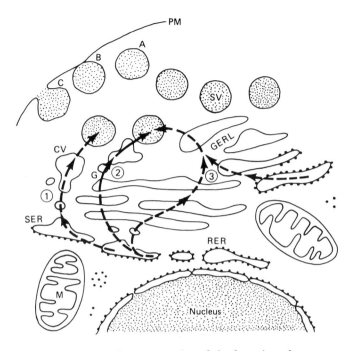

Figure 1. A diagramatic representation of the formation of secretory granules and the release of secretory material during exocytosis. Three pathways of transport of secretory proteins to the secretory vesicles (SV) have been postulated to exist. In each pathway, secretory proteins are synthesized on the rough endoplasmic reticulum (RER) and pass to the smooth endoplasmic reticulum (SER). In pathway (1), secretory material passes via small vesicles to condensing vacuoles (CV), which mature into secretory vesicles. In pathway (2), secretory material passes to the Golgi (G) membranes via small vesicles and thence by small vesicles from the dilated rims of the Golgi cisternae to aggregating vesicles forming the secretory vesicles. In pathway (3), the secretory material may pass through the smooth membranes into the dilations of the GERL or through the Golgi membranes to the GERL. The secretory granules mature from the vesiculated membranes. The process of release of secretory material from the cell involves the movement of secretory granules to the plasma membrane (PM) (step A), followed by fusion to the plasmalemma (B), and then rupture of the membrane and extrusion of the granular contents (C).

condensing vacuoles. Palade and coworkers consider the condensing vacuoles to be part of the Golgi system, existing as dilations of these membranes on the trans side of the Golgi membrane stacks. This conclusion is substantiated by subfractionation studies of Golgi membranes showing no differences in biochemical parameters of the Golgi stacks and other Golgi membranes. In addition, radioactive secretory protein can be localized in the dilated rims of the Golgi cisternae of guinea pig pancreas hyperstimulated by the secreto-gogue carbamylcholine. The transport vesicles may be an independent system in secretory granule formation or may be part of a specialized region of the ER associated with the Golgi apparatus and also involved in lysosome formation, the GERL (Golgi–endoplasmic reticulum–lysosomes). In many glandular cells concentration of secretory material takes place in the dilated ends of the more trans Golgi cisternae or swellings of the innermost saccule. In developing eosinophils, peroxidase activity is localized in the ER and transitional elements, Golgi cisternae, and immature and mature secretory granules; hence the stacked Golgi cisternae take part in the segregation of this secretory protein. Secretory granules arise as vesiculation from these membranes, and in some cells, such as pituitary mammotrophs, these vesicles may fuse, forming an aggregate analogous to the condensing vacuole during maturation of the secretory granule.

The GERL system is found in close relation to the Golgi, but it can be distinguished from the Golgi cisternae stacks by the cytochemical demonstration of acid phosphatase specifically in the former and thiamine pyrophosphatase in the latter. The GERL membranes may be found separated from the Golgi cisternal stacks, whereas separations between adjacent stacked Golgi saccules are not observed. The participation of the GERL in the formation of condensing vacuoles is evidenced by the morphological continuity of condensing vacuoles as expanded cisternae from the GERL and the presence of acid phosphatase activity in both membranous components. In the rat exorbital lacrimal gland, the secretory enzyme peroxidase can be demonstrated in cisternae of the nuclear envelope, RER, Golgi vesicles and saccules, and immature and mature secretory granules; but not the GERL. This suggests that the Golgi saccules are involved in the transport of this secretory protein, and the GERL is engaged in secretory granule formation. In melanoma cells, tyrosinase and acid phosphatase activities have been shown in both the GERL and premelanosomes (secretory granules), whereas in most secretory cell types acid phosphatase activity, although found in condensing vacuoles, is not found in mature secretory granules. Since the GERL appears to participate in both secretory granule and lysosome formation, and the protein constituents of their contents arise via the same synthetic and intracellular transport system, an important question arises concerning the nature of the mechanism by which the GERL can recognize lysosomal and secretory proteins and separate them into the appropriate cellular organelles.

CONCENTRATION OF SECRETORY MATERIAL

The transport of secretory proteins to the Golgi membranes is not the result of a simple concentration gradient between the ER and Golgi, but has been determined to require metabolic energy in the form of ATP. This transport phenomenon is also independent of continued protein synthesis, since preformed proteins move into the Golgi membranes and secretory granules in the presence of protein synthesis inhibitors. The secretory proteins reach the Golgi cisternae and/or condensing vacuoles in a dilute solution. Concentration of the secretory material proceeds in these membranous compartments by an apparent energy-independent process; active pumping of water or other molecules from the condensing vacuoles probably only occurs to a limited extent. It appears that in the condensation process, water outflow is dependent on simple osmosis due to the low osmotic pressure of the vacuolar protein content. This osmotic gradient may be potentiated by the formation of large aggregates of the predominantly basic secretory proteins in ionic interaction with a sulfated polyanion. Such a molecule, a sulfated peptidoglycan, has been found in pancreatic discharge and secretory granule content. The secretory material of prolactin granules of rat pituitary gland appears to be arranged in solid-state organization, since it is unaffected by removal of the limiting membrane by nonionic detergents. In such a membranous granule, prolactin accounts for more than 80% of the protein present, and other macromolecules include sulfated glycosaminoglycans (e.g., heparin and chrondoitin sulfate), which participate in the formation of high-molecular-weight proteoglycans (three to four discrete peptide components of 60,000 to 80,000 daltons molecular weight are present) through their linkage to peptide moieties. The osmotic effects resulting in concentration of secretory material could also be achieved through other ionic interactions leading to paracrystal formation, as in the binding of small peptides to carrier proteins (e.g., neurophysins).

INTRACELLULAR STORAGE

Secretory Granule Membranes

In the formation of the secretory granule, the secretory material is transferred through a variety of subcellular membranes possessing individual properties to a membrane that approximates the plasma membrane. The secretory granule membrane which comes from the Golgi complex has a lipid composition similar to that of the plasma membrane, and as such has a decreased permeability (especially compared to the ER). The study of individual protein components of the secretory granule membrane (2–3% of the total granule protein) has been made difficult owing to contamination by residual granule-content proteins in isolated preparations. The majority of proteins of storage granule membranes appear to be of a relatively limited number of individual species of a molecular weight of 40,000 daltons or greater, and several react in the PAS procedure, suggesting the presence of bound polysaccharide. Pulse labeling experiments using radioactive amino acids indicate that the synthesis of membrane proteins occurs at a rate much slower than that of granule-content proteins. It thus appears that membrane proteins are reutilized following secretory discharge. Few of the vesicular membrane proteins have been identified with respect to their function. Granule proteins possess endogenous protein kinase activity which can phosphorylate several membrane proteins, a phenomenon that may be important in the discharge process. In chromaffin granules ATPase, dopamine β-hydroxylase, cytochrome b 561, and cytochrome b 561:NADH reductase are constitutent membrane proteins (no function has been established for this electron transport system). In addition to protein, secretory granule membranes are rich in lipids. Chromaffin granule membranes, for example, have a high cholesterol-to-lipid-phosphorus ratio, and of the phospholipids, lysolecithin (17% of lipid phosphorus) is present in high concentrations.

Secretory Granule Content

Even though the pancreatic exocrine cell packages a complex mixture of secretory proteins, primarily enzymes and proenzymes, for export, individual secretion granules appear to contain samples of each product. For example, immunocytochemical procedures in the bovine pancreas have shown no qualitative differences in granule or cell distribution of trypsinogen, chymotrypsinogen, deoxyribonuclease, and ribonuclease. In addition, autoradiographic studies show a random distribution of newly formed secretory granules among preexisting granules, and upon discharge of secretory material from these cells, there is also a random appearance of recently and previously synthesized proteins. This suggests a slow diffusion of secretory granules, resulting in mixing of "old" and "new" granules in the apical region of the cell and a parallel processing of the secretory proteins during intracellular transport and at discharge. The major secretory proteins of guinea pig pancreatic lobules in a resting state, or upon stimulation of secretion in vitro, are discharged in constant proportions. However, this situation may not be typical for all exocrine cells, since autoradiography of secretory proteins in rabbit parotid salivary gland shows an absence of randomized distribution of newly formed granules during secretory granule accumulation. The recently acquired granules are found near the site of their assembly and rarely near the apical plasmalemma.

DISCHARGE OF SECRETION

The process of exocytosis, which results in the discharge of secretory material from the secretory granules and from the cell, commences with the fusion of the granule membrane to the plasma membrane. This process involves the elimination of membrane layers, progressing to fission of the membrane, resulting in a continuity of the extracellular space with that of the secretory granule. The interaction of the plasma membrane and granule in initiation of secretion as observed in freeze-fracture electron microscopy in the mast cell is marked by the formation of circular impressions on the E fracture face of the plasmalemma. These sites, which resemble nuclear pores, are 80–100 nm in diameter and are encircled with particles. Sites of fusion for the secretory granule membrane are denoted by the appearance of rings of particles and additional particle-surrounded raised areas (48–87 nm diameter) on the granule E face. There is a high degree of specificity in this process with respect to membrane recognition and fusion; other than the fusion of granule membrane to granule membrane, preliminary to tandem granule discharge, the granule membrane has only been observed to fuse with the plasma membrane. In an exocrine cell, this process is unique to the luminal portion of the plasmalemma.

Exocytosis has generally been found to be dependent upon availability of energy and calcium. Calcium in pancreatic acinar cells is associated with the plasma membrane, secretory granule membranes, smooth-microsomal membranes, and mitochondria. Stimulation of secretion in isolated acini results in a rapid loss of mitochondrial Ca^{2+}, whereas no change is observed in the other membrane fractions. This would suggest that Ca^{2+} may not be involved in stimulus-secretion coupling but may play a role in the structure of the granule. However, Ca^{2+} has been observed to accumulate in chromaffin granules during secretion. In secretion coupled to a stimulus response, the process also often requires a cyclic nucleotide generating system (e.g., cAMP) and the mediation of a protein kinase(s). Certain secretory membrane proteins can be phosphorylated by endogenous protein kinase, but their role in the secretory process has not been established. The release of secretory material can be induced in vitro by ATP and prevented in vivo by blocking ATP synthesis. An ATPase in the granule membrane may participate in the release process and may account for part of the P_i formed. In chromaffin granules, phosphorylation of protein and the lipid, diphosphatidylinositol (phosphorylation of monophosphatidylinositol via phosphatidylinositol kinase), also occurs. At least two high-molecular-weight proteins are phosphorylated but account for less than 10% of the phosphorylated membrane components when compared to the lipids. A role for diphosphatidylinositol or other phospholipids in the secretory process has not been elucidated.

Microtubules have been suggested to play a role in exocytosis, particularly because agents such as colchicine, known to depolymerize microtubules, inhibit secretion. However, the role of microtubules has not been clearly established. For example, few microtubules and microfilaments are present in the apical region of the pancreatic exocrine cell. In addition, colchicine promptly inhibits secretory discharge in hepatocytes at a time before morphological changes of microtubules can be demonstrated. A fibrillar network does appear around discharging granules in the pancreatic exocrine cell and is continuous with the fibrillar elements (terminal web) of the luminal plasmalemma. This network may have a contractile function to assist expulsion of secretory granule contents.

A perplexing question concerning exocytosis has been that of the fate of the secretory granule membrane added to the plasma membrane during the secretory process. There is evidence that excess membrane is removed from the plasma membrane and is reutilized. Studies following endocytosis of cytochemical markers have indicated that membranous vesicles migrate into the cell interior; in cells of the pituitary and vas deferens these vesicles have been localized to the Golgi region. The presence of marker in Golgi saccules and secretory granules suggests the possible addition of granule membrane directly into that of the Golgi. However, the fusion of lysosomes with vacuoles and multivesicular bodies containing marker molecules taken up in endocytic processes implicates these hydrolytic enzymes in the breakdown of retrieved luminal membrane. The manner in which the membrane might be utilized (i.e., as whole membrane pieces, as subunits, or as individual molecular species) is not clear, but these data are in concert with the observation that the rate of incorporation of newly synthesized protein components into secretory granule membranes is slower than that of the secretory proteins of the granule contents, implying that newly synthesized proteins of membrane protein pools are diluted by reutilized membrane proteins.

The formation of the secretory granule is an intermediate step in the total secretory process. However, it is also the culmination of a series of discontinuous steps involving the synthesis, modification, and shuttling of secretory material through a variety of membrane compartments to a point of storage prior to discharge from the cell. Specific properties of the secretory granule membrane appear to control its involvement in the discharge process, particularly in interaction with specific areas of the plasmalemma (e.g., apical plasma membrane in exocrine cells) and possibly also in the release mechanism itself.

SELECTED REFERENCES

Blaschko, H., Firemark, H., Smith, A. D., and Winkler, H. 1967. *Biochem. J.* 104:545–49.
Bogart, B. I. 1975. *J. Ultrastruct. Res.* 52:139–55.
Burwen, S. J., and Satir, B. H. 1977. *J. Cell Biol.* 73:660–71.
Castle, J. D., Jamieson, J. D., and Palade, G. E. 1975. *J. Cell Biol.* 64:182–210.
Chandler, D. E., and Williams, J. A. 1978. *J. Cell Biol.* 76:386–99.
Clemente, F., and Meldolesi, J. 1975. *Br. J. Pharmacol.* 55:369–79.
Farqubar, M. G., Skutelsky, E. H., and Hopkins, C. R. 1975. Structure and function of the

anterior pituitary and dispersed pituitary cells. In vitro studies. In *The Anterior Pituitary*, A. Tixier-Vidal and M. G. Farquhar, eds., pp. 83–135. Academic Press, New York.

Giannattasio, G., and Zanini, A. 1976. *Biochim. Biophys. Acta* 439:349–57.

Hand, A. R., and Oliver, C. 1977. *J. Cell Biol.* 74:399–413.

Jamieson, J. D., and Palade, G. E. 1977. Production of secretory proteins in animal cells. In *International Cell Biology* B. R. Brinkley and K. R. Porter, eds., pp. 308–317. Rockefeller University Press, New York.

Kirshner, N. 1974. *Adv. Cytopharmacol.* 2:265–72.

Morre, J. D. 1977. Membrane differentiation and the control of secretion. A comparison of plant and animal Golgi apparatus. In *International Cell Biology*, B. R. Brinkley and K. R. Porter, eds. pp. 293–303. Rockefeller University Press, New York.

Muller, T. W., and Kirshner, N. 1975. *J. Neurochem.* 24:1155–61.

Novikoff, A. B., Mori, M., Quintana, N., and Yam, A. 1977. *J. Cell Biol.* 75:148–65.

Palade, G. 1975. *Science* 189:347–58.

Pelletier, G. 1974. *J. Ultrastruct. Res.* 43:445–59.

Poisner, A. M., and Douglas, W. W. 1968. *Mol. Pharmacol.* 4:531–40.

Rasmussen, H., Jensen, P., and Goodman, D. B. P. 1976. In *Stimulus-Secretion Coupling in the Gastrointestinal Tract*, R. M. Case and H. Goebell, eds., pp. 33–47. University Park Press, Baltimore.

Serck-Hanssen, G., and Christiansen, E. N. 1973. *Biochim. Biophys. Acta* 307:404–14.

Trifaro, J. M., and Dworkind, J. 1975. *Can. J. Physiol. Pharmacol.* 53:479–92.

Wallach, D., Kirshner, N., and Schramm, M. 1975. *Biochim. Biophys. Acta* 375:87–105.

4.9. Lysosomes

Michael J. Wilson and Said A. Goueli

The concept of the lysosome grew from the original observations of de Duve and coworkers, in the early 1950s, that activities of acid hydrolase enzymes in liver homogenates increased upon standing. This phenomenon was due to the patency of membrane-limited subcellular structures containing these enzymes. In subsequent studies, lysosomes have been found in all cell types as sedimentable vesicles whose most common identifying characteristics are limitation by a single membrane and the presence of hydrolytic enzymes with acidic pH optima. Ultrastructural studies, facilitated by cytochemical localization of acid phosphatase, showed that lysosomes from different cells vary considerably in size, structure, density, and enzyme content. The morphological diversity of lysosomes is suggestive of the variety of cellular processes in which these organelles have been implicated.

LYSOSOME FORMATION

The diversity of structures and enzymatic activities of lysosomes has been recognized, but the presence of certain characteristics has permitted the classification of this family of related particles in the lysosome system. The polymorphism appears to be the result of fusion of primary lysosomes with different endocytized materials and cellular particles forming secondary lysosomes.

The general features of formation of primary lysosomes are similar to those observed in secretory granule formation (see Chapter 4.8). The hydrolytic enzymes of lysosomes appear to be synthesized on polysomes of the rough endoplasmic reticulum and from there translocated through the smooth endoplasmic reticulum to the Golgi apparatus and eventually to lysosomes. Kinetic studies of β-glucuronidase and cathepsin D synthesis and transport in rabbit liver using immunochemical procedures, in addition to other reports showing cytochemical localization of hydrolase activities in the Golgi apparatus, substantiate this route of transit for these enzymes prior to lysosome formation. However, a modification of this scheme involves a specialized region of the smooth endoplasmic reticulum, located at the inner or trans portions of the Golgi apparatus, in lysosome formation. This portion of the smooth endoplasmic reticulum, the GERL (Golgi–endoplasmic reticulum–lysosomes) can be distinguished from the Golgi saccules by the cytochemical demonstration of acid phosphatase in the former and thiamine pyrophosphatase in the latter. Other lysosomal hydrolases, arylsulfatase and esterase activities, have also been localized cytochemically to the GERL. The Golgi and GERL systems are also involved in assembly of secretory granules in addition to lysosome formation; hence an important role undertaken by these membranes is the sequestering of the specific enzymes for each organelle into the individual membrane compartments even though they are apparently being channeled to the packaging site through the same membrane systems. Lysosomal packaging, however, is not an uniform process, since heterogeneity of enzymic composition in lysosomes is found. For example, differential centrifugation studies of liver lysosomes indicate the presence of at least two populations, one sedimenting in the heavy mitochondrial fraction (density of 1.22) and containing high acid nuclease activity and a second fraction of lower density (1.206) possessing higher acid phosphatase and β-glucuronidase activities. In monocytes, various types of primary lysosome can be distinguished cytochemically, and in *Tetrahymena,* protease-rich and glycosidase-rich lysosomes are present.

Lysosomes thus originating from the Golgi or GERL are termed primary lysosomes. Secondary lysosomes are the product of fusion of primary lysosomes with other vesicles or cytoplasmic bodies; the hydrolytic enzymes contributed by primary lysosomes are active in digestion of the enclosed materials. The vesicles that thus become part of the lysosome system originate from a number of sources. Cells are capable of internalizing extracellular material by endocytosis, a process involving enclosure of the material in an invagination of the plasma membrane which then blebs into the cytoplasm. When the endocytic vacuole contains particulate material, the process is referred to as phagocytosis; whereas if it contains soluble material, it is termed pinocytosis. Endocytic vacuoles become digestive vacuoles or phagolysosomes when they receive lysosomal hydrolases upon fusion with primary lysosomes or other digestive vacuoles. Ingested material such as carbon or asbestos particles cannot be digested, whereas biological materials in general can be catabolized. Some types of lipids, however, are degraded slowly and tend to accumulate in secondary lysosomes; their subsequent oxidation results in the colored "aging" pigments known as lipofuscin. Digestive vacuoles containing undigested material, which may be in the form of electron-dense material, membranous whorls, and so on, are referred to as residual bodies. In residual bodies these residues tend to accumulate, and the organelles increase in size. Multivesicular bodies are secondary lysosomes characterized by the presence of a number of internal vesicles. Such a structure has been thought to arise through several possible means, including a collection of pinocytized material, a collection of primary lysosomes remaining as discrete structures, or membrane remnants of lysosome-engulfed material.

The intracellular degradation of cellular components, autophagy, is common during tissue regression (physiological or pathological) and programmed cell death. This process may progress by two means: (1) cytoplasmic constituents may be enclosed by pairs of smooth endoplasmic reticulum membranes forming double-membrane-bound vesicles; or (2) lysosomes may invaginate and engulf a portion of cytoplasm forming a double-membrane-bound vesicle. The inner membrane of either type of autophagic vacuole disappears, and lysosomal enzymes are contributed by fusing lysosomes or the membranes of origin. Autophagy, particularly when autophagic vacuoles are small, can be difficult to recognize with electron microscopy, but in larger vacuoles the presence of certain subcellular organelles such as mitochondria facilitates identification. It is also difficult to estimate the rate of autophagy in a cell or tissue, since it is difficult to determine the half-lives of these vesicles.

METHODS OF STUDY

The separation of various subcellular organelles has relied on differential and density gradient centrifugation methods. But although lysosomes have a slightly greater density than mitochondria, there is considerable overlap between the two; hence these traditional methods do not yield entirely pure fractions. The density of lysosomes, however, can be altered through the uptake by endocytosis of several materials that may increase (Dextran 500, iron, gold) or decrease (Triton WR-1339) lysosome density, facilitating isolation by means of centrifugation. Practically, however, these modified procedures may be limited to study of certain cells or tissues (e.g., following in vivo administration, the nonlytic detergent Triton WR-1339 is accumulated well in liver but not kidney lysosomes). An alternative technique which has proved successful in lysosome isolation is carrier-free continuous electrophoresis. The structural integrity of isolated fractions is evaluated by comparison of the latency and sedimentability of the isolated lysosomes and the original homogenate. The presence of nonlysosomal structures is assessed through the distribution of organelle-specific marker enzymes and electron microscopy and cytochemistry. Because of the heterogeneity of lysosomes, the above isolation procedures often yield purified fractions of a subpopulation of the lysosomal system, mainly secondary lysosomes.

The specific identification of lysosomes in electron micrographs is also hampered because of the heterogeneity of these organelles. One structural characteristic common to lysosomes is that their limiting membrane, like the plasma membrane, is thicker compared to other intracellular membranes. In addition, the lysosome limiting membrane is often separated from the matrix by an electron-lucent halo. Primary lysosomes have a diameter of about 70 nm and are generally smaller than the coated vesicles (average diameter about 140 nm) often found in the region of the Golgi. These coated vesicles apparently arise as interiorized portions of the plasma membrane. Another criterion of lysosome identity is the presence of acid hydrolase activity. Histochemical procedures may be used to localize these activities in the cell, but, unfortunately, at the level of the electron microscope methods that have been developed are limited to only a few enzymes. The most satisfactory cytochemical technique is for acid phosphatase, whereas those available for arylsulfatase, dipeptidyl aminopeptidase I, and nonspecific esterase are less adequate. However, immunocytochemical techniques, commonly using horseradish peroxidase conjugated antibody methods, can be used to localize those lysosomal enzymes (e.g., cathepsin D) to which antibodies have been prepared. Other ultrastructural methods for the study of lysosomes utilize markers that are phagocytosed by cells and can be visualized microscopically. These substances may include: (1) those with high electron density such as colloidal carbon, colloidal metals (thorium dioxide, gold), and iron-containing molecules (ferritin); (2) enzymes that can be visualized cytochemically (peroxidase) and ^{125}I-labeled proteins localized by autoradiography; (3) macromolecules leading to increased lysosomal size (Triton WR-1339, dextran).

COMPOSITION

About 60 enzymes, primarily glycoproteins, have been found to be associated with lysosomes in one or more cell types. This list includes glycosidases, nucleases, proteinases, sulfatases, phospholipases, and phosphatases, with the enzymic capacity to hydrolyze peptide, glycosidic, and ester linkages of macromolecules. The majority of these enzymes are associated with the matrix of the lysosome and are neutral or cationic in nature with isoelectric points usually greater than 7.0. The pH optima of these enzymes are normally acidic although a few show maximal activities at neutral pHs (e.g., myeloperoxidase of the neutrophil leucocyte, an elastase, a lipase, and cathepsin G). The acidic pH optima of lysosomal acid hydrolases have been taken to indicate a role of carboxyl groups (pK 2.2–5.1) in the catalytic mechanism of these enzymes. However, the pK of a cysteine thiol group or the hydroxyl group of serine (functional groups in certain proteinases) may be depressed in the environment of the active site. Some lysosomal enzymes appear to be membrane-bound, and cathepsin B and an elastase have been suggested to be exposed on the external surface of the lysosome. Lysosomal membranes, sedimented following lysis in hypotonic medium, contain about 35% of the protein, 75% of the phospholipid, and 70% of the cholesterol of the original lysosome fraction. The lysosomal membrane contains significant carbohydrate, and is particularly rich in sialic acid (about 16 $\mu g/mg$ protein). The matrix of rat kidney and liver lysosomes is also rich in lipoproteins, which are generally negatively charged, contain some carbohydrate, and are devoid of enzymic activity. They may account for nearly half of the organelle's protein. The control of the activity of the lysosomal hydrolytic enzymes such that self-digestion of lysosomal constituents is prevented may be mediated in part by the close interaction of the cationic enzymes with the anionic lipoproteins. Lysosomal lipids generally resemble those of mitochondria except that they contain significant amounts of cholesterol and sphingomyelin, a property characteristic of plasma membranes. Although lysosomal membranes also resemble plasma membranes in a number of ways (e.g., morphologically), they each contain unique antigens. Lysosomes have also been found to contain high proportions of flavins and several metals (iron, manganese, etc.) compared to other organelles; this may be due to the binding of such positively charged material to the acidic anionic lysosomal lipoproteins.

The rates and control of formation of individual lysosomal components have not been well studied. Some data are available on the rates of synthesis of certain enzymes such as acid ribonuclease in regressing mammary tumor and in the hormonal induction of β-glucuronidase in mouse kidney. In general, increased activity of lysosomal enzymes appears to be dependent upon the synthesis of new enzyme molecules. The rates of degradation of lysosomal soluble and membranous protein constituents have been estimated following labeling with radioactive amino acids. A wide variation in half-lives for individual proteins has been found, ranging from about 24 hours to nearly 30 days. The reason(s) for the stability of lysosomal enzymes to the lysosomal acidic environment and presence of various proteinases has not been established.

FUNCTIONS OF LYSOSOMES

The role of lysosomes in various cellular fractions has been assumed to involve the digestive processes of the organelle whether they be of ingested material or participation in the maintenance of the balance between synthesis and degradation of cellular components. However, little evidence is available to show that autophagy is responsible for the regular turnover of intracellular constituents, and it is also difficult to always correlate the function of a tissue with the number of lysosomes present or the activity of their acid hydrolases. For example, the kidney of the rat is rich in lysosomes, whereas the same organ of the mouse is not. In addition, lysosomes are more numerous in the basal portion of proximal convoluted tubule cells in the rat, whereas in the mouse these organelles are positioned near the brush border of the luminal surface. The presence of greater numbers of lysosomes in cells has, however, been correlated with processes of absorption and digestion of large molecules, whereas the presence of fewer lysosomes correlates with cells utilizing small molecules.

The degradation of endocytized material is an important and well documented function carried out by lysosomes. Examples of this process include the digestion of bacteria by phagocytes, absorption of large molecules by kidney convoluted tubule and intestinal cells, and processing of thyroglobulin in the release of thyroid hormone by thyroid follicular cells. Lysosomes also have a major role in the degradation of intracellular proteins; however, the extent of lysosomal contribution to autophagy of subcellular organelles is not clear, since most cytoplasmic membranous organelles have an endogenous proteolytic system of their own. In protein hormone-secreting cells of the anterior pituitary, lysosomes function in the disposal of excess hormone not required for secretion. This process, termed crinophagy, interestingly does not proceed by the engulfment of the secretory granules by endoplasmic reticulum membranes, as often is observed in other autophagic processes, but by fusion directly with primary lysosomes.

The degradative process of lysosomes involves the breakdown of macromolecules to low-molecular-weight products that diffuse into the cytoplasm where they may be utilized by the cell for metabolic or synthetic purposes. The killing of organisms by phagocytes appears to involve a lysosomal peroxidase (utilizing chloride ion and hydrogen peroxide as substrate) and occurs with changes in permeability and loss of metabolites before significant breakdown of macromolecules occurs. In the breakdown of macromolecules several enzymes may act sequentially in a specific order to accomplish the task. For the catabolism of proteins, lysosomes possess several peptidases; it appears that intralysosomal proteolysis progresses by hydrolysis of internal peptide bonds by cathepsins B1 and D followed by breakdown of the resultant fragments by exopeptidases, cathepsins A and C.

Lysosomes play a role in differentiation through the employment of their digestive and autolytic properties in tissue remodeling or regression. Utilization of food stores upon the rapid mobilization of biosynthetic pathways during histogenesis of sponge gemmules (following hibernation) is carried out by lysosomes. Throughout embryonic development, programmed cell death is an important morphogenetic mechanism; it is observed in the autolysis of the tadpole tail following stimulation by thyroid hormone at metamorphosis and in the regression of the Mullerian duct in the developing male fetus. The role of lysosomes in these processes is not a primary cause of cell death but occurs as a secondary event. The dead cell may be partially digested by its own lysosomal hydrolases released into the cell. Autophagy is also accompanied by an influx of phagocytic cells into the area of necrosis to engulf and degrade the resultant cellular debris. In the necrotic tissue resulting from an infarct, massive tissue degradation occurs, and lysosomal and other cellular constituents may be found in the circulation. However, during mammary gland involution a more controlled process occurs; extensive autophagy is observed but is confined within large autolytic vesicles, and release of enzymes or materials into the circulation does not occur.

Lysosomes respond to cellular damage produced by injurious agents. The effect of the damaging agent to the cell in some cases may be directly upon the lysosome, releasing the hydrolytic enzymes and leading to cellular damage or death. In other circumstances, lysosomes may scavange other cellular organelles damaged by a toxic agent. Lung macrophages phagocytizing silica or asbestos particles may suffer cellular damage through rupture of lysosomal membranes and release of hydrolytic enzymes. The labilization of lysosomal membranes by silica has been suggested to be due to a consequence of increased hydrogen bonding of the particle to the membrane. Anesthetics can damage lysosomal membranes and release hydrolytic enzymes, whereas other substances such as the adrenal steroid hormones cortisone and hydrocortisone have a stabilizing effect on lysosomal membranes. Many drugs act as lysosomal-membrane-stabilizing agents at low concentration owing to an inherent chemical property (e.g., binding free metals or scavenging free radicals) but exhibit detergentlike properties at high concentrations and disrupt lysosomal membranes. In other circumstances (e.g., starvation), lysosomes are involved as a secondary factor in cellular or tissue injury. The detection of lysosomal enzymes in extracellular fluids such as bile or serum is indicative of a role for exocytized lysosomal enzymes. Such functions have been considered in tissue remodeling and in a variety of degradative processes. Increased synthesis and release of acid hydrolases by bone rudiments in culture is observed upon stimulation by parathyroid hormone, or in the presence of excess vitamin A or sucrose. Extracellular lysosomal enzymes also appear to have roles in the mediation of inflammation in rheumatoid arthritis (synovial membrane cells) and gout (polymorphonuclear leukocytes) and in tumor cell invasion of tissues. Lysosomes may also be affected directly in diseases involving genetic defects for a lysosomal enzyme. Glycogenosis II is such an example, in which there is a lack of the lysosomal acid hydrolase α-glycosidase, and glycogen accumulates in liver lysosomes. The topic of lysosomal storage diseases is aptly discussed in Chapter 4.14. In Wilson's disease and in hemochromatosis excessive accumulation of the metals copper and iron, respectively, occurs in the liver lysosomes. The mechanism of the metal accumulation is not known, but it appears responsible for increased lipid peroxidation and accumulation of lipofuscin pigment.

ROLE OF LYSOSOMES IN PLANTS

Vacuoles in plants carry out functions that are very similar to those ascribed to lysosomes in animals. Provacuoles (primary lysosomes) originate from the endoplasmic reticulum and undergo fusion with one another resulting in their enlargement to form small vacuoles. Further fusion of these provacuoles and/or small vacuoles results in the formation of larger vacuoles, ultimately producing the central vacuole, which accounts for most of the cell volume. Because of its meristematic capacity, the vacuolar system can form multiple vacuoles through blebbing. Pinocytosis is also found in plant cells and functions in the uptake of macromolecules; this can be observed regardless of the restriction imposed on the cell by the rigid cell wall. Spherosomes, which are part of the lysosomal system in plants, are principal sites of lipid storage. The balance between storage and lysosomal function depends upon the state of development of the cell. Spherosomes originate from the endoplasmic reticulum and are thus considered to be primary lysosomes. Fusion of spherosomes with the vacuolar system has not been observed, yet "spherosome-like" bodies have been found within vacuoles.

As in animals, protection of the endoplasmic space from the catabolic consequences of lysosomal hydrolases is provided by the lysosomal limiting membrane. In plants, lysosomes play important roles in normal development in addition to those of degradative processes. Mobilization of storage reserves to provide nutrients required for the germination process is achieved through the lysosomal enzymic system. Lysosomes also function in stomatal opening and closing by regulating osmotic concentrations in the guard cells through the release of acid phosphatase. The terminal stage of xylem differentiation in root tips and the development of chloroplasts are accompanied by redistribution of acid phosphatase and other hydrolases from lysosomes to the cytosol. The role of the lysosomal enzymes in these maturational events is not clear. The breakdown of polysaccharides in lysosomes and the secretion of the resulting sugars is part of the transport system of carbohydrates. This is in addition to the role played by the endoplasmic reticulum, Golgi apparatus, and plasmalemma. Cellular damage, as is observed in certain pathological responses and in cellular aging, is mediated through the release of hydrolytic enzymes following disruption of lysosomal membranes.

In the interaction of parasites with plants, lysosomal enzymes are released from each organism before occurrence of actual contact. The survival of the host or the parasite depends on the specificity of the enzymes released by their correspondent lysosomal systems. Also in the preinfection stage, extracellular enzymes secreted by one organism may affect the stability of lysosomes of the other, leading to decompartmentalization of the contained hydrolases and autolysis. Such a process may explain the action in plant and animal cells of fungal or bacterial toxins, respectively. The release of hydrolases in host cells results in digestion of cellular components, and more nutrients become available to the parasite. These enzymes also may act on lysosomal membranes in adjacent cells, setting in motion a chain reaction.

Resistance of plants to infection by pathogens is commonly manifested by hypersensitivity, a response characterized by reaction to the foreign agent greater than that which occurs normally. The hypersensitive reaction results in inactivation of the pathogen but is associated with necrotic changes in the infected tissue including histological changes, increased membrane permeability, and protein denaturation. The mechanism of the hypersensitive reaction is not understood but thus appears to involve the lysosomal system.

ROLE OF LYSOSOMES IN FUNGI

Fungi have a lysosomal system similar to that described above for plants. These lysosomes can take up heavy metals and may function in detoxification of fungicides through the sequestering of these agents. The accumulation of such materials can lead to disruption of lysosomal membranes, thus creating a fungicidal potential due not only to the possible release of hydrolytic enzymes but also to that of the heavy metals or fungicidal substances. The development of means for disrupting lysosomal membranes and the release of their hydrolytic enzymes may be useful in the control of fungal growth.

SUGGESTED READING

Barrett, A. J., and Heath, M. F. 1977. In *Lysosomes, A Laboratory Handbook,* J. T. Dingle, ed., pp. 19–145. North-Holland, Amsterdam.

Davies, M. 1975. *Front. Biol.* 43:305–48.

Davies, M., and Allison, A. C. 1976. *Front. Biol.* 45:61–98.

De Duve, C. 1969. In *Lysosomes in Biology and Pathology,* J. T. Dingle and H. B. Fell, eds., Chapter 1. North-Holland, Amsterdam.

Dean, R. T., and Barrett, A. J. 1976. *Essays Biochem.* 12:1–40.

Lloyd, J. B., and Beck, F. 1974. In *The Cell in Medical Science,* Vol. 1, *The Cell and Its Organelles,* F. Beck and J. B. Lloyd, eds., pp. 273–313. Academic Press, London.

Maggi, V. 1973. In *Cell Biology in Medicine,* E. E. Bittar, ed., pp. 215–264. John Wiley and Sons, New York.

Novikoff, A. B. 1973. In *Lysosomes and Storage Diseases,* H. G. Hers and F. van Hoof, eds., pp. 2–41. Academic Press, New York.

Novikoff, A. B. 1976. *Proc. Natl. Acad. Sci. U.S.A.* 73:2781–87.

Schellens, J. P. M., Daems, W. Th., Emeis, J. J., Brederoo, P., DeBruijn, W. C., and Wisse, E. 1977. In *Lysosomes, A Laboratory Handbook,* J. T. Dingle, ed., pp. 147–208. North-Holland, Amsterdam.

Slater, T. F. 1974. In *Companion to Biochemistry Selected Topics for Further Study,* A. T. Bull, J. R. Lagnado, J. O. Thomas, and K. F. Tipton, eds., Longman, London.

Szego, C. M. 1975. *Front. Biol.* 43:385–477.

4.10. Melanin Pigment Production

Michael J. Wilson

The coloration of mammalian skin is produced by the cutaneous distribution of the pigments hemoglobin, carotinoid, and melanin. The last is the primary factor in variation of pigmentation among individuals, and is synthesized in specialized cells termed melanocytes. Pigmentation due to melanin is determined somewhat by the number and melanin content of melanocytes and primarily by the distribution of melanin within the keratinizing cells (keratinocytes) of the epidermis and hair (Figure 1). The melanocyte hence is a secretory cell and as such exhibits well-developed rough and smooth endoplasmic reticula, a prominent Golgi apparatus, and the distinctive melanin-synthesizing organelle, the melanosome. The melanocyte lacks desmosomes and is typically dendritic in morphology, a feature necessary for the transfer of melanosomes to keratinocytes. This latter phenomenon appears to be a heterophagocytic process in which keratinocytes actively phagocytize portions of melanocyte dendritic, melanosome-filled cytoplasm. The melanocyte and the keratinocytes with which it has this functional relationship have been conceptualized as the "epidermal melanin unit." Increased melanin formation (melanogenesis) results in a morphological color change due to the physical distribution of melanin in the epidermal cells. In many animals, principally poikilotherms, rapid or physiological color changes can occur owing to the movement of pigment granules within dermal chromatophores. The melanophore is an example of such a cell; a darkening response results following the migration of melanosomes into the dendritic processes of the melanophore, and a lightening response is elicited upon concentration of melanosomes around the nucleus in the melanophore cell body. The formation of melanosomes and synthesis of melanin pigment is a function of both melanophores and melanocytes.

TYROSINASE

The initial steps of melanin synthesis, the conversion of the amino acid tyrosine to 3,4-dihydroxyphenylalanine (dopa) and dopa to dopaquinone, are controlled by the oxidase tyrosinase (Figure 2). Subsequent steps to indole-5,6-

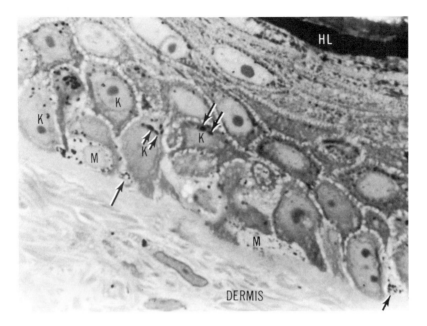

Figure. 1. A cross-sectional view showing the organizaton of mammalian epidermis (scrotal skin of rat). Melanocytes (M) are found in the basal layer of the epidermis and are marked by a cytoplasm filled with melanosomes. Cross sections of melanocyte dendritic processes are present (single arrow). Melanosomes (double arrow) are also present in keratinocytes (K); note the supranuclear location of these granules. The epidermis rests on the dermis and is covered by the horny layer (HL) formed from squamated keratinizing cells.

quinone and to melanin appear to take place nonenzymatically in the presence of oxygen. Tyrosinase is a copper-containing enzyme that requires dopa as a cofactor in addition to utilizing it as a substrate. Based on kinetic studies, two kinds of substrate binding sites on the enzyme moelcule have been suggested; one site would appear relegated for the oxidation of dopa and the other site, at which tyrosine is not oxidized, for the binding of tyrosine during the first phase of the reaction. The enzyme demonstrates a higher affinity for tyrosine than for dopa, whereas, conversely, the V_{max} for the reaction with dopa as substrate is much higher than with tyrosine. The tyrosinase reaction is subject to regulation by substrate and product inhibition and can utilize catechol and various esters of dopa in pigment formation. Tryptophan also may be involved as a precursor for melanin formation, probably following its metabolism through the kynurenine pathway. In addition, it has been suggested that the melanin precursor may be utilized in the form of a peptide or protein, since acid hydrolysis or pepsin digestion of acid

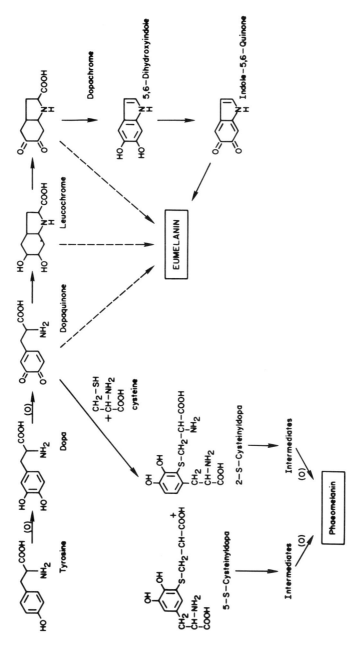

Figure 2. The biosynthetic pathway for eumelanin and pheomelanin formation. The first two steps, the conversion of tyrosine to dopa and dopa to dopaquinone are catalyzed by the enzyme tyrosinase.

precipitates of melanoma homogenates or melanosomal fractions yields large amounts of dopa.

Multiple forms of tyrosinase, both soluble and particulate-bound, have been demonstrated by polyacrylamide gel electrophoresis. Examination of tyrosinase patterns in hair bulbs from various coat color mutants of mice indicates a complex genetic control of the different tyrosinase isoenzymes. Differences in the electrophoretic mobility of the soluble forms of the enzyme may be due to its carbohydrate moiety, since neuraminidase treatment transforms one isoenzyme into a less anodic form but has no effect on the total catalytic activity. The particulate-bound tyrosinase of mouse melanoma is more susceptible to inactivation by acidic pH, heat, and low ionic strength and has a lower thermodynamic constant of inactivation when compared with the two soluble isoenzymes. These constants for the latter forms of the enzyme are similar, suggesting comparable molecular configurations. Granule-bound tyrosinase has a molecular weight of 102,000, whereas molecular weights of two soluble tyrosinases have been estimated to be 66,000 and 56,700. These latter isoenzymes have similar enzymic properties but differ in amino acid composition and do not undergo interconversion. In addition, they may exist as dimers, since tyrosinases separated by Sephadex column chromatography have molecular weights of about 33,000 and amino acid compositions about half that of the 56,700–66,000 isoenzymes. Antisera prepared against tyrosinase solubilized from melanosomes of Harding-Passay mouse melanoma react with tyrosinase purified from mouse B-16 melanoma; antisera against tyrosinase and hair follicles of the C-57 black mouse, also exhibits a high degree of cross-reaction with partially purified human melanoma tyrosinase, but do not react with mushroom tyrosinase.

Tyrosinase may be present in melanocytes in an inactive form, which suggests that a mode of regulation of this enzymic activity occurs in various melanocyte cytoplasmic compartments (e.g., endoplasmic reticulum and GERL) in which tyrosinase activity has been demonstrated but in which melanin formation does not take place in vivo. Proposed mechanisms of control include (1) the presence of a proenzyme from which an inhibitory portion of the molecule must be cleaved for activity, and (2) the presence of specific tyrosinase inhibitors.

The activation of a protyrosinase by means of proteolytic enzymes has been demonstrated in frog epidermis. Two such molecular forms of the enzyme reported by Mikkelsen and Triplett appear to be similar, if not identical, upon comparison of criteria such as amino acid composition, amino-terminal amino acids (arginine for both proteins), and immunologic identity. However, they do differ in their stability to trypsin digestion, and it appears that one of the enzymic forms is localized predominately in the smooth endoplasmic reticulum and the other in premelanosomes. A molecular weight of 30,000–

33,000 was determined for monomeric forms of the enzyme which at low ionic strengths reassociated into tetramers. Protyrosinase isolated from frog skin by McGuire and coworkers has also been reported to be a tetramer, but composed of monomers of 55,000 molecular weight. Chymotryptic activation of protyrosinase, however, produces a peptide and a monomer of 5700 and 50,000 molecular weight, respectively. Both the protyrosinase and the activated tyrosinase demonstrate basic isoelectric points (9.35 and 9.25, respectively), an observation substantiated by the amino acid composition. The presence, however, of a protyrosinase in mammalian pigment cells has not been established.

The role of an endogenous tyrosinase inhibitor in the regulation of melanogenesis has been suggested in a number of experimental systems. For example, variant strains of a human melanoma cell line possess different melanin contents and tyrosinase activities; however, tyrosinase activity is found to be similar among these variants following electrophoresis. Endogenous inhibitors have been described which vary in their dialysability, heat stability, and susceptibility to inactivation by X-ray and ultraviolet radiation. Heat-stable inhibitors have been isolated from melanomas; the presence of a tyrosine residue in these molecules suggests a mechanism of action involving substrate inhibition. Also, thermolabile inhibitors have been reported which appear to be peptides of less than 10,000 molecular weight and may function through binding of tyrosine and dopa.

MELANOSOMES

The melanosome is oval to ellipsoidal in shape and generally may vary in size, 0.3–0.7 $\mu \times 0.6$–1.3 μ, depending upon the tissue source of the pigment cells. Tyrosinase activity has been demonstrated by biochemical, cytochemical, and high resolution autoradiographic methods to be not only in melanosomes but also in the endoplasmic reticulum and Golgi-associated smooth endoplasmic reticulum saccules (GERL), suggesting that the tyrosinase molecule, synthesized by ribosomes on the rough endoplasmic reticulum (RER), is included in or on the melanosome structure during melanosome assembly (Figure 3). Ultrastructural demonstration of electron-dense, fibrillar material in saccules of the smooth endoplasmic reticulum (SER) associated with the Golgi system has implicated these membranes in the initiation of melanosome formation. Premelanosomes appear to develop through the assembly of melanosomal structural subunits within focal dilations of the tubular SER or through coalescence of membranous vesicles arising from the SER, resulting in the formation of a coiled-filamentous to sheetlike superstructure upon which melanin is deposited. The shape of the melanosome becomes apparent as the subunit fibers aggregate and establish crosslinkages during matrix for-

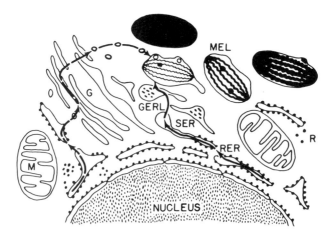

Figure 3. A diagrammatic representation of the formation and melaninization of melanosomes (MEL). The assembly of melanosomal structural elements is shown to take place in vesicles formed from dilations of the smooth endoplasmic reticulum (SER) or GERL membranes. The route from the time of synthesis of melanosomal proteins through assembly of the melanosome is represented by the solid line. The enzyme tyrosinase may enter the melanosomal structure through two proposed routes. One is by way of the same route as the structural components, and the second (following synthesis on the RER) is via small vesicles arising from the Golgi (G) membranes (dashed line represents this route). Melanin deposition occurs upon the structural elements of the melanosome, and in the diagram as melanization proceeds, the elements become darker and in the mature granule are obliterated. Other cytoplasmic organelles represented are ribosomes (R) and mitochondria (M).

mation. Ultrastructural studies of melanized melanosomes from a variety of sources have shown the presence of lucent areas. These vesicular bodies do not appear to be formed in the same manner as the lamellar structural components of the melanosome, since an increase in their number and attachment to the inner structural elements of the melanosome occurs during organization and melanization of the organelle. Such vesicular structures arise from the Golgi and have been suggested to carry tyrosinase, in an inactive form, to the site of melanosome formation where the small vesicles with associated enzyme are added to the assembled lamellar matrix. In the giant melanosomes of human pigmented nevus or gold fish melanophore melanosomes, where the microvesicles are the only structural component (in contrast to the above-described coiled helical filamentous melanosome structure of man and other mammalian species), melanin deposition appears to take place on the surface and between the microvesicles.

The structural integrity of the melanosome appears critical for maximal melanization of the organelle, a factor probably related to the physical attachment of the tyrosinase molecule in the melanosomal framework. Melanin deposition, which is normally uniform on melanosomal filaments, is incomplete in many pigmentary mutations. Alterations in mouse melanosome fine structure suggest that alleles of the B, C, and P loci are genes for structural macromolecules of the melanosomal subunits. Association of tyrosinase with membranous components of the melanosome is suggested by the extraction of lipids from purified frog skin tyrosinase and the solubilization of melanoma particulate tyrosinase upon lipase digestion. The concept that tyrosinase occupies specific in situ sites in the structure of the melanosome is further substantiated by the sequential loss of melanosomal tyrosinase activity observed as melanization of the melanosome progresses. It would appear that inactivation of tyrosinase is due to binding of reaction products to the enzyme, probably at its active sites.

In addition to tyrosinase, melanosome assembly is dependent upon the availability of other macromolecular components, including structural proteins, membranes, and auxillary enzymes. ATPase, β-N-acetylglucosaminidase, β-galactosidase, β-glucoronidase, cathepsin D, peroxidase, aryl sulfatase, and acid phosphatase activities have been demonstrated in melanosomes. ATPase may have a role in transport processes of the melanosomal membrane; however, the function of the lysosomal hydrolases is not clear, although it may include the eventual degradation of melanosomes. In addition, the melanosomal membrane has been suggested to contain a permease system for the concentration of tyrosine. Such a substrate-specific transport system could explain the data in human tyrosinase positive albinism, in which serum levels of tyrosine are normal, and melanization, which does not occur in vivo, will do so in hair bulbs incubated with tyrosine in vitro. Electrophoretic analysis of melanosomal proteins reveals a number of protein components including 6–7 major and about 15 minor bands with a molecular weight range of 25,000 to > 100,000 daltons. A small-molecular-weight (< 1000) darkly pigmented band is also present, which appears to be melanin or melanoprotein. A comparison of the total protein and melanin composition of melanosomes from a variety of tissue sources shows a range of 8–53% for protein and 18–58% for melanin content. A melanoprotein has been isolated from human melanoma that contains 8.8% melanin and in addition is high in sulfur (2.1%) and zinc (21 ng/g dry wt.) content. X-ray microanalysis of melanosomes also demonstrates the presence of iron and calcium.

MELANIN

There are two major classes of melanin formed from tyrosine derivatives through the tyrosinase-catalyzed pathways: eumelanin (brown-black melanin) and pheomelanin (yellow-red melanin). Eumelanin is depicted as a homopolymer of indole-5,6-quinone units (Figure 2), according to the classic Raper-

Mason pathway. However, the use of radioactive labeled precursors has shown this pathway to be oversimplified. For example, the final melanin product appears to contain three or four different quinone configurations and can include the incorporation of the tyrosine carboxyl group. Melanin formed during incubation of cell-free extracts with ^{14}C-l-tyrosine demonstrates a shift with time of melanization in the extent of decarboxylation of the tyrosine incorporated into the melanin structure. In addition, selective degradation of melanin shows the presence of 5,6-dihydroxyindole. Thus, it appears that melanin is either a heteropolymer or group of polymers, and it is believed to be attached by its quinone linkages to the amino and sulfhydryl groups of the structural proteins of the melanosome.

Eumelanin is universally light-absorbing and virtually insoluble in almost all solvents, whereas pheomelanin is soluble in dilute alkali. Pheomelanin is also characterized by its sulfur content, and its synthesis occurs as a deviation of the eumelanin pathway involving the 1,6-addition of cysteine to dopaquinone producing 5-S-cysteinyldopa, and to a lesser extent 2-S-cysteinyldopa, as intermediates (Figure 2). Subsequent steps and products in the phenomelanin biosynthesic pathway have not been established. Eumelanin and pheomelanin synthesis may occur in the same melanocyte. For example, in the agouti mouse, individual hair bulb melanocytes produce eumelanin at the beginning of hair growth, followed by pheomelanin production and reversion to eumelanin formation in order to produce the subterminal yellow band of the otherwise black or brown hair. In addition to the altered melanin biosynthetic pathway, melanosome morphology is also modified. In contrast to the eumelanosome, pheomelanosomes, which appear to arise through maturation of a multivesicular body precursor, are spherical with a disorganized internal structure.

CONTROL OF MELANOGENESIS

The melanocyte system of the adult integument originates from melanoblasts derived from the neural crest which early in embryonic development migrate to prospective skin areas. The effects of specific genes and the tissue environment influence the migration and ultimate differentiation of the melanoblasts. The skin of various body areas has distinct melanocyte population densities; differences in pigmentation of individuals (e.g., the human races) are not due to an altered number of melanocytes in a given skin area, but their melanogenic activity and distribution of melanosomes in surrounding keratinocytes. Although melanogenic function depends ultimately on the genetic competence of the pigment cell, extramelanocytic factors such as ultraviolet light, hormones, and some drugs are known to modulate the pigmentary process.

Ultraviolet-light exposure of skin not only produces erythema but leads to both immediate and delayed tanning responses. The former response begins immediately, is maximal at about one hour, and disappears within 4 hours following UV treatment. The immediate tanning reaction is characterized by the perinuclear to peripheral cytoplasmic organization of microfilaments and microtubules, which may facilitate movement of melanosomes to the dendrites from the perikaryon. The immediate tanning response is elicited by radiation from 320 to 700 nm and appears to involve oxidative reactions resulting from unstable semiquinone-like free radicals in melanin. Delayed tanning, which developes in 48–72 hours, is marked by increased pigment cell melanogenic activity and is initiated most effectively by wavelengths of 290–320 nm. A single exposure of UV irradiation to human or guinea pig skin results in increased tyrosinase activity at 72 hours followed by increased melanocyte cell volume, melanosome number, melanin content, and dendritic cell morphology. However, utilizing cytochemical methods, increased tyrosinase activity can be demonstrated in smooth endoplasmic reticulum and Golgi at 24 hours following UV treatment. The gross pigmentary response to UV is thus associated with an increased number of functional melanocytes, which appear to result from the activation of melanocytes of low melanogenic activity from a dormant or resting cell population. Although melanocytes have been shown to incorporate thymidine into DNA and undergo mitosis, the rate of melanocyte proliferation in response to UV irradiation (about 1% melanocytes demonstrate ^{3}H-thymidine incorporation) is unlikely to account for the increased number of melanin synthesizing pigment cells.

Certain hormones are known to exert profound effects upon melanin pigmentation. Melanocyte stimulating hormone (α-MSH) produces hyperpigmentation in humans, which is marked by increased numbers of melanosomes and highly dendritic melanocytes. In experimental animals MSH has been shown to increase the melanin content of guinea pig epidermis, increase tyrosinase activity in skin of newborn hamsters and mice, and suppress the agouti gene in mice by increasing tyrosinase activity and diverting pheomelanin to eumelanin formation. MSH, which stimulates tyrosinase activity and melanin deposition in melanoma cells, appears to activate adenyl cyclase, leading to an increase in cellular cAMP levels. MSH effects mediated by cAMP include the conversion of preexisting tyrosinase molecules from an inactive to an active state through the inactivation of an inhibitor of the enzyme. However, effects similar to the stimulation by MSH of the rapid dispersion of melanosomes into the dendrites of melanophores of amphibians, reptiles, and fish have not been observed in mammals.

The gonadal hormones are also capable of producing striking color changes which are often limited to the abdomen and sex skin areas. For example, in the human female, pregnancy is marked by increased pigmentation of the nipples, areolae, midline of the abdomen, and genitalia. Estrogen and progesterone treatment of ovariectomized female guinea pigs produces similar findings and suggests that these hormones are responsible for the color changes observed in pregnancy. The scrotal skin of the pigmented rat possesses a population of melanocytes whose melanogenic activity is controlled specifically by testosterone. Stimulation of tyrosinase activity in scrotal skin by testosterone and in chicken feather tract by estrogen can be prevented by inhibitors of protein synthesis. It thus appears that the melanogenic response to these sex hormones involves the synthesis of new proteins necessary for melanin formation (e.g., tyrosinase, melanosomal structural proteins, etc.), a mode of action that differs significantly from that proposed for the early effects for MSH mediated by cAMP.

The process of melanin pigment production is thus a complex series of events including the synthesis of individual components that are assembled into the organelle, the melanosome. Melanin synthesis is carried out at this site. The control of melanin pigmentation involves not only regulation of these steps but also the prior embryonic migration and differentiation of the melanocyte and the distribution of melanin in keratinocytes following its formation. The actual synthesis of melanin from tyrosine has now been found to be more varied than originally proposed, as is evidenced by the number of individual precursors polymerized into the macromolecule. Even the concept of one enzyme catalyzing the two steps, tyrosine to dopa and dopa to dopaquinone, has been challenged. In this latter proposal the first step is thought to be carried out by peroxidase and the second by dopa oxidase. Although much information has been elucidated concerning melanin formation, many questions still remain, particularly related to the control of this process.

REFERENCES

Barisas, B. G., and McGuire, J. 1974. *J. Biol. Chem.* 249:3151–56.

Burnett, J. B. 1971. *J. Biol. Chem.* 246:3079–91.

Chen, Y. M., and Chavin, W. 1969. *Anal. Biochem.* 27:463–72.

Coleman, D. L. 1962. *Arch. Biochem. Biophys.* 96:562–68.

Doezema, P. 1973. *J. Cell. Physiol.* 82:65–74.

Hearing, V. J., and Ekel, T. M. 1975. *J. Invest. Dermatol.* 64:80–85.

Holstein, T. J., Stowell, C. P., Quevedo, W. C., Jr., Zarcaro, R. M., and Bienieki, T. C. 1973. *Yale J. Biol. Med.* 46:560–71.

Iwata, K., and Takeuchi, T. 1977. *J. Invest. Dermatol.* 68:88–92.

Jimbow, K., and Fitzpatrick, T. B. 1973. *J. Ultrastruct. Res.* 48:269–83.

Jimbow, K., Roth, S. I., Fitzpatrick, T. B., and Szabo, G. 1975. *J. Cell Biol.* 66:663–71.

Lerner, A. B. 1971. In *Biology of Normal and Abnormal Melanocytes*, T. Kawamura, T. B. Fitzpatrick, and M. Seiji, eds., pp. 3–16. University of Tokyo Press, Tokyo.

Maul, G. G., and Brumbaugh, J. A. 1971. *J. Cell Biol.* 48:41–48.

Mayer, T. C. 1970. *Dev. Biol.* 23:297–309.

Mikkelsen R. B., and Triplett, E. L. 1975. *J. Biol. Chem.* 250:638–43.

Moyer, F. H. 1966. *Am. Zool.* 6:43–66.

Novikoff, A. B., Albala, A., and Biempica, L. 1968. *J. Histochem. Cytochem.* 16:299–319.

Okun, M. R., Patel, R. P., Donnellan, B., and Eddstein, L. M. 1973. In *Pigment Cell* V. J. McGovern and P. Russell, eds., Vol. 1, pp. 90–110. Karger, Basel.

Pomerantz, S. H., and Warner, M. C. 1967. *J. Biol. Chem.* 242:5308–14.

Quevedo, W. C., Fitzpatrick, T. B., Pathak, M. A., and Jimbow, K. 1974. In *Sunlight and Man, Normal and Abnormal Photobiologic Responses,* T. B. Fitzpatrick, M. A. Pathak, L. C. Harber, M. Seiji, and A. Kukita, eds. pp. 165–94. University of Tokyo Press, Tokyo.

Romsdahl, M. M., and O'Neill, P. A. 1973. In *Pigment Cell,* V. J. McGovern and P. Russell, eds., Vol. 1, pp. 111–17. S. Karger, Basel.

Seiji, M., Fukuzawa, H., Miyazaki, N., Akiba, H., and Kato, T. 1973. *Yale J. Biol. Med.* 46:508–15.

Swan, G. A. 1974. *Prog. Chem. Org. Nat. Prod.* 31:521–82.

Taylor, J. D., and Bagnara, J. T. 1972. *Am. Zool.* 12:43–62.

Wilson, M. J., and Spaziani, E. 1976. *Acta Endocrinol.* 81:435–48.

Witkop, C. J., Jr. 1971. *Adv. Hum. Genet.* 2:61–142.

Wong, G., and Pawelek, J. 1975. *Nature* 255:644–46.

4.11. Metabolic Compartmentation

Jacob Joseph Blum

Compartmentation is an obvious feature of all eukaryotic cells. Not only is the entire cell enclosed within a plasma membrane that regulates the entry of ions, sugars, amino acids, and so on, but numerous internal domains—which may or may not be entirely enclosed within their own boundary membranes—exist within the cell. Within these domains enzyme systems serving particular functional requirements are localized. Srere and Mosbach (1) and, more recently, Srere and Estabrook (2), in comprehensive reviews of this subject (to which the reader is referred for the many references therein as well as for an emphasis somewhat different from that to be presented here), recognized four classes of compartmentation: symbiotic, organelle, multienzyme complexes, and microenvironmental effects. Welch (3) has recently examined in great detail various factors that tend to favor the evolution of multienzyme complexes and the implications of such a tendency for the structural organization of the cell. In this chapter we focus on the organellar organization of intermediary metabolism in eukaryotes and hence on the localization of various pathways in discrete and relatively large domains.*

THE ORGANIZATION OF CARBOHYDRATE METABOLISM

The Glycogen Particle

Until recently glycogen particles were considered as bits of stored carbohydrate suspended in the cytoplasm and acted upon by cytosolic enzymes. It is now clear that glycogen particles should be considered as organelles even

---

* Abbreviations used in this chapter: P_i, inorganic phosphate; cAMP, adenosine 3'5'-cyclic AMP; G6P, glucose-6-phosphate; FDPase, fructose 1,6-diphosphate aldolase; FDP, fructose 1,6-biphosphate; DF6, 2,3-diphosphoglycerate; PFK, phosphofructokinase; MDH, malate dehydrogenase; DHAP, dihydroxyacetone phosphate; CPSase, ATP:carbamate phosphotransferase; OCTase, carbamoyl phosphate:L ornithine carbamoyltransferase; ER, endoplasmic reticulum; SOD, superoxide dismutase; HMG-CoA, β-hydroxy-β-methyl glutaryl-CoA; CP, carbamoyl phosphate; DBH, dopamine-β-hydroxylase

though they are not enclosed within a membrane. Glycogen debranching enzyme, glycogen phosphorylase, glycogen synthetase, and phosphorylase kinase account for over 95% of the protein attached to the glycogen particles of rabbit skeletal muscle (4). The polysaccharide matrix may also serve as a suitable microenvironment for the binding of phosphorylase kinase phosphatase and the phosphatase that acts on glycogen synthetase and glycogen phosphorylase (5, 6). There are at least two classes of glycogen particles, differing in density, enzyme composition, and presumably in function (6). In many tissues, an increase in concentration of cAMP initiates glycogenolysis via a cascade system involving several of the enzymes now known to be present within the glycogen particles. In cardiac muscle a distinct sarcoplasmic reticulum–glycogen particle complex occurs and has kinetic properties indicating that it may function as an effector site for cAMP that modulates both glycogenolysis and calcium transport (7). In skeletal muscle, Ca^{2+} released from the sarcoplasmic reticulum causes a "flash" activation of the glycogenolytic cascade as well as a simultaneous inhibition of the enzymes involved in glycogen synthesis (8). Flash activation is not observed, however, when these enzymes are studied in dilute solution. Furthermore, although several of these enzymes are subject to allosteric modulation in dilute solution by AMP, ADP, ATP, and P_i^+, these modulators have little effect on activity when the enzymes are within the glycogen particle. These examples emphasize the large changes in regulatory behavior that may ensue when a multienzyme system normally present in high concentrations in a structured microenvironment is examined in dilute solution.

Glycolysis

The almost universally held opinion that glycolysis is mediated in the cytosol via the action of the individual (i.e., noninteracting) enzymes of the glycolytic pathway is now being seriously challenged; the reader is referred to a recent comprehensive discussion of this subject for many details that cannot be presented here (9). Several lines of evidence indicate that at least in some cells, and possibly in many, a number of glycolytic enzymes occur in association with one another in the cytosol or attached to membranes (9, 10). These associations tend to be preserved if the cells are disrupted in 0.25 M sucrose, but are generally abolished with increasing ionic strength. Since the ionic strength of the cell is > 0.1 M, some workers feel that the complexes obtained during extraction with sucrose are artifacts (11). Hexokinase, for example, is frequently associated with mitochondria and is released by exposure to high concentrations of NaCl or low concentrations of G6P; it is released from the mitochondria of *Tetrahymena* by a change of one pH unit (12). FDPase, much of which appears to be associated with membranes of the

ER in rat liver, is released by NaCl and by FDP, the latter being about 100-fold more effective than the NaCl (13; see, however, Ref. 11). Skeletal muscle aldolase (and triosephosphate dehydrogenase) appear to be reversibly bound to actin filaments; aldolase binding is sensitive to pH, ionic strength, and low concentrations of FDP, glucose-1,6-diphosphate, and DPG (9). Studies of aldolase, hexokinase, and several other glycolytic enzymes support the generalization that certain glycolytic intermediates may control the proportion of glycolytic enzymes bound to membranes in different metabolic states (8). Changes in the fraction bound to membranes will have metabolic consequences because the kinetic properties of the bound enzyme frequently differ from those of the enzyme in solution. Furthermore, different isoenzymes (with differing kinetic properties) may be preferentially bound or desorbed by changes in pH, ionic strength, or concentration of glycolytic intermediates (9, 10, 13). It has also been postulated that the association of hexokinase with mitochondria allows preferential utilization of ATP for glycolysis (1, 14); a similar rationale may underlie the localization of PFK on the mitochondria of *Tetrahymena* (1, 15). Perhaps the most extensive known association of glycolytic enzymes with membrane occurs in bovine erythrocytes, where the entire set may be membrane-bound (16).

There is considerable evidence for two pools of several glycolytic intermediates in heart and skeletal muscle (9), liver (17), ascites tumor cells (18), and the prokaryote *E. coli,* which has no known intracellular barriers. In *E. coli,* a multienzyme complex with glycolytic activity has been tentatively identified (19). Such complexes probably also occur in eukaryotic cells (e.g., bovine erythrocytes), but in addition two or more distinct compartments containing the enzymes of the glycolytic sequence frequently occur in eukaryotic cells. The nucleus, for example, often contains a complete set of glycolytic enzymes (9), and glycogen particles also appear to contain a complete set of glycolytic enzymes, with the possible exception of hexokinase (6, 10), in addition to their complement of glycogenolytic and glycogenic enzymes (see, however, Ref. 4). Proplastids and chloroplasts also contain a number of glycolytic enzymes (1, 20), as does the sarcoplasmic reticulum of skeletal muscle (9). Because the nuclear membrane has large pores and the glycogen particle is not surrounded by a membrane, it is not yet known whether the glycolytic intermediates of these two organelles mix rapidly with their counterparts in other compartments. It has been reported that the peroxisomes (organelles that we will describe in more detail below) of *Trypanosoma brucei* contain enzymes of the glycolytic pathway (21). In some cells, therefore, several spatially separate glycolytic pathways may operate simultaneously; the unusual effect of insulin on skeletal muscle and that of bicarbonate on rat diaphragm (see Ref. 9 for a fuller discussion) are probably indications of such situations.

The enzymes of the pentose phosphate pathway—which functions in part as a bypass to the glycolytic pathway—are generally believed to be cytosolic although a mitochondrial localization has been suggested (22). The autosomally inherited glucose-6-phosphate dehydrogenase of liver sediments with the microsomal fraction (22), but is not specific for G6P and may be part of the inducible drug-oxidizing system localized on these membranes. A method for quantitative analysis of metabolite fluxes along the glycolytic and pentose phosphate pathways has been published recently (24); extension of the algebraic procedure underlying this analysis to a multicompartmental system is straightforward in principle. A detailed specification of the pool structure of the various intermediates for the cell to be studied would, however, be required before the algebraic and experimental labor would be worthwhile.

Gluconeogenesis

After the formation of P-enolpyruvate, the gluconeogenic pathway shares the same enzymes as the glycolytic pathway with the addition of FDPase and G6P phosphatase. Thus the evidence already presented for compartmentation of the enzymes of glycolysis and for glycolytic intermediates also pertains to this portion of the gluconeogenic pathway. Additional complexities arise when one considers the source of the P-enolpyruvate. In mammalian organs specialized for gluconeogenesis (i.e., liver and kidney), the key enzymes involved in initiation of gluconeogenesis are pyruvate carboxylase and P-enolpyruvate carboxykinase. The former is generally present in the inner mitochondrial compartment (25), while the latter may be in the mitochondria, the cytosol, or both (26). Thus gluconeogenesis will frequently be initiated within the mitochondria, and both carbon and reducing equivalents will need to be transferred out of the mitochondria. The importance of transport of substrates into the mitochondria for the terminal oxidation steps that follow glycolysis and for the export of substrates for gluconeogenesis is attested to by the existence of at least six porter systems (27) which facilitate and control the flux of substrates [as well as of protons and hence of oxidative phosphorylation (28)] across the inner mitochondrial membrane.

In contradistinction to animals, most plants and many protozoa can use substrates that form acetyl-CoA (e.g., acetate and fatty acids) for net gluconeogenesis. This is usually accomplished by means of the enzymes of the glyoxylate cycle—isocitrate lyase and malate synthetase—which bypass the oxidative decarboxylation steps of the Krebs cycle. These enzymes are often localized in peroxisomes (29), a class of single-membrane-bounded organelles, about 0.3–1.5 μm diameter, containing a variable complement of enzymes, which generally include catalase, α-hydroxy acid oxidase, D-amino acid oxidase, urate oxidase, and other oxidases. In addition these organelles may contain malate synthetase, isocitrate lyase, and isocitrate dehydrogenase [i.e., a complete glyoxylate bypass; such peroxisomes are often referred to as glyoxysomes (30)], cytochrome c reductase, malic dehydrogenase, citrate synthase, and NAD-linked α-glycerophosphate dehydrogenase, allantoinase, and several transaminases (31). They generally also contain a complement of enzymes involved in lipid metabolism, as will be described below.

Hydrogen peroxide formed by any of the oxidases is exposed to a high concentration of catalase, thus preventing possible damage to enzymes localized elsewhere. DeDuve (31) has suggested that a terminal flavin oxidation system coupled to catalase is typical of mammalian peroxisomes, and the presence of shuttle systems which could transport reducing equivalents (e.g., MDH, α-glycerophosphate dehydrogenase, several transaminases) supports this concept. Insofar as peroxisomes serve as a terminal oxidation system, however, they reduce the amount of oxidative phosphorylation that could have been achieved had the mitochondrial electron transfer systems been used. The only quantitative estimate of gluconeogenic flux through the peroxisomal compartment is for *Tetrahymena* (32). Under the conditions of those experiments about one-third of the acetate entering the Krebs cycle via citrate synthase was transferred from the mitochondria to the peroxisomes, and about half of this amount was finally used for gluconeogenesis. Although enzymes of the glyoxylate bypass are often localized in the peroxisomes, this situation is not universal; in *Ascaris* larvae the glyoxylate cycle appears to be mitochondrial (33). As with mitochondria, the peroxisome itself may contain several microenvironments. Thus malate synthase and cytochrome c reductase are localized in the peroxisomal membrane, catalase appears to be in the matrix of the soluble portion, and urate oxidase, when present, often occurs as a semicrystalline core (34, 35).

In green plants the initial reactions of gluconeogenesis occur in the chloroplast. In those plants that have appreciable photorespiration the glycolate formed in the chloroplast is transaminated in the peroxisomes to yield glycine, while the glycerate from the chloroplast is both transaminated and oxidized (yielding NADH) in the peroxisomes to form serine. Glycine then enters the mitochondria where serine and CO_2 are formed. A postulated glycolate–glyoxylate shuttle between these two compartments and the mitochondria permits proper balancing of the flow of carbon and of reducing equivalents (35). The main substrate for peroxisomal oxidation in green leaves is thus glycolate (which comprises up to half of the net photosynthetic production), and its oxidation requires substrate flow between three organelles via the cytosol.

Glyoxylate aminotransferase activities with glutamate, serine, leucine, phenylalanine, and alanine occur in differing proportions in peroxisomes from spinach leaves and from rat liver and kidney (36). In liver, these enzymes may function in part to convert glyoxylate to glycine instead of undergoing further oxidation to oxalate by the peroxisomal α-hydroxyacid oxidase or by cytosolic LDH, and may play a role in the degradation of several of these amino acids. The level of glyoxylate aminotransferase activity increases with time after birth and, in adult rats, after the administration of the hypolipidemic drug clofibrate (36). Whatever the evolutionary reason why such a seemingly valuable metabolic pathway as the glyoxylate bypass was lost in mammalian cells, it appears that the peroxisomes have retained a central role in the metabolism of glyoxylate. It is noteworthy that glyoxylate condensation with fatty acids can lead to alternate pathways of fatty acid metabolism in bacteria (37) so that a common localization for enzymes involved in glyoxylate utilization and fatty acid metabolism may have preceded the appearance of peroxisomes in the eukaryotic cell.

Carbon dioxide is produced in the mitochondria while it is being fixed in the chloroplasts. CO_2 fixation plays an important role in lipogenesis (i.e., the formation of malonyl-CoA) and in gluconeogenesis in nonphotosynthesizing cells (e.g., the pyruvate carboxylase reaction) even though the CO_2 so fixed is lost in subsequent steps. CO_2 fixation also occurs during the catabolism of leucine, and this has enabled the first demonstration of CO_2 compartmentation in a nonphotosynthetic cell (38). It is apparent, therefore, that analysis of the control of gluconeogenesis requires consideration of the compartmentation of acetyl-CoA, NAD, ATP, P_i, and CO_2, as well as of pyruvate, oxaloacetate, and several amino acids. Compartmentation of ATP, ADP, and P_i allows a high phosphate potential to be maintained in the cytosol, favoring biosynthetic steps, and a low potential intramitochondrially, favoring oxidative phosphorylation. The two pools communicate via an adenylate transporter system, which thus plays an important role in adjusting the energetic state of the cell. Compartmentation of acetyl-CoA and of long-chain acyl-CoA similarly facilitates control over the balance between fatty acid synthesis and degradation, as well as other aspects of lipid metabolism, as discussed below. Many of these aspects of metabolic control are discussed in a recent publication (39), to which the reader is referred for further detail.

LIPID METABOLISM

Fatty acid synthesis is accomplished in the cytosol by a multienzyme complex (3) that contains all the enzymes necessary for chain elongation of acetyl-CoA. Recent data indicate that the complex exists as apo- and holo-forms, which may be interconverted by cytosol enzymes that insert or remove a 4'-phosphopantotheine onto the acyl carrier protein of the complex (40). Very little is known about the equilibration of metabolites such as acetyl-CoA, malonyl-CoA, ATP, and NADPH, all of which are required for fatty acid synthesis, with other compartments, but it is probable that the holo-synthetase constitutes a separate compartment for at least some of these metabolites.

β-Oxidation of fatty acids was thought for many years to occur exclusively in the inner compartment of the mitochondria. The enzymes that perform this sequence appear to occur as a multienzyme complex within the matrix (41). Several studies indicate that there are at least two pools of acetyl-CoA in mitochondria, one containing the acetyl-CoA derived from pyruvate decarboxylation and participating primarily in the Krebs cycle, the other derived from β-oxidation and feeding into the first pool or serving as the source of ketone bodies (42, 43). Ketone body formation proceeds via the condensation of two molecules of acetyl-CoA, catalyzed by acetoacetyl-CoA thiolase. There are two isozymes of this enzyme in ox liver mitochondria, and their differing kinetic properties suggest that they play a role in regulating ketogenesis with respect to the intramitochondrial NADH/NAD ratio (44). The formation of acetoacetyl-CoA is followed by its condensation with another molecule of acetyl-CoA, forming HMG-CoA, which is cleaved to acetoacetate and acetyl-CoA by an intramitochondrial lyase. An identical sequence of reactions is used to initiate cholesterol biosynthesis in the cytosol. Acetoacetyl-CoA formation is catalyzed by a cytosol thiolase, and HMG-CoA is then formed. The HMG-CoA synthetase that catalyzes this step is a different isozyme from its mitochondrial counterpart, and, as expected, subject to different controls (45). Although the first two reactions of ketone body formation and of cholesterol biosynthesis are identical, they occur in different compartments and are in part catalyzed by different isozymes, thus ensuring ample opportunity for independent control.

The discovery that some plants contained a complete β-oxidation system in their peroxisomes (30) and that this also occurred in *Tetrahymena* (46) and in liver (47) indicated the importance of peroxisomes in lipid metabolism. In *Tetrahymena* about one-third of the total β-oxidation of hexanoate occurs in the peroxisomal compartment in a particular set of conditions (32). The first evidence implicating liver peroxisomes in lipid metabolism came from studies that showed that clofibrate, a drug used in the treatment of hyperlipidemias, caused a marked increase in the number of peroxisomes (48). Glycerol phosphate dehydrogenase, which serves primarily to oxidize glycerol-3-phosphate to DHAP (49, 50), acyl-CoA:DHAP acyl transferase (51), and carnitine acetyl-CoA transferase (52) are also present in liver peroxisomes. Acetyl DHAP synthetase and acyl/alkyl DHAP:NADH oxidoreductase are highly enriched in the lysosomal–peroxisomal fraction of guinea pig liver (51) and are presumably in the peroxisomes. Thus liver peroxisomes not only have the capacity for β-oxidation of fatty acids, but also are able to synthesize glycerolipids containing ester and ether bonds. Treatment with clofibrate caused a 70-fold increase in the mitochondrial carnitine acetyl-CoA transferase, as compared to 6- and 16-fold increases in the peroxisomal and microsomal activities, respectively (52). Clofibrate also caused a large increase in activity of the β-oxidation sequence of the peroxisomes (47). Clofibrate and similar drugs therefore appear to shift the contribution of peroxisomal lipid metabolism from glycerolipid synthesis toward β-oxidation. Clinical implications aside, it is apparent that peroxisomes play a key role in lipid metabolism in addition to mitochondria and the ER. Several enzymes of lipid metabolism are present in membranes of the endoplasmic reticulum (53). Glycerol-3-phosphate acyl transferase, for example, is largely confined to the microsomal fraction of guinea pig liver (51), though it probably also occurs in mitochondria. Mitochondria are also capable of phospholipid synthesis. The enzymes of mitochondrial phospholipid synthesis are apparently synthesized via nuclear genes on cytoplasmic ribosomes, since the complete loss of mitochondrial DNA in a petite mutant of yeast did not alter the total lipid synthesized by a crude mitochondrial fraction (54).

Given that phospholipid synthesis occurs in mitochondria, peroxisomes, and elements of the ER, it is likely that not only are there multiple pools of acetyl-CoA (1, 32, 41–43) in most eukaryotic cells, but of DHAP and glycerol-3-phosphate as well. The NADP of rat hepatocytes is also compartmentalized, part being in the cytosol, part in the ER (55), and part in the mitochondria (56). Enzymes of isoprenoid biosynthesis are present in proplastid and mitochondrial fractions of castor bean endosperm (57). Such extensive compartmentation facilitates control of different aspects of lipogenesis as well as coordination of the rate of the pentose-phosphate pathway with lipogenesis (58) and other reductive biosyntheses.

TERMINAL OXIDATION

Electron transfer in most aerobic eukaryotic cells occurs in the inner mitochondrial membrane via a series of oxidative steps in which the free energy drop is vectorially coupled to oxidative phosphorylation via a proton pump (28). A similar proton pump apparently operates in chloroplasts to achieve transduction of the energy of light quanta into the high-energy bonds of ATP. Details of these mechanisms are considered elsewhere in this treatise. From the standpoint of metabolic compartmentation an important feature is that in mitochondria the terminal oxidation system is in close proximity to the β-oxidation system and to the Krebs cycle, each of which produces the NADH that comprises the direct fuel for oxidative phosphorylation. The NAD/NADH ratio in the mitochondria is about 7, whereas that of the average cytosol pool is about 10^3 (1). The intramitochondrial and cytosolic NADP/NADPH ratios, however, are about 1/84 and 1/40, respectively (56).

The redox state of the cell appears to be controlled in part by the state of phosphorylation of the adenine nucleotides in the cytosol and mitochondria (59), and changes in redox state [e.g., after addition of ethanol (60) or ammonia (57)] cause significant changes in metabolism. It is therefore apparent that compartmentation of terminal oxidation has many consequences besides the formation of ATP.

Terminal oxidation may also occur in species adapted for anaerobic conditions. Such species frequently develop special organelles [e.g., the yellow pigment granules of molluscs (61), the cercidosomes of trypanosomes (9), and the hydrogenosomes found in trichomonads (62)]. Since relatively little is known about the yellow pigment granules or cercidosomes, we will briefly describe only the role of the hydrogenosomes.

Trichomonads are anaerobic protozoa that parasitize the digestive and genito-urinary tracts of both vertebrates and invertebrates. In these organisms, which have no mitochondria, glycolysis leads to the formation of P-enolpyruvate, part of which is carboxylated to oxaloacetate and reduced to succinate in the cytosol (62). The remainder is converted to pyruvate by a cytosolic malic enzyme [decarboxylating, NAD(P)], which then enters a single-membrane-bounded organelle called the hydrogenosome where it is converted to acetyl-CoA and CO_2 by a reversible pyruvate dehydrogenase. Acetate is formed from the acetyl-CoA by another substrate-level phosphorylation step which may involve succinate thiokinase. The reducing equivalents are disposed of inside the hydrogenosome, anaerobically by the action of hydrogenase, yielding H_2, or aerobically by transfer of the electrons to O_2, a process that may utilize in part a cytoplasmic NADH oxidase as well as an as yet unknown process in the hydrogenosome (62).

Although much remains to be learned about the properties of these relatively uncommon organelles (and, indeed, about the organization of terminal oxidation in mitochondria), it is clear that during the course of evolution it was often convenient to compartmentalize terminal oxidation, presumably to provide for efficient control of the flow of reducing equivalents and of ATP formation. Compartmentation of phosphate and of ATP has obvious consequences for the control of metabolism, since many pathways are sensitive to adenine nucleotide ratios (63). While one may be confident that there are at least two pools of ATP and of P_i in most eukaryotic cells, it is probable that there are multiple pools of P_i and ATP in many cells. Indeed, it is likely that there are two pools of ADP and of P_i (64) and of acetyl-CoA (42–44) in mitochondria alone. The consequences of multiple compartmentation of these and other metabolites have yet to be explored, but with the development of methods for quick separation of organelles from cytoplasm (56, 65, 66), for the subfraction of mitochondria (67) and ER (68), and for electrophysiological mapping of intracellular compartments (69) such problems are now becoming amenable to investigation. Quantitation of steady-state fluxes between compartments can be assessed without knowledge of pool size, however, provided that a realistic model of the structural organization of metabolism is used, and a sufficiently large number of well-distributed measurements of label incorporation into suitably chosen metabolites are performed (24,32). Use of both approaches—pool-size measurements and steady-state isotope incorporation studies—can be expected to yield much new information on the flow of metabolites between the major pathways of intermediary metabolism.

THE UREA CYCLE AND NITROGEN METABOLISM

Carbamoyl phosphate (CP) is an intermediate in the synthesis of pyrimidines and of arginine and hence, in ureotelic animals, of urea as well. In *Neurospora* (1) and in rat liver (70) there are two carbamoyl phosphate synthetase isoenzymes, CPSase I in the inner mitochondrial compartment, where OCTase is also present, and CPSase II in the cytosol, where enzymes of the pyrimidine biosynthesis pathway are localized, the CPSase II existing as a multienzyme complex (1). Liver mitochondria also contain several transaminases and glutamine synthetase (71). Since CPSase I of hepatic mitochondria is activated by N-acetylglutamate and is dependent on ammonium for the synthesis of urea, the latter process is sensitive not only to the balance between protein synthesis and degradation, but also the redox potential of the cytosol and the inner mitochondrial compartment (72). Much of the CP used for orotic acid biosynthesis in liver under normal conditions as well as at high levels of ammonia is derived from CPSase I, indicating a considerable net flux of CP (and citrulline) from mitochondria to cytosol.

The most complete analysis of the structural organization of the arginine and ornithine synthesis pathways has been obtained for *Neurospora* as a result of combined genetic and metabolic studies (73). Several important points emerge from this work. First, CP of the arginine pathway is a small intramitochondrial pool, and not normally used in pyrimidine synthesis, which takes place in the nucleolus. Second, the mitochondrial location of CPSase I is consistent with its lack of feedback sensitivity to arginine. It is, however, sensitive to repression by arginine. The only cytosolic enzyme of ornithine synthesis is acetylglutamate kinase, in a feedback-sensitive step, and this sensitivity may be why it is localized in the cytosol. Selection of one type of control sensitivity over another (e.g., feedback control by the end product vs. control by repression) may be an evolutionary consequence of compartmentation. Third, the bulk of the large arginine and ornithine pools is located in vacuoles or vesicles. These vesicular pools are slow-turnover pools. The vesicles probably serve as regulators of the catabolism of these amino acids.

In the absence of external arginine, for example, the vesicles release arginine just fast enough to allow a near-maximal growth rate, but slowly enough to prevent appreciable catabolism by arginase. Thus the control of the catabolism and biosynthesis of these pathways cannot be understood without reference to their compartmental organization.

Remarkably little is known about the subcellular localization of enzymes responsible for purine degradation. Xanthine oxidase appears to be cytosolic in rat liver and carp liver, but xanthine dehydrogenase is in the peroxisomes of chicken liver (74). Urate oxidase is peroxisomal in rat and carp liver and is also present in the peroxisome-like particles of *Acantamoeba* (29, 31). Allantoinase appeared in the cytosol of rat kidney and carp liver (74) but was peroxisomal in frog liver and possibly in castor bean endosperm (75). Allantoicase, the last enzyme of the purine degradative pathway, has so far been found only in the cytosol. If the glyoxylate formed by the action of allantoicase is to be utilized in the peroxisomes, it must reenter these organelles. Studies on a larger number of species will be required for a fuller understanding of the compartmentation of this pathway and its evolutionary implications.

LYSOSOMES

Although lysosomes are dealt with in detail in Chapter 4.9 of this treatise, it is useful to consider them in the context of metabolic compartmentation as well. Since they contain a complement of acid hydrolases that can degrade virtually all cell constituents, they not only play an important role in the turnover of cellular components, thus helping to regulate the amounts present, but also participate more directly in many metabolic processes. The fact that absence of α-1,4-glucosidase in Type II glycogen storage disease results in accumulation of glycogen within secondary lysosomes suggests that considerable glycogen degradation normally occurs in this compartment (76).

An important metabolic role for lysosomes can also be derived from the effect of glucagon on autophagy in liver. In this process a region of cytoplasm (which may contain a mitochondrion or a peroxisome as well as elements of the ER and glycogen particles) is surrounded by a membrane. Upon fusion of the autophagic vacuole thus formed with a primary lysosome, digestion of the vacuolar contents ensues, and amino acids, fatty acids, sugars, and oligonucleotides are formed and released, presumably by passive permeation, into the cytosol. In addition to its other actions, therefore, glucagon enhances the rate of internal generation of nutrients, many of which may supply carbon for gluconeogenesis. Insulin acts in the opposite direction, so that the net rate of nutrient formation by autophagy is in part determined by the balance between these two hormones (77). A similar chain of events occurs in cells that form food vacuoles, so that here too the secondary lysosomes comprise an internal compartment that supplies nutrients.

Lysosomes cannot be considered as a single compartment; much evidence demonstrates that they are a heterogeneous population, with different hydrolase complements (78). Indeed, the acellular slime molds and *Amoeba proteus* have developed a mechanism for intracellular segregation of endocytically ingested substances; particle mixtures of up to five different components, initially engulfed into single large vacuoles, were later separated into smaller vacuoles containing only one type of particle (79).

In cells that cannot eliminate teleolysosomes in which indigestible material remains, a new class of particles arises. These particles contain "age pigments" (lipofuscins) which have been only partially characterized (80). Except for the presence of several acid hydrolases, these particles are thought to be metabolically inert, though they may contribute to cell aging as they accumulate (81, 82). A related process may occur in epithelial cells of the midgut of the adult housefly. Here mineralized deposits are initially formed within Golgi vesicles and then appear in the cytosol as residual bodies. Their average size increases with age, and it has been postulated that they serve as an excretory system for various metals (83).

OTHER ORGANELLES

The metabolite functions of the most common cellular organelles—mitochondria, peroxisomes, chloroplasts, lysosomes, nuclei, glycogen particles, endoplasmic reticulum—have been adumbrated above. The roles of the Golgi apparatus, ribosomes, nucleus, and ER in the synthesis and processing of proteins and nucleic acids are considered elsewhere in this treatise. A complete picture of the complexity of metabolic compartmentation is not feasible, since specialized organelles have been developed in many cells to perform specific functions. Such organelles often use metabolites involved in the major pathways of intermediary metabolism. One such class of organelles consists of the storage vesicles in which the biogenic amines are sequestered. The best-studied of these vesicles are the chromaffin vesicles of the adrenal gland. These multifunctional organelles are designed for the uptake, biosynthesis, storage, and secretion of catecholamines (84). Dopamine, formed from tyrosine in the cytosol, is taken up by the vesicles, in which it is converted to norepinephrine by dopamine-β-hydroxylase. The norepinephrine may be stored or released into the cytosol for conversion into epinephrine and subsequent reuptake into the vesicles. In addition to DBH (which is in part in solution inside the vesicle and in part bound to the inner surface of its membrane), the vesicles also contain a membrane-bound ATPase, which presumably is part of an active transport system for catecholamine uptake via a proton motive gradient (85). Cytochrome b_{561} and an NADH(NADPH):oxidoreductase are present but serve no known function. Catecholamines appear to be stored inside the vesicles as a nondiffusible complex, consisting of about 4 moles catecholamine to 1 mole ATP, stabilized by one or more acidic proteins called chromogranins. Several other proteins of unknown function are also present. Clearly the chromaffin vesicles (and comparable vesicles specialized for the storage of other biogenic amines and acetylcholine) form distinct cellular compartments. Since they contain large quantities of ATP and utilize (albeit indirectly) certain amino acids or acetyl-CoA, S-adenosylmethionine, and choline, the number and composition of these organelles must somehow be coordinated with other aspects of intermediary metabolism.

The role of symbionts as intracellular metabolic compartments has been considered in detail by Srere and Mosbach (1) and needs no further elaboration here. It is, however, worth noting that whether or not this process provides a model for the origin of mitochondria or chloroplasts (86), the possibilities of introducing symbionts into some cells (87) and of removing chloroplasts or mitochondria from other cells provide a potentially valuable technique for studying the effects of compartmentation on intracellular metabolite flux patterns.

WHY COMPARTMENTATION?

When one considers the number and variety of multienzyme complexes and of the more clearly delimited organelles, it is evident that most of the metabolic machinery of the cell is compartmented. A number of advantages of this tendency to maximize compartmentation may be surmised:

1. Potentially dangerous compounds may be generated within an organelle that also contains high concentrations of enzymes that either utilize those compounds or render them harmless. Thus superoxide dismutase (SOD) is typically present in both the cytosol and mitochondria; in leukocytes, the cyanide-insensitive mitochondrial SOD may be involved in the activation of metabolism associated with phagocytosis (88). In the mitochondria-free trichomonads, SOD is present in the hydrogenosomes, where terminal oxidation occurs (89). The participation of catalase in the metabolism of short-chain alcohols in liver depends in part on the relative amounts of catalase present in the cytosol and in the peroxisomes (90), perhaps because the peroxidatic reactions of catalase are favored when the enzyme is present in high concentration. Catalase is also present in the microperoxisomes, a class of organelles of unknown function found in close association with the ER (91).

2. Efficiency of catalysis may be greatly enhanced by the much higher concentrations of enzymes and of substrates that can be attained within the compartment as compared to the entire cell volume, and possible limitations

of reaction velocity to the time required for diffusion are obviated when the reactants are kept in close proximity. Thus in sperm with long tails the mitochondria are often wrapped around the axoneme, thereby removing a limitation on flagellar length due to diffusion at ATP (92), whereas in castor bean seedlings synthesizing sucrose from stored lipid reserves, the peroxisomes are closely apposed to the lipid droplets (30). The gathering of the light-emitting system of many cells into organelles (93) may in part reflect this and related advantages of close proximity.

3. Vectorial pumping, such as that required for oxidative phosphorylation, in principle must occur on a membrane; if the reaction is to occur entirely within the cell and not only on the plasma membrane, a closed compartment is required. Multistep sequences such as the electron transport chain of mitochondria or the trapping of light by chlorophyll arrays and the funneling of energy into appropriate reaction centers in chloroplasts may also require that some close elements be vectorially embedded in a lipid membrane, again implying a closed compartment.

4. Locally favorable ionic environments can be maintained in different compartments. Thus the pH of secondary lysosomes can be lowered to ~ 5 within 15 min after vacuole formation (94). Similarly, electrical activity of the sarcolemma (and T-tubule system when present) allows the graded release of Ca^{2+}, thereby permitting a coordinated mechanical and metabolic response to nerve stimulation. Compartmentalization for regulation of ionic balance is not limited to metazoan cells. Many ciliates have developed structurally complex contractile vacuoles for this purpose. In addition, *Tetrahymena* in stationary phase cultures form membrane-bounded organelles containing Ca^{2+} and other ions (95), presumably to aid the contractile vacuoles in maintaining the ionic conditions appropriate to such an environment.

5. Flexibility of control of pathways or segments of pathways that share common intermediates is greatly enhanced. Compartmentation implies not only that different concentrations of a metabolite may be maintained in each pool, but also that flux through one pool may be changed markedly without necessarily altering the flux of that metabolite in other pools. The appearance of isoenzymes with differing kinetic properties becomes increasingly advantageous if the isoenzymes can be selected for function in specific environments. Control by entirely different mechanisms is facilitated; the amount of one isoenzyme may be adjusted by repression, while the activity of the other may be regulated by feedback inhibition. The tendency toward compartmentation also operates on higher-level control systems. Thus binding of a variety of polypeptide hormones to high-affinity receptors on the plasma membrane of target cells causes an increase in cAMP level in the cell. This in turn causes an increase in the activity of cAMP-sensitive protein kinase, which can modify the activity of a large number of enzymes or structural proteins

in the cell. Compartmentation of cAMP and of some of the cAMP-sensitive protein kinases would provide flexibility in the control of interrelated processes; evidence for such compartmentation in cardiac muscle has recently been obtained (96).

For these and perhaps other reasons as well (3), there has been a strong tendency toward maximizing the compartmentation of cellular function. Compartmentation must therefore be considered as a cardinal principle in the organization of the eukaryotic cell, just as compartmentation of function between organs is an essential feature of all multicellular organisms.

REFERENCES

1. Srere, P., and Mosbach, K. 1974. *Annu. Rev. Microbiol.* 28:61–83.
2. Srere, P., and Estabrook, R. 1978. *Microenvironments and Cellular Compartmentation.* Academic Press, New York.
3. Welch, G. R. 1977. *Prog. Biophys. Mol. Biol.* 32:103–91.
4. Caudwell, B., Antoniw, J. F., and Cohen, P. 1978. *Eur. J. Biochem.* 86:511–18.
5. Meyer, F., Heilmeyer, L. M. G., Haschke, R. H., and Fischer, E. H. 1970. *J. Biol. Chem.* 245:6642–49.
6. Guenard, D., Morange, M., and Buc, H. 1977. *FEBS Lett.* 76:262–65.
7. Entman, M. L., Bornet, E. P., Garber, A. J., Schwartz, A., Levey, G. S., Lehotay, D. C., and Bricker, L. A. 1977. *Biochim. Biophys. Acta* 499:228–37.
8. Heilmeyer, L. M. G., Meyer, F., Haschke, R. H., and Fischer, E. H. 1970. *J. Biol. Chem.* 245:6649–56.
9. Ottaway, J. H., and Mowbray, J. 1977. In *Current Topics in Cell Regulation,* B. L. Horecker and E. R. Stadtman, eds., 12:107–208. Academic Press, New York.
10. Masters, C. J. 1977. In *Current Topics in Cell Regulation,* B. L. Horecker and E. R. Stadtman, eds., 12:75–105. Academic Press, New York.
11. Arion, W. J., and Lange, A. J. 1976. *Biochem. Biophys. Res. Commun.* 68:770–75.
12. Risse, H. J., and Blum, J. J. 1972. *Arch. Biochem. Biophys.* 149:329–35.
13. Foemmel, R. S., Gray, R. H., and Bernstein, I. A. 1975. *J. Biol. Chem.* 250:1892–97.
14. Bessman, S. P. 1974. In *Lipmann Symposium: Energy, Regulation and Biosynthesis in Molecular Biology,* D. Richter, ed., p. 77. Walter de Gruyter, Berlin.
15. Eldan, M., and Blum, J. J. 1973. *J. Biol. Chem.* 284:7745–48.
16. Green, D. E., Murer, E., Hultin, H. O., Richardson, S. H., Salmon, B., Brierly, G. P., and Baum, H. 1965. *Arch. Biochem. Biophys.* 112:635–47.
17. Arion, W. J., Lange, A. J., and Ballas, L. M. 1976. *J. Biol. Chem.* 251:6784–90.
18. Coe, E. L., and Greenhouse, W. V. V. 1973. *Biochim. Biophys. Acta* 329:171–82.
19. Mowbray, J., and Moses, V. 1976. *Eur. J. Biochem.* 65:25–36.
20. Dennis, D. T., and Green, T. R. 1975. *Biochem. Biophys. Res. Commun.* 64:970–75.
21. Opperdoes, F. R., and Borst, P. 1977. *Abstr. 5th Int. Congr. Protozool. New York,* p. 106.
22. Baquer, N. Z., Sochor, M., and McLean, P. 1972. *Biochem. Biophys. Res. Commun.* 47:218–26.
23. Beutler, E., and Morrison, M. 1967. *J. Biol. Chem.* 242:5289–93.
24. Borowitz, M. J., Stein, R. B., and Blum, J. J. 1977. *J. Biol. Chem.* 252:1589–1605.
25. Böttger, J., Wieland, O., Brdiczka, D., and Pette, D. 1969. *Eur. J. Biochem.* 8:113–19.
26. Elliott, K. R. F., and Pogson, C. I. 1977. *Biochem. J.* 164:357–61.
27. Williamson, J. R. 1976. In *Use of Isolated Liver Cells and Kidney Tubules in Metabolic*

Studies, J. M. Tager, H. D. Söling, and J. R. Williamson, eds. pp. 79–95. North-Holland, Amsterdam.

28. Mitchell, P. 1976. *Biochem. Soc. Trans.* 4:399–430.
29. Muller, M. 1975. *Annu. Rev. Microbiol.* 29:467–83.
30. Tolbert, H. E. 1971. *Annu. Rev. Plant Physiol.* 22:45–74.
31. DeDuve, C. 1969. *Proc. R. Soc. London B* 173:71–83.
32. Raugi, G. J., Liang, T., and Blum, J. J. 1975. *J. Biol. Chem.* 250:5866–76.
33. Rubin, H., and Trelease, R. N. 1976. *J. Cell Biol.* 70:374–83.
34. Köller, W., and Kindl, H. 1977. *Arch. Biochem. Biophys.* 181:231–48.
35. McGroarty, E., and Tolbert, N. E. 1973. *J. Histochem. Cytochem.* 21:949–54.
36. Hsieh, B., and Tolbert, N. E. 1976. *J. Biol. Chem.* 251:4408–15.
37. Wegener, W. S., Reeves, H. C., Rabin, R., and Ajl, S. J. 1968. *Bacteriol. Rev.* 31:1–26.
38. Borowitz, M. J., and Blum, J. J. 1977. *J. Biol. Chem.* 252:3402–7.
39. Hanson, R. W., and Mehlman, M. A., eds. 1976. *Gluconeogenesis: Its Regulation in Mammalian Species.* John Wiley and Sons, New York.
40. Kim, M., Qureshi, A. A., Jenik, R. A., Lornitzo, F. A., and Porter, J. W. 1977. *Arch. Biochem. Biophys.* 181:580–90.
41. Stanley, K. K., and Tubbs, P. K. 1975. *Biochem. J.* 150:77–88.
42. Fritz, I. B. 1967. *Perspect. Biol. Med.* 10:643–77.
43. VonGlutz, G., and Walter, P. 1975. *Eur. J. Biochem.* 60:147–52.
44. Huth, W., Jonas, R., Wunderlich, I., and Seubert, W. 1975. *Eur. J. Biochem.* 59:475–89.
45. Clinkenbeard, K. D., Reed, W. D., Mooney, R. A., and Lane, M. D. 1975. *J. Biol. Chem.* 250:3108–16.
46. Blum, J. J. 1973. *J. Protozool.* 20:688–92.
47. Lazarow, P. B., and DeDuve, C. 1976. *Proc. Natl. Acad. Sci. U.S.A.* 73:2043–46.
48. Reddy, J. K. 1973. *J. Histochem. Cytochem.* 21:967–71.
49. Gee, R., McGroarty, E., Hsieh, B., Wied, D., and Tolbert, N. E. 1974. *Arch. Biochem. Biophys.* 161:187–93.
50. Gee, R., Hasnain, S. N., and Tolbert, N. E. 1975. *Fed. Proc.* 34:599.
51. Jones, C. L., and Hajra, A. K. 1977. *Biochem. Biophys. Res. Commun.* 76:1138–43.
52. Kahonen, M. T. 1976. *Biochim. Biophys. Acta* 428:690–701.
53. Groot, P. H. E., Scholte, H. R., and Hulsmann, W. C. 1976. *Adv. Lipid Res.* 14:75–126.
54. Cobon, G. S., Crowfoot, P. D., and Linnane, A. W. 1977. *Arch. Biochem. Biophys.* 181:454–61.
55. Kong, M. S., and Landau, B. R. 1977. *Arch. Biochem. Biophys.* 180:69–74.
56. Sies, H., Akerboom, T. P. M., and Tager, J. M. 1977. *Eur. J. Biochem.* 72:301–7.
57. Green, T., Dennis, D. T., and West, G. A. 1975. *Biochem. Biophys. Res. Commun.* 64:976–82.
58. Krebs, H. A., and Eggleston, L. V. 1974. *In Advances in Enzyme Regulation,* Vol. 12, C. Weber, ed., pp. 421–34. Pergamon Press, Oxford.
59. Krebs, H. A., and Veech, R. L. 1970. In *Pyridine Nucleotide-Dependent Dehydrogenases,* H. Sund, ed., pp. 413–34. Springer-Verlag, Berlin.
60. Thurman, R. G., and Scholz, R. 1977. *Eur. J. Biochem.* 75:13–21.
61. Nagy, I. Z. 1977. In *International Review of Cytology,* Vol. 49, G. H. Bourne and J. F. Danielli, eds., pp. 331–77. Acad. Press, NY.
62. Muller, M. 1976. In *Biochemistry of Parasites and Host–Parasite Relationships,* van den Bossche, ed., pp. 3–13. Elsevier, Amsterdam.
63. Atkinson, D. E., Roach, P. J., and Schwedes, J. S. 1975. In *Advanced Enzymatic Regulation,* G. Weber, ed., 13:393–411. Pergamon Press, New York.
64. Tokumitsu, Y., and Ui, M. 1973. *Biochim. Biophys. Acta* 292:325–37.

65. Siess, E. A., Brocks, D. G., Lattke, H. K., and Wieland, O. H. 1977. *Biochem. J.* 166:225–35.
66. Tischler, M. E., Hecht, P., and Williamson, J. R. 1977. *Arch. Biochem. Biophys.* 181:278–92.
67. Decker, G. L., and Greenawalt, J. W. 1977. *J. Ultrastruct. Res.* 59:44–56.
68. Eriksson, L. C., Bergstrand, A., and Dallner, G. 1977. *Cell Tissue Res.* 179:17–43.
69. Giulian, D., and Diacumakos, E. G. 1977. *J. Cell Biol.* 72:86–103.
70. Tremblay, G. C., Crandall, D. E., Knott, C. E., and Alfant, M. 1977. *Arch. Biochem. Biophys.* 178:264–77.
71. Vorhaben, J. E., and Campbell, J. W. 1977. *J. Cell Biol.* 73:300–10.
72. Krebs, H. A., Hems, R., and Lund, R. 1973. In *Advanced Enzymatic Regulation,* G. Weber, ed., 11:361–77. Pergamon Press, New York.
73. Davis, R. H. 1975. *Annu. Rev. Genet.* 9:39–65.
74. Goldenberg, H. 1977. *Mol. Cell Biochem.* 16:17–21.
75. Scott, P. J., Visentin, L. P., and Allen, J. M. 1969. *Ann. N.Y. Acad. Sci.* 168:244–64.
76. Geddes, R., and Stratton, G. C. 1977. *Biochem. J.* 163:193–200.
77. Neely, A. N., Nelson, P. B., and Mortimore, G. E. 1974. *Biochim. Biophys. Acta* 338:458–72.
78. Davies, M. 1975. In *Lysosomes in Biology and Pathology,* Vol. 4, J. T. Dingle and R. T. Dean, eds., pp. 305–48. North-Holland, Amsterdam.
79. Stockem, W., and Stiemerling, R. 1976. *Cytobiologie* 13:158–62.
80. Hasan, M., and Glees, P. 1972. *Gerontologia* 18:217–21.
81. Timiras, P. S. 1972. *Developmental Physiology and Aging.* MacMillan, New York.
82. Leunenberger, P. M. 1975. In *Cell Impairment in Aging and Development,* pp. 265–78. Plenum Press, New York.
83. Sohal, R. S., Peters, P. D., and Hall, T. A. 1977. *Tissue Cell* 9:87–102.
84. Kirshner, N. 1974. In *Cytopharmacology,* Vol. 2, B. Ceccarelli, F. Clemente, and J. Meldolesi, eds., pp. 265–72. Raven Press, New York.
85. Holz, R. W. 1978. *Proc. Natl. Acad. Sci. U.S.A.* 75:5190–94.
86. Raff, R. A., and Mahler, H. R. 1972. *Science* 177:575–82.
87. Soldo, A. T. 1977. *Abstr. 5th Int. Congr. Protozool. New York,* Abstr. 437.
88. Auclair, C., Hakin, J., and Bowvin, P. 1977. *FEBS Lett.* 79:390–92.
89. Lindmark, D. G. 1977. *Abstr. 5th Int. Congr. Protozool. New York,* Abstr. 107.
90. Makar, A. B., and Mannering, G. J. 1968. *Mol. Pharmacol.* 4:484–91.
91. Gulyas, B. J., and Yuan, L. C. 1977. *Cell Tissue Res.* 179:357–66.
92. Raff, E. C., and Blum, J. J. 1968. *J. Theor. Biol.* 18:53–71.
93. DeSa, R., and Hastings, J. W. 1968. *J. Gen. Physiol.* 51:105–22.
94. Jensen, M. S., and Bainton, D. F. 1973. *J. Cell Biol.* 56:379–88.
95. Nilsson, J. R., and Coleman, J. R. 1977. *J. Cell Sci.* 24:311–25.
96. Corbin, J. D., Sugden, P. H., Lincoln, T. M., and Keely, S. L. 1977. *J. Biol. Chem.* 252:3854–61.

4.12. Lymphokines

John T. Crosson

Animals immunized with certain classes of antigens demonstrate a specific response when challenged locally (usually intracutaneously) with the antigen, a response characterized by erythema and induration beginning 8 to 12 hours after challenge and peaking at 24 to 48 hours. Histologically these reactions show primarily a mononuclear infiltration (monocytes and lymphocytes). This response, called delayed hypersensitivity, is epitomized by the clinical tuberculin reaction. With the demonstration in 1942 by Lansteiner and Chase that this tuberculin reaction can be transferred by live lymphoid cells but not by serum (containing antibody), the distinction between humoral immunity and cell-mediated immunity became evident. The latter is responsible for resistance against protozoal, fungal, viral, and a few bacterial infections, as well as for allograft rejection and resistance to growth of neoplastic cells.

Progress in the field of cell-mediated immunity was hampered by the dependence on an in vivo assay system (the cutaneous delayed hypersensitivity response) until the development of satisfactory in vitro assays in the mid 1960s. These assays depend on the release from sensitized lymphocytes in contact with specific antigens, of soluble effector substances that can affect the biologic function of other cells. Such soluble substances have collectively been termed lymphokines. Most of the lymphokines are also released from nonsensitized lymphocytes when reacted with nonspecific mitogens such as phytohemagglutinin (PHA) or concanavalin A (Con A). It is the purpose of this chapter to review the biological properties of selected lymphokines.

Since the discovery and characterization of macrophage migration inhibitory factor (MIF) in the mid 1960s by such investigators as George, Vaughan, David, and Bloom, a large number of lymphokines have been and are continuing to be discovered, which correlate with the presence of in vivo delayed hypersensitivity. Since it is beyond the scope of this chapter to review all of them, only certain ones with special in vivo or in vitro properties will be discussed. Table 1 is a list of some of these lymphokines.

Most of the lymphokines were initially discovered because of their in vitro activities. However, from direct experimental evidence or from the in vitro properties, there is good reason to believe that most have important in vivo

Table 1. Some Currently Known Lymphokines.

Migration inhibitory factor (MIF)
Leukocyte inhibitory factor (LIF)
Chemotactic factor for monocytes
Chemotactic factor for eosinophils
Chemotactic factor for neutrophils
Lymphocyte mitogenic factor (LMF)
Lymphotoxin (LT)
Transfer factor (TF)
Interferon
Suppressor factors
Helper factors
Osteoclast activating factor

functions. This chapter will focus primarily on the known or presumed in vivo activities.

Since histologic sections from a delayed hypersensitivity reaction contain primarily monocytes and lymphocytes, the lymphokines directed toward these cells are probably of major importance in the development of such reactions. Antigen-activated or mitogen-activated lymphocytes release a factor that is chemotactic for monocytes. Such chemotactic activity is demonstrated in chambers containing two compartments separated by a micropore filter. The movement of monocytes from one compartment toward the other compartment containing the supernatant fluid from activated lymphocytes is quantitated and correlates with the supernatant fluid's chemotactic activity. The release of chemotactic factor is antigen-specific, as is the release of most lymphokines. This substance appears to be a heat-stable protein. Guinea pig chemotactic factor has a molecular weight of 35,000 to 55,000 daltons, while the human factor is smaller with a molecular weight of 12,000 to 25,000 daltons. Both T cells and B cells have been shown to release chemotactic factor for macrophages. Because only a small portion of cells in sites of delayed hypersensitivity have been shown to be specifically sensitized to the antigen, it is likely that this chemotactic factor is responsible for attracting the nonsensitized mononuclear cells (macrophages) to the area.

Once macrophages reach the site, they probably stay in the area, partly owing to the influence of MIF, which was the first lymphokine to be discovered and currently serves as the basis for one of the most valuable in vitro tests for studying cell-mediated immunity. Generally, the test is performed using peritoneal exudate cells from guinea pigs as indicator cells. These cells are responsive to the inhibitory effect of MIF from many species including humans. A capillary tube is filled with a solution containing peritoneal exudate cells, which are then centrifuged to one end. The capillary tube is cut at the fluid-cell interface and placed in a chamber containing tissue-culture fluid, and the cells are allowed to migrate freely from the tip of the capillary tube onto the glass surface of the chamber, usually for 18 hours. The normal fan-shaped pattern of migration can be projected on paper and the area of migration quantitated by weighing the paper or by planimetry. If the cells are incubated with MIF in the supernatant fluid of antigen-stimulated or mitogen-stimulated lymphocytes, the area of migration is reduced. It must be remembered that many nonspecific factors can affect exudate cell migration, making interpretation difficult unless adequate controls are also run. Generally, the assay is run in two stages (generation of MIF from lymphocytes, followed by incubation of MIF with exudate cells), but the assay can be run with lymphocytes, antigen, and exudate cells in the same capillary tube as a one-stage test. More recently migration of cells in an agarose medium has been substituted for the capillary tubes.

Guinea pig MIF appears to be a glycoprotein, has a molecular weight of 35,000 to 55,000 daltons, is inhibited by trypsin and chymotrypsin, has electrophoretic migration in the prealbumin region, and is heat-stable. Human MIF is similar except that it has a molecular weight of 23,000 and migrates with albumin. Macrophages have a receptor for MIF which is destroyed by trypsin and which depends on the presence of an α-L-fucose in the receptor.

It has generally been felt that T cells are responsible for cell-mediated immunity while B cells are responsible for humoral immunity. Recently, however, it has been shown that human MIF is produced by both T cells and B cells. In spite of this fact, most studies (but not all) have shown a very good correlation between the delayed hypersensitivity response and the ability of host lymphocytes to produce MIF after reacting with antigen. It might be that B cells as well as T cells can contribute to the in vivo manifestations of cell-mediated immunity, or that B cell MIF production is only an in vitro phenomenon. In support of the last statement, a T cell lymphokine that can inhibit B cell MIF production has recently been demonstrated.

A factor that inhibits the migration of leukocytes (LIF) in either the capillary tube or the agarose system has been shown also to be produced by B cells as well as T cells. Human LIF can easily be separated from MIF by column chromatography. It is a larger molecule with a molecular weight of about 69,000 daltons. Both are glycoproteins, but LIF in contrast to MIF is a serine esterase.

LIF has been of value in providing a useful in vitro test that is easier to perform than the MIF assay. Most tests are done using the entire leukocyte population, which contains both antigen-responsive lymphocytes, which release LIF, and neutrophils, whose migration is inhibited by LIF but not

MIF. It is also known that macrophage migration is inhibited by MIF and not LIF. In spite of the fact that LIF is produced by both B cells and T cells, there is very good correlation between in vivo delayed hypersensitivity and the production of LIF. Thus, though MIF and LIF are good in vitro correlates of delayed hypersensitivity, neither can be used as a means of evaluating T cell function separate from B cell function.

Though chemotactic factors can be responsible for attracting many nonsensitized cells to a site of delayed hypersensitivity, other amplification mechanisms are probably necessary to account for all of the cells present. Lymphocyte mitogenic factors (LMF) could be responsible for much of this amplification. Nonsensitive lymphocytes when cultured in the presence of supernatants from antigen-stimulated sensitive lymphocytes, undergo blastogenesis, which can be quantitated morphologically or by measuring the amount of ^{3}H-thymidine incorporated into the transformed cells. LMF is nondialyzable, heat-stable, and resistant to RNAse and DNAse, and has a molecular weight of 25,000 to 55,000 daltons. In contrast to MIF, LIF, and macrophage chemotactic factor, LMF is produced by T cells and not B cells. Both T and B cells, however, respond to LMF by undergoing blastogenesis. LMF has been shown to be distinct from other lymphokines. In fact, in certain disease states there is a dissociation between the production of MIF and LMF, with failure to produce MIF in spite of normal proliferative responses and LMF production. In the cell-mediated inflammatory response, LMF reacts with nonsensitized lymphocytes, producing a blastogenic response that leads to the subsequent release of other lymphokines and/or antibody.

The action of transfer factor which leads to an increased number of antigen-responsive cells, represents another probable amplification mechanism in the development of delayed hypersensitivity. Transfer factor is a controversial lymphokine primarily because [1] it differs from other lymphokines in some of its basic biologic properties; [2] there is no satisfactory in vitro assay system; and [3] there was no animal model in which to study it outside of the human.

Many years ago, Lawrence discovered that delayed hypersensitivity could not only be as easily transferred in humans as in guinea pigs using live lymphoid cells, but could be transferred using soluble extracts of these cells. The soluble factor, called transfer factor (TF), could be released from sensitized lymphocytes by the specific antigen but not unrelated antigens, and could transfer the ability to respond with a typical positive delayed hypersensitivity skin test to that particular antigen but to no other antigens. Thus, TF differs from other lymphokines in that its action as well as its release is immunologically specific. Another major way in which TF differs from other soluble mediators is that it is dialyzable, which means the molecular weight is less than 10,000 daltons (probably about 4,000). The exact biochemical composition is uncertain, but it is resistant to RNAse and DNAse, and is not a protein. There is some evidence that it may have a polypeptide and/or polynucleotide composition. It is nonimmunogenic, a property that complicates the study of the molecule but makes it potentially safer to use clinically. Though the exact mechanism of action of TF remains a mystery, it acts as though it uncovers or causes the appearance of specific receptor sites on the recipient lymphocytes, leading to a new clone of cells that can react with specific antigen.

Because of the controversy surrounding TF, attempts to use it clinically have been made only in the past few years. There have been a few reported clinical successes in diseases such as sarcoid, mucocutaneous candidiasis, disseminated tuberculosis, Wiskott-Aldrich syndrome, and ataxia-telangiectasia. TF has been uniformly unsuccessful in restoring delayed hypersensitivity to anergic patients with Hodgkins. Unfortunately, no well-conducted controlled studies have yet been done; so the clinical efficacy of TF is still unproved.

One of the major functions of lymphocytes involved in cell-mediated immunity appears to be lysis of foreign target cells. This reaction is antigen-specific and does not involve antibody or complement. Lysis, which depends on close contact of lymphocytes and target cells without fusion of membranes, is probably mediated in some way by lymphotoxin (LT)—a cytotoxic activity found in the supernatant of antigen- or mitogen-stimulated lymphocytes. By immunologic and physicochemical techniques LT has been shown to be separate from MIF and LMF. Human LT has a molecular weight of 80,000 to 90,000 daltons and is resistant to trypsin, DNAse, and RNAse; but since it is sensitive to pronase, it probably is a protein. Guinea pig LT is smaller, with a molecular weight of 35,000 to 55,000 daltons.

Most assays of LT utilize mouse L cells as the target and measure cytotoxicity either by direct observation or by release of radioactivity from labeled cells. Two effects are observed on different cell populations: (1) a rapid fragmentation of cells in 2 to 5 min and, (2) a gradual swelling over 1 to 2 hours eventually leading to cell rupture. Cells sensitive to LT avidly bind LT, but this binding is readily saturated. It has been estimated that a sensitive target cell can bind up to 600 molecules of LT. The events triggered by LT once it binds to the target cell, which lead to destruction of the cell, have not yet been elucidated.

There is evidence that recently described helper and suppressor T cells exert their influence on other T cells or B cells by releasing soluble factors into the environment. A number of helper and suppressor factors have been described by different workers, but there has not been enough time to determine how many different molecules are involved in helper and suppressor activity and whether they differ from other lymphokines.

The large number of enhancing factors that have been described can be divided into two categories depending on their specificity of action. One group of enhancing factors is released from T cells by interaction with a specific antigen to which that T cell is sensitized, but once released can enhance B cell antibody production to a large number of unrelated antigens. The enhancing factors in the second group, also released by a specific antigen, enhance B cell antibody production to only that special antigen. Mitogens may also release enhancing factors whose action is entirely nonspecific. Characterization of these enhancing factors will certainly be an important goal for future research.

There is also evidence that a number of suppressor systems exist, most probably mediated by soluble substances. Perhaps the most well-defined suppressor substance is the material described by Tada. In studying the IgE response of the rat to a DNP derivative of an ascaris extract, Tada and coworkers have identified a substance derived from T cells that can suppress IgE response. The suppressor substance was found to be a protein with a molecular weight of from 35,000 to 55,000 daltons. It contained determinants coded for by I region genes, which may be important in determining its antigen specificity. There is evidence that this factor is effective by inactivating helper T cell activity.

In summary, this chapter has reviewed the physical properties and in vitro actions of several lymphokines released from sensitized lymphocytes upon coming in contact with the specific antigen. An attempt has also been made to clarify some of the potential in vivo functions of these molecules.

REFERENCES

Barnet, F. M. Transfer factor. 1974. *J. Allergy Clin. Immunol.* 54:1.

David, J., et al. 1964. Delayed hypersensitivity in vitro. I. The Specificity of inhibition of cell migration by antigens. *J. Immunol.* 93:264.

Dutton, R. Suppressor T cells. 1975. *Transplant. Rev.* 26:39.

Lawrence, H. S. 1974. Transfer factor: Initiation and augmentation of cell-mediated immunity. In *Mechanisms of Cell Mediated Immunity,* R. McCluskey and S. Cohen, eds. John Wiley & Sons, New York.

Rocklin, R. 1976. Products of activated lymphocytes. In *Clinical Immunobiology,* F. Bach and R. Good, eds. Academic Press, New York.

Rocklin, R. 1974. Products of activated lymphocytes: Leukocyte inhibitory factor distinct from migration inhibitory factor. *J. Immunol.* 112:1461.

Rocklin, R. 1976. Mediators of cellular immunity, their nature and assay. *J. Invest. Dermatol.* 67:372.

Rocklin, R., et al. 1974. Studies on mediator production by highly purified human T and B lymphocytes. *J. Exp. Med.* 140:1303.

Rosenau, W., and Tsoukas, C. 1976. Lymphotoxin. *Am. J. Pathol.* 84:580.

Soborg, M., and Bendixin, G. 1967. Human lymphocyte migration as a parameter of hypersensitivity. *Acta Med. Scand.* 181:247.

Tada, T., et al. 1975. Properties of primed suppressor T cells and their products. *Transplant. Rev.* 26:87.

Yoshida, T., and Cohen, S. 1974. In vivo manifestations of lymphokine and lymphokine-like activity. In *Mechanisms of Cell Mediated Immunity,* R. McCluskey and S. Cohen, eds. John Wiley & Sons, New York.

4.13. Phagocytosis

Elaine L. Mills and Paul G. Quie

The first description of phagocytosis was made by Haeckel in 1862. It was not recognized until 30 years later, however, when the Russian biologist Eli Metchnikoff published his classic descriptions of phagocytosis, that the process of phagocytosis was essential to host survival. Metchnikoff was the first to appreciate that phagocytic cells are protective to the host, that they ingest and kill invading microorganisms, and that they perform this function as part of the inflammatory response. Then, as it is now, it was recognized that phagocytosis does not occur in multicellular organisms as an isolated event, but that it takes place in the presence of a complex interaction between the phagocytic cell, humoral mediators, and tissue factors. For this reason, the phagocytic process will be discussed here in the context of the inflammatory response and microbial killing but with emphasis on the elemental functions of recognition, attachment, and ingestion.

Phagocytosis, narrowly defined, is the process by which certain cells transport particulate objects from the extracellular environment into intracellular vacuoles. Phagocytosis, or cellular eating, can be distinguished from pinocytosis, or cellular drinking. The term phagocytosis is generally used to describe the uptake of particles large enough to be visible by light microscopy, ranging from red cells and crystals to bacteria, fungi, and possibly some viruses. During uptake there is close apposition of a segment of the plasma membrane to the surface of the particle, excluding most, if not all, of the surrounding fluid. The term pinocytosis is used to describe uptake of a wide range of materials from small particles such as lipoproteins to soluble macromolecules such as enzymes to fluid and low-molecular-weight solutes.

The phagocytic cell must make contact with invading microorganisms in order for phagocytosis to occur. Invading microorganisms that enter via the lymphatic or blood circulation are removed by the fixed phagocytic cells of these vascular systems (i.e., macrophages of the lymph nodes, lungs, liver, and spleen). However, once the organisms become lodged in the tissues, phagocytic cells from the bloodstream or from adjacent tissue move into the site of challenge to remove the foreign particles.

THE PHAGOCYTIC CELLS

Polymorphonuclear neutrophils are the primary circulating phagocytes, and together with mobile tissue macrophages (also called histiocytes) they comprise the major defense system of tissue spaces. Neutrophils exist in three phases and have a total life span of 16 to 17 days. After a 14-day developmental period in the bone marrow, they are released as mature cells into the peripheral blood, where they spend 6 to 7 hours as part of the circulating or the marginal pool, and then enter the tissues for a final 24 to 48 hours.

The mononuclear phagocytes form a continuum cells from bone marrow monoblast through the blood monocyte to the immature and the mature large tissue macrophages and multinuclear giant cells. The bone marrow phase of the monocyte cell-line is very rapid, with a developmental time between stem cell and blood monocyte of 24 hours. Monocytes exist in the circulation from hours to days, but once they leave the circulation, they do not return. In the tissues, monocytes undergo transformation into macrophages and may survive in this form for many months, or even years. Tissue macrophages are found in the pleural and peritoneal spaces and in the alveoli, and are particularly abundant in lymph nodes and in the sinusoids of the liver and spleen.

Eosinophils and basophils are also capable of particle ingestion. After bone marrow development, from 3 to 6 days for the eosinophil and an unknown period for the basophil, the cells are released into the peripheral blood. Their half-life in the circulation is probably measured in minutes before they migrate into the tissues where they remain for an undetermined period of time.

LOCOMOTION

Both monocytes and neutrophils move from the circulation to tissues in a random fashion under physiologic conditions, and accumulate in vast numbers at localized sites in response to attraction by inflammatory stimuli. Little is known about factors that influence mononuclear mobilization into these areas, but neutrophil locomotion and chemotaxis have been studied extensively. Circulating neutrophils are exquisitely sensitive to inflammatory stimuli and respond by adhering to the walls of capillaries and small venules and crawling (diapedesis) through spaces between endothelial cells into the tissues. The small-molecular-weight factors released during inflammatory reactions by bacteria, leukocytes, plasma, and tissues which attract neutrophils include activated complement components (C_3 fragment, C_5 fragment, and $C_{\overline{567}}$), bacterial peptides, neutrophil and lymphocyte products, bradykinin, and many others.

While neutrophils are capable of random migration, it is the gradient of chemoattractants that brings about the directed locomotion of phagocytic cells (chemotaxis) toward the center of the inflammatory response. Chemoattractants stimulate the leukocyte membrane to produce cytoplasmic contraction and relaxation in sequential regions of the neutrophil or monocyte to effect locomotion.

RECOGNITION AND ATTACHMENT

Phagocytosis begins when the phagocytic cell recognizes a microbe or other particle as "nonself." Some microbes, particularly nonpathogenic strains, are intrinsically attractive to phagocytes and present little opposition to attachment and ingestion. Other microbes, such as encapsulated organisms with antiphagocytic factors on their surface, become appetizing only following opsonization.

To "opsonize" means to "prepare to eat" (from the Greek), and an "opsonin" refers to any serum factor that acts on particles to make them more readily ingested by phagocytes. Opsonins act by neutralizing antiphagocytic factors on the surface of particles and by binding with receptors on the cell surface to provide ligands between the particle and phagocytic membrane. Serum opsonins include both heat-stable factors, chiefly antibacterial antibodies, and heat-labile factors, primarily components of the complement system. Specific antibacterial antibody, if present in sufficiently high concentrations, can opsonize on its own and directly promote ingestion. Consequently, antibody-coated microorganisms, erythrocytes, platelets, and neutrophils can be ingested by macrophages and neutrophils. The opsonically active antibodies are usually 7S, IgG molecules, though 19S antibody, IgM, may also perform this function. Under physiological conditions, however, the primary opsonin appears to be activated complement C_3. This key opsonic factor may be activated by two separate pathways, the classical complement and the properdin systems. Antibody is absolutely required for opsonic activity mediated by the classical complement pathway. Specific antibody also serves as an initiator or accelerator of opsonization by the properdin system, but this heat-labile system can operate in the absence of specific antibody. Thus, specific antibody directly, or the opsonically active fragment of C_3 alone, or both in concert, facilitate the binding of particles to the surface of phagocytic cells. It appears that opsonically active C_3 is bound very tightly to particle surfaces, but the physical and chemical properties of this binding remain obscure. It is clear that antibody binds to particles via its Fab region, and that the part of the immunoglobulin molecule that activates ingestion is the Fc region. It is also fairly well established that human neutrophils possess surface receptors that are specific for the Fc region of IgG and for the opsonic fragment of C_3.

INGESTION

Despite morphologic and functional diversity, human phagocytic cells all exhibit remarkable similarities in the morphologic changes associated with ingestion. In monolayer cultures, the entire cell periphery attached to the substrate appears to be well organized (hyaline ectoplasm), while the cell interior (endoplasm) appears to be in a fluid phase with organelles in constant vibrating motion or streaming in rushes from one part of the cell to the other. The relative proportion of the cell that is fluid "endoplasm" or "hyaline ectoplasm" appears to change constantly. When the cell encounters a particle to which it will become attached, an area of ectoplasm enlarges to form pseudopodia that flow about the particle, surround it, and fuse to form a vacuole (Figure 1A–C). The pseudopod response and ingestion are localized to the region of the membrane adjacent to the particle initiating the stimulus; the stimulus does not spread or elicit a general membrane response. The clear hyaline ectoplasm as seen by electron microscopy is composed of the contractile proteins, microfilaments, and microtubules, and is devoid of any organelles (Figure 1B).

Phagocytic leukocytes contain actin and myosin, and it appears that these proteins probably play a central role in the phagocytic process. Actins purified from diverse phagocytic cells are strikingly similar, though not identical, to muscle actin in structural and functional properties. In muscle cells, the monomeric subunits (G actin) are fully polymerized (F-actin), and the actin filaments are aligned in an organized parallel fashion to provide static contractile strength. In phagocytic cells, where fluidity and rigidity appear to alternate in response to assembly and disappearance of localized microfilament networks, a highly organized and rigid filamentous structure would not be practical. A state of reversible polymerization of actin would permit flexibility, but there is little evidence that this occurs. Among the proteins identified in the actomyosin complex of the phagocytes are cytoplasmic myosins which crosslink actin filaments and an unstable protein that in the presence of Mg and ATP, increases the rate of contraction of the actomyosin complex. Microtubules have also been identified in phagocytic cells, but little is known concerning the structure and function of their subunit protein, tubulin.

Phagocytosis is an energy-consuming process. During ingestion, all phagocytic cells increase their rates of glucose uptake, phosphorylation, and utilization, as well as lactate and CO_2 production. While these metabolic changes suggest increased ATP consumption and/or generation, ATPase activity may not be a requirement but instead may be a metabolic consequence of ingestion.

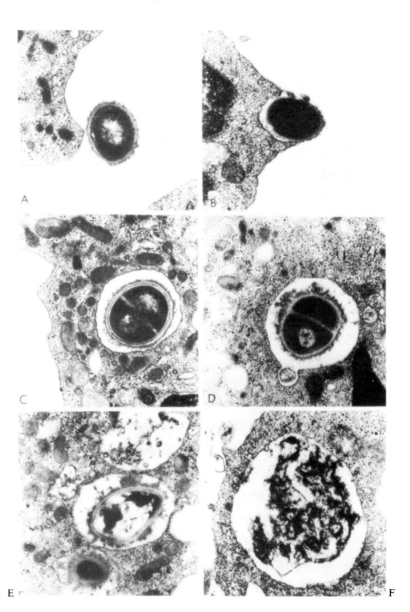

Figure 1. Sequence of events in bacterial phagocytosis by a human polymorphonuclear leukocyte. (A) Magnification of polymorph and staphylococcus. (×10,000) (B) Attachment of opsonized bacterium to phagocytic membrane. (C) Membrane engulfment of the bacterium. (D) Intracellular bacterium within a phagocytic vacuole. (E) Bacterial death. (F) Bacterial digestion. (Courtesy of Drs. J. G. White and C. C. Clawson.)

In any event, the energy expended during ingestion is derived from metabolism of endogenous or exogenous carbohydrates. The process of engulfment in human neutrophils is non-oxygen-dependent, since phagocytosis proceeds normally in the absence of oxygen, and patients with defective oxidative metabolism engulf particles normally.

Once particles are engulfed and the phagocytic vacuole is formed, degranulation follows in rapid sequence. As granules of the leukocyte come into apposition with the vacuole, the membranes of the granule and vacuole fuse and the granules rupture, discharging their enzyme-rich contents into the vacuole (Figure 1C,D). Degranulation in the neutrophil occurs within 5 to 30 min of particle ingestion, with the extent of degranulation dependent upon the amount of material phagocytized.

INTRACELLULAR KILLING

Perturbation of the neutrophil plasma membrane by particle attachment stimulates a sudden surge in cellular oxidative metabolism. A rapid sequence of metabolic events follows which involves uptake of large amounts of oxygen (the "respiratory burst"), a concomitant tenfold rise in glucose metabolism via the hexose monophosphate shunt, and generation of large amounts of H_2O_2 and superoxide. These metabolic consequences of phagocytosis, while not energy requirements for particle ingestion, are essential for normal intracellular killing. The activating factor responsible for the respiratory burst has yet to be identified. Oxygen consumption, however, is almost certainly a response of the plasma-membrane enzyme, nicotinamide adenine dinucleotide (NADH) oxidase, and the azurophil granule enzyme, nicotinamide adenine dinucleotide phosphate (NADPH) oxidase.

Oxidative processes have been shown by studies of inherited leukocyte abnormalities to play a major role in the armamentarium of neutrophils against both fungi and bacteria. Patients with chronic granulomatous disease (CGD) have severe infections, their leukocytes are markedly defective in microbicidal activity, and they fail to show phagocytosis-stimulated oxidative metabolism. Similarly, patients with leukocytes deficient in the granular enzyme myeloperoxidase (MPO) or those that have a complete absence of glucose-6-phosphate dehydrogenase have increased infections. Their neutrophils are defective in generation of certain products of oxygen reduction, and they have delayed or decreased microbicidal activity.

Phagocytizing cells generate several products of oxygen reduction: H_2O_2 and superoxide, which have been measured directly; the hydroxyl radical, which has been indirectly quantitated; and singlet oxygen, which has been postulated from compelling experimental evidence (Table 1). The superoxide anion, a powerful oxidation–reduction agent, is found in abundant supply

Table 1.   Antimicrobial Systems of Human Granulocytes.

OXYGEN-DEPENDENT	OXYGEN-INDEPENDENT

I. Oxygen products
  1. Hydrogen peroxide
  2. Superoxide anion
  3. Hydroxyl radicals
  4. Singlet oxygen
II. Enzyme-mediated
  1. Myeloperoxidase–halide–
    hydrogen peroxide
	1. Lysozyme
	2. Lactoferrin
	3. Acid
	4. Cationic proteins
	5. Myeloperoxidase

in stimulated phagocytes. Its highly reactive properties coupled with the fact that neutrophils of patients with intracellular killing defects (CGD) generate virtually no superoxide during phagocytosis, suggest that this radical, or one of its derivatives, is involved in microbial killing. There is good evidence that superoxide does indeed participate in the bactericidal event, but that the anion itself has little bactericidal activity. Similarly, hydrogen peroxide alone has limited bactericidal activity, but hydrogen peroxide acting in concert with myeloperoxidase (MPO) and halide, forms a powerful antimicrobial system. The hydroxyl radical and singlet oxygen are both potentially bactericidal agents produced during this reaction, but the nature and extent of their participation in microbicidal activity is not known.

Human neutrophils also possess non-oxygen-dependent microbicidal systems which are responsible for the intracellular killing of certain bacterial and fungal species. Some of these bactericidal agents are granule-derived cationic proteins, lysozyme, lactoferrin, and myeloperoxidase (Table 1).

Recently, neutrophils, monocytes, macrophages, and eosinophils have all been observed to emit photons of light during phagocytosis. Spectral analysis of this light, measurable with a beta-spectrophotometer, has shown emission over a broad region of the visible light spectrum. These findings are consistent with oxidation of a variety of particle constituents (such as microbial unsaturated lipids and nucleic acids) producing a heterogenous group of electronically excited species. Relaxation of these species yields light emission in multiple regions of the visible spectrum. While the electronically excited species responsible for this chemiluminescence* has not been identified, there is good evidence to suggest that chemiluminescence and microbial killing are related. The most compelling evidence is the finding that granulocytes of CGD patients with severe intracellular killing defects produce virtually no chemiluminescence.

---

* The dissipation of excess energy from a biochemical reaction in the form of light emission, rather than heat, is termed chemiluminescence.

CONCLUSION

While the events described in phagocytizing granulocytes are strikingly similar to those associated with particle ingestion by certain unicellular organisms such as amoeba, phagocytosis is more than a primitive and curious phenomenon. The phagocytic system is essential for host defense against invasion by microorganisms and recovery from microbial disease.

BIBLIOGRAPHY

Allen, R. C., Stjernholm, R. L., and Steele, R. H. 1972. Evidence for the generation of an electronic excitation state(s) in human polymorphonuclear leukocytes and its participation in bactericidal activity. *Biochem. Biophys. Res. Commun.* 47:679–84.

Babior, B. M., Kipnes, R. S., and Curnutte, J. T. 1973. Biological defense mechanisms. The production by leukocytes of superoxide, a potential bactericidal agent. *J. Clin. Invest.* 52:741–44.

Bainton, D. F. 1973. Sequential degranulation of the two types of polymorphonuclear leukocyte granules during phagocytosis of microorganisms. *J. Cell Biol.* 58:249–64.

Bellanti, J. A., and Dayton, D. H., eds. 1975. *The Phagocytic Cell in Host Resistance.* Raven Press, New York.

Cheson, B. D., Curnutte, J. T., and Babior, B. M. 1977. The oxidative killing mechanism of the neutrophil. In *Progress in Clinical Immunology,* Vol. 3, R. S. Schwartz, ed. Grune and Stratton, New York.

Cline, M. J. 1975. *The White Cell.* Harvard University Press, Cambridge, Massachusetts.

Gotze, O., and Muller-Eberhard, H. J. 1976. Alternative pathway of complement activation. *Adv. Immunol.* 24:1–35.

Klebanoff, S. J. 1975. Antimicrobial mechanisms of neutrophil polymorphonuclear leukocytes. *Semin. Hematol.* 12:117–42.

Metchnikoff, E. 1968. *Lectures on the Comparative Pathology of Inflammation.* Dover Publications, New York.

Quie, P. G. 1975. Pathology of bactericidal power of neutrophils. *Semin. Hematol.* 12:143–60.

Quie, P. G., Mills, E. L., and Holmes, B. 1978. Molecular events during phagocytosis by human neutrophils. In *Progress in Hematology,* Vol. X, E. B. Brown, ed. Grune and Stratton, New York.

Quie, P. G., White, J. G., Holmes, B., and Good, R. A. 1967. In vitro bactericidal capacity of human polymorphonuclear leukocytes: Diminished activity in chronic granulomatous disease of childhood. *J. Clin. Invest.* 46:668–79.

Shawn, R., Gigli, I., and Austen, K. F. 1972. The complement system of man. *N. Engl. J. Med.* 287:489–642.

Silverstein, S. C., Steinman, R. M., and Cohn, Z. A. 1977. Endocytosis. *Annu. Rev. Biochem.* 46:669–722.

Stossel, T. P. 1974. Phagocytosis (first of three parts; second of three parts; third of three parts). *N. Engl. J. Med.* 290:717–23; 774–80; 833–39.

Stossel, T. P. 1975. Phagocytosis: Recognition and ingestion. *Semin. Hematol.* 12:83–116.

van Oss, C. J., and Gillman, C. F. 1972. Phagocytosis as a surface phenomenon. II. Contact angles and phagocytosis of encapsulated bacteria before and after opsonization by specific antiserum and complement. *J. Reticuloendothel. Soc.* 12:497–502.

Wright, D. E., and Douglas, S. R. 1903. An experimental investigation of the role of blood fluids in connection with phagocytosis. *Proc. R. Soc. London B Biol. Sci.* 72:357–62.

4.14. Pathologic Forms of Cellular Storage

Randolph C. Steer

The ability to degrade a variety of macromolecules is an important function of many living cells. When this ability is diminished or absent, the accumulation of these substances becomes apparent by bulging and vacuolation of affected cells. Numerous storage disease have been discovered in which complex macromolecules such as mucopolysaccharides, glycolipids, and others are found in vast abundance within cells. Almost all of these genetically determined disorders represent the lack of a specific enzyme with a resultant block in a normal biochemical pathway. The metabolic defect presumably results from a mutation, and the genetic mechanism involved may be simple or very complex. Most storage diseases are familial, and their transmission almost always follows an autosomal recessive pattern with traits becoming clinically manifest in homozygotes. In some cases, evidence of dominant or sex-linked patterns of inheritance has been presented. The exact enzymatic defect that results, the identity of the substance that is stored in excess, and the altered cellular and systemic functions that produce the clinical stigmata are not completely understood in many of the storage diseases.

Despite the fact that some defective basic mechanisms appear to be common among almost all of these disorders, their clinical presentations are often strikingly different. Thus, it is not surprising that only recently have they been considered to represent a broadly related group of diseases. The systemic manifestations that occur depend upon several factors, including the tissue distribution of the enzyme defect, the specific nature and extent of the defect, and the stage in organismal development at the time the enzyme defect becomes manifest. Some storage diseases may predominantly involve localized dysfunction, such as the central nervous system involvement in Tay-Sachs disease. Others may present evidence of widespread involvement, as the abnormal (in type and/or amount) storage product "overflows" into the systemic circulation and is picked up by reticuloendothelial cells, producing hepatosplenomegaly, lymphadenopathy, and marrow infiltration. An example of such a disseminated type is the adult form of Gaucher's disease.

The purpose of this chapter is to describe briefly the general features of some selected disorders of cellular storage. For more extensive considerations of the biochemistry and pathology of these diseases, several recent journal articles and books are cited. Although these storage diseases are relatively uncommon among the general population, their study is indicated for several reasons: With increased knowledge of the altered genetic and biochemical mechanisms involved, we may hopefully increase our ability to detect these disorders during the prenatal period and among carriers in general; we may learn to treat patients in a beneficial way and thus avoid or reduce their often critical and even fatal sequelae; and perhaps we may learn to better understand the manner in which cells utilize macromolecules both in disease and in health.

GLYCOGENOSES

The "glycogenoses" is a collective term used to represent a group of disorders that share some abnormality involving the structure or metabolism of glycogen. The term is frequently and erroneously equated with the term "glycogen storage disease," which implies a defect in the breakdown of glycogen. Such a defect exists in some, but certainly not all of the glycogenoses. Table 1 includes some of the main features of the seven most common disorders in this group.

Type I (von Gierke's disease) is frequently called "hepatorenal glycogenosis" because it is mainly characterized by excessive glycogen storage in the liver and kidneys. A deficiency of the microsomal enzyme, glucose-6-phosphatase, prevents the hepatic formation of glucose from glycogen. Glucose-6-phosphate that is formed by the breakdown of glycogen cannot be hydrolyzed, and it does not accumulate. Rather, its utilization in the pentosephosphate and Embden-Meyerhof pathways generates 5-ribosylpyrophosphate and lactate, respectively. The former is a precursor of uric acid, which is characteristically elevated in the blood of these patients. The elevated lactate levels result in chronic acidosis. Although some glucose is probably produced by the action of nonspecific phosphatases on glucose-6-phosphate, the fasting hypoglycemia produced in severe. This decrease in blood glucose causes enhanced fat mobilization from peripheral stores, and, because of the availability of glycolytic intermediates in the liver, massive reesterification of fatty acids occurs. Accordingly, a fatty liver and hyperlipidemia result. The abnormal biochemical findings of hyperlactatemia, hyperuricemia, and hyperlipidemia may be reversed by administration of glucose. In addition to the hepatomegaly resulting from excess storage of fat and glycogen within liver cells, glycogen deposits cause renal tubular cell vacuolation and renal enlargement. Infants so afflicted fail to thrive and commonly die as a result of infection.

Type II (Pompe's disease) is a fatal disorder that usually causes death

Table 1. The Glycogenoses.

TYPE	EPONYM/SYNONYM	AFFECTED TISSUES	ENZYME DEFICIENCY	MODE OF TRANSMISSION
I	von Gierke's disease; glucose-6-phosphatase deficiency	liver, kidney	glucose-6-phosphatase	autosomal recessive
II	Pompe's disease; acid maltase deficiency	all tissues	alpha-1,4-glucosidase	autosomal recessive
III	Cori/Forbes disease; limit dextrinosis	all tissues	amylo-1,6-glucosidase (debranching enzyme)	autosomal recessive
IV	Andersen's disease; amylopectinosis	all tissues	amylo-1,4-1,6-transglucosidase (branching enzyme)	autosomal recessive
V	McArdle's syndrome; myophosphorylase deficiency	muscle	myophosphorylase	autosomal recessive with male predominance
VI	Hers' disease; hepatic phosphorylase-complex deficiency	liver	hepatic phosphorylase kinase (majority of patients)	sex-linked recessive, autosomal recessive
VII	Tarui's disease; muscle phosphofructokinase deficiency	muscle	muscle phosphofructokinase	autosomal recessive

during the first year of life. In 1963, Hers demonstrated the deficiency of lysosomal alpha-1,4-glucosidase (acid maltase) in the liver of patients with Pompe's disease, and subsequently the enzyme was shown to be deficient in skeletal muscle, brain, heart, pancreas, fibroblasts, and leukocytes of patients with this disease. Heterozygotes not clinically manifesting the disease can be detected by assay of phytohemagglutinin-stimulated lymphocytes for alpha-1,4-glucosidase. Deficiency of this exoglucosidase produces lysosomal swelling with accumulated glycogen. Since the enzyme is confined to lysosomes, its deficiency does not apparently alter the normal cytoplasmic pathways of glycogen synthesis and breakdown. Lysosomes in all tissues are affected, but cellular damage is most evident in heart and skeletal muscle. Although mental development appears normal, severe muscular weakness, failure to thrive, and subsequent congestive heart failure result in progressive deterioration and death.

Type IV (Andersen's disease) may be the rarest form of glycogenosis, with fewer than 15 cases reported. It is one of the most lethal forms and almost always causes death during infancy. Deficiency of amylo-1,4-1,6-transglucosidase (branching enzyme) results in the formation of an abnormal glycogen molecule with an excess of straight chains and few branch points. The abnormal glycogen is present in all glycogen-containing organs; however, the major clinical problem is confined to the liver. Infants fail to thrive early during the course of the disease, which almost invariably results in diffuse portal cirrhosis with resultant liver failure and death.

Type VI (Hers' disease) is a disorder in which patients show a decrease in, but not an absence of, activity of the hepatic phosphorylase complex. Increased liver glycogen content produces hepatomegaly, and patients with this disorder may demonstrate marked hypoglycemia. Patients with Type VI glycogenosis actually have one of three different disorders: decreased activity of phosphorylase kinase, of the protein kinase, or of phosphorylase itself. Most patients appear to lack activity of phosphorylase kinase. Unlike the other glycogenoses, this disorder is inherited as a sex-linked recessive trait. In some cases, however, the inheritance appears to follow an autosomal recessive pattern.

MUCOPOLYSACCHARIDOSES

Mucopolysaccharides, in association with reticulin, collagen, and elastin, are the major polymers of connective tissue and ground substance. Because previous reports in the literature erroneously equated the terms "mucin," "mucopolysaccharide," "mucoprotein," and so one, the clarification provided by Jeanloz has been of great value. His introduction of the term "glycosaminoglycan" (GAG) more clearly defined the chemical nature of mucopolysaccharides

(GAGs) as being high-molecular-weight polymers composed of repeating dimers of an amino sugar usually linked to a hexuronic acid.

The mucopolysaccharidoses constitute a group of genetic diseases with a total incidence of about 4:100,000. These disorders are characterized by storage of incompletely degraded glycosaminoglycans, a storage that results from deficiency of specific lysosomal hydrolases essential for their degradation. With the exception of Type IV (Morquio's disease), all of the mucopolysaccharidoses involve a defect in the lysosomal catabolism of either one or both of the polymeric compounds heparan sulfate and dermatan sulfate. These substances are composed of alternating residues of sulfated hexosamine (either glucosamine or galactosamine) and uronic acid. Their degradation is accomplished primarily by lysosomal exoenzymes such as glycosidases and sulfatases, which cleave the molecules by sequentially removing individual carbohydrate residues or sulfate groups. Because each chemically distinct moiety is acted on by a different enzyme, the combined action of multiple enzymes is normally involved in order to disrupt the chain. When an enzyme is deficient, degradation of the glycosaminoglycan is incomplete. Normally, degradation of dermatan sulfate and heparan sulfate produces sulfate, which is excreted, and uronic acid and hexosamine, which enter the hexosemonophosphate shunt and Embden-Meyerhof pathway, respectively. In the mucopolysaccharidoses, the degradation of these compounds produces fragmented molecules, which are somehow trapped within lysosomes. The lysosomal distention that results is progressive, and the associated dysfunction presumably leads to cellular and systemic injury.

In 1968 it was confirmed that these disorders were due to deficient degradation of mucopolysaccharides, on the basis of kinetics of $^{35}SO_4$-glycosaminoglycan accumulation in cultured fibroblasts obtained from skin biopsies of patients with Hunter's and Hurler's diseases. Shortly after these observations, it was discovered that when cells from patients with Hurler's disease were mixed with cells from patients with Hunter's disease, mutual correction of the defect occurred, and the cells then behaved as normal cell cultures. In fact, the cells did not even need to be mixed because the medium itself appeared to contain a substance that would correct the abnormal accumulation of glycosaminoglycans. Thus, the medium from a normal person's fibroblast culture contained some diffusible material that would correct the defect in Hurler or Hunter cells. The diffusible material was referred to as a "corrective factor." Since 1970, extensive experimentation on these corrective factors has led to the discovery of the identities of enzymes whose deficiencies produce the genetic mucopolysaccharidoses.

The mucopolysaccharidoses fulfill the criteria established by McKusick for lysosomal storage diseases: Evidence of storage always exists; the stored material is usually heterogeneous and enclosed in membrane-bound vesicles;

several tissues are usually affected; and the disease is usually progressive. Table 2 includes some important features of these disorders.

SPHINGOLIPIDOSES

Sphingolipids are complex lipids containing sphingosine (4-sphingenine), or a related base. They are present in large amounts in brain and other tissues of the nervous system but exist in only trace amounts in the fat depots of the body. These complex molecules are formed during the natural turnover of erythrocyte and other cell membranes and are normally catabolized within lysosomes in a sequence of enzymatic steps. Sphingolipids contain three characteristic components: one molecule of a fatty acid, one molecule of sphingosine (a long-chain amino alcohol) or one of its derivatives, and a polar head group. The long-chain base (e.g., sphingosine) possesses a hydroxyl group on its first and third carbons, and an amino group on the second carbon. When a long-chain fatty acid is attached to the amino group by an amide bond, the resulting compound is called a *ceramide,* which has two nonpolar tails and is the characteristic parent structure of all sphingolipids. The structures of sphingosine and ceramide are shown in Figure 1.

Various chemical groups can be attached to the hydroxyl group of the first carbon of sphingosine. When the group attached is a carbohydrate, the resulting compound is called a *cerebroside;* it may also be called a ceramide if the attached carbohydrate moiety is specified (e.g., glucocerebroside or ceramide glucoside). When sialic acid is attached to one of the carbohydrates, the resuling molecule becomes charged (a net negative charge at pH 7.0) and is called a *ganglioside.* The sialic acid usually found in human gangliosides is N-acetylneuraminic acid (NANA). Gangliosides are most abundant in the gray matter of brain tissue; however, smaller amounts of these glycosphingolipids may also be found in nonneural tissues. The normal function of gangliosides is not well understood; however, because of their relative abundance in nerve endings, it has been proposed that they play a role in the transmission of impulses across synapses. They are also believed to be present at receptor sites for acetylcholine and other neurotransmitter substances.

The terminology used in the study of gangliosides is derived from the work of Svennerholm. Subtypes are indicated by the letter G, which is followed by M, D, or T, which denotes the number of sialic acid groups. Thus, GM is monosialic acid, GD is disialic acid, and GT is trisialic acid. The subscript numbers 1, 2, and 3 refer to the presence of 4, 3, and 2 hexoses, respectively. For example, GM_2 has one sialic acid and three hexose groups. Groups other than sugars may also be attached to the ceramide. For instance, when phosphorylcholine is attached, the resultant compound is sphingomyelin, which is particularly abundant in the membranes of myelinated nerve tissue.

Table 2. The Mucopolysaccharidoses[a]

CURRENT DESIGNATIONS	PREVIOUS DESIGNATION	GENETICS	ENZYME DEFICIENCY	ACCUMULATED PRODUCT	CLINICAL FEATURES
Mucopolysaccharidosis (MPS), dysostosis multiplex	Gargoylism	autosomal recessive (except Type II)	Variable	glycosaminoglycans	Impressive phenotypic disturbances
MPS I H, Hurler disease	Lipochondrodystrophy	Homozygous for MPS I H gene	Alpha-L-Iduronidase	Heparan sulfate Dermatan sulfate	Early clouding of cornea; death usually before age 10
MPS I S, Scheie disease	Spat-Hurler	Homozygous for MPS I S gene	Alpha-L-Iduronidase	Heparan sulfate Dermatan sulfate	Stiff joints, cloudy cornea, aortic regurgitation, normal intelligence
MPS I H/S, Hurler-Scheie compound	—	Genetic compound of MPS I H and I S genes	Alpha-L-Iduronidase	Heparan sulfate Dermatan sulfate	Phenotype intermediate between MPS I H and I S
MPS IIA Hunter disease, severe	—	Hemizygous for X-linked gene	L-Iduronosulfate sulfatase	Heparan sulfate Dermatan sulfate	No clouding of cornea, death usually before age 15
MPS IIB Hunter disease, mild	—	Hemizygous for X-linked allele for mild form	L-Iduronosulfate sulfatase	Heparan sulfate Dermatan sulfate	Survival 30–50 years, fair intelligence
MPS IIIA Sanfilippo type A	Polydystrophic oligophrenia	Homozygous for Sanfilippo A	Heparan sulfate sulfamidase	Heparan sulfate	Identical phenotype
MPS IIIB Sanfilippo type B	Heparan sulfaturia	Homozygous for Sanfilippo B (at different locus)	N-acetyl-α-D-glucosaminidase	Heparan sulfate	Mild somatic, severe CNS effects

Type	Eponym	Genetics	Enzyme deficiency	Urinary MPS	Clinical features
MPS IV Morquio type I	Morquio-Brailsford	Homozygous for Morquio gene (probably more than one allelic form)	N-acetylhexosamine-6-SO₄ sulfatase	Keratan sulfate Chondroitin sulfate	Severe bone changes, cloudy cornea, aortic regurgitation, normal intelligence
MPS IV Morquio type II	Chondro-osteodystrophy	Homozygous for Morquio gene (probably more than one allelic form)	N-acetylhexosamine-6-SO₄ sulfatase	Non-KS-CS-secreting	Similar radiographic features as MPS IV—type I
MPS V None	Formerly type IS	—	—	—	—
MPS VI A Maroteaux-Lamy, classic form	Polydystrophic dwarfism	Homozygous for M-L gene	N-acetylgalactosamine-4-sulfate sulfatase (arylsulfatase B)	Dermatan sulfate	Severe bone and corneal changes, normal intellect, cardiac disease, WBC inclusions
MPS VI B Maroteaux-Lamy, mild form	—	Homozygous for allele at M-L locus	—	Dermatan sulfate	Severe bone and corneal changes, normal intellect, cardiac disease, WBC inclusions
MPS VII beta-glucuronidase deficiency disease	—	Homozygous for mutant gene at beta-glucuronidase locus	Beta-D-glucuronidase	Dermatan sulfate Heparan sulfate Chondroitin sulfate	Hepatosplenomegaly, WBC inclusions, mental retardation

[a] Modified from Victor A. McKusick, *Heritable Disorders of Connective Tissue*, 4th ed. The C. V. Mosby Co. St. Louis, 1972.

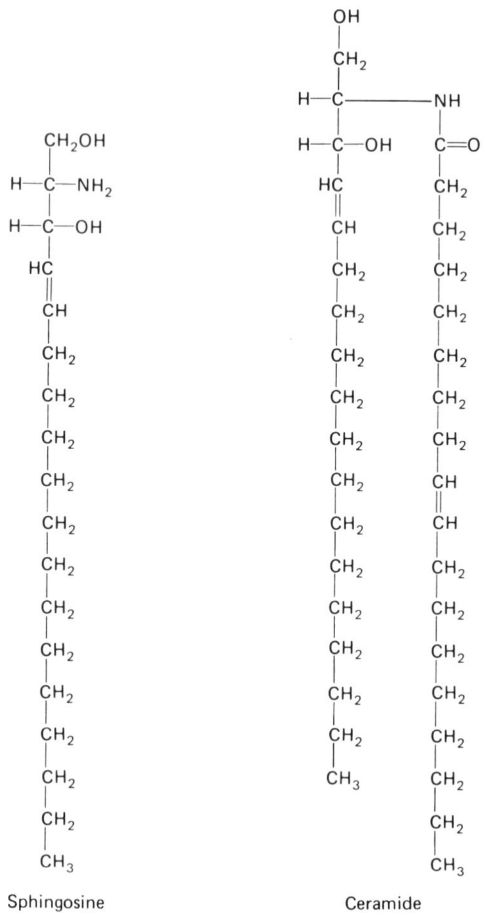

Figure 1. Structures of sphingosine and ceramide.

When a sulfate group is added to a galactose attached to ceramide, a *sulfatide* is formed, which is also present in myelinated nerve.

The group of diseases known as sphingolipidoses results from deficiencies in the pathways of catabolism of sphingolipids. There are ten such inherited disorders for which the deficient enzymology is established. Excessive amounts of these compounds accumulate in lysosomes of various tissues of patients with these disorders. Although the rate of synthesis of the accumulating substances (storage products) is normal, the activity of a lysosomal enzyme essential for the hydrolysis of the accumulating lipid is decreased. Each sphingolipidosis, with the exception of Fabry's disease, is transmitted in an autosomal recessive fashion. Fabry's disease is inherited in an X-linked recessive fashion. Figure 2 schematically shows the catabolism of sphingolipids and the sites of action of enzymes whose deficiencies result in the associated diseases. The designations, clinical features, identities of stored products, and enzyme deficiencies involved in these disorders are listed in Table 3. One disorder, Tay-Sachs disease, will be discussed in greater detail.

Tay-Sachs disease (GM₂ gangliosidosis, variant B) is the most common gangliosidosis. Since the original independent descriptions by Tay in 1881 and Sachs in 1887, several thousand cases have been reported. The disorder is found almost entirely within Jewish populations and mostly among the descendants of the Ashkenazi Jews, where the estimated carrier frequency is 1 in 30. Clinically the infant appears normal at birth; however, mental and motor deterioration become apparent after 6 to 9 months. After the

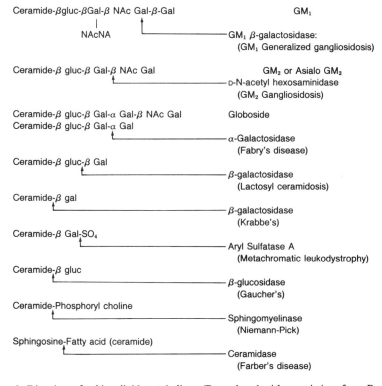

Figure 2. Disorders of sphingolipid metabolism. (Reproduced with permission, from Rochelle Hirschhorn and Gerald Weissmann, Genetic disorders of lysosomes, *Prog. Med. Genet.* 1:49–101, 1976. Publishers: Grune and Stratton, Inc., New York.)

Table 3. Lysosomal Storage Diseases: Disorders of Sphingolipid Metabolism.[a]

DESIGNATION	CLINICAL FEATURES	PRODUCT STORED	ENZYME DEFICIENCY
Generalized gangliosidosis (Gangliosidosis GM₁)	Acute infantile cerebral disorder; onset at birth; death by age 2 with decerebrate rigidity; similar to Hurler's coarsening of facial features; bone changes, hirsutism, hepatosplenomegaly. Lipids in liver, spleen, marrow, kidney, and blood cells.	Ganglioside GM_1 and asialo derivative in brain; visceral storage of mucopolysaccharide	β-Galactosidase (GM_1 β-galactosidase)
Juvenile gangliosidosis GM₁	Onset age 1; locomotor ataxia, frequent falling, internal strabismus, progressing to decerebrate rigidity by age 3. No hepatosplenomegaly. Mild bony abnormalities.	Same as above.	β-Galactosidase (GM_1 β-galactosidase)
Gangliosidosis GM₂ Type I: Tay-Sachs	Normal at birth, onset 4–6 months; weakness progressive mental and motor deterioration, blindness, macrocephaly, hyperacusis, paralysis, and dementia. Cherry red spot in macula. Jewish parentage.	GM_2 ganglioside	N-Acetyl hexosaminidase A
Type II: Sandhoff	Clinically indistinguishable from above. Non-Jewish parentage.	GM_2 ganglioside and globoside in viscera	N-Acetyl hexosaminidase A and B
Type III: Juvenile gangliosidosis GM₂	Onset 2–6 years; locomotor ataxia, loss of speech, progressive spasticity, and weakness progressing to decerebrate rigidity and blindness. Death by age 5–15. No cherry red spots.	GM_2 ganglioside	Partial deficiency hexosaminidase A and B
Fabry's disease	Males have crises of severe incapacitating burning pain in extremities, fever, characteristic skin lesion, angiokeratoma corporis diffusum universale, corneal opacities, anhidrosis, multiple system involvement, renal impairment, hypertension, cardiac failure. Heterozygous females may have limited disease. X-linked inherited.	Ceramide trihexoside widespread deposition, blood vessels, nerve cells, RES, myocardium, kidney	α-Galactosidase
Lactosyl ceramidosis	Childhood onset. Slowly progressive CNS impairment. Hepatosplenomegaly, foam cells. Macrocytic anemia, leukopenia, and thrombocytopenia (one case).	Lactosyl ceramide	β-Galactosidase (?)

Table 3. *(continued)*

DESIGNATION	CLINICAL FEATURES	PRODUCT STORED	ENZYME DEFICIENCY
Krabbe's globoid cell leukodystrophy	Rapidly fatal infantile neurologic disorder. Globoid cells in brain tissue.	No overt accumulation of galactocerebroside	β-Galactoside galactocerebrosidase; psychosine β-galactosidase
Metachromatic leukodystrophy (sulfatide lipidoses) Late infantile	Onset 1–4 years; gait disturbance, incoordination leading to dementia; macular changes. Vegetative state by 5 years. Nerve biopsy: metachromasia.	Galactosyl (SO_4) ceramide	Aryl sulfatase A
Juvenile	As above but later onset. Sometimes seen in same kindred as above.		Aryl sulfatase A; levels higher than in infantile
Adult	Rare; onset in adult life with psychosis and dementia; motor signs much later (up to 30 years).	Galactosyl (SO_4) ceramide	Aryl sulfatase A diminished but not absent
Variant (Austin type)	Rare; onset 1–3 years. Dysostosis multiplex. Hepatosplenomegaly with generalized CNS involvement; early death. Nerve biopsy: metachromasia.	Galactosyl (SO_4) ceramide and sulfated mucopolysaccharides, steroid sulfates	Aryl sulfatase A, B, and C; steroid sulfatase deficiencies
Gaucher's Infantile (cerebrovisceral)	Normal at birth; death by age 2; severe cerebral involvement with hyperextension of head, strabismus, retraction of lips. Hepatosplenomegaly, Gaucher cells in marrow.	Glucocerebroside	β-Glucosidase deficiency
Adult (visceral)	Chronic nonneuronopathic: no cerebral involvement. Hepatosplenomegaly; episodic bone pain with involvement of hip and long bones. Gaucher cells in marrow; lymphadenopathy. Spectrum of benign to more malignant course.	Glucocerebroside	Diminished pH, 4.0; β-glucosidase activity (?)
Juvenile	Heterogeneous group; hepatosplenomegaly and neurologic abnormalities. Gaucher cells.	? Glucocerebroside	

Table 3. *(continued)*

DESIGNATION	CLINICAL FEATURES	PRODUCT STORED	ENZYME DEFICIENCY
Niemann-Pick Cerebrovisceral	Onset in infancy; death by age 3, progressive rapid neurologic deterioration. Hepatosplenomegaly, cachexia, 30% with cherry red spot in macula; foam cells in marrow stain for lipid and phosphorus.	Sphingomyelin + cholesterol (neural and visceral)	Sphingomyelinase (no artificial substrate)
Visceral	Older onset; visceral involvement only. Pulmonary infections, hepatosplenomegaly, normal intelligence.	Sphingomyelin + cholesterol (visceral)	Sphingomyelinase
Visceral-cerebral	Moderate course, lesser visceral involvement and late onset of CNS involvement. May have cherry red spot. Death between 5 and 15. Older onset (2–6 years).	Sphingomyelin + cholesterol (visceral and neural)	Sphingomyelinase (?)
Visceral-cerebral	Nova Scotia variant. Ataxia and dyskinesia, early jaundice with hepatosplenomegaly. Protracted degenerative course.	Sphingomyelin + cholesterol (primary cholesterol)	(?) Diminished or ↑ sphingomyelinase
Farber's disease (lipogranulomatosis)	Childhood onset; progressive arthropathy. Subcutaneous nodules, nutritional failure, and psychomotor retardation.	Ceramide	Ceramidase

[a] Reproduced by permission, from Rochelle Hirschhorn and Gerald Weissmann, Genetic disorders of lysosomes, *Prog. Med. Genet.* 1:49–101, 1976. Publishers: Grune and Stratton, Inc., New York.

first year, blindness and deafness occur, and a condition of decerebrate rigidity follows. Death usually occurs between 2 and 5 years of age.

The storage of GM_2 ganglioside is associated with the absence of N-acetylhexosaminidase A, the enzyme that catalyzes the hydrolysis of the terminal N-acetylgalactosamine. There is also an associated increase in GA_2, the asialo derivative of GM_2. The manifestations of Tay-Sachs disease are consequences of the accumulation of these compounds in ganglion cells, glial cells, and perivascular tissue cells of the nervous system. Increased concentrations of N-acetylglucosamine and mannose in brain dialyzable glycopeptides are also found.

The gross pathologic features of this disorder are numerous. During the first 12 to 14 months of illness, there are pallor and mild atrophy of the basal ganglia and thalami. The ventricular system, particularly the third ventricle, is moderately dilated. Between the fifteenth and twenty-fourth months, the brain weight increases moderately with slight enlargement of the cerebral hemispheres and swelling of the gyri. The white matter is edematous, and its swelling compresses the lateral ventricles, although the remainder of the ventricular system appears normal. Pallor of the basal ganglia increases. After the second year of this disorder, brain weight markedly increases as the cerebral hemispheres become diffusely enlarged. The base of the brain commonly shows protrusion of the third ventricle, which pushes down the optic chiasm, and the optic nerves are atrophic. The white matter of the frontoparietal lobes contains areas of cystic changes. In the cerebellum, the folia of all lobules are atrophic, and there is brown discoloration of the white matter.

The histopathologic features of Tay-Sachs disease are likewise numerous. Neurons in the central nervous system are uniformly involved by the lipid storage process. Neuronal loss and glial proliferation occur in varying degrees with alterations in the cerebral cortex more severe than those of the deep gray matter, brain stem, and spinal cord. During the first 12 to 14 months of illness, there is moderate loss of neurons. The remaining neurons do not appear to be swollen, but under high magnification they are noted to contain fine intracytoplasmic vacuoles. After the second year of the disorder, extensive loss of neurons and glial proliferation occur in the cerebral cortex. The white matter contains few axons or oligodendroglial cells, which are replaced by astrocytic and microglial cells. Most of the neurons in the gray matter of the spinal cord are very swollen and filled with granules and cytoplasmic vacuoles. The retina shows neuronal loss, and the remaining cells are distended. The characteristic "cherry red spot" is due to involvement of the ganglion cells and thinning of the nerve cell layer so that more of the underlying choroidal coat is visible on ophthalmoscopic examination.

With regard to the involvement of other organ systems, some authors have described extraneuronal cellular inclusions in the liver, spleen, pancreas, lungs, and lymph nodes; however, electron microscopy has established the presence of such findings only in liver. Skeletal muscle displays neurogenic atrophy as a result of degeneration of anterior horn cells. Some authors have also noted the existence of vacuoles in a small percentage of lymphocytes.

Studies employing enzyme histochemistry have shown that the activities of oxidative enzymes in neurons are decreased, whereas the activity of acid phosphatase is significantly increased. Accumulating gangliosides appear to displace to the cell periphery those cellular organelles that contain oxidative enzymes. There appears to be a greater relative decrease in oxidative enzyme activity of neurons in the phylogenetically younger parts of the brain, such as the cerebral cortex. In neurons located in the medulla, a phylogenetically older part of the brain, oxidative enzyme activity appears to be only slightly decreased.

MUCOLIPIDOSES

This group of genetic disorders of lysosomes includes features of both lipid and mucopolysaccharide storage diseases. Storage of mucopolysaccharides without mucopolysacchariduria, and storage of glycolipids and/or sphingolipids, are also observed. Included in this group are four disorders previously encountered in this chapter: gangliosidoses GM_1 and GM_2, Farber's disease, and metachromatic leukodystrophy of the variant Austin type. The other mucolipidoses, which will be briefly described here, include fucosidosis, mannosidosis, and mucolipidosis Types I through IV.

Fucosidosis. In this disorder, all of the isoenzymes of alpha-L-fucosidase are deficient. Vacuolation of lymphocytes is impressive, and the liver contains lipid whirls, as well as empty vacuoles indicative of water-soluble polysaccharide accumulation. The exact nature of the materials that accumulate in tissues is unknown, but in liver great increases in the concentrations of acid mucopolysaccharides and glycoproteins have been detected. Ceramide tetra- and pentahexosides abound in the livers of these patients, and in those glycolipids the terminal hexose was identified as fucose. Clinically, progressive psychomotor and mental retardation occur.

Mannosidosis. A deficiency of the heat-stable acidic form of alpha-mannosidase is responsible for this disorder. This enzyme's activity is reduced in several tissues, while increased activity of other lysosomal hydrolases occurs. The patients' phenotypes have not been adequately classified on the basis of the few patients described thus far. In one patient, however, the clinical manifestations were very similar to those of patients with Hurler's disease.

Mucolipidosis Type I. Also called "lipomucopolysaccharidosis," this disease has not been clearly defined. No enzymatic deficiency has yet been demonstrated. It appears to be a Hurler-like disorder, but there is storage of lipid as well as acid mucopolysaccharides within lysosomes.

Mucolipidosis Type II. "I-Cell disease," as it is also called, because of the very impressive cytoplasmic inclusions ("I") observed, clinically resembles Hurler's disease. Unusual storage materials have been observed in brain, kidney, liver, skin, cornea, and other tissues. Interestingly, there is a lack of storage products in hepatic Kupffer cells. The most striking biochemical abnormality is found in cultured skin fibroblasts, where each lysosomal acid hydrolase, except beta-glucosidase, acid phosphatase, and beta-xylosidase, appears to have only 10 to 20% of normal activity. In the fibroblast culture medium, however, the activity of those enzymes is in excess in approximately the same proportion as it is absent within the cells. This observation correlates well with the increased activity of acid hydrolases measured in the blood, urine, and spinal fluid of patients with Type II disease. These findings were previously interpreted to mean that lysosomal membranes in this disorder are "leaky"; however, it was later shown that the lysosomal enzymes do not "leak out" from within the cells. Another theory states that the enzymes possess normal acid hydrolase activity, but a conformational change in their structures ultimately prevents their uptake into the cell.

Mucolipidosis Type III. This disorder, also called "psuedo-Hurler polydystrophy," shares many features of Hurler's disease and of Type II mucolipidosis. Cultured skin fibroblasts contain inclusions very similar to those found in I-cell disease. As in the latter disorder, the specific mutant- enzyme(s) causing the abnormalities has not yet been determined.

Mucolipidosis Type IV. The first patient diagnosed as having this disease was reported in 1974. Since then, four unrelated Jewish (Ashkenazi) children with Type IV disease have been diagnosed. Clinical findings include small head circumference, normal facies and bone X-rays, corneal clouding, and motor retardation. Assays of lysosomal acid hydrolases in cultured skin fibroblasts, plasma, and leukocytes were normal. Abnormal accumulation of ganglioside and other sugar polymers in cultured fibroblasts has been described. Similarly, unusual storage products have been observed in marrow histiocytes.

BIBLIOGRAPHY

Books

Hers, H. G., and Van Hoof, F., eds. 1973. *Lysosomes and Storage Diseases.* Academic Press, New York.
McKusick, V. A. 1972. *Heritable Disorders of Connective Tissue,* 4th ed. C. V. Mosby Co., St. Louis.
Volk, B. W., and Schneck, L., eds. 1975. *The Gangliosidoses.* Plenum Press, New York.

Journal Articles

Brady, R. O. 1973. The abnormal biochemistry of inherited disorders of lipid metabolism. *Fed. Proc.* 32(6):1660–67.
Dorfman, A. and Matalon, R. 1976. The mucopolysaccharidoses (a review). *Proc. Natl. Acad. Sci. U.S.A.* 73(2):630–37.

Hirschhorn, R., and Weissmann, G. 1976. Genetic disorders of lysosomes. *Prog. Med. Genet.* 1:49–101.

Huijing, F. 1975. Glycogen metabolism and glycogen storage diseases. *Physiol. Rev.* 55(4):609–58.

Legum, C. P., Schorr, S., and Berman, E. R. 1976. The genetic mucopolysaccharidoses and mucolipidoses: Review and comment. *Adv. Pediat.* 22:305–47.

Mahler, R. F. 1976. Disorders of glycogen metabolism. *Clin. Endocrinol. Metab.* 5(3):579–98.

Neufeld, E. F. 1974. The biochemical basis for mucopolysaccharidoses and mucolipidoses. *Prog. Med. Genet.* 10:81–101.

O'Brien, J. S. 1971. Ganglioside storage diseases. *N. Engl. J. Med.* 284(16):893–96.

Pennock, C. A., and Barnes, I. C. 1976. The mucopolysaccharidoses. *J. Med. Genet.* 13:169–81.

Senior, B., and Sadeghi-Nejad, A. 1976. The glycogenoses and Other inherited disorders of carbohydrate metabolism. *Clin. Perinatol.* 3(1):79–98.

Svennerholm. L. 1963. Chromatographic separation of human brain gangliosides. *J. Neurochem.* 10:613–23.

Volk, W., Adachi, M., and Schneck, L. 1975. The gangliosidoses. *Hum. Pathol.* 6(5):555–69.

SECTION 5
BIOLOGICAL OXIDATIONS AND ENERGY METABOLISM

CHUNG S. YANG, SECTION EDITOR

5.1. Energy Metabolism: Basic Concepts and Design

Chung S. Yang

PRINCIPLES OF BIOENERGETICS

Living cells are characterized by a dynamic state of continuous synthesis and breakdown of macromolecules. The cells are constantly engaged in the synthesis of amino acids, proteins, lipids, polysaccharides, nucleic acids, and other compounds, as well as in the performance of mechanical, transport, and bioelectric activities. In order to carry out the energy-requiring processes of life, the cells are continuously extracting energy from their surroundings. In heterotrophic ("feeding on others") cells, the energy is derived from the oxidation of nutrient molecules acquired from the environment or derived from their own cellular components. In autotrophic ("self-feeding") organisms, the energy comes mainly from the sun via photosynthesis. This section deals with the general principles of biological energy transformation, the nature of biological oxidation reactions, and the important role of adenosine triphosphate (ATP) in bioenergetics.

The Application of Thermodynamic Laws in Living Systems

The first law of thermodynamics states that energy can neither be created nor destroyed, but that it can be changed from one form to another. In other words, the total energy of a system, the living system plus surroundings, remains constant, although chemical energy may be transformed into mechanical, electrical, radiant, or thermal energy. The second law of thermodynamics states that in all processes the *entropy* of the system plus the surroundings always increases until equilibrium is reached. Entropy is a measurement of disorder or randomness. The meaning of this law is that there is always a driving force for the living system to become disordered or to reach equilibrium with the surroundings. The living system cannot violate this natural law. In order to maintain their form and functions, living systems have to adapt to these laws by maintaining a steady state. There is constant degradation of cellular components or even death of cells, but biological molecules and cells are also constantly being made so that cells and multicellular organisms can maintain their forms. Energy is required for the biosynthetic processes.

In dealing with energy transformation in biological systems, the concept of *free energy* is of great importance and wide usefulness. Since the absolute energy of a system is difficult to measure, the change in free energy, ΔG, is usually used in bioenergetics. The free-energy change of a system is related to the change of enthalpy, ΔH, and the change in entropy, ΔS, by the equation

$$\Delta G = \Delta H - T\Delta S \tag{1}$$

where T is the absolute temperature. Almost all biological processes occur at constant (usually atmospheric) pressure, essentially constant volume, and constant temperature. Free energy can be defined as the component of the total energy that is available for useful work under these conditions. Consider the reaction

$$A + B \rightleftharpoons C + D \tag{2}$$

The free-energy change of this reaction is given by

$$\Delta G = \Delta G^0 + RT \ln \frac{[C][D]}{[A][B]} \tag{3}$$

where [A], [B], [C], and [D] are the molar concentrations, R is the gas constant and equal to 1.987 cal $\deg^{-1}$ mol^{-1}, and T is the absolute temperature. The quantity ΔG^0, the *standard free-energy change*, is the free-energy change under standard conditions, usually defined as a concentration of 1.0 molar (or molal) for all components, at a temperature of 25°C, and a pressure of 1.0 atm.

ΔG^0 is related to the equilibrium constant, K_{eq}, of the reaction by

$$\Delta G^0 = -RT \ln K_{eq} \tag{4}$$

Most biological reactions take place at neutral pH; the denotations $\Delta G^{0'}$ and K'_{eq} are usually used for a system at pH 7.

It can be seen from equations (3) and (4) that the free energy change of a reaction depends on both the equilibrium constant and the concentrations of the reactions and products. If ΔG is negative, the reaction proceeds spontaneously in the direction written. If ΔG is positive, the reaction does not proceed spontaneously; instead it tends to go in the reverse direction. If ΔG is equal to zero, the system is at equilibrium, and no net reaction can take place. Although the values of ΔG^0 or $\Delta G^{0'}$ of chemical reactions are usually given in the literature, it is important to stress that the criterion of spontaneity for a reaction is ΔG, not ΔG^0.

Oxidation–Reduction Reactions

Reactions that involve transfer of electrons from one molecule to another are called oxidation–reduction or *redox* reactions. The molecule that loses electrons is oxidized, and the molecule that gains electrons is reduced. In the reaction

$$\text{Cytochrome } b \text{ (Fe}^{2+}) + \text{Cytochrome } c \text{ (Fe}^{3+}) \rightarrow$$
$$\text{Cytochrome } b \text{ (Fe}^{3+}) + \text{Cytochrome } c \text{ (Fe}^{2+}) \quad (5)$$

cytochrome b loses an electron from the iron of the heme prosthetic group and is oxidized. Cytochrome c gains an electron to convert the heme iron from the ferric to the ferrous state and, therefore, is reduced. The former is considered a *reducing agent* and the latter an *oxidizing agent*. In this case hydrogen atoms are not involved in the reaction. In other reactions, for example, the dehydrogenation (oxidation) of ethanol by nicotinamide adenine dinucleotide (NAD$^+$)

$$\text{CH}_3\text{CH}_2\text{OH} + \text{NAD}^+ \rightarrow \text{CH}_3\overset{\displaystyle O}{\overset{\displaystyle \|}{\text{C}}}\!\!-\!\!\text{H} + \text{NADH} + \text{H}^+ \quad (6)$$

the transfer of hydrogen atoms is involved. One hydrogen atom carrying two electrons, usually known as a hydride ion (H:$^-$), is transferred from ethanol to NAD$^+$, and another hydrogen atom is released to the solvent as a proton (H$^+$).

The tendency for redox reactions to proceed is dependent upon the difference in the *redox potential* of the components. The redox potential is an electrochemical concept. Consider a substance that can exist in an oxidized form A_{ox} and a reduced form A_{red}. Such a pair is called a *redox couple*. The redox potential of this couple can be determined by measuring the electromotive force generated by a half-cell (consisting of 1 M A_{ox} and 1 M A_{red}) with respect to a standard reference half-cell (consisting of 1 M H$^+$ in equilibrium with 1 atm H$_2$ gas) (see Figure 1). The observed voltage is the *standard redox potential (E_0)* of the redox couple A_{ox}/A_{red}. If the electrons flow from the half-cell (A_{ox}/A_{red}) to the reference half-cell, the E_0 of the A_{ox}/A_{red} has a negative value. Thus, a substance with a negative E_0 has lower affinity for electrons than does the reference H$^+$/H$_2$ couple and would donate electrons to the latter system under standard conditions. Conversely, a substance

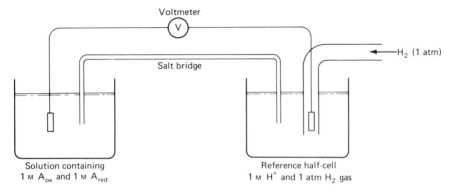

Figure 1. Measurement of the standard redox potential of a redox couple.

with a positive E_0 has higher affinity for electrons than does the reference H^+/H_2 couple. A strong biological reducing agent such as NADH has a negative redox potential, $E_0' = -0.32$ V; whereas a strong oxidizing agent such as O_2 has a positive redox potential, $E_0' = +0.815$ V. The standard redox potentials of a number of important redox couples are given in Table 1.

Free-Energy Change in a Redox Reaction

Under standard conditions, the direction of electron flow is determined by the differences in standard redox potential of the components, $\Delta E_0'$ (V), which is related to $\Delta G^{0'}$ (cal $\cdot$ mol^{-1}) by equation (7):

$$\Delta G^{0'} = -nF \Delta E_0' \tag{7}$$

where n is the number of electrons transferred, F is the faraday (23,062 cal $\cdot$ V^{-1} mol^{-1}), and $\Delta E_0'$ is equal to the E_0' of the oxidizing agent minus the E_0' of the reducing agent. For example, in the reaction

$$A_{ox} + B_{red} \rightleftharpoons A_{red} + B_{ox} \tag{8}$$

$\Delta E_0'$ is given by

$$\Delta E_0' = E_0' \text{ (of } A_{ox}/A_{red} \text{ couple)} - E_0' \text{ (of } B_{ox}/B_{red} \text{ couple)}$$

The relationship is illustrated by the following example. In the oxidation of NADH by molecular oxygen, a two-electron transfer process,

$$NADH + 1/2 \, O_2 + H^+ \rightarrow NAD^+ + H_2O \tag{9}$$

Table 1.   Standard Redox (Reduction) Potentials of Some Biological Redox Couples.[a]

HALF-REACTION	E_0', mv
$O_2 + 4H^+ + 4e^- \longrightarrow 2H_2O$	+815
$Fe^{3+} + e^- \longrightarrow Fe^{2+}$	771
$NO_3^- + 2H^+ + 2e^- \longrightarrow NO_2^- + H_2O$	421
Cytochrome f $(Fe^{3+}) + e^- \longrightarrow$ Cytochrome f (Fe^{2+})	365
$Fe(CN)_6^{3-}$ (ferricyanide) $+ e^- \longrightarrow Fe(CN)_6^{4-}$	360
$O_2 + 2H^+ + 2e^- \longrightarrow H_2O_2$	295
Cytochrome a $(Fe^{3+}) + e^- \longrightarrow$ Cytochrome a (Fe^{2+})	290
p-Quinone $+ 2H^+ + 2e^- \longrightarrow$ Hydroquinone	285
Cytochrome c $(Fe^{3+}) + e^- \longrightarrow$ Cytochrome c (Fe^{2+})	254
Adrenodoxin $(Fe^{3+}) + e^- \longrightarrow$ Adrenodoxin (Fe^{2+})	150
Cytochrome b_2 $(Fe^{3+}) + e^- \longrightarrow$ Cytochrome b_2 (Fe^{2+})	120
Ubiquinone $+ 2H^+ + 2e^- \longrightarrow$ Ubiquinone H_2	100
Cytochrome b $(Fe^{3+}) + e^- \longrightarrow$ Cytochrome b (Fe^{2+})	075
Dehydroascorbic acid $+ 2H^+ + 2e^- \longrightarrow$ Ascorbic acid	058
Fumarate^{2-} $+ 2H^+ + 2e^- \longrightarrow$ Succinate^{2-}	031
Methylene blue $+ 2H^+ + 2e^- \longrightarrow$ Leucomethylene blue (colorless)	011
Crotonyl-CoA $+ 2H^+ + 2e^- \longrightarrow$ Butyryl-CoA	−015
Glutathione $+ 2H^+ + 2e^- \longrightarrow$ 2-Reduced glutathione	−100
Oxaloacetate^{2-} $+ 2H^+ + 2e^- \longrightarrow$ Malate^{2-}	−166
Pyruvate$^-$ $+ 2H^+ + 2e^- \longrightarrow$ Lactate$^-$	−185
Acetaldehyde $+ 2H^+ + 2e^- \longrightarrow$ Ethanol	−197
Riboflavin $+ 2H^+ + 2e^- \longrightarrow$ Dihydroriboflavin	−208
Acetoacetyl-CoA $+ 2H^+ + 2e^- \longrightarrow$ β-Hydroxybutyryl-CoA	−238 (38°C)
$S + 2H^+ + 2e^- \longrightarrow H_2S$	−274
Lipoic acid $+ 2H^+ + 2e^- \longrightarrow$ Dihydrolipoic acid	−290
$NAD^+ + H^+ + 2e^- \longrightarrow$ NADH	−320
$NADP^+ + H^+ + 2e^- \longrightarrow$ NADPH	−324
Ferredoxin $(Fe^{3+}) + e^- \longrightarrow$ Ferredoxin (Fe^{2+}) (clostridia)	−413
$2H^+ + 2e^- \longrightarrow H_2$	−414
$CO_2 + H^+ + 2e^- \longrightarrow$ Formate$^-$	−420
Ferredoxin $(Fe^{3+}) + e^- \longrightarrow$ Ferredoxin (Fe^{2+}) (spinach)	−432

[a] Data obtained from D. E. Metzler, *Biochemistry: The Chemical Reactions of Living Cells*, Academic Press, New York, 1977.

the standard free energy change is as follows:

$$\Delta G^{0'} = -2 \times 23{,}062 \times [0.815 - (-0.32)] \text{ cal} \cdot \text{mol}^{-1}$$
$$= -46{,}124 \times 1.135 \text{ cal} \cdot \text{mol}^{-1}$$
$$= -52{,}350 \text{ cal} \cdot \text{mol}^{-1} \text{ or } -52.3 \text{ kcal} \cdot \text{mol}^{-1}$$

In a system that is not under standard conditions, the free-energy change is given by

$$\Delta G = -nF\Delta E \qquad (10)$$

where ΔE is related to ΔE_0 by the Nernst equation:

$$\Delta E = \Delta E_0 - \frac{RT}{nF} \ln \frac{[A_{red}] [B_{ox}]}{[A_{ox}] [B_{red}]} \tag{11}$$

ATP: The Universal Currency in Bioenergetics

The free energy derived from biological oxidation reaction is usually conserved in the synthesis of adenosine triphosphate (ATP) (Figure 2). The "~" denotes a "high-energy bond," meaning that much free energy is released upon hydrolysis of the compound at that bond. The standard free energy of hydrolysis of ATP, leading to the formation of adenosine diphosphate (ADP) and inorganic phosphate (P_i) or to adenosine monophosphate (AMP) and pyrophosphate, is -8.4 and -8.5 kcal $\cdot$ mol^{-1} respectively, at pH 7.0.

$$ATP + H_2O \rightleftharpoons ADP + P_i \qquad \Delta G^{0'} = -8.4 \text{ kcal} \cdot \text{mol}^{-1} \tag{12}$$

$$ATP + H_2O \rightleftharpoons AMP + \text{pyrophosphate} \qquad \Delta G^{0'} = -8.5 \text{ kcal} \cdot \text{mol}^{-1} \tag{13}$$

ATP, ADP, and AMP are interconvertible in the reaction

$$ATP + AMP \rightleftharpoons ADP + ADP \tag{14}$$

The reaction is catalyzed by the enzyme adenylate kinase, also known as myokinase.

Although the hydrolysis of ATP is generally considered to be a driving force for most energy-requiring reactions in living cells, the hydrolysis of ATP as shown in equation (12) does not usually take place; rather, the high-

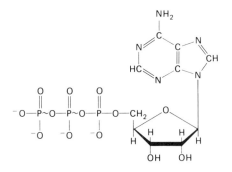

Figure 2. The structure of adenosine triphosphate (ATP).

energy phosphate group is transferred to other molecules in *transphosphorylation* reactions. For example, the phosphorylation of glucose

$$\text{Glucose} + P_i \rightarrow \text{Glucose-6-phosphate} + H_2O \quad \Delta G^{0\prime} = +3.9 \, \text{kcal} \cdot \text{mol}^{-1} \quad (15)$$

is energetically unfavorable. However, glucose-6-phosphate can be synthesized by the transphosphorylation shown below:

$$\text{ATP} + \text{Glucose} \rightleftharpoons \text{ADP} + \text{Glucose-6-phosphate}$$
$$\Delta G^{0\prime} = -4.5 \, \text{kcal} \cdot \text{mol}^{-1} \quad (16)$$

Both the reaction and energetics of equation (16) can be obtained by the addition of reaction (12) and reaction (15). In fact, transphosphorylation is the most commonly used mechanism of energy transduction in living organisms.

In addition to the direct synthesis of ATP in oxidative phosphorylation, the high-energy phosphate bond is also formed in the formation of compounds such as phosphoenolpyruvate and 3-phosphoglyceroyl phosphate, which have free energies of hydrolysis of -14.8 and $-11.8 \, \text{kcal} \cdot \text{mol}^{-1}$, respectively. These compounds are said to have higher "phosphate group transfer potential" than ATP, and their high-energy phosphate group can be transferred to ADP to synthesize ATP. Through transphosphorylation reactions, ATP can drive a variety of anabolic reactions. The terminal phosphate group of ATP can also be transferred to different nucleoside diphosphates to make the corresponding nucleoside triphosphates which are needed for many metabolic processes. The transferring of high-energy phosphate groups in this *ATP–ADP cycle* is the fundamental mode of energy transfer in biological systems. The production and utilization of ATP are subjected to refined regulations in the cell.

A Summary of Biological Energy Transformation

A summary of biological energy transformation is shown in Figure 3. The proteins, carbohydrates, and lipids ingested by heterotrophic organisms are degraded and oxidized in stepwise reactions leading to the formation of CO_2 and H_2O as the end products. The free energy derived from these reactions is utilized for the synthesis of ATP from ADP and P_i. ATP, which plays a unique role in bioenergetics, is required for various important processes such as biosynthesis, mechanical work, and active transport. Heat is also produced in these processes and is indicated by the increase in entropy, ΔS. In autotrophic organisms, the chemical energy is primarily derived from solar energy captured during photosynthesis, in which carbon dioxide and water are con-

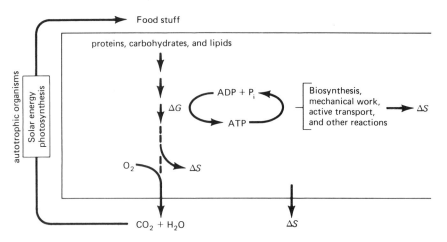

Figure 3. Energy flow in biological systems.

verted into hexose and other sugars. Larger molecules of carbohydrates, proteins, and lipids are subsequently synthesized in these organisms. Heterotrophs have to feed on these organisms to acquire the chemical energy. The figure shows that the general direction of energy flow in biological systems is unidirectional and irreversible.

OXIDATION–REDUCTION ENZYMES AND COENZYMES

Biological oxidation is characterized by stepwise degradations and oxidations catalyzed by specific enzymes. One important type of these enzymes consists of the oxidation–reduction enzymes, which are classified into three broad categories according to function. The *dehydrogenases* catalyze reactions involving the transfer of electrons or hydrogen without the direct participation of molecular oxygen. The *oxidases* catalyze the oxidation of substrate by molecular oxygen, and the oxygen atoms are used for the formation of water. The *oxygenases* catalyze the addition of one or two atoms of oxygen to the substrates. Structurally, owing to the coenzymes or prosthetic groups involved, oxidation–reduction enzymes can be classified as nicotinamide nucleotide–linked dehydrogenases, flavin nucleotide–linked dehydrogenases, cytochromes, iron–sulfur proteins, and others. These enzymes will be described in this section.

Nicotinamide Nucleotide–Linked Dehydrogenases

This class of dehydrogenases requires either nicotinamide adenine dinucleotide (NAD^+) or nicotinamide adenine dinucleotide phosphate ($NADP^+$) as coenzyme. The structure of NAD^+ is shown in Figure 4. With $NADP^+$, a phosphate ester exists at the $2'$-position of the ribose ring. Most of the nicotinamide nucleotide–linked dehydrogenases are specific for either NAD^+ or $NADP^+$; but a few, such as glycerol dehydrogenase and glutamate dehydrogenase, can use either NAD^+ or $NADP^+$ as the coenzyme. NAD^+-linked dehydrogenases function primarily in the catabolic pathways, transferring electrons from substrates to the oxidative phosphorylation system. $NADP^+$-linked dehydrogenases, on the other hand, serve primarily in the biosynthetic pathways. Many $NAD(P)^+$-linked dehydrogenases also contain tightly bound divalent metal ions; for example, the Zn^{2+} in alcohol dehydrogenase.

The dehydrogenases catalyze the general reactions

$$SH_2 + NAD(P)^+ \rightleftharpoons S + NAD(P)H + H^+ \tag{17}$$

where SH_2 and S denote the reduced and oxidized forms of the substrate respectively. The reaction involves the transfer of a hydride ion ($H:^-$) from the substrate to the 4-position of the nicotinamide ring of the coenzyme, and the other hydrogen is removed from the substrate as a free proton (H^+). Depending on the enzyme, the hydride ion can be added at either the A or B side of the nicotinamide ring (Figure 5). For example, isocitrate dehydroge-

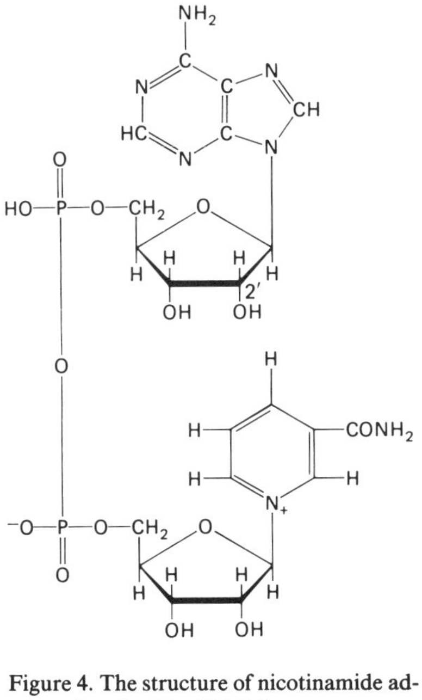

Figure 4. The structure of nicotinamide adenine dinucleotide (NAD^+).

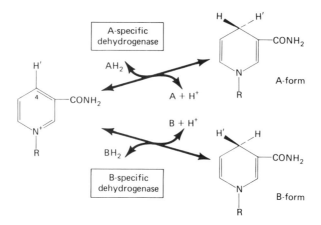

Figure 5. Stereospecificity of nicotinamide adenine dinucleotide–linked dehydrogenases.

nase of heart, ethanol dehydrogenase of yeast, and lactic dehydrogenase of heart are A-specific dehydrogenases; glucose 6-phosphate dehydrogenase of yeast, glutamate dehydrogenase of liver, and glycerol 3-phosphate dehydrogenase are B-specific dehydrogenases.

NAD⁺ and NADP⁺ can exist in two types of conformation: the open (extended) and closed (stacked) forms. In solution, they exist predominantly in the stacked form, in which the planar nicotinamide and adenine rings are parallel to each other. When binding to a dehydrogenase, they assume the open conformation. The nicotinamide nucleotides, NAD⁺ and NADP⁺, are relatively loosely bound to the dehydrogenase. They usually bind to the active site of the enzyme, acquire electrons, and then dissociate. The reduced form of the coenzymes, NAD(P)H, can then be oxidized by other dehydrogenases. These coenzymes thus serve as dissociable carriers of electrons. When NAD(P)⁺ is reduced, an absorption maximum at 340 nm appears. Since NAD(P)H is not auto-oxidized in air, the appearance and disappearance of the absorption at 340 nm can be used conveniently for assaying the reactions catalyzed by these dehydrogenases. The mechanisms of nicotinamide nucleotide–linked dehydrogenases have been extensively studied. These enzymes usually have an ordered sequence for the binding of coenzymes and substrate at the active sites. This is shown as follows:

The nicotinamide nucleotide must bind to the enzyme prior to the binding of the substrate SH_2. After the transfer of the electron equivalents from substrate to coenzyme on the active site, the oxidized substrate, S, departs first, followed by the reduced coenzyme. The reverse sequence is followed in the reverse reaction, in which the enzyme binds NADH first and then S.

Nicotinamide nucleotide–linked dehydrogenases catalyze the dehydrogenation of a variety of substrates. More than 250 dehydrogenases of this class are known, some of which are shown in Table 2. The dehydrogenases exhibit a wide range of molecular weights. Most show catalytic activity only when the subunits are combined to form the proper dimers, tetramers, or hexamers. For example, the catalytically active lactate dehydrogenase is a tetramer. In most cases, identical subunits spontaneously assemble into the stable and functionally active polymers. In certain cases, the cells may make more than one type of subunit with different amino acids in certain segments of the polypeptide chain. The assembly of different subunits allows the formation of isoenzymes. For example, mammalian tissues synthesize two types of subunits of lactate dehydrogenase, α and β, and five isoenzymes, α_4, $\alpha_3\beta$, $\alpha_2\beta_2$, $\alpha\beta_3$, β_4, can occur.

Flavin Nucleotide–Linked Dehydrogenases and Oxidases

This class of enzymes contains either riboflavin phosphate (flavin mononucleotide, FMN) or flavin adenine dinucleotide (FAD) as prosthetic groups. The structures of these coenzymes are shown in Figure 6.

FMN (FAD) can be reduced to $FMNH_2$ ($FADH_2$) by a two-electron transfer process or to the half-reduced "semiquinone" $FMNH\cdot$ ($FADH\cdot$) by a one-electron transport process (Figure 7).

The oxidation–reduction takes place at the isoalloxazine ring of the riboflavin moiety. Although some enzymes function by shuttling between fully oxidized and fully reduced states of the flavin coenzyme, others appear to transfer only one electron at a time. Thus, they serve to split the electron pair, generally from nicotinamide nucleotide coenzymes.

Flavin nucleotide–linked enzymes differ from nicotinamide nucleotide–linked dehydrogenases in that the flavin nucleotide is very tightly bound to the enzyme protein, and the flavin nucleotide does not leave the enzyme during or after the catalytic cycle. This class of enzyme is also known as flavoproteins, characterized by a yellowish color due to the absorption near 450 nm of the oxidized form of the coenzymes. In most flavoproteins, the flavin nucleotide is noncovalently bound. However, the flavin is covalently linked to the polypeptides of some enzymes. For example, the coenzyme is linked through the 8α-position of the isoalloxazine ring to a histidine residue

Table 2. Some Nicotinamide Nucleotide–linked Dehydrogenases.[a]

SUBSTRATE	PRODUCTS	COENZYME	PREPARATIVE SOURCE
Acyclic polyols	Ketoses	NAD	Rat liver, *Aerobacter*
Aldehydes	Carboxylic acids	NAD	Liver
Aspartic β-semialdehyde	β-Aspartyl phosphate	NAD	Liver
Betaine aldehyde	Betaine	NAD	Rat liver
Dihydrofolate	Tetrahydrofolate	NADP	Liver
Ethanol	Acetaldehyde	NAD	Liver, kidney, yeast
D-Fructose	5-Keto-D-fructose	NADP	*Glyconobacter cirinus*
D-Glycerate	Hydroxypyruvate	NAD	Liver
Glycerol	Dihydroxyacetone	NAD or NADP	Pig liver, rat liver, *E. coli*
Glycerol 3-phosphate	Dihydroxyacetone phosphate	NAD	Yeast, muscle, liver
Glucose 6-phosphate	6-Phosphogluconate	NADP	Liver, erythrocytes, yeast
Glutamate	α-Ketoglutarate + NH$_4^+$	NAD or NADP	Muscle, liver
L-Gulonate	Xylulose + CO$_2$	NAD	Kidney
L-Gulonate	D-Glucuronate	NADP	Kidney
ω-Hydroxy acids	ω-Aldehyde acids	NAD	Liver
D(−)-β-Hydroxybutyrate	Acetoacetate	NAD	Liver
L(−)-β-Hydroxybutyryl-CoA	Acetoacetyl-CoA	NAD	Liver
3β-Hydroxysteroids	3-Ketosteroids	NAD (NADP)	*Pseudomonas* (Liver)
17β-Hydroxysteroids	17-Ketosteroids	NAD	*Pseudomonas*
Inosinate	Xanthylate	NAD	*E. coli, Aerobacter aerogenes*
Isocitrate	α-Ketoglutarate + CO$_2$	NAD (NADP)	Beef heart, rat liver, yeast mitochondria (Heart cytosol)
Lactate	Pyruvate	NAD	Muscle, other animal tissues
Malate	Oxaloacetate	NAD	Muscle, other animal tissues
Malate	Pyruvate + CO$_2$	NADP	Pigeon liver cytosol, heart
Malonic semialdehyde	Malonate	NAD	*Pseudomonas*
D-Mannitol	D-Fructose	NAD	*Acetobacter*
3-Phosphoglyceraldehyde	1,3-Diphosphoglycerate	NAD	All animal tissue, yeast, bacteria
Reduced glutathione (GSH)	Glutathione (G-SS-G)	NADP	Yeast, liver
Ribitol	Ribulose	NAD	Liver
Shikimate	Dehydroshikimate	NADP	Peas, *E. coli*
Succinic semialdehyde	Succinate	NAD	Brain, bacteria
Tartronic semialdehyde	Glycerate	NAD	*Pseudomonas*

[a] Modified from A. White, P. Handler, E. L. Smith, R. L. Hill, and I. R. Lehman, *Principles of Biochemistry*, 6th ed., McGraw-Hill, New York, 1978.

572

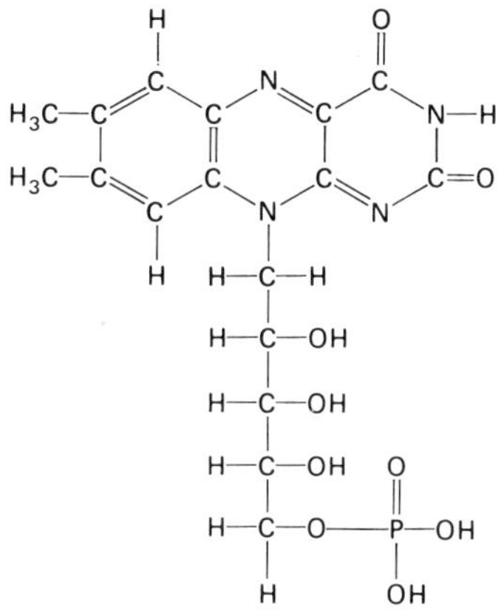

Figure 6. Structures of riboflavin phosphate (FMN) and flavin adenine dinucleotide (FAD).

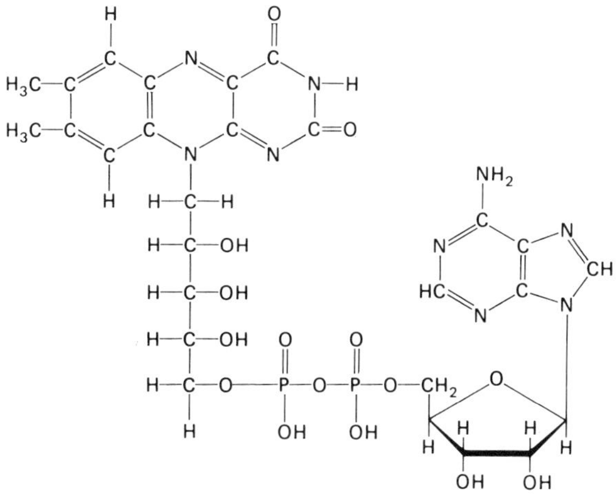

of succinate dehydrogenase, or to a sulfur atom of a cysteine residue of monoamine oxidase.

Flavoproteins may be classified into *dehydrogenases* and *oxidases,* according to function. In the dehydrogenases, such as NADH dehydrogenase, succinate dehydrogenase, and dihydrolipoyl dehydrogenase, the natural electron acceptor is not molecular oxygen. The electron equivalents of the reduced flavin nucleotides are usually transferred to other electron carriers such as ubiqui-

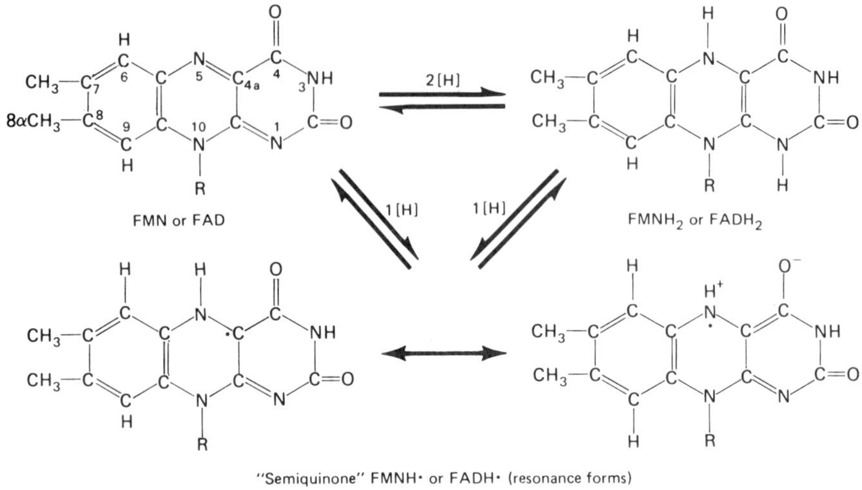

"Semiquinone" FMNH· or FADH· (resonance forms)

Figure 7. Oxidation and reduction of flavin coenzymes. R represents the remaining part of the coenzyme molecule.

none, NAD^+, iron–sulfur proteins, or cytochromes. In the oxidases, such as D-amino acid oxidase and xanthine oxidase, the reduced flavin nucleotide is oxidized by molecular oxygen to yield hydrogen peroxide. The reaction is believed to involve the addition of molecular oxygen to the reduced isoalloxazine ring at position 4a and the formation of a hydroperoxide intermediate. A subclass of flavoprotein oxidases consists of the monooxygenases or hydroxylases. The reduced flavin of these enzymes helps to introduce one atom of oxygen from O_2 into a substrate. The substrate is thus oxygenated or hydroxylated. The other atom of oxygen is used in the formation of water.

Flavoproteins are quite diverse in structure, with molecular weights ranging from 12,000 to 700,000. They may consist of a single polypeptide chain with a single flavin nucleotide, or they may have several subunits with several flavins. Some also contain one or more metals, such as iron–sulfur complexes, heme, and molybdenum. Some examples of flavoproteins are shown in Table 3.

Cytochromes

The cytochromes are electron-transferring proteins found in aerobic cells. Some cytochromes are found in the mitochondrial inner membranes of eukaryotic cells and in prokaryotic cells, participating in the transporting of electrons from various dehydrogenases toward molecular oxygen. Other cytochromes are found in the endoplasmic reticulum and other cell fractions,

Table 3. Some Flavoproteins.[a]

SUBSTRATE	PHYSIOLOGICAL ELECTRON ACCEPTOR	FLAVIN	OTHER FUNCTIONAL COMPONENTS	SOURCE
D-Amino acids	O_2	FAD	—	Liver, kidney
L-Amino acids	O_2	FAD or FMN	—	Kidney, snake venoms
Monoamines	O_2	FAD	—	Liver, kidney, brain
Diamines	O_2	FAD	—	Liver, kidney, brain
Glucose	O_2	FAD	—	Liver, molds
α-Hydroxy acids	O_2	FMN	—	Kidney
Acyl CoA (C_6–C_{12})	ETF[b]	FAD	—	Mitochondria
Butyryl-CoA	ETF	FAD	—	Mitochondria
H_2, photosynthesis	NADP reductase	FMN	—	Anaerobes, blue-green algae
Dihydrolipoate	NAD^+		Internal disulfide	Mitochondria, E. coli
NADPH	Glutathione	FAD	Internal disulfide	Liver, yeast, E. coli
NADPH	Thioredoxin	FAD	Internal disulfide	Liver, E. coli
NADH	H_2O_2	FAD	Internal disulfide	Streptococcus faecalis
NADH	Cytochrome b_5	FAD	—	Liver microsomes
NADPH	Cytochrome P_{450}	FAD + FMN	—	Liver microsomes
NADPH	Putidaredoxin	FAD	—	Pseudomonas putida
D-Lactate	Cytochrome c	FAD	Zn^{2+}	Yeast
Ferredoxin	$NADP^+$	FAD	—	Chloroplasts
NADPH	Adrenodoxin	FAD	—	Adrenal cortex mitochondria
Dihydroorotate	NAD^+	FAD + FMN	$(FeS)_n^c$	Zymobacterium oroticum
NADH	Ubiquinone	FMN	$(FeS)_n$	Mitochondria
Succinate	Ubiquinone	FAD	$(FeS)_n$	Mitochondria
Reduced ETF	Ubiquinone	FAD	$(FeS)_n$	Mitochondria
Choline	Ubiquinone	FAD	$(FeS)_n$	Mitochondria
α-Glycerophosphate	Ubiquinone	FAD	$(FeS)_n$	Mitochondria
Sarcosine	Ubiquinone	FAD	(FeS),	Mitochondria

Table 3. Some Flavoproteins.[a] *(Continued)*

SUBSTRATE	PHYSIOLOGICAL ELECTRON ACCEPTOR	FLAVIN	OTHER FUNCTIONAL COMPONENTS	SOURCE
Purines	O_2	FAD	Mo, $(FeS)_4$	Milk
Purines	NAD^+	FAD	Mo, $(FeS)_4$	Liver
Aldehydes	O_2	FAD	Mo, $(FeS)_4$	Liver
NADPH	NO_2^-	FAD	Siroheme	*Neurospora crassa*
NADPH	SO_3	FAD + FMN	$(FeS)_4$, siroheme	*E. coli*
L-Lactate	Cytochrome *c*	FAD	Heme	Yeast

[a] Modified from A. White, P. Handler, E. L. Smith, R. L. Hill, and I. R. Lehman, *Principles of Biochemistry*, 6th ed., McGraw-Hill, New York, 1978.
[b] ETF = electron-transferring flavoprotein.
[b] $(FeS)_n$ = iron–sulfur center.

playing a role in the oxygenation or hydroxylation of various compounds. The cytochromes use hemes (Fe–porphyrin) as prosthetic groups. The iron–porphyrin complex undergoes reversible Fe(II)–Fe(III) valence changes during the catalysis of the cytochromes.

Cytochromes can be grouped into three classes: a, b, and c. Some properties of the cytochromes are shown in Table 4. Cytochromes of the b type contain protoheme, an iron–protoporphyrin IX complex, as the prosthetic group. The structures of protoheme and the prosthetic groups of a and c type cytochromes are shown in Figure 8. In mammalian cells, the b type cytochromes are generally integral membrane proteins. The cytochromes b are those of lowest potential among cytochromes. The standard oxidation–reduction potential (E_0') for isolated cytochrome b in aqueous solution is -340 mV, whereas in mitochondria it behaves as if E_0' were about $+30$ mV. The detailed structure and properties of mitochondrial cytochrome b have not been clearly established. The cytochrome b_5 found in the endoplasmic reticulum is involved in the desaturation of fatty acids. Other b type cytochromes, cytochromes P450, are found in the endoplasmic reticulum and mitochondria. They are involved in the oxygenation and hydroxylation of steroids, fatty acids, and various xenobiotics. The b type cytochromes are also found in the electron transport chains of bacteria.

In cytochromes of the c type, the heme is bound to the protein via thioether bridges between the porphyrin ring and two cysteine residues of the polypeptide chain. Cytochrome c is a small-molecular-weight (13,000 daltons) water-soluble protein. It has been obtained in pure form from a great variety of animals, plants, and microorganisms. Complete amino acid sequences have been determined for over 70 species, and the structures of some have been determined by X-ray crystallography. It is known that the heme moiety lies in a hydrophobic crevice with the fifth and sixth coordination positions of iron occupied by the imidazole group of a histidine residue and the sulfur atom of a methionine residue. This coordination arrangement prevents cytochrome c from reacting with molecular oxygen. Cytochrome c_1, an integral protein of the mitochondrial membrane, has spectroscopic properties similar to those of cytochrome c. It also has identical prosthetic groups and modes of attachment to the protein. In mitochondria, cytochrome c and c_1 form a rather tight complex, serving as electron carriers from cytochrome b to cytochrome oxidase in the electron transport chain. Different types of cytochrome c are also found in various bacteria.

Cytochromes a and a_3 contain heme A, which differs from protoheme in having a formyl group replace the methyl group at position 8, no methyl group at position 5, and a long hydrophobic 17-carbon isoprenoid side chain at position 2 instead of a vinyl group (Figure 8). Cytochrome a_3 differs from cytochrome a in that it is auto-oxidizable at low O_2 tension and binds CO

Table 4. Properties of Some Cytochromes.[a]

CYTOCHROME	SOURCE	ABSORPTION MAXIMA—REDUCED FORMS			E_0', mV	REACTION WITH O_2
		α, nM	β, nM	γ, nM		
a	Mitochondria	605	517	414	+340	−
a_3	Mitochondria	600	—	445	+200	+
a_1	E. coli	590	—	—	+147	+
a_2	Azotobacter vinelandii, Pseudomonas	652	629	460	—	+
b	Mitochondria	563	530	430	+30	−
b_t	Mitochondria	565	535, 528	430	−30[b] (+245)	−
b_5	Microsomes	557	527	423	+0.03	−
P450	Microsomes	540	—	410	−330	+
b_1	E. coli, Azotobacter	560	530	426	+250	−
b_{562}	E. coli	562	532	427	+35	−
b_4	Hemophilus (Micrococcus)	554	521	418	+180	−
c	Mitochondria	550	521	416	+260	−
c_1	Mitochondria	554	523	418	+225	−
o	E. coli, Acetobacter	568	—	—	—	+
c_2	Rhodospirillum rubrum	550	521	416	+320	−
c_3	Desulfovibrio desulfuricans	552	522	418	−205	+
c_4	Azotobacter	551	522	418	+300	−
c_5	Azotobacter	555	523	418	+320	−
c_{551}	Psuedomonas	551	521	416	+286	−
c_{552}	Chromatium	552	523	416	+10	+
"Cytochromoid c"	R. rubrum	568	—	424	−8	+
"Cytochromoid c"	Chromatium	565	—	426	−5	+

[a] Modified from A. White, P. Handler, E. L. Smith, R. L. Hill, and I. R. Lehman, *Principles of Biochemistry*, 6th ed., McGraw-Hill, New York, 1978.
[b] The E_0' of cytochrome b_t in mitochondria is affected by ATP; in the absence of ATP $E_0' = -30$ mV, whereas in the presence of ATP $E_0' = 245$ mV.

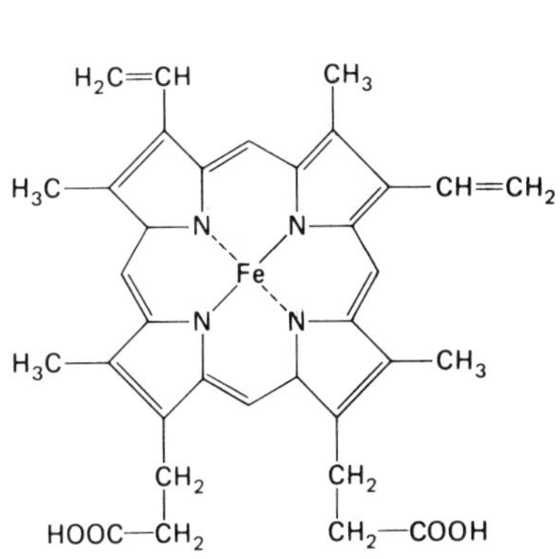

Ferroprotoporphyrin IX or (proto) heme (IX).
Prosthetic group of cytochromes of class B,
hemoglobin, and other proteins

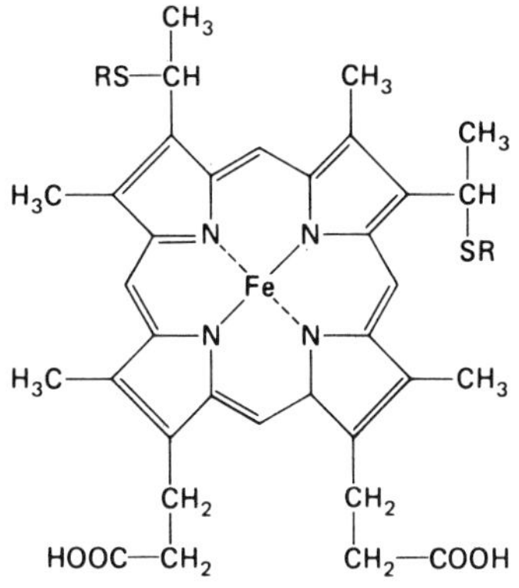

Heme C
Prosthetic group of
cytochromes of class C

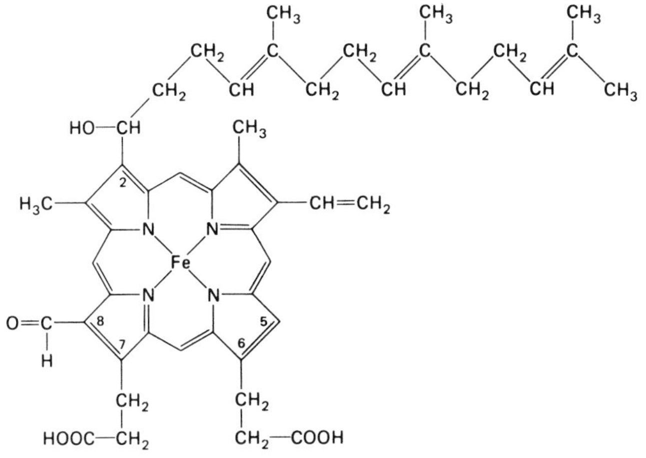

Heme A
Prosthetic group of cytochromes of class A

Figure 8. The structures of the prosthetic groups of cytochromes.

and CN^-. Both cytochromes are parts of a functional cytochrome oxidase or cytochrome c oxidase complex, the terminal oxidase of the mitochondrial electron transport chain which transfers electrons to molecular oxygen. Cytochrome oxidase is a larger protein complex with a molecular weight of about 200,000, composed of seven distinct subunits. It contains two molecules of heme A and two atoms of copper. The protein complex is known to traverse the inner mitochondrial membranes. The detailed arrangement of subunits will be discussed in Chapter 5.2 Cytochromes a_1 and a_2 are also found in bacteria (Table 4).

Iron–Sulfur Proteins

In iron–sulfur proteins, the iron atoms are not bound to a porphyrin ring; rather, they are chelated to the sulfur atoms of cysteine residues of the protein and inorganic sulfide (S^{2-}). Therefore they have also been referred to as nonheme iron proteins. The structure of the iron–sulfur center (Fe_2S_2) of ferredoxins is shown in Figure 9. Chloroplast ferredoxins are small soluble proteins with molecular weights around 10,500 daltons. They are important electron carriers in photosynthesis. In the oxidized form of ferredoxin both irons are in the Fe^{3+} state. The iron–sulfur center can be reduced by accepting one electron to become the $Fe^{3+} \cdot Fe^{2+}$ form.

Several types of iron–sulfur proteins with iron–sulfur centers represented by F_4S_4, $(F_4S_4)_2$, and other structures have been observed, and they participate in a variety of biological oxidation–reduction reactions. Some representative iron–sulfur proteins, their properties, and occurrences are shown in Table 5. Iron–sulfur centers are important components of the mitochondrial electron transport chain and exist in different parts of the chain. For example, the NADH dehydrogenase complex contains 16 Fe^{3+} and 16 S^{2-} per FMN. A detailed description of the electron transport chain is included in Chapter 5.2.

Ubiquinone

Ubiquinone, or coenzyme Q, is a lipid-soluble electron carrier found in the mitochondrial electron transport chain. Ubiquinone contains a long isoprenoid side chain (Figure 10); in animals it has 10 isoprene units ($n = 10$), and in some microorganisms $n = 6$. This coenzyme can be reversibly reduced by a two-electron process (see Figure 10).

Because of its lipophilic properties, ubiquinone has been postulated to function as a mobile electron carrier between the electron transport complexes of the mitochondrial electron transport chain (see Chapter 5.2). In plants, the closely related plastoquinones perform a similar electron transfer function in photosynthetic electron transport.

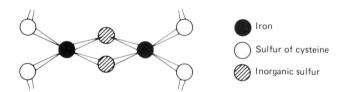

Figure 9. Structure of the iron–sulfur center of ferredoxins.

Table 5.   Some Iron–Sulfur Proteins[a]

CENTER	MW	E_0', mV	SOURCE
Fe rubredoxin	6,000	−60	Clostridia (obligate anaerobes)
(Fe$_2$S$_2$) proteins			
Ferredoxins	10,600	−420	Spinach chloroplast
	10,300	−400	*Microcystis* (blue-green alga)
	21,600	−350	*Azotobacter* (aerobic, N$_2$-fixing)
	12,600	−360	*E. coli* (enteric bacterium)
Putidaredoxin	12,500	−240	*P. putida* (aerobic bacterium)
Adrenodoxin	12,500	−270	Adrenal cortex
(Fe$_4$S$_4$) proteins			
Ferredoxins	6,000	−330	*Desulfovibrio* (anaerobic SO$_4$-reducing)
	8,800	−380	*Bacillus* (soil, N$_2$-fixing)
(Fe$_4$S$_4$)$_2$ proteins			
Ferredoxins	6,000	−395	Clostridia (obligate anaerobe)
	10,000	−490	*Chromatium* (red sulfur, photosynthetic)
	15,000	−420	*Azotobacter* (aerobic, N$_2$-fixing)
(Fe$_2$S$_2$)-HiPiP[b]	30,000	+280	Complex III, heart mitochondria
(Fe$_4$S$_4$)-HiPiP	9,650	+350	*Chromatium* (red sulfur, photosynthetic)

[a] Modified from White, A., Handler, P., Smith, E. L., Hill, R. L., and Lehman, I. R., *Principles of Biochemistry* 6th ed., McGraw-Hill, New York, 1978.
[b] HiPiP, high-potential iron proteins.

MAJOR PATHWAYS IN ENERGY METABOLISM

Energy metabolism is composed of many catabolic pathways catalyzed by enzymes. This design enables the reaction to proceed efficiently and allows the rate to be regulated. In the first stage of catabolism, large polymers are degraded to their monomeric building blocks such as monosaccharides, amino acids, fatty acids, and glycerol. The major pathways for the metabolism of these compounds are illustrated in Figure 11. Monosaccharides, mainly hexoses, are largely metabolized by the glycolytic pathway to pyruvate and then

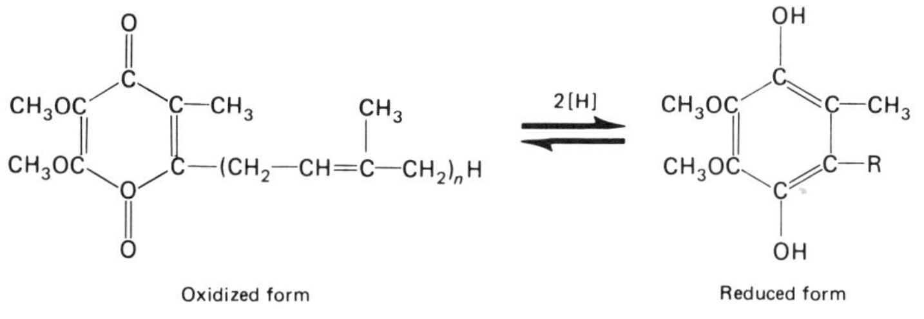

Figure 10. The oxidized and reduced forms of ubiquinone.

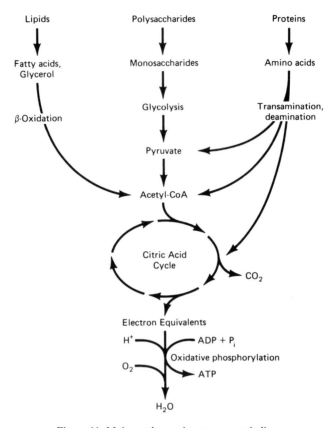

Figure 11. Major pathways in energy metabolism.

to acetyl-CoA. Acetyl-CoA is a key common intermediate in metabolism, since it is also the product of the β-oxidation of fatty acids and of the degradation of some amino acids. The two-carbon unit in acetyl-CoA is metabolized in the citric acid cycle, in which electron equivalents are harvested in NADH and FADH$_2$. This section deals with these pathways. The oxidation of NADH and other substrates by the mitochondrial electron transport system and the coupled oxidative phosphorylation reaction will be discussed in Chapter 5.2.

Glycolysis

Glycolysis, also known as the Embden-Meyerhof pathway, is the most ancient pathway for obtaining energy from fuel molecules such as glucose. It is the sole energy-producing process in anaerobic cells and in cells that do not possess mitochondria, such as erythrocytes. In most aerobic cells, glycolysis is an obligatory first stage in the catabolism of hexose. In eukaryotic cells, all the enzymes in the glycolytic pathway are found in the cytosol fraction of the cell. The reactions, intermediates, and enzymes involved in glycolysis are shown in Figure 12. Glucose enters into the pathway by being phosphorylated to glucose-6-phosphate. This is accomplished by the enzyme hexokinase, or by glucokinase which is present in the livers of nonruminants. ATP is required as the phosphate donor, and Mg^{2+} is required as the cofactor of the reaction. Glycogen, other hexoses, and pentoses can also enter into the glycolytic pathway by being converted to glucose-6-phosphate. The latter compound is converted to fructose-6-phosphate by phosphoglucose isomerase. It is then phosphorylated by ATP in the presence of phosphofructokinase to fructose-1,6-diphosphate. This compound is split by aldolase into two triose phosphates, glyceraldehyde-3-phosphate and dihydroxyacetone phosphate, which are interconvertible by triose phosphate isomerase. In the next step, glyceraldehyde-3-phosphate is oxidized in the presence of inorganic phosphate to form 1,3-diphosphoglycerate. The oxidation is catalyzed by glyceraldehyde-3-phosphate dehydrogenase. In this reaction, a pair of electrons are transferred to NAD^+ to form NADH; energy is also conserved in the formation of the "high-energy" phosphate bond in 1,3-diphosphoglycerate. Because of the interconvertibility of the trioses, dihydroxyacetone phosphate is also oxidized to 1,3-diphosphoglycerate via glyceraldehyde-3-phosphate. In the presence of phosphoglycerate kinase, the high-energy phosphate bond is transferred to ADP to synthesize ATP. The resulting 3-phosphoglycerate is converted, in the presence of phosphoglycerate mutase, to 2-phosphoglycerate, which is subsequently dehydrated by enolase. The dehydration and rearrangement of the molecule results in the formation of a high-energy phosphate bond in phosphoenolpyruvate. In the presence of pyruvate kinase, the phosphate group of phosphoenolpyruvate is transferred to ADP to form ATP and pyruvate.

Pyruvate is a key intermediate in energy metabolism. In aerobic cells, pyruvate is oxidized to acetyl-CoA, which then enters the citric acid cycle pathway for further oxidation. The conversion of glucose to pyruvate is known as *aerobic glycolysis*. In cells devoid of this oxidative pathway or functioning under hypoxic circumstances, pyruvate is usually reduced to lactate. The reaction is catalyzed by lactate dehydrogenase and oxidizes NADH to NAD^+. The conversion of glucose to lactate is known as *anaerobic glycolysis*. The purpose of the final oxidation–reduction reaction is to regenerate NAD^+ for the glyceraldehyde-3-phosphate dehydrogenase reaction (Figure 12). In this pathway, glycolysis can proceed by shuttling electrons between the two dehydrogenase systems, glyceraldehyde-3-phosphate dehydrogenase and lactate dehydrogenase, without relying on oxidizing power from the environment.

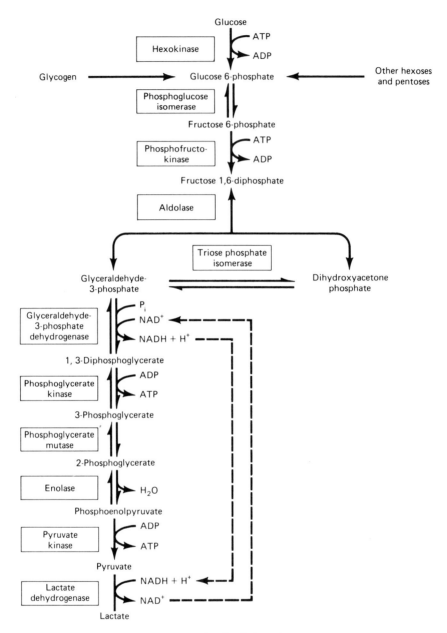

Figure 12. The glycolytic pathway.

In anaerobic glycolysis, ATP is formed by the phosphoglycerate kinase and pyruvate kinase reactions. Since one molecule of glucose is converted to two molecules of trioses, 4 moles of ATP are formed when 1 mole of glucose is converted to lactate. Considering that 2 moles of ATP are used in the phosphorylation of hexose in the hexokinase (glucokinase) and phospho-fructokinase reactions, a net of 2 moles of ATP is formed from ADP when 1 mole of glucose is metabolized in the anaerobic glycolic pathway. This is relatively inefficient as compared to aerobic glycolysis, in which, when glucose is converted to 2 moles of pyruvate, 2 moles of NADH are formed in addition to the net production of 2 moles of ATP. Upon oxidation of the 2 moles of NADH in the mitochondria, and depending on the shuttle system used in different cells, 4 or 6 moles of ATP can be produced. Thus, 6 or 8 moles of ATP are produced per mole of glucose in aerobic glycolysis.

Citric Acid Cycle

This cyclic pathway is also known as the tricarboxylic acid cycle or the Krebs cycle. The citric acid cycle enzymes are located in the matrix of the inner mitochondrial membrane. The only exception is succinate dehydroge-nase, which is embedded in the inner membrane of mitochondria. In aerobic cells, the citric acid cycle is probably the most important common pathway for the oxidation of carbohydrates, fatty acids, and amino acids. These nu-trients enter the citric acid cycle in the form of acetyl-CoA. Some amino acids are not converted to acetyl-CoA but enter the cycle by being metabolized to the intermediates of the cycle. Pyruvate, the product of glycolysis, is con-verted to acetyl-CoA in an oxidative decarboxylation step in which NADH and carbon dioxide are also formed. The reaction is catalyzed by the pyruvate dehydrogenase system, which consists of three types of enzymes in a large molecular complex with a particle weight of over several million and requires five coenzymes: thiamine pyrophosphate, lipoic acid, coenzyme A, FAD, and NAD^+, for activity.

Acetyl-CoA enters the citric acid cycle by reacting with oxaloacetate to form citrate, the first tricarboxylic intermediate in the cycle (Figure 13). The condensation reaction is catalyzed by citrate synthase, also known as citrate synthetase. In the next step, citrate is converted to isocitrate via an intermediate cis-aconitrate, the enzyme that catalyzes this reaction being aconitase, also known as aconitate hydratase. Isocitrate is oxidized by isoci-trate dehydrogenase to form α-ketoglutarate; in this reaction a pair of electrons are captured in NADH, and one molecule of CO_2 is released. α-Ketoglutarate is converted to succinyl-CoA by the α-ketoglutarate dehydrogenase complex. The structure of this enzyme complex and mechanisms of action are analogous to the pyruvate dehydrogenase complex system. NADH and CO_2 are pro-

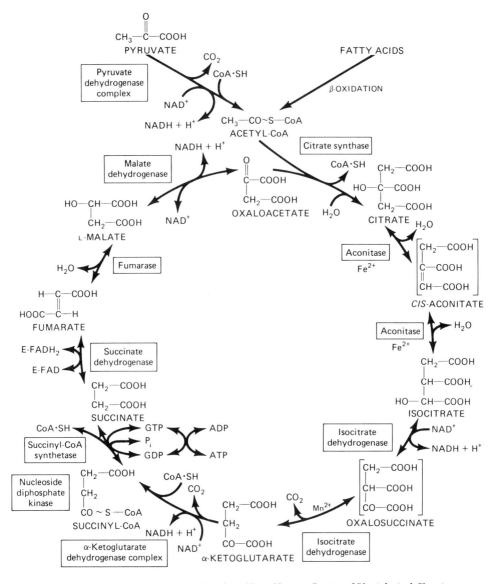

Figure 13. The citric acid cycle. (Modified from H. A. Harper, *Review of Physiological Chemistry*, 14th ed., Lange Medical Publications, Los Altos, California, 1973.)

duced in the reaction. Because of the thioester bond, succinyl-CoA is able to react with GDP and P_i to form GTP plus succinate and coenzyme A. The reaction is catalyzed by succinyl-CoA synthetase. The GTP formed then transfers its terminal phosphate group to ADP to form ATP, a reaction catalyzed by nucleoside diphosphate kinase. The next step of the cycle is the dehydrogenation of succinate by succinate dehydrogenase, an enzyme directly associated with the mitochondrial oxidative phosphorylation system. The product of the dehydrogenation of succinate is fumarate, which is subsequently hydrated in the presence of fumarase, also known as fumarate hydratase, to form L-malate. L-Malate is oxidized by malate dehydrogenase to regenerate oxaloacetate to complete the cycle. In the reaction, the electron equivalents are transferred to NAD^+ to form NADH.

In one turn of the citric acid cycle, the "acetyl" unit of acetyl-CoA is metabolized to two molecules of CO_2. The oxidation of 1 mole of the acetyl unit also allows the formation of 3 moles of NADH and 1 mole of $FADH_2$, which can be oxidized subsequently in the oxidative phosphorylation system to produce 9 and 2 moles of ATP, respectively. This ATP plus the 1 mole of ATP formed in the succinyl-CoA synthetase reaction totals 12 moles of ATP. Since 1 mole of NADH produced in the conversion of pyruvate to acetyl-CoA can result in the formation of 3 moles of ATP, a total of 15 moles of ATP can be produced upon the oxidation of 1 mole of pyruvate by the citric acid cycle and oxidative phosphorylation pathway.

β-Oxidation of fatty acids

Fatty acids yield more energy than other biological molecules upon oxidation and are the major form of energy reserve in animals. Most aerobic cells can oxidize fatty acids completely to CO_2 and H_2O, a process that takes place within the matrix of the mitochondria. The major mechanism of this pathway is β-oxidation, in which two carbon units of the fatty acids are removed each time to form acetyl-CoA (Figure 14). In the first step, fatty acids are converted to fatty acyl-CoA by acyl-CoA synthetase. ATP and coenzyme A are required for this activation process. The activated thioester of fatty acid undergoes enzymic dehydrogenation at carbons 2 and 3 to form Δ^2-*trans*-enoyl-CoA as product. The reaction is catalyzed by acyl-CoA dehydrogenase, which contains tightly bound FAD as a prosthetic group. The FAD is reduced to form $FADH_2$, and the reducing power is transferred to the mitochondrial electron transport system. The fatty enoyl-CoA is then hydrated at the 2 and 3 positions to form L-3-hydroxyacyl-CoA by the enzyme enoyl-CoA hydratase. In the next step of this pathway, L-3-hydroxyacyl-CoA is dehydrogenated to form 3-ketoacyl-CoA by 3-hydroxyacyl-CoA dehydrogenase, which uses NAD^+ as the electron acceptor. The electron equivalents in NADH are then transferred to the mitochondrial electron transport chain. In the last step of the fatty acid oxidation cycle, the 3-ketoacyl-CoA is cleaved by acetyl-CoA acetyltransferase, also known as thiolase, in the presence of coenzyme A to yield acetyl-CoA and a fatty acyl-CoA that is two carbons shorter than the starting substrate. The shortened fatty acyl-CoA then undergoes another cycle of oxidation.

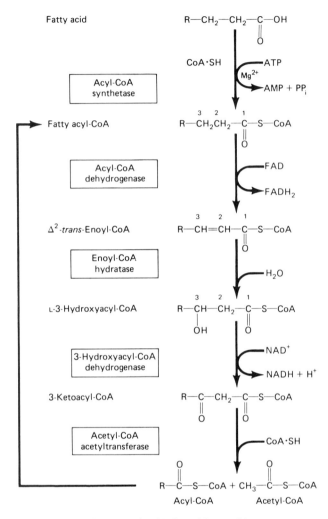

Figure 14. β-oxidation of fatty acids.

The overall equation for one turn of the β-oxidation cycle for palmitoyl-CoA is:

$$Palmitoyl\text{-}CoA + CoA + FAD + NAD^+ + H_2O \rightarrow Myristoyl\text{-}CoA$$
$$+ Acetyl\text{-}CoA + FADH_2 + NADH + H^+ \quad (18)$$

For the seven turns of the cycle required for the degradation of palmitoyl-CoA, the equation is:

$$\text{Palmitoyl-CoA} + 7\text{CoA} + 7\text{FAD} + 7\text{NAD}^+ + 7\text{H}_2\text{O} \rightarrow 8 \text{ Acetyl-CoA}$$
$$+ 7\text{FADH}_2 + 7\text{NADH} + 7\text{H}^+ \quad (19)$$

When linked to the citric acid cycle and mitochondrial oxidative phosphorylation pathway, 1 mole of acetyl-CoA, NADH, and FADH$_2$ can result in the formation of 12, 3, and 2 moles of ATP, respectively. The total amount of ATP produced is $8 \times 12 + 7 \times 3 + 7 \times 2 = 131$ moles ATP per mole of palmitoyl-CoA. Since two high-energy bonds are used for the activation of the fatty acid, the complete oxidation of 1 mole of palmitate, a molecule containing 16 carbons, can support the synthesis of 129 moles of ATP from ADP and P$_i$.

Metabolism of Amino Acids

The major site of amino acid catabolism in mammals is the liver. Although there are many different pathways for the oxidation of different amino acids, the most common feature of amino acid catabolism is the combination of transamination and deamination reactions shown by Figure 15. The α-amino group of many amino acids is transferred to α-ketoglutarate to form glutamate, which is then oxidatively deaminated to yield α-ketoglutarate and NH$_4^+$. During the deamination reaction, the electron equivalents are captured in either NADH or NADPH. With some amino acids, the α-amino group can be transferred directly to α-ketoglutarate in the presence of glutamate transaminase (aminotransferase). With other amino acids, the amino group is transferred to pyruvate to form alanine, which subsequently donates the amino

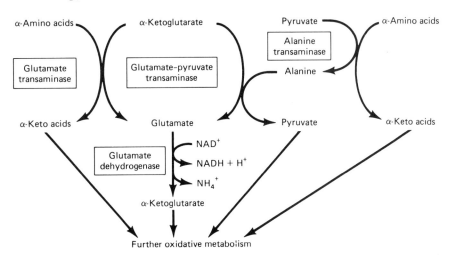

Figure 15. Common pathways of the oxidative metabolism of amino acids.

group to α-ketoglutarate. These reactions are catalyzed by alanine transaminase and glutamate–pyruvate transaminase, respectively. The NH_4^+ formed is disposed of by the urea cycle, an energy-requiring process. The resulting carbon skeletons of the amino acids are generally converted to pyruvate, acetyl-CoA, acetoacetyl-CoA, or one of the intermediates of the citric acid cycle, and are metabolized further.

Cellular Regulation of Energy Metabolism

The rate of energy metabolism is generally controlled not by the availability of nutrients in the cell, but by the cell's needs; that is, cells consume their fuels only as fast as is necessary to furnish the energy required for the activities of the cells. The regulation of a metabolic pathway may occur at several levels:

Concentrations of Substrates and Products. Although the overall rate of catabolic metabolism is generally not regulated by the concentration of available nutrients, the rates of individual pathways may be regulated by the availability of substrates. For example, the rate of the citric acid cycle is in part regulated by the concentrations of acetyl-CoA and oxaloacetate in the matrix of the mitochondria. The production of acetyl-CoA is regulated by the rates of oxidative decarboxylation of pyruvate, β-oxidation of fatty acids, and other pathways. The concentration of oxaloacetate is dependent mainly on the level of NADH, which affects the rate of malate dehydrogenase (see above, under "Citric Acid Cycle"), and on the rate of pyruvate carboxylase, which catalyzes the synthesis of oxaloacetate from pyruvate and CO_2. In addition to the rates of metabolic reactions, intercellular and intracellular transport of nutrients are also important factors affecting the cellular level of the substrates for enzyme systems.

Cellular Concentration of Enzymes. A metabolic pathway requires the catalytic activities of many enzymes. The rate of the pathway is, however, usually determined by the slowest step of the metabolic sequence. This step is usually known as the rate-limiting step. By varying the cellular concentration of the enzyme that catalyzes this step, the rate of metabolism can be regulated. For example, the induction of β-galactosidase and other proteins in *E. coli* by lactose would allow this substrate to be metabolized at a faster rate. Enzyme induction may also play a role in regulating energy metabolism in animals; for example, the glycerol 3-phosphate dehydrogenase in mitochondria is induced many-fold by triiodothyronine.

Allosteric Control of Enzyme Activity. Many allosteric enzymes are inhibited by the end product of the sequence in which they function. These enzymes are usually the control points of metabolic pathways. ATP, the end product of catabolic metabolism, is an allosteric inhibitor of several enzymes in the catabolic pathways of carbohydrates, lipids, and amino acids. In addition, some regulatory enzymes are activated or stimulated by specific metabolites, sometimes by their own substrates. Some allosteric enzymes are located at branch points of the metabolic pathways. Such enzymes usually can respond to two or more activators or inhibitors which may be the products of the two branching pathways. By this mechanism the rate of two or more metabolic pathways can be regulated.

Energy Charge and Respiratory Control. It has been proposed that the rates of many metabolic pathways are regulated by *energy charge,* which is a measure of the high-energy phosphate state of a cell. The energy charge is defined as follows:

$$\text{energy charge} = \frac{[\text{ATP}] + \frac{1}{2}[\text{ADP}]}{[\text{ATP}] + [\text{ADP}] + [\text{AMP}]} \tag{20}$$

It has been shown that some enzymes in the ATP-generating pathways are inhibited by a high energy charge, whereas those in the ATP-utilizing pathways are stimulated by a high energy charge. In other words, the energy charge, like the pH of a cell, is buffered. The energy charge of most cells is in the range of 0.8 to 0.95. If the energy charge decreases below this range, the ATP-generating pathways are accelerated through the response of their regulatory enzymes to the relative concentrations of ATP, ADP, and AMP; at the same time the ATP-utilizing pathways slow down.

Respiratory control, also known as acceptor control, is the phenomenon that the rate of mitochondrial electron transport (cellular respiration) is controlled by the concentration of ADP. Since the cellular adenylate exists mainly in the form of either ATP or ADP, a high concentration of ATP is accompanied by a low ADP concentration. This low ADP concentration serves to decrease the rate of mitochondrial electron transport, a process that provides free energy for the synthesis of ATP. By this mechanism, the overall rate of the oxidative metabolism can be regulated by the cells' need for ATP.

Regulation by Hormones. In higher multicellular organisms, hormones secreted in one organ can regulate the metabolism of certain target tissues. For example, the insulin secreted by the pancreas increases the transport of glucose into cells and thus increases the utilization of this nutrient. Epinephrine can initiate a series of reactions including the actions of cyclic AMP and protein kinases, and cause an increase in the breakdown of glycogen.

REFERENCES

Atkinson, D. E. 1968. *Biochemistry* 7:4030–34.

Boyer, P. D., ed. 1975, 1976. *Oxidation–Reduction,* Vols. XI–XIII of *The Enzymes,* 3rd ed. Academic Press, New York.

Guengerich, F. P., Ballou, D. P., and Coon, M. J. 1975. *J. Biol. Chem.* 250:7405–14.

Hayaishi, O., ed. 1974. *Molecular Mechanisms of Oxygen Activation.* Academic Press, New York.

King, T. E., Mason, H. S., and Morrison, M., eds. 1973. *Oxidases and Related Redox Systems.* University Park Press, Baltimore.

Krebs, H. A., and Kornberg, H. L. 1957. *Energy Transformation in Living Matter.* Springer-Verlag, Berlin.

Lehninger, A. L. 1975. *Biochemistry,* 2nd ed. Worth Publishers, New York.

Lovenberg, W., ed. 1973, 1974, 1977. *Iron–Sulfur Proteins,* Vols. I–III. Academic Press, New York.

Lowenstein, J. M., ed. 1969. *Citric Acid Cycle: Control and Compartmentation.* Marcel Dekker, New York.

Meister, A. 1965. *Biochemistry of the Amino Acids,* 2nd ed., Vols. I and II. Academic Press, New York.

Metzler, D. E. 1977. *Biochemistry: The Chemical Reactions of Living Cells.* Academic Press, New York.

Morowitz, H. J. 1968. *Energy Flow in Biology.* Academic Press, New York.

Pigman, W. W., and Horton, D., eds. 1972. *The Carbohydrates: Chemistry and Biochemistry.* Academic Press, New York.

Ryan, D. E., Thomas, P. E., Korzeniowski, D., and Levin, W. 1979. *J. Biol. Chem.* 254:1365–74.

Singer, T. P., ed. 1976. *Flavins and Flavoproteins.* Elsevier Scientific, Amsterdam.

Stryer, L. 1975. *Biochemistry,* W. H. Freeman and Co., San Francisco.

Wakil, S. J., and Barnes, E. M., Jr. 1971. *Comp. Biochem.* 185:57–104.

White, A., Handler, P., Smith, E. L., Hill, R. L., and Lehman, I. R. 1978. *Principles of Biochemistry,* 6th ed. McGraw-Hill, New York.

5.2. Structure and Function of Mitochondria

Chung S. Yang

Mitochondria are found in aerobically growing yeast, in protozoa, and in almost every cell of higher plants and animals. These subcellular organelles are the most important site of energy metabolism. This chapter deals with the structure of these organelles, the process of oxidative phosphorylation, compartmentation, and the intracellular transport of nutrients.

THE STRUCTURE OF MITOCHONDRIA

The shapes of mitochondria are different in different types of cells. Mitochondria are spherical in brown fat cells, elliptical in liver cells, cylindrical in kidney cells, and threadlike in fibroblasts, whereas yeast mitochondria have very complex irregular structures. The size of the mitochondria appears to be in the order of 0.5 by 3 μm. The mitochondria of rat liver, which are most intensively studied, are about 2 μm long and less than 1 μm wide, a size similar to bacteria. The number of mitochondria varies with the size and energy requirement of cells; for example, there are approximately 250 mitochondria per sperm cell, 800 per liver cell (rat), and 500,000 in some amoebas. Mitochondria are often aligned in a manner that facilitates the acquisition of nutrients and the delivery of ATP to the energy-requiring systems. For example, mitochondria are generally located adjacent to cytoplasmic fat droplets, arranged along the contractile fibers of muscle cells, or coiled about the midpiece of a spermatozoon. The mitochondrion is a major component of aerobic cells; for example, the mitochondrial protein accounts for approximately 20% of the protein of liver cells. The mitochondria also make up about 20% of the volume of liver cells and over 50% of heart-muscle cells.

The structure of mitochondria is illustrated in Figure 1. The organelle is characterized by a double membrane structure; oxidative enzymes are embedded, attached, or enclosed in the membranes. The *outer membrane* is smooth and somewhat elastic, whereas the *inner membrane* has inward folds called *cristae*. The cristae appear to be a device for increasing the surface area of

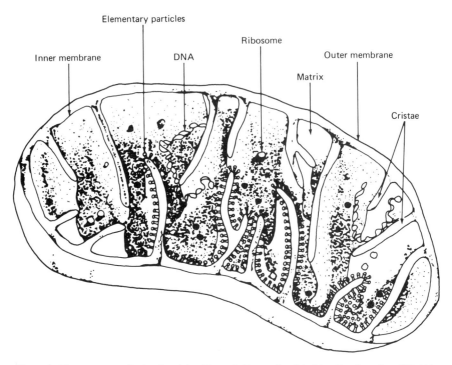

Figure 1. The structure of mitochondria. (From J. Bernstein, *Biochim. Biophys. Acta* 205:464–72, 1970.)

the inner membrane, and may vary in number and structure depending on the cell type. In liver mitochondria, the cristae are continuous with the inner membrane, but this continuity is less obvious in other types of mitochondria. Inside the inner membrane is the *matrix,* which contains many oxidative enzymes as well as DNA and ribosomes. The mitochondrial genetic materials and the biogenesis of mitochondria will be discussed in Chapter 5.3.

Outer Membrane

The outer membrane of liver mitochondria is 5 to 7 nm thick, is composed of about 50% lipids and 50% proteins, and has a density of about 1.1 g/cm^3. The outer membrane is permeable to water, NADH, ATP, and most substances with molecular weighs under 10,000 daltons. If the outer membrane is removed from liver mitochondria, the remaining structure still retains oxidative phosphorylation activities. Although the oxidative phosphorylation enzymes are not located on the outer membrane, certain enzymes such as monoamine oxidase, kynurenine 3-monooxygenase, and fatty acyl-CoA synthetase are known to be associated with this membrane. Monoamine oxidase, a flavoprotein that catalyzes the oxidation of various monoamines (e.g., epinephrine) is commonly used as a "marker" enzyme for the presence of the outer membrane. Other enzymes known to be located on the outer membrane are shown in Table 1, together with enzymes located in other fractions of the mitochondria. To accurately determine the suborganelle location of enzymes is a difficult task. The possible contamination by enzymes from other fractions and redistribution of enzymes during the preparation of the suborganelle fraction are sometimes hard to avoid.

Inner Membrane and Cristae

The inner membrane contains about 80% proteins and 20% lipids. It has a density of 1.21, higher than that of the outer membrane. The inner membrane is a lipid bilayer composed predominately of choline- and ethanolamine-con-

Table 1. Localization of Enzymes in Mitochondria[a]

OUTER MEMBRANE	INNER MEMBRANE
Cytochrome b_5	Cytochromes b, c_1, c, a, a_3
Cytochrome b_5 reductase	NADH dehydrogenase
Monoamine oxidase	Succinate dehydrogenase
Kynurenine hydroxylase	Ubiquinone
Fatty acyl-CoA synthetase	Electron-transferring flavoprotein
Fatty acid elongation system	ATPase
Glycerophosphate acyl transferase	β-Hydroxybutyrate dehydrogenase
Choline phosphotransferase	Carnitine-palmityl transferase
Phospholipase A	Fatty acid elongation system
Nucleoside diphosphokinase	ADP–ATP translocase
	P_1-OH$^-$ translocase
MATRIX	Dicarboxylate translocase
	Tricarboxylate translocase
Pyruvate dehydrogenase	α-Ketoglutarate–malate translocase
Citrate synthase	Pyruvate translocase
Aconitase	Aspartate–glutamate translocase
Isocitrate dehydrogenase	
Fumarase	INTERMEMBRANE SPACE
α-Ketoglutarate dehydrogenase	
Malate dehydrogenase	Adenylate kinase
Fatty acid oxidation system	Nucleoside diphosphokinase
Phosphopyruvate carboxylase	Sulfite oxidase
Glutamate dehydrogenase	
Aspartate–glutamate aminotransferase	
Ornithine transcarbamoylase	

[a] Modified from A. White, P. Handler, E. L. Smith, R. L. Hill, and I. R. Lehman, *Principles of Biochemistry*, 6th ed., McGraw-Hill, New York, 1978.

taining phosphoglycerides, and lesser amounts of those containing serine, inositol, and glycerol. About two-thirds of the fatty acids are unsaturated to some degree. Cardiolipin (diphosphatidylglycerol) makes up approximately 20% of the lipid in the inner membrane; this lipid is almost exclusively found in this type of membrane. In the inner membrane of mitochondria, many biologically active proteins are embedded in the phospholipid bilayer, including the oxidative enzymes and electron carriers, the ATP synthetase complex, and the transport proteins.

The ultrastructure of the inner membrane has been studied by electron microscopy following negative-contrast staining. It has been shown that the inner surface of the inner membrane is covered with regularly spaced spherical particles, with diameters of 8 to 9 nm, connected to the membrane by narrow stalks. These knoblike structures are known as *elementary particles* or *inner membrane particles.* (See Figure 2.) When the mitochondria are subjected to a brief sonic irradiation, submitochondrial particles are formed; they are vesicles formed by rupture and resealing of the inner membrane, and are in an "inside-out" configuration relative to the disposition of the inner membrane of the intact mitochondria (Figure 2). The elementary particles of the submitochondrial particles are thus on the external surface and are exposed to the external environment. These particles are much smaller and structurally simpler than mitochondria but still retain the ability to catalyze oxidative phosphorylation. The preparation of submitochondrial particles has proved to be a fruitful approach in studying the mechanism of oxidative phosphorylation.

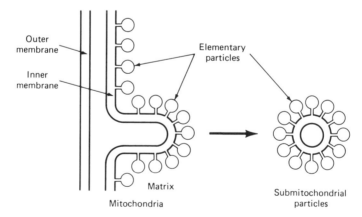

Figure 2. Structure of mitochondrial inner membrane and submitochondrial particles. (Modified from A. White, P. Handler, E. L. Smith, R. L. Hill, and I. R. Lehman, *Principles of Biochemistry,* 6th Ed., McGraw-Hill, New York, 1978.)

Intermembrane Space

Between the outer and inner membranes, there is a space about 7 nm thick. When the outer membrane is ruptured by osmotic shock or by exposure to phospholipase, intermembrane fluid and enzymes are released. A few enzymes are found in this space (Table 1). Adenylate kinase, a key enzyme involved in equilibrating ATP and AMP with ADP (Chapter 5.1, reaction 14), is one of the enzymes thought to be characteristically present in the intermembrane space.

Matrix

Enclosed in the inner membrane is the matrix. This gel-like compartment contains the component enzymes of the citric acid cycle, fatty acid oxidation system, and amino acid degradation pathways. Some of the enzymes are organized into reticular networks apparently attached to the inner surface of the inner membrane. Such arrangements facilitate the transfer of NADH produced by these enzyme systems to the electron transport chain in the inner membrane. The matrix also contains DNA and ribosomes.

THE ELECTRON TRANSPORT CHAIN

The NADH and $FADH_2$ formed in glycolysis, fatty acid oxidation, and the citric acid cycle are oxidized in the mitochondria to generate energy for the synthesis of ATP. The electrons are transferred through several electron carriers and finally to O_2. This chain is generally referred to as the *electron transport chain*, the *respiratory chain*, or the *respiratory assembly*.

The Components and Sequence of the Chain

The electron transport chain has been fractionated into four complexes following a detergent treatment of submitochondrial particles. The four complexes are: Complex I, NADH–ubiquinone reductase; Complex II, succinate–ubiquinone reductase; Complex III, reduced ubiquinone–cytochrome c reductase; and Complex IV, cytochrome oxidase (Figure 3). This work was accomplished by Hatefi, Green, and coworkers. Each complex still retains some of the membrane lipids which are believed to be functionally important. The partial or complete electron transport chain can be reconstituted with some or all four electron transfer complexes. For example, succinate oxidase activity can be reconstituted with complexes II, III, and IV. The alignments, constituents, and particle weights of the complexes are shown in Figure 3. Although evidence exists showing that the four complexes are the basic structural units

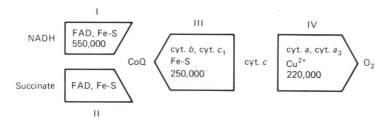

Figure 3. The four complexes of the mitochondrial electron transport chain. (Modified from D. E. Green and R. F. Goldberger, *Molecular Insights into the Living Process,* Academic Press, New York, 1967.)

of the electron transport chain, the concept remains to be firmly established. The components and the electron transfer sequence of the chain as well as the "sites" of phosphorylation and the sites of action of inhibitors are shown in Figure 4.

The first enzyme of the chain is NADH dehydrogenase. A purified preparation of this enzyme has a molecular weight of 70,000 daltons and contains one FMN and one (Fe_4S_4) iron–sulfur (Fe–S) center. This enzyme uses artificial electron acceptors such as ferricyanide and cytochrome c but not ubiquinone as electron acceptors. The functional NADH–ubiquinone reductase (Complex I) is a much larger entity, containing at least seven polypeptides ranging from 25,000 to 75,000 daltons as well as 16 Fe–S complexes per FMN. Recent studies with electron paramagnetic resonance suggests that there are four and perhaps six distinct Fe–S centers with standard redox potential (E_0') ranging from −400 to −20 mV. These Fe–S centers are reducible by NADH. Inhibitors of NADH–ubiquinone reductase such as rotenone, amytal, and piericidin appear to block the electron transfer between Fe–S centers. Owing to the hydrophobic and multicomponent nature of the NADH–ubiquinone complex, its structure has not been clearly established. Of a similar structure is the succinate–ubiquinone reductase (Complex II).

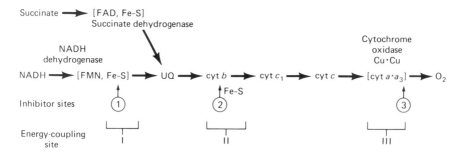

Figure 4. The mitochondrial electron transport chain.

A soluble succinate–dehydrogenase has been shown to consist of a subunit of 70,000 daltons with a covalently bound FAD and two (Fe_2S_2) centers, as well as a small subunit of 27,000 daltons containing one (Fe_4S_4) center. Values of E_0' for these two types of Fe–S centers are +30 and −260 mV, respectively. The isolated enzyme reacts with electron acceptors such as ferricyanide and phenazine methosulfate but is unable to transfer electrons to ubiquinone. The functional succinate–ubiquinone reductase is also composed of two polypeptides CII-3 (molecular weight, 13,500) and CII-4 (molecular weight, 7000) in a molecular complex. The complex has been shown to span the mitochondrial inner membrane with the succinate dehydrogenase flavoprotein on the matrix side and CII-3 on the cytoplasmic side.

The reduced ubiquinone is oxidized by cytochrome b. Two forms of cytochrome b, b_K and b_T have been detected in mitochondria. The standard redox potential of b_K is +30 mV. The standard redox potential of b_T, however, rises from −30 to +245 mV when ATP is added. This has been suggested as an event of energy coupling, but the mechanism remains to be elucidated. The electron transfer sequence among ubiquinone, b_K, and b_T has not been clearly established. The reduced form of cytochrome b does not auto-oxidize. The physiological electron acceptor of this cytochrome is cytochrome c_1. The latter has been isolated as an aggregate consisting of polypeptides of 31,000 daltons. The ferrous form of neither the cytochrome nor its aggregate can react directly with cytochrome oxidase. Addition of a catalytic amount of cytochrome c permits rapid oxidation of cytochrome c_1 by cytochrome oxidase. Cytochrome c and c_1 form a rather tight complex, and reaction between them is extremely rapid; the second-order rate constant is 3.3 × 10^3 M^{-1} sec^{-1} at pH 7.4. The functional reductase ubiquinone–cytochrome c reductase has been isolated as Complex III. Complex III has a particle weight of 250,000 daltons consisting of nine different polypeptides. In addition to cytochromes b and c_1, it also contains an Fe–S protein with E_0' of +280 mV.

Cytochrome c is a small (molecular weight 13,000) water-soluble protein. It is the only electron carrier of the electron transport chain that can be readily extracted into diluted buffer. The structure and properties of cytochrome c have been studied extensively with samples from a great variety of species. The three-dimensional structure and the structure of the heme environment have been elucidated. At neutral pH, ferrocytochrome c does not react with O_2 or CO, and the ferri- form does not bind with CN^-, S^{2-}, or N_3^-. The detailed mechanism of electron transfer from cytochrome c_1 through cytochrome c to cytochrome oxidase is not yet clearly understood. Phospholipids may play an important role in facilitating this process.

Cytochrome oxidase (Complex IV) is the only component of the chain that transfers electron equivalents to O_2. The enzyme contains cytochromes

a and a_3. Of these, a_3 is auto-oxidizable at low O_2 tension and can combine with CO and CN^-, whereas cytochrome a does not. Therefore, the sequence of electron transfer appears to be $a \rightarrow a_3 \rightarrow O_2$. The E_0' for cytochrome a is $+200$ mV and for a_3 is $+340$ mV. In the presence of ATP, the E_0' of a_3 falls to about 160 mV, a phenomenon that may be related to energy coupling. The reduction of O_2 is a four-electron process; in addition to one molecule each of cytochromes a and a_3, two copper ions are also components of a functional unit of cytochrome oxidase. Cytochrome oxidase has been isolated as a molecular complex of about 200,000 daltons consisting of seven distinct subunits: I, 40,000; II, 33,000; III, 22,000; IV, 14,500; V, 13,000; VI, 12,700; VII, 4,600 daltons. This molecular complex traverses the inner membrane of mitochondria. The topographical arrangement of cytochrome oxide has been studied. Subunits II and III are believed to span both sides of the membrane. Subunits IV, V, and VIII protrude on the matrix side, whereas subunits I and VI are buried in the membrane. The concentrations of the components of the electron transport chain have been studied with some tissues. For example, the cytochrome b content in rat liver mitochondria is 0.28 μmol/g of proteins. The amounts of other components, expressed as ratios to cytochrome b, are shown in Table 2. It is seen that cytochromes b, $c + c_1$, a and a_3, which constitute the main chain, exist at approximately equimolar amounts, whereas quantities of ubiquinone and iron–sulfur proteins are several times that of cytochrome b. NADH dehydrogenase content, on the other hand, is only about one-seventh that of cytochrome b.

Although the components of the electron transport chain have been studied extensively, the topographic arrangement of these electron carriers in the mitochondria inner membrane is not completely understood. Cytochromes

Table 2. Components of the Mitochondrial Electron Transport Chain.[a]

COMPONENT	RAT LIVER MITOCHONDRIA	BEEF HEART MITOCHONDRIA
Cytochrome b	1.0	1.0
Cytochrome c_1	0.63	0.33–0.51
Cytochrome c	0.78	0.66–0.85
Cytochrome a	1.0	1.1
Cytochrome a_3	1.0	1.1
Copper		2.2
Ubiquinone	3–6	7.0
Iron–sulfur protein		5.5
NADH dehydrogenase		0.14

[a] Modified from D. E. Metzler, *Biochemistry: The Chemical Reaction of Living Cells.* Academic Press, New York, 1977.

a, c, and c_1 appear to be located on the cytoplasmic side of the inner membrane, accessible to macromolecular or impermeant probes added to mitochondria. Cytochrome a_3 and flavoproteins are on the matrix side of the inner membrane and are accessible to impermeant probes added to submitochondrial particles.

The Transport of Electrons from Some Substrates to the Main Chain

In addition to NADH and succinate, the electron transport chain also receives electrons from substrates such as fatty acyl-CoA, glycerol 3-phosphate, choline, and sarcosine. The electrons usually transfer through iron–sulfur flavoproteins to ubiquinone, which funnels electrons to the electron transport chain. The lipophilic ubiquinone is believed to serve as diffusible electron carriers in the mitochondrial membrane, shuttling electrons from various dehydrogenases to cytochrome b. The electron transfer sequences of some substrates are shown in Figure 5. Fatty acid oxidation is a major energy source of the cell; the electron transfer sequence from fatty acyl-CoA through acyl-CoA dehydrogenase and the electron-transferring flavoprotein to ubiquinone is thus an important pathway. Glycerol 3-phosphate dehydrogenase is a part of the "glycerol phosphate shuttle" which serves to transfer electron equivalents of the cytosolic NADH to the mitochondrial electron transport chain, and is of considerable importance in affecting the glycolytic pathway. The electrons from other substrates such as choline and sarcosine also enter the chain through ubiquinone (Figure 5.)

Inhibitor of the Electron Transport Chain

The use of site-specific inhibitors is an important approach in studying the sequence of electron transport of the mitochondria. For example, rotenone

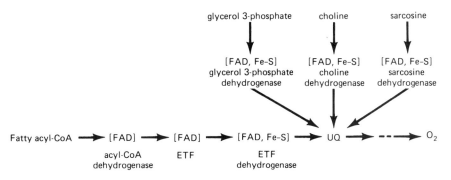

Figure 5. Transport of electrons into the electron chain. ETF, electron-transferring flavoprotein.

prevents reduction of the cytochrome system by NADH but allows reduction by succinate. Antimycin inhibits the oxidation of both NADH and succinate but not ferrocytochrome *c* by the electron transport chain. These results together with the isolation of the four functional complexes and the information on the standard redox potentials of various electron carriers provide the basis of elucidating the sequence of the electron transport chain. The sites of action of some commonly used inhibitors are shown in Figure 4. (1) The inhibitors that block electron transfer between NADH and ubiquinone include: rotenone, a poison from plant roots; piericidin A, a structural analogue of ubiquinone; amytal, a barbiturate drug; progesterone, a steroid hormone; and theonyltrifluoroacetone [4,4,4-trifluoro-1-(2-thienyl)-1,3-butadione]. The detailed mechanisms and specific sites of the inhibitory actions are not known, although rotenone, amytal, and piericidin appear to block the electron transfer between the Fe–S centers of Complex I. (2) Antimycin A, a *Streptomyces* antibiotic, inhibits the electron transfer from cytochrome *b* to *c*. (3) The inhibitors that prevent the electron transfer from cytochrome oxidase to O_2 include cyanide, azide, hydrogen sulfide, and carbon monoxide.

THE SYNTHESIS OF ATP AND OTHER ENERGY-DEPENDENT REACTIONS

Coupling of Oxidative Phosphorylation to Electron Transport

When the electron equivalents of NADH and succinate are transferred through the mitochondrial electron transport chain to O_2, the free energy derived from the oxidation–reduction reactions is used to drive the synthesis of ATP in a process known as *oxidative phosphorylation* or *respiratory-chain phosphorylation*. With NADH, 3 moles of ATP are synthesized when two equivalents of electrons are transferred to one gram atom of molecular oxygen. The overall equation for the reaction can be written as

$$NADH + H^+ + 3ADP + 3P_i + \tfrac{1}{2}O_2 \rightarrow NAD^+ + 4H_2O + 3ATP \quad (1)$$

The quantitative relationship between oxidation and phosphorylation is usually expressed as the P/O ratio; for NADH, the P/O ratio = 3. With succinate, the overall equation for oxidative phosphorylation is

$$Succinate + 2ADP + 2P_i + \tfrac{1}{2}O_2 \rightarrow Fumarate + 3H_2O + 2ATP \quad (2)$$

with P/O ratio = 2. Other substrates that enter the electron transport chain through ubiquinone also have P/O ratios of 2. The linking of the oxidation reaction to phosphorylation reactions is generally referred to as *energy cou-*

pling. Thermodynamic calculations based on standard redox potentials have shown that the free energy changes of the electron transfer from NADH to ubiquinone, cytochrome *b* to *c,* and cytochrome *a* to O_2 are sufficient for driving the synthesis of 1 mole of ATP at each site per two equivalents of electrons. These are shown as energy-coupling sites I, II, and III in Figure 4. The sites of energy coupling pertain closely to the mechanism of oxidative phosphorylation, and both will be discussed in detail in subsequent sections.

The coupling of oxidation with phosphorylation also means that the rate of electron transport is dependent on the rate of ATP synthesis. In intact mitochondria, electron transport proceeds at a maximal rate only when sufficient amounts of phosphate and ADP are present. When ADP is lacking, the rate of cellular respiration (mitochondrial electron transfer) is very low, and no phosphorylation occurs because there is no phosphate acceptor. This condition, known as "state 4 respiration," is the idling or resting state of cellular respiration. When ADP is added to this system, the oxidation abruptly increases to a maximum with concomitant synthesis of ATP. This is known as "state 3" or "active" respiration. When all the added ADP has been phosphorylated, the rate of cellular respiration abruptly returns to the idling state (state 4). This phenomenon, in which the rate of cellular respiration is controlled by the concentration of ADP, is called *respiratory control* or *acceptor control;* it is an important mechanism for the cell in regulating its rate of oxidative metabolism. The mitochondria can lose their respiratory control because of cellular damage or the presence of *uncoupling agents (uncouplers).* Under these conditions, oxidation proceeds at a maximal rate in the absence of ADP and without the phosphorylation reaction.

Several classes of compounds are known to uncouple oxidative phosphorylation. Some are lipid-soluble substances containing an acidic group and an aromatic ring. Examples of this class of uncouplers are 2,4-dinitrophenol, carbonylcyanide *p*-trifluoromethoxyphenylhydrazone, dicumarol, and 5-chloro-3-t-butyl-2'-chloro-4'-nitrosalicylanilide. The structures of the first two compounds are shown in Figure 6. The uncouplers prevent the synthesis of ATP by oxidative phosphorylation, but do not affect ATP synthesis by other pathways such as glycolytic phosphorylation. The mechanism of uncoupling will be discussed in a subsequent section, together with the mechanism of oxidative phosphorylation. In fact, uncouplers have been an important tool in elucidating the mechanism of energy-coupling.

Ionophores which can carry ions through the mitochondrial inner membrane are also uncouplers of oxidative phosphorylation. Over 50 different ionophores with similar activity have been described. The most commonly used ones in the study of oxidative phosphorylation are valinomycin, nigericin, and nonactin, which require K^+ for the uncoupling action; and gramicidin, which functions in the presence of either K^+ or Na^+. Valinomycin (Figure 6) is a

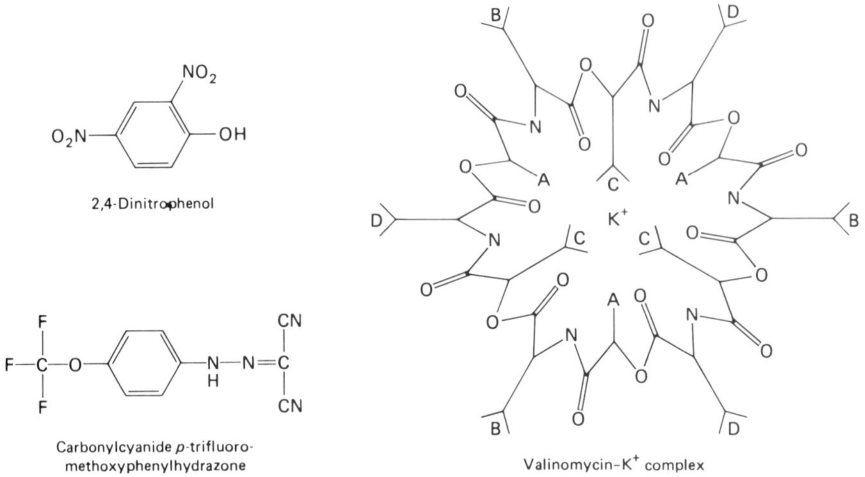

Figure 6. Structures of uncouplers. For the valinomycin–K$^+$ complex, A = L-lactate, B = L-valine, C = D-hydroxyisovalerate, and D = D-valine.

prototype of these compounds. Valinomycin is specific to K$^+$, and, upon binding, the lipid-soluble valinomycin–K$^+$ complex readily passes through the mitochondrial inner membrane, which has very low permeability for K$^+$ in the absence of the ionophore. Valinomycin and other ionophores, therefore, can uncouple oxidative phosphorylation by abolishing the ionic gradient across the mitochondrial membrane.

The Mitochondrial ATP Synthesis System

The enzyme system that is responsible for the synthesis of ATP is generally known as *ATPase,* although it should be more appropriately named *ATP synthetase.* The ATPase activity of mitochondria is normally very low, but it can be greatly stimulated by 2,4-dinitrophenol and other uncouplers, whereas the stimulated ATPase activity is inhibited by oligomycin. The ATPase activity is believed to represent the reversal of the normal ATP synthesis function of the mitochondria. It can be demonstrated experimentally that the ATP synthetase system also catalyzes exchange reactions that are partial reactions of oxidative phosphorylation. Some of the exchange reactions are as follows:

1. *Phosphate–ATP exchange:*

$$AMP \sim P \sim P + {}^{32}P_i \rightleftharpoons AMP \sim P \sim {}^{32}P + P_i \qquad (3)$$

The terminal phosphate group of ATP exchanges rapidly with inorganic phosphate in the absence of electron transport. The reaction is completely inhibited by either 2,4-dinitrophenol or oligomycin.

2. *ADP–ATP exchange:*

$$*AMP \sim P + AMP \sim P \sim {}^{32}P \rightleftharpoons *AMP \sim P \sim {}^{32}P + AMP \sim P \qquad (4)$$

The terminal phosphate group is reversibly transferred to the terminal phosphate group of ADP. It is also inhibited by 2,4-dinitrophenol and oligomycin.

3. *Phosphate–water exchange:*

$$HPO_{4_-} + H_2\,{}^{18}O \rightleftharpoons HP^{18}O_4{}^{-2} + H_2O \qquad (5)$$

The oxygen atom in the phosphate is exchanged with that in the water, with no net disappearance of phosphate. The exchange is inhibited by 2,4-dinitrophenol and oligomycin. These properties of the partial reactions strongly indicate that the sequence by which ATP is formed from ADP and P_i is reversible.

The ATP synthetase system has been isolated in soluble form as coupling factor F_1 or Complex V. In the presence of Mg^{2+}, F_1 catalyzes the slow hydrolysis of ATP to ADP and phosphate; this reaction is not inhibited by oligomycin. Coupling factor F_1 is an enzyme complex consisting of five polypeptides designated α, β, γ, δ, and ϵ with molecular weights of 56,000, 52,000, 32,000, 21,000, and 11,500 daltons, respectively. The functional unit of F_1 is built of two of each of the subunits; the proposed structure is shown in Figure 7. None of the separate subunits has ATPase activity, but this activity can be obtained by combining subunits α and β.

The isolated enzyme contains two tightly bound ADP per molecule. The active form of the ATP synthetase in the mitochondria is also believed to have tightly bound ADP. The bound nucleotides can exchange with medium nucleotides upon energization. The F_1 complex has been shown to undergo profound conformational changes when the membrane is activated by electron flow. These observations have been considered as important clues in elucidating the mechanisms of oxidative phosphorylation.

Another specific protein functioning in the coupling of ATP synthesis to electron transport is F_0 or *oligomycin-sensitivity-conferring factor.* When the F_0 factor is added to the F_1 factor, the ATPase activity is inhibited by oligomycin. F_0 is a protein complex composed of at least four polypeptide chains. The hydrophobic nature of F_0 allows it to be secured in the lipid bilayer of the membrane and serves as a binding site for F_0. F_1 appears to be attached

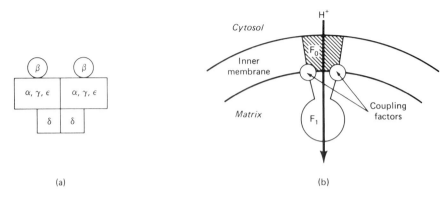

(a)   (b)

Figure 7. Proposed structure of the ATP synthetase system. (A) Subunit structure of coupling factor F_1. (B) Topography of F_0 and F_1 in the membrane. The ATP synthetase or the proton pump also consists of other coupling factors such as F_2 and F_6. (Modified from E. Racker, *Ann. Rev. Biochem.* 46:1006–1014, 1978.)

to F_0 specifically by the δ chains. Removal of F_1 from the membrane makes the latter highly permeable to protons; and these leaks can be plugged by rebinding F_1 or by certain inhibitors. These observations have led to the view that F_0 offers a channel through which protons cross the membrane to the active site on the ATP synthetase. The proton may create a microenvironment at the active site that drives ATP formation. This idea is illustrated in Figure 7.

Energy-Dependent Transport of Ions

The existence of a proton transport system in mitochondria coupled to respiration was elucidated by Mitchell and Moyle. In their experiment mitochondria were suspended in a medium that contained no oxygen, and then the number of protons translocated outside of the mitochondrial membrane was measured after a known quantity of oxygen was injected into the solution. The proton concentration was found to rise immediately and rapidly; when the oxygen was exhausted, the concentration slowly returned to normal as protons leaked back across the membrane. It is commonly believed that six protons are transported outside the mitochondria when each electron pair passes from NADH to oxygen, although there are reports showing that more than six protons are translocated. Thus the electron transport is able to create a proton gradient accompanied by a membrane potential across the mitochondrial membrane. The proton gradient has been found to consist of a pH difference of about 1.4 pH units (acid outside) and a membrane potential of approximately 140 mV (positive outside). The addition of proton ionophore immediately dissipates the gradient. Other ions also pass across the membrane as a result of the transmembrane electrochemical gradient. Their passage is affected by the membrane activities and coupling. Uptake of K^+, Ca^{2+}, Mn^{2+}, Sr^{2+}, and other cations is associated with ejection of H^+ from inside the mitochondria. Anions such as phosphate, arsenate, acetate, sulfate, and metabolites of the citric acid cycle can also accumulate within the mitochondria. Of these, phosphate movements are coupled to the counterflux of OH^-. Other ion movements are concerted in that the influx of some species is associated with the efflux of other species. Membrane carriers or transport protein are required for these processes.

The transport of K^+ and Ca^{2+} have been well characterized. The intramitochondrial concentration of K^+ exceeds that in the surrounding medium. The concentration of K^+ depends on the energy generated from the electron transport system, since antimycin A and DNP inhibit K^+ uptake. Reaccumulation of K^+ in potassium-depleted mitochondria is related to the H^+ efflux. At pH 6.6, K^+ uptake can be driven by two energy sources: one is the oxidation of succinate or other substrates, and the other is ATP. Other studies revealed that the succinate-dependent accumulation is markedly increased by oligomycin. The addition of P_i and ADP leads to a net loss of potassium. The energy-dependent uptake of Ca^{2+} by mitochondria has been studied throughly by Lehninger and coworkers. Accumulation of Ca^{2+} is accompanied by uptake of an equivalent amount of phosphate. For every pair of electrons passing from NADH to O_2, about six Ca^{2+} ions are accumulated from the medium. Under these conditions no ATP is synthesized. Thus, the energy derived from oxidation can be used to carry out either Ca^{2+} accumulation or ATP formation but not both.

Energy-Dependent Ultrastructure Changes of Mitochondria

The ultrastructure of mitochondria can undergo drastic changes as a reflection of the state of the energy-coupling process. In the absence of ADP, the inner-membrane-matrix compartment of the respiring mitochondria (state 4 respiration) completely fills the space bounded by the outer membrane (Figure 8). This is called the *orthodox state*. When ADP is added to the system to initiate state 3 (active) respiration, the matrix condenses to a volume that is only about half of that in the orthodox state; the inner membrane and cristae become more tightly folded and more contorted. This is called the *condensed state*. The orthodox state is believed by some authors to represent an "energized" state which can drive the synthesis of ATP and ADP and P_i; whereas the condensed state is the "relaxed" state after utilizing the energy for ATP synthesis. In intact respiring liver cells the mitochondria are halfway between state 4 and state 3.

Orthodox conformation

Condensed conformation

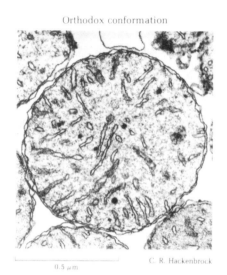 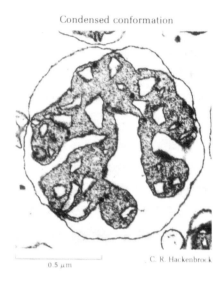

0.5 μm   C. R. Hackenbrock   0.5 μm   C. R. Hackenbrock

Figure 8. Ultrastructural changes of mouse liver mitochondria. Electron micrographs showing the ultrastructural changes in mouse-liver mitochondria during the transition from resting (state 4) to active (state 3) respiration. (From A. L. Lehninger, *Biochemistry,* 2nd Ed., Worth Publishers, Inc., New York, 1975.)

Energy-Dependent Reverse Flow of Electrons

When ATP is added into a system that consists of mitochondria, succinate, oxaloacetate, and cyanide, electrons will flow from succinate to oxaloacetate. The sequence of electron flow is believed to be a reversal of the normal electron transfer reaction:

Succinate → succinate dehydrogenase → ubiquinone → NADH dehydrogenase → NAD^+ → oxaloacetate

The function of cyanide is to inhibit the electron flow to O_2. ATP undergoes cleavage to ADP and P_i by reversal of the energy-coupling reaction of site 1. The energy from the hydrolysis of ATP is thus required to reverse energy-coupling electron transport. The other two energy-coupling steps of the chain can also be reversed under suitable conditions. These reactions demonstrate that the reactions of oxidative phosphorylation are indeed reversible.

The energy from electron transport or ATP can also drive the *transhydrogenation* between NADH and $NADP^+$:

$$NADH + NADP^+ + energy \rightarrow NAD^+ + NADPH \tag{6}$$

The reaction is strongly exergonic, and the reverse process is not readily measured. It can be demonstrated in respiring mitochondria in the absence of ATP or can operate anaerobically with utilization of one equivalent of ATP per mole of NADPH formed. In the presence of these energy sources, the NADPH/NADH ratio can greatly exceed that predicted from the equilibrium constant. The enzymes that catalyze the transhydrogenase reaction are located in the mitochondrial inner membrane, but the mechanism is not clearly understood.

THE MECHANISMS OF OXIDATIVE PHOSPHORYLATION

The mechanism of oxidative phosphorylation has been intensively investigated in many laboratories over the past 30 years. During the past several years evidence has accumulated in favor of the chemiosmotic hypothesis, orginally proposed in 1961 by P. Mitchell. This hypothesis not only addresses itself to oxidative phosphorylation, but also applies to photosynthetic phosphorylation and membrane transport. The mechanism of photosynthetic phosphorylation in chloroplasts is believed to be similar to mitochondrial oxidative phosphorylation. In the former system, the absorption of light by photoactive centers allows reducing and oxidizing components to form; subsequent electron transfers between these components provide energy for the synthesis of ATP. Because of the important contribution of this hypothesis in understanding various aspects of bioenergetics, Mitchell was awarded a Nobel Prize in chemistry in 1978. The chemiosmotic hypothesis, however, has not been universally accepted. The chemical-coupling and conformational-coupling hypotheses, or some of their features, still merit serious consideration.

The Chemical-Coupling Hypothesis

The earliest mechanism proposed for oxidative phosphorylation is the chemical-coupling hypothesis. According to this hypothesis, the first step in energy coupling is the formation of a high-energy intermediate $X \sim B$, where B is a component of electron transport enzymes or coenzymes. The high-energy bond is consecutively transferred through common intermediates to ADP forming ATP. One version of the chemical-coupling hypothesis is shown in Figure 9. A major weakness of this hypothesis is that the proposed high-energy chemical intermediate has never been demonstrated despite many years of intensive search. Phosphohistidine, discovered in a protein in the 1960s and originally thought to be an intermediate in oxidative phosphorylation, is in fact an intermediate of the substrate-level phosphorylation in the citric acid cycle. A later suggestion of a protein acyl phosphate as an energy-coupling intermediate has been abandoned. The second shortcoming

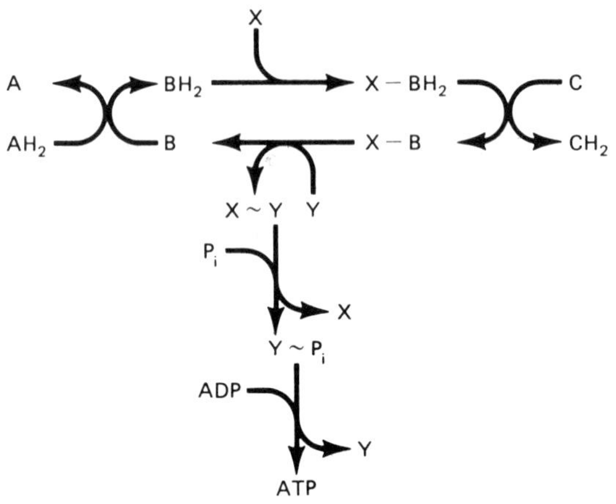

Figure 9. One version of the chemical-coupling hypothesis.

is that the chemical-coupling hypothesis provides no satisfactory explanation for the fact that an intact membrane is required for energy coupling.

The Conformational-Coupling Hypothesis

The conformational-coupling hypothesis postulates that the energy yield by electron transport is conserved in the form of high-energy conformational states in electron carriers or coupling factors; the energy inherent in this high-energy conformation is used to drive the synthesis of ATP from ADP and P_i. The high-energy conformational states have not been well defined in chemical terms, but the conformational changes occurring in the actomyosin system of skeletal muscles as ATP is bound and hydrolyzed, have been used as a model by some authors to illustrate the concept of energy-dependent conformational changes. The striking ultrastructural changes of respiring mitochondria caused by the addition of ADP (Figure 8) have previously been used as evidence in support of the conformational-coupling hypothesis. Rapid conformational changes of the inner mitochondrial membrane are also known to take place as electrons pass along the respiratory chain; they are detected by membrane-bound fluorescence probes, such as 1-anilinonaphthalene 8-sulfonic acid. It is not known, however, whether these conformational changes are the primary events in energy-coupling, or are just consequences of the energy-coupling processes. Recently, Boyer and coworkers have proposed that an energy-dependent conformational change is the key step in the synthesis and release of ATP by coupling factor F_1, as illustrated in Figure 10. F_1 is proposed to have two symmetrical catalytic sites with one site usually occupied by a tightly bound ATP. After the binding of ADP and P_i at the

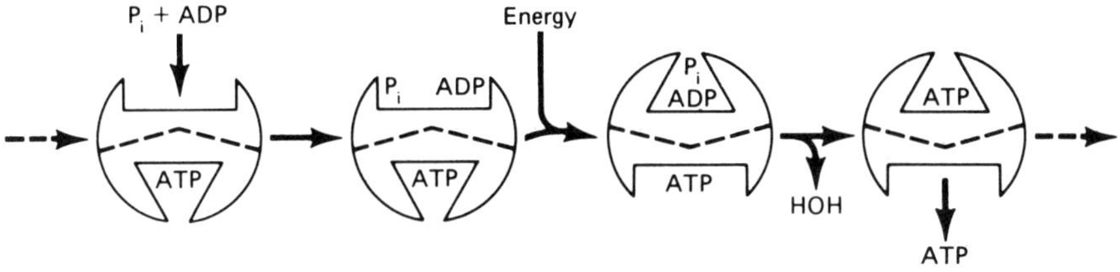

Figure 10. Steps in an alternating site model for conformational coupling to ATP synthesis. (From P. D. Boyer, *Annu. Rev. Biochem.* 46:957–66, 1977.)

second site, an energy-dependent conformational change would allow ATP to be released from the first site and ATP to form in the second site. The conformation in the second site enables ADP and P_i to be converted to tightly bound ATP without any further input of energy. However, the ATP formed is not released until the first site again binds ADP and P_i and until the key energy-dependent conformational change occurs.

The Chemiosmotic-Coupling Hypothesis

To account for the inability to identify high-energy intermediates of oxidative phosphorylation, Mitchell offered the chemiosmotic hypothesis of oxidative phosphorylation. Simply stated, the hypothesis postulates that the function of mitochondrial electron transport is to translocate protons across the mitochondrial membrane and thereby generate an electrochemical potential gradient described as protonmotive force. The protonmotive force, which consists of a pH gradient and a membrane potential, is utilized for the synthesis of ATP from ADP and P_i by the ATP synthetase complex, also known as the proton pump. Exactly how the protons are translocated and how the proton gradient drives ATP synthesis are not known, although different mechanisms have been proposed.

A recent illustration of the chemiosmotic-coupling process by the mitochondrial inner membrane is shown in Figure 11. Although there are some uncertainties, this figure serves to delineate some of our current understandings of the structure and function of the oxidative phosphorylation system. It shows that when FMN is reduced by NADH, the former receives two electrons and picks up two protons to form $FMNH_2$. Upon oxidation by Fe–S proteins, $FMNH_2$ can release two protons into the medium on the cytosol side, and two electrons return to the inner surface of the membrane. There the two electrons are transferred to two molecules of ubiquinone (Q), each of which acquires a proton from the matrix to form the semiquinone (QH·). The semiquinones then take on two more electrons from cytochrome b and two more protons from inside the mitochondrion to become fully reduced

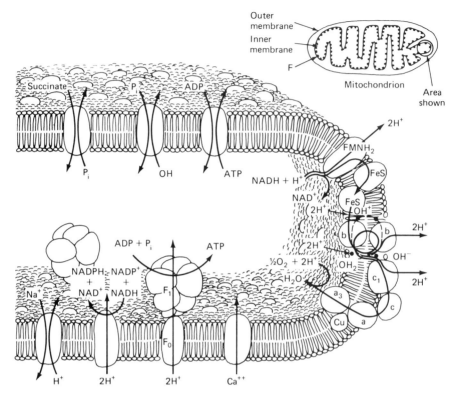

Figure 11. A schematic illustration of the structure of mitochondrial inner membrane and mechanism of oxidative phosphorylation. Features shown: (1) the electron transfer causes protons to translocate across the membrane, and (2) the protonmotive force drives the synthesis of ATP by the ATP synthetase complex. Also shown are the carrier systems that are required for the transport of ADP, ATP, P_i Na^+, Ca^{2+}, succinate, and other ions as well as the energy-dependent transphosphorylation system. (From P. C. Hinkle and R. E. McCarty, *Sci. Am.* 238:No 3, 104–23, 1978.)

hydroquinone (QH_2). Each hydroquinone gives up one electron to cytochrome c_1 and releases one proton outside. The remaining two electrons are then returned to the cycle through cytochrome *b*, and the last two of the six protons are released to the cytosol side. The two electrons are then transported through cytochromes c_1, *c*, *a*, and a_3 to oxygen, which picks up protons to form water. The proton circuit is completed by the proton pump (F_1–F_0 complex), where each pair of protons moving inward drives the synthesis of one ATP molecule from ADP and P_i. It should be noted that the sites and stoichiometry of proton translocation have not been firmly established. The above scheme uses redox reactions that are known to pick up or release protons at the active center of the enzyme or coenzyme. It is also possible that protons can become associated with or dissociated from the electron carriers owing to conformational changes during their oxidation or reduction.

Experimental Results That Are Consistent with the Chemiosmotic Hypothesis

Some of the predictions of the chemiosmotic hypothesis, such as the generation of a proton gradient across the mitochondrial and chloroplast membranes, have been verified. When the proton gradient is generated by artificial means, the protonmotive force can drive the synthesis of ATP. These experiments as well as many others are consistent with and thus supportive of the chemiosmotic hypothesis. Some of the results are summarized as follows:

Upon illumination of a suspension of chloroplasts, protons are translocated into the chloroplast. In the steady state, the electrochemical potential is expressed almost entirely as a difference in proton concentration. The membrane potential is negligible because the membrane is permeable to chloride ions. The pH gradient can reach a magnitude of 3.5 units, and the interior matrix of chloroplasts can become acidic, reaching a pH of about 4. In order to test the chemiosmotic hypothesis, Jagendorf and Uribe subjected chloroplasts to an artificial pH gradient. The chloroplasts were suspended in a pH 4 buffer to make their interior matrix moderately acidic, and then the chloroplasts were exposed to a buffer at pH8. This artificial gradient is able to drive the synthesis of ATP from ADP and P_i corresponding to 100 molecules for each ATP synthetase complex (cF_1). This experiment was performed in 1966 and was considered as one of the early evidences in support of the chemiosmotic hypothesis. Similar experiments with mitochondria were performed later by Mitchell, who demonstrated the synthesis of ATP upon subjecting mitochondria to a pH transition from basic to acidic. This synthesis occurs because the normal direction of the energy-driven proton flow of the mitochrondria is the opposite of the chloroplast. Thayer and Hinkle have also elicited ATP synthesis from ADP and P_i by imposing a combined pH gradient and membrane potential over inverted vesicles made from mitochondrial membrane. The maximum yield was about 10 ATP for each F_1. They also compared the rate of ATP synthesis in these submitochondrial vesicles driven by electron transport with that driven by an artificial protonmotive force. Initially, the artificial gradient drove ATP synthesis faster than the oxidation of NADH, but thereafter the rate of ATP synthesis driven by the artificial gradient declined as the gradient decayed. This result suggests that the rate of phosphorylation is controlled by the magnitude of the electrochemical gradient.

One of the main features of the chemiosmotic hypothesis is that energy coupling requires an intact membrane system to maintain the cross-membrane electrochemical gradient but does not require direct interactions of the oxidation enzymes with the ATP synthetase system. This has been demonstrated in synthetic vesicles. Kagawa and Racker incorporated the mitochondrial F_1–F_0 complex into the lipid bilayer of vesicles. The F_1 knobs were on the outer surface of the vesicles and were inverted with respect to normal mitochondria. ATP was able to drive the transport of protons inward in this system. Hinkle and coworkers used a similar method to study different segments of the electron transport chain separately. By addition of suitable reductants and oxidants, the electron flow in each system was found to be coupled to the transport of protons with a stoichiometry similar to that observed in mitochondria. Racker and coworkers also showed that when the F_1–F_0 complex and segments of the respiratory chain were incorporated into the vesicles, the vesicles were capable of carrying out oxidative phosphorylation. The topographic arrangement of the enzymes was found to be very important in the reconstitution of the oxidative phosphorylation system. An even more dramatic demonstration of the chemiosmotic coupling process was recently accomplished by Racker and Stoeckenius. They incorporated *bacteriorhodopsin,* a rhodopsin-like substance from the bacterium *Halobacter halobium,* into synthetic vesicles. Upon illumination, the vesicles pumped protons inward across the membrane. When the F_1–F_0 complex was incorporated into this proton pump system with the headpiece at the outer surface of the vesicles, ATP synthesis was observed upon illumination. These experiments clearly demonstrate that the electron transport chain and the F_1–F_0 complex can function independently, and the two systems can be coupled by a proton gradient across the membrane system.

The mode of action of uncouplers of oxidative phosphorylation can also be explained readily by the chemiosmotic hypothesis. For example, the classical uncoupler 2,4-dinitrophenol is a lipophilic weak acid and is believed to migrate through the lipid phase of the membrane in both the ionized and un-ionized forms; hence it can abolish the proton gradient by ferrying protons through the mitochondrial membrane. The uncoupling actions of ionophores can be considered as even more clear evidence in support of the chemiosmotic hypothesis. The common feature of the ionophores is that they allow ions to translocate across the membrane and abolish ionic gradients.

Mechanism of ATP Synthesis by the Proton Pump

Since most of the available evidence appears to be in favor of the chemiosmotic hypothesis, the mechanism by which a proton flux drives the synthesis of ATP has received some attention. Several mechanisms have been proposed. According to Mitchell's recent postulation, P_i is directly accessible to the proton flux at the active site of coupling factor (Figure 12A). The proton

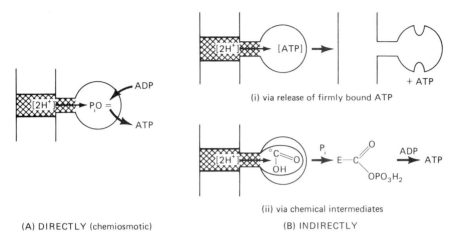

(A) DIRECTLY (chemiosmotic)　　　　　　(B) INDIRECTLY

Figure 12. Possible mechanism of ATP synthesis by the proton pump (from E. Racker, *Annu. Rev. Biochem.* 46:1006–14, 1978).

serves to activate the P_i, and this activated P_i reacts with ADP, resulting in the formation of ATP. This is known as the direct mechanism. The proton-motive force may also drive the synthesis of ATP indirectly (Figure 12B). In one version of the indirect synthesis, the proton flux is proposed to provide the energy for a conformational change of the enzyme and thus allows a tightly bound ATP to be released; the mechanism of ATP formation can be similar to that described in Figure 10. Alternatively, the proton flux may cause the formation of a phosphorylated intermediate that can react with ADP to form ATP. Racker has recently proposed a model utilizing conformational changes and a phosphoenzyme intermediate (Figure 13). In this model, coupling factor F_1 first interacts with Mg^{2+} and P_i. The binding of Mg^{2+} causes a conformational change that favors the formation of a high-energy phosphoenzyme intermediate. The proton gradient allows protons to displace the firmly bound Mg^{2+} from the enzyme, and the high-energy phosphate is transferred to ADP for ATP formation. The F_1 then releases the protons and assumes a conformation that can interact with Mg^{2+} and P_i for a second round of proton flux–driven phosphorylation. This model is proposed on the basis of studies with Ca^{2+}–ATPase and Na^+, K^+–ATPase; its applicability to the mitochondrial ATP synthesis system remains to be demonstrated.

COMPARTMENTATION AND TRANSPORT OF METABOLITES

Glycolysis occurs in the cytosol, but the citric acid cycle and oxidative phosphorylation take place in the mitochondria. Fatty acid oxidation is catalyzed

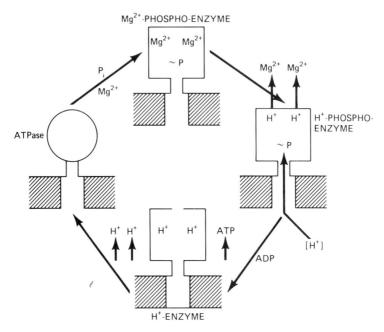

Figure 13. Hypothetical mechanism of ATP formation via a phosphoenzyme intermediate (from E. Racker, *Annu. Rev. Biochem.* 46:1006–14, 1978).

by enzymes in the mitochondria, whereas fatty acid synthesis is accomplished by cytosol enzymes. The inner membrane of the mitochondria is not freely permeable to most metabolites and nucleotides, such as ADP and NADH. Thus, it is possible to form cytosol and mitochondrial pools of various metabolites. The two pools, however, communicate quite efficiently through specific membrane transport systems known as *translocases* or *carriers*. The compartmentation and specific transport of various metabolites across the mitochondrial membrane are important in the regulation of metabolic pathways.

Specific Transport Systems of the Mitochondria

These transport systems or translocases are located in the inner membrane of the mitochondria. They are species-specific and genetically determined. Although most tissues contain transport systems for P_i and ADP–ATP, other transport systems vary in their species distribution. Some of the major transport systems of rat liver mitochondria are shown in Figure 14. They have the following properties:

ADP–ATP translocase promotes the reversible exchange of a molecule of external ADP for a molecule of internal ATP. The carrier is specific for ATP–ADP and dATP–dADP, but does not transport AMP, GTP, GDP, CTP, or CDP. The exchange of ATP with ADP involves the net movement of one charge across the membrane, and can be powered by the membrane potential. The carrier system is specifically and strongly inhibited by the toxic plant compound atractyloside and the antibiotic bongkrekic acid.

Phosphate translocase promotes the exchange of $H_2PO_4^-$ ion and OH^- ion, and is inhibited by certain sulfhydryl reagents.

Dicarboxylic translocase promotes equimolar exchanges among dicarboxylic acids such as malate, succinate, and fumarate, or between a dicarboxylic acid and HPO_4^-.

Tricarboxylic translocase can promote equimolar exchange of citrate and isocitrate as well as equimolar exchange of a tricarboxylate with a dicarboxylate.

Asparate–glutamate translocase, α-ketoglutarate–malate translocase, and pyruvate translocase: The first two translocates facilitate the exchange trans-

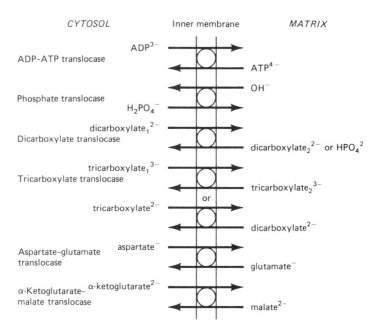

Figure 14. Transport systems of the mitochondria. (Modified from A. L. Lehninger, *Biochemistry*, 2nd Ed., Worth Publishers Inc., New York, 1975.)

port of the substrates as indicated by the names. The counter ion for the pyruvate transport by the pyruvate translocase is not known.

The Coupling of Proton Gradient with Metabolic Transport

The passive transport system described above can be coupled to the proton gradient generated by electron transport. This could allow transport of metabolites into or out of the mitochondria against a gradient at the expense of energy. An example is shown in Figure 15. A pH gradient across the membrane (basic inside) would drive the inward flow of $H_2PO_4^-$ against a gradient through the phosphate carrier. When $H_2PO_4^-$ is dissociated to HPO_4^{2-}, the outward flow of this ion can be coupled to the inward transport of malate against a gradient. The malate gradient can in turn cause the uptake of citrate by the mitochondria via the tricarboxylic acid carrier. The K^+, Ca^{2+}, and other ions are all transported in response to the outward flow of H^+ and the negative inside potential.

Shuttle Systems

There are shuttle systems that transport otherwise impermeable metabolites into or out of the mitochondria. The following are two of the best known of these systems.

The Glycerol Phosphate Shuttle. The inner membrane of mitochondria is not permeable to NADH. Thus the NADH generated in the cytosol requires a shuttle system to transfer the electron equivalents into the electron transport chain. With the glycerol phosphate shuttle (Figure 16), the electrons from NADH are transferred to dihydroxyacetone to form glycerol phosphate. The latter passes readily through the outer membrane and donates its electrons to glycerol phosphate dehydrogenase, which is a flavoprotein located on the outside surface of the inner membrane. The electrons are then captured by ubiquinone and enter into the electron transport chain. The oxidation of NADH by this mechanism leads to the formation of 2 moles of ATP per mole of NADH. This shuttle is operative in certain muscle and nerve cells.

The Malate–Aspartate Shuttle. This shuttle system is found in many tissues, particularly the liver and heart. It requires the participation of cytoplasmic and mitochondrial isoenzymes of malate dehydrogenase and aspartate–glutamate transaminase as well as mitochondrial transport systems. The operation of the shuttle is shown in Figure 17. This complex shuttle functioning in a cyclic manner is bidirectional. It can transport electron equivalents from cytosol NADH to mitochondrial NADH or in the reverse direction. With this shuttle, 3 moles of ATP can be synthesized when 1 mole of cytosol

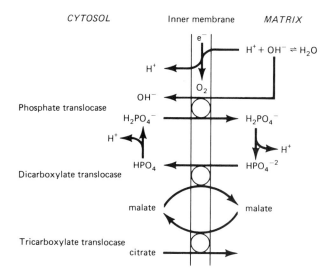

Figure 15. Energy-dependent transport of metabolites. (Modified from A. L. Lehninger, *Biochemistry,* 2nd Ed., Worth Publishers, Inc., New York, 1975.)

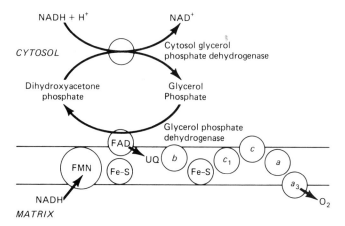

Figure 16. The glycerol phosphate shuttle. (Modified from A. L. Lehninger, *Biochemistry,* 2nd Ed., Worth Publishers, Inc., New York, 1975.)

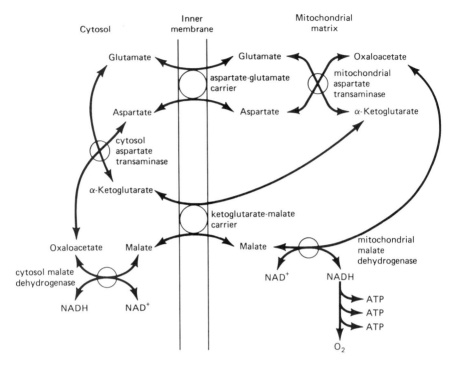

Figure 17. The malate–aspartate shuttle (from A. L. Lehninger, *Biochemistry,* 2nd ed., Worth Publishers, Inc., New York, 1975).

NADH is oxidized. In addition, this shuttle system also allows other metabolites such as oxaloacetate to be transported into and out of the mitochondria.

REFERENCES

Alexandre, A., Reynafarje, B., and Lehninger, A. L. 1978. *Proc. Natl. Acad. Sci. U.S.A.* 75:5296–5300.

Bernstein, J. 1970. *Biochim. Biophys. Acta* 205:464–72.

Boyer, P. D., Chance, B., Ernster, L., Mitchell, P., Racker, E., and Slater, E. C. 1977. *Annu. Rev. Biochem.* 46:955–1026.

Boyer, P. D., Cross, R. L., and Momsen, W. 1973. *Proc. Natl. Acad. Sci. U.S.A.* 70:2837–39.

Brand, M. D., Reynafarje, B., and Lehninger, A. L. 1976. *Proc. Natl. Acad. Sci. U.S.A.* 73:437–41.

Bridger, W. A., Millen, W. A., and Boyer, P. D. 1968. *Biochemistry* 7:3608–16.

Capaldi, R. A., Sweetland, J., and Merli, A. 1977. *Biochemistry* 16:5707–10.

Cross, R. L., and Boyer, P. D. 1973. *Biochem. Biophys. Res. Commun.* 51:59–66.

Davis, K. A., and Hatefi, Y. 1971. *Biochemistry* 2509–16.

Eytan, G. D., Carrol, R. C., Schatz, G., and Racker, E. 1975. *J. Biol. Chem.* 250:8598–8603.

Hatefi, Y., and Djavadi-Ohaniance, L., eds. 1976. *The Structural Basis of Membrane Function.* Academic Press, New York.

Hilkle, P. C., and McCarty, R. E. 1978. *Sci. Am.* 238:104–23.

Kenny, W. C., Mowery, P. C., Seng, R. L., and Singer, T. P. 1976. *J. Biol. Chem.* 251:2369–73.

King, T. E., Mason, H. S., and Morrison, M., eds. 1973. *Oxidases and Related Redox Systems.* University Park Press, Baltimore.

Lehninger, A. L. 1965. *The Mitochondrion: Molecular Basis of Structure and Function.* Benjamin, Menlo Park, California.

Lehninger, A. L. 1975. *Biochemistry,* 2nd ed. Worth Publishers, New York.

Ludwig, B., Downer, N. W., and Capaldi, R. A. 1979. *Biochemistry* 18:1401–1047.

Merli, A., Capaldi, R. A., Ackrell, B. A. C., and Kearney, E. B. 1979. *Biochemistry* 18:1393–1400.

Metzler, D. E. 1977. *Biochemistry, The Chemical Reactions of Living Cells.* Academic Press, New York.

Mitchell, P. 1961. *Nature* 191:144–48.

Mitchell, P. 1967. *Adv. Enzymol.* 29:33–87.

Mitchell, P. 1974. *FEBS Lett.* 43:189–94.

Mitchell, P., and Moyle, J. 1967. *Biochem. J.* 104:588–600.

Mitchell, P., and Moyle, J. 1967. *Biochem. J.* 105:1147–62.

Racker, E. 1972. *A New Look at Mechanisms in Bioenergetics.* Academic Press, New York.

Racker, E., and Stoeckenius, W. 1974. *J. Biol. Chem.* 249:662–63.

Thayer, W. S., and Hinkle, P. C. 1973. *J. Biol. Chem.* 248:5395–402.

Thayer, W. S., and Hinkle, P. C. 1975. *J. Biol. Chem.* 250:5330–42.

White, A., Handler, P., Smith, E. L., Hill, R. L., and Lehman, I. R. 1978. *Principles of Biochemistry,* 6th ed. McGraw-Hill, New York.

Wilson, D. F., Erecinska, M., and Dutton, L. P. 1974. *Annu. Rev. Biophys. Bioeng.* 3:203–30.

5.3. Biogenesis of Mitochondria

Leonard Baskin and Chung S. Yang

In all eukaryotic cells that use oxygen for respiration, mitochondria are present as double-membraned organelles with associated oxidative phosphorylation, Krebs cycle, and other enzymatic activities. In rat liver cells which are about 20 μm in diameter, the mitochondria are 1–2 μm in diameter, similar in size to *E. coli* bacterial cells. This chapter describes the molecular biology of mitochondrial biogenesis.

THE GENOME OF THE MITOCHONDRIA

Mitochondria are semiautonomous eukaryotic cell organelles which arise only by growth and division of preexisting mitochondria. Their propagation and assembly during the cell cycle require the contribution of both the nuclear chromosomal genetic system (haploid size 10^4–10^8 kilobase pairs) and a considerably smaller extrachromosomal or cytoplasmic genetic system (10–100 kilobase pairs) in the mitochondria. Similar to the nuclear genome, the mitochondrial genetic material is DNA (see Table 1). However, the genome of the mitochondria resides in double-stranded, covalently closed circular mitochondrial DNA (mtDNA) molecules similar to certain viruses and bacteria. Exceptions are the linear mtDNA molecules of the ciliated protozoa *Tetrahymena* and *Paramecium* (Table 1).

Within a mitochondrion, the DNA is generally localized in discrete regions called *nucleoids,* analogous to similar regions in prokaryotes. The mtDNA is often seen under the electron microscope attached to fragments of membrane following gentle lysis of the mitochondria. In HeLa cell mtDNA, the membrane fragments are always attached to the same locus on the mtDNA. Apart from this attachment, isolated mtDNA is generally not complexed with histones or other proteins (excepting possibly the replication and transcription apparatus) in the manner of chromosomes of the nucleus. Exceptions are the highly condensed mtDNA of slime molds, which appear to be complexed with a basic protein, and the mtDNA of *Xenopus* oocytes, which can be isolated in association with protein in the form of a structure reminis-

Table 1. DNA Characteristics of Some Mitochondria.[a,b]

SOURCE	DNA STRUCTURE	TOTAL DNA GENOME SIZE (KBP/HAPLOID CELL)	DNA MW (10^6 DALTONS)	ESTIMATED dsDNAs/ MITOCHONDRION	APPROXIMATE CONTOUR LENGTH (μm)
Beef heart	CD	26	10	1–2	5
Mouse L cells (fibroblasts)	CD	90	10	6	5
Rat liver	CD	90–160	10	6–9	5
Chicken liver	CD	70	10	4	5
Turnip	CD	500	70	4–5	36
Baker's yeast (Saccharomyces)	CD	60–370	49	1–4	25
Paramecium aurelia	LD	370	27	20	28
Tetrahymena	LD	370	30–36	61–74	15–18

[a] Calc. from data in Smith, p. 473.
[b] Abbreviations used: CD, circular duplex; LD, linear duplex; kbp, kilobase pairs; dsDNA. double-stranded DNA.

cent of the nucleosomes of chromatin. Although methylated bases occur, distinctive unusual bases have not been found in mtDNA. However, occasional ribonucleotides have been found in mammalian mtDNAs, rendering them alkali-labile. Their function and origin are unknown.

In alkaline CsCl gradient centrifugation, animal mtDNA separates into heavy and light strands, seen as two bands with a density difference of from 0.005 g/cc in sea urchin to 0.044 g/cc in chicken (Table 2). The density difference between the separated heavy (H) and light (L) strands is correlated with the higher thymine content of the H-strand. Exploiting the density difference between the strands to separate them, researchers have found quantitative DNA–DNA renaturation and more recently specific restriction endonuclease digestion to strongly indicate that all mtDNA molecules in a single normal organism are identical, and that mtDNA contains no major gene repetitions. The exception is *Tetrahymena,* where some strands have up to 30% of the total mtDNA present in gene duplications of unknown function. In nuclear DNA, of course, extensive gene repetition occurs.

While each organism appears to have a unique, single type of mtDNA without gene duplications, the number and packaging of mtDNA vary from organism to organism and can vary at different stages during the life cycle. The mtDNA is packaged into as few as one mitochondrion in some trypanosomes (flagellated protozoa) to as many as 3×10^5 mitochondria in some oocytes (which form ova upon undergoing meiosis). *Chlamydomonas* (green algae) haploid cells have about 46 mtDNAs (molecular weight 1.24×10^8) packaged in many small mitochondria at certain stages of their life cycle and in a few large mitochondria at other times. A typical rat liver cell has been estimated to contain more than 1000 mitochondria, each with about six to nine mtDNAs per mitochondrion (Tables 1 and 3). The number of mitochondria genes is limited by the small size of the mtDNA. Molecules of mtDNA range from about 5 μm in length (about 10^7 daltons or 15 kilobase

Table 2. Buoyant Density Difference ($\Delta\rho$) of mtDNA Heavy and Light Strands.[a]

mtDNA SOURCE	ALKALINE CsCl $\Delta\rho$ (G/ML)
Sea urchin	.005
Chicken	.044
Human	>.010
Rat	>.010
Tetrahymena	.006

[a] Data from Borst (1972), p. 338.

Table 3. Number of mtDNA per Cell.[a]

ORGANISM	TISSUE	mtDNA MW $(10^6$ DALTONS)	ESTIMATED NO. mtDNA MOLECULES/CELL
Yeast	Vegetative diploid	49	1×10^2
Mouse	L-cell line	10	1×10^3
Rat	Liver	10	2×10^3
Toad	Egg	11	1×10^8

[a] From Borst (1977), p. 32, Table II.

pairs) in animals to about 30 μm (6×10^7 daltons or 90 kilobase pairs) in pea plants (see Table 1).

THE PHYSICAL PROPERTIES OF mtDNA

Following the discovery in 1966 that the mtDNA of animal tissues consists of a stable, homogeneous population of small double-stranded closed circles (see electron micrograph, Figure 1) which are easy to isolate, the mtDNA from a variety of organisms has been characterized. Some of the physical-chemical properties obtained are summarized in Table 1.

All normal animal cells contain, to varying degrees (2–15%), catenated (interlocked) oligomers of mtDNA, that is, two or more mtDNA molecules interlocked as rings in a chain (Figure 2A). In addition to catenated oligomers, unicircular dimers consisting of two monomers identical in base sequence and linked head to tail (i.e., twice the length of mtDNA), higher unicircular oligomers, and other complex forms (Figure 2B, C) such as D-loops have been seen under the electron microscope. When isolated, these forms display different sedimentation properties, allowing identification as well as isolation (Table 4). The D-loop conformation found in some animal mitochondria has been shown to be a replication intermediate. However, the biological significance, if any, of most of the complex forms is not known. In some cases, they may be part of the replicative process, which very often involves mtDNA structural or topological changes from a closed, relaxed duplex to that of a supercoil or superhelix. Such topological tertiary winding represents an energy-consuming process and may involve various DNA-binding proteins such as the various topoisomerases and the DNA gyrase which catalyzes both relaxation and tightening of this higher-order coiling as well as unwinding of the Watson-Crick duplex during replication. Some aspects of this tertiary winding are associated with DNA complexes other than circular, duplex mtDNA molecules, including prokaryotic and eukaryotic chromosomes. Thus

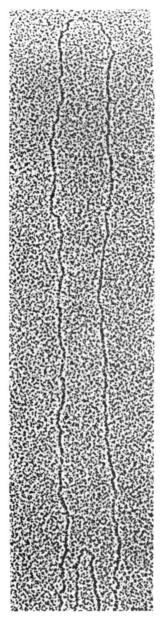

Figure 1. Circular mitochondrial DNA from chick-liver (open circular configuration) 89,440×
[from van Bruggen et al. (1966), *Biochim. Biophys. Acta* 119:439, Fig. 1d].

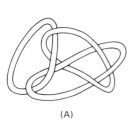 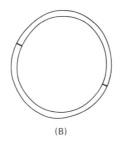 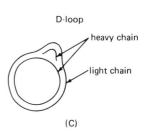

(A)   (B)   (C)

Figure 2. Complex forms of mtDNA in adult rat liver. (A) Catenated trimer. (B) Unicircular dimer. (C) D-Loop mtDNA.

the physical-chemical study of mtDNA offers insight into the coiling process of DNA.

The supercoiling of a DNA molecule is usually expressed as the superhelix density, σ, which is equal to the number of superhelical turns (τ) per ten basepairs. In naturally occurring circular DNA molecules, σ is often negative (i.e., having left-handed turns), a typical value being -0.05 (5 superhelical turns per 1000 basepairs). The presence of superhelices in circular DNA molecules can be recognized by sedimentation properties. Supercoiled duplex DNA sediments rapidly, whereas after one of the strands is nicked by brief treatment with a single-strand-specific DNase, the resulting relaxed form of the molecule sediments more slowly.

When an uncoiled DNA duplex is wound, the number of turns made (the winding number), α, equals the sum of the secondary turns, β, expected

Table 4.   Sedimentation Coefficients of mtDNA Forms.[a]

DNA FORM	$S^0_{20,w}$ (NEUTRAL pH)	S_{obs} (ALKALINE pH)
Monomers		
Open monomer	26.2	
Closed monomer (D-loop)	27	
Closed monomer (without D-loop)	37.1	80
Dimers		
Open circular dimer	33	
Doubly open catenated dimer	36.5	
Triply open catenated dimer	45.1	
Singly open catenated dimer	55.0	
Closed circular dimer	51	
Doubly closed catenated dimer	51.5	
Triply closed catenated dimer	62.7	

[a] Adapted from Clayton and Smith, p. 33, Table VII.

by the unconstrained twisting of one strand about the other (as in a Watson-Crick linear DNA structure) plus the number of superhelical turns, τ, or coiling of the duplex axis in space:

$$\alpha = \tau + \beta$$

The value of β is always positive, but that of τ can be negative (i.e., having left-handed superhelical turns).

The cyclic form of DNA such as found in mitochondria has been described for bacterial chromosomes and plasmids as well as several viruses. To date, all closed duplex DNAs isolated from mitochondrial systems have been found to have a supercoiled configuration. This property provides the DNA molecule with a decreased sensitivity to shear and also alters its chemical reactivity.

Covalently closed circular DNA molecules bind dyes with aromatic rings by a process known as intercalation, that is, insertion of their flat aromatic rings between the stacks of basepairs in a DNA duplex. The extent of such binding is operationally related to the superhelix density. Many antibiotics, drugs, and dyes are capable of inserting themselves into DNA molecules in this way. The aromatic rings of amino acid side chains in proteins which interact with nucleic acids may also intercalate into DNA helices, thus serving as a biochemical "bookmark" for DNA-requiring enzyme systems of the cell. Intercalation is often used to estimate the amount of negative supercoiling of DNA molecules. The binding of intercalative dyes such as ethidium bromide causes partial unwinding of duplex structures which induces buoyant density differences linearly related to the initial superhelix density. These differences can be measured in an ultracentrifuge by adding varying amounts of ethidium bromide to the DNA. As increasing intercalation occurs, the secondary turns of DNA are unwound (the value of β decreases in the expression $\alpha = \beta + \tau$). Each intercalated dye molecule bound unwinds the helix about $26°$. Since for a closed covalent duplex DNA α is constant, the decrease in β caused by increased intercalation leads to an increase in the value of τ. After sufficient intercalation has occurred to raise τ to zero, a minimum sedimentation rate is observed. Addition of further intercalating agent then causes positive supercoiling. Intercalation also affects the electrophoretic mobility of DNA on gels and the viscosity of DNA in solution.

REPLICATION OF mtDNA

Multiple DNA polymerases have been extracted from both the cytoplasm and nuclei of higher eukaryotic cells. They have been classified as DNA polymerase α, β, or γ on the basis of their molecular weight, sensitivity to sulfhydryl inhibitors, and reactions with the DNA template and a variety of primer molecules (see Table 5). Essentially all of DNA polymerase α

Table 5. Properties of DNA Polymerases in Higher Eukaryotes.[a]

DNA POLYMERASE	NATURAL TEMPLATE	PRIMER	MW (10³ DALTONS)	NEM-SENSITIVITY[b]	COMMENTS
α	Nuclear DNA	RNA	(Large) 120–300	+	Complexes with 60,000-dalton ATPase and DNA binding protein
β	Nuclear DNA	DNA	(Small) 30–50	−	
γ	mtDNA	DNA	(Large) 150	+	Present in relatively low amounts

[a] Data from Weissbach, pp. 25–47; Sheinin and Humbert, pp. 277–316.
[b] NEM, N-ethyl maleimide.

629

and β is associated with nuclei. The DNA polymerase γ of rat liver cells or HeLa cells appears to be mitochondrial DNA polymerase.

Although the detailed biochemistry of DNA replication remains somewhat obscure, the mechanics of replication of mtDNA are best understood in a mouse tissue culture cell line (see Figure 3). In these cells, growing exponentially in culture, the majority of the mtDNA not actively undergoing replication is in the form of a closed circular molecule (A), which contains a region in which the two circular strands do not form the Watson-Crick helical structure, but instead one strand (the "heavy" strand in alkaline cesium chloride, designated here by thick lines) becomes a single strand, and the complementary light strand (symbolized by thin lines) in this region forms a duplex with a small linear piece of DNA about 450 nucleotides long. This small single-stranded piece of DNA (represented by heavy dashed lines) sediments at 7S and is termed the 7S frament or 7S initiation sequence. The region of the molecule containing this unusual structure is termed a D-loop, and molecules containing D-loops are termed D-mtDNA. D-mtDNA has a superhelix density in solution that is close to zero, and thus has the sedimenta-

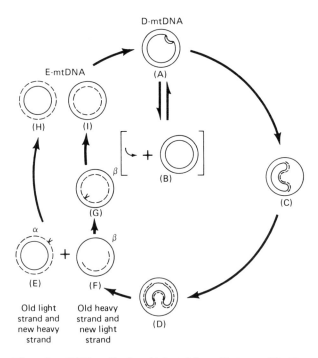

Figure 3. mtDNA replication. (Adapted from Clayton and Smith, p. 41, Fig. 12.)

tion properties of nicked circular mtDNA. It appears that a process by which the 7S fragment is lost and resynthesized occurs in the mitochondrion. If the 7S fragment is lost, during DNA isolation, the closed circular molecule (B) attains a significant negative superhelix density and has the altered hydrodynamic properties characteristic of superhelical DNA.

The replication cycle begins by using the 7S fragment as a primer for DNA synthesis, displacing the heavy parental strand as a single strand. Newly synthesized DNA is represented by dashed lines. These replicating molecules are referred to as expanding D-loop molecules (C), and can be isolated so that neither parental strand contains a nick. This, plus the topological requirements of replication, indicates that the molecule undergoes nicking–ligation events as replication proceeds. When displacement replication has proceeded at least 60% of the length of the molecule (D), synthesis of the other daughter strand, using the displaced heavy strand as template, begins and proceeds unidirectionally back toward the origin of replication (F). Because of the asynchronous nature of this replication, the heavy daughter strand (E) nears completion before the light daughter strand. Separation of the two daughter molecules occurs before completion of the light-strand synthesis, probably at a time near the completion of heavy-strand synthesis, forming the alpha daughter (E), a circle with a nick or small gap in the heavy strand, and the beta daughter, (F), a molecule with a large gap in the light strand. The beta daughter (G) then completes synthesis of the light strand, and, if not complete at separation, the heavy strand of the alpha daughter is also then completed, leaving both daughter molecules (E, G) as simple nicked ($<$) circles. These circles are then closed, forming a species called E-mtDNA (H, I) which is a closed mtDNA free of D-loops with superhelix densities close to zero. The 7S fragments are then synthesized on this E-mtDNA, again with at least one nicking–ligation event at the end of synthesis, to form D-mtDNA. The complete cycle is accomplished in about 120 min.

THE TRANSLATION CAPABILITIES OF THE MITOCHONDRION

In addition to having their own mitochondrial DNA (mtDNA) plus the enzymes necessary for its maintenance and replication, mitochondria have their own transcription system (including mitochondrial RNA polymerases), as well as their own protein synthesis apparatus complete with mitochondrial ribosomes, transfer RNAs, and the ancillary enzymes and cofactors needed for translation. The mitochondrial RNA polymerase of *Neurospora crassa* like the bacterial RNA polymerases is inhibited by rifampicin, but is insensitive to α-amanitin, an inhibitor of certain of the nuclear RNA polymerases. Like T7 bacteriophage RNA polymerase, mtRNA polymerase in most species is a single polypeptide chain with a molecular weight of 64,000 daltons. This is unlike the large multisubunit structures of nuclear or bacterial RNA polymerases. Furthermore, translation on mitochondrial ribosomes is inhibited by chloramphenicol and other antibiotics that block bacterial protein synthesis, but not by inhibitors of protein synthesis on eukaryotic cytoplasmic ribosomes.

Mitochondrial ribosomes are sometimes referred to as mitoribosomes to differentiate them from the cytoribosomes in the cytoplasm. Mitoribosomes were first identified with electron microscopy. Subsequently they were isolated and characterized. The properties of mitoribosomes are summarized with those of cytoribosomes in Table 6. Both types of ribosomes participate in the synthesis of mitochondrial proteins. A special class of cytoribosomes is bound to the outer membrane of mitochondria; this type of cytoribosomes dissociates poorly in 0.4 M KCl compared to free or endoplasmic-recticulum-bound cytoplasmic ribosomes. Mitoribosomes of animal or fungal sources, although different in size, are similar in shape under the electron microscope to bacterial ribosomes. They do not contain a 5S RNA. Subunit exchange between mitoribosomes and cytoribosomes does not occur. The rRNA of mitoribosomes is synthesized in the mitochondria by a DNA-dependent RNA polymerase. Most if not all of the 50 to 80 proteins associated with mitoribosomes are synthesized, however, on cytoplasmic ribosomes.

A considerable effort has been expended toward identifying the proteins coded for by mtDNA (the mitochondrial genome) and synthesized in the mitochondria, particularly from the viewpoint of whether they function as subunit components of known enzymes. It has been established that all the mitochondrial polypeptide chain products are associated with the inner membrane. The major enzyme constituents of the inner membrane consist of four electron-transport chain complexes plus the ATP synthetase complex (Complex V) or the oligomycin-sensitive ATPase (see Chapter 5.2). These enzymes jointly carry out the process of oxidative phosphorylation. The re-

Table 6. Some Properties of Ribosomes.[a]

ORGANISM	CYTORIBOSOMES	MITORIBOSOMES
Eukaryote:		
Rat liver	80S (60S; 40S subunits)	60S (40S; 30S subunits)
	51% protein (70–80 proteins)	75% protein
	49% RNA (28S, 18S, 5.8S, 5S)	25% RNA
Prokaryote:		
E. coli	70S (50S; 30S subunits)	
	37% protein (50–60 proteins)	
	63% RNA (23S + 5S; 16S)	

[a] Adapted from Neupert, pp. 257–296; Spirin, pp. 72–120; and Metzler.

quirement of a functional system of mitochondrial protein translation for the biosynthesis of these enzymes has been investigated in yeast grown in the presence of various prokaryotic- or eukaryotic-specific inhibitors of cytoplasm protein synthesis. Table 7 summarizes the results of these studies. Of all the enzymes examined, only the biosynthesis of cytochrome oxidase, coenzyme QH_2–cytochrome c reductase, and the oligomycin-sensitive ATPase appear to depend on both mitochondrial and cytoplasmic protein synthesis. This is indicated by the inhibitory effect of both chloroamphenicol (a prokaryotic ribosome inhibitor) and cycloheximide (a eukaryotic cytoribosome inhibitor) on the biosynthesis of these enzymes.

The biosynthetic origin of the different polypeptide chain components of the ATPase and cytochrome oxidase, and of coenzyme QH_2–cytochrome c reductase has been studied using the basic experiment shown in Figure 4. Yeast are labeled with radioactive leucine in the presence of either cycloheximide or chloroamphenicol. The cells are fractionated, and the enzyme is purified from the mitochondrial fraction either by standard procedures of protein purification or by immunoprecipitation with antiserum to the native enzyme. The radioactive polypeptide chains isolated from the purified enzyme are analyzed by SDS–polyacrylamide gel electrophoresis.

In the case of cytochrome oxidase, the three largest subunit polypeptide chains of the enzyme are mitochondrially synthesized, whereas the four low-molecular-weight subunits are made on cytoplasmic ribosomes. Similar results

Table 7. Effect of Protein Synthesis Inhibitors on the Biosynthesis of Mitochondrial Enzymes.[a]

MITOCHONDRIAL COMPARTMENT	ENZYME	INHIBITION	
		CHLORAMPHENICOL	CYCLOHEXIMIDE
Outer membrane	Cytochrome b_5 reductase	No	Yes
Matrix	Citric acid cycle enzymes	No	Yes
	β-Oxidation enzymes	No	Yes
Inner membrane	Complex I (NADH–CoQ reductase)	No	Yes
	Complex II (Succinate–CoQ reductase)	No	Yes
	Complex III (CoQH$_2$–cytochrome c reductase)	Yes	Yes
	Complex IV (Cytochrome oxidase)	Yes	Yes
	Complex V (ATPase)	Yes	Yes

[a] From Tzagoloff, p. 19, Table 1.

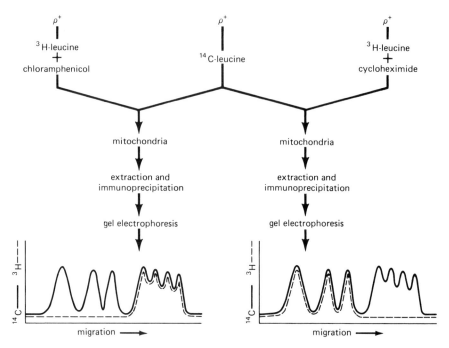

Figure 4. Experimental protocols used to identify the biosynthetic origin of subunit proteins of cytochrome oxidase labeled with ^{14}C-leucine in wild-type (ρ^+) yeast. The dashed trace represents either mitochondrial (right) or cytoribosomal (left) products of the enzyme synthesized in the presence of the two different inhibitors. (From Tzagaloff, p. 20, Fig. 3.)

have been obtained for ATPase and for coenzyme QH_2–cytochrome c reductase which have been derived both from mitochondrial and cytoplasm protein synthesis. Table 8 shows the compositions of cytochrome oxidase, coenzyme QH_2–cytochrome c reductase, and ATPase. The three complexes contain a total of eight proteins that originate in the mitochondria; these proteins account for nearly all the major mitochondrial polypeptide chain products present in the organelle.

Since mitochondrial proteins are synthesized by both mitoribosomes and cytoribosomes, coordination of these synthetic processes is important. Several models have been suggested to correlate these processes. According to one model the nuclear genome contains genes that code for the translation of several compounds involved in regulation of the synthetic mitochondrial activity. The system is controlled by a feedback mechanism in the nucleus through a specific repressor protein of mitochondrial origin. Variations in either direction ensure a high degree of coordination.

Table 8. Composition and Site of Synthesis of the Subunit Polypeptides of Inner Membrane Complexes.[a]

ITEM	ATPASE	CYTOCHROME OXIDASE	$COQH_2$– CYTOCHROME c REDUCTASE
Number of subunits	10	7	6
Number of mitochondrial products	4	3	1
Identified components	Membrane factor	Cytochrome a	Cytochrome b
Number of cytoplasmic products	6	4	5
Identified components	F_1, OSCP[b]	—	Cytochrome c_1

[a] From Tzagoloff, p. 20, Table 2.
[b] OSCP, oligomycin-sensitivity-conferring protein; F_1, coupling factor F_1 or ATPase.

MAPPING THE mtDNA GENOME

Besides biochemical methods, genetic approaches have been utilized to map the mitochondrial genome. To further understand the role of mtDNA in the biogenesis of mitochondria, mapping of the mtDNA genome has been carried out in unicellular eukaryotes such as yeast *(Saccharomyces cerevisiae)* as well as mammalian cells (HeLa cells) and hybrid mammalian cells (rat or mice and human hybrid cells). In mammalian mitochondria, both the H and L complementary strands of mtDNA are transcribed although it is not clear that the L-strand is transcribed 100%.

In 1949, Ephrussi reported finding mutants of baker's yeast, *Saccharomyces cerevisiae,* that were unable to grow on a nonfermentable substrate (e.g., glycerol), and whose metabolism depends on mitochondrial respiration and oxidative phosphorylation. When cloned on glucose-containing agar plates, these mutants could be easily distinguished by their small colony size. Such *petite* mutants were thus capable of growing on the energy derived from the glycolytic breakdown of sugars, but when replicated onto agar plates containing a nonfermentable substrate, glycerol, they were unable to grow. Ephrussi showed the petite phenotype to be caused by a mutation inherited in a non-Mendelian fashion and due to the irreversible loss or damage of a cytoplasmic factor that he called rho (hence the nomenclature ρ for petite mutants). Such ρ mutants irreversibly lose the ability to synthesize functional mitochondria. They are viable because yeast can live by glycolysis alone.

We now know that ρ is identical to mtDNA and that in the cytoplasmic petite mutants mtDNA has undergone either extensive deletions (ρ⁻ mutants) compared to the wild type (ρ⁺) or has been lost altogether (ρ⁰ mutants). A loss of mtDNA implies the loss of mitochondrial-directed protein synthesis.

Hence, all ρ^0 petites must be specified by nuclear genes and made on cytosol ribosomes. It is, therefore, interesting to see that these petite mutants still contain mitochondria-like structures under the electron microscope, including a mitochondrial outer membrane, an (altered) mitochondrial inner membrane, as well as most of the enzymes of the Krebs cycle, large sections of the mitochondrial respiratory chain, the soluble part of the mitochondrial ATPase, and enzymes involved in mtDNA and mtRNA synthesis.

Since mtDNA is by far the smallest replicon in nature that contains genes for rRNAs, tRNAs, and mRNAs, a detailed map of these genes will not only help to catalog all mitochondrial genes, but also serve to help identify regions in the mtDNA genome involved in the regulation of DNA replication and gene expression.

A large number of different ρ clones are obtained by treatment with a DNA-intercalating dye such as ethidium bromide. However, a genetic analysis of mitochondrial DNA deletions requires the identification of new classes of mtDNA mutants which are specific and less severe than the ρ mutation. One such class of mitochondrial mutants consists of antibiotic-resistant mutants. At present there are two broad classes of such antibiotic-resistant mutants (Table 9). One of these classes resists antibiotics that selectively inhibit

Table 9.   Antibiotic-resistant Yeast Mutants.[a]

1. *Mitochrondrial rRNA Mutants:*

GENETIC LOCI	AFFECTED COMPONENT
cap, ery	Chloramphenicol and erthromycin resistance, respectively. Specifies 21S rRNA (given in Figure 5 outside the middle ring, the bar indicating uncertainty in the exact positions; the open part represents an intervening sequence) of the large ribosomal subunit.
par-1	Paromomycin resistance. Thought to be the gene for 15S rRNA (given in Figure 5 outside the middle ring, the bars indicating uncertainty in the exact position) of the small ribosomal subunit.

2. *Mitochondrial (Mit⁻) Mutants:*

GENETIC LOCI	AFFECTED COMPONENT
oli-1,2,3; pho-1,2	Class I mutants, oligomycin-sensitive ATPase deficient.
cob-1,2	Class II mutants, cytochrome b biosynthesis deficient.
oxi-1,2,3	Class III mutants, cytochrome oxidase deficient.
cob + oxi	Class IV mutants, double-deficient class II and III.

[a] For references see Figure 1.

protein synthesis on mitochondrial ribosomes but not cytoplasmic ribosomes. This class includes mutants resistant to antibacterial agents such as chloramphenicol, erythromycin, and paromomycin. The genetic loci (Figure 5) involved in chloramphenicol and erythromycin are called cap and ery, respectively. Since yeast possesses two haploid mating types a and α which give rise to diploid vegetative yeast cells, it is possible to carry out genetic recombination mapping. Such data indicate that the two loci are closely linked and probably represent the gene that specifies the RNA of the large ribosomal subunit. Paromomycin is associated with another genetically unlinked locus,

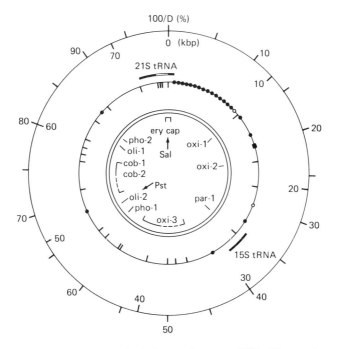

Figure 5. Genetic and physical map of yeast mtDNA. The genetic markers are indicated within the innermost double-ring. See Table 9 for explanation. The physical map in the outer ring given in kilobase pairs (kbp) is of mtDNA from *Saccharomyces cerevisiae*, strain KL14–4A. The middle ring gives the cleavages sites (τ) for restriction endonucleases *Hind II* and *III* (from *Haemophilus influenzae* RD) and *Eco R1* (from *Escherichia coli* RY 13) and the approximate position of the 4S RNA (tRNA) genes (●,○). The open circles are tRNA met genes. The arrows marked Sal and Pst indicate the single cleavage sites for restriction endonucleases *Sal 1* (from *Streptomyces albus* G) and *Pst 1* (from *Providentia stuarti*). (Adapted from Tzagoloff, p. 22, Fig. 6; Borst and Grivell, p. 706–7, Table 1 and Fig. 1.)

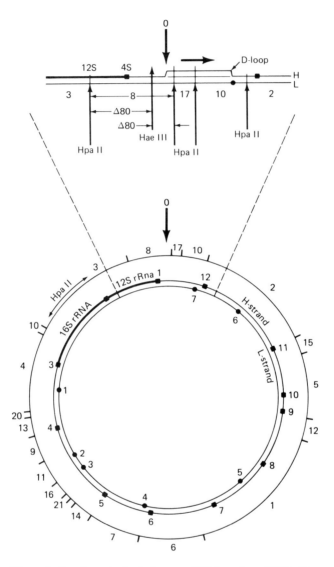

Figure 6. Genetic and physical maps of HeLa cells mtDNA. The restriction endonuclease map determined with the enzyme *Hpa II* (from *Haemophilus parainfluenzae*) has been aligned with the *Eco RI* (from *Escherichia coli* RY 13) and the *Hind III* (from *Haemophilus influenzae* RD) maps and with the map of the positions of the complementary sequences for the 12S and 16S rRNA on the H-strand and for 4S RNAs (tRNAs) on the H (■) and L strands (●). In the upper part, a region of the *Hpa II* physical map of HeLa cell mtDNA has been expanded to show the precise positions of the origin of

par-1, which is thought to be the gene for the RNA of the small ribosomal subunit.

The second class consists of antibiotic-resistant mutants that grow in the presence of inhibitors of oxidative phosphorylation, such as oligomycin. In this case three distinct genetic loci, oli-1, 2, and 3, have been found. Although all the gene products involved in the resistance have not been identified, it is assumed that the mutations result in the modification of some polypeptide components of the oligomycin-sensitive ATPase.

Four mutant oxidative phosphorylation phenotypes have also been found and are designated mit⁻ mutations (Table 9). Each is characterized by the absence of one or two of the three enzyme complexes known to have subunit proteins made on mitochondrial ribosomes. Class I, characterized by the presence of a normal cytochrome spectrum, contains mutants that are deficient in oligomycin-sensitive ATPase. Mutants in class II do not have spectral cytochrome b ($\lambda_{max} = 560$ nm) or any measurable $CoQH_2$–cytochrome c reductase. This class, therefore, is characterized by a specific loss of cytochrome b. The third class is composed of strains that lack spectral cytochromes a and a_3 and do not have cytochrome oxidase activity. The fourth class is composed of double-deficient mutants, which lack both coenzyme QH_2–cytochrome c reductase and cytochrome oxidase. The spectra in this class show the presence of only c-type cytochromes.

With these markers, it has been possible to begin to quantitatively map different ρ^- clones by statistical analysis of a large number of crosses whereby following mating, for instance, of the mit_1^- to ρ_1^-, the wild-type phenotype is restored, indicating that the DNA segment retained in ρ_1^- has the region allelic to the mit_1^- mutation, whereas the mtDNA segment retained by ρ_2^- does not.

Another useful mapping technique combines sequence-specific restriction endonuclease digestion with hybridization techniques. These studies have helped to generate the yeast and human physical mtDNA maps (Figures 5 and 6). To locate the genes for rRNAs and tRNAs on human mtDNA (HeLa cell), electron microscopy of DNA–RNA hybrids has been carried out. The two rRNA (12S and 16S) genes together with 12 tRNA (4S RNA genes) were scattered around the H- and the L-strands of mtDNA.

---

replication (vertical arrow marked ◯) and of the D-loop. The rightward arrow indicates the direction of H-strand synthesis. H, heavy strand; L, light strand. The arrows marked *Hpa II* indicate *Hpa II* cleavage sites; the arrow marked *Hae III* indicates an *Hae III* site in *Hpa II* fragment 8. The numbers in the outer ring represent mtDNA fragments obtained from restriction endonuclease cleavage. (Adapted from Crews et al., p. 193, Fig. 1.)

BIBLIOGRAPHY

Barnett, W., Schwartzback, S. D., and Hecker, L. I. 1978. *Prog. Nucl. Acid Res. Mol. Biol.* 21:143–79.

Bauer, W. R. 1978. *Annu. Rev. Biophys. Bioeng.* 7:287–313.

Birsky, C. W. 1978. *Annu. Rev. Genetics* 12:471–512.

Borst, P. 1972. *Annu. Rev. Biochem.* 41:333–76.

Borst, P. 1977. *Trends Biochem. Sci.* 2:31–34.

Borst, P., and Grivell, L. A. 1978. *Cell* 15:705–23.

Crews, S., Ojala, D., Posahony, J., Nishiguichi, J., and Attardi, G. 1979. *Nature* 277:192–98.

Clayton, D. A., and Smith, C. A. 1975. *Int. Rev. Exp. Pathol.* 14:1–67.

Freedman, J. A., and Chan, S. H. P. 1978. *Mol. Cell. Biochem.* 19:135–46.

Helinski, D. R., and Clewell, D. B. 1971. *Annu. Rev. Biochem.* 40:899–942.

Kasamatsu, H., and Vinograd, J. 1974. *Annu. Rev. Biochem.* 43:695–719.

Lehninger, A. L. 1973. *Biochemistry*. Worth, New York.

Metzler, D. E. 1977. *Biochemistry, The Chemical Reactions of Living Cells*. Academic Press, New York.

Neupert, W. 1977. *Horizons Biochem. Biophys.* 3:257–96.

Roodyn, D. B., and Wilkie, D. 1968. *The Biogenesis of Mitochondria*. Methuen, London.

Rubenstein, J. L. R., Brutlag, D., and Clayton, D. A. 1977. *Cell* 12:471–82.

Schatz, G., and Mason, T. L. 1974. *Annu. Rev. Biochem.* 43:51–87.

Sheinin, R., and Humbert, J. 1977. *Annu. Rev. Biochem.* 47:277–316.

Smith, H. H. ed. 1972. *Evolution of Genetic Systems*. Gordon and Breach, New York.

Spirin, A. S., 1973. In *Subunits in Biological Systems, Part B*, G. D. Fasman, and S. N. Timasheff, eds., pp. 72–120. Marcel Dekker, New York.

Tzagoloff, A. 1977. *Bioscience* 27:18–23.

van Bruggen, E. F. J., Borst, P., Ruttenberg, G. J. C. M., Gruber, M., and Kroon, A. M. 1966. *Biochim. Biophys. Acta* 119:439–442.

Watson, J. D. 1975. *Molecular Biology of the Gene*. W. A. Benjamin, New York.

Weissback, A. 1977. *Annu. Rev. Biochem.*

5.4. The Endoplasmic Reticulum

John J. Mieyal and Jeffrey L. Blumer

I. INTRODUCTION

The endoplasmic reticulum is the complex network of membrane-bound channels, vesicles, and connected vesicles (cisternae) that is present in all eukaryotic cells, but missing in prokaryotes. The network was so named by Keith Porter and associates at the Rockefeller Institute because it was observed in the thinnest margins of the cell, that is, in the gelled region sometimes called the ectoplasm (1). Varying in size, shape, and amount, this system of microcanals is not an isolated and closed system; rather it appears to extend from the cell membrane, to coat the nucleus and surround the mitochondria, and to connect directly with the Golgi apparatus. This description of the interconnections of the endoplasmic reticulum represents the current consensus of interpretation of histological and biochemical data; however, the associations among the membranous structures of the cell need not be so much direct physical connections as they are close spatial arrangements that allow for functional interactions. For example, it is believed that the endoplasmic reticulum is responsible for synthesizing the lipids necessary for mitochondrial membranes, and that the Golgi apparatus (see Chapter 4.7) is the site where the final stage of glycoprotein synthesis (see Section III, below) is completed, which was initiated in other parts of the endoplasmic reticulum. Other examples of functional interrelationships are discussed in the various subsections below.

The quantitative importance of the endoplasmic reticulum is evidenced by electron micrographs, which show that it is present throughout the cytoplasm. Estimates of its surface area reveal that it comprises about 50% of the total membrane surface in intact mammalian liver tissue, including plasma and mitochondrial membrane (2). The endoplasmic reticulum itself may be classified as smooth-surfaced (SER) or rough-surfaced (RER), the latter being studded with ribosomes and usually comprising the greater proportion of the ER. Discussion of the composition of the ribosomes and consideration of their role in protein synthesis are presented in Section 8 of this textbook. In general, cytoplasmic polyribosomes occur in two forms, membrane-attached (RER) and free cytoplasmic. In cells synthesizing protein for secretion (see Section III, below) the majority of the ribosomes are attached to membranes of the ER, probably via specific ribosome-binding proteins ("ribophorins," see Section II, below).

When tissues are homogenized and cellular disruption occurs, the endoplasmic reticulum usually cannot be isolated in the form of tubules as it apparently exists in the intact cell. Instead, even gentle homogenization leads to breakage of the ER membrane and the formation of closed lipoprotein vesicles of various sizes and shapes. These vesicles were named *microsomes* by Claude (5), and this terminology has been retained. Like the intact ER the microsomes can be classified as rough or smooth, and they can be separated according to whether they possess attached ribosomes. Figure 1 is an electron micrograph of a section of a rat hepatocyte, illustrating various regions of the SER and RER; a schematic representation of the ER and its disruption is depicted in Figure 2; and Figure 3 is an electron micrograph of a purified preparation of microsomes. The formation of microsomes is viewed (6) as an active "pinching-off" process that neither entraps cytoplasmic components nor allows for the release of secretory proteins from the lumen. Since the microsomal surface has a high net negative charge density, basic (positively charged) cytoplasmic proteins do become absorbed and must be removed before the actual composition of the microsomes per se can be determined (see Section II).

Delineation of the composition of the microsomes and characterization of the many enzymic activities associated with it (3) have been made possible by the various techniques of cell fractionation and histochemistry including differential ultracentrifugation, density gradient centrifugation, detergent solubilization, and immunological localization. Certain of these techniques have been described in Section 1 of this textbook, in Chapters 1.1 and 1.3. A recent critical review of techniques for the characterization of the ER was presented by De Pierre and Dallner (7). In addition, Berthet and Beaufay and their coworkers have published a series of articles over the past several years (Refs. 8-I–8-VI) that illustrate the application of all of the techniques listed above, as well as specific assays for many of the ER-associated enzymes. These references have served as the basis for the consideration of the structural features of the ER (Section II, below), but the techniques themselves will not be discussed further in this context. It is understood that conclusions concerning the subcellular localization of enzyme systems and functional metabolic pathways are only as certain as the techniques are successful for separating the individual fractions and eliminating cross contamination.

With the exception of the mature erythrocyte of animals, all eukaryotic cells have been found to contain some type of endoplasmic reticulum within the cytoplasm. The system varies according to cell type, being a characteristic

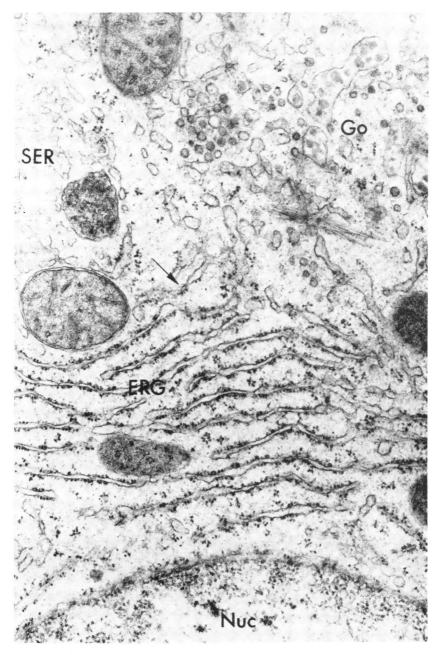

Figure 1. Portion of hepatic parenchymal cell of fasted rat. The nucleus (Nuc) is at the bottom, and part of a Golgi zone (Go) is at the upper right. An aggregate of smooth tubules (SER) is seen at the upper left, and stacks of rough-surfaced cisternae (ERG) are in the middle. The arrows indicate an area of anastomosis between rough and smooth tubules. ×25,400. (Reprinted with permission from Ref. 19, p. 1107.)

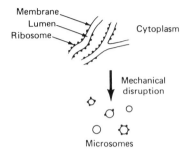

Figure 2. A schematic representation of the morphology of the endoplasmic reticulum. (Reprinted with permission from Ref. 4, p. 238.)

of differentiation. For example, electron micrographs of spermatocytes and cells involved in fat metabolism like adipose cells show many smooth-surfaced circular or oval profiles apparently scattered randomly, with only a few rows suggestive of the reticular arrangement. The other extreme is exemplified by cells that actively synthesize protein for secretion, such as plasma cells and the enzyme-producing cells of the digestive glands. In these cells the

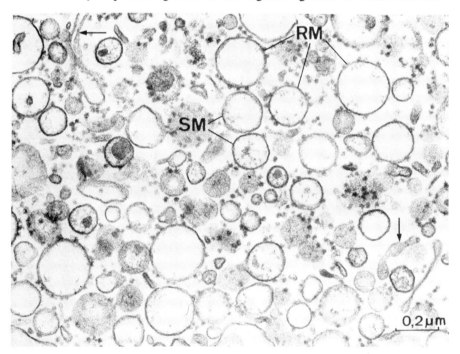

Figure 3. The microsomal fraction contains rough (RM) and smooth (SM) vesicles as well as irregularly shaped membranes (arrow). ×62,000. (Reprinted with permission from Ref. 2, p. 573.)

RER predominates and takes the form of a parallel array of flattened vesicles (cisternae). In muscle cells a highly specialized adaptation of the system called the sarcoplasmic reticulum takes the form of lacelike sleeves around the myofibrils, and it appears to be segmented in phase with the striations of the myofibrils. It is believed that this specialized system within muscle cells may serve to effect relaxation by specifically sequestering ionized Ca^{2+} (9). Thus, the ER of each different type of cell in each organism may have certain specialized structural, compositional, and functional peculiarities. A comprehensive compendium of tabulated data and corresponding literature citations on plant and animal endoplasmic reticulum systems, their lipid and protein composition, enzymes, and associated organelles has recently been published (10). By far the most widely studied ER system both structurally and functionally is that of the rat hepatocyte. Therefore it will serve as the focus of the ensuing subsections of this review, although comparisons will be made with systems from other tissues and other organisms where appropriate.

Studies of the composition of rat liver microsomes have shown that the ER membrane is ~60–70% protein, and 30–40% phospholipid by weight. This ratio corresponds roughly to ~35 molecules of phospholipid (molecular weight ~ 800) per polypeptide chain (molecular weight ~ 50,000). The lipids serve a structural role, they participate in the control of membrane permeability, and they apparently modulate the expressed activity of the various microsomal enzymes which are localized differentially within the ER structure. Rat liver microsomes are fully permeable to uncharged molecules with molecular weights as large as 600 daltons, whereas charged species with molecular weights as low as 90 daltons and macromolecules are impermeable (4). Because treatment of microsomes with proteases does not alter their barrier to macromolecules, this approach may be used in delineating the localization of enzymes within the transverse plane of the ER (see Section II, below).

A large number of enzymes and enzyme systems are associated with the endoplasmic reticulum. Among the functions of this organelle are the metabolism of drugs and other xenobiotics; the synthesis of a number of proteins including glycoproteins and lipoproteins for incorporation into the ER membrane, for transport to other intracellular membranes (e.g., mitochondrial), or for secretion; the synthesis of cholesterol, phospholipids, unsaturated fatty acids and triglycerides, prostaglandins, and ascorbic acid (vitamin C). Microsomes are also involved in the anabolic and catabolic metabolism of endogenous steroids and other molecules (11). Details of the primary functions of the ER are described in Section III, below.

An outstanding feature of the liver endoplasmic reticulum is its remarkable ability for adaptation. For example, the activities of the fatty acid desaturase and elongation enzymes not only respond to diet changes and saturation, but they decrease in diabetes and can be restored with insulin (11). Chronic administration of phenobarbital or many other drugs causes proliferation of the SER, elevation of the activities of the drug hydroxylases and glucuronide transferases, alterations in steroid metabolism, and so on. Other inducing agents more selectively alter the composition and activities of the ER (see Section IV, below).

The importance of the ER and associated enzymic activities in the economy of the cell and the survival of the organism has been emphasized perhaps most strongly by Wickramasinghe and Ville (12) who have proposed that the activity of microsomal cytochrome P450 systems of primitive organisms may have played an important role in the mutation of these forms and in species formation.

II. STRUCTURAL CONSIDERATION

A. Preparation and Characterization of Total Liver Microsomes

1. Ultrastructure of the Endoplasmic Reticulum. The ER of rat hepatocytes consists of a network of tubules, vesicles, and lamellae, about 60% of which are dotted with ribosomes. This ribosome-studded portion, generally termed the rough endoplasmic reticulum (RER), is arranged in parallel arrays of broad flattened cisternae. The smooth endoplasmic reticulum (SER), which is usually found in the region of the Golgi apparatus and then associated with deposits of glycogen, consists mainly of widely dispersed tubules and vesicles. While the morphometric characteristics of the ER may vary from region to region in the liver lobe, the membranes are generally 50–80 Å thick with the lumens of the RER and SER ~ 260 Å and ~ 430 Å wide, respectively (13).

The ER occupies approximately 15.3% of the total cell volume and has a surface area of roughly 63,000 μm^2 per hepatocyte. In comparison to other organelles this represents 37.5 times the area of the plasma membrane and 8.5 times the area of the outer mitochondrial membrane.

2. Isolation of Total Liver Microsomes. The goal of microsomal isolation is to obtain a membrane fraction in high yield that is as free as possible from contamination by other organelles and yet retains the morphological, chemical, and enzymic properties of the intact ER. In practice it is impossible to achieve all of these goals, and often a compromise between purity and yield must be made. In any event, it is crucial in interpreting biochemical data obtained with microsomal systems to be critically aware of the methods employed in their preparation.

Liver, the most often used tissue for the preparation of microsomes contains two major cell types, namely, parenchymal cells (usually termed hepatocytes) and Kupffer cells, the reticuloendothelial cells that line the hepatic sinusoids. The former are rich in endoplasmic reticulum and are relatively susceptible to disruption by the routine techniques employed for tissue homogenization. Kupffer cells contain only sparse endoplasmic reticulum and are relatively resistant to mechanical shearing forces. Thus with liver tissue the hepatocyte is the principal source of the isolated microsomal membranes (14).

The yield and purity of the microsomal fraction obtained depend on the conditions selected for initial tissue disruption and homogenization. An outline of the general procedure for preparing total microsomes is presented in Chart 1. When it is prepared in this fashion, there is little contamination of the microsomal pellet by nuclei or mitochondria. However, with vigorous homogenization fragments of the nuclear envelope (for which there is no good biochemical marker) and outer mitochondrial membrane (evidenced

Chart 1. Microsome Preparation

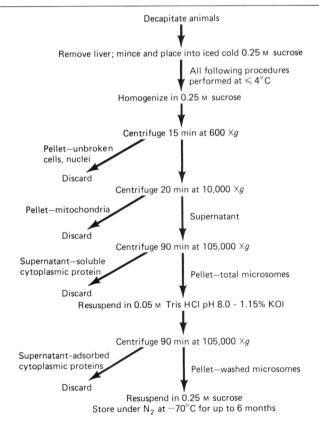

by the presence of monoamine oxidase) are found in the microsomal fraction. Biochemical evidence has also been presented that suggests contamination of microsomes by lysosomes and peroxisomes.

Major contaminants of the microsomal fraction probably derive from two sources, the plasma membrane and the Golgi apparatus (15). While no good enzymic markers exist for hepatocyte plasma membrane, the activity of the enzyme 5'-nucleotidase is often employed. With standard homogenization procedures, as much as 40–50% of the homogenate 5'-nucleotidase activity is recovered in the microsomal fraction. Nevertheless the observation that the specific content of gangliosides in microsomes prepared by standard techniques is 12 times less than that found in purified plasma membranes suggests that the extent of contamination may be far less. In either case the overall contamination would not be quantitatively large (<1.5%) owing to the abundance of ER relative to plasma membrane (14).

The Golgi apparatus is in many ways morphologically similar to the membranes of the ER. It consists of large cisternae, which remain intact only under the mildest of homogenization conditions, and small peripheral vesicles. Because of the similarity in size and density between the Golgi membranes and the ER and the ease with which the former fragment, total microsomal preparations from rat liver contain 40–50% of the Golgi content of homogenate.

Another potentially significant contaminant of total microsomal preparation is free ribosomes. Approximately half of the number found in rat liver homogenate appear later in the 105,000 × g pellet.

Various modifications of the procedure depicted in Chart 1 have been employed in attempts to increase the yield and/or purity of the microsomal fraction or to eliminate the stress of high-speed centrifugations. In addition, total microsomes are often subfractionated by various gradient techniques. When such subfractionation is anticipated, modified preparative techniques are employed in order to prevent particle aggregation which interferes with gradient resolution. The advantages and technical details of each of these approaches have been recently reviewed (15).

3. Protein Content of the Microsomal Fraction.   The protein content of the endoplasmic reticulum comprises 19% of the protein in the rat hepatocyte. By weight, protein constitutes 50 to 70% of the microsomal membrane. The nature of these protein components has been the subject of intensive investigation since microsomes were first isolated. The proteins of the microsomal membrane can be broadly classified into two categories termed "peripheral" or "extrinsic" and "integral" or "intrinsic" (16–18). Peripheral proteins are released from membranes with relatively mild treatment (e.g., by increases in ionic strength or by addition of chelating agents), they dissociate from the membrane free of lipids, and they are relatively soluble in neutral aqueous solutions. In contrast, the integral proteins require drastic treatments such as detergents, bile salts, protein denaturants, proteolytic and lipolytic enzymes, or organic solvents to effect their release from the membrane. In many instances they are lipid-associated when isolated and are usually highly insoluble in neutral aqueous buffers when freed of lipids.

For a variety of technical reasons, it is sometimes difficult to distinguish between these two categories of proteins in microsomes. Moreover, a clear distinction between microsomal peripheral proteins and microsomal membrane-associated proteins is often difficult to make. It is estimated that almost half the protein isolated in the microsomal fraction is nonmembranous. Microsomal membranes carry a high net negative charge density. Therefore, during homogenization many basic cytoplasmic proteins are adsorbed to the surface of the microsomal vesicles. Such proteins account for approximately 30% of the total microsomal protein. In most studies adsorbed protein is removed by washing the microsomal pellet with solutions of high ionic strength— typically 0.1 to 0.5 M KCl (see Chart 1).

The remaining 20% of the nonmembranous microsomal protein is comprised chiefly of proteins trapped within the microsomal vesicles. Convincing evidence has been presented indicating that these proteins are normally found in the lumen of the ER in vivo (13). As described above, during tissue homogenization the ER forms semipermeable vesicles by an active pinching-off process. It is significant that vesicles so formed appear to preserve the cytoplasmic–luminal membrane orientation typically observed for the ER in situ. Consequently, secretory proteins and lipoprotein-containing cholesterol packets are sequestered within. Essentially two major types of secretory proteins are present. One type, for which albumin is the prototype, is released into the lumen of the ER from the ribosomes and is transported in a non-membrane-bound form from the ER to the Golgi apparatus and finally secreted. The second group of proteins is the glycoproteins. They are transported along the ER to the Golgi in a membrane-bound form that facilitates the stepwise addition of hexose moieties by enzymes present on the luminal surface (6).

In contrast to the removal of adsorbed proteins, the removal of luminal proteins while maintaining functionally intact microsomal membranes presents a technical challenge. Consequently such procedures are attempted only when absolutely necessary. Three approaches to the removal of secretory proteins from microsomal vesicles have been developed (13).

The least effective of the three employs mechanical forces which temporarily disrupt the membrane. Sonication, Ultra Turrax, and the French press have been used, but all have proved generally ineffective and in some instances deleterious. Loosely bound peripheral proteins such as nucleoside diphosphatase may be released.

A second approach involves a hypotonic rupture of the vesicles. While this procedure is effective in removing 50% of the luminal protein without affecting microsomal cytochromes or enzyme activity, it results in an irreversible increase in membrane permeability to ions (15).

Perhaps the most effective means of removing secretory proteins involves incubation of microsomes with low concentrations of deoxycholate (0.025–0.05%) at 0°C for 30 min. When membranes treated in this fashion are examined by electron microscopy, it is found that vesicle size is decreased by 30%, but otherwise they look intact with ribosomes still bound to the membrane. Biochemical analysis of deoxycholate-treated vesicles suggests that relatively small amounts of integral membrane components are released (e.g., 3% of phospholipids, 5% of the NADPH-cytochrome c reductase, 6% of the NADH-cytochrome c reductase, and 2% of the cytochrome b_5) concomitant with a substantial reduction in luminal protein. Thus this technique appears to be an effective way to release the trapped contents of microsomes. One drawback, however, is that such treatment also quantitatively removes β-glucuronidase and nucleoside diphosphatase from the membranes as well.

The peripheral and intrinsic membrane proteins of the ER constitute approximately 50% of the protein in the total microsomal fraction. Among these proteins are enzymes involved in carbohydrate, protein, fatty acid, phospholipid, nucleotide, steroid, and xenobiotic metabolism (11, 20). When microsomes, freed of adsorbed and secretory proteins, are subjected to electrophoresis under dissociating conditions, 60 to 70 protein bands are identified (21, 22). Not all of these bands have been associated with a specific enzyme activity, and some have been clearly shown to represent subunits and/or isozymes of intrinsic membrane proteins. A list of the microsomal enzyme activities is shown in Chart 2.

As with all membrane systems there is considerable debate concerning the existence within the membranes of so-called structural proteins that have no enzymic function. It is conceivable that such proteins may serve to maintain the structural integrity of the microsomal membrane, but none has been characterized as such to date. Nevertheless two polypeptides of 63,000 and 65,000 daltons molecular weight without known enzymic function have recently been identified as ribosome binding sites in the RER (21). These proteins, termed ribophorins, are intrinsic membrane proteins present in a fixed stoichiometric relationship with the ribosomes, that is, 2 ribophorin I : 2 ribophorin II per ribosome. It is likely that other "organizational" proteins will be identified among the many electrophoretic bands as further insight is gained relative to the molecular mechanisms of the specialized functions of the ER (see Section III, below).

Many of the enzymic activities of the ER are linked together in multienzyme complexes such as the enzymes involved in steroid, xenobiotic, and fatty

Chart 2. Representative Enzyme Activities of the Endoplasmic Reticulum.[a]

CARBOHYDRATE METABOLISM
  Glucose-6-phosphatase
  L-ascorbic acid synthesis
  UDP–glucose dephosphorylation
  UDP–glucuronic acid metabolism
PROTEIN METABOLISM
  Protein synthesis, variety of
    peptidases, amidases
  Incorporation of iodine into amino
    acids and protein
DRUG METABOLISM
  N- and O-dealkylations
  Hydroxylation of azo dyes, various
    aromatic carcinogens, others
  N-demethylation, glucuronidation
  Side-chain and thio-ether oxidation,
    deamination, desulfuration,
    deiodination
FATTY ACID METABOLISM
  Reductive synthesis of short-chain
    fatty acids
  Acylation with acyl-CoA (ligase)
  Neutral glyceride synthesis
PHOSPHOLIPID METABOLISM
  Phosphatidic acid synthesis
  Phosphatidylcholine synthesis
  Decarboxylation of phosphatidylserine
  Transmethylation and deacylation
    of phosphatides
  Redistribution of phosphatides in
    membranes

STEROID METABOLISM
  Synthesis of cholesterol from acetate
  Interconversion and degradation of
    steroids: hydroxylations, aromati-
    zation, variety of steroid dehydrogenases
    and hydroxylases
OTHER LIPIDS
  Synthesis of glycolipids and plasmalogens
NUCLEOTIDE METABOLISM
  Nucleoside diphosphates,
    (5'-nucleotidase) NAD and NADH
    pyrophosphatase, NADase
BINDING PROPERTIES
  Azo dyes, K^+, Na^+, Ca^{2+}, iodide
    (in vitro), epinephrine and
    norepinephrine
OXIDATION–REDUCTION
  NADH and NADPH cytochrome c reduc-
    tase activity, pyridine nucleotides, non-
    specific and NADP diaphorase,
    cytochromes b_5 and P450
TRANSPORT AND TRANSMISSION
  Sarcoplasmic AMPases, cholinesterase
  Ion-stimulated (Mg^{2+}, K^+, Na^+) AMPases

[a] Chart adapted from *Handbook of Molecular Cytology*, p. 1115 (19).

acid metabolism. Others operate in a sequential fashion even though they are physically separate. For example, a drug may first be hydroxylated by the cytochrome P450–containing mixed-function oxidase system, and then conjugated to glucuronic acid by UDP–glucuronyltransferase; an epoxide product of the mixed–function oxidase system may be converted to a diol by microsomal epoxide hydrase and then conjugated by the transferase. The organization of these proteins within the microsomal membrane is discussed below.

4. Lipid Content of Microsomal Membranes.

The endoplasmic reticulum contains 48% of the total phospholipid of the hepatocyte (23, 24). Of this about 55% is phosphatidylcholine, 20–25% phosphatidylethanolamine, 5–10% phosphatidylserine, 5–10% phosphatidylinositol, and 4–7% sphingomyelin. The nature of the fatty acid moieties of these lipids varies substantially with dietary changes. In addition the microsomes contain small amounts of cholesterol (0.6 mg/g liver), triglycerides, and vitamin K. Microsomal lipids are important determinants of the microenvironment of the various microsomal systems. As such they play a key role in the modulation of microsomal enzyme activities.

It is generally accepted that the lipid portion of the microsomal membrane forms a bilayer into which the intrinsic proteins are inserted. In this bilayer the phospholipids are arranged with their polar tails extending toward the luminal and cytoplasmic surfaces and their hydrophobic heads apposed. Several of the enzymes identified as integral membrane proteins (e.g., ATPase) have been reported to require phospholipid for activity. With other enzymes such as cytochrome P450, glucose-6-phosphatase, and UDP–glucuronyltransferase the microenvironment provided by microsomal lipid is essential to maximal activity and/or stability.

In the cytochrome P450 system a relative specificity for phosphatidylcholine has been demonstrated in solubilized reconstituted systems (25). Studies employing purified phospholipases, organic solvents, and scanning calorimetry have suggested that the role of lipids in the function of this system is very much dependent on the substrate employed (26). In addition, further studies with a reconstituted microsomal mixed-function oxidase system from phenobarbital-treated rats have shown that several nonionic detergents could substitute for lipid in supporting the N-demethylation of benzphetamine. Similar observations have also been reported with respect to a reconstituted cytochrome P450 system from adrenocortical microsomes. Taken together they suggest that the role of lipid in drug and steroid metabolism may be physical rather than chemical.

The microsomal UDP–glucuronyltransferase systems demonstrate the effects of the microsomal lipid milieu (27). UDP–glucuronyltransferase activity is markedly enhanced by treatment of the microsomes with various detergents, phospholipases A_2 and C, sonication, and exposure to pH 9.7. These perturbations tend to increase both V_{max} and K_M. These observations suggest that UDP–glucuronyltransferase is normally constrained from expressing its maximal activity by microsomal phospholipids.

5. Carbohydrate and RNA Content of Microsomal Membranes.   Microsomal membranes are approximately 2–3% carbohydrate by weight. Essentially all of this carbohydrate is in the form of glycoproteins (28–30). While it is possible that these glycoproteins are simply contaminating serum glycoproteins derived from those contained within the lumen of the ER, this is

unlikely because the membrane glycoproteins differ from serum glycoproteins in structure, composition, ability to bind concanavalin A, and susceptibility to hydrolytic enzymes.

The microsomes contain both neutral sugars and amino sugars in addition to sialic acid (29, 30). The function of these intrinsic membrane glycoproteins is unknown, but it has been suggested that several intrinsic microsomal enzymes including nucleoside pyrophosphatase, AMPase, cytochrome b_5, cytochrome P450, and β-glucuronidase may be glycoproteins.

Washed microsomes contain the neutral sugars mannose and galactose in a ratio of about 2.7 : 1. Variable amounts of glucose are also present, being derived either from the sucrose used in their preparation or glycogen. The major amino sugar is glucosamine, which is present in amounts equivalent to the most abundant neutral sugar mannose.

Almost 60% of the total hepatocellular RNA is found associated with the ER (13). This RNA is primarily ribosomal (28S and 18S) in type. Its structure and function will be covered in detail in Section 8 of the text.

B. Structural Heterogeneity of Microsomal Membranes

1. General Considerations.   Homogenization of rat liver results in the formation of microsomes from the membranes of the ER by an active pinching-off process. This breakage occurs transversely, that is, perpendicular to the plane of the lipid bilayer. Isolated microsomes are clearly very different morphologically from the intact ER. Therefore the relevance of in vitro studies to in vivo structure might be questioned. Nevertheless, evidence suggests that despite the fragmentation a certain degree of structural integrity is maintained (4, 6, 13, 15). When viewed by electron microscopy, microsomal vesicles have ribosomes only on their outer surfaces. Biochemical studies indicate that secretory proteins, such as albumin, known to be present in the lumen of the ER are located inside of the vesicles. Thus it appears that the outside of the microsomal vesicle corresponds to the cytoplasmic surface of the ER and the inside to the luminal surface.

It is also possible that during homogenization vesicles might fuse, forming vesicle hybrids, and thus distort any biochemical heterogeneity in the lateral plane. Two types of evidence suggest that this does not occur to any appreciable extent. First, it is possible to isolate smooth and rough microsomes in the approximate ratio expected from morphological studies of intact tissues (4, 6, 13, 15). Second, when rough microsomes are sonicated in a solution of smooth microsomes previously labeled in vivo with [3H] glycerol or [14C] leucine, little or no radioactivity can be detected in the rough microsomes when they are reisolated (13, 21).

In general, therefore, studies of biochemical heterogeneity among microsomal membranes in vitro are considered to reflect accurately the biochemical heterogeneities of the ER membranes in vivo. The asymmetrical distribution of protein, lipid, and carbohydrate moieties within biological membranes is not a new concept. Such heterogeneity has been well documented for erythrocyte, reticulocyte, and inner mitochondrial membranes and hepatocyte plasma membranes as well (4). The asymmetric distribution of the various membrane components may be vital to the functional integrity of the various microsomal enzyme systems.

2. Heterogeneity in the Lateral Plane.   Early attempts to subfractionate the ER concentrated on separating smooth and rough microsomes. The heterogeneous distribution of ribosomes along the membranes of the ER constitutes the major qualitative difference along the membranes of the ER. While the size distributions of the RER and SER vesicles are heterogeneous and overlapping, they do show a small but significant difference in density distribution. The SER has an equilibrium density of 1.10–1.18 g/cm^3 in sucrose, whereas the rough vesicles have a density of ~1.2. Separation of rough and smooth vesicles is generally achieved by centrifugation on discontinuous sucrose gradients in the presence of CsCl. This procedure takes advantage of both the differences in density and the differential effect of monovalent cations on the state of aggregation of membranes derived from the SER and RER. The affinity of the RER for Cs^+ is appreciably greater than that of the SER. It is thought that the binding of small amounts of Cs^+ by the RER decreases their surface charge, causing them to aggregate and thus increasing their sedimentation velocity four- to ninefold.

A list of characteristics that distinguish rough from smooth microsomes is presented in Chart 3. Virtually all of the differences listed are quantitative rather than qualitative. As described previously, the major qualitative difference between the SER and RER is the presence of ribosomes. Recently electrophoretic analysis of these microsomal subfractions has led to the recognition of two protein bands present in membranes of the RER and absent from the SER. These proteins, termed ribophorins, have subunit molecular weights of 63,000 and 65,000 and appear to function in ribosome attachment (21).

A great deal of effort has been expended in search of biochemical differences between rough and smooth ER. However, histochemical, immunochemical, and biochemical techniques have failed to disclose any qualitative differences in enzyme activity between rough and smooth microsomes. On the other hand, quantitative differences are abundantly reported.

It is difficult to assess the significance of these quantitative differences. Discrepancies in the literature may be related to the technical skill required to prepare good rough and smooth microsomal fractions, problems in enzyme assay, and the effects of storage and dilution, which may differentially affect

Chart 3. Comparative Characteristics of the Membranes of the Rough and Smooth Endoplasmic Reticulum.[a]

PROPERTY	ROUGH	SMOOTH
I. Physico-chemical		
Net negative charge	High	Low
Monovalent cation affinity	High	Low
Equilibrium density	High	Low
Tendency to aggregate	Less	More
II. Composition		
RNA	High	Low
Ribosomes	Present	Absent
Ribophorins	Present	Absent
Dolichol phosphate	High	Low
Galactose, sialic acid	Low	High
III. Functional		
Protein synthetic capability	Present	Absent
Appearance of secretory protein after in vivo labeling	First	Later
Developmental expression of electron transport and glucose-6-phosphatase activities	First	Later

[a] Adapted from Ref. 13.

various enzyme activities. In addition, microsomal enzyme activities and their distribution are markedly affected by the physiological state of the animals (31, 32). When all of these caveats are considered, results to date suggest that the enzyme activities in the rough and smooth vesicles (except for activities associated with ribosomes) are both qualitatively and quantitatively similar. Moreover, heterogeneities *within* the rough and smooth microsomal fractions are greater than the differences between them.

Further subfractionation of rough and smooth microsomes based on size and/or density has also been used in an effort to demonstrate biochemical heterogeneity in the lateral plane. Heterogeneous distributions have been reported for the components of both the NADH- and the NADPH-dependent electron transport chains, glucose-6-phosphatase, nucleoside diphosphatase, ATPase, UDP–glucuronyltransferase, and esterase (2). The starting preparations for such studies have included total microsomes, rough microsomes, and smooth microsomes.

The most thorough and analytical study of the subfractionation of total microsomes was that of Beaufay and his coworkers (8). In their studies microsomes were centrifuged to near-equilibrium in various gradients. In all of their systems the following activities or contents, NADPH–cytochrome c reductase, NADH–cytochrome c reductase, cytochrome P450, cytochrome

b_5, and aminopyrine-N-demethylase (termed group b enzymes), showed similar distributions; and glucose-6-phosphatase, nucleoside diphophatase, esterase, β-glucuronidase, and UDP–glucuronyltransferase (termed group c enzymes) were distributed similarly but in fractions different from group b enzymes. It was found that the median density of the vesicles enriched in group c enzymes was greater than the median density of the vesicles enriched in group b enzymes. Further, when the vesicles were treated under conditions that detach ribosomes, a more marked reduction in the median density of group c enzymes than group b enzymes was noted, suggesting that the former might be concentrated in ribosome-rich portions of the ER.

These observations of Beaufay et al. have been substantiated by studies of subfractions of the RER in which the electron transport chains were found to be relatively more concentrated on rough microsomes with fewer ribosomes. The phosphatase and transferase were likewise enriched in the heavier subfractions.

Treatment of either isolated smooth or rough vesicles by sonication, which dramatically reduces their size, and their subfractionation on the basis of density have revealed markedly different distributions for the two pyridine nucleotide-dependent electron transport chains.

The phospholipid-to-protein ratios in washed rough and smooth microsomes and the subfractions thereof are similar (i.e., ~0.4). All five major phospholipids found in total microsomal fractions are present in both rough and smooth membranes, and no quantitative differences in distribution are apparent. Microsomal neutral lipid content is also similar in rough and smooth membranes. Some of the data reported suggest that smooth membranes are enriched in cholesterol and triglycerides compared to rough membranes, but the possibility of contamination by plasma membrane fragments and cytosol lipids was not completely eliminated (23).

Both rough and smooth vesicles are rich in protein-bound mannose. On a phospholipid basis, the SER appears to be relatively mannose-enriched. A similar pattern of distribution is observed when galactose is studied. However, when the mannose-to-galactose ratio among total microsomes, smooth vesicles, and rough vesicles is compared, the ratio in the rough microsomes is about 1.7 times that of the smooth. The distribution of microsomal glucosamine is similar to galactose. Sialic acid, on the other hand, is two times more concentrated in the smooth than in the rough membranes.

Thus, studies of lateral asymmetry in the membranes of the ER have generally revealed a biochemical heterogeneity in which the differences in membrane composition tend to be quantitative rather than qualitative. The role of these quantitative differences in the multifarious functions of the ER remains to be elucidated. Clearly, more investigation into the functional roles of the carbohydrate and lipid moieties is required before these membrane asymmetries can be fully understood.

3. Heterogeneity in the Transverse Plane. The distinction between integral and peripheral proteins has already been discussed. Integral proteins must generally be solubilized with agents that disrupt membrane structure. In addition, it appears that some if not all of these intrinsic membrane proteins are amphipathic, and their binding to microsomal membranes has been studied in detail (4, 6).

Cytochrome b_5 is an intrinsic membrane protein that functions as part of the NADH-dependent electron transport system (see Section III, below). It can be solubilized from the membrane by trypsin treatment or by treatment with various detergents. The enzyme can be purified after either solubilization procedure. In the former instance, the t-b_5 has a molecular weight of about 11,000, while in the latter, the d-b_5 has a molecular weight of about 16,700. Both forms are catalytically active.

The elegant work of Strittmatter (33) and Sato (34) has shown that an extra 44 amino acid residues present in the d-b_5 but not in the t-b_5 is responsible for "anchoring" the hemoprotein to the microsomal membrane. These amino acids are about 60% hydrophobic, and the d-b_5 can be specifically reincorporated into microsomal membranes to yield specific contents 5 to 20 times above constitutive levels. The t-b_5 cannot be reincorporated at all, nor can the d-b_5 be reincorporated into erythrocyte membranes.

These observations suggest that the hydrophobic tail is responsible for the specific interaction between the cytochrome and the microsomal membrane. Moreover, if one considers the permeability properties discussed in the introduction and the maintenance of vectoral (inside–outside) integrity in the active pinching-off process involved in microsome formation from the ER, the above results suggest that cytochrome b_5 resides on the cytoplasmic side of the ER membrane.

Similar results have been reported with respect to binding of the NADH–cytochrome b_5 reductase to the microsomal membrane. Studies of the NADPH-dependent cytochrome c reductase have revealed that the detergent-solubilized enzyme but not the trypsin-solubilized enzyme can be combined with purified cytochrome P450 to reconstitute active drug-metabolizing systems, apparently because the detergent-solubilized form retains a required hydrophobic peptide (106). Thus it seems that at least some of the intrinsic membrane proteins possess hydrophobic moieties, both to anchor them to the membrane and to modulate certain intramembranous protein–protein interactions.

In the above sections the biochemical heterogeneity of the microsomal membrane has been discussed in terms of the lateral plane, but it can be appreciated that the information provides little insight with regard to the juxtaposition or mutual orientation of the various enzymes, lipids, or carbohydrates that comprise the integral components of these membranes. The amphipathic nature of certain of the intrinsic membrane proteins coupled with the apparent functional differences between the cytoplasmic and luminal sides of the membrane suggest a marked biochemical asymmetry in the transverse plane. In fact, recent studies employing a variety of biochemical techniques have suggested that the distribution of protein and lipid within the microsomal membrane may be asymmetric (6, 13, 35).

The investigative efforts employed to describe these membrane asymmetries have involved treatment with proteolytic enzymes, labeling with ^{125}I, use of antibodies to specific membrane proteins, studies of impermeable substrates and enzyme latency, localization of products, and most recently the use of low concentrations of detergents for selective release of proteins from the cytoplasmic portion of the membrane and/or the introduction of proteolytic enzymes into the vesicle for the release of luminal components (2).

Treatment of microsomal membranes with trypsin quantitatively released cytochrome b_5 and NADPH–cytochrome c reductase. NADH–cytochrome b_5 reductase and nucleoside diphosphatase were also solubilized, and 50 to 60% of the cytochrome P450 was denatured. At the same time microsomal esterase, nucleoside diphosphatase, UDP–glucuronyltransferase, and 75 to 80% of the glucose-6-phosphatase were unaffected. Because microsomes are not permeable to macromolecules, it is assumed that the trypsin was exerting its effect only at the outer surface of the microsomal vesicle. Thus the enzymes solubilized by the treatment were considered to reside on the cytoplasmic surface of the membrane. This conclusion was further substantiated when microsomes were treated with trypsin in the presence of low detergent concentrations in order to permit trypsin access to the enzymes on the luminal surface of the vesicles. This treatment resulted in greater reduction in esterase, nucleoside diphosphatase, and glucose-6-phosphatase activities than that achieved by either agent alone.

The labeling of microsomal membrane proteins with ^{125}I using lactoperoxidase has been widely employed. The results obtained from such experiments have suggested a more uniform distribution of the proteins within the microsomal membranes than those employing proteolytic enzymes. However, the results of these experiments have been seriously questioned. Treatment of microsomes with lactoperoxidase, iodide, and hydrogen peroxide was found to result in the peroxidation of microsomal phospholipids, which likely resulted in alterations in membrane permeability and structure. This could easily explain the labeling of proteins not ordinarily ascribed to the outer surface.

Antibodies are large protein molecules (molecular weight $\sim 160,000$) that are generally hydrophobic and thus not expected to cross biological membranes. Inhibition of a microsomal enzyme activity by a specific antibody provides reasonably good evidence for the localization of the enzyme on the cytoplasmic surface of the ER. This approach has been taken with several microsomal enzymes. The catalytic activities of cytochrome b_5, NADH–cytochrome b_5 reductase, and NADPH–cytochrome c reductase are markedly inhibited by treatment of microsomes with specific antibodies, while antibodies to nucleoside diphosphatase and esterase had no effect on their respective enzyme activities.

Antibodies have also been used to examine the location of enzymes within the ER membranes by electron microscopy. The antibodies are labeled with ferritin, and then the antibody–membrane complexes "stained" with anti-ferritin antibody. This approach has been used to localize cytochrome b_5 (8-VI) and NADPH–cytochrome c reductase to the cytoplasmic surface (36).

The permeability characteristics of microsomal membranes have been described above. The restrictions noted for small ionized molecules and macro-molecules suggest that the accessibility of substrate and cofactors to enzyme active sites may be limited by membrane properties. Thus molecules such as NADH, NADPH, and cytochrome c penetrate little if at all into microsomal membranes. The full expression of NADH and NADPH–cytochrome c reductase activities in intact microsomes supports their location on the cytoplasmic side of the membrane. In contrast, only ~20% of microsomal nucleoside diphosphatase activity is expressed in intact microsomes, and very little glucose-6-phosphatase and UDP–glucuronyltransferase activity is detectable. However, the full expression of these enzyme activities may be obtained after treatment with detergents or phospholipases or after mechanical disruption using an Ultra Turrax Blender. It is, however, difficult to draw conclusions regarding intramembranous localization after these latter treatments because of their many possible effects on membrane integrity.

Probably the most useful technique for elucidating protein asymmetry in the transverse plane is a combination of low detergent and trypsin or chymotrypsin. This technique has been employed most recently by Nilsson and Dallner (35), and the following represents their conclusions with respect to enzyme distribution in the transverse plane. They suggest that NADPH–cytochrome c reductase, cytochrome b_5, and at least part of the GDP–mannose-transferase system are located on the cytoplasmic surface of the membrane. At the inner surface are found nucleoside- and glucose-6-phosphatase. AMPase and UDP–glucuronyltransferase are thought to be buried within the lipid bilayer inaccessible to attack by proteolytic enzymes from either membrane surface. In this study cytochrome P450, the most abundant enzyme in the ER, shows a unique homogenous distribution in the transverse plane. They postulate that since it occurs in multiple forms, these forms may be differentially compartmentalized in different parts of the membrane.

A general summary of the transverse localization of various microsomal enzymes and the criteria used for making the assignment is presented in Chart 4.

Chart 4.   Asymmetric Distribution of Microsomal Enzymes and Lipids in the Transverse Plane.

CYTOPLASMIC SURFACE	INNER MEMBRANE	LUMINAL SURFACE
Cytochrome P450	Cytochrome P450	Cytochrome P450
Phosphatidylcholine	Phosphatidylcholine	Phosphatidycholine
Cytochrome b_5	DT-diaphorase	Esterases
GDP–mannosyl transferase	Nucleoside pyrophosphatase	Glucose-6-phosphatase
NADPH–cytochrome c reductase	Phosphatidylinositol	β-Glucuronidase
NADH diaphorase	Sphingomyelin	Nucleoside diphosphatase
5'-Nucleotides	UDP–glucuronyltransferases	
Nucleoside triphosphatase		
Phosphatidylethanolamine		
Phosphatidylserine		

Transverse membrane asymmetry with respect to phospholipid content has been studied in a manner similar to that used for studying protein asymmetry except that various phospholipases have been employed along with or instead of proteases (13, 35). These studies are performed in the presence of albumin to bind the lysophospholipids produced. Under carefully controlled conditions it would appear that about 90% of the phosphatidylserine and phosphatidylethanolamine are located at the cytoplasmic surface along with roughly 50% of the phosphatidylcholine. Phosphatidylinositol and sphingomyelin appear to be accessible to attack by phospholipase only after disruption of the membrane by detergent. Therefore it is concluded that these lipids are buried within the membrane bilayer.

Still another aspect of phospholipid asymmetry in the transverse plane relates to certain physical-chemical differences between lipids in close proximity to various microsomal enzymes and those in the bulk phase. Most of these studies involve electron spin resonance spectroscopy of spin labels of lipid molecules (37).

Studies of microsomal cytochrome–phospholipid interaction have suggested that these proteins restrict the free lateral mobility of the membrane phospholipids in their vicinity, and that these lipids are more highly organized than those in the bulk phase. These studies have led to the suggestion that microsomal cytochrome P450 is enclosed in a phospholipid "halo" which is more rigid than the bulk of microsomal lipids. This halo is thought to contain less than 20% of the microsomal phospholipids and to undergo a crystalline–liquid crystalline phase transition at 32°C compared to 0°C for the bulk phase. It is interesting that critical effects on the K_M for microsomal oxidation of aniline and aminopyrine, two lipid-soluble substrates, are seen at 34–36°C and 27–29°C respectively 38, 39).

III. CHIEF FUNCTIONS UNIQUE TO THE ENDOPLASMIC RETICULUM

A. Macromolecule Synthesis and Transport

The proteins produced by the endoplasmic reticulum of liver may be classified in two main categories, namely, proteins for intracellular use and plasma proteins for export to the circulation. The latter type includes albumin, glycoproteins like prothrombin and fibrinogen, and high- and low-density lipoproteins. Since albumin is the major secretory protein of the liver and is relatively easily purified, the mechanism of its synthesis, transport, and secretion into the blood has been the most fully characterized (40). On the other hand, much of our knowledge of the overall secretory process for export proteins has come from studies of the mammalian pancreatic exocrine cell and related cells which are specialized to produce such proteins in large amounts and at high rates. In general, the process follows the established pathway (RER → SER → Golgi system → blood), and it may be divided into six steps: synthesis, segregation in the cisternal space of the RER, intracellular transport, concentration of the proteins in secretory granules, intracellular storage, and exocytosis (41). In the initial part of the process, the exportable proteins are synthesized in the cytosol on polysomes attached to the endoplasmic reticulum. At some point during elongation of the nascent polypeptide chain, it is vectorally inserted through the RER membrane toward the cisternal space. This insertion is apparently dependent on a specific amino acid sequence ("signal") originally incorporated into the primary structure of the protein, which serves as a recognition site for a complementary site on the RER membrane (42). The completion of the synthesis of the glycoproteins takes place in a sequential process during their transport in the channel system. The first sugar added (at least for prothrombin and fibrinogen) is glucosamine covalently bound to asparagine by an N-glycosidic linkage. The glycoprotein is in a free form in the SER where additional glucosamine moieties may be attached.

The mechanism of glycosidic bond formation with the developing glycoprotein apparently involves the intermediacy of phosphorylated forms of a polyprenoid substance dolichol (16–23 isoprene units), which serves to transport sugars through the lipid barrier of the ER and activate them for coupling to the glycoprotein (43). The completion of the oligosaccharide chain apparently takes place in the Golgi system where the terminal sugars galactose, fucose, and sialic acid are attached.

In a similar manner, assembly of the various lipoproteins takes place in the ER lumen where appropriate molecules of polypeptides released from ribosomes interact with triglycerides, cholesterol, and phospholipids. Each of these types of lipid is also synthesized within the endoplasmic reticulum as part of its main functions (11). The intracellular transport process itself from RER to the Golgi complex appears to operate independently of protein synthesis (i.e., the latter can be blocked without affecting the former), but it is an energy-dependent process (i.e., ATP production is required). In contrast, the concentration of the export proteins in the secretory granules does not require energy; rather it is the result of the interaction of the predominantly basic secretory proteins with large sulfated peptidoglycan polyanions that were synthesized in the Golgi complex. After their formation the secretory granules reside in the cytoplasm for varying times until an appropriate stimulus (hormone or neurotransmitter) causes large and sudden increases in the rate of discharge (exocytosis). The process of exocytosis involves fusion of the secretion granule membrane to the luminal plasma membrane; then fission of the fused membranes leads to the formation of an opening through which secretory discharge occurs. The sequence of events from stimulus to discharge ("stimulation–secretion coupling") is calcium-dependent and energy-dependent, and it involves elevation in the intracellular level of a cyclic nucleotide in response to hormone–receptor interaction (44). The ERs of various cells carry out the processing of different export proteins in different ways. For example, some proteins like albumin are completed at the ribosomal level, whereas others are completed during intracellular transport. Although albumin and certain lipoproteins are concentrated and to a limited degree stored in the mammalian hepatocyte, their discharge does not appear to be hormonally controlled.

Besides the synthesis and transport of secretory proteins, the ER is also involved in the synthesis of various phospholipids, glycoproteins, lipoproteins, and enzymes for incorporation into the ER membrane itself as well as for other intracellular membranes including mitochondrial, nuclear, and plasma membranes. A separate theory entitled the "trigger hypothesis" has been proposed to describe the mechanism whereby such integral proteins are fitted into their appropriate functional conformations and localizations within the membrane (107). Moreover the pathway described above for serum glycoprotein synthesis apparently does not apply to intracellular membrane glycoproteins because instead of a stepwise addition of sugar moieties, the entire oligosaccharide core is transferred to the protein acceptor as a unit. After addition of the terminal sugars galactose and sialic acid in the Golgi complex, the completed products are released to the cytoplasm where they may aggregate with lipids or lipoproteins before being incorporated into the appropriate membranes. The incorporation appears to be enzymically mediated, and it represents an exchange reaction without a net increase of the membrane glycoproteins (6). The transfer of lipids from the ER to other intracellular membranes also appears to be stimulated by cytoplasmic effectors; for example, phosphatidyl choline is transported through the cytoplasm sequestered in a protein molecule (45).

B. Electron Transport Systems

Mammalian hepatic endoplasmic reticulum contains two electron transport systems, whose components are depicted below in a fashion representative of their separate functions. In isolation each system can operate independently of the other, but within the ER there are notable interactions between the sytems, which will be mentioned below as each system is considered.

I. $NADPH \rightarrow$ cytochrome $\rightarrow$ cytochrome P450 $\rightarrow O_2$
    P450 reductase
    (FP$_1$)

II. $NADH \rightarrow$ cytochrome $\rightarrow$ cytochrome $b_5 \rightarrow$ fatty acid $\rightarrow O_2$
    b_5 reductase   desaturase
    (FP$_2$)   ("CN-sensitive
                                                        factor")

1. Cytochrome P450 Systems. The oxidative metabolism of many endogenous substances such as steroids, fatty acids, and bile acids, as well as the metabolism of a wide variety of drugs and environmental agents including insecticides and polycyclic hydrocarbon carcinogens, occurs primarily within the endoplasmic reticulum of mammalian hepatocytes. The fact of metabolic alteration of exogenous agents has been known for some time (46), but our knowledge of the localization and characterization of the systems responsible for such metabolism has developed only over the last several decades, and it is still evolving (47–49). The operational metabolic system of the microsomes is composed of at least two protein components. One of these, the terminal electron acceptor, was characterized as a hemeprotein and a b-type cytochrome, and it was named cytochrome P450 because in the reduced (ferrous) form the Soret absorption band of the carbon monoxide complex (P450^{2+}– CO) appears at 450 nm. Most other hemeproteins like hemoglobin which bind CO display Soret maxima for the ferrous–CO complex at ~420 nm. The unusual character of P450 has been attributed to occupation of the sixth ligand position of the heme iron atom by sulfur (cysteine or methionine moiety of the apoprotein) (50). Isolation and purification of P450 from liver microsomes of various species has revealed that multiple isozymes of P450 exist. There is evidence for as many as six to seven different forms in rat liver microsomes (51) and in rabbit liver microsomes (52). The isolated P450s appear as aggregates of molecular weight ~280,000–600,000; each heme-containing subunit of the various isozymes has a molecular weight of ~50,000.

The other protein component of the metabolic system serves to shuttle electrons between the required cofactor NADPH and cytochrome P450. Hence it is named the NADPH-dependent cytochrome P450 reductase. It is a flavoprotein containing two prosthetic groups, one FAD and one FMN group per enzyme molecule of molecular weight ~78,000 (53). In order to reconstitute full hydroxylase activity with isolated P450 and reductase, a lipid component (phosphatidylcholine) must be added to the two protein components before combination with substrate and NADPH. Although recent evidence from studies of such a reconstituted system suggested that the most efficient combination of the two protein components is a 1:1 complex (54), the stoichiometry within mammalian microsomes shows a large excess of cytochrome P450 molecules; that is, the ratio of cytochrome P450 to P450 reductase molecules may be ≥ 10, depending on the species and the method of estimating the content of reductase molecules (55, 56). This imbalance suggests either that each reductase molecule may serve many P450 molecules, or that not all of the P450 molecules are involved in metabolism. In conjuction with the latter thought, a provocative hypothesis has been offered that P450 may serve as a tissue O_2-carrier like myoglobin (57). The antithesis, namely, that the blood O_2-carrier hemoglobin could serve in certain circumstances as a monooxygenase enzyme like P450, has also been proposed (58, 59).

Cytochrome P450 is not unique to the liver endoplasmic reticulum. In fact, much of the early characterization of the P450 system was carried out in the laboratories studying steroid metabolism by adrenal microsomes (60). To date, mixed-function oxidase activity has been demonstrated in various mammalian tissues including liver, adrenal gland (cortex microsomes and mitochondria), kidney, lung, intestine, mammary gland, testes, spleen, skin, aorta, placenta, reticulocytes, lymphocytes macrophages, platelets, brain, and so on. In addition, similar activity has been found in insects, various microorganisms, yeast, and plants. In many but not all of these cases, cytochrome P450 content has been demonstrated specifically. (Listings of the various sources of the mixed-function oxidase systems and their substrates along with citations of the original articles describing them are contained in Ref. 48, p. 8; Ref. 49, pp. 13–15; and Ref. 61.) Perhaps the most well-studied and characterized nonmammalian P450 system is that of *Pseudomonas putida,* which catalyzes the hydroxylation of camphor and related compounds (62). Unlike the mammalian liver microsomal system, the P450 system of *P. putida* is a soluble enzyme system, it utilizes NADH as the initial electron donor, and it contains three protein components. In addition to a cytochrome P450 and an NADH-dependent reductase enzyme, this bacterial system also contains a non-heme iron protein (putidaredoxin) which serves as an intermediate electron carrier between the reductase (putidaredoxin reductase) and the P450. It is interesting that the P450 system of mammalian adrenal mitochondria is analogous in this way to this bacterial system; that is, the adrenal mitochondrial system also contains a non-heme iron electron transport protein (adrenodoxin) which bears many physical and chemical similarities to the bacterial protein (putidaredoxin). This analogy is consistent with the theory of the symbiotic evolution of eukaryotic mitochondria from prokaryotes. Figure 4 shows the importance of the cytochrome P450 systems in the synthesis of steroids by the mammalian adrenal gland (63), and it shows the interrelationships of the endoplasmic reticular and mitochondrial systems in the overall metabolic scheme.

In contrast to the P450 systems of the adrenal gland, which are primarily

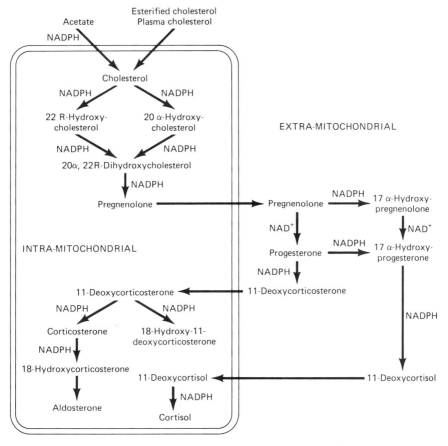

Figure 4. Biosynthesis of corticosteroids. The intracellular locations of enzymes for steroid conversions in the adrenal. [Reprinted with permission from Schulster (1974), in M. H. Briggs and G. A. Christie (eds.), *Adv. Steroid Biochem. Pharmacol.* 4:233–95. Academic Press Inc., Ltd., London.]

involved in steroid anabolism, the liver microsomal systems catabolize steroids and have a much broader substrate specificity, which includes most exogenous agents like drugs, environmental pollutants, and xenobiotics in general. This very broad substrate specificity and the relatively slow substrate turnover rates of the liver microsomal systems are both atypical properties for enzymes, which are characterized generally by their narrow specificity and high catalytic efficiency. Some examples of reactions catalyzed by the liver microsomal P450 systems are depicted in Chart 5 below.

As depicted in the chart, all of these oxidative reactions catalyzed by cytochrome P450 may be viewed as *hydroxylation* reactions (see underscored –OH in each reaction scheme); that is, every reaction shows the involvement of a hydroxylated species. The general reaction is expressed by the following equation, which shows the requirements for NADPH and molecular O_2:

$$\underset{\substack{(2e^-)}}{NADPH} + H^+ + O_2 + \underset{\substack{(substrate)}}{S\text{-}H} \xrightarrow{\substack{P450 \text{ enzyme} \\ system}} \underset{\substack{(product)}}{S\text{-}OH} + H_2O + NADP^+$$

The enzyme system that catalyzes the reaction is called a *mixed-function oxidase* because it utilizes oxygen as well as reducing equivalents to form the oxidized product and H_2O (fully reduced oxygen); it has also been termed a *mono*oxygenase, because only one O-atom of O_2 is transferred to the substrate while the other forms H_2O. The current consensus regarding the mechanism of the overall reaction is represented by Figure 5.

Cytochrome P450 exists in the ER of liver slices predominantly in the ferric state (64), and it is known that most substances do bind to $P450^{3+}$ as evidenced by substrate-induced changes in the visible spectrum of $P450^{3+}$. Furthermore, the presence of substrate alters the redox state of adrenal $P450^{3+}$ and *Pseudomonas* $P450^{3+}$ such that reduction is facilitated (62). All of these data are consistent with formation of a substrate–$P450^{3+}$ complex as the first step of the reaction. This complex can be reduced by the P450 reductase and then acquire O_2 to form a ternary complex. The simplest system would involve then donation of a second electron from FP_1 to commit the ternary complex to activation of oxygen and formation of products. Some investigators have suggested that this "second" electron might come from NADH via FP_2 and b_5, but contrary evidence has made this hypothesis doubtful as a general rule although it might operate in certain cases (48). It is also conceivable and speculative to suggest that the NADH system (which is analogous to the methemoglobin reductase system of erythrocytes) might serve to maintain a certain fraction of P450 in the ferrous oxygenated state ($P450^{2+}$–O_2). Then binding of substrate to that complex might initiate the metabolic scheme, followed by donation of the "second" electron from NADPH and FP_1. The

Chart 5. Reactions Catalyzed by the Liver Microsomal P450 Systems.

REACTION	SUBSTRATE	PRODUCT

Side-chain oxidation

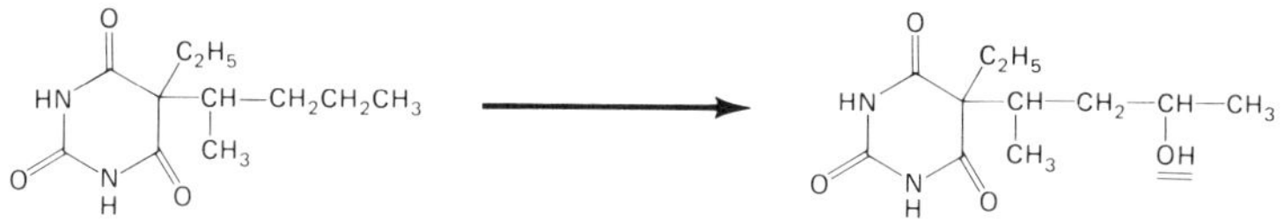

Pentobarbital (anesthetic agent)

Aromatic hydroxylation

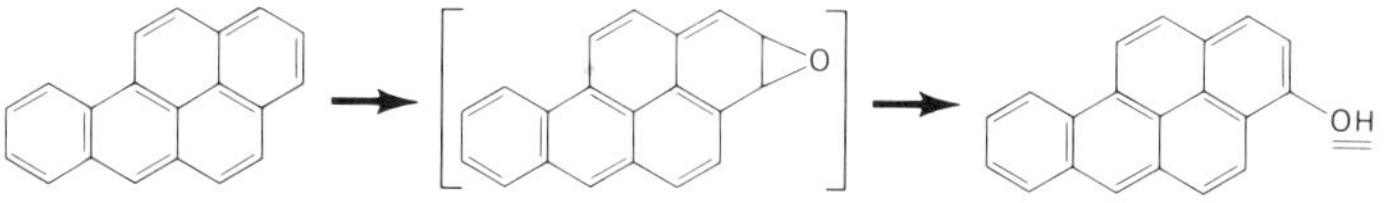

Benzpyrene (cf. cigarette smoke)

O-Dealkylation

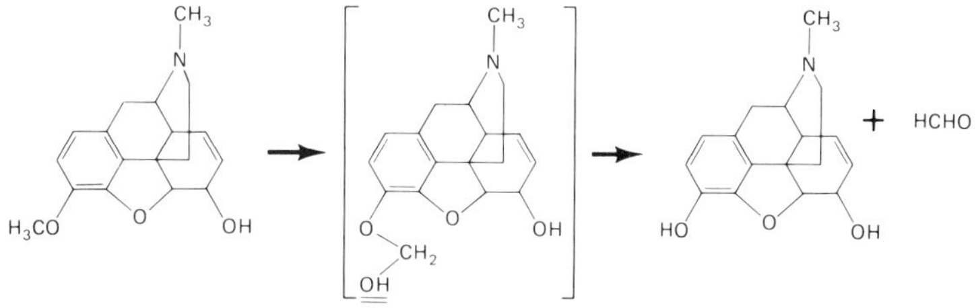

Codeine (narcotic analgesic agent)

N-Dealkylation

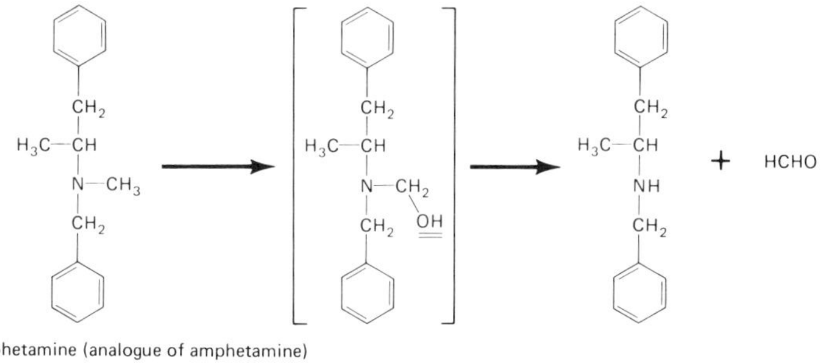

Benzphetamine (analogue of amphetamine)

Deamination

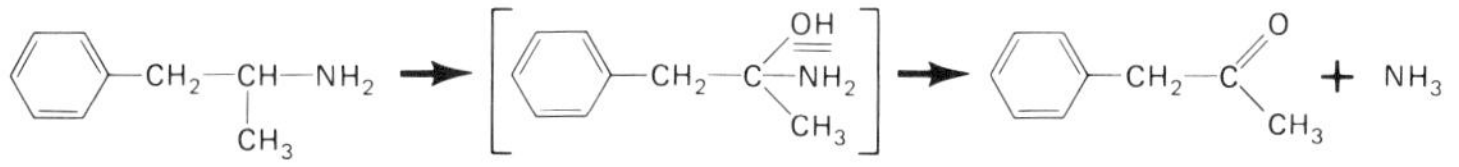

Amphetamine (central nervous system stimulant)

Structures shown in brackets are proposed intermediates.

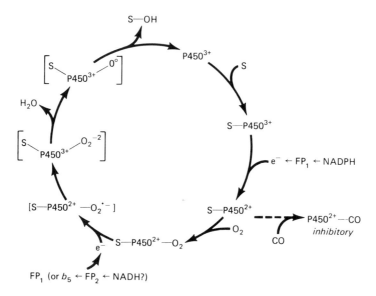

Figure 5. Reactions catalyzed by cytochrome P450. Abbreviations: S = substrate; P450³⁺ = ferricytochrome P450; P450²⁺ = ferrocytochrome P450; FP₁ = P450 reductase; FP₂ = b_5 reductase; O₂⁻ = superoxide; O⁰ = atomic oxygen.

series of intermediates shown in brackets after the "second" electron are hypothetical. It is plausible that the activation of oxygen, hydroxylation of substrate, and formation of water could occur in a concerted fashion, rather than in the stepwise fashion depicted. The side reaction with CO displays how CO can compete with O_2 and thereby inhibit the reaction. Such inhibition has been used as the chief diagnostic tool for testing the involvement of P450 in biotransformation reactions. In this way evidence was obtained that P450 catalyzes certain reduction reactions also, and that a third microsomal flavoprotein exists that functions independently of P450 in catalyzing the oxidation of di- and tri-substituted amines and certain sulfhydryl compounds (65). This FP₃ does not discriminate between NADH and NADPH.

A remarkable feature of the activity of the ER cytochrome P450 systems is their inducibility by a wide variety of chemical agents (see Section IV, below). Many of the products of P450 action serve as substrates for other enzymes which complete the metabolic conversion of the original agents to water-soluble excretory products (see section IIIC, below).

2. Fatty Acid Desaturase System. The following scheme depicts the conversion of stearyl-CoA to oleyl-CoA by the fatty acid desaturase system of endoplasmic reticulum:

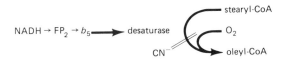

In this case three proteins have been isolated and characterized as requirements for the enzymic system (66). The requirements for molecular oxygen and a reduced pyridine nucleotide were first reported by Bloomfield and Bloch (67) for a cell-free system from yeast. In mammals, there are functional desaturase enzyme systems in the liver, lung, and adipose tissue, the last containing the highest activity. A recent study of kidney cortex microsomes (68), which contain FP_2 and b_5 but lack a functional desaturase system, showed that their combination with liver microsomes gave a higher desaturase activity than that of the liver microsomes alone. This result prompted the authors to suggest that there may be a fourth component in the overall desaturase system present in liver but lacking in kidney, but the evidence for this hypothesis was only indirect, and it is subject to alternative interpretation. The desaturase system from rat hepatocytes has been the most extensively studied.

Unlike the cytochrome P450 system, the desaturase system is insensitive to carbon monoxide; instead the activity is completely abolished by cyanide, which binds to the terminal oxidase. For this reason, the desaturase enzyme was originally named the "cyanide-sensitive factor" (CSF) (69). Initially it was thought that the desaturase was a hemoprotein (70), but studies of the solubilized and purified enzyme have shown that it is a hydrophobic non-heme protein with a molecular weight of $\sim$53,000, containing one atom of catalytically active iron that apparently is ligated with several tyrosine hydroxyl groups (71). This latter property is similar to that of the transferrins which bind iron via tyrosyl residues.

The purified cytochrome b_5 and the reductase (FP_2) are amphipathic proteins consisting of a hydrophilic catalytic segment and a hydrophobic portion involved in binding to microsomes or to lipid vesicles in reconstituted systems. Cytochrome b_5 has been isolated from rat, rabbit, calf, pig, horse, and human liver microsomes, and it has been observed in various tissues from many other species. The calf liver cytochrome b_5 has been purified to homogeneity (72) and characterized as a single polypeptide chain with molecular weight of $\sim$16,000 containing one molecule of iron protoporphyrin IX. The amino-terminal peptide is a typical globular, charged structure, and it contains the heme moiety; the carboxyl-terminal is nonpolar and serves as the membrane-binding segment.

A soluble cytochrome b_5 in the form of a heme peptide segment is found in erythrocytes. In general, the spectral and redox properties of microsomal cytochrome b_5 are essentially identical to those of the isolated heme peptide segment.

The b_5 reductase (FP_2) has been detergent-solubilized and purified from calf and rabbit liver microsomes. It is composed of a hydrophilic segment bearing the FAD prosthetic group and a hydrophobic segment responsible for binding to microsomes and lipid vesicles. The molecular weight has been estimated as 33,000 and 43,000 daltons for the rabbit and calf enzymes, respectively (73, 74). In aqueous solution, the reductase enzymes form large aggregates ranging in molecular weight from ~360,000 to 600,000. A soluble form of cytochrome b_5 reductase has been purified from erythrocytes, and like the soluble b_5 it is immunologically similar to the isolated microsomal enzyme (75).

The in vitro reconstitution of the overall desaturase system from the isolated component parts has been accomplished by combining the three proteins with lecithin vesicles. Consistent with the amphipathic nature of the protein constituents, such preparations appear to contain the three proteins bound to the outer surface of the vesicles (76). Although a detailed mechanism of the overall desaturase reaction has not been proposed, certain facts have been gleaned from studies of the reconstituted system. A survey of the specificity of substrate and inhibitor binding and reactivity has suggested that the substrate may bind in a specific conformation (i.e., with the two hydrocarbon chains at C-9 and C-10 arranged in a *gauche* conformation) in order to facilitate the formation of the *cis* alkene. This concept is illustrated in Chart 6 for the conversion of stearyl-CoA to oleyl-CoA.

Among the physiologically significant fatty acyl-CoA's, stearyl-CoA was found to be the best substrate for the isolated rat liver system. This finding is consistent with the fact that oleic acid is the major monounsaturated fatty acid of rat liver. In fact, the microsomal $\Delta 9$ stearyl-CoA desaturase appears to be the most widely distributed fatty acid desaturating enzyme in nature, occurring not only in various tissues in animals and in plants, but also in low forms of life (11). It should be pointed out, however, that the oxygen-dependent fatty acid desaturase system described here in detail for the rat liver is not the universal enzyme system that accomplishes this reaction in all of nature (77). For example, in *Euglena* the electron-donating cofactor is NADPH, and the non-heme iron protein ferredoxin (instead of b_5) serves as the intermediate electron carrier between the flavoprotein and the desaturase; moreover, the system is soluble rather than membrane-bound. In addition oxygen-independent pathways exist in anaerobic organisms. Other desaturases besides the well-studied $\Delta 9$ system are also known (e.g., $\Delta 6$, $\Delta 5$, and $\Delta 4$, which form $C_6 = C_7$, $C_5 = C_6$ and $C_4 = C_5$ double bonds, respectively) which participate in the synthesis of polyunsaturated fatty acids (11).

As illustrated in Chart 6, the net $\Delta 9$ desaturase reaction is a complex

Chart 6. Conformational Relationships in Conversion of Stearyl-CoA to Oleyl-CoA.

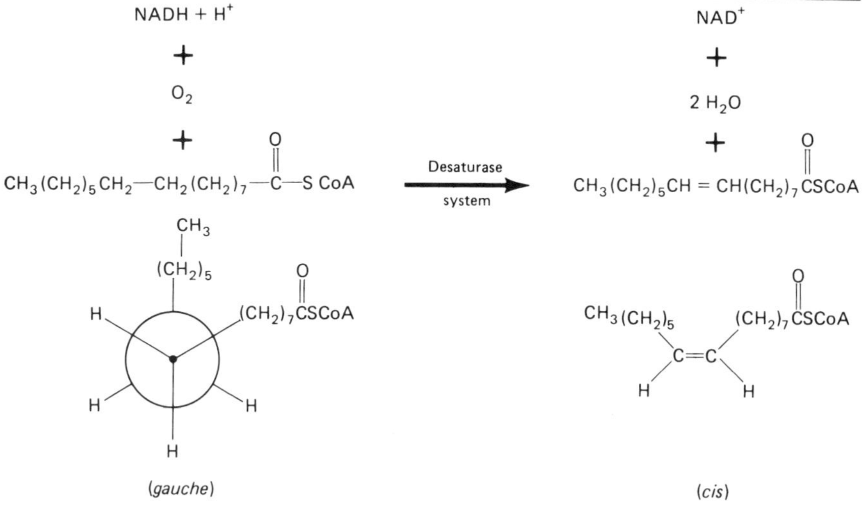

$$NADH + H^+$$
$$+$$
$$O_2$$
$$+$$

$$CH_3(CH_2)_5CH_2-CH_2(CH_2)_7-\overset{\overset{\displaystyle O}{\|}}{C}-S\ CoA$$

$$\xrightarrow[\text{system}]{\text{Desaturase}}$$

$$NAD^+$$
$$+$$
$$2\ H_2O$$
$$+$$

$$CH_3(CH_2)_5CH=CH(CH_2)_7\overset{\overset{\displaystyle O}{\|}}{C}SCoA$$

(gauche)

(cis)

four-electron reaction in which oxygen is reduced to H_2O by the oxidation of two molecules of reduced cytochrome b_5 (one equivalent of NADH) and dehydrogenation of the substrate. It is conceivable that the reaction could proceed stepwise such that C-9 or C-10 would be hydroxylated initially and 1 mole of H_2O formed; then dehydration of the hydroxylated intermediate would yield the desaturated product and the second mole of H_2O. No evidence for this "mixed-function oxidase-like" sequence, or for any other detailed molecular mechanism is yet available (77). Isotope discrimination studies with 9,10-deuterated (or tritiated) stearyl-CoA have indicated that hydrogen removal may be the rate-limiting step of the overall reaction (77).

As alluded to in the previous section, considerable attention has been devoted to possible interactions between the NADH and NADPH electron transport systems. It is known that both P450 and b_5 can be reduced by either NADPH or NADH, although one or the other pyridine nucleotide is favored as described above. In one case a P450-mediated reaction (hydroxylation of lauric acid) was shown to be inhibited by antibody to b_5 (78). Inhibition of P450-dependent mixed-function oxidation reactions by stearyl-CoA has been interpreted as resulting from a diversion of electrons from the NADPH-dependent P450 pathway to the b_5-dependent desaturase system (68, 79); however, since substantial inhibition required concentrations of stearyl-CoA corresponding to $\sim100 \times K_m$ for desaturation (68, 76), an alternate interpretation might be that the fatty acyl-CoA could have a nonspecific detergentlike effect on the P450 system.

Although the desaturase activity apparently is not susceptible to induction by the wide variety of agents that induce the P450 system (see Section IV, below), it is quite sensitive to dietary influences. For example, feeding rats a high-carbohydrate, fat-free diet may result in as much as a 10–15-fold increase in liver desaturase activity and a 2–3-fold increase in lung activity (80, 81). The desaturase activity is decreased in diabetes, but it can be restored with insulin (82). It is curious that such changes in activity apparently are not accompanied by elevations in cytochrome b_5 content. This finding may be reflective of the excess of cytochrome b_5 molecules relative to b_5 reductase (33, 55). Cytochrome b_5 is also involved in the microsomal elongation reaction of fatty acids (e.g., conversion of palmityl-CoA to stearyl-CoA), which is accomplished by a coordinated group of enzymes. The precursor fatty acyl-CoA is condensed with malonyl-CoA; then sequential decarboxylation, hydrogenation, dehydration, and reduction lead to the $n + 2$ homologue of the original fatty acid (11). The activity of the elongation system is also influenced by certain dietary conditions, but it appears to be less sensitive than the desaturase system.

C. Other Enzymic Activities Associated with the Endoplasmic Reticulum

The host of additional enzymic activities localized specifically to the endoplasmic reticulum may be classified generally as conjugative (synthetic) reactions or hydrolytic reactions. In addition certain of these activities are closely associated with the functions of the two electron transport systems; hence they might be termed ancillary enzymes. For example, the first step necessary for transformation of fatty acids and synthesis of lipids is the activation of the endogenous or exogenous fatty acids to the corresponding fatty acyl-CoA's by an enzyme called fatty acyl-CoA synthetase [Fatty acid:CoA ligase (AMP)] (11, 83). The reaction requires ATP and Mg^{+2}, and it results in the cleavage of the ATP to AMP and pyrophosphate. This activity has been studied with microsomes from many sources, and it has generally been found that the enzyme operates on long-chain (>5 carbons) saturated and unsaturated fatty acids; acetic, propionic, and butyric acids are inactive. In contrast, there are acyl-CoA synthetase enzymes localized to the mitochondria and the cytosol that are specific for simple alkyl and aromatic acids. The action of the microsomal fatty acyl-CoA synthetase on substrates for desaturation or elongation can be competitively inhibited by the products of those reactions; however, at least for rat liver microsomes, the activation of the fatty acids is not the rate-limiting enzyme in the overall pathway of fatty acid metabolism because it is much faster than the rates of elongation or desaturation of the corresponding acyl-CoA's.

Also associated with microsomal fatty acid metabolism is the quantitatively minor, but physiologically important synthesis of arachidonic acid derivatives. The prostaglandins and their endoperoxides as well as thromboxane and prostacyclin are all derived from prostanoic acid:

Prostaglandin synthetase activity has been observed in a wide variety of tissues including human prostate gland (hence the name), sheep seminal vesicles, guinea pig intestine, rat stomach, pig iris, human heart, liver, kidney, thymus, uterus, and so on. Oxygen functional groups are incorporated into the polyunsaturated structures of the various arachidonic acid derivatives by the action of an endoperoxidase enzyme which, unlike cytochrome P450, initially introduces both atoms of molecular oxygen into the fatty acid structure. The biosynthesis, metabolism, and physiological functions of the various arachidonic and derivatives have recently been reviewed (84).

There are two enzyme activities that are closely coupled to the action of the cytochrome P450 hydroxylase system, namely, glucuronyltransferase (a synthetic enzyme) and epoxide hydrase (a hydrolytic enzyme). Microsomal UDP–glucuronyltransferase catalyzes the transfer of the glucuronic acid moiety from uridine-5′-diphospho-α-D-glucuronic acid to various acceptors. The transfer reaction involves inversion of configuration and yields the corresponding β-D-glucuronides as products. Glucuronide formation is probably the most common conjugation reaction, occurring in all mammals and most other vertebrates (85). Substrates for glucuronidation include the various hydroxylated products formed by the P450 system. Thus, primary, secondary, and tertiary alcohols and phenols form ether-type (hemiacetal) glucuronides. In addition, carboxylic acids form ester-type glucuronides, various amines form N-glucuronides, and certain sulfur-containing compounds form S-glucuronides. In general, the formation of the glucuronide conjugate of a drug increases its water solubility and leads to abolition of pharmacological activity and to excretion. Besides the role of glucuronidation in drug elimination, many endogenous compounds are metabolized via glucuronide formation. For example, steroids form ether-type glucuronides, and the major route of elimination of bilirubin is biliary excretion of bilirubin glucuronides. The various types of glucuronides apparently are formed by a number of isozymic transferases with overlapping substrate selectivities. As with other microsomal enzymes, the activity of solubilized isolated glucuronyltransferases is enhanced by the presence of phospholipids. Hence the native membrane-associated environment in vivo appears to be important for these enzymes as well.

As described above, mammalian microsomal monooxygenases (P450 systems) can convert olefinic and aromatic drugs and xenobiotics to arene and alkene oxides. These reactive epoxides have been shown to bind irreversibly to DNA, RNA, and proteins and thereby potentially interfere with the normal functioning of the cell, leading to tissue necrosis or cancer. Relatively recently a microsomal enzyme has been characterized that transforms epoxides to much less reactive vicinal *trans*-diols (86). In some cases, however, the action of epoxide hydrase may be on the direct path to formation of the most highly carcinogenic metabolite of polycyclic hydrocarbons; thus the putative ultimate carcinogen formed from benzpyrene is thought to be the 7,8-diol 9,10-epoxide derivative (87). The enzyme has been isolated and purified from rat liver microsomes (86). The purified enzyme displays a minimum molecular weight of ~49,000 in the presence of detergent, but its relatively high content of aromatic and hydrophobic amino acid residues causes it to form large aggregates in the absence of detergent. It is active with a wide variety of substrates, including both arene and alkene oxides. The epoxide hydrase appears to be inducible by the same agents that induce the aryl hydrocarbon hydroxylase P450 system (see Section IVB).

Besides the various enzymes described above, there are many hydrolytic enzymes associated with the endoplasmic reticulum whose functions are not clearly defined. These include glucose-6-phosphatase, β-glucuronidase, sulfatase, 5'-nucleosidases, nucleotide diphosphatases, nucleotide triphosphatases, nucleotide pyrophosphatases, 5'-nucleotidases, esterases, and so on. It has been suggested that one specific role of β-glucuronidase and sulfatase might be in regulating the levels of active steroids by regenerating them from inactive sulfate or glucuronide conjugates. A speculative role for glucose-6-phosphatase is to maintain blood glucose levels by catalyzing the final step in glycogen breakdown and thereby regenerating glucose within the ER channels that exit to the extracellular space; conversely, during hyperglycemia, the glucose-6-phosphatase might act as a transferase to initiate gluconeogenesis by generating G-6-P in the cytoplasm. It has been suggested that glucose-6-phosphatase might catalyze the synthesis of other "high-energy phosphate" compounds as well (89).

IV. BIOCHEMICAL ADAPTATION OF THE ENDOPLASMIC RETICULUM

A. Ontogeny

In mammals, the structure and activity of the ER changes markedly throughout gestation and during extrauterine maturation. The precise physiologic stimulus for these alterations is unknown, but the pattern of the changes appears to be very similar among the animal species that have been studied (30).

Prior to birth the hepatocytes comprise one-third to one-half of the cell population of the liver. The remainder is composed mainly of erythropoietic cells. At this stage (~day −3) the hepatocytes are small, and the ER consists mainly of randomly arranged rough-surfaced tubules and distended cisternae. The membranes are intimately associated with relatively large glycogen deposits. Ribosomes are present in tightly packed arrays in rosette, spiral, and double-row configurations. SER is sparsely represented despite the rather mature-appearing Golgi complex (90).

At birth several marked changes occur. The cell population of the liver becomes more uniform with the decline in the number of erythroid elements present. At the same time the number and size of the hepatocytes increases. The ER greatly enlarges, and while its elements are still largely rough-surfaced, the membranes are positioned in elaborate arrays. There is still little change in the frequency of smooth elements, and the ribosomes and glycogen deposits are increased in number.

By the third postpartum day the hepatocytes have reached their full differentiated size and appearance. The rough-surfaced membranes, while still predominant, are much less tightly packed, and the smooth-surfaced membranes have greatly increased in number.

In conjunction with these structural alterations the chemical makeup of the ER changes as well. The protein content of the ER increases from 80 to 90 mg/g wet weight of liver at day −3, to 110 to 140 mg/g in the newborn and adult. The RNA content is highest before birth, and its relative concentration decreases with the rapid membrane proliferation in the neonate. Phospholipid content rises rapidly after birth from 14 mg/g in the fetus to 22 mg/g in the newborn (90).

The specific activities of the microsomal electron transport enzymes are low in fetal rats. NADPH–cytochrome c reductase and NADPH-diaphorase activities show a marked increase in activity at the time of birth and reach adult levels of activity by day +1. Microsomal cytochromes P450 and b_5 are difficult to detect before birth, but low levels of mixed-function oxidase activity are measurable in the fetus. After birth the microsomal cytochrome specific contents gradually increase, attaining 70 to 80% of adult levels by day +8. However, during this same period of time demethylase activity reaches only 30% of adult levels, suggesting that additional maturation processes are essential to the expression of full enzymic activity even in the presence of a full complement of enzymes. The NADH-dependent reductase activities rise more slowly than the corresponding NADPH-dependent systems. They often achieve adult levels of activity only after several months (91).

The microsomal phosphatases show three different developmental patterns.

Nucleoside triphosphatase activity remains essentially constant from day -3 through maturity. In contrast, nucleoside diphosphatase activity increases slowly after birth but is hardly detectable in the fetus. Finally, glucose-6-phosphatase activity displays a large increase in activity after birth to levels that exceed that found in the adult (91).

Microsomal glucuronyltransferase activity is generally reported to be low in the term fetus and neonate, but the actual level of activity detected depends upon the substrate, strain, and species studied. Postnatal increases in glucuronyltransferase activity often overshoot adult values, and evidence has accumulated suggesting that certain pituitary hormones are responsible. Another important factor in the expression of glucuronyltransferase activity is the membrane conformation. Dissimilarities have been reported between infant and adult mouse glucuronyltransferase in response to deoxycholate (27).

Whether the postnatal increases in enzyme activity described above result from an activation of enzyme molecules already present in the ER or result from protein synthesis is an important question. Studies of microsomes isolated from rats treated with actinomycin D or puromycin have indicated that these increases are dependent upon protein synthesis (90). However, a strong controversy exists relative to the presence of apocytochrome P450 in the membranes of the developing rat ER (22, 92).

There is also an asymmetric distribution of microsomal enzyme activities in the lateral plane during the maturation process at birth. The specific activities of NADPH–cytochrome c reductase and glucose-6-phophatase are much higher in the rough membranes than in the smooth. Even though enzyme activities increase in the SER during the first 3 days of life, they remain far below those of the RER. In contrast nucleoside triphosphatase activity, the activity of which changes little with age, is higher in the SER (91).

The most detailed work concerning the lateral distribution of microsomal enzyme activities has concentrated on glucose-6-phosphatase. The time courses of appearance of enzyme activity in the smooth and rough membranes are not parallel. Phosphatase activity appears later and its activity increases more slowly in smooth than in rough vesicles, suggesting a gradual transfer of the enzyme from the rough to the smooth ER. This developmental pattern, in which enzyme activity appears first in the RER and then the SER, is considered to apply to most microsomal enzymes. Whether this results from a gradual transformation of rough into smooth membranes or from the de novo synthesis of smooth membranes with the subsequent insertion of the enzymes into the lipid–protein matrix remains uncertain (13, 17, 18, 91).

In addition to changes in microsomal protein content, the amount of microsomal phospholipid also increases with age (24). No major differences are observed in types or relative amounts of phospholipid obtained from fetal, newborn, or adult rats. However, the fatty acid composition among the phospholipids differs markedly with each, showing relatively unique patterns of distribution with age. This stability in microsomal lipid content throughout the maturation process renders it unlikely that general or specific lipid deficiencies are responsible for the low activities displayed by certain enzymes during ER ontogeny (90).

In summary, it appears that the constitutive enzymes of the ER are produced at different times and at different rates during development. Enzymes are synthesized in the RER and subsequently transferred to the SER. Lipid membrane components, which also appear to be first incorporated into the RER, remain compositionally stable during development and seem to have no effect on the biochemical maturation of the microsomal enzymes.

B. Pharmacologic Stimuli

The adaptive responses of the various enzymes of the ER to a variety of chemical stimuli have been best characterized with respect to the two microsomal electron transport systems. The activities of these enzymes can be altered by dietary and nutritional factors, hormonal changes, and ingestion of or environmental exposure to various xenobiotic compounds (31, 32). In most cases the effect of these various chemical agents is expressed as an increase in enzyme activity, which is often referred to as enzyme induction. Although it has not been determined for each enzyme whether this increase in enzyme activity represents an increase in enzyme synthesis, a decrease in enzyme degradation, an activation of preexisting apoenzyme, or some combination thereof, it has been shown that for cytochrome P450 induction requires an increase in enzyme synthesis (93). In addition to the chemical nature of the inducer employed, the extent of induction depends on the species, strain, age, sex, and nutritional status of the animal studied (31).

The enzyme most often studied with respect to pharmacologic induction is the mixed-function oxidase cytochrome P450. Nevertheless recent investigations have made it clear that other microsomal enzymes including NADPH–cytochrome c reductase, cytochrome b_5, fatty acid desaturase, and UDP–glucuronyltransferase are all induced to varying degrees by various agents. Recent work has suggested that induction of the P450 reductase requires the increased synthesis and translation of m-RNA by polysomes tightly bound to the ERA members (108), whereas increased synthesis of cytochromes P450 and b_5 is apparently mediated by free polysomes (108,109).

More than 200 agents, including drugs, environmental chemicals, and steroid hormones, have been reported to increase the activity of the microsomal electron transport enzymes. It is interesting that most of these compounds are neither chemically nor pharmacologically related. One of the unique aspects of this induction phenomenon is that virtually all of these so-called inducing agents are also substrates for the mixed-function oxidase system. This property of substrate inducibility is rather unique in eukaryotes but is strongly reminiscent of the lac operon system in bacteria (94).

Based upon differences in their profile of biological activity, pharmacologic inducing agents may be divided into three general groups: (a) the phenobarbital type, (b) the polycyclic hydrocarbon type, and (c) anabolic steroids. In addition to these three major types of inducing agents, there are several other well studied agents. The polychlorinated biphenyls, for which Arochlor 1254 is the prototype, are important environmental pollutants that possess the inducing properties of both of the main classes of microsomal enzyme inducers, namely, phenobarbital and methylcholanthrene (95). Another well-studied agent is 2,3,7,8-tetrachlorodibenzo-p-dioxin TCDD, which has been shown to be an inducer of the methylcholanthrene type, but is 30,000 times more potent than the latter (96). Its major importance as an inducer of microsomal enzyme activity consists of its role in evaluating the molecular basis for the genetically determined lack of responsiveness of certain mouse strains to polycyclic hydrocarbon induction (100).

Administration of phenobarbital results in increased metabolism of a large number of drugs, hormones and environmental chemicals. This is accomplished by effects on at least four levels. First phenobarbital increases hepatic blood flow to more metabolically active tissue. The second major effect is an increase in microsomal protein per gram wet weight of liver. Associated with this proliferation of the ER is an increase in the specific content of both cytochrome P450 and its reductase. Finally phenobarbital treatment increases the specific activity of the microsomal drug-metabolizing enzymes.

In general all animal species respond to phenobarbital in a similar fashion. Maximal induction of microsomal enzymes requires daily administration for 3–5 days. During that time the specific content of cytochrome P450 rises to approximately 2–3 times its constitutive (uninduced) level. Characteristically the observed increase in drug metabolism is directly proportional to the increase in microsomal enzyme content. Thus even though the specific activity of the enzyme (moles of product formed per unit time per gram microsomal protein) is increased, the turnover number (moles of product formed per unit time per mole of enzyme) is unchanged. The observations suggest that treatment with phenobarbital increases the microsomal content of the same enzyme(s) that was present in the constitutive state. This concept is further supported by the observation that while phenobarbital treatment increases the maximal velocity (V_{max}) of various drug oxidation reactions, it has no significant effect on the Michaelis constant (K_m).

The prototype inducing agent of the polycyclic hydrocarbon type is 3-methylcholanthrene. There are several fundamental differences between the inductive effects of methylcholanthrene and those of phenobarbital (Chart 7). In contrast to the rather generalized increase in metabolism of both endoge-

Chart 7. Comparative Characteristics of Phenobarbital- and Methylcholanthrene-Type Inducing Agents.

PROPERTY	PHENOBARBITAL	METHYLCHOLANTHRENE
Liver weight	Increase	No change
Proliferation of ER membranes	Yes	No
Increase in microsomal protein content	Large	Small
Increase in cytochrome P450 content	2–3-fold	1.4–2-fold
Cytochrome b_5 content	Increase	No change
NADPH–cytochrome c reductase activity	Increase	No change or decrease
Time to maximal mixed-function oxidase induction	72–120 hr	24–48 hr
Shift in Soret maximum for reduced CO-bound cytochrome	No	Yes
Species- and strain-specific	No	Yes
Relatively substrate-specific	No	Yes
Change in substrate turnover number	No	Yes
Increased fatty acid content in phospholipids	Linoleic	Oleic

nous and exogenous substrates that results from phenobarbital treatment, methylcholanthrene treatment increases the metabolism of far fewer compounds. Along with this increase in metabolic capacity there is relatively little proliferation of the ER, and there are only slight increases in microsomal protein content. Nevertheless microsomal content of cytochrome P450 is significantly elevated.

There is now good evidence indicating that the predominant cytochrome synthesized in response to polycyclic hydrocarbon treatment is different from that which predominates in the constitutive state. Initial observations suggesting this difference were made soon after the role of cytochrome P450 in xenobiotic metabolism was established. It was found that in microsomes from methylcholanthrene-treated rats the reduced CO-bound cytochrome showed a 2-nm hypsochromic shift when compared to controls. Further, it was observed that the increase in specific mixed-function oxidase activity was accompanied by an increase in substrate turnover number. Analysis of microsomal protein from methylcholanthrene-treated rats by SDS–polyacrylamide gel electrophoresis revealed a marked increase in a heme-containing band at MW = 54,000, in contrast to phenobarbital, which caused an increase in a heme containing band at MW = 49,000 (95). Antibodies prepared against purified cytochrome P450 isolated from phenobarbital- and methylcholanthrene-treated animals showed little or no cross reactivity in Ouchterlony double diffusion assays.

Several other characteristics of polycyclic hydrocarbon induction provide an interesting contrast to phenobarbital induction. The maximal inductive effects of methylcholanthrene are achieved in 24 to 48 hours rather than 3 to 5 days. Also the increases in substrate metabolism and substrate turnover number occur without any apparent increases in NADPH-specific reductase concentration. This suggests that the increase in metabolism is related to an increase and/or change in a single component within the multienzyme system involved. This concept becomes even more extraordinary because in the constitutive state there is already at least a 10:1 cytochrome P450–to–NADPH-specific reductase ratio. Thus methylcholanthrene induction must increase the efficiency of the interaction between the cytochrome and the reductase in order to manifest the observed change in metabolic activity.

Induction by phenobarbital and methylcholanthrene appears to be additive, suggesting that different molecular mechanisms are responsible (31). Although the induction of microsomal mixed-function oxidase activity by the two proto-type inducers phenobarbital and methylcholanthrene has been described as a rather generalized phenomenon, this is not always the case. While among mammalian species, there do not seem to be any exceptions to the inductive effects of phenobarbital, with polycyclic hydrocarbon inducers certain inbred strains of mice appear to be relatively insensitive to treatment. This lack of responsiveness appears to be genetically determined and is inherited in an autosomal recessive manner (98). Another curious effect of polycyclic hydro-carbon inducing agents is seen in rabbits. When newborn and young rabbits are treated with methylcholanthrene, the previously described changes in microsomal enzyme content and activity occur. However, when mature rabbits are similarly treated, the expected alterations in microsomal enzyme content and spectral parameters occur without concomitant changes in enzyme activity (99). These results have prompted further investigations concerning the control of gene expression related to microsomal enzyme induction. Evidence has been presented to support the existence of structural (97), regulatory (100), temporal (101), and architectural genes (56) in the control of these microsomal enzyme systems.

Insofar as the other microsomal enzymes are concerned, with two excep-tions very little work has been done related to their adaptive responses to pharmacologic stimuli. The first of these exceptions is the enzyme DT diapho-rase. It is a dicoumarol-sensitive electron transport enzyme with no pyridine nucleotide specificity found in rat liver microsomes (102). Its activity is specifi-cally increased after methylcholanthrene treatment, but it has been shown to have no specific role in xenobiotic metabolism (103). The activity cannot be detected in mouse microsomes but is present in mouse liver cytosol. In the mouse the cytosolic enzyme is under the same genetic control as micro-somal cytochrome P450 with respect to induction by polycyclic hydrocarbons (101).

The other well-studied inducible microsomal enzyme is UDP–glucuronyl-transferase (27). Present evidence indicates that there are probably multiple transferases or multiple enzyme active sites present in microsomes. The inductive effects of various agents seem to depend upon the substrates investigated. This fundamental observation has led to a plethora of conflicting results. As with the mixed-function oxidase system, the principal inducers used have been phenobarbital and methylcholanthrene.

Induction alters the membrane environment and thereby alters the activation, kinetic properties, and substrate specificity of the enzyme. It appears that after inducer treatment there is an "increased latency" of the enzyme activity. Although the inductive effects of phenobarbital and methylcholanthrene are not additive as they are for the mixed-function oxidase system, the membrane constraints imposed by the two agents are different, as shown by susceptibility to solubilization by trypsin and phospholipase and by the use of fluorescent probes.

Alterations in substrate specificity after treatment with one inducing agent or another are well documented. These alterations appear to be associated with the protein itself rather than the membrane because they persist after solubilization. These differences also show marked species variability, and in inbred mice some of the activities appear to be under genetic control identical to that for polycyclic hydrocarbon induction of the mixed-function oxidase system (104).

In conjunction with the alterations in microsomal protein content and enzyme activity following treatment with either phenobarbital of methylcholanthrene, alterations in microsomal lipid content have also been documented (105). Treatment with either agent resulted in a decrease in the cholesterol-to-phospholipid ratio in the membrane. Phenobarbital treatment increased the proportion of phosphatidylcholine in the membrane. It also increased the proportion of linoleic acid in phosphatidylcholine and phosphatidylethanolamine while decreasing the amount of oleic, arachidonic, and docosahexanoic acid. It is significant that the time course of the increased incorporation of linoleic acid corresponds exactly to that of the increase in cytochrome P450 and the increase in mixed-function oxidase activity. In contrast methylcholanthrene caused an increase in the proportion of oleic acid in phosphatidylcholine and phosphatidylethanolamine. These changes in microsomal lipid content associated with microsomal enzyme induction support the concept of lipid modulation of enzyme activity within the ER. Further, they suggest that specific lipid environments are required for the expression of different substrate specificities following treatment with different types of inducing agents.

CONCLUDING REMARKS

The endoplasmic reticulum plays an important role in the economy of each cell both structurally and functionally, serving as the major site of synthesis of many complex molecules which comprise the membranes of various other intracellular organelles as well as the ER membrane itself. This tubular network appears to provide a physical continuity between the plasma membrane and the intracellular environment as well as possibly serving as a biochemical communications system among the intracellular organelles. It is compositionally complex, multifunctional, enzymically diverse, and highly adaptable to dietary changes and chemical insults. The relatively high concentration of the unique mixed-function oxidase system within the ER provides an interface between the external chemical environment and the biological organism.

REFERENCES

1. Porter, K. R. 1961. In *The Cell,* Vol. 2, J. Brachet and A. E. Mirsky, eds., p. 621. Academic Press, New York.
2. Bolender, R. P., Paumgartner, D., Losa, G., Muellener, D., and Weibel, E. R. 1978. Integrated stereological and biochemical studies on hepatocyte membranes. *J. Cell. Biol.* 77:565–83.
3. Moulé, Y. 1968. Biochemical characterization of the components of the endoplasmic reticulum in rat liver cell. In *Structure and Function of the Endoplasmic Reticulum in Animal Cells,* FEBS Symposium, F. C. Gran, ed., pp. 1–12. Academic Press, New York.
4. De Pierre, J. W., and Ernster, L. 1977. Enzyme topology of intracellular membranes. *Annu. Rev. Biochem.* 46:201–62.
5. Claude, A. 1946. Fractionation of mammalian liver cells by differential centrifugation. *J. Exp. Med.* 84:51–89.
6. Dallner, G., and Ericsson, J. L. E. 1976. Molecular structure and biological implication of the liver endoplasmic reticulum. In *Progress in Liver Diseases,* H. Popper and F. Schaffner, eds., pp. 35–50. Grune and Stratton, New York.
7. De Pierre, J., and Dallner, G. 1976. Isolation, subfractionation and characterization of the endoplasmic reticulum. In *Biochemical Analysis of Membranes,* A. H. Maddy, ed., pp. 79–131. John Wiley & Sons, New York.
8. Analytical study of microsomes and isolated subcellular membranes from rat liver:
     I. Biochemical methods. Beaufay, H., Amar-Costesec, A., Feytmans, E., Thines-Sempoux, D., Wibo, M., Robbi, and Berthet, J. 1974. *J. Cell. Biol.* 61:188–200.
    II. Preparation and composition of the microsomal fraction. Amar-Costesec, A., Beaufay, H., Wibo, M., Thines-Sempoux, D., Feytmans, E., Robbi, M., and Berthet, J. 1974. *J. Cell. Biol.* 61:201–12.
   III. Subfractionation of the microsomal fraction by isopycnic and differential centrifugation in density gradients. Beaufay, H., Amar-Costesec, A., Thines-Sempoux, D., Wibo, M., Robbi, M., and Berthet, J. 1974. *J. Cell. Biol.* 61:213–31.
    IV. Biochemical, physical and morphological modifications of microsomal components induced by digitonin, EDTA and pyrophosphate. Amar-Costesec, A., Wibo, M., Thines-Sempoux, D., Beaufay, H., and Berthet, J. 1974. *J. Cell. Biol.* 62:717–45.
     V. Immunological localization of cytochrome b_5 by electron microscopy: Methodology and application to various subcellular fractions. Fowler, S., Remacle, J., Trouet, A., Beaufay, H., Berthet, J., Wibo, M., and Hauser, P. 1976. *J. Cell. Biol.* 71:535–50.
    VI. Electron microscope examination of microsomes for cytochrome b_5 by means of ferritin-labeled antibody. Remacle, J., Fowler, S., Beaufay, H., Amar-Costesec, A., and Berthet, J. 1976. *J. Cell. Biol.* 71:551–64.

9. Peachey, L. D. 1965. The sarcoplasmic reticulum and transverse tubules of the frog's sartorius. *J. Cell. Biol.* 25:209–31.

10. Siekevitz, P. 1976. Endoplasmic reticulum, microsomes and Golgi. In *Cell Biology,* FASEB Handbook, pp. 231–313. FASEB, Bethesda, Md.

11. Brenner, R. R. 1977. Metabolism of endogenous substances by microsomes. In *Drug Metab. Rev.* 6:155–212.

12. Wickramasinghe, R. H. and Ville, C. A. 1976. Possible similar role of cytochrome P450 in primordial evolution of species and in chemical carcinogenesis. *Perspect. Biol. Med.,* 473–75. (Summer issue)

13. De Pierre, J. W., and Dallner, G. 1975. Structural aspects of the membrane of the endoplasmic reticulum. *Biochim. Biophys. Acta* 415:411–72.

14. Blouin, A., Bolender, R. P., and Weibel, E. R. 1977. Distribution of organelles and membranes between hepatocytes and nonhepatocytes in rat liver parenchyma. *J. Cell Biol.* 72:441–55.

15. Eriksson, L. C., De Pierre, J. W., and Dallner, G. 1978. Preparation and properties of microsomal fractions. *Pharmacol. Ther.* 2:281–317.

16. Singer, S. J., and Nicolson, G. L. 1972. The fluid mosaic model of the structure of cell membranes. *Science* 175:720–31.

17. Singer, S. J. 1974. The molecular organization of membranes. *Annu. Rev. Biochem.* 43:805–33.

18. Gulik-Kuzywicki, T. 1975. Structural studies of the associations between biological membrane components. *Biochem. Biophys. Acta* 415:1–28.

19. Goldblatt, P. J. 1969. The endoplasmic reticulum, Chapter 40 in *Handbook of Molecular Cytology,* A. Lima-De-Faria, ed., pp. 1101–29. John Wiley and Sons, New York.

20. Testa, B., and Jenner, P. 1976. *Drug Metabolism. Chemical and Biochemical Aspects.* Marcel Dekker, New York.

21. Kreibich, G., Ulrich, B. L., and Sabatini, D. D. 1978. Proteins of rough microsomal membranes related to ribosome binding. I. Identification of ribophorins I and II, membrane proteins characteristic of rough microsomes. *J. Cell Biol.* 77:464–87.

22. Siekevitz, P. 1973. The differentiation of rat liver endoplasmic reticulum membranes: Apocytochrome P450 as a membrane protein. *J. Supramol. Struct.* 1:471–89.

23. Glaumann, H., and Dallner, G. 1968. Lipid composition and turnover of rough and smooth microsomal membranes in rat liver. *J. Lipid Res.* 9:720–29.

24. Dallner, G., Siekevitz, P., and Palade, G. 1965. Phospholipids in hepatic microsomal membranes during development. *Biochem. Biophys. Res. Commun.* 20:142–48.

25. Lu, A. Y. H., and Levin, W. 1974. The resolution and reconstitution of the liver microsomal hydroxylation system. *Biochim. Biophys. Acta* 344:205–40.

26. Vore, M., Hamilton, J. G., and Lu, A. Y. H. 1974. Organic solvent extraction of liver microsomal lipid. I. The requirement of lipid for 3,4-benzpyrene hydroxylase. *Biochem. Biophys. Res. Commun.* 56:1038–44.

27. Dutton, G. J., and Burchell, B. Newer aspects of glucuronidation. In. *Progress in Drug Metabolism,* Vol. 2, J. W. Bridges and L. F. Chasseaud, eds., pp. 1–70. John Wiley & Sons, New York.

28. Bergman, A., and Dallner, G. 1978. Incorporation of N-acetylglucosamine from UDP–N-acetylglucosamine into proteins and lipid intermediates in microsomal and Golgi membranes from rat liver. *Biochim. Biophys. Acta* 512:123–35.

29. Bergman, A., and Dallner, G. 1976. Distribution of protein-bound sugar residues in microsomal subfractions and Golgi membranes. *Biochim. Biophys. Acta* 433:496–508.

30. Helgeland, L., Christensen, T. B., and Janson, T. L. 1972. The distribution of protein-bound carbohydrates in submicrosomal fractions from rat liver. *Biochim. Biophys. Acta* 285:62–71.

31. Conney, A. H., and Burns, J. J. 1972. Metabolic interactions among environmental chemicals and drugs. *Science* 178:576–86.
32. Conney, A. H. 1967. Pharmacological implications of microsomal enzyme induction. *Pharm. Rev.* 19:317–66.
33. Strittmatter, P., Rogers, M. J., and Spatz, L. 1972. The binding of cytochrome b_5 to liver microsomes. *J. Biol. Chem.* 247:7188–94.
34. Envmoto K., and Sato, R. 1973. Incorporation in vitro of purified cytochrome b_5 into liver microsomal membranes. *Biochem. Biophys. Res. Commun.* 51:1–7.
35. Nilsson, O. S., and Dallner, G. 1977. Enzyme and phospholipid asymmetry in liver microsomal membranes. *J. Cell Biol.* 72:568–83.
36. Moritmoto, T., Matsuura, S., Sasalsi, S., Tashiro, Y., and Omura, T. 1976. Immunochemical and immunoelectron microscope studies on localization of NADPH–cytochrome *c* reductase on rat liver microsomes. *J. Cell Biol.* 68:189–201.
37. Stier, A. 1976. Lipid structure and drug metabolizing enzymes. *Biochem. Pharmacol.* 25:109–13.
38. Duppel, W., and Ullrich, V. 1976. Membrane effects on Drug Monooxygenation activity in hepatic microsomes. *Biochim. Biophys. Acta* 426:399–407.
39. Becker, J. F., Mecharr, T., and Bartholomew, J. C. 1978. Fatty acid requirements and temperature dependence of monooxygenase activity in rat liver microsomes. *Biochim. Biophys. Acta* 512:136–46.
40. Glaumann, H. 1978. Albumin secretory pathway in the hepatocyte. In *Proceedings of the 11th FEBS Meeting,* Vol. 50, *Albumin: Structure, Biosynthesis, Function,* pp. 41–50. Pergamon Press, New York.
41. Jamieson, J. D., and Palade, G. E. 1977. Production of secretory proteins in animal cells. In *International Cell Biology,* B. R. Brinkley and K. R. Porter, eds., pp. 308–17. Rockefeller University Press, New York.
42. Blobel, G. 1977. Synthesis and segregation of secretory proteins: The signal hypothesis. In *International Cell Biology,* B. R. Brinkley and K. R. Porter, eds., pp. 318–25. Rockefeller University Press, New York.
43. Behrens, N. H. 1974. Polyprenol sugars and glycoprotein synthesis. In *Biology and Chemistry of Eucaryotic Cell Surfaces,* E. Y. C. Lee and E. E. Smith, eds., pp. 159–80. Academic Press, New York.
44. Schramm, M., and Selinger, Z. 1975. The functions of cyclic AMP and calcium as alternative second messengers in parotid gland and pancreas. *J. Cyc. Nucleotide Res.* 1:181–92.
45. Kamp, H. H., Spregers, E. D., Wisterman, J., Wirtz, K. W. A., and van Deenan, L. L. M. 1975. Action of phospholipases on the phosphotidylcholine exchange protein from beef liver. *Biochem. Biophys. Acta* 398:415–23.
46. Williams, R. T. 1959. *Detoxication Mechanisms. The Metabolism and Detoxication of Drugs, Toxic Substances and Other Organic Compounds.* John Wiley & Sons, New York.
47. Gilette, J. R. Davis, D. C., and Sasame, H. A. 1972. Cytochrome P450 and its role in drug metabolism. *Annu. Rev. Pharmacol.* 12:57–84.
48. Lu, A. Y. H., Kuntzman, R., and Conney, A. H. 1976. The liver microsomal hydroxylation enzyme system. Induction and properties of the functional components. In *Frontiers of Gastrointestinal Research,* Vol. 2, *Enzymology of the Liver,* L. van der Reis, ed., pp. 1–31. S. Karger, New York.
49. Fleischer, S., and Packer, L., eds., 1978. *Methods in Enzymology,* Vol. LII, *Biomembranes, Part C: Biological Oxidations—Microsomal, Cytochrome P450, and Other Hemoprotein Systems.* Academic Press, New York. pp. 595.
50. Dawson, J. H., Trudell, J. R., Linder, R. E., Barth, G., Bunnenberg, E., and Djerassi,

C. 1978. Magnetic circular dichroism of purified forms of rabbit liver cytochromes P-450 and P-420. *Biochemistry* 17:33–42.

51. Coon, M. J., Vermillion, J. L., Vatsis, K. P., French, J. S., Dean, W. L., and Haugen, D. A. 1977. Biochemical studies on drug metabolism: Isolation of multiple forms of liver microsomal cytochrome P450. In *Drug Metabolism Concepts*, D. M. Jerina, ed., ACS Symposium #44, pp. 46–71. Am. Chem. Soc., Washington, D.C.

52. Thomas, P. E., Lu, A. Y. H., Ryan, D., West, S. B., Kawalek, J., and Levin, W. 1976. Immunochemical evidence for six forms of rat liver cytochrome P450 obtained using antibodies against purified rat liver cytochromes P450 and P448. *Mol. Pharmacol.* 12:746–58.

53. Yasukochi, Y., and Masters, B. S. S. 1976. Some properties of a detergent-solubilized NADPH cytochrome P450 reductase purified by biospecific affinity chromatography. *J. Biol. Chem.* 251:5337–44.

54. Miwa, G. T., West, S. B., and Lu, A. Y. H. 1978. Studies on the rate-limiting enzyme component in the microsomal monooxygenase system. *J. Biol. Chem.* 253:1921–29.

55. Blumer, J. L., and Mieyal, J. J. 1978. Genetic expression of microsomal electron transport in mice. *J. Biol. Chem.* 253:1159–66.

56. Estabrook, R. W., Franklin, M. R., Cohen, B., Shigamatzu, A., and Hildebrandt, H. G. 1971. Influence of hepatic microsomal mixed-function oxidation reactions on cellular metabolic control. *Metabolism* 20:187–99.

57. Longmuir, I. S., Sun, S., and Soucie, W. 1973. Possible role of cytochrome P450 as a tissue oxygen carrier. In *Oxidases and Related Redox Systems*. T. E. King, H. S. Mason, and M. Morrison, eds., pp. 451–61. University Park Press, Baltimore.

58. Mieyal, J. J. 1978. Mechanisms of enzyme-like reactions involving human hemoglobin, Chapter 12 in *Bioorganic Chemistry*, Vol. IV, E. E. van Tamelan, ed., pp. 315–48. Academic Press, New York.

59. Blisard, K. S., and Mieyal, J. J. 1979. Characterization of the aniline hydroxylase activity of erythrocytes. *J. Biol. Chem.*, 254:5104–5110.

60. Estabrook, R. W., Cooper, D. Y., and Rosenthal, O. 1963. The light-reversible carbon monoxide inhibition of the steroid C-21 hydroxylation system of the adrenal cortex. *Biochem. Z.* 338:741–55.

61. Madyastha, K. M., Ridgway, J. E., Dwyer, J. G., and Coscia, C. J. 1977. Subcellular localization of a cytochrome P450–dependent monooxygenase in vesicles of the higher plant *Catharanthus roseus. J. Cell. Biol.* 72:302–13.

62. Gunsalus, I. C., Pederson, T. C., and Sligar, S. G. 1975. Oxygenase-catalyzed biological hydroxylations. *Annu. Rev. Biochem.* 44:377–407.

63. Schulster, D., Burstein, S., and Cooke, B. A. 1976. *Molecular Endocrinology of the Steroid Hormones.* John Wiley & Sons, New York.

64. Sies, H., and Weigl, K. 1977. Nicotinamide nucleotide systems and drug oxidation in the liver cell. In *Microsomes and Drug oxidations.* V. Ullrich, ed., pp. 307–14. Pergamon Press, New York.

65. Ziegler, D. M., and Poulsen, L. L. 1978. Hepatic microsomal mixed-function amine oxidase. In Ref. 49, pp. 142–51.

66. Strittmatter, P., Spatz, L., Corcoran, D., Rogers, M. J., Setlow, B., and Redline, R. 1974. Purification and properties of rat liver microsomal stearyl coenzyme A desaturase. *Proc. Natl. Acad. Sci. U.S.A.* 74:4565–69.

67. Bloomfield, D. K., and Bloch, K. 1960. The formation of Δ^9-unsaturated fatty acids. *J. Biol. Chem.* 235:337–45.

68. Montgomery, M. R., and Cinti, D. L. 1977. Pyridine nucleotide–dependent electron trans-

port in kidney cortex microsomes: Interaction with desaturase and other microsomal mixed function oxidases. *Mol. Pharmacol.* 13:60–69.

69. Oshino, N., Imai, Y., and Sato, R. 1966. Electron-transfer mechanism associated with fatty acid desaturation catalyzed by liver microsomes. *Biochim. Biophys. Acta* 128:13–28.

70. Gaylor, J. L., Moir, N. J., Seifried, H. E., and Jefcoate, C. R. E. 1970. Assay and isolation of a cyanide-binding protein of rat liver microsomes. *J. Biol. Chem.* 245:5511–13.

71. Enoch, H. G., and Strittmatter, P. 1978. Role of tyrosyl and arginyl residues in rat liver microsomal stearyl coenzyme A desaturase. *Biochemistry* 17:4927–32.

72. Strittmatter, P., Fleming, P., Connors, M., and Corcoran, D. 1978. Purification of cytochrome b_5. In Ref. 49, pp. 97–101.

73. Mihara, K., and Sato, R. 1978. Detergent-solubilized NADH–cytochrome b_5 reductase. In Ref. 49, pp. 102–8.

74. Spatz, L., and Strittmatter, P. 1973. A form of NADH–cytochrome b_5 reductase containing both the catalytic site and an additional hydrophobic membrane-binding segment. *J. Biol. Chem.* 248:793–99.

75. Kuma, F., Prough, R. A., and Masters, B. S. S. 1976. Studies on methemoglobin reductase: Immunological similarity of soluble methemoglobin reductase and cytochrome b_5 of human erythrocytes with NADH–cytochrome b_5 reductase and cytochrome b_5 of rat liver microsomes. *Arch. Biochem. Biophys.* 172:600–7.

76. Enoch, H. G., Catala, A., and Strittmatter, P. 1976. Mechanism of rat liver microsomal stearyl-CoA desaturase. *J. Biol. Chem.* 251:5095–103.

77. Bloch, K. 1969. Enzymatic synthesis of monounsaturated fatty acids. *Acc. Chem. Res.* 2:193–202.

78. Sasame, H. A., Thorgeirsson, S. S., Mitchell, J. R., and Gillette, J. R. 1974. The possible involvement of cytochrome b_5 in the oxidation of lauric acid by microsomes from kidney cortex and liver of rats. *Life Sci.* 14:35–46.

79. Correia, M. A., and Mannering, G. J. 1973. NADH synergism of the NADPH-dependent mixed function oxidase system of hepatic microsome-effects on activation and inhibition of the fatty Acyl-CoA desaturation system. *Mol. Pharmacol.* 9:455–69.

80. Montgomery, M. R. 1976. Characterization of fatty acid desaturase activity in rat lung microsomes. *J. Lipid Res.* 17:12–15.

81. Oshino, N., and Sato, R. 1972. The dietary control of the microsomal stearyl-CoA desaturation enzyme system in rat liver. *Arch. Biochem. Biophys.* 149:369–77.

82. Gellhorn, A., and Benjamin, W. 1964. The intracellular localization of an enzymatic defect of lipid metabolism in diabetic rats. *Biochim. Biophys. Acta* 84:167–75.

83. Marcel, Y. L., and Suzue, G. 1972. Kinetic studies on the specificity of long chain Acyl-CoA synthetase from rat liver microsomes. *J. Biol. Chem.* 247:4433–36.

84. Moncada, S., and Vane, J. R. 1979. Pharmacology and endogenous roles of prostaglandin endoperoxides, thromboxane A_2, and prostacyclin, *Pharmacological Reviews* 30:293–331.

85. Dutton, G. J. 1971. Glucuronide-forming enzymes. In *Handbook of Experimental Pharmacology*, Vol. 28, part 2, Chapter 45, pp. 378–400. Springer Verlag, Berlin.

86. Oesch, F. 1973. Mammalian epoxide hydrases: Inducible enzymes catalyzing the inactivation of carcinogenic and cytotoxic metabolites derived from aromatic and olefinic compounds. *Xenobiotica* 3:305.

87. Jerina, D. M., Lehr, R., Schaefer-Ridder, M., Yagi, H., Karie, J. M., Thakker, D. R., Wood, A. W., Lu, A. Y. H., Ryan, D., West, S., Levin, W., and Conney, A. H. 1977. Bay-region epoxides of dihydrodiols: A concept explaining the mutagenic and carcinogenic activity of benzo[a]pyrene and benzo[a]anthracene. In *Origins of Human Cancer*, H. Hiatt, J. D. Watson and I. Winsten, eds., pp. 639–58. Cold Spring Harbor Laboratory, Cold Spring Harbor, New York.

88. Bentley, P., and Oesch, F. 1977. Isolation of rat liver epoxide hydratase: Properties and substrate specificity of the pure enzyme. In *Microsomes and Drug Oxidations*, V. Ullrich, ed., pp. 646–53. Pergamon Press, New York.

89. Nordlie, R. C. 1974. Metabolic regulation by multifunctional glucose-6-phosphate. In *Current Topics of Cellular Regulation*, B. L. Horecker and E. R. Stadtman, eds., Vol. 8, pp. 33–117. Academic Press, New York.

90. Dallner, G., Siekevitz, P., and Palade, G. E. 1966. Biogenesis of endoplasmic reticulum membranes. I. Structural and chemical differentiation in developing rat hepatocyte. *J. Cell Biol.* 30:73–96.

91. Dallner , G., Siekevitz, P., and Palade, G. E. 1966. Biogenesis of endoplasmic reticulum membranes. II. Synthesis of constitutive microsomal enzymes in developing rat hepatocyte. *J. Cell Biol.* 30:97–117.

92. Negishi, M., and Kreibich, G. 1978. Coordinated polypeptide synthesis and insertion of protoheme in cytochrome P-450 during development of endoplasmic reticulum membrane. *J. Biol. Chem.* 253:4791–97.

93. Haugen, D. A., Coon, M. J., and Nebert, D. W. 1976. Induction of multiple forms of mouse liver cytochrome P-450 evidence for genetically controlled de novo synthesis in response to treatment with β-naphthoflavone or phenobarbital. *J. Biol. Chem.* 251:1817–27.

94. Jacob, F., and Monod, J. 1961. Genetic regulatory mechanisms in the synthesis of proteins. *J. Mol. Biol.* 3:318–56.

95. Alvares, A. P., and Kappas, A. 1977. Heterogeneity of cytochrome, P-450s induced by polychlorinated biphenyls. *J. Biol. Chem.* 252:6373–78.

96. Lucier, G. W., McDaniel, O. S., Hook, G. E. R., Fowler, B. A., Sonawane, B. R., and Faeder, E. 1973. TCDD-induced changes in rat liver microsomal enzymes. *Environ. Health Perspect.* 5:199–209.

97. Welton, A. F., and Aust, S. D. 1974. Multiplicity of cytochrome P-450 hemoproteins in rat liver microsomes. *Biochem. Biophys. Res. Commun.* 56:898–906.

98. Nebert, D. W., Robinson, J. R., Niwa, A., Kumaki, K., and Poland, A. P. 1975. Genetic expression of aryl hydrocarbon hydroxylase activity in the mouse. *J. Cell Physiol* 85:393–414.

99. Atlas, S. A., Boobis, A. R., Felton, J. S., Thorgeirsson, S. S., and Nebert, D. W. 1977. Ontogenetic expression of polycyclic aromatic compound–inducible monooxygenase activities and forms of cytochrome P-450 in rabbit. *J. Biol. Chem.* 252:4712–21.

100. Poland, A., and Glover, E. 1975. Genetic expression of aryl hydrocarbon hydroxylase by 2,3,7,8-tetrachlorodibenzo-p-dioxin: Evidence for a receptor mutation in genetically nonresponsive mice. *Mol. Pharmacol.* 11:389–98.

101. Kumaki, K., Jensen, N. M., Shire, J. G. M., and Nebert, D. W. 1977. Genetic differences in induction of cytosol reduced-NAD(P): Menadione oxidoreductase and microsomal aryl hydrocarbon hydroxylase in the mouse. *J. Biol. Chem.* 252:157–65.

102. Lind, C., and Ernster, L. 1974. A possible relationship between DT diaphorase and the aryl hydrocarbon hydroxylase system. *Biochem. Biophys. Res. Commun.* 56:392–400.

103. Lind, C., Vadi, H., and Ernster, L. 1978. Metabolism of benzo(a)pyrene-3,6-quinone and 3-hydroxybenzo(a)pyrene in liver microsomes from 3-methylcholanthrene-treated rats. *Arch. Biochem. Biophys.* 190:97–108.

104. Owens, I. S. 1977. Genetic regulation of UDP glucuronyltransferase induction by polycyclic aromatic compounds in mice. *J. Biol. Chem.* 252:2827–33.

105. Davison, S. C., and Wills, E. D. 1974. Studies on the lipid composition of the rat liver endoplasmic reticulum after induction with phenobarbitone and 20-methylcholanthrene. *Biochem. J.* 140:461–68.

106. Black, S. D., French, J. S., Williams, C. H. Jr., and Coon, M. J. 1979. Role of a hydrophobic polypeptide in the N-terminal region of NADPH-cytochrome P-450 reductase in the complex formation with P450$_{LM}$. *Biochem. Biophys. Res. Comm.* 91:1528–1535.
107. Wickner, W. 1979. The assembly of proteins into biological membranes: The membrane trigger hypothesis. *Ann. Rev. Biochem.* 48:23–45.
108. Gonzalez, F. J., and Kasper, C. B. 1980. Phenobarbital induction of NADPH-cytochrome C (P-450) oxidoreductase messenger ribonucleic acid. *Biochem.* 19:1790–1796.
109. Colbert, R. A., Bresnick, E., Levin, W., Ryan, D. E., and Thomas, P. E. 1979. Synthesis of liver cytochrome P-450b in a cell-free protein synthesizing system. *Biochem. Biophys. Res. Comm.* 91:886–891.

SECTION 6
DNA AND ASSOCIATED ENZYMES

THERESA CAMPANA, SECTION EDITOR

Many of the areas discussed in the following sections are the subject of intense experimental work at present. As a consequence, hypotheses that appear valid based on present knowledge may be invalidated by new data in the near future. In addition, much published material is speculative because of the paucity of hard data. Some of this material has been included in order to stimulate the formulation of testable hypotheses, as well as further discussion.

The references included at the end of each chapter do not represent an exhaustive survey of the literature. Instead, recent papers that are of interest either because of new experimental procedure, new data, or new theories have been listed. Recent review articles that survey the available literature more exhaustively are cited when available as a guide to the student seeking further information.

6.1. The Nucleic Acids: Composition and Cellular Localization

Theresa Campana and Lazar M. Schwartz

CHEMICAL CONSTITUENTS

Nucleic acids are macromolecules composed of equimolar amounts of sugar and phosphate, and a mixture of heterocyclic bases. The two main classes of nucleic acids, DNA and RNA, take their names from the sugar moiety present in the molecule (Figure 1).

The heterocyclic bases found in the nucleic acids belong to two classes: purines and pyrimidines (Figure 2). Each base can exist in two tautomeric forms, as shown for uracil in the figure. The other bases are represented in the tautomeric form that predominates as pH 7.0. Tautomerism is thought to play a role in spontaneous point mutations found in nucleic acids (see Chapter 7.7), by allowing mispairing of bases during DNA synthesis.

The bases found in the nucleic acids may be subdivided into major and minor components. The major bases found in DNA are adenine, guanine, cytosine, and thymine. In RNA, uracil is found in place of thymine. These bases constitute about 95% of the total; minor components include methylated derivatives and certain other unusual bases listed in Table 1. In general, RNA contains more minor bases than does DNA.

Chargaff (1) has shown that, in DNA, the sum of the purines is equal to

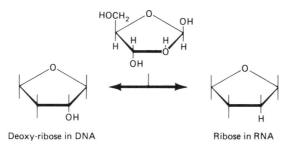

Deoxy-ribose in DNA   Ribose in RNA

Figure 1. Sugar moieties in nucleic acids.

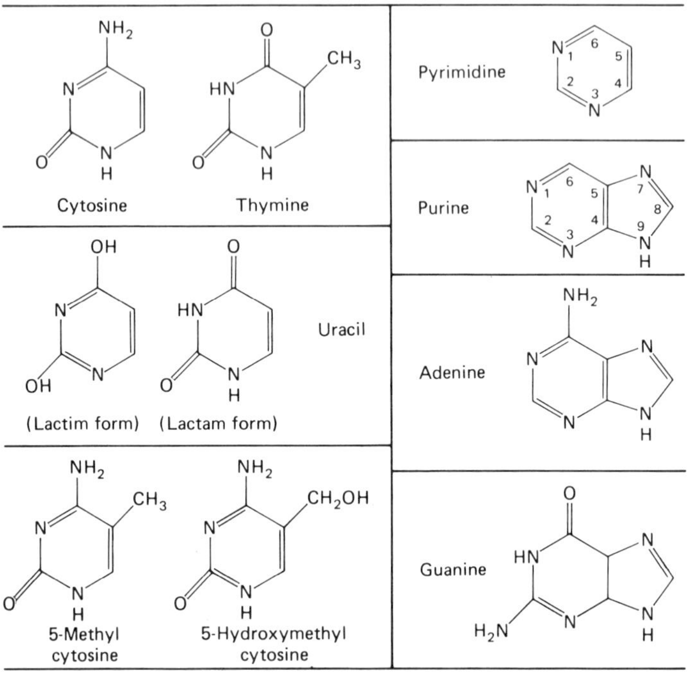

Figure 2. Examples of heterocyclic bases in nucleic acids.

the sum of the pyrimidines, and that the sum of the 6-amino bases (adenine and cytosine) is equal to that of the 6-keto bases (guanine and thymine). Specifically, there are equimolar quantities of adenine and thymine (A = T), and of guanine and cytosine (G = C). DNA from different sources may be relatively enriched in A–T base pairs, and that from still other organisms contains nearly equivalent amounts of each type of base pair. As the G + C content increases, the buoyant density and the thermal stability of the nucleic acid also increase. This characteristic allows separation of nucleic acids from several sources by density gradient centrifugation.

NUCLEOSIDES

The nitrogenous bases of nucleic acids are linked to the C-1 carbon of the sugar moieties by glycosidic bonds. The bond involves the N-1 position of pyrimidines, or the N-9 position of purines. This combination of base and sugar is called a nucleoside. The nucleoside forms of the major bases found in the nucleic acids are commonly called adenosine, guanosine, cytidine, uridine, and thymidine. The nucleosides that contain deoxyribose are usually abbreviated as dA, dG, dC, or dT. The dG·dC pair is more stable than

Table 1. Minor Bases in the Nucleic Acids.

DNA	RNA
	thymine
	pseudouracil
uracil	dihydrouracil
5-hydroxyuracil	5-hydroxyuracil
(bacteriophages)	2-thiouracil
	4-thiouracil
	1-methyluracil
	3-methyluracil
	5-methyluracil (thymine)
	5-hydroxymethyluracil
	5-methylaminomethyl-2-thiouracil
5-methylcytosine	2-thiocytosine
(higher plants)	N^6-acetyl cytosine
	3-methylcytosine
5-hydroxymethylcytosine	N^4-methylcytosine
(bacteriophages)	5-methylcytosine
	5-hydroxymethylcytosine
	6-amino-N^5-methylformamido-isocytosine
	N^1-methylcytosine
6-methylaminopurine	N^6-aminoacyladenine
(bacteria and bacteriophages)	1-methyladenine
	2-methyladenine
	6-methyladenine
	6-dimethyladenine
	7-methyladenine
	N^6-dimethyladenine
	1-methyl-N^6-methyladenine
	N^6-isopentyladenine
	1-methylguanine
	7-methylguanine
	N^2-methylguanine
	N^2-dimethylguanine
	orotic acid
	xanthine
	hypoxanthine
	7-methylxanthine
	1-methylhypoxanthine

the dA·dT pair (about 1 kcal/mole difference), but the dA·dT pair binds about 2 moles more of water than does the dG·dC pair (2). The sugar in the nucleoside is in the furanose configuration, and the glycosidic linkage is always β. The orientation of the glycosidic bond is *anti*, while the conforma-

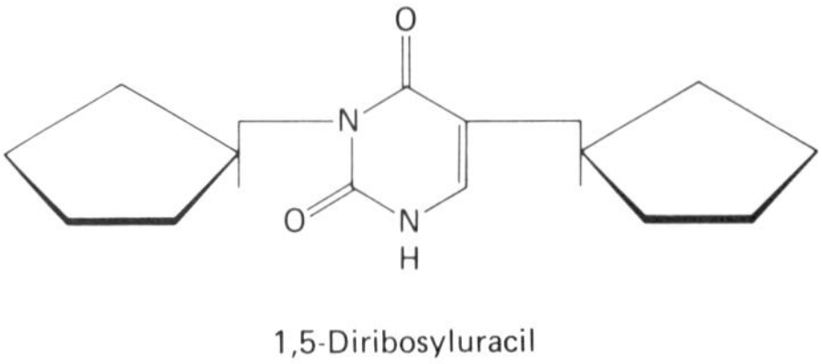

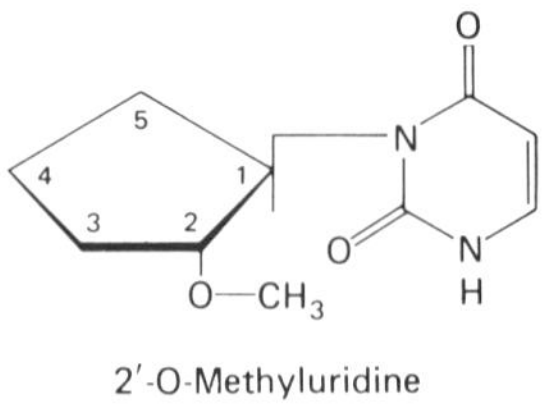

1,5-Diribosyluracil   2′-O-Methyluridine

Figure 3. Unusual nucleosides.

tion of the furanose ring is *endo* (3). In a few exceptional nucleosides, generally found in RNA, a base is found linked to two sugar molecules, or the glycosidic linkage involves a methylated sugar (Figure 3).

NUCLEOTIDES

Esters of nucleosides with phosphate are strong acids called nucleotides. The phosphate group may be linked to any of the hydroxyl groups found on the sugar. (See Figure 4.) Ribose nucleotides have been found with phosphate groups at positions, 2′, 3′, and 5′. Since deoxyribose does not contain a hydroxyl group at position 2, the deoxynucleotides can be phosphorylated only at the 3′ and 5′ positions. As many as four phosphate groups may be sequentially esterified to the 5′ position (Figure 5 and 6). It is generally accepted that the actual substrates for nucleic acid biosynthesis are the nucleoside 5′-triphosphates (4).

Another nucleotide which occurs naturally is a stable 3′,5′ cyclic compound that contains a single phosphate group esterified to the 3′ and 5′ positions of a single ribose molecule. Cyclic AMP, cyclic GMP, and cyclic CMP have been found in cells from a wide range of organisms. They appear to act as mediators of hormone action (5). Another cyclic nucleotide has also been described. This 2′,3′-cyclic nucleotide class occurs only as an intermediate in the alkaline hydrolysis of RNA (Figure 7).

CELLULAR LOCALIZATION OF NUCLEIC ACIDS

The name "nucleic acids" arose from the fact that the early preparations of this material used nuclei of sperm and other cells as a source of this

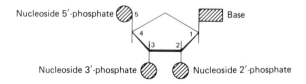

Figure 4. Nucleoside phosphates.

Figure 5. Nucleoside-diphosphate.

Figure 6. Nucleoside-tetraphosphate.

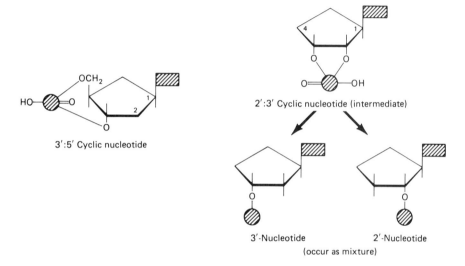

3':5' Cyclic nucleotide

2':3' Cyclic nucleotide (intermediate)

3'-Nucleotide   2'-Nucleotide
(occur as mixture)

Figure 7. Cyclic nucleotides.

highly acidic material. These early preparations were actually isolations of DNA, which is the form of nucleic acid found predominantly in the cell nucleus of eukaryotic cells. Some DNA is found in the cytoplasm; it is a small fraction of the total. Cytoplasmic DNA is, to a large extent, localized in the mitochondria in higher organisms.

Since the early isolation of RNA was from plant cells, it was first thought that the two types of nucleic acids were specific, RNA for plants and DNA for animal. Actually both forms exist in plants and animals. The bulk of the cellular RNA, unlike DNA, is found in the cytoplasm. DNA is generally found to be the carrier of genetic information, whereas RNA is the mediator responsible for the translation of this information into proteins. In some viruses RNA is the primary genetic material. The cellular localization of the nucleic acids in eukaryotes corresponds generally to their physiological roles. RNA, as well as DNA, is synthesized in the nucleus; RNA, however, is then transported to the cytoplasm in order that protein synthesis may take place (see Sections 8 and 9).

APPENDIX

In nucleic acids, the spatial relationship of the furanosic sugar linked through a glycosidic bond to the base, takes into account three parameters:

Figure 8

a. Orientation of the hydroxyl function at C 1', which may be below the ring (α) or above the ring (β) (Figure 8).

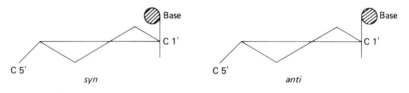

Figure 9

b. Orientation of the sugar molecule with respect to the glycosidic bond represented by *syn* and *anti* (Figure 9).

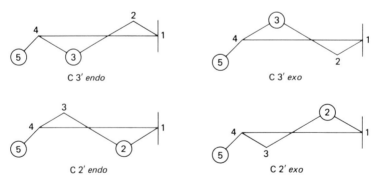

Figure 10

c. Displacement of either C 2' or C 3' with respect to C 5'. Four of the five atoms of the furanose ring are in co-planar orientation, and the fifth (either C 2' or C 3') displaced from the plane. The representation takes into account the most out-of-plane atom (either one) and its displacement with respect to C 5'. Displacement on the same side is called *endo,* while displacement in the opposite side is called *exo* (Figure 10).

REFERENCES

1. Chargaff, E. 1963. Essays on Nucleic Acids. Elsevier, Amsterdam.
2. Felsenfeld, G., and Miles, H. T. 1967. *Annu. Rev. Biochem.* 36:407.
3. Preobrazhenskaya, N. N., and Shabarova, Z. A. 1969. *Russ. Chem. Rev.* 38:111.
4. Goulian, M. 1971. *Annu. Rev. Biochem.* 40:855.
5. Robison, G. A., Sutherland, E. W., and Butcher, E. W. 1971. *Cyclic AMP.* Academic Press, New York.

6.2. Synthesis of the Components of Nucleic Acids

Theresa Campana

THE PYRIMIDINES

The nitrogenous bases required for the formation of both DNA and RNA are synthesized from simple precursors in all living cells. The biosynthetic pathway for the pyrimidines is shown in Figure 1. Of the enzymes that are required for this series of reactions, the first, aspartate transcarbamylase, seems to control the rate of reaction of the whole pathway. This enzyme is an allosteric protein which consists of several copies (perhaps six) of each of two types of subunits: regulatory and catalytic. The catalytic subunit contains the active site of the enzyme and the binding sites for both aspartic acid and carbamyl phosphate, the two substrates of the reaction. When isolated from the complex, the catalytic subunits are capable of catalyzing the condensation of the two substrates, in the absence of the other subunits; the regulatory subunit alone shows no catalytic activity.

What, then, is the role of these subunits? There is a site on the regulatory subunit that binds to CTP, the end product of the reaction pathway. When excess CTP is present owing to some imbalance in metabolism, it binds to the regulatory site, thereby causing a conformational change in the protein. This change in turn alters the conformation of the catalytic subunit so as to alter the active site, prevent binding of the substrates, and thereby shuts off the synthesis of pyrimidines. If, on the other hand, ATP is present in excess, this compound will bind to the regulatory subunit and prevent binding of CTP. This acts to maintain the active site in the appropriate conformation for the binding of substrates, and the biosynthetic pathway proceeds.

Other control mechanisms have also been reported to play a role in pyrimidine biosynthesis (1, 2). The other enzymes of the pathway appear to aggregate into a complex in at least one species; this complex controls activity by polypeptide interactions (1, 2). In other bacteria studied, the formation of the enzymes as well as control of their catalytic rate appears to be under allosteric modulation (3, 4, 5).

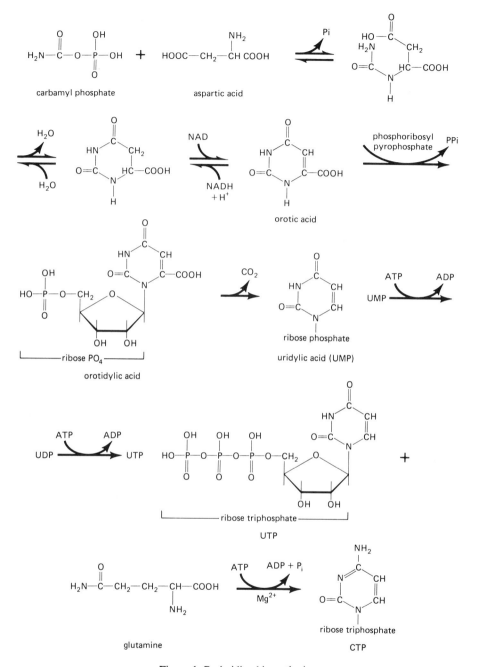

Figure 1. Pyrimidine biosynthesis.

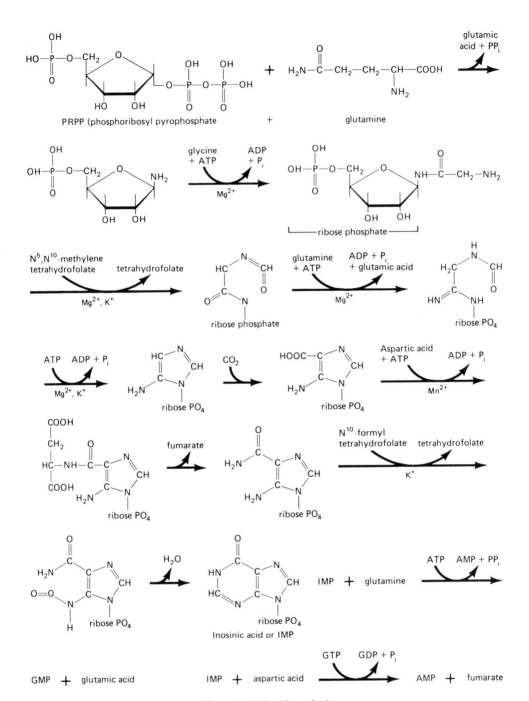

Figure 2. Purine biosynthesis.

THE PURINES

Purine biosynthesis (reviewed in Refs. 6 and 7) is carried out through a more complex series of reactions, shown in Figure 2. The first enzyme required for this pathway is again an allosteric protein subject to end-product inhibition. The enzyme, an amidotransferase is more complex than is aspartate transcarbamylase, since there are two sites on the regulatory subunit. The two sites respond to different inhibitors. One site binds AMP, ADP, and ATP; the other binds the phosphorylated derivatives of guanine. When these nucleotides are present in excess of the amount required for nucleic acid synthesis and energy requirements, the purine biosynthetic pathway is slowed down or stopped.

The final steps in the pathway involve the formation of AMP and GMP, which can be further phosphorylated through the various kinases that are present in the cell. The formation of AMP requires the presence of GTP, and GMP can only be formed in the presence of ATP. The reactions will be inhibited respectively by the presence of ATP or GTP; by means of such regulatory steps, the cell is able to control the formation of nucleic acid precursors in order to prevent build-up of nucleotide pools to levels that are higher than needed.

It is of interest to note that the vitamin folic acid is required for the biosynthesis of purines. Because of the requirements for this compound, various anti-tumor agents have been developed that are structural analogues of folic acid; these agents will be discussed later in this chapter.

REDUCTION OF THE RIBONUCLEOTIDES

The biosynthesis of purines and pyrimidines results in the formation of ribonucleotides which are used directly in the synthesis of RNA. In order to allow formation of DNA, however, these compounds must be reduced to the deoxyribose compounds. Both prokaryotic and eukaryotic systems have been described; mammalian cells appear to use the same type of mechanism as do *E. coli,* whereas the *Lactobacilli* system differs slightly. In each group, the first step required is the reduction of a disulfide bridge in a small, heat-stable protein called thioredoxin. The enzyme required for this reaction, thioredoxin reductase, is a flavoprotein; bound FAD and a disulfide group are required for activity. The reaction is:

$$\text{Thioredoxin-S}_2 + \text{NADPH} + \text{H}^+ \rightleftharpoons \text{Thioredoxin-(SH)}_2 + \text{NADP}^+$$

The reduced thioredoxin then acts as a hydrogen donor in the reduction of the ribonucleotides. In *E. coli,* and probably also in eukaryotes, a non-heme iron molecule and Mg^{2+} ions are required as cofactors in the reaction:

$$\text{Thioredoxin-(SH)}_2 + \text{XDP} \xrightarrow[\text{enzyme}]{\text{Fe} \cdot \text{H, Mg}^{2+}} \text{dXDP} + \text{Thioredoxin-S}_2$$

The required substrates are the diphosphate nucleosides, and the reaction involves the specific reduction of the 2' position of the ribose ring. The enzyme required for this reaction is called ribonucleotide reductase.

In *E. coli,* the enzyme has been shown to consist of two nonidentical subunits, with a molecular weight of about 250,000 daltons. It is an allosteric enzyme, and is regulated by the deoxyribonucleoside triphosphates (7). Specific deoxyribose triphosphates act as inhibitors or stimulators of the reduction of each of the ribonucleotides. For example, formation of dCDP is stimulated by dATP, but inhibited by dTTP. In general, dATP tends to inhibit reduction of purines but tends to promote the reduction of the pyrimidines. The enzyme is a complex protein; one of the subunits contains four separate binding sites which differ in their affinity for various nucleotides. It appears possible that inactivation may result from the formation of a specific complex of the two nonidentical subunits (see Refs. 6 and 7 for review).

In *Lactobacilli,* ribonucleotide reductase also appears to be an allosteric protein with control properties similar to the *E. coli* enzyme. However, the substrates for this enzyme are the ribonucleoside triphosphates, not the diphosphates. In addition, the coenzyme requirements of the two enzymes differ; the enzyme from *Lactobacilli* requires 2'-deoxyadenosylcobalamin, a conjugated form of vitamin B_{12}, rather than non-heme iron. The specificity of the enzymes are alike in that only the 2' position of the ribose ring can be reduced.

THYMIDYLATE SYNTHESIS

Deoxythymidylic acid is required for DNA but not RNA synthesis; this compound is formed by a specific reaction that simultaneously adds a methyl group to dUMP and reduces the hydroxymethyl compound that is formed (Figure 3). The one-carbon group that is added is contributed by N^5,N^{10}-methylenetetrahydrofolic acid, which also contributes the hydrogen required for the reduction. The structures of the vitamin, folic acid, and of its methylene derivative are shown in Figure 4. Folic acid, in a reduced form, functions as a one-carbon carrier for many important reactions, including purine biosynthesis. The reduction of folic acid to tetrahydrofolic acid is carried out by two enzymes. Structural analogues of folic acid, such as methotrexate and

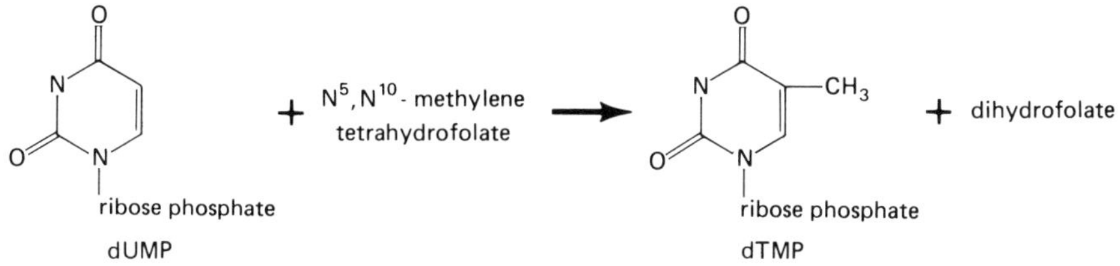

Figure 3. Generation of dTMP.

aminopterin (Figure 5), can act as competitive inhibitors of these enzymes. In this way, such compounds prevent cell growth by interfering with the formation of purines and of dTTP, and thus preventing the synthesis of nucleic acids. Since most tissues in the normal body replicate very slowly, agents such as these will kill neoplasms with little effect on normal cellular function for some time. Long-term use, however, can interfere dramatically with certain tissues such as the red blood cells and the intestinal mucosa. In addition, replacement of proteins in other tissues is also inhibited, since mRNA, and therefore new proteins, cannot be synthesized if purines are unavailable.

Thymidylate synthetase, the enzyme required for the formation of dTTP, differs from the other enzymes of purine and pyrimidine metabolism in that it shows no allosteric control (3, 7). Both eukaryotic and prokaryotic systems have been extensively tested for inhibition or stimulation by nucleotides, but modulation has never been demonstrated. At present, it is unclear why dTTP

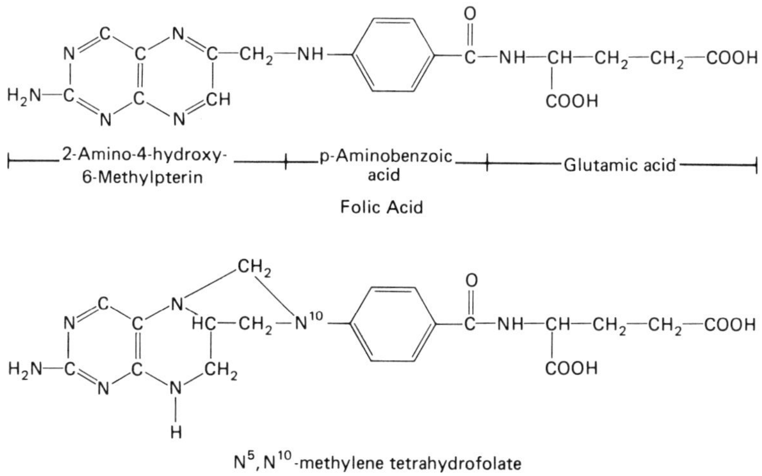

Figure 4. Structure of folic acid and of N^5,N^{10}-methylene tetrahydrofolate.

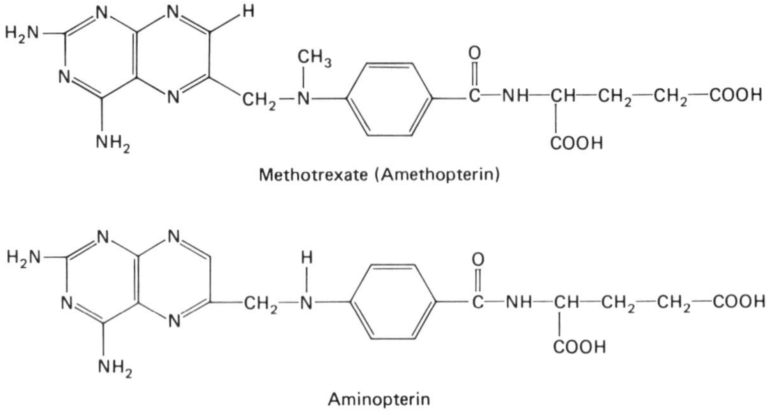

Methotrexate (Amethopterin)

Aminopterin

Figure 5. Folic acid analogues.

is incorporated into DNA and dUTP is not, since both serve as substrates for DNA-synthesizing enzymes in vitro. Regulation could take place at several points, such as some mechanism that prevents phosphorylation of dUMP, or perhaps binding of dUTP to the polymerase. At present, no such mechanism has been found in vivo; this is an interesting problem which merits further study.

SALVAGE PATHWAYS

Since the pyrimidine bases are preformed during biosynthesis, and the phosphorylated ribose is added to the base, pyrimidines in the diet may be directly utilized by the biosynthetic pathways. Purines, on the other hand, are built up on the sugar, and do not exist in the body as preformed bases. Purines in the diet require a separate metabolic pathway in order to be utilized; such pathways are known as salvage mechanisms (Figure 6). The physiological role of these enzymes may be more important than was originally thought,

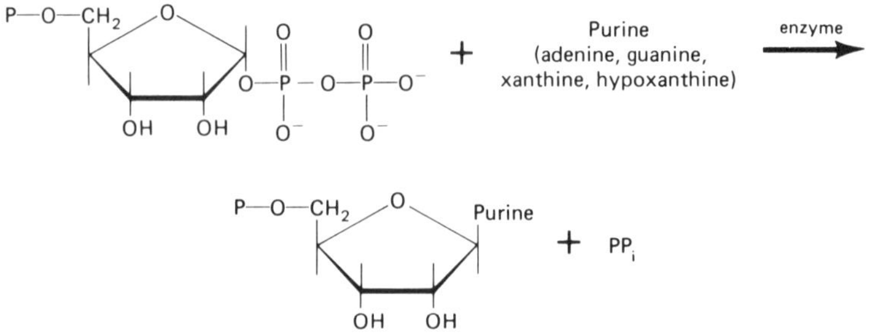

Figure 6. "Salvage" of preformed purines.

since severe disturbances result in humans when these enzymes are deficient. The enzymes involved are called adenine phosphoribosyltransferase and hypoxanthine–guanine phosphoribosyltransferase. In each system nucleotides are formed directly, not through the formation of nucleosides. In addition to their role in the utilization of dietary purines and pyrimidines and their roles in the breakdown of nucleic acids (reviewed in Ref. 8), phosphoribosyltransferases are important in the use of purine analogs given as pharmacological agents. These enzymes show a complex mechanism of control, and appear to have several sites to which different inhibitors may bind (9). It appears likely that phosphoribosyl pyrophosphate binds first to the enzyme, and the purines can bind only to the complex (10). Further studies with these enzymes may completely elucidate their physiologic roles; it would be of great interest to determine the reasons for the devastating effects of deficiencies in these transferases in man.

REFERENCES

1. Murray, A. W., Elliot, D. C., and Atkinson, M. R. 1970. *Prog. Nucl. Acid Res. Mol. Biol.* 10:87.
2. Gadd, R. E. A., and Henderson, J. F. 1970. *J. Biol. Chem.* 245:2979.
3. Henderson, J. F., Gadd, R. E. A., and Miller, H. 1970 *J. Biochem* 40:573.
4. O'Donovan, G. A., and Neuhard, J. 1970. *Bacteriol. Rev.* 34:278.
5. Calvo, J. M., and Fink, G. R. 1971. *Annu. Rev. Biochem.* 40:943.
6. Henderson, J. F., and Paterson, A. R. P. 1973. *Nucleotide Metabolism.* Academic Press, New York.
7. Potvin, B. W., Kellcher, R. J., and Gooder, H. 1975. *J. Bacteriol.* 123:604.
8. Condon, S., Condon, J. K., and O'Donovan, G. A. 1976. *J. Gen. Microbiol.* 92:375.
9. Wild, J. R., and Belser, W. L. 1977. *Biochem. Genet.* 15:157.
10. Wild, J. R., and Belser, W. L. 1977. *Biochem. Genet.* 15:173.

6.3. DNA Structure

Theresa Campana and Lazar M. Schwartz

THE DOUBLE HELIX

The first isolation of DNA was accomplished by Miescher in 1869, but its physiological role was not established until 1943. In that year, Avery, Mac-Leod, and McCarty established that a genetic trait was co-transferred from one strain to another with cellular DNA. The next ten years saw many laboratories devote their efforts to further elucidation of the structure of DNA. Chargaff and his coworkers had established that the DNA content of a given organism was a constant in all tissues except the germ line; the base equivalence within DNA molecules was also established by this group. Some X-ray diffraction studies had been carried out in 1938 by Astbury with an impure specimen of DNA. These studies were refined and expanded on a purer sample by Franklin and Wilkins in the early 1950s. Other laborator-

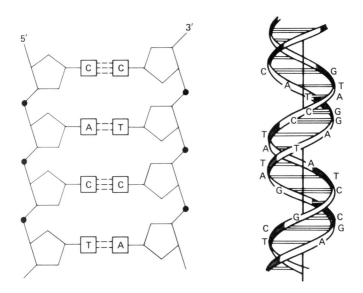

Figure 1. Schematic representation of the double helix.

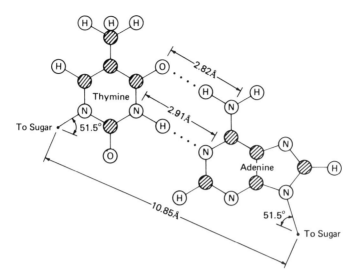

Figure 2. Secondary hydrogen bonds in the T–A base pair.

ies were investigating the chemistry of purines and pyrimidines (see Ref. 1 for extensive review).

With remarkable insight, two young investigators, Watson and Crick, were able to coordinate all these facts into a model of the structure of DNA. This model, the double helix, which was proposed in 1953, has been confirmed by much work since that time.

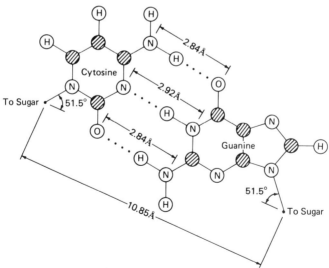

Figure 3. Secondary hydrogen bonds in the C–G base pair.

The basic unit in this structure is a right-handed helix formed by a single polynucleotide chain. Two of these units coil around a single axis to form a double helix with an overall diameter of 20 Å. The two chains are antiparallel; that is, the 3' end of one polynucleotide chain is paired with the 5' end of the second chain (Figure 1).

The external backbone of the double helix is formed by alternate sequences of deoxyribose and phosphate groups. The bases of each strand are located in the interior of the double helix and slightly twisted relative to each other (Figure 1). Secondary hydrogen bonds form between the bases (Figures 2 and 3). The length of the interbase hydrogen bonds is 2.80 to 3.0 Å. The bases are stacked at a center distance of 3.4 Å from each other, while the distance between the C_1 carbon atoms of the deoxyribose rings is about 11 Å.

PHYSICAL AND CHEMICAL PROPERTIES

DNA is a strong polybasic acid because of the phosphate groups which are fully ionized above pH 4.0. This allows strong binding to simple divalent cations such as Ca^{2+} and Mg^{2+}, as well as to basic proteins such as the histones (see Chapter 6.6). In nature, DNA is found in tight association with proteins in the eukaryotic organisms, but apparently it is naked (that is with no tightly held proteins) in the prokaryotes.

The DNA molecule is very long in relation to its small diameter, and is rigid because of the double-helix structure. For these reasons DNA in solution has a high viscosity except when the DNA is broken into small pieces, or when DNA is denatured. Denaturation, the unfolding of the double helix, can be monitored by decreases in the viscosity of a solution of DNA (2).

Denaturation of a solution of DNA can also be monitored in a spectrophotometer. The purines and pyrimidines have characteristic absorption spectra in the ultraviolet range, and, as a consequence, DNA has a strong absorption band at 260 nm. In the double helix, electrostatic interactions between the stacked bases reduce the amount of light each base can absorb. On denaturation, these electrostatic interactions are disrupted, since breakage of hydrogen bonds releases the molecule from the rigid constraints of the double helix. Denatured DNA can absorb 20 to 60% more light at 260 nm than can DNA in the natural double helix. This hyperchromic shift can be measured by following UV absorption in a spectrophotometer. The absorption is monitored while the DNA solution is heated to its melting temperature, which is the temperature at which the secondary bonds of the double helix have been completely disrupted (Figure 4.)

As the G + C content increases, the melting temperature is raised, since more energy must be applied to break the three hydrogen bonds of G–C

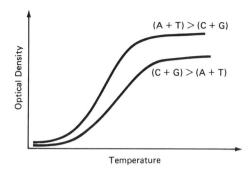

Figure 4. Heat denaturation of two DNA samples and subsequent hyperchromic shift.

pairs as compared to the two hydrogen bonds of A–T base pairs. The A–T content of a given molecule, however, shows a direct correlation with the hyperchromism of that molecule. The hyperchromic effect becomes more pronounced as A + T content increases. Molecules of undenatured, linear double-stranded DNA from different sources each show a characteristic melting pattern. Denaturation also depends on the ionic strength, or dielectric constant of the solution, and can be influenced by the presence of various drugs that can intercalate in the double helix (3).

MOLECULAR WEIGHT OF DNA MOLECULES

The mass of macromolecules is usually expressed in daltons, a term used to indicate a unit of mass equal to the mass of the hydrogen molecule, or 3.32×10^{-24}g. The mass, or molecular weight, of DNA is usually determined by ultracentrifugation of a solution containing a low concentration of DNA. Because of the extreme fragility of DNA, which can be sheared even on pipetting of a solution, it is difficult to obtain the molecular weights of large molecules. Recently, advanced physical chemistry measurements have been used to estimate the molecular weight of DNA in the chromosomes of fruit flies (4). Accurate determinations of the molecular weights of several DNA molecules are available. Viral DNAs range in molecular weight from 10^6 to 10^8 daltons, depending on the size and complexity of the virus. The *E. coli* genome appears to have a mass of about 3×10^9 daltons; other bacterial genomes are probably in the same general range of 10^8–10^{10} daltons. The chromosomes of the fruit fly have now been shown to have a mass of 10^{10}–10^{11} daltons (4), while chicken erythrocyte nuclei appear to contain DNA of 2.5×10^{12} daltons, according to cytochemical studies (5). Mitochondria and plasmids contain DNA that is much smaller.

MOLECULAR CONFORMATION OF DNA

Naturally occurring nucleic acids consist of polynucleotide chains. The linkage between the nucleotides is formed by phosphodiester bonds between the 5′ phosphate of one nucleotide and the 3′-OH end of a second. These polymers can exist as linear or circular molecules (see Chapter 6.4). The conformation of the molecule in solution depends on many factors (see Chapter 6.5), including the presence of counterions, pH, and temperature. Physical forms that have been described include:

1. Random coil, a linear, disorganized form.
2. Single-stranded, a helical, linear, or circular form which may contain intrastrand hydrogen bonds.
3. Multistranded, a helical form which contains interstrand hydrogen bonds; eukaryotic DNA generally occurs as a double-stranded molecule.
4. Circular, a continuous strand(s) with no free ends; natural form of some prokaryotic and organelle DNA.
5. Supercoil, a helical form with added tight coiling; found in eukaryotic chromosomes and some circular DNA molecules.
6. Intercalated double helix, in which the DNA is associated with certain molecules, often mutagenic and/or carcinogenic. This association leads to increased rigidity and thermal stability.
7. Branched molecules, an in vitro form of DNA synthesized by DNA polymerase I; not found in naturally occurring DNA.
8. Single-stranded ends: double-stranded molecules with single-stranded regions at the ends; found in certain bacteriophages which have complementary "sticky ends." This allows circularization of the molecule in suitable circumstances. Single-stranded ends may also form in vitro on incomplete renaturation of denatured DNA.
9. Catenated forms, interlocked circular DNA molecules found in organelles.

REFERENCES CITED

1. Henderson, J. F., and Paterson, A. R. P. 1973. *Nucleotide Metabolism, An Introduction.* Academic Press, New York.
2. Felsenfeld, G., and Miles, H. T. 1967. *Annu. Rev. Biochem.* 36:407.
3. Waring, M. J. 1970. *J. Mol. Biol.* 54:247.
4. Kavenoff, R., and Zim, B. H. 1973. *Chromosoma* 41:1.
5. Rasch, E. M., Barr, H. J., and Rasch, R. W. 1971. *Chromosoma* 33:1.

OTHER REFERENCES

Books and Review Articles:

1. Voet, D., and Rich, A. 1970. *Prog. Nucl. Acid Res. Mol. Biol.* 10:183.
2. Spencer, J. H. 1972. *The Physics and Chemistry of DNA and RNA.* Saunders, Philadelphia.
3. Feldma, M. Y. 1973. *Prog. Nucl. Acid Res. Mol. Biol.* 13:1.
4. Guschlbauer, W. 1976. *Nucleic Acid Structure.* Springer Verlag, New York.

Research Articles:

1. Bram, S. 1971. *Nature New Biol.* 232:174.
2. Bram, S., and Tongard, P. 1972. *Nature New Biol.* 239:128.
3. Pilet, J., and Brahms, J. 1972. *Nature New Biol.* 236:99.

6.4. Naturally Occurring Forms of DNA

Theresa Campana and Lazar M. Schwartz

Linear DNA Molecules

The DNA of eukaryotic chromosomes appears to occur as a long, linear, continuous double helix (1). This molecule is found in tight association with protein in the nucleus and is present in a highly condensed form. On lysis (breakage of the cell) the DNA is partially relaxed from this constricted form; careful isolation of the strands has shown that this less condensed form can be 5000 times longer than the original chromosome (2). Various techniques, including the kinetics of reassociation of denatured DNA, have been used to determine the size of the unbroken DNA in mammalian cells. These estimates indicate that the total DNA in a single cell may be about 2 meters long (3).

Some viral DNA is also isolated as a linear molecule. A virion of less than 100 Å in length may contain DNA with a total contour length of 50 μ, or 5000 times longer than the particle from which it was obtained. In viruses, as in prokaryotes in general, the DNA is not tightly associated with specific proteins, but is packaged within an envelope of protein. Many viruses, however, do not contain linear DNA, nor do prokaryotes in general.

CIRCULAR DNA

Most prokaryotes contain DNA that has no free ends in the single, continuous molecule. This form of DNA, circular DNA, may be a single-stranded molecule or may contain two strands that form a circular double helix. Circular DNA is found in bacteria, many viruses, plasmids, and eukaryotic organelles such as mitochondria and chloroplasts (4). Plasmids, semiautonomous, self-replicating DNA molecules that may exist independent of the cellular genome or be integrated into it, are discussed in detail in Section 8.

Monomeric circular DNA is generally found in bacterial cells and viruses, but the DNA can also be isolated as dimeric or higher oligomeric forms (Figure 1). These oligomeric forms appear in some cases to be intermediates

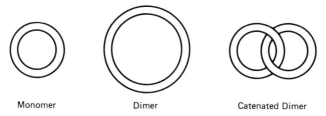

Monomer   Dimer   Catenated Dimer

Figure 1. Forms of circular duplex DNA.

in replication. Most bacterial viruses, referred to as bacteriophages or phages, contain double-stranded DNA (T phages, λ phages), but a few small phages generally contain single-stranded DNA which becomes double-stranded only on infection of a bacterium (φ X phages). The double-stranded circular DNA of mitochondria is found in the form of interlocked circles in a low but constant frequency (5). These forms are known as catenated oligomers (Figure 1).

SUPERCOILED DNA

Double-stranded circular DNA is often found in supercoiled configuration which is resistant to exonuclease attack and thermal denaturation, and has many compact twists of the helix (Figure 2, Form I). The physiological significance of supercoiling is not known with certainty, but it may play a role in the regulation of replication (4). It appears probably that a relaxation of the suprcoiling is required for unwinding of the double helix prior to DNA replication. Nicking of one strand of the supercoiled duplex by an endonuclease relieves the tightness, resulting in Form II, or open circle (Figure 2). Nicks on both strands of the circular duplex cause the molecule to become linear (Figure 2, Form III).

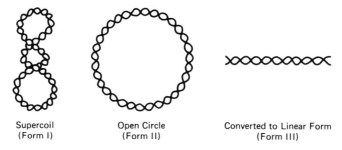

Supercoil   Open Circle   Converted to Linear Form
(Form I)   (Form II)   (Form III)

Figure 2. Supercoiled circular DNA and the effects of nicking by endonucleases

MATHEMATICAL FORMULATIONS OF SUPERCOILING

The supercoiled circular forms may be described in terms of superhelix winding, or the number of superhelical turns per ten base pairs (6). Two equations were developed for this purpose:

$$\tau = \alpha - \beta \qquad \sigma \equiv \frac{\tau}{\beta^\circ}$$

where:

τ = superhelix winding; the number of revolutions made by the helix about the superhelix axis.

α = topological winding; the number of revolutions made by one strand about the duplex axis constrained to be in a single plane.

β = duplex winding; the number of revolutions made by one strand about the unconstrained duplex axis.

σ = superhelix density; the number of superhelical turns per ten base pairs.

β^0 = normalization factor; numerically equal to one-tenth the number of base pairs per molecule.

PROPERTIES OF SUPERCOILED MOLECULES

Supercoiled circular forms of DNA differ from open circles in several physical and chemical properties, including electron microscopic appearance, higher sedimentation coefficients, increased electrophoretic mobility in agarose gels, denaturation at higher pH, higher melting temperature, lower intrinsic viscosity, and decreased sensitivity to shear (7). In addition these supercoiled molecules exhibit biphasic behavior on the intercalation of specific dye molecules with formation of superhelices in the opposite direction (8). Circular DNA seems to contain few, if any, supercoils in vivo at the time of formation. They appear with changes in the ionic environment, as is also true in vitro (4).

RELAXATION FACTOR

Several proteins that combine with supercoiled duplex circular DNA and cause relaxation of the supercoiling have been identified and isolated. One of these, ω protein, isolated from *E. coli*, induces relaxation but not permanent unwinding of the DNA strand (7). The mode of action of this protein appears to consist of nicking of one strand, with conservation of the energy from the broken phosphodiester bond. The energy, perhaps stored in the form of

One strand covalently
bound; one strand
nicked; protein
plastering gap.

Both strands covalently
linked; protein contains
patent nickase activated
by treatment.

Both strands covalently linked;
one strand in activated state
bound as stable enzyme-
substrate intermediate.

Figure 3. Models of relaxation complex of circular DNA.

an intermediate, is then used to re-form the phosphodiester bond after relaxation of the supercoiling (7). Other relaxation factors are known; synthesis of at least one is blocked by chloramphenicol (4). In some cases the relaxed form of the supercoiled double helix can be separated into two equal peaks on sedimentation in alkaline sucrose density gradients. One of these peaks contain a single-stranded linear DNA, while the remaining strand in the other peak is circular (8, 9). Three postulated models for the relaxation complex are shown in Figure 3.

INTERCONVERSION OF CIRCULAR AND LINEAR DNA FORMS

Some circular DNA molecules appear to be permanently fixed in this form. Apparently this category includes the DNA of eukaryotic organelles such as mitochondria, which are generally present as one to two copies per cell (10), whereas organelle DNA isolated from protists is almost always found to be linear (11). Some bacteria contain a group of small extrachromosomal DNA bodies called plasmids (discussed in greater detail in Section 8); the circular DNA of some plasmids, as well as that of certain phages, can be integrated into the bacterial chromosome as a linear insertion. The intimate mechanism of incorporation is still poorly understood, but it is known that integration occurs at a specific site on the chromosome, called attachment region. The process of insertion is known as recombination (a general term related to many aspects of DNA metabolism), and results from reciprocal crossover events at regions of homology between the recombining DNA molecules (Figure 4).

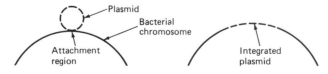

Figure 4. Integration of bacterial plasmids.

The integrated plasmid or viral DNA can be transferred together with the chromosome during bacterial conjugation or can also dissociate from the genome, apparently by a reversal of the integration process.

TERMINALLY REPETITIOUS DNA

Some DNA molecules, notably some phage and viral genomes, exist as double-stranded molecules that can be either circular or linear permutations of each other. These genomes have DNA sequences that are terminally repetitious and complementary in the linear form. The repetitious sequences range in size from about 300 bases in phages T_3 and T_4 (12) to about 10,000 nucleotides in phage T_5 (13). Circular permutation requires treatment with a specific enzyme. *E. coli* exonuclease III sequentially removes nucleotides from the 3' ends of a chain, exposing complementary ends that can then anneal to form a circular molecule (Figure 5).

In the λ and P_2-type phages, prior exonuclease treatment is not required for circular permutation of the linear forms (Figure 6). These types of phage DNA are packaged into the virion as a linear duplex, but cyclize rapidly after infection into the host cell. It has been determined that these phages have short, repetitious single-stranded ends in their linear form, which are called cohesive ends. The base sequence of the cohesive ends of bacteriophage λ has recently been determined. It consists of 12 nucleotides (GGGCGGC-GACCT) on one end matched by a complementary sequence on the other (14). Purified phage DNA must contain at least one of these cohesive ends for infectivity; it appears probable that cyclization is mandatory for successful infection.

The DNA of several animal viruses has also recently been shown to undergo cyclization when subjected to annealing conditions after denaturation to single strands (15). Unlike the bacteriophages, animal virus DNA which can undergo circular permutation has a specific sequence on each molecule of the duplex,

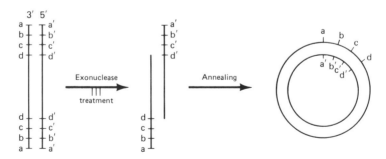

Figure 5. Formation of double-stranded circular DNA from linear duplex molecules as found in many T-type bacteriophages.

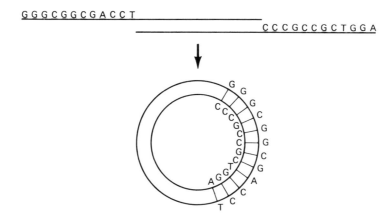

Figure 6. Formation of circularly permuted λ phage DNA.

with a complementary sequence on the other end of the same strand (Figure 7). This allows the formation of a "panhandle form," which involves about 2% of the total genome. Such a form has not been unequivocally demonstrated by electron microscopy, but single-stranded, twisted circular forms have been seen (16).

It is not clear what role cyclized forms play in viruses other than phages. It has recently been suggested (17) that these forms may arise as a consequence of dimerization during replication of the DNA. Oligomeric forms, perhaps with single-stranded ends, have been shown in *E. coli* infected with some of the larger bacteriophages. Watson (17) considers that multigenic forms are necessary for proper packaging of the DNA into the virion heads.

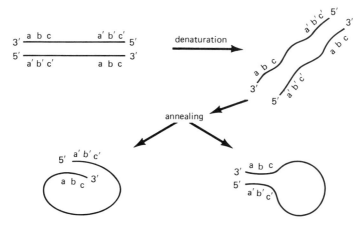

Figure 7. Circularization of animal virus DNA.

REFERENCES

1. Laird, C. D. 1973. *Annu. Rev. Genet.* 7:177.
2. Kavenoff, R., and Zimm, B. 1973. *Chromosoma* 41:1.
3. Du Prow, E. J. 1970. In *DNA and Chromosomes*. Holt, Rinehart and Winston, New York.
4. Helinski, D. R., and Clewell, D. B. 1971. *Annu. Rev. Biochem.* 40:899.
5. Jardon, J. M., Van der E. A., and Vinograd, J. 1970. *Fed. Proc.* 29:725.
6. Vinograd, J., Lebowitz, J., and Watson, R. 1968. *J. Mol. Biol.* 33:173.
7. Wang, J. C. 1971. *J. Mol. Biol.* 55:523.
8. Robberson, D. L., and Clayton, D. A. 1972. *Proc. Natl. Acad. Sci. U.S.A.* 69:3810.
9. Salzman, N. P., Sebring, E. D., and Radonovich, M. 1973. *J. Virol.* 12:669.
10. Miller, P. L., ed. 1970. *Control of Organelle Development.* Cambridge University Press, London.
11. Borst, R. 1972. *Annu. Rev. Biochem.* 41:333.
12. Ritchie, D. A., Thomas, C. A., McHattie, L. A., et al. 1967. *J. Mol. Biol.* 23:365.
13. Rhoades, M., and Rhoades, E. A. 1972. *J. Mol. Biol.* 69:187.
14. Wu, R., and Taylor, E. 1971. *J. Mol. Biol.* 57:491.
15. Koczot, F. J., Carter, B. J., Garonaud, C. F., et al. 1973. *Proc. Natl. Acad. Sci. U.S.A.* 70:215.
16. Garon, C. F., Berry, K. W., and Rose, J. A. 1972. *Proc. Natl. Acad. Sci. U.S.A.* 69:2391.
17. Watson, J. D. 1972. *Nature New. Biol.* 239:197.

6.5. Properties of DNA in Solution

Theresa Campana

ACID–BASE PROPERTIES

The acidic nature of DNA is due to the ionization of the secondary phosphate groups of the phosphodiester bonds, which is essentially complete at pH = 4.0. The nitrogenous bases also ionize, and pK'_a values have been determined for each. The first pK'_a, at pH = 3.3 to 4.5, corresponds to the removal of the hydrogen from position N-1 in A and C, and from position N-7 in G. The keto group at C-6 of G, T, and U, has a pK'_a of 9.2 to 9.9. A third dissociation can be measured in bases. This corresponds to the titration of the hydrogen at N-9 (purines) or N-3 (pyrimidines). Since this is not present in nucleosides and nucleotides, these compounds have no pK'_{a3}. On titration of a duplex polynucleotide, however, the apparent pK_a of the bases is altered, owing to stability conferred by hydrogen bonding (1). Ionization of the bases in DNA takes place above pH = 5.0, since it depends on the disruption of the hydrogen bonds.

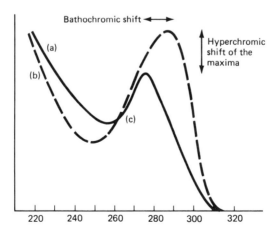

Figure 1. Titration of DNA from acid to neutral pH (curve a) and from neutral to alkaline pH (curve b). Point c, where the two curves cross, is the isosbestic point.

On titration of nucleic acids, a hypsochromic shift toward the red end of the spectrum is seen when the DNA is back-titrated to neutrality from an acid pH. Correlated with this is a hypochromic shift to lower optical density (Figure 1a). Titration from neutrality to alkaline pH gives rise to the opposite effects; the peak undergoes a bathochromic shift to the blue end of the spectrum and a hyperchromic shift (Figure 1b).

The point where two curves, obtained by titrating from different pH values, cross each other is known as the isosbestic point or point of equal extinction (Figure 1c). The sharpness of these curves can be used as a measure of the purity of the DNA. The isosbestic point can be used in calculating the amount of a specific base present in the sample.

DENATURATION OF DNA

Hydrogen bonding is disrupted by the addition of appropriate energy. Heating a sample causes these bonds to break, but does not influence covalent bonds. A duplex DNA molecule will denature, that is, separate into two single-stranded molecules, at a temperature that allows complete disruption of hydrogen bonding. This denaturation depends on the ionic strength of the solution, the concentration of DNA, the presence of specific ions in the solution, and the composition of the DNA.

At neutral pH, in 0.15 M NaCl, most DNA duplex molecules will denature at 75–95°C, depending on the G–C content of the DNA. By decreasing the NaCl concentration about 150-fold, the melting temperature can be decreased by about 30°C, but the G–C content still determines the exact melting point. Most divalent cations will increase thermal stability of a specific DNA; the exception is Ca^{2+}. This cation depresses the melting temperature, apparently by destroying hydrogen bonds and preventing their re-formation. Acidic or basic conditions greatly decrease the melting temperature. Denaturation at pH = 2.6 will take place at ambient temperature. However, if the temperature is lowered to 0.4°C, denaturation will not occur even at extremes of pH. Reductions in the ionic strength of the solution enhance these pH effects, while increases in salt concentration inhibit the disruption of hydrogen bonding.

VISCOSITY

Neutral solutions of DNA have a high visocity due to the length and rigidity of the double helix. The viscosity of a DNA solution is directly related to the hydrated volume of the DNA molecules and has a complex relationship with the molecular weight. Intrinsic viscosity $[\eta]$ cannot be measured directly, but can be obtained from the relative viscosity. η_{rel}, which can be measured in a viscometer. The time required for a solution, and for the solvent, to pass between two points marked on a viscometer is measured, and the η_{rel} is calculated:

$$\eta_{rel} = \frac{t_{solution}}{t_{solvent}} \tag{1}$$

where t = time required to pass between the marked points. The specific viscosity, η_{sp}, is then calculated

$$\eta_{sp} = \eta_{rel} - 1$$

Finally, $[\eta]$ is calculated from:

$$[\eta] = \lim_{C \to o} \left(\frac{\eta_{sp}}{C} \right) \tag{2}$$

where C is the concentration of the DNA.

Generally $[\eta]$ is computed by extrapolation to $C = O$ from a plot of η_{sp} vs. C (Figure 2). However, as the ionic strength approaches zero, the DNA tends to denature, and extrapolation becomes difficult (Figure 3), owing to interactions between the charged phosphate groups in the absence of salt. When salt is added, the charged groups are neutralized, and there is no charge repulsion.

The intrinsic viscosity can be related to the molecular weight by the Scherager-Mandelkern equation:

$$\frac{NS \, [\eta]^{1/3} \, \eta_o}{100 \, 1/3 \, MW^{2/3} \, (1 - \bar{v}p)} = \beta \left(\frac{a}{b} \right) \tag{3}$$

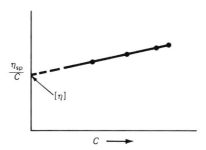

Figure 2. Determination of $[\eta]$ from measurements of η_{rel} in NaCl solutions

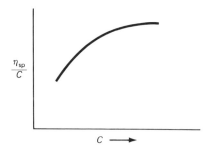

Figure 3. Curve obtained when η_{rel} is measured in a solution containing little or no salt.

where

$N =$ Avogadro's number
$S =$ Svedberg unit
$\eta_o =$ viscosity of the solvent

$\beta \left(\dfrac{a}{b} \right) = \dfrac{\text{Unit of function of the shape of the molecule that is obtained}}{\text{from light scattering studies}}$

$(1 - \bar{v}\rho) =$ Bouyancy factor where
$\bar{v} =$ partial specific volume of the solution, and
$\rho =$ density of the solvent
$MW =$ molecular weight

Recent work indicates that the nucleotide composition of the DNA molecule also has an influence on viscosity. Synthetic homopolymers and heteropolymers of known composition have been studied; those more nearly resembling natural DNA appear to be closest to the native polymer in most physicochemical measurements (2). However, these measurements indicate that specific repeating sequences dictate structural properties, but are somewhat masked in native DNA owing to the complexity of the molecule (1).

OPTICAL MEASUREMENTS

DNA has several optical properties that can be measured; these include ultraviolet absorption, optical rotatory dispersion, and circular dichroism. These measurements provide information on the secondary and tertiary structure of macromolecules. As discussed in Chapter 6.3, the base composition of DNA molecules determines the hypochromicity found on denaturation. Optical density (O.D.) measurements are carried out at 260 nm, since the ring systems of the bases absorb ultraviolet light most strongly in this region of the spectrum. The O.D. must be measured at a pH that is 2 or more units from any measurable pK value, to minimize interactions between salt and acid or alkali. In addition, the O.D. must be measured in the presence of salt (NaCl = 10^{-3}M) to prevent denaturation with consequent hyperchromicity. Temperature must also be kept at or lower than ambient temperature to prevent denaturation.

The molar extinction coefficient (ϵ) of DNA solutions has been determined. It is expressed as ϵ(P), the molar extinction coefficient with respect to phosphorus content (in number of gram atoms of P per liter), since this number is smaller than ϵ. For the most native (i.e., least denatured) DNA samples, ϵ(P) = 6–7 × 10^3. Studies on synthetic polynucleotides have shown that nucleotide sequence influences ϵ(P), with the lowest values found for duplex molecules containing a single base on each strand (1). On the basis of quantum-mechanical calculations, it has been determined that the hypochromicity of native DNA also depends on the sequence (3).

Both optical rotatory dispersion (ORD) and circular dichroism (CD) have been used to study the secondary and tertiary structure of macromolecules. The optical activity of DNA depends on helicity, interactions of the bases, and hydrogen bonding. Transitions from helical to random coil conformation can be monitored by ORD and CD. The nucleotide composition and sequence also influence CD spectra, as shown by studies with synthetic polynucleotides (1, 4). Polymers that contain both purines and pyrimidines on both strands give CD spectra consistent with those obtained from natural DNA samples. Those consisting of one purine and one pyrimidine strand, on the other hand, appear to assume conformations that differ widely from that of native DNA (4, 5). This does not imply that there are no homogenous sequences in DNA, but that these sequences are influenced by the heterogenous sequences surrounding them. Studies of this type, using synthetic polymers, can be used to decipher the contribution of specific sequences to the activity of DNA.

SEDIMENTATION PROPERTIES OF DNA

DNA solutions can be centrifuged on density gradients prepared of sucrose, cesium chloride, or cesium sulfate. When such a gradient is centrifuged to equilibrium, macromolecules will band at a point where they are equal in density to the solution. Cesium salts, especially CsCl, are usually used because of their high solubility and low viscosity. The gradient need not be performed, since it will form with time on centrifugation. The DNA solution, mixed with 6 M CsCl, is centrifuged to equilibrium, and the DNA will band at some density. This bouyant density is determined by the base composition of the DNA molecule, and can be directly related to the G–C content (Figure

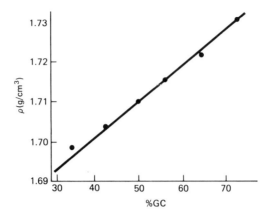

Figure 4. Relationship between bouyant density and GC content in several microorganisms.

4). The G–C content can be calculated from the density in CsCl gradients:

$$\rho = 1.660 + 0.098 \text{ (G–C)} \tag{4}$$

where ρ = bouyant density of the DNA sample. Denaturation of a given DNA sample causes it to band at a higher density than the native duplex molecule, owing to intramolecular hydrogen bonding, which causes a denser and more compact conformation.

The sedimentation coefficient, S, for DNA molecules, however, is usually determined by velocity sedimentation in an alkaline sucrose density gradient. In this method equilibrium is not attained, but S can be determined by comparison to a standard DNA of known S or can be calculated from

$$S = \frac{dx/dt}{\omega^2 \, x} \tag{5}$$

where

$$x = \text{distance from center of rotation}$$
$$\omega = \text{angular velocity (radians/sec)}$$
$$t = \text{time (sec)}$$

The S value obtained for a globular molecule can be directly related to molecular weight (MW).

$$MW = \frac{RTS}{D(1 - \bar{v}\rho)} \tag{6}$$

where

$$R = \text{gas constant (ergs/mole/deg)}$$
$$T = \text{absolute temperature}$$
$$D = \text{diffusion coefficient}$$
$$\bar{v} = \text{partial specific volume}$$
$$\rho = \text{density of the solvent}$$

This relationship however, does not hold for long rods; in order to determine the molecular weight of a DNA molecule, a more complex equation must be used. From this method, S values for various DNA molecules and their molecular weights have been determined.

The sedimentation coefficient is usually expressed in terms of Svedberg units, S being defined as 1×10^{-13} S. For mitochondrial DNA molecules, centrifugation in alkaline sucrose gradients has established a particle size of about 80–90S (6). It appears that pH has an effect on the S values obtained for at least some mitochondrial DNA molecules, since S increases with the pH up to pH = 12.6 (6). Circular DNA and linear DNA of the same molecular weight will differ greatly in S values; circularity and single-strandedness of a DNA molecule will each cause it to band at a higher density than will a linear double-stranded molecule of equal molecular weight. The molecular weights of some bacterial plasmids (7, 8) and those of some satellite DNAs (9) have been determined from their S values.

HYBRIDIZATION IN SOLUTION

Double-stranded DNA will melt on heating; if the solution is cooled quickly, the denatured single strands cannot re-form the double helix to any appreciable degree. This property has been used to study the homology of genomes from various species. The greater the degree of double-stranded areas formed, the greater the sequence homology and therefore the closer the two species are in evolution. DNA molecules from bacteria will hybridize much better with each other than with mammalian DNA. This method can be used with two DNA fractions or with RNA from one sample and the DNA from a different species (10).

DNA is denatured and cooled quickly to prevent reannealing. The other nucleic acid (denatured or single-stranded DNA, or single-stranded RNA) is added, with temperature and pH strictly controlled. The temperature is lowered very gradually to allow reannealing, and hybrid duplex molecules can be isolated from the mixture. One of the two nucleic acids is usually radioactively labeled to allow detection of even a small degree of homology. The double-stranded hybrids can be detected and isolated by the use of hydroxyapatite column chromatography, CsCl density gradient centrifugation, or other column chromatography methods (10). These methods have also been useful in the restriction endonuclease mapping of viral DNA (11), as well as the in situ localization of specific RNA fractions (12).

REFERENCES CITED

1. Wells, R. D., and Wartell, R. M. (1974). In *Biochemistry of Nucleic Acids,* Vol. 6, K. Burton. ed. University Park Press, Baltimore.
2. Grant, R. C., Kodama, M., and Wells, R. D. 1972. *Biochemistry* 11:805.
3. Pysh, E. S., and Richards, J. L. 1972. *J. Chem. Phys.* 57:3680.
4. Gray, D., and Tinoco, I., Jr. 1970. *Biopolymers* 9:223.
5. Allen, F. S., Gray, D. M., Roberts, G. P., et al. 1972. *Biopolymers* 11:853.
6. Borst, P. 1972. *Annu. Rev. Biochem.* 41:333.
7. Guerry, P., and Falkow, S. 197. *J. Bacteriol.* 107:372.
8. Helinski, D. R. 1973. *Annu. Rev. Microbiol.* 26:437.
9. Laird, C. D. (1973. *Annu. Rev. Genet.* 7:177.
10. Ayad, S. R. 1972. *Techniques of Nucleic Acid Fractionations.* Wiley Interscience, New York.
11. Lebowitz, P., Siegel, W., and Skar, J. 1974. *J. Mol. Biol.* 88:105.
12. Winber, D. E., and Steffensen, D. 1974. *Annu. Rev. Genet.* 7:205.

ADDITIONAL REFERENCES

1. Von Hippel, P. and Kwok-Ying, W. 1971. *J. Mol. Biol.* 61:587.
2. Klotz, L. C., and Zimm, B. H. 1972. *J. Mol. Biol.* 72:779.
3. Szala, S., and Chorazy, M. 1972. *Acta Biochim. Pol.* 19:235.

6.6. Structural Organization of Genetic Information in Eukaryotes

Kenneth S. McCarty, Sr. and Kenneth S. McCarty, Jr.

Four prominent features contribute to the complexity of the structural organization of genetic information in eukaryotes: (1) The eukaryotic nuclear DNA is three orders of magnitude more complex than in prokaryotes and is composed of highly repetitive, middle repetitive, and single copy sequences (ref. 1). (2) The DNA coding for specific RNAs is temporally amplified. Although this is well established as a mechanism of ribosomal genome amplification during oocyte maturation, recent observations suggest that it may also extend to somatic cells as a possible mechanism of drug resistance. Thus under conditions of stress, the cell is able to cope with its environment by increased protein synthesis of a particular enzyme coded for by an mRNA transcribed from an amplified DNA sequence (ref. 2). (3) The DNA in eukaryotes, as well as that of many mammalian viruses, exists in a highly condensed form associated with proteins. (4) The primary DNA sequence is not colinear with the final mRNA transcript. Thus the initial RNA transcript requires precise splicing of intervening sequences (introns) and a ligation of the RNA coding sequences (exons) into functional RNA units (ref. 3).

INTRODUCTION AND MAGNITUDE OF THE PROBLEM

It is essential to define the highly complex organization of DNA and chromosomal proteins in order to form a reasonable mechanism to account for the storage and selection of genetic information. This section will first consider the DNA sequence complexity and then the molecular organization of chromatin. It is hoped that this discussion will provide the background for us to consider the molecular controls of transcription to be described in Chapter 12.1.

DNA SEQUENCE COMPLEXITY IN EUKARYOTES

The DNA content of the eukaryote exceeds that of the prokaryote by three orders of magnitude (2–3 pg per haploid nucleus, e.g., 2–3×10^9 DNA base pairs) (4). In addition there is no obvious relationship between position on the evolutionary scale and DNA content (thus amphibian DNA content ranges as high as 100 pg per haploid nucleus).

The apparent excess of DNA in eukaryotes suggests other functions than direct coding for specific mRNAs. The eukaryote (1000–10,000 genes per cell) with an average mRNA size equivalent to ovalbumin of 2800 nucleotides) would require only 2.8×10^6 to 2.8×10^7 base pairs of DNA. This represents at least two to three orders of magnitude excess DNA, some of which is never transcribed, and some of which is transcribed but not transported to the cytoplasm. The excess nucleotides are likely to serve some control functions.

The differences in the eukaryotic DNAs demonstrate the presence of sequence complexities very different from that of prokaryotic DNA. Thus renaturation studies reveal a reiteration frequency, with 10% highly repetitive DNA (1,000,000 copies), 15% middle repetitive (1,000–100,000 copies), and 70% unique single copy (1 copy), when compared to prokaryotic DNA with predominantly unique single copy DNA.

Highly Repetitive DNA

With the possible exception of yeast, repetitious DNA occurs in all eukaryotes (5). The most rapidly renaturing DNAs are represented by satellite DNA with repeating units that vary from 110 to 390 base pairs. The sequence complexity is low, species-specific, and not transcribed into RNA. The species specificity is revealed by the absence of competitive cross hybridization between guinea pig, calf, and mouse satellite DNA (6). Cytological hybridization of satellite DNA with metaphase arrested intact chromosomes is confined to both specific heterochromatic regions and centromeres of mitotic cells.

Middle Repetitive DNA

Until recently, gene amplification of middle repetitive DNA was presumed to be limited to a few specific genomes, as ribosomal DNA (rDNA), transfer RNA (tDNA), 5S RNA (5S DNA), and so on. The ribosomal genes of the developing oocytes represent a unique situation in which these genes are only temporally amplified. Recent experiments by Schimke et al. (7) utilizing mouse, S-180, and L1210 cells cultured for a number of generations in the presence of methotrexate, however, provide evidence that drug-induced resistance to this dihydrofolate analogue may be accounted for by increased production (200 ×) of dihydrofolate reductase. cDNA probes prepared from dihydrofolate reductase mRNA indicated a 200-fold amplification of the folate reductase DNA genome. The significance of these observations will be discussed in Chapter 12.1 in relation to transcription control.

In contrast to the transcriptionally active middle repetitive DNA sequences, satellite DNA is not transcribed. The technique of Thomas and Dancis (8) in the formation of DNA closed circles has been useful in identifying the frequency of middle repetitive DNA's based on the observation that these sequences have the capacity to form closed circles whose circumference is dictated by the number of base pairs of the unique single copy DNA sequences. For example, the alternating sequence elements of the repetitive and unique sequences in the *Xenopus* DNA genome are 200–400 nucleotides and 650–900 nucleotides, respectively.

MOLECULAR ORGANIZATION OF CHROMATIN

The remarkable feature of chromatin in eukaryotes is that its DNA is wound around an octomer of histones that form a structural lattice resulting in DNA compaction ratios of 7/1 and 10,000/1 in euchromatin and heterochromatin, respectively. Although many of these observations had been suggested by electron microscopy in the early 1970s, it is only within the past few years that chromatin has begun to yield to the newer techniques of molecular analysis.

We will present evidence here that histones H2A, H2B, H3, and H4 represent the primary scaffold on which 140 base pairs of DNA are wrapped (9). The intermolecular hydrophobic interaction of each of these histones represents a well-defined structure, the *nucleosome*. The molecular properties of the nucleosome are a consequence of the interaction of centrally located hydrophobic amino acid residues (10). Amino terminal basic amino acid residues, which extend from these hydrophobic centers, interact with the aqueous environment to provide a configuration in which electrostatic charge interactions are maintained within the major groove of the DNA. Although these interactions impart the primary DNA configuration, histone H1 is required in addition to attain the maximal compaction observed in heterochromatin and in mitotic chromosome structures (11). Histone H1 is located in the linker region between nucleosomes, as well as on the outer surface of the first ten base pairs of the nucleosome.

Chemical Composition of the Basic Structural Chromosomal Proteins

The major delineation between prokaryotes and eukaryotes is the presence in eukaryotes of a macromolecular complex of DNA and histones confined to a nucleus.

Although prokaryotes are defined by the absence of a nucleus, specific DNA–basic protein interactions result in a higher level of organization of the genome. To formulate a mechanism of storage and regulation of gene expression, it is essential to provide a critical analysis of the proteins involved in these macromolecular complexes.

Proteins in Prokaryotes.   Although the association between histones and DNA in eukaryotes has been studied for many years, structures imposed by the packing of the DNA in the bacterial nucleoid have only recently received attention. In fact, the simple concept of a protein-free circular double-stranded DNA helix has already begun to yield to the notion that bacterial linkage groups also attain a higher level of organization.

Studies of the *E. coli* nucleoid have shown it to contain approximately 60% DNA, 30% RNA, and 10% proteins. Thus the bacterial DNA assumes a highly folded configuration, sedimenting at $1500S_{20,W}$, arranged in approximately 50 independent supertwisted loops attached to a RNA core.

Evidence of folding constraints imposed on the DNA by the interaction of both RNA and protein is obtained by utilizing the fact that different conformational transitions result from ribonuclease and/or trypsin treatment of the nucleoid complex.

The probability that bacterial DNA might either permanently or transiently complex with proteins is suggested by the presence of a specific class of DNA binding proteins, some of which bear close resemblance to histones (HU_E, HU_A, etc.) (12) (see Table 1). Although the protein to DNA ratio of 0.1 to 0.15 (weight basis) represents only 1/10 that of the histone/DNA ratio in eukaryotes, it is reasonable to suggest that HU proteins play a structural role in the condensation of bacterial or phage DNA. This role resembles the interaction between eukaryotic DNA and histones. For example, a preferential shift (T_m decrease) in melting of certain AT-rich portions of DNA has been observed in prokaryotes, not unlike the effect of calf thymus histone H1 on DNA melting. Electron microscopy and sedimentation analysis also show a DNA compaction of the type seen with histone interactions.

Histones in Eukaryotes.   In addition to the presence of a nucleus, a specific, highly conserved set of histone/DNA interactions defines the chromatin of eukaryotes. The ratio of histones/DNA is constant (1 ± 0.15) on a weight

Table 1. Basic Proteins Associated with DNA.

PROTEIN	ORIGIN	M.W.	(RESIDUES)	CHARACTERISTICS
Basic Proteins				
HU$_E$	*E. coli*	10,000		Lysine-rich
HU$_A$	Blue-green algae	10,000–11,000		
Histones				
Histone	Mycoplasmas			Lysine-rich
Histone	*Euglena*			5 histones
H1G	*Chlamydomonas*			
H1-2	"			
H1-3	"			
HMGT	Rainbow trout	28,133		
HMG1	Calf thymus	28,190		
HMG2	" "	28,423		
A24	" "			
HMG17				
HMG14				
Histones				
TH1	Calf thymus	20,000–22,000	(220)	Tissue-specific differentiation
X	" "	" "	"	" "
H1-3B	" "	" "	"	" "
H2A.1	All tissues	14,000	(129)	Lysine-rich (No Met)
H2A.	" "	"	"	Met residue 51
H2B.1	" "	13,774	(125)	Lysine-rich
H2B.2	Mouse only	"	"	Ser residue 75
H2B.3	All tissues	"	"	Glu residue 76
H3.1	" "	15,324	(135)	Arginine-rich (2 Cys)
H3.2	" "	"	"	Ser 75
H3.3	" "	"	"	Val 68, Ser 76
H4	" "	11,282	(102)	Arginine-rich
VII	Adenovirus type 2	18,500		Histone H4–like
V	" "	48,500		Histone H1–like
X$_1$	Rat testis			X$_1$ Histone H1–like
X$_2$	" "			X$_2$ Histone H3–like
X$_3$	" "			X$_3$ Histone H2B–like
Polyamines				
Protamines				
Spermines				
Spermadines				

The nucleosome core particle is composed of an octomer of eight histones molecules, two each of H3, H4, H2A, and H2B. During the course of development, minor forms of three of the four histone types are expressed: H2A.1, H2B.2, H2B.3, H3.2, H3.3. Only H4 is invariant (22).

The DNA, 1¾ turns, is wound around the circumference of the nucleosome core histone complex (dimensions 50 Å × 110 Å) (23).

Histone H1 is primarily associated with the linker region of DNA between the nucleosome core particles with only a portion associated exterior to the nucleosome (24).

basis. The nonhistone protein content of chromatin varies significantly, (0.21–.95)/1, as does that of the RNA (0.02–0.13) (see Table 2).

Histones are synthesized only during the S phase of the cell cycle and represent an exceedingly metabolically stable class of proteins (13). In fact, the metabolic turnover $T_{1/2}$ is equal to that of the DNA.

All eukaryotes including yeast, *Neurospora, Physarum,* and many mammalian viruses demonstrate the presence of five histones, H1, H2a, H2b, H3, and H4. The sequence determinations of four of the histones, H2a, H2b, H3, and H4, show them to have an exceedingly low calculated mutation rate, which represents for histone H4 less than 0.06 residue change per 100 total amino acid residues, over a period of a hundred million years (13). A striking example is the observation that only a 2% divergence in amino acid residues has been detected in this histone class, even in species as widely separated as the pea and the calf. It should be noted that this divergence is limited to the hydrophobic sequence and represents conservative amino acid substitutions (Figure 1) (e.g., in pea histone H4 leucine for valine at residue 60 and arginine for lysine at residue 77). The sequence analyses of histone H4 from calf thymus, pig thymus, rat lymphosarcoma, Novikoff hepatoma, trout, sea urchin, and pea all reveal only single amino acid sequence substitutions (Figure 1).

Histone H3 sequence conservation (Figure 1) approaches that of H4, and its sequence has been determined in the calf, chicken, carp, trout, shark, *Drosophila,* sea urchin, mollusc, pea, and cycad. Despite its evolutionary sequence stability, high resolution gel electrophoresis of histone H3 has recently revealed three amino acid sequence substitution subclasses within a single tissue. Histone H3 is exceptional in that it is the only histone with cysteine residues. In calf thymus 80% of the H3 has two cysteine residues (96 and 110), whereas 20% has a serine replacement for cysteine residue 96. Marzluff et al. (14) have shown that these histone H3 subclasses can be differentiated by the presence of interdisulfide versus intradisulfide linkages induced by oxidization.

Histone H2A and H2B appear to have evolved at a more rapid rate than

Table 2. Chemical Composition of Chromatins.

SOURCE	RNA	NHP	HISTONES	DNA
Rat liver	0.04	0.95	1.15	1
Pig cerebellum	0.13	0.50	1.00	1
Chicken erythrocyte	0.02	0.54	1.08	1
Calf thymus	0.05	0.21	0.89	1
HeLa cell	0.05	0.70	1.08	1

This tabulation shows that in addition to core histones in the nucleosome complex both nonhistone proteins (300–500 different molecules) and RNA are associated with the linker region of the DNA (25).

either H3 or H4. H2A also exists in two forms, both of which have been observed within the same tissue (15). The fact that H2A.1 does not have methionine at residue 51 (replaced by leucine) permits its separation and detection by cyanogen bromide cleavage. Histone H2B has three forms, H2B.1, H2B.2, H2B.3, with amino acid sequence differences in residues 75 and 76 (see Figure 1).

The Nucleosome. Three cardinal features of histones essential to provide a structural lattice on which the DNA is wound, are: (1) a rigidly conserved amino acid sequence, (2) a metabolic stability, and (3) a unique asymmetric amino acid sequence. Histones H3–H4–H2A–H2B are all essential to form the protein backbone interactions necessary for nucleosome structures. All of these histones have positively charged amino terminal regions. Although the arginine-rich H3 and H4 have been proposed to be sufficient to partially define the nucleosome structure when tested by reconstruction experiments discussed below, H2A and H2B are invariably found in the isolated complete nucleosome.

Histone H1 (rabbit thymus fraction 3)

Ac—Ser—Glu—Ala—Pro—Ala—Glu—Thr—Ala—Ala—Pro—Ala—Pro—Ala—Glu—Lys—Ser—
    1   10

Pro—Ala—Lys—Lys—Lys—Lys—Ala—Ala—Lys—Lys—Pro—Gly—Ala—Gly—Ala—Ala—Lys—
        20   30
            Ser—P   P

Arg—Lys—Ala—Ala—Gly—Pro—Pro—Val—Ser—Glu—Leu—Ile—Thr—Lys—Ala—Val—Ala—
                        40   50
P

Ala—Ser—Lys—Glu—Arg—Asn—Gly—Leu—Ser—Leu—Ala—Ala—Leu—Lys—Lys—Ala—Leu—
                                60

Ala—Ala—Gly—Gly—Tyr—Asp—Val—Glu—Lys—Asn—Ser—Arg—Ile—Lys—Leu—Gly—Leu—
        70   80

Lys—Ser—Leu—Val—Ser—Lys—Gly—Thr—Leu—Val—Glu—Thr—Lys—Gly—Thr—Gly—Ala—
                90   100
                P   Lys—Pro

Ser—Gly—Ser—Phe—Lys—Leu—Asp—Lys—Lys—Ala—Ala—Ser—Gly—Glu—Ala—Lys—Pro—
                            110   120

Lys—Lys—Ala—Gly—Ala—Ala—Lys—Pro—Lys—Lys—Pro—Ala—Gly—Ala—Ala—Lys—Lys—
                                130

Pro—Ala—Gly—Ala,Ala,Lys,Ala,Pro(Thr,Pro,Lys)(Val—Ala—Lys)(Lys—Ala—Val—Lys)(Ala—Lys—
    140   150

Lys)(Ser—Pro—Lys)(Lys—Ala—Lys)(Lys—Pro—Lys)(Ala—Pro—Lys)(Ser—Ala—Ala—Lys)(Ser—
    160   170

Pro—Ala—Lys—Pro—Lys)(Ala—Ala—Lys—Pro—Lys—Ala—Pro—Lys—Pro—Lys)(Ala—Ala—Lys)
        180   190

(Lys)(Ala—Ala—Lys)(Ser—Pro—Ala—Lys)(Ala—Val—Lys—Pro—Lys)(Ala—Ala—Lys—Pro—Lys)
                        200   210

(Ala—Ala—Gly—Ala—Lys)(Lys—Lys—COOH
                        220

Figure 1

Histone H2a (1 = Calf Thymus 2 = Rat) (K.W. = 14,004)

```
              P                    Ac
1)  Ac—Ser—Gly—Arg—Gly—Lys—Gln—Gly—Gly—Lys—Ala—Arg—Ala—Lys—Ala—Lys—
2)  — — — — — — — — — — Thr—Ser— — — — — — — — —
S        1                                    10

                       P
1)  Thr—Arg—Ser—Ser—Arg—Ala—Gly—Leu—Gln—Phe—Pro—Val—Gly—Arg—Val—His—
2)  Ser— — — — · — — — — — — — — — — — —
S              20                               30

1)  Arg—Leu—Leu—Arg—Lys—Gly—Asn—Tyr—Ala—Glu—Arg—Val—Gly—Ala—Gly—Ala—
2)  — — — — — — — — — — — — — — — —
S                        40

1)  Pro—Val—Tyr—Leu—Ala—Ala—Val—Leu—Glu—Tyr—Leu—Thr—Ala—Glu—Ile—Leu—
2)  — — — — Met — — — — — — — — — — Val — —
S             50                                  60

1)  Glu—Leu—Ala—Gly—Asn—Ala—Ala—Arg—Asp—Asn—Lys—Lys—Thr—Arg—Ile—Ile—
2)  — — — — — — — — — — — — — — Thr— —
S                    70

1)  Pro—Arg—His—Leu—Gln—Leu—Ala—Ile—Arg—Asn—Asp—Glu—Glu—Leu—Asn—Lys—
2)  — — — — — — — — — — — — — — —
S   80                               90

1)  Leu—Leu—Gly—Lys—Val—Thr—Ile—Ala—Gln—Gly—Gly—Val—Leu—Pro—Asn—Ile—
2)  — — — — — — — — — — — — — —
S               100                              110

1)  Gln—Ala—Val—Leu—Leu—Pro—Lys—Lys—Thr—Glu—Ser—His—His—Lys—Ala—Lys—
2)  — — — — — — — — — — — — — —
S                          120

1)  Gly—Lys—COOH
2)  — — — —
S           129
```

Figure 1 (Continued)

Two molecules of each of the four histones are rigidly maintained by hydro-phobic interactions. A 140 base-pair DNA fragment is wound on the outside of the histone octamer with a variable DNA spacer filament between nucleo-somes representing 20–60 base-pair nucleosome linkages (Table 3). Determi-nation of the significance of the minor histone sequence differences in the nucleosome will have to await further studies.

Polyamines in Eukaryotes.   It is now well established that in a late stage of spermatogenesis, protamine, a low-molecular-weight basic protein (4,200) with a high arginine content (see Figure 2), replaces the histones in a process that appears to be essential to provide an additional compaction of the DNA within the small volume of the sperm head. Nearly two-thirds of the amino

Histone H2b (Forms 1, 2, 3) (M.W. = 13,774)

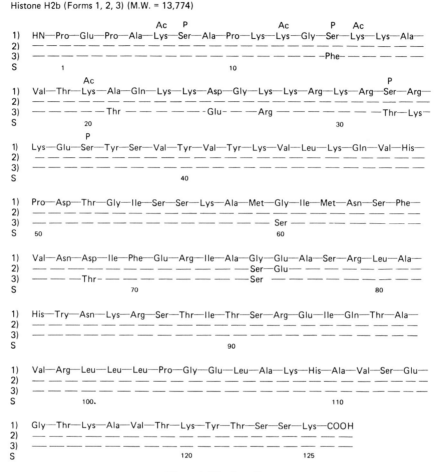

Figure 1 (Continued)

acid residues in protamines are basic, usually found in clusters of four or five arginine residues.

In developing trout testis, all five major histone fractions H1, H2A, H2b, H3, and H4 have been shown to be phosphorylated in the early stages of spermatogenesis. Thus 5% of H2b and H3, 15–20% of H2a, 10–20% of H4, and 40–50% of H1 are found in the phosphorylated state (16). At a later stage, the H1 histone is replaced by TH1-X and testis specific protein (TSP) (Table 1), which in addition to the usual H2B type histone X_3 and the protamines (Table 1) serve as useful markers of specific stages of spermatogenesis.

Histone H3 (Forms 1, 2, 3) (M.W.–15,324)

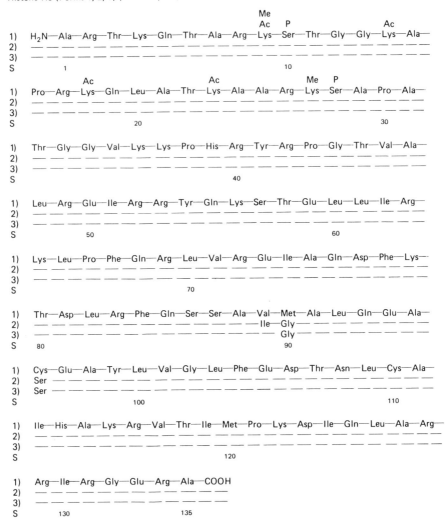

Figure 1 (Continued)

A major thrust has been directed to determining the mode of binding between protamine and double-helical DNA. Neutron diffraction methods, spectroscopic techniques, electron microscopy, and chemical modification have all been used to elucidate the details of the protamine–DNA interaction. The amino acid sequences of several fish sperm protamines have been

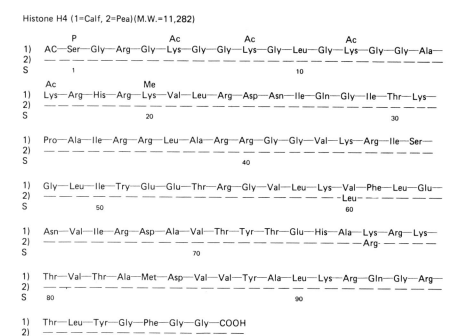

Figure 1 (Continued)

Table 3. Average Spacer Distance Between Nucleosomes.

NUCLEOSOME SOURCE	CORE BASE PAIRS	AVERAGE SPACER DISTANCE BASE PAIRS
Chicken erythrocyte	140	58
HeLa	140	47
Yeast	140	19
Neurospora crosses	140	30
Rat liver	140	60
Duck reticulocyte	140	45
Calf thymus	140	60
Satellite chromatin	140	30

This tabulation illustrates the fact that the number of base pairs associated with the core histones in invariant, independent of species; the number of base pairs in the linker region (average spacer distance) is variable (26).

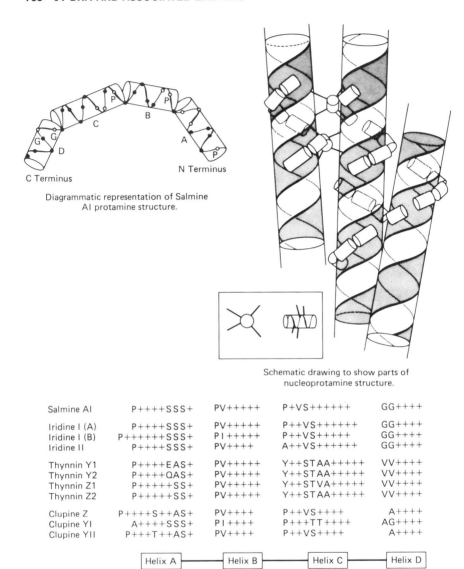

C Terminus

N Terminus

Diagrammatic representation of Salmine
AI protamine structure.

Schematic drawing to show parts of
nucleoprotamine structure.

Salmine AI	P++++SSS+	PV+++++	P+VS+++++++	GG++++
Iridine I (A)	P++++SSS+	PV+++++	P++VS++++++	GG++++
Iridine I (B)	P++++++SSS+	PI+++++	P++VS+++++	GG++++
Iridine II	P++++SSS+	PV++++	A++VS++++++	GG++++
Thynnin Y1	P++++EAS+	PV+++++	Y++STAA+++++	VV++++
Thynnin Y2	P++++QAS+	PV+++++	Y++STAA+++++	VV++++
Thynnin Z1	P+++++SS+	PV+++++	Y++STVA+++++	VV++++
Thynnin Z2	P+++++SS+	PV+++++	Y++STAA+++++	VV++++
Clupine Z	P++++S++AS+	PV++++	P++VS++++	A++++
Clupine YI	A++++SSS+	PI++++	P+++TT++++	AG++++
Clupine YII	P+++T++AS+	PV++++	P++VS++++	A++++

Helix A		Helix B		Helix C		Helix D

Sequences of protamines

Figure 2. Illustration of the interaction of Salmine AI protamine structure as discussed in the text (17). The histone H1 may be replaced by HMG1, HMG2, HMG17, HMG14, etc. During the course of spermatogenesis the histones are replaced by basic proteins, protamines (17).

determined and found to have a number of structural features in common (Figure 2). These features emphasize that protamine appears to be composed of at least three segments, with middle joints being a proline, tyrosine, or alanine residue, and with the last segment divided in two with a joint before a pair of glycines or valines (Figure 2). Based on single crystal X-ray diffraction and circular dichroism analysis of protamine–tRNA complexes, it has recently been proposed that all protamine–DNA complexes have a structure composed of three or four α-helical domains connected by two or three flexible joints as shown in Figure 2.

In the model shown in Figure 2 the α-helical domains maintain a structural rigidity of sufficient length to stabilize the DNA double helix to double helix crosslinking or condensation. Thus the joints between the α-helical domains provide the flexibility essential in the orientation of the domains to assure that two DNA double helices can be brought together even though they assume a variety of orientations. It should be emphasized that the extensive DNA–protamine condensation would exceed that of the histone–DNA nucleosome molecular constraints calculated to be sufficient to account for the high degree of compaction of DNA observed in the sperm nuclei; it would also account for the inhibition of DNA-dependent RNA synthesis by protamines observed in in vitro systems (17).

In summary, and to be discussed in greater detail in Chapter 12.1, histone phosphorylation is an essential first step in sperm maturation. The phosphorylated H1 histone is then replaced by TH1-X, and TSP. There is evidence to suggest that the unusual histone X_3 may also replace H2B. The resulting negative charge induced by phosphorylation appears to facilitate the progressive release of histones from the DNA. The newly synthesized protamines are usually phosphorylated at serine residues. In the model shown in Figure 2 it is proposed that these modified protamines would efficiently displace the phosphorylated histones and prevent DNA condensation. Once the histone displacement is almost complete, dephosphorylation of protamine is initiated, and the DNA condensation becomes complete, representing a necessary progression in the sperm maturation process.

Structural Aspects of Chromatin

DNA-Histone Interactions. *Physical Methods.* Recent studies using physical techniques including scanning electron microscopy, transmission electron microscopy, low-angle neutron diffraction, circular dichroism, and other optical measurements suggest a condensed form of DNA in chromatin (Table 4). Amino acid residues, such as proline, serine, and glycine, which favor extended chain structures, and basic amino acid residues, including lysine, arginine, and histidine, characterize the amino terminal segments of histones

Table 4.   Physical Techniques.

TECHNIQUE	OBSERVATION	INTERPRETATION
Circular dichroism	↑ Ellipticity 260–300 mM.	Urea affects protein secondary structure. Low ionic strength ↑ the effective (−) charge of the nucleoprotein backbone. Intermediate ionic strength weakens histone–DNA backbone.
Neutron diffraction	Concentration-dependent peak 10–11 nm. Contrast match 5.5 and 3.7 nm difference from 11 nm. Radius of gyration of 185 bp five; diameter 120–150 Å.	Interparticle space of a subunit. Histone and DNA have different spatial arrangement in subunit globular model in which apolar amino acid residues form a core surrounded by DNA complexed with basic amino terminal residues. Not all DNA is in an external shell.
^{13}C Nuclear magnetic resonance spectra	Many narrow resonances are evident in histone spectrum.	Propensity to form secondary structure at N terminal is low; therefore, free tails H4–H3, H2A–H4, H3, H2A, H3 attached to each other via hydrophobic interactions and each a tail for attachment to DNA.
Proton magnetic resonance	C terminal H4 monomer PMR "invisible."	C terminal is relatively rigid secondary structure.
Nuclear magnetic resonance spectra	CNBr peptide Met84 to amino terminal versus carboxyl terminal.	Flexible amino terminal and rigid carboxyl terminal.
X-ray diffraction	Peak at 11 nm is concentration-dependent.	Neighboring subunits have a tendency to align themselves close to the axis of the fiber, or each subunit has three turns per 200 bp.
Electron microscopy	100 or 200–250 Å diameter fibers dependent on solvent condition.	There may be considerable configurational heterogeneity in chromatin dependent on salt condition. Freeze-fracture shows DNA enters and leaves at same site.
First derivative thermal denaturation	$T_{mIII} = 72°C$ $T_{mI} = 47°C$ $T_{mIV} = 82°C$ $T_{mII} = 57°C$.	$79 \pm 3\%$ DNA bp bound by histones. 3.4 ± 0.4 amino acids per nucleotide.
Electron microscopy	Nucleosome structures 125 Å in diameter.	Nucleosome spacing and size is a constant feature of chromatin preparations.
Neutron diffraction	10-nm peak has maxima that	Coil of nucleosomes of pitch of 10

Table 4. *(continued)*

TECHNIQUE	OBSERVATION	INTERPRETATION
	form a cross pattern with semimeridional angle 8°–9°. Low angle reflections 400, 200, and 140.	nm and outer diameter 30 nm. Higher-order structure pitch 500 Å radius 130 Å.
Centrifugation	Distribution of histones in alkali-denatured metrizamide gradients.	Alkaline denaturation favors a bilateral model.

Regarding Tables 4, 5, and 6, a number of techniques have been used in a multidisciplinary approach to the analysis of the nucleosome core particle. These techniques are reviewed here. For details see Ref. 27.

H2A, H2B, H3, and H4 (Figure 1). The central regions of H2A and H2B, as well as the carboxyl halves of H3 and H4, possess high proportions of apolar and other amino acid residues that appear to favor helix formation. Thus, in general, aqueous solutions of histones are considered predominately to favor random coils, which are induced to interact with an increase in ionic strength. Under these conditions, NMR studies demonstrate that well-defined structures predominate in the apolar regions to represent sites of histone–histone interactions. These hydrophobic interactions provide a configuration in which the amino terminal residues have access to the aqueous environment, presumably providing primary sites of interaction between individual histones within the major groove of the DNA. When histones are dissolved in water, the circular dichroism spectrum resembles that of a random coil, in agreement with the fact that the fluorescence polarization of the tyrosines is low, providing evidence of free rotation of these aromatic residues. On the addition of salt, however, there is an immediate change in both the CD and fluorescence anisotrophy of all the histones, suggesting fewer degrees of freedom. Histones H3 and H4 demonstrate an additional slower change that takes place in minutes or hours, depending on the histone concentration. The fast step in CD change is interpreted as best attributed to the formation of an α-helix, whereas the slow step is more likely to represent the formation of β-pleated sheets. Van Holden and Isenberg propose that only limited histone sequences are involved in these molecular conformations. Histones in solution show specific cooperative folding that alters the degree of aggregation. Sedimentation equilibrium data show that $(H4–H3)_2$ represents a tetramer, while H4–H2B and H2A–H2B represent dimers in which H3–H4 and H2A–H2B have the highest binding constants. This undoubtedly explains the ease with which Kornberg and Thomas were able to crosslink H2A–H2B. Some of the observations are outlined in Table 5.

Table 5.   Crosslinking Experiments.

TECHNIQUE	OBSERVATION	INTERPRETATION
UV	Covalent linkage of histones at 280 nm H2A–H2B. CNBr analysis of crosslinked histones.	Histones must first interact with each other before being deposited on DNA. Histone H2B has separate binding sites for H2A and H4.
Tetranitromethane	Crosslinked H2A–H2B.	H4 is essential to proper reconstitution of H2A and H2B with DNA. H4, H2A, and H2B interact specifically in chromatin.
Dimethyl suberimidate	(H4)₂ (H3)₂ (H2A–H2B).	Tetramer of $(H4)_2$ $(H3)_2$; oligomer of H2A–H2B; monomer H1.
Methyl-4-mercaptobutyrimidate	H3–H2B, H3–H4, H2B–H2A at high frequency.	Proposes a model.
Reporter dye	Does not interfere with histone binding.	Histones in major groove.
Schiff base formation	Crosslink histone to DNA in nucleosome, 5′ DNA termini identified.	Determined histone arrangement within nucleosome.
Formaldehyde	Formation of a reversible covalent bond between DNA and histone.	Determines distribution of DNA on histones.
Surface tension	H2B in the presence or absence of chromatin at ionic strength 0.01 and 0.10.	Calculates amount of histone bound to DNA.

Enzyme Probe Analysis. Enzymatic digestion of chromatin has been exceedingly useful in the analysis of the nucleosome. Proteases have been used to define histone–DNA interactions and nucleases to define the unit length of DNA. Some of these data and their interpretations are outlined in Table 6.

The fact that trypsin digestion of intact nucleosomes is limited to 20 to 30 amino terminal residues of H3, H4, H2B, and H2A is in agreement with nuclear magnetic resonance studies suggesting these basic amino acid residues as prime candidates to interact with the DNA. In addition, a more detailed analysis of the order of cleavage has been able to clarify a number of specific histone–DNA and histone–histone interactions. The observation that trypsin rapidly destroys histone H1 without disrupting the nucleosome subunit structure is consistent with the concept that this histone is external to the nucleosome, most probably in the linker or spacer DNA region.

A number of nucleases have been used, as a probe to analyze the organization of chromatin at the level of the basic repeating unit, as a technique to

Table 6.   Enzyme Probe Analysis of Nucleosome Structure.

ENZYME	OBSERVATION	INTERPRETATION
Trypsin	Digestion of only 20% of histone, change in properties of nucleosome. Cleavage of chromatin with trypsin cleaves only 20–30 amino acids H3, H4, H2B, H2A. Order of cleavage H1, H5, H3, H4, H2A, and H2B.	Histones essential to maintain the compact structure. Basic amino terminus defines coordinates of DNA binding sites and folding of DNA fiber in chromosome.
DNAse I and II	DNA products from digestion form a regular series of fragment size classes, all being integral multimers of the smallest DNA unit.	200 base pairs is a reflection of the regularity in distribution of protein.
Staph nuclease	Digestion product of DNA of 185 and 140 base pairs.	Limit digest of 140 bp.
Ca²⁺Mg²⁺ endonuclease	Series of double-stranded fragments with single-stranded breaks.	Double-stranded fragments result from a regular series f single-strand fragments.
Micrococcal nuclease	Shows 3.4, 5.3, 8.6, 17, 22, and 26S fractions.	Suggests either several types of subunits or asymmetric cleavages at any one of four or more sites.
Restriction nuclease	Specific cleavage by *Eco* RIII	Repetitive DNA part of the nucleosome.

resolve the unit size of the DNA associated with the nucleosome (Table 6), and, as will be discussed in Chapter 12.1, to obtain specific details of the structure of transciptionally active versus inactive nucleosomes.

Four classes of nucleases have been used to provide this information:

1. DNase I and DNase II have been shown to cleave a wide range of DNA sites on the chromatin substructure restricted by histone–DNA interactions. DNase I has been useful to distinguish active from inactive nucleosomes.

2. The Ca²⁺–Mg²⁺-dependent endonucleases cleave those DNA sites that are regularly spaced along the repeating chromatin substructure without the release of mono- or oligonucleotides.

3. Micrococcal nuclease attacks the same sites as the Ca²⁺–Mg²⁺ endonuclease, differing, however, in the release of mono- and oligonucleotides as acid-soluble fragments.

4. Restriction enzymes, as, for example, *Eco* RII, have been most useful in demonstrating that most, if not all, satellite and repetitive DNAs assume a nucleosome configuration.

Early evidence of a subunit structure of chromatin using nucleases was first presented by Hewish and Burgoyne as an extension of the work of Williamson. These studies, using endogenous DNAse, show a 200 base-pair limit digest fragment of DNA as a reflection of the regularity in the nucleotide chain length protected by the nucleosome protein–DNA interaction. Noll obtained similar results when nuclei were treated with staphylococcal nuclease.

It is assumed that the nucleosome monomer excised by gentle nuclease digestion is derived from the larger chromatin structure by clipping the DNA at relatively susceptible nucleotides between subunits. It is now generally accepted that the 140 base pairs obtained from a limit digest represent a nucleosome core DNA fragment found wrapped around the nucleosome complex. It is presumed that these enzymatic probes reveal, in some way, the arrangement of histones with DNA wound on the exterior surface of the nucleosome subunit.

Finally, the combined use of trypsin and nuclease, as seen in the work of Weintraub and Van Lente, has been valuable in showing specific histone–DNA interactions. These studies of trypsin and DNase-resistant DNA–histone fragments imply that both specific histone amino terminal and carboxyl terminal residues are associated with the DNase resistance. These results are confirmed using cyanogen bromide cleavage of histone H4, to demonstrate that the amino terminal fragment (1–83) binds DNA with an affinity equivalent to the whole molecule. In contrast, the C-terminal fragment (84–102) of H4 is weakly bound under the same conditions.

DNA–Protein Crosslinking Analysis. The elegant work of Simpson (18) has recently revealed a number of fine details of the nucleosome structure, showing that the histones H3 and H4 interact at the ends of the nucleosomal DNA. In these studies, the DNA of the nucleosome core particle of 140 nucleotide base-pair lengths is first labeled with (α-^{32}P) ATP and polynucleotide kinase. The DNA is then methylated at a guanine residue, using dimethyl sulfate, gently depurinated, and crosslinked with histone in the formation of a Schiff base. The Schiff base is reduced with sodium borohydride to form a covalent linkage of histone and DNA. The DNA is then digested to permit the identification of a histone complex associated with the nucleotide as a marker. The most significant observations of these studies is the suggestion of symmetry in the arrangement of histones within the nucleosomes.

It should be emphasized that there is no evidence for base specificity in the nucleosome DNA interaction. Thus the objective achieved in DNA–protein crosslinking experiments determines the location of specific histone domains.

Histone–Histone Interactions. A more detailed analysis of the nucleosome has been undertaken using histone crosslinking experiments, as shown in Table 5. These studies have already contributed a great deal to our knowledge of the nature of strong histone interactions within the histone octamer subunit.

Protein–Protein Crosslinking Analysis. Two crosslinking reagents, UV at 280 nm and tetranitromethane, may be considered as zero-length crosslinking reagents converting noncovalent interactions among the histones into covalent bonds, without the interposition of bridges. Both crosslinkers penetrate hydrophobic clusters and activate tryosine residues. These studies show that histone H2B is crosslinked to both H2A and H4. Characterization of the cyanogen bromide peptide fragments shows that the amino terminal half, at tyrosine residue 40 of H2B, is crosslinked to the amino terminal half of histone H2A at residue phenylalanine 25, whereas the tyrosine carboxyl terminal residue 121 of H2B is crosslinked to the phenylalanine residue 61 of histone H4. In addition, it is most intriguing that two H2A molecules, one of which has a methionine, have both been observed to be crosslinked to H2B. The significance of this observation also warrants further study.

Formaldehyde represents the shortest of the "spanner" crosslinking agents reacting with lysine residues in chromosomal proteins. Using this agent, Van Lente has confirmed the observation that H2B is in close proximity to both H2A and H2B. Both dimethylsuberimidate, 1-ethyl-3-(3-dimethylaminopropyl) carbodimide, and the sulfhydryl methylmercaptobutyrimidate show, in addition, that H3–H2B, H3–H4, and H2B–H2A are in close proximity.

Immunochemical Analysis. The nature of chromatin subunits has been examined in some detail using two innovative techniques: immunosedimentation and immunoelectron microscopy.

The information obtained by crosslinking experiments does not have the capacity to resolve the question of whether every nucleosome contains a complete complement of histones. The technique of immunoelectron microscopy provides a unique approach to this question. Simpson and Bustin (19) have shown that 90% of the chromatin nucleosomes react with antibodies to histone H2B, suggesting that most if not all the nucleosomes contain this histone. In addition, these investigators have also used these techniques to demonstrate the presence of H3 and H4 in most if not all nucleosomes.

The use of anti-H2B-IgG molecules has shown that the ratios of both H2A and (H2B + H3) to H4 are identical, suggesting that each nucleosome has an identical histone complement of two each of histones H2A, H2B, H3, and H4.

Antibodies to histone H1 have also been useful in detecting subtle irreversible changes as a result of the usual fractionation techniques, using strong acid or urea extraction.

Nucleosome as a Repeating Unit. Physical properties of chromatin preparations that have been depleted of the lysine-rich histone H1 are all in agreement with the concept that the fundamental macromolecular structure is best represented by a chain of nucleosomes, each with dimensions of $57 \times 110 \times 110$ Å (Table 4) connected by a flexible DNA filament. The protein–protein and protein–DNA interactions described above are dictated by stringent constraints resulting in an invariant structure that, once established, has ramained resistant to change.

Characteristics of the DNA Spacer. Intranuclear digestion of eukaryotic chromatin by staphylococcal nuclease produces a series of discretely sized DNA fragments (oligomers), the length of which are integral multiples of a basic (monomer) size, 140 base pairs of DNA. Although the 140 base-pair monomer size is invariant in different cell types, the length of the nuclease-sensitive DNA between nucleosomes varies. The average spacer distance between nucleosomes varies from 19 to 60 base pairs (Table 3). The significance of these differences is not immediately obvious. It should be emphasized that these values represent averages and thus do not exclude the possibility of nonuniform distribution of nucleosomes along the DNA double strand.

Histone H1 Interstrand DNA Associations. The fifth histone, class H1, can be selectively extracted from the chromatin using salt concentrations in the range of 0.6 M. Upon removal of histone H1, the 19–60 base-pair DNA bridge exhibits an increase in nuclease susceptibility, which is also accompanied by an increase in accessibility of the chromatin to DNA polymerase I. Both of these observations are in agreement with those of Bradbury and others in implying that histone H1 is complexed directly with DNA, providing a DNA–protein complex. This is in contrast to the hydrophobic protein–protein interactions proposed as the predominant force in the tetramers of $(H3–H4)_2$ and dimers of $(H2A)_2$ and $(H2B)_2$ within the nucleosome core.

The primary sequence of H1 has undergone extensive interspecies and interorgan variation as a result of both conservative and nonconservative amino acid replacements. The number of H1 subfractions varies from two to five. Although there is considerable variation in amino acid residues 1–40 and 110–212, it is proposed that residues 72–106 in the globular region are involved in the recognition of superhelical DNA. Since the carboxyl terminal halves of the histone H1 are enriched in lysine and proline, it is reasonable to presume that they represent the DNA-binding site. In contrast, the amino terminal halves of these proteins are enriched in acidic residues and, therefore, might be expected to associate with components other than DNA. For example, two low molecular weight (M.W. <30,000) proteins have been fractionated and characterized by their solubility in trichloroacetic acid. They have been termed "high-mobility group" (HMG) proteins, HMG1 and HMG2, and have been obtained in relatively pure form (Table 1). From their amino acid sequences, these proteins are closely related, found in large quantities, and seem to associate with histone H1. H1-b and H1-2 appear to interact only with the HMG1. Subfractions of histone H1, H1-3, and H1-3B bind both HMG1 and HMG2. These protein–protein interactions may account for some of the heterogeneity characteristic of histone H1.

Satellite Chromatin. The homogeneous highly repetitive fraction that comprises nearly a quarter of the African green monkey genome has been isolated utilizing the restriction enzyme *Eco* RI. This fraction of αDNA has been shown to be composed of nucleosomes with a repeat periodicity of 176 $\pm$ 4 nucleotide base pairs. The α-nucleosomes appear to be free of H1 histones in the interstrand DNA nucleosome linker region. Certain classes of non-histone proteins are present in this region of the chromatin. The presence of this protein appears to render the oligonucleosome less sensitive to *Eco* RI nucleolytic cleavage, and unlike histone H1 this protein is resistant to salt extraction with 0.6 M NaCl. It is possible that the tightly bound protein(s) determine the highly condensed, heterochromatic organization found in satellite sequences.

The significance of these studies is that the heterochromatic, nontranscribed satellite DNAs are organized in a subunit structure similar to the bulk chromatin.

Minichromosome. The chromatin structures of the animal viruses have been designated as minichromosomes (20). The minichromosome, because of its small size and defined sequence, is exceedingly useful as a tool to study the properties of protein–DNA interactions. In fact, it is quite probable that all animal viral DNAs are complexed with proteins in a nucleosome-like subunit structure.

The chromosomes of at least two animal viruses, polyoma and simian virus 40 (SV40), are condensed into 109 Å subunits complexed with cellular histones. The DNA of SV40 is composed of 5200 base pairs of double-stranded closed circular DNAs complexed with a total of 21 subunits. The viral subunits of SV40 resemble those of all other eukaryotic nucleosomes composed of eight histones (two each of H2A, H2B, H3, and H4) with the DNA wrapped around the outside of the subunits, giving a protein to DNA ratio of one. The SV40 nucleosomes are associated with 140 base pairs interspersed with 55 base-pair linker regions.

In contrast to polyoma, and SV40, adenovirus synthesizes its own basic histone-like proteins. The DNA is a linear duplex of 35,000 base pairs complexed with protein VII. This major core protein is a highly arginine-rich protein (almost 23 mole % arginine) with an asymmetric distribution of basic residues at the amino terminal. There are similarities of this protein to histone H4, which is also arginine-rich. This nucleoprotein VII is synthesized as a precursor molecule observed to be packaged in immature virions. The final stage of virus maturation utilizes a specific endoprotease that processes a 20-residue fragment from the amino end of the molecule. Staph nuclease cleaves adenoviral DNA with a repeat unit of 200 base pairs. The 23×10^6-dalton adenoviral DNA molecule can accomodate 180 nucleosomes. Based on this stoichiometry of core polypeptides, it is suggested that each viral nucleosome contains six copies of polypeptide VII (M.W. 18,500) and a single copy of polypeptide V.

The adenovirus nucleosome core particle is remarkably similar to that of the eukaryote. They both have 140 base pairs of DNA, associated with either six polypeptides VII (M.W. 110,000) or eight histones (M.W. 108,768) in the adenovirus or eukaryotic nucleosome, both with a ratio of protein to DNA of 1.2. Either two molecules of Hl (M.W. 42,000) or one molecule of polypeptide V, which is Hl-like in its amino acid composition (M.W. 48,500), is associated with the 200 base-pair nucleosome unit observed by mircococcal nuclease cleavage of either the eukaryotic or adenovirus molecule, respectively.

Nucleosome Superstructure

A number of recent experiments have emphasized the key role played by Hl in higher orders of nucleosome packing and its temporal association with phosphorylation in the cell cycle.

Finch and Klug (11, 21) have shown that chromatin prepared by a brief digestion of nuclei with micrococcal nuclease and then extracted with 0.2 mM EDTA appears as loosely coiled filaments. In the presence of 0.2 mM Mg^{2+}, however, these nucleofilaments condense into a supercoil or "solenoidal structure" of a 10-nm pitch with six nucleosome particles per turn. It should be emphasized that the solenoidal structures require histone Hl for stabilization of higher orders of nucleosome packing (Chapter 12.1).

Addition of histone H2A, H2B, H3, and H4 to SV40 DNA (3×10^6 daltons) under proper salt concentrations results in the formation of a 19–22 nucleosome minichromosome in the form of a DNA circle. If histone Hl is included, a contraction of the minichromosome results, demonstrating morphological characteristics that resemble the solenoidal structure proposed by Finch and Klug.

SUMMARY OF CHROMATIN STRUCTURE

It is now generally accepted that the nucleosome is an essential structural component on which the double-stranded DNA is organized. The basic structure is invariant, composed of a heterotypic tetramer of two copies of each of four histones H2A, H2B, H3, and H4, rigidly maintained by hydrophobic interaction provided by the histone apolar residues. The nucleosome provides a scaffold with dimensions of 110×50 Å on which 140 base pairs of DNA are folded with a compaction ratio of 7/1 (folded vs. extended structure). Histone H1 is located outside the 140 DNA base-pair nucleosome subunit. Recent evidence suggests that histone H1 is directly associated by salt interactions with the DNA linker regions, contributing to the further compaction (up to 10,000) observed in heterochromatin, metaphase chromosomes, satellite DNAs, and so on.

The presence of "nonhistone" proteins with pK values of 3–8 is primarily associated with the DNA nucleosome linker region. The extreme complexity of these proteins is evidenced by the fact that protein species have been demonstrated to be associated with the linker DNA. A detailed discussion of these proteins is unwarranted at this time, however; and we elect to await further research before attempting to review this aspect of chromatin structure. The significance of nucleosome compaction in relation to its role in RNA transcription and replication, in addition to its interactions with other chromosomal proteins, will be amplified in Chapter 12.1.

RNA processing is defined as the collection of enzymatic reactions that transform a primary transcript, the hnRNA product, into a mature functioning molecule. We are now painfully aware of the fact that the final mRNA product is not necessarily sequentially collinear with the DNA template. In fact, almost all mRNAs that have been isolated indicate that they are synthesized as a large precursor product and that this RNA processing of the intervening sequences is a result of a series of enzymatic reactions that transforms a primary transcript product into a mature functioning mRNA molecule. We are led to the conclusion that RNA processing is a major mechanism in the expression of the eukaryotic gene. The reliability of this complex processing is emphasized by the fact that oviduct cells can easily endure seven intervening sequences in the ovalbumin gene and remove all of them accurately to within a single base pair. These recent observations suggest that RNA splicing may play a major role in differentiation.

This concept of the split gene and mRNA processing represents an intensely active area of investigation amenable to the tools (cloning of plasmids, nucleotide sequencing, recombinant DNA) of the molecular biologist.

REFERENCES

1. Davidson, E. H., and Britten, R. J. 1979. Regulation of gene expression: Possible role of repetitive sequences. *Science* 204:1052–59.
2. Alt, F. W., Kellems, R. E., Bertino, J. R., and Schimke, R. T. 1978. Selective multiplication of dihydrofolate reductase genes in methotrexate-resistant variants of cultured murine cells. *J. Biol. Chem.* 253:1357–70.
3. Crick, F. 1979. Split genes and RNA splicing. *Science* 204:264–71.
4. Davidson, E. H., ed. 1976. *Gene Activity in Early Development,* 2nd ed. Academic Press, New York.

5. Davidson, E. H., Klein, W. H., Hough-Evans, B. R., Smith, M. J., Galau, G. A., Crain, W. R., Angerer, R. C., Wold, B. J., Davis, M. M., and Britton, R. J. 1977. The organization of functional DNA sequences in animal genomes. In *The Organization and Expression of the Eukaryotic Genome*, Bradbury and Javaherian, eds., pp. 373–91. Academic Press, New York.

6. Lewin, B. 1974. Sequences of eukaryotic DNA. In *Gene Expression—2, Eukaryotic Chromosomes*, Chapter 4, pp. 148–228. Wiley, New York.

7. Schimke, R. T., Alt, F. W., Kellems, R. E., Kaufman, R. J., and Bertino, J. R. 1977. Amplification of dihydrofolate reductase genes in methotrexate-resistant cultured mouse cells. *Symp. Quant. Biol.* 42:649–57.

8. Thomas, C. A., Jr. and Dancis, B. M. 1973. Ring stability. *J. Mol. Biol.* 77:43.

9. Shaw, B. R., Herman, T. M., Kovacic, R. T., Beaudreau, G. S., and Van Holde, K. E. 1976. Analysis of subunit organization in chicken erythrocyte chromatin. *Proc. Natl. Acad. Sci.* 73:505–9.

10. Lilley, D. M. J., Pardon, J. F., and Richards, B. M. 1977. Structural investigations of chromatin core protein by nuclear magnetic resonance. *Biochemistry* 16:2853–60.

11. Finch, J. T., and Klug, A. 1976. Solenoidal model for superstructure in chromatin. *Proc. Natl. Acad. Sci.* 73:1899–1901.

12. Rouviere-Yaniv, J. 1977. Localization of the HU protein on the *Escherichia coli* nucleoid. *Cold Spring Harbor Symp. Quant. Biol.* 42:439–47.

13. DeLange, R. J., and Smith, E. L. 1971. Histones: Structure and function. *Annu. Rev. Biochem.* 40:279–314.

14. Marzluff, W. F., Jr., Sanders, L. A., Miller, D. M., and McCarty, K. S. 1972. Two chemically and metabolically distinct forms of calf thymus histon F3. *J. Biol. Chem.* 247:2026–33.

15. McCarty, K. S., Sr. and McCarty, K. S., Jr. 1978. Some aspects of chromatin structure and cell-cycle-related postsynthetic modifications. In *Cell Cycle Regulation*, J. R. Jeter, Jr., I. L. Cameron, G. M. Padilla, and A. M. Zimmerman, eds., pp. 9–35. Academic Press, New York.

16. Gurley, L. R., Tobey, R. A., Walters, R. A., Hildebrand, C. E., Hohmann, P. G., D'Anna, J. A., Barham, S. S., and Deaven, L. L. 1978. Histone phosphorylation and chromatin structure in synchronized mammalian cells, In *Cell Cycle Regulation*, J. R. Jeter, Jr., I. L. Cameron, G. M. Padilla, and A. M. Zimmerman, eds., pp. 37–60. Academic Press, New York.

17. Warrant, R. W. and Kim, S. H. 1978. α-Helix–double helix interaction shown in the structure of a protamine-transfer RNA complex and a nucleoprotamine model. *Nature* 271:130–35.

18. Simpson, R. T. 1976. Histones H3 and H4 interact with the ends of nucleosomal DNA. *Proc. Natl. Acad. Sci.* 73:4400–4.

19. Simpson, R. T., and Bustin, M. 1976. Histone composition of chromatin subunits studied by immunosedimentation. *Biochemistry* 15:4305–12.

20. Griffith, J. D. 1977. The structure of condensed DNA; similarities between higher cells and bacteria. In *The Molecular Biology of the Mammalian Genetic Apparatus*, Vol. 1, P. O. P. Ts'o, ed., pp. 273–80. North Holland, Amsterdam.

21. Reny, M., Nehls, P., and Hozier, J. 1977. Histone H1 involvement in the structure of the chromosome fiber. *Cold Spring Harbor Symp. Quant. Biol.* 42:245–52.

22. Newrock, K. M., Alfageme, C. R., Nardi, R. V., and Cohen, L. H. 1977. Histone changes during chromatin remodeling in embryogenesis. *Cold Spring Harbor Symp. Quant. Biol.* 42:421–31.

23. Pardon, J. F., Cotter, R. I., Lilley, D. M. J., Worchester, D. L., Campbell, A. M., Wooley, J. C., and Richards, B. M. 1977. Scattering studies of chromatin subunits. *Cold Spring Harbor Symp. Quant. Biol.* 42:11–22.

24. Goodwin, G. H., Mathew, C. G. P., Wright, C. A., Venkov, C. D., and Johns, E. W. 1979. *Nucl. Acids Res.* 7:1815–36.
25. Stein, G., Stein, J., and Kleinsmith, L. J., eds. 1978. *Methods Cell Biol.* (Part D, Fractionation and characterization of nonhistone chromosomal proteins) 17:253–409.
26. Noll, M. 1977. Internal structure of the nucleosome: DNA folding in the conserved 140-base-pair core particle. *Cold Spring Harbor Symp. Quant. Biol.* 42:77–85.
27. Ts'o, P. O. P., ed., 1977. *The Molecular Biology of the Mammalian Genetic Apparatus,* Vols. 1 and 2, North Holland, Amsterdam; 1977. *Cold Spring Harbor Symp. Quant. Biol.* 42 (Parts 1 and 2).

6.7. Prokaryotic DNA Polymerases

Theresa Campana and Lazar M. Schwartz

DNA POLYMERASE I OF *E. COLI*

The major portion of DNA polymerase activity found in extracts of wild-type *E. coli* is contributed by an enzyme known as DNA polymerase I. This enzyme, first described by A. Kornberg and coworkers in 1956, has been studied extensively. It consists of a single, large polypeptide with a molecular weight of 109,000 daltons, and contains several distinct enzymatic activities. The evidence that DNA polymerase I consists of a single chain comes from several lines of investigation:

1. Migration on polyacrylamide gel electrophoresis shows a single band unaffected by pH as well as urea.
2. Only a single amino terminus has been found in the molecule.
3. The enzyme contains one group, and a single binding site for all deoxyribosetriphosphates.
4. Molecular weight determination on density gradient sedimentation equilibrium is not affected by treatment with guanidium chloride mercaptoethanol.
5. Recovery of activity after denaturation and removal of the denaturing agent by dilution is concentration-independent.

The constituent enzyme activities of DNA polymerase I are: (1) polymerase, (2) 3′ to 5′ exonuclease, (3) 5′ to 3′ exonuclease, and (4) pyrophosphorylase.

It is possible to recover all the activity after limited proteolysis in the presence of DNA. This gives rise to two fragments, one of which contains the 5′ to 3′ exonuclease, with the other three activities recovered in a single, larger fragment.

The amino acid composition of DNA polymerase I has been determined. The enzyme has a relatively high concentration of neutral amino acids. The two cysteines appear to be located near the surface, forming a disulfide bridge that can react with a variety of reagents but is not essential for enzymatic activity. The enzyme is a metalloenzyme, containing Zn^{2+}. The metal is essential for activity, but its exact function is not yet completely understood. An *E. coli* cell contains about 400 molecules of DNA polymerase I, and polymerizes nucleotides at a rate of about 20/sec. The enzyme appears to contain four sites which must be intact for polymerase activity (Figure 1).

Early work held out the promise that this enzyme was the replicating enzyme in vivo, especially since a biologically active ϕX 174 bacteriophage DNA molecule could be synthesized in vitro. However, with the use of less denatured templates, it was found that DNA polymerase I could not use an undenatured DNA as a template, and requires a 3'-OH end. In addition, the rate of polymerization catalyzed by the enzyme is much too low to account for *E. coli* replication.

Presently, the consensus of scientific opinion holds that DNA polymerase I is required for dark-rapair of DNA, and for replication of a plasmid (Col E1) but not for replication of *E. coli* DNA, or most plasmids and bacteriophages. Mutants of *E. coli* that lack DNA polymerase I replicate normally, but certain DNA repair processes are impaired. One of these is excision of pyrimidine dimers formed when DNA is irradiated with ultraviolet light. These dimers are most often formed of adjacent thymidine bases, but C–T and C–C dimers can also form.

The enzyme recognizes a distortion in the DNA double helix caused by the dimers, and attaches near this site. A single-stranded nick is introduced by an endonuclease, and DNA polymerase I repairs the damage (Figure 2). The 5' to 3' exonuclease of the enzymes removes the dimer and several

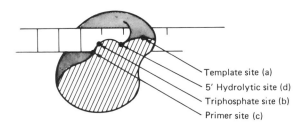

Template site (a)
5' Hydrolytic site (d)
Triphosphate site (b)
Primer site (c)

Figure 1. Active sites of DNA polymerase I. (a) Template site: binding site to template. The affinity of this site varies with the type of template used. Binding does not result in active catalysis unless other conditions are met. (b) Triphosphate site on the large fragment: binding site for the nucleosides to be polymerized. Single site for all four deoxynucleoside triphosphates. (c) Primer site—nucleoside monophosphate site: binding site to 3'-OH terminus of the primer. Once bound the enzyme cannot be removed, inverted, or modified. Also called 3'-OH ribonucleotide site because it binds equally well to 3'-OH ribonucleotides. Both b and c are adjacent in the large fragment. The primer site will also be the binding site for phosphorolytic activity. (d) 5' to 3' hydrolytic site, on the small fragment. The 5'-OH hydrolytic site would be adjacent to the triphosphate site and important in removal of nonpaired base dimers (e.g., T–T) concurrent to the progression of the nick repair. Binding of polymerase to DNA is influenced by the structure of the template. It does not require Mg^{2+} and forms stable complexes.

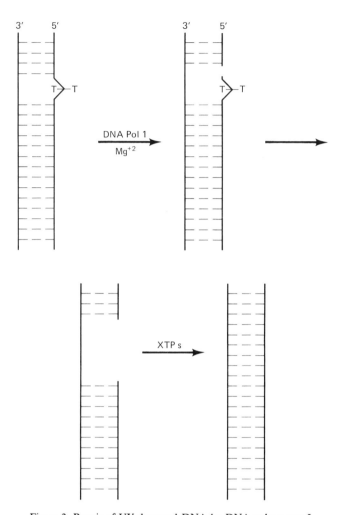

Figure 2. Repair of UV-damaged DNA by DNA polymerase I.

other bases at the 5' end of the nick. At the same time, the polymerase activity adds nucleotides, using the free 3'-OH at the nick as a primer; and the other types of single-stranded breaks in DNA by DNA polymerase I also require both the 5' to 3' exonuclease and the polymerase.

Recent work has indicated that DNA polymerase I may play a required role in replication, but *not* as a polymerase. It has been reported that mutants lacking this enzyme but still capable of replication retain the 5' to 3' exonuclease normally associated with DNA polymerase I, some mutants maintaining almost normal levels of nuclease. Recent reports indicate that mutants that have a temperature-sensitive nuclease are not viable at the restrictive temperature, implying a necessary role for the nuclease in normal replication. In contrast, however, is another mutant, which lacks 5' to 3' nuclease; this strain grows, albeit poorly, but does not repair UV damage well. Further characterization of such mutants may resolve the role of DNA polymerase I. It seems safe to assume that this enzyme may participate in maintenance of normal DNA sequences by virtue of its nuclease activity, and may play a facultative role in replication. Recent work has shown that the primer for prokaryotic DNA synthesis in vivo is an RNA molecule, and that DNA polymerase I is able to covalently join a DNA polynucleotide strand to an RNA primer. At present, no information is available as to whether the other polymerases can carry out this reaction.

DNA POLYMERASE II OF *E. COLI*

In 1970, several laboratories reported the presence of a new polymerase activity. DNA polymerase II was demonstrated in both membrane complexes and cells made permeable to small molecules by treatment with toluene. Both systems appear to carry out replication, and are able to support replication of several bacteriophages. By several independent criteria, the enzyme is not an altered form of DNA polymerase I:

1. Antibodies against DNA polymerase I do not inhibit the new activity.
2. Sulfhydryl groups are necessary for the activity of DNA polymerase II but not I.

On purification of the enzyme, it was found that this enzyme, like DNA polymerase I, could not catalyze true replication. It, too, requires a 3'-OH primer, it cannot use native DNA as a template, and the rate of catalysis is too low to account for in vivo replication. The enzyme works best with a DNA molecule containing relatively large single-stranded gaps. DNA polymerase II has a molecular weight of 120,000 daltons and is present at low concentration in the cell. Depending on the method used for isolation, there appear to be 17 to 100 molecules per cell.

Genetic studies have not been able to clarify the in vivo role of DNA polymerase II. Mutants deficient in this enzyme have been isolated; they appear to function normally, showing no defects in replication, DNA repair, or recombination. Based on all the above data, the present consensus is that DNA polymerase II does not play a necessary role in replication. There are, however, several points that do not accord well with this hypothesis.

A nucleotide analogue, arabinofuranosylcytidine-5'-triphosphate (ara-CTP), interferes with the in vivo role of this enzyme. In addition, an unwinding protein known to be required for optimal synthesis of phage M13 DNA interacts well in vitro only with DNA polymerase II. These observations have not yet been explained. It is possible that the polymerase activity solubilized from membrane complexes is incomplete. The activity retained by the complexes, however, has not been further studied, and it is as yet unclear whether it represents a part of the DNA polymerase II, residual activity due to other known polymerases, or some new activity. It has been suggested that the in vivo role of DNA polymerase II is the repair of gaps introduced into DNA by exonuclease activity. These gaps would be produced during excision of mismatched bases while replication proceeds. At present, no evidence exists to confirm or deny such a role. Further studies will be required for elucidation of the in vivo role of DNA polymerase II.

DNA POLYMERASE III

Kornberg and Gefter discovered a third polymerase activity, DNA polymerase III, while studying DNA polymerases in a mutant lacking DNA polymerase I. Like the other known polymerases, this enzyme also requires a primer, but it can be distinguished by several properties. Salt concentrations above 0.05 M are inhibitory, while the addition of ethanol to the in vitro assay mixture stimulates the activity. The rate of polymerization catalyzed by this enzyme is much higher than that found with the other enzymes, and is high enough to account for in vivo replication rates.

The enzyme has a molecular weight of about 140,000 daltons and consists of two identical subunits each with a molecular weight of 90,000 daltons. There are apparently only ten copies of the enzyme molecule present in each cell. In vivo, the enzyme appears to be present as a complex with other proteins. Wickner and Kornberg have described three forms of this enzyme (Figure 3): (1) pol III, the dimeric enzyme, itself; (2) pol III*, apparently a tetrameric form of pol III, isolated by chromatography on phosphocellulose; and (3) holoenzyme, a tetrameric form of pol III in association with a peptide of molecular weight of 70,000 daltons, known as copol III*.

The holoenzyme is presumed to be the native, active form of the enzyme in vivo. The molecular weight of the tetramer is 330,000 daltons. It consists of two pol III subunits (90,000 daltons each) and two copol III* subunits (70,000 daltons each). The core enzyme is not active in the absence of copol III*. In the presence of this peptide, together with an RNA primer, DNA unwinding protein, and ATP, the core enzyme can catalyze the conversion of a single-stranded, circular DNA from some bacteriophages into the double-stranded replicative form. With the addition of other proteins, this system will also catalyze the synthesis of other DNA molecules.

Evidence from genetic studies has clearly demonstrated a necessary role

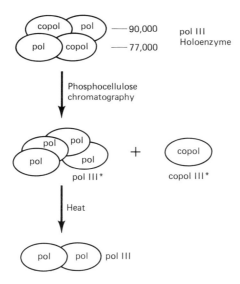

Figure 3. Structure of DNA polymerase III (after W. Wickner and A. Kornberg, *J. Biol. Chem.* 249:6244, 1974).

for DNA polymerase III in cellular replication. No viable strains have been found with significant deficiency in the enzyme. Several strains whose replication is temperature-sensitive have been isolated; these cells are viable at permissive temperatures, but cannot replicate at higher temperatures. In several cases, it has been demonstrated that the mutation lies within the *dna E* locus, which is the structural gene for DNA polymerase III. The enzyme from these strains has been partially purified, and was shown to be temperature-sensitive; that is, in vitro, the enzyme is more sensitive to heat denaturation at relatively low temperature. In general, DNA polymerase III is more heat-labile than the other known polymerases, and has not yet been purified to homogeneity as a consequence.

The present evidence indicates that DNA polymerase III is required for replication, whereas the other polymerases may participate in specific stages, but are not essential. Possible roles for each polymerase and the general models for replication are discussed in Chapter 7.1.

OTHER BACTERIAL DNA POLYMERASES

The bacterium *Bacillus subtilis* has been shown to contain three distinct DNA polymerase activities. DNA polymerase I of *B. subtilis* is somewhat smaller than the corresponding *E. coli* enzyme, with a molecular weight of

110,000 daltons. Like the *E. coli* DNA polymerase I, this enzyme carries out DNA repair, is least sensitive to high salt concentrations, does not depend on sulfhydryl group for reactivity, and is not affected by ara-CTP. However, *B. subtilis* DNA polymerases, including polymerase I, appear to lack the nuclease activity of the corresponding *E. coli* enzymes. Polymerase II has a molecular weight of 160,000–180,000 daltons, and constitutes about 10% of the total polymerase activity in wild-type strains. Like the *E. coli* enzyme, it is sensitive to reagents that bind sulfhydryl groups, and is strongly inhibited by ara-CTP. No specific role in vivo has yet been assigned to this enzyme.

As in the case in *E. coli,* *B. subtilis* DNA polymerase III has been shown to be required in vivo for replication. The enzyme has a molecular weight of 140,000–150,000 daltons, and represents only about 1% of the wild-type polymerase activity. The gene locus has been shown to be unlinked to that of DNA polymerase I. Mutants that are temperature-sensitive in this enzyme may show mutator characteristics; that is, the rate of mutation is increased. Of the three *B. subtilis* polymerases, this enzyme has been reported to co-purify with a nuclease activity, but the fraction involved was not homogeneous. Like the *E. coli* enzyme, DNA polymerase III of *B. subtilis* appears to be sensitive to salt concentrations above 0.05 M, and to be heat-labile.

In vitro studies of *B. subtilis* DNA polymerase III have shown that this enzyme is specifically inhibited by 6-(*p*-hydroxyphenylazo)-uracil, which may occupy the triphosphate binding site and interact with deoxycytidine residues on the template strand. Recently, the effects of this inhibitor on synthesis of nascent DNA fragments were studied in vivo. Both the rate of synthesis and the size of the nascent chains were affected. As drug concentration increased, there was a decrease in both parameters. The single-stranded fragments can be isolated on hydroxyapatite columns; investigation of these fragments shows that they are not capable of self-annealing. Since the fragments are not complementary, they are apparently generated from only one parental strand. This fact appears to fit well with the postulated replication mechanism which holds that DNA synthesis is continuous on the other strand (see Chapter 7.1).

In *E. coli,* DNA fragments (Okazaki fragments) formed during replication apparently can be joined together by the combined action of DNA polymerase and ligase. When *B. subtilis* nascent fragments are formed under conditions of partial inhibition of DNA polymerase III, the rate of joining is also inhibited. This indicates that the other polymerases are also inhibited, or that they are not required for this step. Anderson and Ganesan postulate that a form of *B. subtilis* pol III analogous to the core enzyme of *E. coli* may be responsible for this step, and that a holoenzyme form of the enzyme carries out synthesis of Okazaki fragments.

DNA POLYMERASES OF BACTERIOPHAGE

The larger DNA phages induce the formation of their own DNA polymerase (viral-specific) after infection of the host. Several of these enzymes have been studied extensively. The best characterized phage polymerases are those from the T-phages, relatively large *E. coli* viruses. Evidence for T-phage–specific polymerase was obtained before 1960, and the enzyme has been purified to homogeneity from the T4 and T7 bacteriophages. Like the bacterial enzymes, these polymerases may also be incapable of initiation of synthesis. The polymerases which have been extensively studied appear to contain a 3′ to 5′ exonuclease activity, as do the *E. coli* enzymes.

Phage T4 polymerase is coded for by gene 43 of the phage, and requires the product of T4 gene 32 for activity. The polymerase has a molecular weight of 105,000–110,000 daltons, and requires a 3′-OH primer. In vitro the enzyme can utilize gapped DNA, but not nicked DNA, as template primer, or may use the 3′ end of a single-stranded DNA containing a hairpin loop near the 3′ end of the polymer (Figure 4). In vivo this polymerase and the gene 32 protein are required for phage DNA synthesis; bacterial proteins cannot be used.

The gene 32 protein binds to single-stranded DNA. In vivo the protein

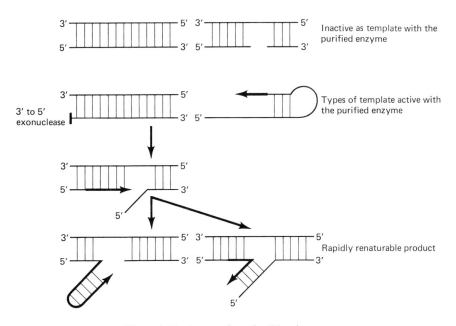

Figure 4. *In vitro* templates for T4 polymerase.

probably participates in replication by facilitating the unwinding of the parental double helix. The purified protein is an asymmetric molecule with a molecular weight of 35,000 daltons which does not bind to *E. coli* polymerase.

Studies of the phage T4 enzyme from several mutants have shown that the enzyme contains both polymerase and a 3′ to 5′ exonuclease activity. The relative proportions of the two activities in these mutants lead to interesting properties. These strains show a mutator or antimutator phenotype; mutators induce a high rate of mutation in the strain, while antimutators depress the rate of introduction of mutations. These two phenotypes can arise in phage T4 as a consequence of mutations in the same gene, gene 43; other mutations in this gene may arise which do not influence mutation rates. The mutator phenotype has been shown to correlate well with a decreased rate of nuclease activity leading to retention of errors, or to a defect in the polymerase activity such that errors are introduced at a higher rate. An experimental anticancer agent, adriamycin, has been shown to inhibit T4 polymerase differentially in wild-type, mutator, and antimutator strains. In mutator strains, there is less inhibition of the polymerase activity, but the nuclease activity is equally inhibited.

The polymerase from phage T7 has also been purified. It is coded for by gene 5, contains no endonuclease activity, but does include a 3′ to 5′ exonuclease. The enzyme has a molecular weight of 80,000 daltons and contains sulfhydryl groups which are required for activity.

This enzyme, like other known polymerases, requires several proteins for replication to proceed. They include the products of genes 3 and 6, which are nucleases, and of 2 and 4, whose function is as yet unknown. Attempts have been made to reconstitute the DNA replication complex in vitro, but have not been completely successful. The system obtained was able to initiate synthesis but not to carry the reaction to completion. However, these experiments demonstrated a requirement for a phage-specific RNA polymerase in replication of DNA, and work is continuing to elucidate the mechanisms of in vivo synthesis.

BIBLIOGRAPHY

DNA Polymerase I of E. coli:

Klenow, H., and Overgaard-Hansen, K. 1970. *FEBS Lett.* 6:25.
Huberman, J. A., and Kornberg, A. 1970. *J. Biol. Chem.* 245:5236.
Slater, J. P., Mildvan, A. S., and Loeb, L. A. 1971. *Biochem. Biophys. Res. Commun.* 44:37.
Brutlag, D., Schekman, R., and Kornberg, A. 1971. *Proc. Natl. Acad. Sci. U.S.A.* 68:2826.
Wells, R. D., Fluegel, R. W., Larson, J. E., Schendel, P. F., and Sweet, R. W. 1972. *Biochemistry* 11:621.
Goulian, M. 1972. *Prog. Nucl. Acid Res. Mol. Biol.* 12:28.
Setlow, P., Brutlag, D., and Kornberg, A. 1972. *J. Biol. Chem.* 247:224.

Kingsbury, D., and Helinski, D. 1973. *J. Bacteriol.* 114:1116.

Veltkamp, E., and Nijkamp, H. 1973. *Mol. Gen. Genet.* 125:329.

Glickman, B. W., van Sluis, C. A., Heijeneckar, H. L., and Rörsch, 1973. *Mol. Gen. Genet.* 124:53.

Konrad, E., and Lehman, I. 1974. *Proc. Natl. Acad. Sci. U.S.A.* 71:2048.

Emmerson, P. T. 1974. In *Biochemistry Series One,* Vol. 6, *Biochemistry of Nucleic Acids* K. Burton, ed., p. 141. University Park Press, Baltimore.

Dressler, D. 1975. *Ann. Rev. Microbiol.* 29:525.

DNA Polymerase II of E. coli:

Knippers, R., and Strätling, W. 1970. *Nature* 226:713.

Moses, R. E., and Richardson, C. C. 1970. *Biochem. Biophys. Res. Commun.* 41:1557.

Kornberg, T., and Gefter, M. 1970. *Biochem. Biophys. Res. Commun.* 40:1348.

Rama Reddy, G. V., Goulian, M., and Hendler, S. S. 1971. *Nature New Biol.* 234:286.

Knippers, R. 1971. *Nature* 228:1050.

Wickner, R. B., Ginsberg, B., Berkower, I., and Hurwitz, J. 1972. *J. Biol. Chem.* 247:489.

Campbell, J., Soll, L., and Richardson, C. C. 1972. *Proc. Natl. Acad. Sci. U.S.A.* 69:2090.

Hirota, Y., Gefter, M., and Mindich, L. 1972. *Proc. Natl. Acad. Sci. U.S.A.* 69:3238.

Schekman, R., Wickner, W., Westergaard, O., Brutlag, D., Geider, K., Bertsch, L. L., and Kornberg, A. 1972. *Proc. Natl. Acad. Sci. U.S.A.* 69:2691.

Sigal, N., Delius, H., Kornberg, T., Gefter, M. L., and Alberts, B. 1972. *Proc. Natl. Acad. Sci. U.S.A.* 69:3537.

Fujiwara, T., and Komano, T. 1974. *Agr. Biol. Chem.* 38:1281.

Tait, R. C., and Smith, D. W. 1974. *Nature* 249:116.

Campana, T., and Shapiro, H. S. 1976. *Biochim. Biophys. Acta* 442:216.

DNA Polymerase III:

Kornberg, T., and Gefter, M. L. 1971. *Proc. Natl. Acad. Sci. U.S.A.* 68:761.

Goulian, M. 1972. *Prog. Nucl. Acid Res. Mol. Biol.* 12:28.

Kornberg, T., and Gefter, M. 1972. *J. Biol. Chem.* 247:5369.

Wickner, W., Schekman, R., Geider, K., and Kornberg, A. 1973. *Proc. Natl. Acad. Sci. U.S.A.* 70:1764.

Wickner, W., and Kornberg, A. 1974. *J. Biol. Chem.* 249:6244.

Dressler, D. 1975. *Annu. Rev. Microbiol.* 29:525.

Other Bacterial DNA Polymerases:

Kuempel. P., and Veomett, G. 1970. *Biochem. Biophys. Res. Commun.* 41:973.

Okazaki, R., Arisawa, M., and Sugino, A. 1971. *Proc. Natl. Acad. Sci. U.S.A.* 68:2954.

Yehle, C. O., and Ganesan, A. T. 1972. *J. Virol.* 9:263.

Ganesan, A. T., Yehle, C. O., and Yu, C. C. 1973. *Biochem. Biophys. Res. Commun.* 50:155.

Gass, K. B., and Cozzarelli, N. R. 1973. *J. Biol. Chem.* 248:7688.

Mackenzie, J., Neville, M., Wright, G., and Brown, N. 1973. *Proc. Natl. Acad. Sci. U.S.A.* 70:512.

Anderson, J. J., and Ganesan, A. T. 1976. *J. Mol. Biol.* 106:285.

DNA Polymerases of Bacteriophage:

Alberts, B. M. 1970. *Fed. Proc.* 29:1154.

Nossal, N. G., and Hershfield, M. S. 1971. *J. Biol. Chem.* 246:5414.

Sinha, N., and Sunstad, D. P. 1971. *J. Mol. Biol.* 62:267.

Huberman, J. A., Kornberg, A., and Alberts, B. M. 1971. *J. Mol. Biol.* 62:39.

Grippo, P., and Richardson, C. C. 1971. *J. Biol. Chem.* 246:6867.

Studier, F. 1972. *Science* 176:367.

Muzyczka, N., Poland, R. L., and Bessman, M. J. 1972. *J. Biol. Chem.* 247:7116.

Hershfield, M. 1973. *J. Biol. Chem.* 248:1417.

Schnaar, R. L., Muzyczka, N., and Bessman, M. J., 1973. *Genetics Suppl.* 73:137.

Knippers, R., Strätling, W., and Krause, E. 1973. In *DNA Synthesis in Vitro,* R. D. Wells and R. B. Inman, eds., p. 451. University Park Press, Baltimore.

Goodman, M. F., Bessman, M., and Bachur, N. R. 1974. *Proc. Natl. Acad. Sci. U.S.A.* 71:1193.

6.8. Eukaryotic DNA Polymerases

Theresa Campana

GENERAL PROPERTIES

DNA polymerases have been described in mammalian cells and in yeast; these studies have utilized both cells grown in cell culture systems and cells obtained from living organisms. Eukaryotic cells in general contain multiple DNA polymerases; these include a mitochondrial enzyme as well as two or three cellular polymerases. The enzymes described share several characteristics, and, to a degree, are similar to prokaryotic polymerases (Table 1). Thus, each requires a divalent cation, generally Mg^{2+}, and none seems to initiate new DNA strands. The different forms described are distinct enzymes, although there have been some reports of antigenic and structural similarities.

Unlike the bacterial polymerases, these eukaryotic enzymes contain little or no associated exonuclease activity. ATP appears to inhibit the eukaryotic polymerases, whereas it has generally been reported that ATP stimulates DNA synthesis in bacteria. Neither prokaryotic nor eukaryotic DNA polymerases appear to use an intact, double-stranded DNA molecule on purification, but they preferentially replicate molecules with extensive single-stranded gaps. Originally, the α and β polymerases had been reported to be localized to the cytoplasm and the nucleus, respectively, on the basis of cell fractionation techniques using aqueous solvents. It has now been postulated that this was an artifact and that all cellular polymerases are indeed associated with the

Table 1. Characteristics of Eukaryotic DNA Polymerases.

POLYMERASE	PREFERRED TEMPLATE	SIZE IN 10^3 DALTONS	ATP	INHIBITION BY		
				NACL	NEM	HEAT
α	gapped DNA	150	+++	+	+	++
β	" "	30–40	n.d.	−	−	+
γ	RNA*	110–150	n.d.	−	+	n.d.
m	m DNA	100–150	+	**	+	++

* The preferred template has been reported to be the synthetic polymer poly rA:oligo dT. ** NaCl at 0.2 M stimulates some of the mitochondrial enzymes.

cell nucleus, because of the finding that over 90% of the cellular polymerase activity is associated with the nucleus when nonaqueous solvents are used for fractionation. The earlier finding appears to indicate leakage of polymerases out of the nucleus because of permeability changes induced by aqueous solvents.

As was noted for the bacterial enzymes, it is probable that further studies will implicate other proteins in the processes of cellular DNA replication. The role of each of the eukaryotic polymerases is not as yet clear; further studies may allow a definition of the reactions catalyzed by each enzyme. Several properties of each of these enzymes have been reported, and some preliminary attempts made to define a physiological role for each. The next few years should see a clearer picture emerging on the specific role of these polymerases in vivo.

THE α POLYMERASE

This large enzyme, originally thought to be localized to the cellular cytoplasm, was generally called DNA polymerase I. The polypeptide dimerizes easily to a form with a molecular weight of about 300,000 daltons. Like the bacterial polymerases, this enzyme requires the deoxyribonucleoside triphosphates and Mg^{2+}, and prefers a gapped template-primer, although it can elongate a natural RNA primer. The pH optimum of the α polymerase is about pH 7.0, and the protein has an isoelectric point of about 5.6.

The enzyme also catalyzes pyrophosphate exchange and hydrolysis. Sulfhydryl groups are required for activity, although the exact number of such groups and their specific role have not yet been determined. The enzyme is inhibited by salt concentrations above 0.2 M, and by ara-CTP, a potent inhibitor of in vivo replication. These properties are reminiscent of those described for DNA polymerases II and III of E. coli (see Chapter 6.7), and have been cited as evidence for an in vivo requirement for α polymerase in replication. Direct evidence for such a requirement is not available, since genetic studies of the type that proved so fruitful in bacterial systems have not yet been carried out. However, the observation that the levels of α polymerase vary during the cell cycle accords well with such a role. The increase is noted also in human lymphoblasts that have been induced with phytohemagglutinin and in proliferating rat liver.

Baril and his coworkers have isolated the α polymerase in a fraction containing membrane fragments and several associated enzymes. These enzymes, thymidine kinase, thymidylate synthetase, and ribonucleotide reductase, remain associated with the polymerase in rat liver even after treatment with agents known to disrupt membranes. Such complexes may be artifacts, or they may really exist in vivo and be required for DNA replication. In vitro, these enzyme complexes have been shown to catalyze the phosphorylation and incorporation of thymidine into DNA. The nature of the membrane fragments has not yet been established; it should be noted that many scientists working in eukaryotic DNA synthesis are unsure of the role of membranes in replication. These results should stimulate further studies of these points.

Some studies have led to the conclusion that the α polymerase may be required to fill in gaps in newly synthesized DNA that result from the removal of RNA primers. The requirement of eukaryotic DNA for RNA primers has not been unequivocally demonstrated, but there is much experimental evidence for such a system in bacteria (see Section 7). According to this theory, some one of the other polymerases would form Okazaki fragments. However, the only polymerase that has been shown to use natural RNA as a primer is α. It would therefore seem to be as justified—if not more so— to assume that this enzyme is directly involved in Okazaki fragment production as to assign a gap-filling role. In any case, by analogy to the bacterial systems, eukaryotic DNA replication will doubtless be shown to involve several enzymes acting together in a coordinated fashion. The present state of knowledge indicates that the α polymerase will probably be one of these.

THE β POLYMERASE

This enzyme differs from all other known polymerases in size; it is considerably smaller than the others, with a molecular weight of only about 35,000 daltons. It has been called the nuclear, or the mini polymerase, but the preferred nomenclature is β. The enzyme has been extensively purified, and resembles the α polymerase in many properties. Thus, both enzymes fill in gaps in double-stranded DNA, require Mg^{2+} and the four ribonucleoside triphosphates, and have little or no associated nuclease activity. There have been reports of antigenic and structural similarities between the two enzymes, but the present consensus is that these results were artifactual. This could have been the result of cross contamination of samples, since the two enzymes are each capable of aggregation to similar sizes.

There are several important differences in the properties of the α and β polymerases. The isoelectric point of the two enzymes is very different: for α it is below pH 7.0, whereas for β it is about pH 9.2. The pH optimum of β is also considerably more alkaline than that of the larger polymerase. The small β polymerase is less heat-labile than α, and is not inhibited by salt, NEM, or ara-CTP. In addition, the cellular levels of β remain constant throughout the cell cycle, and do not change when cells are induced to proliferate. It has been noted, however, that the cellular levels of this enzyme are high enough to account for replication, whereas the α levels are very low except near the time of division.

Another difference between the two enzymes lies in the template-primers each will accept. The preferred template is gapped DNA for both α and β; however, each enzyme can use other templates and primers. As noted above, α will accept a natural RNA primer; β will not. The β polymerase can, on the other hand, use the synthetic polymer poly rA:oligo dT. Both enzymes will elongate an oligo rA when poly dT is included as a template. The β polymerase has not been reported to be associated with other enzymes in vivo and in vitro, and has no real distinctive characteristics that allow much postulation of an in vivo role.

It has been suggested that β is the enzyme that fills in the gaps formed after removal of RNA primers, although Hunter and Franke have suggested that it is the enzyme required for the formation of Okazaki fragments. It is interesting to note that this enzyme will not repair a mismatched base in vitro, but will copy the mistake. None of the eukaryotic polymerases is as proficient in replacing mismatches as are the bacterial enzymes, possibly because of the lack of associated nucleases, but β seems least able to correct these errors. At present, it seems safe to speculate that this enzyme will be found to play a facultative role in some aspects of DNA metabolism, or perhaps will be shown to participate in recombination.

THE γ POLYMERASE

This enzyme, described in several mammalian systems, has been called a cellular or endogenous RNA-dependent DNA polymerase, since it efficiently uses the synthetic template-primer poly dA:oligo dT, as does β. However, γ also uses poly dT:oligo rA and other DNA templates, and cannot use natural RNA as a primer. Therefore, it has now been decided to call this enzyme γ. The activity of γ polymerase is sensitive to RNAase but not to DNAase, and appears to be linked to cellular proliferation. About 1% of the total cellular polymerase activity has been ascribed to γ.

Several properties of this enzyme have been determined. The K_m of this polymerase for the deoxyribonucleoside triphosphates is much lower than that of α and β. This may have some implications for in vivo replication, since the pools of triphosphates may be lowered by various drugs that prevent gap-filling, but not the formation of Okazaki fragments. Since variations in pool size could be expected to have the least effect on the enzyme with a low K_m, which would be the γ polymerase in this case, it is postulated that this enzyme is required for formation of Okazaki fragments. The sensitivity of γ to sulfhydryl-binding reagents is also consistent with a cellular requirement for this enzyme.

Prior to purification, crude preparations of γ appear to utilize viral 70S

RNA as a template. On purification of the enzyme from phytohemagglutinin-stimulated normal human lymphocytes, however, this property is lost; the purified enzyme prefers a gapped DNA molecule as template-primer. This puzzling observation might be explained by the loss of some neccessary cofactors during purification, or might be due to some contaminant present in the crude fraction. The present state of knowledge is inadequate to explain fully why this is so.

Several properties differentiate the cellular γ polymerase from viral-induced RNA-dependent DNA polymerase, although they do share some properties. Under certain assay conditions, the cellular enzyme prefers Mn^{2+} ions to the Mg^{2+} required by other polymerases. The viral enzyme has an associated ribonuclease activity called RNase H; this endogenous activity co-purifies with the viral reverse transcriptase and appears to be part of the same polypeptide molecule. It acts as an exonuclease, as do all other nucleases that have been shown to form integral parts of polymerases. An activity that has also been called RNase H has been found associated with the γ polymerase, but it is not yet certain whether this enzyme activity is part of the same protein or a separate polypeptide. This nuclease, however, is an endonuclease; it could then be required to cut an RNA primer at the point of attachment to the DNA chain. These properties could lead to speculation that this enzyme is required during replication, and deserve attention from scientists in the field.

Another point that it would be of interest to define is the effect of ara-CTP on the purified γ polymerase. This has not yet been reported, but should be studied, since several properties of γ are consistent with a neccessary role for this enzyme in vivo. The physiological roles of the cellular polymerases are as yet unclear, as are their interactions with other enzymes that may be required in replication. Proteins analogous to the gene products of *dna* genes in *E. coli* have not yet been described in eukaryotic systems, but further work may identify such proteins. Eukaryotic systems will probably be shown to be much more complex than bacterial systems, but is resonable to assume that some basic mechanisms will be shared by both.

THE MITOCHONDRIAL (m) POLYMERASE

Mitochondria are cellular organelles that contain a small, circular DNA that codes for mitochondrial rRNA, some specific tRNA molecules, and a few proteins specific to the organelle. The mitochondria from yeast and some mammals have also been shown to contain a specific DNA polymerase. This enzyme may be membrane-bound in some species, since it has been reported that the enzyme can be extracted from rat liver mitochondrial membranes with 1 M NaCl or with detergents. It is not yet clear what the specific physiological role of this enzyme is; it may be responsible for the replication of mitochondrial DNA, or perhaps be required for repair of lesions in this DNA. In *Tetrahymena pyriformis*, it has been reported that the levels of m polymerase increase dramatically after damage to the DNA. This process requires the synthesis of both RNA and protein, and appears to be directed by the cell nucleus, since it is inhibited by cycloheximide but not by chloramphenicol. Cycloheximide inhibits cellular but not mitochondrial protein synthesis, while the chloramphenicol inhibits just the mitochondrial process.

The m polymerase from several sources differs in several properties. Rat liver mitochondria contain a polymerase that is strongly stimulated by salt (0.15 M NaCl or KCl; the enzyme isolated from calf liver or HeLa cell mitochondria are slightly stimulated; the enzyme in yeast mitochondria shows no influence of salt. The rat liver enzyme is the most labile of those studied, and can use denatured DNA quite effectively as a template. Gapped DNA, on the other hand, is the preferred template for HeLa m polymerase; duplex DNA, including the DNA from the mitochondria, can be used, since the enzyme preparation includes a low but significant level of an endonuclease activity. The m polymerase appears to be similar in size to cellular polymerases in mammalian cell systems, but not in protozoan systems.

The mitochondrial polymerase from the protozoan *Tetrahymena pyriformis* has been purified, and several characteristics have been determined. The enzyme is a relatively small polypeptide, and prefers a denatured template. The K_m for Mg^{2+} is 11 times higher for this enzyme than for the cellular polymerases of the same organism, and appears to be about 5 times greater than that of the major cellular polymerases of other organisms. Like the rat liver m polymerase, this protozoan enzyme is stimulated by salt, in this case, by 0.2 M NaCl. On exposure to agents that damage the mitochondrial DNA, there is a 40-fold increase in the levels of this polymerase, so that, in this organism at least, the role of this enzyme appears to be closely linked to repair of damage. This repair would certainly require the presence of nuclease activity; such an activity has been demonstrated to co-purify with some of the m polymerases, but has not yet been shown to be an integral part of the enzyme.

DNA replication in mitochondria appears not to be synchronous with cellular DNA replication, implying a need for an organelle-specific replication system. At the same time, the process may be controlled indirectly by the cell nucleus, and certainly depends on cellular protein synthesis. Further studies on the process of mitochondrial DNA synthesis should shed some light on these control processes, and may also clarify the interrelationships between cellular organelles and the cell.

BIBLIOGRAPHY

General Properties:

Wintersburger, U., and Wintersburger, E. 1970. *Eur. J. Biochem.* 13:20.

Meyer, R. R., and Simpson, M. V. 1970. *J. Biol. Chem.* 245:3426.

Chang, L. M. S., and Bollum, F. J. 1971. *J. Biol. Chem.* 246:5835.

Baril, E. F., Brown, O. E., Jenkins, M. D., and Laszlo, J. 1971. *Biochemistry* 10:1981.

Weissbach, A., Schlabach, A., Fridlender, B., and Bolden, A. 1971. *Nature New Biol.* 231:167.

Smith, R. G., and Gallo, R. C. 1972. *Proc. Natl. Acad. Sci. U.S.A.* 69:2879.

Chang, L. M. S., and Bollum, F. J. 1972. *Science* 175:1116.

Lazarus, L. H., and Kitron, N. C. 1973. *J. Mol. Biol.* 81:529.

Hecht, N. B. 1973. *Nature New Biol.* 245:199.

Gallo, R. C., Sarin, P. S., Bobrow, S. N., Sarngadharan, M. G., Reitz, M. S., Jr., and Abrell, J. W. 1973. In *DNA Synthesis in Vitro,* R. D. Wells and R. B. Inman, eds., p. 251. University Park Press, Baltimore.

Tibbets, C. J. B., and Vinograd, J. 1973. *J. Biol. Chem.* 248:3367, 3380.

Frey, M., and Weissbach, A. 1973. *Biochemistry* 12:3602.

Baril, E. F., Baril, B., Elford, H., and Luftig, R. B. 1974. In *Mechanism and Regulation of DNA Replication,* A. R. Kolber and M. Kohiyama, eds., p. 275. Plenum Press, New York.

Bollum, F. J., and Chang, L. M. S. 1974. In *Mechanism and Regulation of DNA Replication,* A. R. Kolber and M. Kohiyama, eds., p. 253. Plenum Press, New York.

Foster, D. N., and Gurney, T., Jr. 1974. *J. Cell Biol.* 249:2991.

Edenberg, H. J., and Huberman, J. A. 1975. *Annu. Rev. Genet.* 9:245.

Weissbach, A. 1975. *Cell* 5:101.

The α Polymerase:

Keller, W. 1972. *Proc. Natl. Acad. Sci. U.S.A.* 69:1660.

Sedwick, W. D., Wang, T. S. S., and Korn, D. 1972. *J. Biol. Chem.* 247:5026.

Spadari, S., and Weissbach, A. 1974. *J. Biol. Chem.* 249:5809.

Bollum, F. J. 1975. *Prog. Nucl. Acid Res. Mol. Biol.* 15:109.

Hunter, T., and Franke, B. 1975. *J. Virol.* 15:759.

Spadari, S., and Weissbach, A. 1975. *Proc. Natl. Acad. Sci. U.S.A.* 72:503.

The β Polymerase:

Chang, L. M. S., Brown, McK., and Bollum, F. J. 1973. *J. Mol. Biol.* 74:1.

Chang, L. M. S. 1973. *J. Biol. Chem.* 248:3789.

Wang, T. F.-S., Sedwick, W. D., and Korn, D. 1975. *J. Biol. Chem.* 250:7045.

Wang, T. F.-S., Sedwick, W. D., and Korn, D. 1975. *J. Biol. Chem.* 250:7040.

The γ Polymerase:

Skoog, L., and Nordenskjold, B. 1971. *Eur. J. Biochem.* 19:81.

Kang, C.-Y., and Temin, H. M. 1972. *Proc. Natl. Acad. Sci. U.S.A.* 69:1550.

Bobrow, S. N., Smith, R. G., Reitz, M. S., and Gallo, R. C. 1972. *Proc. Natl. Acad. Sci. U.S.A.* 69:3228.

Sarngadharan, M. G., Sarin, P. S., Reitz, M. S., and Gallo, R. C. 1972. *Nature New Biol.* 240:67.

Bolden, A., Frey, M., Muller, R., Citarella, R., and Weissbach, A. 1972. *Arch. Biochem. Biophys.* 153:26.

Baltimore, D., and Smoler, D. 1972. *J. Biol. Chem.* 247:7282.
Leis, J. P., Berkower, I., and Hurwits, J. 1973. *Proc. Natl. Acad. Sci. U.S.A.* 70:466.
Laipis, P. J., and Levine, A. J. 1973. *Virology* 56:580.
Salzman, N. P., and Thoren, M. M. 1973. *J. Virol.* 11:721.
Skoog, L., and Bjursell, G. 1974. *J. Biol. Chem.* 249:6434.
Spadari, S., and Weissbach, A. 1974. *J. Mol. Biol.* 86:11.

The Mitochondrial Polymerase:

Westergaard, O., Marcker, K. A., and Kerding, J. 1970. *Nature* 227:708.
Westergaard, O. 1970. *Biochim. Biophys. Acta* 213:36.
Ojala, D., and Attardi, G. 1973. *J. Mol. Biol.* 78:275.

6.9. Other Enzymes of DNA Metabolism

Theresa Campana and Lazar M. Schwartz

LIGASES

The need for an enzyme capable of joining together pieces of DNA was first noted in studies of recombination. With the report that replication may proceed by means of the formation of Okazaki fragments, a role for a joining enzyme in replication also became obvious. Such enzymes have now been identified in both prokaryotic and eukaryotic systems; in general, the same reaction mechanism appears to be shared by all the ligases thus far studied.

Ligases catalyze the formation of a phosphodiester bond between the 5'-phosphoryl and the 3'-hydroxyl termini of adjacent oligonucleotides. All ligases join DNA polymers; some phage-induced ligases can also use RNA polymers as substrates. The mechanism of action of the ligases consists of three reversible steps:

1. An activated enzyme intermediate is formed by the transfer of an adenyl group from the coenzyme to the epsilon-amino group of a lysine residue in the enzyme. The coenzyme is NAD in bacteria; in viruses and in animal cells, ATP serves this function.

2. The adenyl group is transferred from the lysine residue to the 5'-phosphate terminus of one oligomer; this transfer activates the phosphoryl group. Pyrophosphate will also allow this transfer to take place, but will inhibit further ligase activity.

3. The phosphodiester bond is then formed by an attack of the 3'-hydroxyl group of the adding oligomer onto the activated 5'-terminus. Formation of the bond proceeds with the elimination of one molecule of AMP.

In vivo, bacteriophage T4 induces a fivefold increase in the ligase activity of host cells. A mutation in gene 30 of the phage can prevent this increase, causing accumulation of short viral DNA fragments, so that very few viable phage are produced. On infection of a mutant line of E. coli with abnormally high ligase concentration, this mutant phage is able to reproduce normally, an indication that the ligase plays a necessary role in replication of the virus. Studies with E. coli mutants that have a temperature-sensitive ligase support a similar role for this enzyme in bacterial replication.

The enzyme has been purified from *E. coli;* the ligase is a single polypeptide chain with a molecular weight of 75,000 daltons. An estimate of the number of molecules per cell has also been published; wild-type bacteria seem to contain about 3000 molecules per cell. A mutation in the presumed structural gene for the *E. coli* ligase has been described; this strain contains less than 5% of the normal ligase concentration. Replication and viability are normal, while some repair processes may be impaired. Studies with this mutant indicate that fewer than 150 molecules of ligase should suffice for normal replication; other studies support the possibility that as few as ten molecules of the ligase are actually required for DNA synthesis. The great bulk of the normal concentration is probably needed for recombination and repair, but definitive evidence on this point is still lacking.

"SWIVEL" AND "UNWINDING" PROTEINS

Other proteins have been described that appear to be required for normal DNA synthesis. Some of them appear to be required for the unwinding of the duplex ("unwinding" proteins), whereas others relieve the torque generated during the denaturation of large duplex molecules ("swivelases"). In a strict sense, these proteins may not be enzymes, since stoichiometric rather than catalytic concentrations appear to be needed. Proteins capable of such roles have been described in both prokaryotic and eukaryotic systems.

Unwinding proteins have been shown to be capable of reducing the T_M, or melting temperature, of a duplex DNA molecule by about $40°C$, probably because of tight binding at single-stranded regions. At relatively low temperatures, transient single-stranded regions can form in a double-stranded molecule. These regions are often rich in A–T pairs, since less energy is required to break these hydrogen bonds than those of C–G pairs. Unwinding proteins can attach to these regions, stabilizing them in a denatured conformation. The molecules interact with each other, attaching along the DNA strand in close alignment. The energy of binding is thought to cause the two strands of the duplex to unwind further, allowing attachment of other molecules of the unwinding protein.

In addition, this binding causes the single-stranded regions to assume a conformation that will allow for efficient reannealing. This conformational change may be responsible for the increase in polymerase activity in vitro when unwinding proteins are added. The proteins from various organisms appear to be species-specific; only the polymerase from the parental organism is stimulated by a particular unwinding protein. The molecular weight of these proteins varies from 10×10^3 to 74×10^3 daltons; the largest is that from *E. coli,* which exists naturally as a tetramer, while the others have been determined to be monomers. In plant cells and in animal spermatocytes, the unwinding proteins have been reported to be associated with the nuclear membrane. The number of molecules of unwinding protein present in any species appears to be correlated with the number of replication forks formed during DNA synthesis. In *E. coli,* there have been reported to be about three replication forks, and about 800 copies of the unwinding protein. On the other hand, the bacteriophage T4, which has 60 replication forks, contains 10,000 ligase copies. Both replication and transcription require at least local denaturation of a duplex molecule; the unwinding proteins may facilitate both processes.

Swivel proteins act in cooperation with unwinding proteins and are required for the replication of circular duplexes and very large, linear double-stranded DNA. Supertwisting and torque are generated in such molecules during the unwinding of the two strands. Swivel proteins correct this supertwisting and relieve the torque by a little-understood mechanism. It has been postulated that the ω protein of *E. coli* may nick the duplex but remain attached to one of the free ends of the DNA strands. Such a mechanism would conserve the energy of the phosphodiester bond while permitting rotation of the nicked strands. The ω protein cannot seal nicks in DNA molecules of itself, but conservation of the phosphodiester bond energy may allow the bond to re-form when the swivel protein detaches.

Evidence to support this hypothesis is not yet available. It has, however, been shown that both the *E. coli* ω and a mammalian equivalent can relieve superhelical turns in DNA while conserving the intactness of the molecule. Further studies of such molecules should help elucidate the physical properties of intact chromosomes.

TERMINAL NUCLEOTIDYL TRANSFERASE

This enzyme has been described in plants and in the cells of thymus glands. It catalyzes the polymerization of deoxyribonucleotides in the absence of a template. In some buffers, no primer is required for the reaction to proceed, albeit at a slow rate. Generally, however, a single-stranded oligomer containing at least three nucleotides is required for polymerization. This primer must have both a hydroxyl group at the 3'-terminus and a 5'-phosphoryl terminus. In the presence of such primers, the oligomeric product may contain as many as 500 nucleotides. Poly dG molecules cannot serve as primers, since such oligomers easily form duplex molecules.

Terminal nucleotidyl transferase has been described in both the nucleus and the cytoplasm of thymus cells. In crude extracts of this gland, the transferase activity cannot be assayed, perhaps as a result of interactions of the enzyme with other proteins in some complex. It has been estimated that fewer than 50% of the cells in the thymus contain the enzyme, and that these cells may be specifically the T cells. The exact physiological role of terminal nucleotidyl transferase remains doubtful; The enzyme is found only in lymphoid tissues.

The enzyme has been purified from the cytoplasm of thymus glands. It has a molecular weight of 33,000 daltons, and consists of two subunits, a small (8000 daltons) and a large (26,000 daltons) polypeptide chain. The enzyme activity is influenced by the buffer, pH, and presence of metal ions. It uses only deoxyribonucleotides as substrates, in contrast to the nuclear enzyme, which can also incorporate ribonucleotides.

In vitro, this transferase has been used to form polymer chains of defined composition. These synthetic polymers can then be used to study other enzymes such as ligase, polymerase, and specific endonucleases. In addition, a dimeric viral genome has been produced from monomeric SV40 DNA by the use of the specific endonuclease III and the transferase. Studies of this type may help to define the possible regulatory role of homopolymeric regions in a genome, and can be used in the synthesis of genes.

DNA EXONUCLEASES

Exonucleases degrade nucleic acids by sequentially breaking phosphodiester bonds beginning at the terminal nucleotide. This sequential degradation may go to completion, releasing the constituent mononucleotides, or may be partial, allowing recovery of oligomers. Exonucleases show no specificity for base sequence, but each of them shows a preference for a specific terminus (3′ or 5′, phosphorylated or not), and for a single- or double-stranded substrate. The physiological roles of such enzymes include participation in repair and recombination; they may be required also for degradation of ingested nucleic acids. It has been postulated that specific exonucleases participate in replication of viruses by forming cohesive ends needed for circularization of the genome.

Many exonucleases have been described; eight such activities are known in *E. coli.* The enzyme activity may be found associated with a protein which is known to have other enzymatic functions, as is the case for exonucleases II and VI of *E. coli.* These two activities, as well as an endonuclease, cannot be separated from DNA polymerase I. It is thought that they are required in excision repair and in "copy-reading," that is, the removal of mismatched bases during replication. Another multifunctional protein, the gene product of *rec B, C,* has two exonucleases, an ATPase and an endonuclease. From genetic studies, it is known that this gene is required for recombination and repair, but the exact contribution of each constituent enzyme is not known in detail. The exonuclease activities thus far described in *E. coli* are shown in Table 1.

Table 1.   Exonucleases of *E. coli.*

NAME	SUBSTRATE	PRODUCTS
Exonuclease I	3'-OH, single-stranded DNA	5'-mononucleotides + terminal dinucleotide
Exonuclease II	3'-OH, single-stranded DNA	5'-mononucleotides (polymerase I)
Exonuclease III	3'-OH or 3'-PO$_4$, double-stranded	5'-mononucleotides + large oligomer single-stranded
Exonuclease IV	3'-OH, single-stranded oligomers	5'-mononucleotides
Exonuclease V	3'-OH, single-stranded 5'-PO$_4$, double-stranded	*(rec B,C)* oligonucleotides
Exonuclease VI	5'-OH, PO$_4$ or tri-PO$_4$, double-stranded	(polymerase I) mono- and oligonucleotides
Exonuclease VII	3' or 5' end, single-stranded	oligonucleotides

Exonuclease III has been useful in vitro for the preparation of substrates for DNA polymerase assays. This enzyme attacks a double-stranded DNA molecule from both ends, degrading the DNA until only single-stranded oligonucleotides remain. Limited digestion allows the preparation of molecules with single-stranded ends, which can then serve as primer-templates for a DNA polymerase.

Exonucleases have also been described in other bacteria, in virus-infected cells, and in eukaryotes. Some of them are described in Table 2. The enzyme produced by *B. subtilis* is of interest, since it is found extracellularly, with

Table 2.   Other Exonucleases.

ORGANISM	SUBSTRATE	PRODUCTS
B. subtilis	single-stranded, 3' end double-stranded, 5' end	mononucleotides
N. crassa	single-stranded, 5' end	mononucleotides
Snake venom	single-stranded 3' end	5' mononucleotides
Spleen	single-stranded 5'-OH	3' mononucleotides
Rabbit (liver III IV)	single-stranded 3' double-stranded 5'	mono- + dinucleotides mononucleotides
Phage T4	single-stranded 3'	mono- + oligonucleotides
T5	single + double 5'	mono- + oligonucleotides
T7	double-stranded 5'	dinucleotides
SP3	double-stranded 5'	mononucleotides
λ	single + double 5'	

very low concentrations in the interior. It appears to have two activities, one of which prefers single-stranded substrates, and digests both DNA and RNA. The *N. crassa* enzyme can also degrade both polymers, as can the spleen and snake venom phosphodiesterases. The exonucleases coded for by viruses may serve to produce substrates for viral replication; in one case, the λ phage, the nuclease appears to be required for viral recombination.

ENDONUCLEASES

These enzymes do not require free ends, but attack DNA at some point within the chain. Some endonucleases recognize distortions in the secondary structure caused by incorrect base-pairing or by the presence of pyrimidine dimers. They then introduce a nick near the distortion, allowing excision by an exonuclease.

Other endonucleases appear to recognize specific short sequences of bases; these enzymes include pancreatic DNase I, *E. coli* endonuclease I, T_4 endonuclease IV, and spleen DNase II. These sequences may consist of only three or four bases, except for the T4 phage–induced enzyme, which cleaves specifically TpC sequences. Reaction conditions, such as the cations present and the ionic strength of the solution, influence rate and relative specificity of sequences with different K_M values.

Endonucleases are required in repair, recombination, and restriction, and play a role in the replication of circular DNA molecules. Restriction endonucleases are described in detail below; the role of endonucleases in replication, repair, and recombination is more fully explored in Section 7. In general, it should be stated that endonucleases introduce nicks, and exonucleases then remove a certain number of bases from the polymer. The products of endonuclease activity are oligonucleotides, not the mononucleotides formed by most exonuclease activity. In addition, the oligonucleotides formed almost invariably have $5'$-PO_4 ends.

A few endonucleases can act on RNA as well as DNA; this group includes the enzymes from *N. crassa* and *Aspergillus oryzae*, both of which show a strong preference for single-stranded DNA. The repair endonucleases act on double-stranded DNA with lesions of some sort, while those phage-induced endonucleases that have been shown to function during replication prefer single-stranded substrates.

MODIFICATION ENZYMES

The DNA of certain bacterial strains has been shown to contain methylated bases. This modification is carried out by specific methylases on complete DNA chains after replication of the bacterial genome. The DNA of lysogenized bacteriophage in these strains is also methylated by the same enzymes, but infecting DNA of other bacteriophage is not so modified. It is thought that this modification may protect the host cell DNA from degradation by specific restriction endonucleases. Some methylases, however, do not appear to protect the DNA from restriction enzymes; these methylases are found in many organisms, including both plants and animal cells. In these cases, the methylases, using S-adenosyl methionine as a methyl group donor, modify both adenine and cytosine to form 6-methylamino purine and 5-methyl cytosine. The methylases in modification restriction systems use the same donor, but only one base is modified. This base is usually adenine, although the methylase carried by the *E. coli* plasmid RII modifies the cytosine residues.

A third modification system has also been described; this system is associated with the *E. coli* bacteriophages known as the T-even phages. In these systems, cytosine is replaced by hydroxymethyl cytosine, which is glucosylated to a large extent by the phage-induced modification enzyme. The glucose donor, uridine diphosphate glucose (UDPG), is produced by the *E. coli* host; glucosylation is catalyzed by specific phage α and β glucosyl transferases. In host cells defective in UDPG formation, the phage that are produced on infection lack the glucose residues. These phage consequently are unable to infect most *E. coli,* since the viral DNA will be destroyed by *E. coli* restriction enzymes on infection. The restriction system that affects these phage may be associated with the membrane, since nonglucosylated DNA formed intracellularly is not degraded, but DNA entering the cell can be restricted.

The *E. coli* plasmids RTFI and RTFII each code for a modification methylase. These enzymes may be associated with the restriction endonucleases of these resistance transfer factors, and share the same substrate sites. The *Eco* RI enzymes recognize the sequence:

$$3' \underline{\quad\quad} C-T-T\;|-A^*-A-G \underline{\quad\quad} 5'$$
$$5' \underline{\quad\quad} G-A-A^*|-T\;-T-C \underline{\quad\quad} 3'$$

A* refers to the base that is methylated, and the arrows show the sites of endonuclease scission. The sequence shows a specific axis of symmetry, indicated by the dotted line. The sequence at the site of methylation and restriction by *Eco* RII enzymes is:

$$-C-G-G-A-C^*-C-G-5'$$
$$5'-G-C-C^*-T-G-G-C-$$

The methylases which have been studied extensively include those from *E. coli* B, *E. coli* phage P1, and *E. coli* K. Of these, the first two are separate from restriction endonucleases in the cell, whereas the *E. coli* K methylase is a subunit of the *E. coli* K restriction enzyme. This subunit, β, is present in the enzyme complex in two copies, and has a molecular weight of 60,000 daltons. The complex has been shown to methylate adenine residues in unmodified DNA, but studies have failed to find methylated bases at restriction sites. For this reason, the exact function of this methylase in vivo remains in dispute. The methylases from *E. coli* B and phage P1 have both been shown to consist of two unlike subunits. The *Eco B* methylase catalyzes the transfer of four methyl groups to two sites on unmodified DNA. These sites are arranged symmetrically in the specific modification–restriction sequence.

RESTRICTION ENDONUCLEASES

Specific endonucleases, which can recognize certain nucleotide sequences in DNA, have been isolated from several bacterial strains. Some of these enzymes are found associated with modification enzymes in a complex. The Class I restriction nucleases fail to produce cleavage fragments with distinctive termini. Class II endonucleases are generally simpler molecules and show site-specific cleavage. Class I enzymes require S-adenosyl-methionine, ATP, and Mg^{2+}; restriction enzymes of Class II need only Mg^{2+} ions. The first type of enzyme shows site-specificity in binding, but apparently makes a nick at one of several points. Class II enzymes require a specific nucleotide sequence with twofold symmetry. "Limit" digestion by Class II enzymes produces a defined number of restriction fragments which can be characterized.

The DNA is digested with a purified restriction enzyme until an invariant electrophoretic pattern of fragments is seen. The fragments are separated by electrophoresis on either polyacrylamide or agarose, the latter being more useful for fragments of large molecular weight, while fractionation of oligonucleotides of molecular weight below 10^6 daltons is best carried out in polyacrylamide gels. The bonds formed can be visualized by staining, and a useful fluorescent stain for these DNA fragments is ethidium bromide. If the DNA to be characterized is radioactively labeled, the bands may be visualized by autoradiography.

This technique has been useful in determining the physical map of several viral genomes. The genome of ϕX 174 has been extensively mapped by characterization of restriction fragments. In addition, using purified mRNA from the virus, a transcriptional map may also be constructed. The RNA can be hybridized to single-stranded restriction fragments of viral DNA. Alternatively, the nucleotide sequences of the RNA and DNA can be compared. Previously, it was difficult to sequence DNA; the availability of specific restriction endonucleases has greatly expanded the possibility of such analyses.

In eukaryotic systems, restriction analysis is most useful in the study of repetitive DNA sequences in chromosomes. Studies of this type have been used to localize some genes in the giant salivary glands of the fruit fly. The genes that are present in low copy number, however, cannot be analyzed as yet. These studies would require the use of molecular cloning to amplify this type of gene. Given such clones, restriction analyses would allow determination of the sequence of specific genes.

BIBLIOGRAPHY

Ligases:

Gellert, M., and Bullock, M. L. 1970. *Proc. Natl. Acad. Sci. U.S.A.* 67:1580.
Masamune, Y., Frenkel, G. D., and Richardson, C. C. 1971. *J. Biol. Chem.* 246:6874.
Modrich, P., and Lehman, I. R. 1971. *Proc. Natl. Acad. Sci. U.S.A.* 68:1002.
Okazaki, R., Arisawa, M., and Sugino, A. 1971. *Proc. Natl. Acad. Sci. U.S.A.* 68:2954.
Hosodo, J., and Mathews, E. 1971. *J. Mol. Biol.* 55:155.
Sgaramella, V. 1972. *Proc. Natl. Acad. Sci. U.S.A.* 69:3389.
Modrich, P., Anraku, Y., and Lehman, I. R., 1973. *J. Biol. Chem.* 248:7495.
Pedrali-Noy, G. C. F., Spadari, S., Ciarrocchi, G., and Pedrini, A. M. 1973. *Eur. J. Biochem.* 39:343.
Soderhall, S., and Lindahl, T. 1973. *J. Biol. Chem.* 248:672.
Sugino, A., Goodman, H. M., Heyneker, H. L., Shine, J., Boyer, H. W., and Cozzarelli, N. R. 1977. *J. Biol. Chem.* 252:3987.

"Swivel" and "Unwinding" Proteins:

Wang, J. C. 1971. *J. Mol. Biol.* 55:523.
Champoux, J. J., and Dulbecco, R. 1972. *Proc. Natl. Acad. Sci. U.S.A.* 69:143.
Champoux, J. J., and Dulbecco, R. 1972. *Proc. Natl. Acad. Sci. U.S.A.* 69:139.
Basse, W. A., and Wang, J. C. 1974. *Biochemistry* 13:4299.
Gellert, M., Mizuuchi, K., O'Dea, M. H., and Nash, H. A. 1976. *Proc. Natl. Acad. Sci. U.S.A.* 73:3872.
Champoux, J. J. 1976. *Proc. Nat. Acad. Sci. U.S.A.* 73:3488.
Champoux, J. J. 1977. *Proc. Nat. Acad. Sci. U.S.A.* 74:3800.

Terminal Nucleotide Transferase:

Brunngraber, E. F., and Chargaff, E. 1970. *Proc. Natl. Acad. Sci. U.S.A.* 67:107.
Brunngraber, E. F., and Chargaff, E. 1973. *Biochemistry* 12:3005.
Brunngraber, E. F., and Chargaff, E. 1977. *Proc. Natl. Acad. Sci.* 74:3226.

Nucleases:

Churchill, J. R., Urbanczyck, J., and Studzinski, G. P. 1973. *Biochem. Biophys. Res. Commun.* 53:1009–16.
Hewish, D. R., and Burgoyne. L. A. 1973. *Biochem. Biophys. Res. Commun.* 52:475–81.
Studzinski, G. P., and Fischman, G. J. 1974. *Anal. Biochem.* 58:449.
Radman, M. 1976. *J. Biol. Chem.* 251:1438.
Sierakowska, H., and Shugar, D. 1977. *Prog. Nucl. Acid Res. Mol. Biol.* 20:59.
Riazuddin, S., and Grossman, L. 1977. *J. Biol. Chem.* 252:6280, 6287.

Baril, E., Mitchener, J., Lee, L., and Baril, B. 1977. *Nucl. Acids Res.* 4:2641.

Gates, F. T., III and Linn, S. 1977. *J. Biol. Chem.* 252:1647.

Ljungquist, S. 1977. *J. Biol. Chem.* 252:2808.

Gates, F. T., III and Linn, S. 1977. *J. Biol. Chem.* 252:2802.

Restriction and Methylation Enzymes:

Kelly, T. J., and Smith, H. O. 1970. *J. Mol. Biol.* 51:393.

Boyer, H. W. 1971. *Annu. Rev. Microbiol.* 25:153.

Meselson, M., Yuan, R., and Heywood, J. 1972. *Annu. Rev. Biochem.* 41:447.

Haberman, A., Heywood, J., and Meselson, M. 1972. *Proc. Natl. Acad. Sci.,* 69:3448.

Eskin, B., and Linn, S. 1972. *J. Biol. Chem.* 247:6183.

Hedgpeth, J., Goodman, H. M., and Boyer, H. W. 1972. *Proc. Natl. Acad. Sci.* 69:3448.

Eskin, B., and Linn, S. 1972. *J. Biol. Chem.* 247:6183.

Smith, J., Arber, W., and Kuehnlein, U. 1972. *J. Mol. Biol.* 63:1.

Brockes, J. P. 1973. *Biochem. J.* 133:629.

Roy, P. H., and Smith, H. O. 1973. *J. Mol. Biol.* 81:427, 445.

Arnheim, M., and Southern, E. M. 1977. *Cell* 11:363.

SECTION 7
DNA REPLICATION AND ASSOCIATED PHENOMENA

THERESA CAMPANA AND LAZAR M. SCHWARTZ

7.1. Replication: General Mechanisms

COMPONENTS AND LOCALIZATION

Replication is defined as the process whereby a single DNA molecule is duplicated to give rise to two identical molecules of DNA. This term should not be used to describe synthesis of segments of a DNA strand, but should be reserved for the synthesis of a new genome. However, some of the earlier assays for DNA synthesis actually measure this "repair synthesis" and may lead to spurious results if this fact is not taken into account. In general, the process of replication is similar in all organisms, although details in different cells may be quite different. Most of the available information on replication comes from studies using either bacteria or viruses, although progress has been made in understanding some of the particular mechanisms involved in the replication of eukaryotic chromosomes.

The necessary elements involved in replication include a template, a primer, substrates, enzymes, and a source of energy. However, it has become clear that many proteins are required for replication to proceed; the specific functions of most of these proteins have not yet been determined. It is clear that an enzyme capable of elongating the DNA chain is required, and that the two strands of the original double helix must be separated. In addition, the bulk of available information implicates another protein, sometimes called a primase, which is required for the formation of primer molecules needed for the initiation of DNA synthesis. Theoretically, the double helix should be able to replicate because of base-pairing, without the need of an elongation enzyme; however, the energy required to allow this process to take place with a low frequency of introduction of errors is high. Thus, the actual role of the DNA polymerases that participate in elongation of new DNA chains may be the lowering of energy barriers to allow essentially error-free replication. The energy required for this process may come from the triphosphonucleotides, which are generally accepted as the substrates for replication. However, some data available suggest that this process requires the addition of ATP in vitro. This compound is assumed to act as a source of energy to drive the reaction forward. In general, the proteins required for DNA synthesis appear to be species-specific, and to vary in number in the different organisms that have been studied. Specific proteins whose functions are known will be discussed later in this section.

In eukaryotic organisms, DNA is localized within the cell nucleus, and is present in the form of separate chromosomes, rather than as a single DNA molecule as is found in prokaryotes. Proteins, on the other hand, are produced in the cytoplasm of the cell, and those that are required for replication must be transported across the nuclear membrane, since replication takes place only in the nucleus. The transport of these proteins, as well as of the nucleotides that serve as substrates for the reaction, presents many unsolved questions. In addition, the complexing of eukaryotic DNA with nuclear proteins adds a further complication to the understanding of replication in these cells. In addition to the fact that unwinding of the helix must occur prior to the initiation of replication, the complexed proteins must be removed in order for this unwinding to take place. This procedure may involve enzymes that alter the charge characteristics of the nuclear proteins, and the unwinding proteins probably differ significantly from those studied in simpler systems.

SEMICONSERVATIVE REPLICATION

Watson and Crick postulated that each of the daughter strands resulting from the replication of a DNA helix would be composed of one parental and one new strand of DNA. Two other mechanisms can, however, be postulated to account for the formation of two new identical molecules from a single double helix. These three mechanisms, shown in Figure 1, are known as conservative, semiconservative, and dispersive replication. In each case, the new DNA molecules that are formed each contains all the genetic material of the parental strands. The difference lies in the distribution of the original duplex molecule which served as the template for replication. In semiconservative replication, the mechanism that was originally proposed and which is accepted by molecular biologists, the two old strands each go to one of the

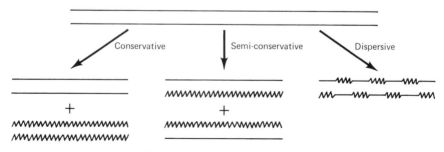

Figure 1 Models of replication.

daughter strands formed. Conservative replication, instead, proposed that the original strands would be retained as one of the daughter molecules, while the other would be formed by the two newly synthesized strands. The theory of dispersive replication, finally, proposed that the daughter molecules would each contain fragments of the original strand which had been broken up and dispersed into the new strands.

The classical experiments of Meselson and Stahl in 1957 and 1958 established the semiconservative nature of replication, at least in the bacterium *E. coli*. These bacteria were grown in media containing a heavy isotope of nitrogen, ^{15}N, for several generations so that all the DNA was labeled with this isotope and could be easily identified by its greater bouyant density in a cesium chloride gradient. These cells were then transferred to media containing the normal or light isotope of nitrogen, ^{14}N, and grown for one or more generations. The DNA was then extracted and analyzed on density gradients. All of the DNA isolated after one generation showed a bouyant density intermediate between molecules grown in either heavy or light media. This could be due to either semiconservative or dispersive replication, but is not consistent with conservative mechanisms. With increasing generation time in the light media, the DNA shifted in density until it was all essentially of light bouyant density. These results, together with other experiments, have clearly established that DNA replicates by a semiconservative mechanism. Similar results have been obtained in other systems, both prokaryotic and eukaryotic in nature, and it is generally accepted that all DNA replication proceeds in this manner.

THE PRECURSORS OF DNA

There is general agreement that the substrates required for DNA replication are the deoxyribonucleoside triphosphates. In vitro, the diphosphates can be used in some cases, but it has been shown that kinases which can form the triphosphates from the diphosphates are invariably present in the mixture in these cases. The apparent K_m for these substrates is about 20 μM, and all four nucleotides are required for replication to take place. Repair synthesis of DNA also uses these compounds; in this case, however, some incorporation of the radioactive triphosphates will take place even if all four are not present. Direct evidence that the triphosphates are required in vivo is not presently available; however, replication in toluenized cells or in membrane complexes does require these compounds. It is thought that these systems are to some extent analogous with in vivo conditions, so that this is good preliminary evidence for the participation of the triphosphates under physiological conditions.

Werner, however, has argued that all in vitro systems measure only repair synthesis, not replication, and that the in vivo situation is therefore quite different. He has proposed that the two processes utilize different precursor pools, and that triphosphates are used in vivo only for repair, not for replication. The diphosphates are postulated to align along the template, with the polymerase acting only to ligate these compounds together. As mentioned above, energy considerations make it unlikely that the polymerase does not participate in the alignment of the bases in the correct positions. In addition, this theory was put forth before the essential role of DNA polymerase III in *E. coli* replication was known, and before systems more analogous to in vivo conditions were available. No evidence exists to support a role for the diphosphates as the direct substrates for replication, nor does DNA polymerase III use these compounds in vitro.

TEMPLATE AND PRIMER MOLECULES

In order for replication to proceed correctly to form an exact copy of the parental DNA molecule, this molecule must in some way direct the correct alignment of the substrates, even though the polymerase(s) may play an active role in this alignment. The "central dogma" of molecular biology expresses this concept as:

$$DNA \longrightarrow RNA \longrightarrow protein$$

This implies that DNA itself is the only template that can function in the formation of new DNA molecules. There is one exception to this rule; in some systems, RNA may occasionally serve as a template for DNA synthesis in the presence of the enzyme reverse transcriptase, or RNA-dependent DNA polymerase. In all other cases, when DNA is the genetic material, it serves as its own template, each strand directing the synthesis of a complementary strand of new DNA (Figure 2).

Evidence however, indicates that the presence of a template molecule is not sufficient for replication and that in addition, a small primer molecule must also be available. The chemical nature of this primer is still the subject of experimental verification, but most available evidence indicates that the

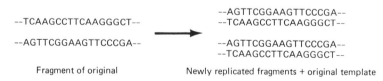

--TCAANGCCTTCAAGGGCT--

--AGTTCGGAAGTTCCCGA--

Fragment of original

--AGTTCGGAAGTTCCCGA--
--TCAAGCCTTCAAGGGCT--

--AGTTCGGAAGTTCCCGA--
--TCAAGCCTTCAAGGGCT--

Newly replicated fragments + original template

Figure 2 The template function of the two strands of DNA.

molecule consists of some small number of ribonucleotides, that is, an RNA oligomer. Such primers were first postulated by Brutlag and his coworkers. In vitro studies have shown that replication can proceed in the presence of a preformed RNA molecule to which deoxyribonucleotides are covalently linked to form a growing DNA chain. In vivo there is some evidence that an RNA oligomer is synthesized directly during the initiation of replication, and then the DNA chain is elongated under the direction of the appropriate polymerase. At a later stage, the primers are removed from the growing chain, and the gaps are filled in and ligated together. Most of the evidence presently available comes from studies with prokaryotic systems, but the little work that has been done with eukaryotic cells supports a similar mechanism in these organisms.

Such a primer role for RNA may explain the puzzling inability of the DNA polymerases actually to initiate the growth of new strands of DNA; none of the enzymes that have been isolated to date is capable of initiation. In addition, genetic studies indicate that the genes required for initiation in bacteria do not code for DNA polymerases. A more complete model of replication requires the identification of all the other components that have been shown to be needed, but a general model can be established. The DNA double helix is unwound and prepared by various proteins for replication. Initiation then takes place by the formation of small RNA oligomers which are synthesized under the direction of an RNA polymerase, or of a protein that is specific for this role and could be called a primase. There is some evidence that such a specific protein is the product of one of the *E. coli* genes which is known to participate in initiation. When a primer, which may be as few as 10 ribonucleotides, or perhaps as many as 29, has reached the desired length, DNA polymerase III in *E. coli* begins to elongate, covalently linking the first deoxyribonucleotide to the primer. Elongation may proceed by the formation of small fragments on one or both strands (see section on Okazaki fragments, below), and continues until the complete new molecule is formed. Various other steps are required, including the removal of primers, filling in the gaps left by such removal, and ligation of all fragments.

Excision of the RNA primers probably takes place early in elongation, since it is difficult to isolate these fragments when replication has been allowed to proceed for any length of time. Some information on primer molecules is now available; chemical analysis is proceeding, but much more information will be required. Okazaki has presented evidence that the RNA primer may end with the dinucleotide AU, and that the first base of the DNA appears to be a dC. Eliasson, Martin, and Reichard have found that nascent DNA from polyoma virus can be isolated attached to RNA fragments containing about 10 bases, and beginning with the base G or A. Kornberg, however, finds that the primer molecule may contain as many as 29 bases in some systems, and he also argues that the primer may contain both ribo- and deoxyribonucleotides. It seems clear, however, that all replication requires some primer molecules which are necessary for initiation.

OKAZAKI FRAGMENTS IN REPLICATION

Much evidence presently available in both prokaryotic and eukaryotic systems indicates that newly replicated DNA is found in the form of oligonucleotides, which appear to be about 2×10^3 residues long in bacteria. In eukaryotic cells, even smaller fragments are found. These oligonucleotides, generally called Okazaki fragments, can be shown to eventually become part of larger fragments, and to finally be joined to the bulk DNA that has been replicated. Ligase is known to be required for the joining of these pieces to the bulk DNA. In ligase-deficient mutants, in vitro studies have indicated that all the newly replicated DNA can be accounted for in the form of such fragments, with no new large molecules formed. This finding has been interpreted to indicate that both strands of the DNA molecule replicate by a discontinuous mechanism that results in the formation of Okazaki fragments. However, electron microscopic photographs do not support such a conclusion, but rather are consistent with a mechanism whereby one of the two strands is

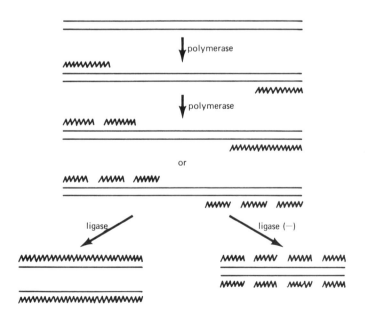

Figure 3 Discontinuous synthesis and formation of Okazaki fragments.

replicated as a single large molecule, while the other is duplicated by the formation of Okazaki fragments.

Since the known polymerases all elongate DNA in the 5' to 3' direction, continuous synthesis of one strand is theoretically possible. However, these enzymes would not be capable of replicating the other strand in the same manner, but could direct the synthesis of relatively small oligonucleotides. Some evidence presently available indicates that both strands may replicate by discontinuous synthesis under specific defined growth conditions. In addition, repair of incorrect bases in the newly replicated large strand could introduce gaps, leading to the isolation of fragments if ligase had not yet repaired these gaps. This artifactual condition might be interpreted to indicate that both strands were undergoing discontinuous replication.

In general, however, discontinuous synthesis of one strand of DNA is well accepted as the probable in vivo mechanism whereby replication takes place. This hypothesis is diagrammatically represented in Figure 3. Also shown in this figure is the condition that arises when a ligase-deficient mutant undergoes replication, both in the case where only one strand is discontinuously synthesized, and assuming that both strands replicate by such a mechanism.

ENZYMES AND PROTEINS REQUIRED FOR REPLICATION

As was discussed extensively in Section 6, several enzymes that act as polymerizing agents for deoxyribonucleotides have been described in both prokaryotic and eukaryotic synthesis. These enzymes participate in the elongation of growing DNA chains, as well as in the repair of lesions introduced into these chains. None of these enzymes, however, can initiate replication. In *E. coli,* the initiating enzyme has been tentatively identified as the product of the *dnaG* gene, and has been called a primase. It may be a specific RNA polymerase capable of producing short ribonucleotide chains, or it may catalyze the polymerization of both ribo- and deoxyribonucleotides to give rise to the required polymers. Further studies of this enzyme, which has not yet been purified, may clarify the actual chemical nature of the primer.

Prior to initiation, several proteins are required to prepare the template DNA for replication. One protein unwinds the two strands of the double helix, while others interact with the unwound, or denatured, strands to prevent their renaturation. An *E. coli* protein, gyrase, has been described that nicks the closed, circular DNA and introduces superhelical twists into the molecule. The actual mechanism of its role in preparing DNA for replication is not yet clear. However, studies with two types of antibiotics that are known to interfere with DNA synthesis have made it clear that gyrase is needed for this process. In addition, some information about the gyrase protein itself has been provided by these studies. The gyrase molecule consists of two subunits, one of which is responsible for ATP hydrolysis and is inhibited by novobiocin and related antibiotics. The larger subunit, which is required for the nicking of the circular DNA, is affected by nalidixic acid. Both subunits are required for activity.

Although much less is known about the proteins involved in eukaryotic replication, it seems likely that similar enzymes will be found in these systems. However, other proteins, such as the histones and the acidic nuclear proteins, are also involved in stabilizing the double helix in eukaryotes; so it seems clear that at least some of the required eukaryotic proteins act stoichiometrically rather than catalytically. In general, however, much more work will be required before the mechanisms of replication of chromatin will be well understood.

Termination of replication and completion of the new double helix also require the participation of several proteins. Primers must be removed during replication, leaving gaps in the chains. These gaps must be filled in, probably by the action of one of the polymerases, although it is not at present clear which of these enzymes is specific for this step. Errors that have been introduced during replication must also be removed. Specific nucleases may cata-

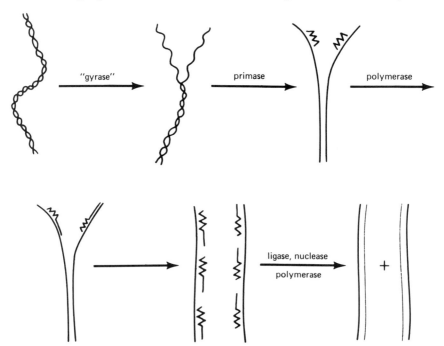

Figure 4 A possible model for replication.

lyze this step, and gaps will result that must be filled in. Again, a polymerase will be required; this enzyme is probably DNA polymerase I. Finally, Okazaki fragments and newly repaired gaps must be ligated to the bulk DNA; the enzyme ligase is responsible for this step.

It is clear from the above schematic description that much remains to be learned about the specific mechanisms of replication. It is at present difficult even to present a comprehensive model that would serve to describe the process in general terms valid for all systems. A current model, which includes much of the information derived from the studies of bacterial replication, is shown in Figure 4. Much of these steps remain speculative, and it is probable that the situation is even more complex than that represented. In the immediate future, much more information should become available, and more refined models can be elaborated.

THE ROLE OF THE MEMBRANE IN REPLICATION

Both electron microscopy and biochemistry have contributed some evidence that the bacterial membrane plays some role in replication. It is clear that the DNA of the bacteria is in some way attached to the cellular membrane, and complexes of DNA and membrane have been reported to carry out replication for short periods in vitro. In addition, the chemical properties of DNA polymerase III are consistent with its localization in the membrane, rather than free in the cytosol of the cell. Both polymerase activity and nuclease activity have been shown to be present in membrane fractions. However, direct evidence for the participation of the membrane as an active component in replication has not yet been found.

The evidence from which such a role may be inferred includes the fact that so many proteins are required for replication, and that the site of action of each should be relatively localized. This fits well with the concept that the membrane may provide a required matrix for DNA synthesis. In addition, in both prokaryotic and eukaryotic systems, at least some of the required proteins appear to co-purify with membrane fragments, implying the necessity for such a matrix. The fact that in vitro systems generally cannot carry out replication at physiological rates and for sufficiently long periods of time may also indicate that factors that are lost during purification of the required components may be associated with the membrane. Much further work will be required to clarify these points.

BIBLIOGRAPHY

Goulian, M. 1971. *Annu. Rev. Biochem.* 40:855.
Klein, A., and Bonhoeffer, F. 1972. *Annu. Rev. Biochem.* 41:301.
Kaufman, D. G., Grisham, J. W., and Stenstrom, M. L. 1972. *Biochim. Biophys. Acta* 272:212.

Sugino, A., and Okazaki, R. 1972. *J. Mol. Biol.* 64:61.
Bird, R. E., Louarn, J., Maruscelli, J., and Caro, L. G. 1972. *J. Mol. Biol.* 70:549.
Hohlfeld, R., and Vielmetter, W. 1973. *Nature New Biol.* 242:130.
Wake, R. G. 1973. *J. Mol. Biol.* 77:569.
Rodriquez, R. L., Dalbey, M. S., and Davern, C. I. 1973. *J. Mol. Biol.* 74:599.
Blumenthal, A. B., Kriegstein, H. J., and Hogness, D. 1973. *Cold Spring Harbor Symp. Quant. Biol.* 38:205.
Louarn, J., Funderburgh, M., and Bird, R. E. 1974. *J. Bacteriol.* 120:1.
Schekman, R., Weiner, A., and Kornberg, A. 1974. *Science* 186:987.
Oho, B., and Reichard, P. 1975. *J. Virol.* 15:259.
Hiraga, S. 1976. *Proc. Natl. Acad. Sci. U.S.A.* 73:198.
Ogawa, T., Hirose, S., Okazi, T., and Okazaki, R. 1977. *J. Mol. Biol.* 112:121.

Proteins Required for Replication:

Wechsler, J. A., and Gross, J. D. 1971.*Mol. Gen. Genet.* 113:273.
Pettijohn, D. 1972. *Nature New Biol.* 235:204.
Wickner, S., Wright, M., and Hurwitz, J. 1973. *Proc. Natl. Acad. Sci. U.S.A.* 70:1613.
Gautschi, J. R., and Kern, R. M. 1973. *Exp. Cell Res.* 80:15.
Gautschi, J. R. 1974. *J. Mol. Biol.* 84:223.
Beyersmann, D., Messer, W., and Schlicht, M., 1974. *J. Bacteriol.* 118:783.
Bouché, J. P., Zechel, K., and Kornberg, A. 1975. *J. Biol. Chem.* 250:5995.
Ogawa, T. 1975. *J. Mol. Biol.* 94:327.
Scheckman, R., Weiner, J. H., Weiner, A., and Kornberg, A. 1975. *J. Biol. Chem.* 250:5859.
Wechsler, J. A. 1975. *J. Bacteriol.* 121:594.
Masters, M. 1975. *Mol. Gen. Genet.* 143:105.
Wickner, S., and Hurwitz, J. 1975. *Proc. Natl. Acad. Sci. U.S.A.* 72:921.
Wickner, S., and Hurwitz, J. 1976. *Proc. Natl. Acad. Sci. U.S.A.* 73:1053.
Geider, K. 1976. *Curr. Top. Microbiol. Immunol.* 74:55.
Schuster, H., Schlicht, M., Lanka, E., Mikolajczyk, M., and Edelbluth, C. 1977. *Mol. Gen. Genet.* 151:11.
Marsh, R. C., and Worcel, A. 1978. *Proc. Natl. Acad. Sci. U.S.A.* 74:2720.

The Role of Membrane in Replication:

Ballesta, O. P., Cundliffe, E., Daniels, M. J., Silverstein, J. L., Susskind, M., and Schaechter, M. 1972. *J. Bacteriol.* 112:195.
Worcel, A., and Burgi, E. 1972. *J. Mol. Biol.* 71:127.
Van Tuyle, G., and Kalf, G. F. 1972. *Arch. Biochem. Biophys.* 149:425.
Freinenstein, C., Freitag, H., and Suss, R. 1973. *FEBS Lett.* 30:170.
Infante, A., Nanta, R., Gilbert, S., Hobart, P., and Firshein, W. 1973. *Nature New Biol.* 242:5.
Lovett, M. A., Guiney, D. G., and Helinski, D. R. 1974. *Proc. Natl. Acad. Sci. U.S.A.* 71:3854.
Liebowitz, P. J., and Schaecter, M. 1975. *Int. Rev. Cytol.* 41:1.
Griffith, J., Dieckman, M., and Berg, P. 1975. *J. Virol.* 15:167.
Shearman, C. W., and Kalf, G. F. 1975. *Biochem. Biophys. Res. Commun.* 63:712.
Shearman, C. W., and Kalf, G. F. 1977. *Arch. Biochem. Biophys.* 182:573.
Albring, M., Griffith, J., and Attardi, G. 1977. *Proc. Natl. Acad. Sci. U.S.A.* 74:1348.
Sinha, A., and Mizuno, N. S. 1977. *Cell Tiss. Res.* 183:191.

7.2. Replication of the Bacterial Genome

THE DNA OF BACTERIA

The genome of bacteria consists of naked DNA, that is, DNA that is not closely associated with specific proteins in the cell. The molecule may be either circular or linear in shape, but is always present as a double helix with superimposed superhelical twists. A single bacterial cell may contain more than one copy of the genome, but the genome itself is a single molecule of DNA. This large DNA duplex is not localized to a single specific membrane-bound region of the cell, but is generally found in one area of the cytosol. It is a very compact molecule, held together by the superhelical turns, and appears to be attached to the cellular membrane. The compactness of the genome can be demonstrated graphically on breakage of the cell, since the DNA will then be seen as long, unwound fibers with a length much greater than that of the cell itself. No specialized proteins like the eukaryotic nuclear proteins can be identified in bacteria. In the cell, ribosomes and various proteins including enzymes are often seen lying close to, or even attached to, the genome, but these interactions are generally not permanent.

The genomes of several bacterial strains have been reasonably well mapped. In many cases, they can be represented in circular forms, for which some electron microscopic evidence is also available. A representation of the genome of the enterobacterium *E. coli* is shown in Figure 1. Genes are identified on these maps by three-letter codes; some of them are identified in Table 1. In many cases, related genes, that is, genes that code for allied proteins, are found to be clustered together in specific regions of the genome. This is not true for all related genes, however; those that are linked are most likely to be under a single regulatory system.

The numbers in Figure 1 represent the time of entry in minutes of the genes on an F′ factor into the genome. Each minute represents 50–100 genes.

THE REPLICON THEORY

In the early 1960s, Jacob and coworkers proposed and elaborated a general theory for the replication of the bacterial chromosome. This theory postulated a structural unit necessary for replication, the replicon. This entity would

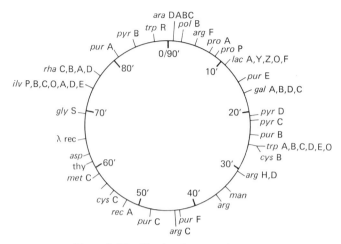

Figure 1. The Circular Genome of *E. coli.*

Table 1.   Meaning of Some 3-Letter Codes of the *E. coli* Genome

SYMBOL	FUNCTION	MAP POSITION (IN MINUTES)
arg A	—arginine biosynthesis	54
asp	—aspartate biosynthesis	61
cys B	—cysteine biosynthesis	25
gal R	—galactose utilization (operon)	55
gly A	—glycine biosynthesis	49
ilv A,B,C,D,E	—isoleucine and valine biosynthesis	74
lac O	—lactose utilization (operon)	10
met A	—methionine biosynthesis	78
mot A,B	—mobility	36
phe S	—phenylalanyl-tRNA synthetase	33
pro C	—proline synthesis	10
pur A	—purine biosynthesis	80
pyr A	—pyrimidine biosynthesis	0
rec A,B	—recombination	51,55
rha A,B,C,D	—utilization of rhamnose	76
str	—streptomycin sensitivity	64
sup B	—suppressor of ochre mutations	15
thi	—thiamine biosynthesis	77
uvr A		79
uvr B	repair of UV damage to DNA by excision	17
uvr C		36

contain the replicating unit of the DNA together with required proteins, and would be attached to the cellular membrane. The membrane portion of the replicon might serve as a matrix that would maintain the various necessary elements in the proper configurations relative to each other. The proteins associated with the replicon would include all the enzymes needed for replication, as well as unwinding proteins and other polypeptides with specific functions. Since this theory was proposed, data from many laboratories have been cited in support of, or against, such a structural entity.

Protein synthesis is known to be required before replication can take place. However, the specific products that are required have not been identified. It is possible that the primase, an enzyme that catalyzes the production of primers required for initiation, or DNA polymerase III, required for elongation, must be made immediately prior to replication. Several other proteins, whose functions have not been clarified completely (see below), are also necessary for replication; any or all of these may be synthesized directly before initiation.

Early experiments appeared to indicate a unique origin of replication on the genome; the replicating fraction appeared to be tightly bound to the membrane. More recent work, however, is more in accord with several points of attachment of the genome to the membrane. These points of attachment may represent DNA with some specific base sequence that is required for attachment, or may merely be dependent on the physical location of particular DNA segments. The relationship between these sites of attachment and replication forks has not been established. If a direct relationship were to be shown, this would be clear confirmation of the replicon theory. Instead, the hypothesis at present is supported by indirect biochemical and electron microscopic data. This includes demonstrations that the DNA is held to the membrane, as well as the chemical characteristics of some of the required enzymes.

In Gram-positive bacteria, a clear attachment of the genome to invaginations of the cellular membrane known as mesosomes (see below) can be seen. In Gram-negative organisms, there is biochemical evidence of such an attachment. Complexes that contain DNA attached to membrane fragments have been isolated; these compounds contain enzymatic activity that appears to bear some relationship to in vivo replication. At present, it is not clear if the proteins that are associated with these complexes are attached directly to the DNA or to the membrane. Most of the proteins known to be required for replication will bind to DNA; it is possible that the membrane–protein–DNA complexes that have been isolated result from some artifactual association of these components, although the associations appear to be specific. After extraction of polymerase activity from these membrane complexes, some residual activity is still found to be associated; it might be due to DNA polymerase III, the chemical properties of which are consistent with a membrane localization. On the other hand, this residual activity may have no actual physiological significance; further studies will be required to determine this.

If bacterial replicons exist, the actual size of the replicon must be determined. It is possible that the entire bacterial genome might constitute a single replicon, for example, in which case one might expect that there is a single replication fork in the whole molecule. In *E. coli,* there appear to be at least two or three separate replication forks, but it is not clear if they are found on the same DNA molecule, since this bacterium may contain more than one double helix within a single cell. In any case, it would appear that the putative bacterial replicons are rather large, especially when compared to the apparent size in eukaryotic systems (see Chapter 7.3).

MESOSOMES

Electron micrographs of Gram-positive bacteria show extensive invaginations of the bacterial membrane, forming structures known as mesosomes. The genome of the bacteria appears to be directly attached to the mesosomes. When exposed to 0.5 M sucrose, the mesosomes become evaginated so that a single cellular membrane is seen; the DNA is seen to be directly attached to the cellular membrane. During replication, the mesosome appears to double, or perhaps to split into two; the newly replicated DNA is split into daughter cells by the movement of the two mesosomes in opposite directions.

It has been postulated that replication takes place at the site of attachment of the DNA to the mesosome. The replicon, then, would be a structural component of the mesosome. No direct evidence in support of such a theory is available. This hypothesis is, on the other hand, consistent with the electron microscopic evidence, but is not the only possible explanation of it. The simplest explanation would be to assume that the association is artifactual, induced during preparation of the samples for analysis. This appears unlikely, however, given the fact that such attachments have been reported by many laboratories, and also because of the biochemical evidence that has been reported in Gram-negative bacteria (see Section 6 for further information).

SYNCHRONIZATION OF REPLICATION AND CELL DIVISION

Replication results in the doubling of the amount of DNA needed for a single cell; this DNA is then partitioned between two daughter cells, an event which requires a close correlation between the time of replication and the division of the parent cell into two new cells. Such a division requires the formation of a new cellular membrane, the septum, together with a new cell wall, which will divide the cell into two parts that may or may not be equal in size. Each daughter, even if it is much smaller than the parent, will receive one copy of the genome as well as some portion of the cytoplasm which contains ribosomes, enzymes, and other components of the cell. In Gram-positive bacteria, formation of the septum is closely correlated with the doubling of the mesosome, which appears to increase in size and to form a separation between what will be the two new cells.

Any asynchrony in the associated processes can result in the formation of new cells with bizarre shapes. If the septum forms too early, minicells devoid of DNA can result. Replication without septum formation, on the other hand, can result in large cells that contain twice the appropriate DNA concentration. It is possible that the synchronous replication and cell division may be controlled by specific membrane proteins, but no evidence as yet exists to identify such proteins, or to identify the mechanisms.

In vitro, cell wall formation may be inhibited by the use of antibiotics like penicillin. This prevents the formation of the polysaccharides that form the cell wall, and results in the production of fragile spheroplasts. In vivo, such a mechanism is responsible for the bactericidal action of these antibiotics. The spheroplasts will lyse easily on minor changes in salt concentration; they have been very useful in the laboratory for studies of bacterial DNA.

PROTEIN REQUIRED FOR REPLICATION

In *E. coli,* six genes have been identified which code for proteins required for the replication of the bacterial genome; some of these genes are also required for replication of certain bacteriophages. The genes, known generally as *dna* genes, are not necessarily closely linked, nor do they share common functional characteristics. Some are known to be required during initiation, whereas others participate in elongation of the newly synthesized DNA. Some of these gene products have been identified as specific proteins, while others are as yet unknown. These genes do not include those that specify ligase function.

Cell-free systems have been developed that contain all the *dna* gene products, and can be used to identify the requirements for each of these proteins. The six genes are known as *dna A, B, C-D, E, F,* and *G.* The genes whose products have been unequivocally identified are *dna E* and *dna F;* the first specifies DNA polymerase III, while *F* codes for ribonucleotide reductase, required for the formation of the deoxyribonucleotides which serve as the substrates for replication. The *dna G* gene product appears to be required for the formation of small Okazaki fragments, and it has been suggested that the actual protein coded for is the primase, an enzyme that forms primers. The actual nature of this enzyme has not been conclusively established; it could be a specific polymerase-type molecule that forms the small primers thought to be composed of ribonucleotides. The other proteins that are the products of these *dna* genes have not been identified.

The other DNA polymerases do not appear to be required for replication itself, but may participate in editing out of errors introduced during DNA synthesis. Ligase is required to form the large molecules of DNA from the Okazaki fragments, and specific nucleases probably excise the primer molecules from the newly synthesized strands. It is possible that one of the as yet unidentified *dna* genes codes for such an endo- or exonuclease, but this is as yet uncertain. Some or all these proteins participate also in the synthesis of bacteriophage DNA; each system appears to have different requirements. In some cases, the virus specifies its own polymerase, while others use the bacterial enzyme. This seems to depend in part on the size of the phage genome; larger phages code for more viral-specific proteins than do the very small ones. Those phages that are single-stranded also require some proteins that are specific to them, while the complexity of other genomes dictates how many of the *dna* gene products will be used. The situation in other bacteria is probably similar to that in *E. coli,* but less is known about these systems.

ROLLING CIRCLE MODELS OF REPLICATION

Various models of replication have been proposed, but most have not stood the test as further information has been accumulated. The model that retains usefulness for circular genomes such as that of *E. coli* is known as the rolling circle. Such a mechanism was first proposed in 1968 by Gilbert and Dressler, and extended by Sinsheimer's group in 1969. This model proposes that the initial step in replication consists of the nicking of one of the two strands of the DNA molecule by an endonuclease. This is followed by the addition of bases (catalyzed by DNA polymerase III) to the free 3'-hydroxyl end formed by the nick. The nicked parental strand thus serves as a primer, while the other strand serves as the template for the new strand. As the 3'-end is extended, the 5'-terminus is displaced by the clockwise rolling of the template (Figure 2). This end is replicated by the addition of Okazaki fragments, again using the nonnicked strand as a template.

Ligase activity is required to tie together the Okazaki fragments, and an endonuclease will be needed to separate the new strand from the original nicked strand which has served as a template. The main problem with this model is the fact that the other proteins discussed above play no role, whereas genetic evidence makes it clear that they are required. Another problem arises from electron microscopic photographs that show replication intermediates shaped like the Greek letter θ (see Figure 3). Such intermediates cannot be formed by a simple rolling circle model, but a modification has been

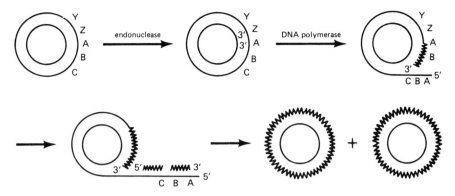

Figure 2. Rolling circle model of replication.

proposed that could account for their formation. This model is known as the double rolling circle (Figure 4), and requires as the first steps two separate endonuclease cuts, one in each of the two template strands. Two separate free tails are thus formed, each of which replicates as described above for the single tail of the simple rolling circle model. The intermediates formed during this process are the θ-shaped intermediate, followed by a form that is a double-size circular duplex. These forms are shown schematically in Figure 4. The large, double-size circle is then cleaved into two linear, double-stranded molecules by the action of a specific nuclease which leaves so-called sticky ends. These are single-stranded regions with complementary base pairs, which can circularize to give rise to two normal circular genomes.

This model, too, suffers from the lack of a role for the *dna* gene products, but accounts for much of the other evidence known concerning the replication of circular genomes. In addition, such a model is consistent with the apparent mechanism for conjugation in *E. coli* (see Chapter 7.6). It is possible that the rolling circle model may indeed account for conjugation, but that replica-

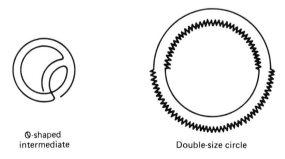

Ø-shaped
intermediate   Double-size circle

Figure 3. Replication intermediates.

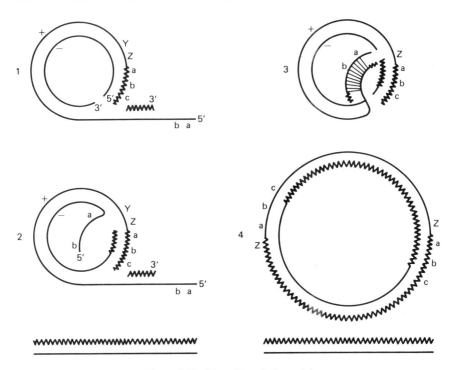

Figure 4. Double rolling circle model.

tion, which is a more complex system, requires further modifications of the model. At present, it is obvious that initiation of replication requires an enzyme of a primase type; this enzyme appears to make primers from ribonucleotides rather than using DNA oligomers as the primer. Modification of the rolling circle model to include such a possibility may be the only requirement to extend this model to normal DNA replication of circular genomes. For linear molecules, the first nick may not be essential, but rather the mere unwinding of the double helix progressively will provide the necessary template. Even in the rolling circle model, the very first step that must take place is the relaxation of the superhelical winding, followed by the local denaturation of the double helix. As the specific roles of the *dna* gene products are further defined, better models of bacterial replication can be postulated.

BIBLIOGRAPHY

Bacterial DNA:

Bachman, B. J., Low, B., and Taylor, A. L. 1976. *Bacteriol. Rev.* 40:116.

RNA Primers and Discontinuous Replication:

Brutlag, D. L., Schekman, R., and Kornberg, A. 1971. *Proc. Natl. Acad. Sci. U.S.A.* 68:2826.
Fuchs, J. A., Karlstrom, H. O., Warner, H. R., and Reichard, P. 1972. *Nature New Biol.* 238:69.
O'Sullivan, A., and Sueoka, N. 1972. *J. Mol. Biol.* 69:237.
Olivera, B. M., and Bonhoeffer, F. 1972. *Proc. Natl. Acad. Sci. U.S.A.* 69:25.
Olivera, B. M., and Bonhoeffer, F. 1972. *Nature* 240:233.
Schaller, H., Otto, B., Nusslein, V., Huf, J., Herrmann, R., and Bonhoeffer, F. 1972. *J. Mol. Biol.* 63:183.
Keller, W., 1972. *Proc. Natl. Acad. Sci. U.S.A.* 69:1560.
Wickman, W., Brutlag, D., Schekman, R., and Kornberg, A. 1972. *Proc. Natl. Acad. Sci. U.S.A.* 69:965.
Sugino, A., and Okazaki, R. 1972. *J. Mol. Biol.* 64:61.
Sugino, A., Hirose, S., and Okazaki, R. 1972. *Proc. Natl. Acad. Sci. U.S.A.* 69:1863.
Sugino, A., and Okazaki, R. 1973. *Proc. Natl. Acad. Sci. U.S.A.* 70:88.
Hirose, S., Okazaki, R., and Tamanoi, F. 1973. *J. Mol. Biol.* 77:501.
Lark, K. G. 1973. *J. Mol. Biol.* 64:47.
Schekman, R., Weiner, A., and Kornberg, A. 1974. *Science* 186:987.
Kurosawa, Y., Ogawa, T., Hirose, S., Okazaki, T., and Okazaki, R., 1975. *J. Mol. Biol.* 96:653.
Ogawa, T., Hirose, S., Okazaki, T., and Okazaki, R. 1977. *J. Mol. Biol.* 112:121.

Replication Forks:

Wolfson, J., Dressler, D., and Magazin, M. 1972. *Proc. Natl. Acad. Sci.* 69:499, 998.
Bird, R. E., Lovarn, J., Martuscelli, J., and Caro, L. *J. Mol. Biol.* 1972. 70:549.
Prescott, D. M., and Kuempel, P. L. 1972. *Proc. Natl. Acad. Sci.* 69:2842.
Gyurasits, E. B., and Wake, R. G. 1973. *J. Mol. Biol.* 73:55.
Wake, R. G. 1973. *J. Mol. Biol.* 77:569.

Proteins Required for Replication:

Schneiderman, M. H., DeWey, D. C., and Highfield, D. P. 1971. *Exp. Cell Res.* 67:147.
Suzuki, N., and Mano, Y. 1973. *Dev. Growth Differ.* 15:113.
Suzuki, N., and Mano, Y. 1974. *J. Biochem.* 75:1349.
Suzuki, N., Neki, T., and Mano, Y. 1977. *Experientia* 33:15.
Ogawa, T. 1975. *J. Mol. Biol.* 94:327.
Wechsler, J. A. 1975. *J. Bacteriol.* 121:594.
Wickner, S., and Hurwitz, J. 1975. *Proc. Natl. Acad. Sci.* 72:921.
Wickner, S., and Hurwitz, J. 1976. *Proc. Natl. Acad. Sci.* 73:1053.
Schuster, H., Schlicht, M., Lanka, E., Mikolajcyk, M., and Edelbluth, C. 1977. *Mol. Gen. Genet.* 151:11.

Models of Replication:

Dressler, D. 1970. *Proc. Natl. Acad. Sci. U.S.A.* 67:1934.
Francke, B., and Ray, D. 1972. *Proc. Natl. Acad. Sci. U.S.A.* 69:475.
Borst, P. 1972. *Annu. Rev. Biochem.* 41:333.
Schroder, C., and Kaerner, H. 1972. *J. Mol. Biol.* 71:351.
Schroder, C., Erben, E., and Kaerner, H. 1973. *J. Mol. Biol.* 79:599.
Hourcade, D., Dressler, D., and Wolfson, J. 1973. *Cold Spring Harbor Symp. Quant. Biol.* 38:537.
Wolstenholme, D., Katsure, K., and Cochran-Fouts, P. 1973. *Cold Spring Harbor Symp. Quant. Biol.* 38:267.

Kasamatsu, H., Grossman, L., Robberson, D., Watson, R., and Vinograd, J. 1973. *Cold Spring Harbor Symp. Quant. Biol.* 38:281.

Gyurasits, E., and Wake, R. 1973. *J. Mol. Biol.* 73:55.

Wake, R. 1973. *J. Mol. Biol.* 77:569.

Hourcade, D., Dressler, D., and Wolfson, J. 1973. *Proc. Natl. Acad. Sci. U.S.A.* 70:2926.

Rochaix, J., Bird, A., Bakken, A. 1974. *J. Mol. Biol.* 87:473.

Takahashi, S. 1975. *Mol. Gen. Genet.* 142:137.

7.3. Replication in Eukaryotes

GENERAL MECHANISM

DNA synthesis in eukaryotic organisms, as in prokaryotes, is semiconservative, as predicted by the Watson-Crick model. This was first demonstrated in the cells of the fava bean, *Vicia fava,* in 1957, and has since beeen confirmed in many other organisms. Both strands of a chromosome, known as sister chromatids, can be tritiated by growth of the cells in a medium that contains [^{3}H]-thymidine, which will be incorporated into the newly synthesized DNA strands. If growth in this medium takes place for only a single replication cycle, one of the new sister chromatids will be labeled, but growth for several cycles in this medium allows the labeling of both strands. If the cells are then transferred to cold medium (without the radiolabel), the radioactivity can be chased from the newly replicated DNA, resulting in a new molecule that again contains only one tritiated strand of DNA.

In many eukaryotic organisms, the S phase, during which DNA replication takes place, lasts about 8 hours (see Section 11). The replication rate required for the complete synthesis of the new DNA thus appears to be about 100 times faster than the corresponding rate found in prokaryotes, such as *E. coli.* This rate will differ, however, during different stages of differentiation, since the length of the S phase varies. At early embryonic stages, the S phase may last only about 1 hour, while the S phase in spermocytes of newts lasts about 200 hours. The replication rate in the first case is thus about 800 times greater than that of *E. coli,* while the spermocytes replicate with an apparent rate only about 4 times that of the bacteria.

The major difference between prokaryotic and eukaryotic replication rates arises from the difference in the size of the genome and the replicon, as well as from the presence of associated nuclear proteins in eukaryotic chromosomes. This difference may also be reflected in the greater complexity of regulatory processes in eukaryotic organisms. In both cases, the same substrates are used; the enzymes involved are of similar type, although there are differences between them. The actual replication mechanism involves many similar or identical steps, with differences due to the greater complexity of eukaryotic chromatin. Thus, in each case, there is local denaturation of the double helix, formation of a primer, chain elongation, perhaps discontinuous, and ligation of segments formed by discontinuous synthesis as well as those resulting from the removal of primers. The eukaryotic replicon appears to be much smaller than the prokaryotic unit, and the mechanism required will be more complex, since the proteins associated with the chromatin must be removed prior to, or at the same time as, the unwinding of the duplex.

EUKARYOTIC REPLICONS

The replication of different segments of the eukaryotic genome appears to follow a specific time sequence; initiation of replication occurs simultaneously at a number of different sites on the genome, with the formation of replication forks at each site. Replication proceeds bidirectionally from each initiation site, and will complete the synthesis of a replicon, or replicating unit, but will not proceed into the neighboring replicon. The number and the size of replicons in a specific DNA molecules vary in a complex fashion. In dipteran flies, the replicon may correspond to the individual chromomeres which can be seen in the giant salivary gland chromosomes. In general, the average size of replicons appears to be 50 μm, with a range of 15 to 120 μm. The size range in other eukaryotic genomes has been reported to be from 10 to 250 μm, except in the case of embryonic tissues. Replication in these cells is extremely rapid, and the replicon is only about one-tenth the size found in adult organisms, at least in the case of the dipteran flies.

DNA replication proceeds bidirectionally within each replicon; the replication fork can be seen and identified as a distinctive structure in electron micrographs. The movement of this fork is correlated with replication, and estimates of the rate of movement can be determined. Published estimates of this rate in eukaryotic organisms range from 6 to about 30 μm per hour. This is only about 2% of the estimated rate of movement of the bacterial replication fork. Although this rate is low in eukaryotes, the actual replication rate is much higher than in bacteria, as calculated from the amount of DNA present and the known length of the S phase, owing to the fact that each eukaryotic genome contains many more replication forks, and therefore a greater number of replicons, than do bacteria.

OKAZAKI FRAGMENTS AND DISCONTINUOUS DNA REPLICATION

Early attempts to demonstrate discontinuous DNA synthesis in eukaryotic chromatin were not very successful. Indeed, many authors argued that Okazaki-type fragments were never formed in eukaryotes. Recent evidence indicates, on the other hand, that such fragments may be found. The earlier lack of isolation was due to problems such as the fact that the pulses used for bacteria are, in general, too long; most authors indicate that pulses of only 10 to 90 sec give the best results in eukaryotic cells. If longer pulses are used, the label will be found associated with bulk DNA. In addition, the isolation and purification procedures used must be carefully controlled in order to detect Okazaki fragments in eukaryotic replication. Such fragments are single-stranded in nature, and are considerably shorter than prokaryotic Okazaki fragments. Because of these factors, these fragments may be lost easily during purification. They could be retained in the phenol interface, for example, or stick to the walls of the cellulose nitrate tubes used during extraction or centrifugation. It appears that eukaryotic Okazaki fragments contain only about 100 bases, whereas those found in bacterial cells are about 1000 bases long. The reason for this difference is not known, but might be related to the smaller size of the replicon.

It is difficult to account for bidirectional DNA synthesis in eukaryotic cells in the absence of a mechanism for discontinuous replication of at least one strand of the chromosome. Like the DNA polymerases of the bacteria, those of eukaryotic organisms cannot catalyze replication in both directions, nor do they seem to be capable of the initiation of synthesis. Some of the evidence that has been published appears to accord well with discontinuous synthesis of both strands of the DNA, but the generally accepted theory is that only one of the two strands is normally replicated in this fashion. When pulse-labeled DNA is analyzed on an isopycnic gradient, short Okazaki fragments can be isolated. If the cells are transferred to media containing no radiolabel and incubated for varying periods of time before analysis, the radioactivity gradually shifts from these small fragments to DNA of intermediate size ranges. After a chase of 1 hour or longer, all the label is found to be associated with bulk DNA. A possible mechanism to explain these shifts is shown in Figure 1.

As represented in the figure, this mechanism can account for the discontinuous replication of either one or both strands of the DNA. The available evidence could support either hypothesis, although it appears more likely that, under normal physiological conditions, there would be no advantage to discontinuous replication of both strands. In either case, the most probable sequence of reactions appears to be that the newly replicated DNA which is formed as Okazaki fragments would gradually be ligated to form intermediate-size oligomers, which would then be ligated to the bulk DNA.

The postulated mechanism involves several proteins and enzymes. First, there must be local denaturation, accompanied by some release of the chromatin from its associated nuclear proteins. This would require an unwinding protein of some kind, which might act either catalytically or stoichiometrically. Then the primase-type enzyme might initiate replication, and the polymerase would elongate the new chains. Okazaki fragments, if formed, would then require the action of ligase to be joined to the bulk DNA; fragments formed by the removal of primers would also be ligated to the chain by such an enzyme. This fact leads to an alternative hypothesis to explain the

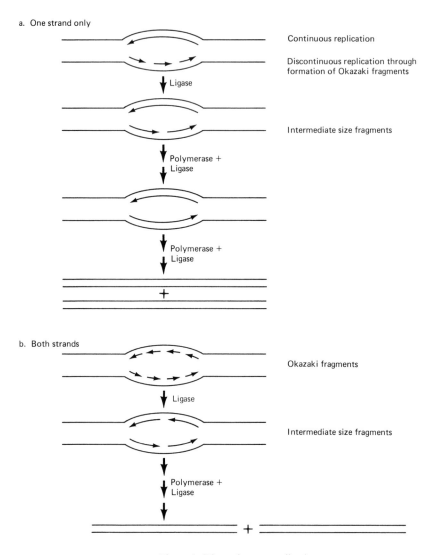

Figure 1. Discontinuous replication.

small fragments found in newly replicating DNA, as shown in Figure 2, which assumes that the removal of primers is all that is required to allow small fragments to be isolated; with time, the fragments would be ligated together, as postulated above. In this case, it is difficult to account for the intermediate-size fragments that have been detected. These findings would appear to be accounted for more satisfactorily by the assumption of discontinuous replication with the formation of Okazaki fragments.

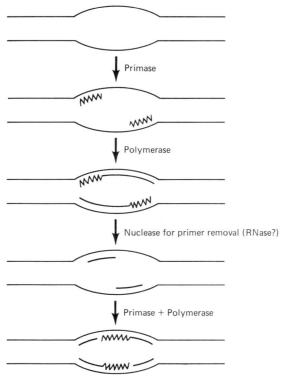

Figure 2. Gaps introduced by the removal of primers.

RNA PRIMERS

In prokaryotes, the role of RNA primers in the initiation of DNA replication appears to be well established (see Chapter 7.1). It would appear likely that these small ribonucleotide oligomers could also participate in the eukaryotic mechanism of DNA synthesis. In recent years, evidence has been accumulating that this is indeed so. Generally, these reports are based on isopycnic gradient centrifugation of newly replicating DNA. The nascent DNA is found to band at a density higher than that expected if only deoxyribonucleotides were present, a density characteristic of that found for hybrid molecules containing both DNA and RNA sequences.

Some authors, however, have not been able to isolate such hybrid molecules, and have therefore postulated that no such mechanism exists in eukaryotic organisms. Others feel that the evidence is consistent with a primer composed of deoxyribonucleotides, while still others opt for a primer that consists of mixed nucleotides (i.e., both ribo- and deoxyribonucleotides). In any case, most authors accept the idea that some small, specific oligomers act as primers in eukaryotic replication. Several explanations can be postulated for the problems reported by some investigators in isolating nascent DNA covalently linked to primers. First, the size of Okazaki fragments in eukaryotic DNA is very small, and they are difficult to isolate. The band linking the primer to the nascent DNA may also be quite labile, or particularly susceptible to digestion by a specific nuclease. In addition, it is not yet clear whether the primers are removed continuously during replication, so that only a small number of such oligomers can be found at a given moment. At present, this field of research is quite active, with many laboratories working to clear up these possible conflict. The near future may see these questions resolved, and more specific mechanisms proposed.

NUCLEOSOMES AS POSSIBLE STRUCTURAL UNITS OF REPLICATION

Nucleosomes, or ν bodies, have been identified in electron micrographs of eukaryotic DNA. These are small units of chromatin that appear to contain about 140 base pairs, complexed with a group of histone proteins including H2A, H2B, H3, and H4. Each of these units is separated by a linker region of DNA containing about 30 to 70 base pairs. This linker region can be unwound more easily than can the nucleosome itself. In vitro, nucleosomes can be dissociated by treatment with solutions containing high salt and high urea concentrations; these solutions cause the histones and nonhistone proteins to detach from the DNA. If the dissociated nucleosomes are dialyzed to return to low-salt, low-urea conditions, some of the nucleosomes can reform. The DNA in nucleosomes is supercoiled, and contains about 25 left-handed superhelical turns in SV40 DNA. Apparently, the number of superhelical turns is directly correlated with the number of nucleosomes found in a DNA molecule. Histone H1 appears to bind to the linker DNA and to participate in the characteristic "beads on a string" conformation seen in some electron microscopic photographs.

Figure 3. (a) The structure of nucleosomes with and without histone H1. (b) Dissociation and reassociation of nucleosomes. Effects of dilution on nucleosomes in SV40 genome. [Part (a) from *Science* 201:406, 1978, Fig. 10; (b) from *Science* 201:406, 1978, Fig. 7.]

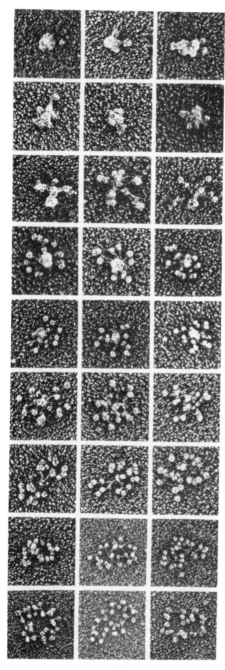

Figure 3. (b) Electron micrograph of native SV40 chromatin complexes diluted 20-fold with water and kept at room temperature (10 minutes) before spreading. Compact globular structures, beaded-string complexes, and intermediates can be observed. Selected examples of different degrees of unfolding are shown and illustrate the transition of the compact globular native structure to the beaded appearance of SV40 chromatin. In each row, complexes at a similar stage of unfolding are grouped together.

The nucleosome could reflect an organization of the genome into specific genes. Transcription can be demonstrated to occur with reconstituted nucleosomes, even when they contain only about 10% of the original number of these bodies, so it would not appear that the structure is itself necessary for transcription. It would appear likely that the strong complexing of the DNA with proteins, as well as the known supercoiling of the DNA, prevents replication or transcription, at least partially. Further information will be required to resolve these points. The structure of nucleosomes in the presence and absence of H1 histone is shown in Figure 3a, while the dissociated and reassociated nucleosomes are shown in Figure 3b.

ASSEMBLY OF CHROMATIN

Eukaryotic chromosomes are a complex of nucleic acids with proteins and must be assembled during or shortly after the replication of the original helix, prior to partition to daughter cells. Chromatin, the nucleoprotein complex, is much more resistent to nuclease digestion than is naked DNA. It appears that the complexing of the DNA with histone and nonhistone proteins protects the nucleic acid, perhaps by limiting access of the enzymes. When replicating DNA is exposed to DNase, more digestion can be observed than when chromatin which is not replicating is reacted with nuclease. The newly replicated DNA is, however, more resistant to digestion than is purified DNA that has been freed of associated proteins. In chick cells, newly replicating DNA acquires resistance to nuclease digestion during the first minute after initiation of replication, reaching a plateau level of resistance which is maintained for about 2 hours.

It has been suggested by several authors that the DNA may be coiled around the histones of the core. This model is shown schematically in Figure 4. The histones in the core include H2A, H2B, H3, and H4. Each histone

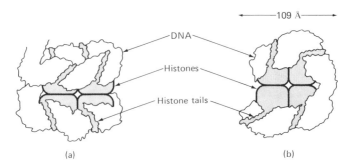

Figure 4. Schematic model of the interaction of DNA and histones in the nucleosome core. (a) View from the side. (b) View looking down along the axis.

appears to be present as a dimer, with the DNA gently coiled onto the surface. The organization may include a dyad arrangement of the nucleosome into identical halves. Such an organization has been suggested by Weintraub and his coworkers to be reponsible for information transfer within and between genes.

If protein synthesis is inhibited, the DNA replication rate very rapidly decreases to about one-half the normal rate of 75 base pairs/sec. The specific proteins that must be synthesized for replication to proceed have not been identified, but it has been postulated that the histones play this role. Using these facts and postulates, Weintraub has suggested the following theory to explain the assembly of chromatin and the related control processes. Within the first minute after initiation of replication, DNA strands start to associate with histone proteins. The rate of histone synthesis is therefore coordinated with, and controls, the rate of replication. A postulated small pool of free histone molecules could simultaneously inhibit histone synthesis and stimulate replication. As the pool becomes depleted because all the histone becomes associated with the newly replicating DNA, histone synthesis would be increased, and replication would be inhibited.

It appears that histones are not rapidly degraded; this has been interpreted to mean that the original histones are recycled to complex again with DNA, rather than being degraded to component amino acids. In addition, Weintraub postulates that these "old" histones would recomplex with the "old" DNA strands, and newly synthesized histones would associate with the newly synthesized DNA. Thus each new DNA molecule would contain one strand complexed with recycled histones, while the other was associated with histones from the pool of new histones.

Direct evidence bearing on this theory is not yet available; it should be possible to determine if such a pool of free histones does exist. It appears likely from studies of nucleosomes that the histones are required for the structural integrity of the chromatin, stabilizing the DNA into supercoiled regions held to each other by unwound DNA that is complexed to a specific histone, H1 (see above). Histones have also been postulated to control the availability of the chromatin for replication and transcription; the strong binding of these proteins makes such a role likely.

SPECIALIZED REPLICATION IN THE NUCLEOLUS

The nucleolus is a suborganelle of the cell nucleus; it is known to be associated with the DNA that codes for the formation of rRNA. In some organisms, like *Xenopus,* ribosomal RNA genes (rDNA) are highly amplified; that is, many copies of these genes exist, during at least some stages during development. When these nucleoli are examined in the electron microscope, a small

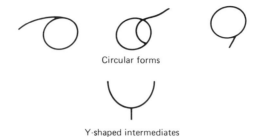

Circular forms

Y-shaped intermediates

Figure 5. Circular and Y-shaped DNA in amplified genes.

but significant fraction of the DNA (2 to 5%) has been shown to be present as circular molecules. Some of these molecules show forms that appear characteristic of a rolling circle model of replication (see Chapter 7.2). A still smaller fraction of the DNA is found in Y-shaped forms, which could result from the breakage of circles. Figure 5 shows schematic representations of such forms.

The physiological significance of these circular molecules has not been established. If eukaryotic chromosomes contain a single, large DNA molecule, it would appear that small circular molecules must be the artifactual result of breakage of segments of the genome. On the other hand, they may indeed represent some specific mechanism for the replication of amplified genes, which may perhaps be only loosely associated with the rest of the genome. If these forms are not artifacts of preparation, they may represent a unique opportunity to demonstrate that some bacterial mechanisms may also be directly applied to specialized eukaryotic systems. Similar molecular forms have been reported in eukaryotic organelles, which contain small circular genomes. Here, it is easier to see that a rolling circle mechanism could be used. Future studies of amplified genes may be expected to determine whether these extra copies of a gene can be compared to plasmids, or whether they are actually joined to the rest of the chromatin.

BIBLIOGRAPHY

General Mechanisms

Goulian, M. 1971. *Annu. Rev. Biochem.* 40:855.
Klein, A., and Bonhoeffer, F. 1972. *Annu. Rev. Biochem.* 41:301.
Probst, G. S., Bikoff, E., Keller, S. J., and Meyer, R. R. 1972. *Biochim. Biophys. Acta* 281:244.
Kaufman, D. G., Grisham, J. W., and Stenstrom, M. L. 1972. *Biochim. Biophys. Acta* 272:212.
Kubinski, H., Gibbs, P., and Kasper, C. B. 1972. *Biochim. Biophys. Acta* 281:244.
Edenberg, H. J., and Huberman, J. 1973. *Annu. Rev. Genet.* 9:245.
Kolber, A. R. 1975. *J. Virol.* 15:322.
Gautschi, J. R., and Clarkson, J. M. 1975. *Eur. J. Biochem.* 50:403.

Reinhard, P., Burkhalter, M., and Gautschi, J. R. 1977. *Biochim. Biophys. Acta* 474:500.
Gautschi, J. R., Burkhalter, M., and Reinhard, P. 1977. *Biochim. Biophys. Acta* 474:512.

Eukaryotic Replicons:

Tobia, A. M., Schildkraut, C. L., and Maio, J. J. 1970. *J. Mol. Biol.* 54:499.
Painter, R. B., and Schaefer, A. W., 1971. *J. Mol. Biol.* 58:289.
Amaldi, F., Carnavale, F., Leoni, L., and Mariotti, D. 1972. *Exp. Cell Res.* 74:367.
Callan, H. G. 1972. *Proc. R. Soc. London Ser. B* 181:19.
Weintraub, H. 1972. *Nature New Biol.* 236:195.
Laird, C. D. 1973. *Annu. Rev. Genet.* 9:177.
Wolstenholme, D. R. 1973. *Chromosoma* 43:1.
Remington, J. A., and Klevecz, R. R. 1973. *Exp. Cell Res.* 76:410.
Huberman, J. A., and Tsai, A. 1973. *J. Mol. Biol.* 78:261.
Hand, R., and Tamm, I. 1973. *J. Cell Biol.* 58:410.
McFarlane, P. W., and Callan, H. G., 1973. *J. Cell Sci.* 13:821.
Amaldi, F., Buongiorno-Nardelli, M., Carnevale, F. Leoni, L., Mariotti, D., and Pomponi,
    M. 1973. *Exp. Cell Res.,* 80:79.
Kavenoff, R., and Zimm, B. H. 1973. *Chromosoma,* 41:1.
Kriegstein, H. J., and Hogness, D. S. 1974. *Proc. Natl. Acad. Sci. U.S.A.* 71:135.
Lee, C. S., and Pavan, C. 1974. *Chromosoma* 41:429.
Newlon, C. S., Petes, T. D., Hereford, L. M., and Fangman, W. L. 1974. *Nature* 247:32.
Burke, W., and Fangman, W. L. 1975. *Cell* 5:263.
Kowalski, J., and Cheevers, W. P. 1976. *J. Mol. Biol.* 104:603.

Okazaki Fragments, Discontinuous DNA Replication and RNA Primers:

Sato, S., Tonaka, M., and Sugimura, T. 1970. *Biochim. Biophys. Acta* 209:43.
Verma, I. M., Meuth, N. L., Bromfel, E., Manly, K. F., and Baltimore, D. 1971. *Nature New
    Biol.,* 233:131.
Leis, B. P., and Hurwitz, J. 1972. *J. Virol.* 9:130.
Flugel, R. M., and Wells, R. D. 1972. *Virology* 48:394.
Sato, S., Ariake, S., Saito, M., and Sugimura, T. 1972. *Biochem. Biophys. Res. Commun.* 49:827.
Francke, B., and Eckhart, W. 1973. *Virology* 55:127.
Fox, R. M., Mendelsohn, J., Barbosa, E., and Goulian, M. 1973. *Nature New Biol.* 245:234.
Reichard, P., Eliasson, R., and Soderman, G. 1974. *Proc. Natl. Acad. Sci. U.S.A.* 71:4901.
Neubort, N., and Bases, R. 1974. *Biochim. Biophys. Acta* 340:31.
Housman, D., and Huberman, J. 1975. *J. Mol. Biol.* 94:173.
Francke, B., and Hunter, T. 1975. *J. Virol.* 15:97.
Otto, B., and Reichard, P. 1975. *J. Virol.* 15:259.
Hunter, T., and Francke, B. 1975. *J. Virol.* 15:759.
Gautschi, J. R., and Clarkson, J. M. 1975. *Eur. J. Biochem.* 50:403.

Nucleosomes as Possible Structural Units of Replication:

Kleiman, L., and Huang, R.-C. C. 1972. *J. Mol. Biol.* 64:1.
Olins, A. L., and Olins, D. E. 1974. *Science* 183:330.
Kornberg, R. D. 1974. *Science* 184:868.
van Holde, K. E., Sahasrabuddhe, C. G., and Show, B. R. 1974. *Nucl. Acids Res.* 1:1579.
Noll, M. 1974. *Nucl. Acids Res.* 1:1573.
Germond, J. E., Hirt, B., Oudet, P., Gross-Bellard, M., and Chambon, P. 1975. *Proc. Natl.
    Acad. Sci. U.S.A.* 72:1843.
Keller, W. 1975. *Proc. Natl. Acad. Sci. U.S.A.* 72:4876.

Stein, G. S., Mains, R. J., Gabby, E. J., Stein, J. L., Davis, J., and Adawadkar, P. D. 1975. *Biochemistry* 14:1859.

Shure, M., and Vinograd, J. 1976. *Cell* 8:215.

Oudet, P., Gross-Bellard, M., and Chambon, P. 1975. *Cell* 4:281.

Zuckerkandl, E. 1976. *J. Mol. Evol.* 9:73.

Varshavsky, A. J., Bakayev, V. V., and Georgiev, G. P. 1976. *Nucl. Acids Res.* 3:477.

Whitlock, J. P., and Simpson, R. T. 1976. *Biochemistry* 15:3307.

Woodcock, C. L. 1977. *Science* 195:1350.

Noll, M., and Kornberg, R. D. 1977. *J. Mol. Biol.* 109:393.

Hozler, J., Renz, M., and Nehis, P. 1977. *Chromosoma* 62:301.

Pardon, J. F., Worchester, D. L., Wooley, J. C., Cotter, R. I., Lilley, D. M. J., and Richards, B. M. 1977. *Nucl. Acids Res.* 4:3199.

Eicken, I., and Keller, W. 1978. *Science* 201:406.

Muller, U., Zentgraf, H., Eicken, I., and Keller, W. 1978. *Science* 201:406.

Assembly of Chromatin:

Weintraub, H. 1972. *Nature* 240:449.

Fakan, S., Turner, G. N., Pagano, J. S., and Hancock, R. 1972. *Proc. Natl. Acad. Sci. U.S.A.* 69:2300.

Weintraub, H. 1973. *Cold Spring Harbor Symp. Quant. Biol.* 38:247.

Specialized Replication in the Nucleolus:

Gall, J. G., Cohen, E. H., and Polan, M. L. 1971. *Chromosoma* 33:319.

Hennig, W. 1972. *J. Mol. Biol.* 71:407, 419.

Kram, R., Botchan, M., and Hearst, J. E. 1972. *J. Mol. Biol.* 64:103.

Sutton, W. D. 1972. *Nature New Biol.* 237:70.

7.4. Uptake of Exogenous Nucleic Acid by Cells

BACTERIAL TRANSFORMATION

Some DNA molecules can enter certain bacterial cells from the media, and may become integrated into the bacterial genome. The DNA that is taken up can be homospecific (i.e., it arises from the same bacterial strain as the acceptor cell), or it may be heterospecific (donor and acceptor strains are different). Integration of the DNA into the genome is more efficient in homospecific cases because of the intracellular events required (see below). Attachment and integration of the foreign DNA to the cell surface are dependent both on the physical characteristics of the DNA and on certain surface characteristics of the bacterial strain. Only a few strains of bacteria are competent for this process, which is called transformation.

A protein has been identified that can transfer competence from one bacterial cell to another; this competence factor has also been reported to inhibit replication, but this behavior may be due to a bacteriocin that co-purifies with the protein. Competent bacteria are usually found only during late logarithmic stages of the growth cycle, and these cells have specific DNA receptors on the cell surface. Although it is known that protein synthesis is required for competence, the actual nature of the protein products is not known. They could include the specific competence factor, and the receptors on the cell surface.

In order actually to transform a cell, the extracellular DNA must have certain properties. The molecule must be double-stranded, and of relatively large size. DNA fragments smaller than 5×10^5 daltons cannot transform bacterial cells. There appears to be no upper limit to the size of the transforming DNA. Single-stranded DNA will not bind to the receptors, but apparently only one of the two bound strands actually enters the cell. The attachment of the DNA to the cell surface appears to be a two-step process. In the first step, the DNA is reversibly bound and is sensitive to digestion by DNase. After attachment, the bound DNA is apparently denatured, since antibody to single-stranded DNA will inhibit further steps in transformation. At this point, the transforming DNA is irreversibly bound and is no longer sensitive to nuclease digestion. The process requires Mg^{+2} ions, and takes place within the bacterial envelope; only one of the two strands subsequently enters the cell.

In the cell, the single strand of DNA is aligned along the bacterial genome in regions of base homology. When the transforming DNA came from the same strain as the recipient cell, the homology between the two DNA molecules is essentially complete. The merozygote that forms in such homospecific transformation is therefore very stable. In heterospecific transformation, on the other hand, although merozygotes form, they are less stable owing to interspersed nonhomologous sequences. The new genetic material can then be integrated into the host DNA by the recombination system of the cell. Once integrated, these genes form a stable part of the genome, and are replicated, transcribed, and translated exactly like the original genetic material. In this way, competent strains of bacteria can change their genetic properties, a characteristic that could be an advantage during selection and evolution.

TRANSFECTION

Nucleic acids from viruses and from animal cells have been isolated and used to infect competent cells; either DNA or RNA can enter the cell. In this process, known as transfection, the nucleic acid is not integrated into the cellular genome, but both RNA and protein of the transfecting species may be produced. In one specific case, the tobacco mosaic virus (TMV), new virions can also be produced, but this behavior is due to certain specific properties of this virus. Purified TMV RNA is used to infect the cell, albeit at a lower efficiency than that of intact virus. Both RNA and viral proteins are produced, and they give rise to intact virions. *In vitro*, intact virions can also be formed when all the RNA and the proteins that make up this virus are mixed together. This behavior is not necessarily a property of all viruses, but has been shown to occur with TMV.

In general, however, transfection results in the production of viral mRNA which is then translated by the cellular protein-synthesizing system to produce viral proteins. In bacteria, a helper virus such as the bacteriophage λ may be required for transfection to take place, and the acceptor bacterial strain must be competent for transformation. When the nucleic acids from animal viruses are isolated, they can be used to transfect either competent bacterial strains or the animal cells that are normally sensitive to those particular viruses. This implies that specific cellular receptors on the surface of the cell may be required for the attachment and entry of this extracted nucleic acid. It is not clear if these receptors are identical to those used in transformation. In general, closely related viruses appear to recognize receptors that are similar, and the same may be true for the isolated nucleic acid from these virions.

The early stages of transfection appear to be very similar to those found in transformation. In both cases, the nucleic acid must attach to the cell surface and enter by traversing the membrane. Once it is in the cell, however, the fate of the nucleic acid differs in the two mechanisms. In transfection, unlike transformation, the nucleic acid is not integrated into the cellular genome but retains its own structural integrity. The cell appears to be able to transcribe and translate this foreign material so that the exogenous genes are expressed, but this genetic material never becomes part of the hereditary genome of the transfected cell. In general, animal virus DNA appears to act in this manner. Oncogenic C-type RNA viruses are thought to be at least partially integrated as DNA copies into the cellular genome, and may therefore act in a manner more akin to bacterial transformation.

TRANSDUCTION

Bacteriophage infection of host bacterial cells can sometimes result in the transfer of genetic material from one bacterium to another. Very few genes can be transferred in this manner, but the use of transducing phage has been most useful in the fine mapping of bacterial genes. There are two general types of transduction, restricted and generalized. In the first, the phage can integrate into the bacterial genome (see "Lysogeny," Chapter 7.5), at a site that is specific, and can, on excision from the bacterial DNA, carry with it a few genes that are proximate to the integration site. In generalized transduction, on the other hand, it is not necessary that the phage be integrated into the bacterial genome, and the viral vector can carry bacterial genes from any region of the bacterial DNA.

Since the virion itself is small (compared to the bacterial host, it may be less than one-hundredth the size), it carries relatively few genes, and can therefore transport only a very limited number of bacterial genes from one host to another. Some part of the viral genome itself must generally be lost when bacterial genes are introduced into the virion in order to allow packaging of a limited amount of DNA into the viral head, and may therefore become defective phage, incapable of productive infection without the aid of a helper virus. When these transducing phage enter a new host cell, they carry this small subset of bacterial genes, which can then be integrated into the bacterial genome by recombination (see Chapter 7.6). Co-transduction of two such genes by a single vector implies a close linkage between them, and analysis of co-transduction allows fine mapping of linkage groups on the bacterial genome.

A similar mechanism may also be operative in eukaryotic cells, but the situation is much less clear. Some DNA viruses have been reported to transfer genetic material to their animal cell hosts, but it is not yet known if these genes are of viral or animal origin. One example that has been reported is the papilloma virus which causes warts on the ears of certain large rabbits. Humans can be infected by this virus, which does not, however, give rise to warts, nor can viruses be recovered after infection. Even in the absence of recoverable virus, an alteration in arginine metabolism can be found. This altered metabolism is not characteristic of human cells, but it is not clear whether it is caused by the retention and expression of a viral gene, or by transduction of a rabbit gene to the human host. Alternatively, this alteration in metabolism could arise as a consequence of the induction of a normally inactive human gene. Until these alternative hypotheses have been more completely studied, it will not be possible to determine if transduction can take place in eukaryotic cells as well as in bacteria.

CONJUGATION

Conjugation is a specialized bacterial mechanism that allows the sexual reproduction of certain bacterial strains. A specific gene or cluster of genes allows transfer of all or part of the genome of an F^+ (male) bacterium to an F^- (female) recipient. Only the enterobacterium *E. coli* has been shown to be capable of conjugation, and this process takes place in only a small number of all available cells. Generally, the whole genome is not transferred during conjugation, but only a part of it, always including the F factor, so that all recipient cells become male. In some cases, the F factor alone is transferred; this generally occurs when this factor exists in the donor cell as an episome, that is, a circular piece of DNA that can replicate independently of the bacterial genome. In a few cases, the F factor is integrated into the cellular genome; strains carrying such an integrated F factor are known as Hfr (high frequency of recombinant) strains. These Hfr strains are capable of inducing the transfer of several genes during conjugation, and at least theoretically could cause the entire genome of a male cell to enter the recipient cell. This is a very rare event, however; in most cases, the entering DNA will break at some point during conjugation, perhaps owing to the mechanical disruption of the bridge between the two cells.

Conjugation takes place through the sex pilus, a specialized structure of male cells, which extends from the F^+ or Hfr cell to the F^- cell. The F factor itself specifies a surface antigen that allows the required intimate contact between the donor and the recipient, and codes for the formation of the sex pilus. The entering DNA is formed in the donor cell by replication, probably through a rolling circle mechanism, and crosses to the recipient cell through the pilus. After transfer, the donor genome undergoes recombination with the recipient DNA, and a number of genes become integrated into the female cell. Judicious choice of gene markers in the two strains

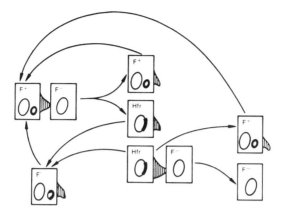

Figure 1. Conjugation in *E. coli.*

allows mapping of genes which are transferred together during recombination. Several Hfr strains, each of which has a specific site for the integration of the F factor, are available. By the use of several of them, the genome of *E. coli* has in essence been almost completely mapped. A schematic representation of conjugation is shown in Figure 1.

UPTAKE OF EXOGENOUS NUCLEIC ACIDS IN EUKARYOTES

Since bacterial transformation and conjugation have been so useful in the mapping of bacterial genomes, many laboratories have attempted to discover analogous mechanisms in eukaryotic cells. In most cases, these attempts have not been fruitful, although a few isolated instances of uptake of nucleic acids by eukaryotic cells have been reported. In general, however, even in these cases, the nucleic acid that enters the cell is not integrated into the cellular genome. A possible exception, noted above, arises in the oncogenic viruses which contain reverse transcriptase, or RNA-dependent DNA polymerase. This enzyme, which appears to be capable of producing DNA using an RNA template, may allow the integration of some genetic information from viruses into their animal cell host genome.

Specific receptor sites for nucleic acids on eukaryotic cell membranes have not yet been identified. However, there is some evidence that accords with the possible adsorption of nucleic acids to the surface of these cells. Such adsorption appears to be dependent on several factors, including the type of cell, the concentration of the nucleic acid, and its physical properties. If DNA is injected into an animal, the bulk of it is degraded by cellular nuclease, and adsorbed DNA may also be digested in this fashion. Some injected DNA is taken up by macrophages and lymphocytes, perhaps by pinocytosis; little if any can be shown to reach the nucleus. No phenotypic changes can be

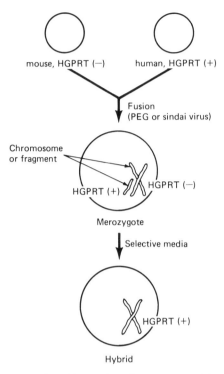

Figure 2. Schematic representation of integration of exogenous nucleic acids in eukaryotic cells.

shown to occur as a result of the adsorption or injection of DNA into the animal cells, although there are reports of chromosomal abnormalities that appear to arise in consequence. RNA is less quickly degraded than is DNA, and has been reported to result in an increased rate of protein synthesis. In general, however, it must be noted that evidence for mechanisms similar to transformation in eukaryotic cells has not been presented as yet.

Recently, there have been reports that exogenous genes carried on chromatin may enter an animal cell and be integrated into the host genome. It has been known for some time that hybrid cells which carry the chromosomes of both host and donor can be formed in cell culture. For example, a cell of a mouse line deficient in the enzyme hypoxanthine–guanine phosphoribosyl transferase (HGPRT) can be fused in culture with a human line that carries an active human HGPRT gene. A stable merozygote is formed, with the retention of the human chromosome, and the hybrid cell can be isolated in selective media that prevent growth of both parent cell lines (Figure 2). The mouse and the human enzymes can be identified on electrophoresis, and the human chromosome can be shown by karyotyping. In most of these hybrids, a large enough piece of the human chromosome is retained for such analysis, but in a few lines no human chromosome fragment can be identified.

A recent report states, however, that the exogenous HGPRT gene need not be associated with a chromosome or fragment, but may be integrated directly into the mouse genome. According to this report, the HGPRT gene is integrated into a chromosome other than the mouse X chromosome, which is the normal site for the gene. If this report, and similar experiments with other genes, should be confirmed, integration of exogenous genes into eukaryotic DNA will be accepted. In general, no site of integration has yet been defined for these genes, and it is not known whether intact chromatin is required for such a mechanism. If animal cells are indeed able to incorporate exogenous genes, this fact may become of great clinical interest, since biochemically defective cells may be able to be cured of their metabolic ailments by such a mechanism.

GENERAL REFERENCES

Bader, J. P. 1973. *Science* 180:1069.
Tiraby, J. G., and Fox, M. S. 1973. *Proc. Natl. Acad. Sci. U.S.A.* 70:3541.

7.5. Lysogeny

VIRULENT AND TEMPERATE VIRUSES

Viruses may generally have either of two effects on host cells, assuming that the virus contains all necessary genes (i.e., that the virus is not defective). Virulent viruses enter cells, shut off host nucleic acid and protein synthesis, and reproduce, eventually killing the cells to release the newly formed virus. Many bacterial and eukaryotic viruses show such infectious lytic cycles. Occasionally, such infections may be nonproductive, owing to restrictions arising from either the host or the virus. The virus may be defective in a late gene required for packaging of the DNA into its protein coat, for example. In this case, entry into the host cell and DNA replication may take place, but mature viruses will not be released. Such a virus may be able to complete its cycle if a "helper virus" is added. The "helper" may supply the necessary missing viral function so that mature virions of both defective and helper viruses are released. Another mechanism, this one host-dependent, that results in nonproductive infection, is the presence of an appropriate restriction enzyme system (see Chapter 6.9). The virus adsorbs normally to the host cell, and viral DNA enters the cell. However, host restriction enzymes recognize specific DNA sequences present in the viral DNA, and degrade it. This prevents viral reproduction, and the host cell continues to grow normally.

Other viruses, however, enter the cell, are not degraded, and yet do not cause virion production, nor do they kill the cell. These temperate viruses remain in the cell for varying periods of time. In some cases, the virus may be induced to replicate by one of several mechanisms, and a lytic cycle can occur as a consequence. With bacteriophages, induction of a temperate virus may be mediated by infection with another phage. Certain eukaryotic viruses can infect several types of host cells, only one of which may be lysed. In this case, fusion of an infected cell unable to undergo lysis with a permissive host cell that is normally lysed causes the induction of a lytic cycle. The viral DNA that enters a host cell and remains there without causing lysis is integrated into the host genome. This process is called lysogeny, and such viruses are known as lysogenic viruses. Generally, temperate viruses are capable of both lysogenic and lytic cycles.

THE PROCESS OF LYSOGENIC INTEGRATION

The mechanism whereby a lysogenic rather than a lytic infection occurs with a particular virus is unknown. Often, infection of a culture results in both; some cells are lysed, while others can be shown to contain a lysogenic virus. The presence of an integrated viral genome renders the lysogenized host immune to lytic infection by a virus of the same strain. This implies that one or more of the viral genes may be active, perhaps including one that changes host cell surface characteristics to prevent entry of other viral genomes. This changed behavior may result from an alteration in the viral receptors on the host cell.

The viral DNA molecule in a lysogenic infection pairs with the host DNA. This pairing will by no means be complete; it may involve just a few sequences which are homologous in the two molecules. After base pairing, an endonuclease introduces nicks; with circular molecules, there may be one nick per genome. Recombination (Chapter 7.6) then takes place between the two DNA molecules, so that the viral genome becomes an integral part of the host chromosome. This integration prevents full expression of the viral genes; replication of the integrated genome is under the control of the host and takes place only during host chromosome replication. Several copies of the viral DNA may be integrated into the host chromosome. In some cases, the viral genomes are in tandem next to each other (Figure 1a); in other cases, the viral DNA molecules may integrate at several sites on the host chromosome (Figure 1b). The integrated bacteriophage genomes are known as prophages; each descendant of a lysogenized bacterium will contain a prophage molecule in its genome.

VIRAL TRANSFORMATION OF CELLS

Lysogeny has been exhaustively studied in bacterial systems, but also occurs in animal cells. In the latter, integration of a viral genome leads to transformation, a process that may be linked to cancer. The word "transformation" here refers to a complex of biochemical and cytological changes noted in vitro in cultures of cells that contain an integrated viral genome. Some changes that have been noted pertain to the surface characteristics of the cells; they include altered surface antigens, and loss of contact inhibition. Normal cells

| a virus | virus | virus | virus | b | a virus | b c d e virus f g virus |

a. In tandem integration   b. Integration at different sites

Figure 1. Integrated viral genomes.

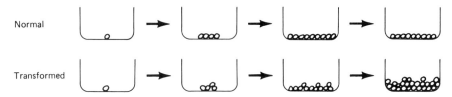

Figure 2. Cell growth in normal and transformed cells.

in culture stop growing as they make contact with other cells, and grow only to a confluent monolayer. Transformed cells continue to grow and form a multilayered culture (Figure 2).

In at least one human transformant, the integration of a viral genome results in local unwinding of the DNA. Cytologically, the integration of the SV40 virus causes an apparent gap to appear in a specific chromosome. This gap has been shown to be caused by local unwinding of the DNA, perhaps with some loss of chromosomal proteins. As a result, chromosomal stains cannot bind to this region, so that the chromatin appears to be missing in that segment.

Cytologically, transformed cells may become aneuploid or polyploid; that is, the chromosome number may change. Chromosomal abnormalities may be seen in such cultures, and the frequency of sister chromatid exchange may increase. A new cytological method allows the visualization of genetic exchanges between the two chromatids of a single chromosome. Normally, this rate is rather low, but in some transformed lines, such exchanges are common. This may be a reflection of an increased rate of breakage and repair. It is interesting to note that a disease state in man, Bloom's syndrome, which is associated with a high frequency of cancer, shows an abnormally high rate of sister chromatid exchange.

LYSOGENIC BACTERIOPHAGE

Some of the strains of bacteriophage that can be integrated into a host cell are the phages lambda (λ), φ80, P-1, and P22 in *E. coli*. Other bacteria can also be lysogenized by specific phages, but the process has been most extensively studied with λ phage and *E. coli*. This virus genome contains fewer than 30 genes, and is known to be circular. It is integrated into one specific site on the chromosome of its host, and appears to be present as a single copy. Mutations in a single region of the viral genome, called the cI region, cause a loss of the temperate nature of λ phage. These mutants are capable only of lytic infection. The integration into the bacterial genome is controlled by a viral gene, and another viral gene which specifies the host cell range.

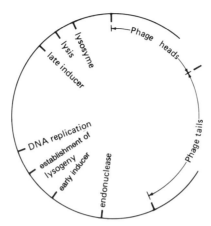

Figure 3. A schematic map of the λ genome. (Note: The actual phage genome is double-stranded; it is represented as a single line for simplicity.)

The λ phage always integrates into the *E. coli* genome at a site near the *gal* locus of the bacterial chromosome. The attachment region on the viral genome is closely linked to genes required for the synthesis of the components of the viral tail, as shown in the schematic map of the λ phage in Figure 3. On the other side of the attachment site lie genes required for the viral DNA synthesis; these genes together make up the C region of the viral genome. Two viral genes are required for integration and excision of the genome; these are the *int* and *xis* genes. Excision requires both gene products, whereas integration requires only the *int* protein. One or more host genes are also required for lysogeny.

Some of the sequences in the attachment region of the viral genome are complementary to sequences on the bacterial DNA. In lysogeny, these complementary sequences pair to each other, and an endonuclease introduces a nick into each of the DNA molecules. Recombination (see Chapter 7.6) between the two genomes then occurs, resulting in the integration of the viral genome into the bacterial chromosome. This integration takes place with a specific polarity; excision of the lysogenized virus requires another recombinational event. Figure 4 represents the integration and excision of the λ phage into the *E. coli* genome.

THE INDUCTION OF PROPHAGES

The spontaneous release of infectious viral particles from a lysogenized host is rare. Generally, some external stimulus is required for this induction. Ultraviolet light, for example, may serve as an inducing agent for some lysogenic

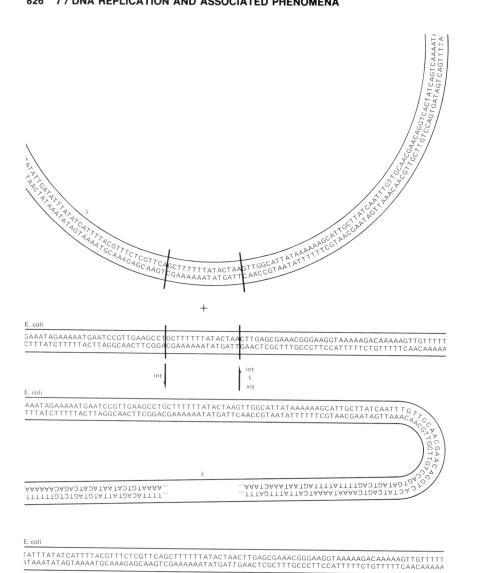

Figure 4. Integration and excision of lysogenized λ.

bacteriophage at low levels of intensity. Not all prophages are inducible; the mechanisms that prevent the excision of a prophage under all circumstances are not well understood; it is possible that further work on these systems will prove that these prophage are also inducible under the proper conditions, which merely have not yet been discovered.

In order to understand how lysogeny can be maintained, it can be assumed that the integrated viral genome produces only a single gene product. This is probably an oversimplification; several genes may be active within the prophage, as long as viral replication is inhibited. For purposes of the model, however, we will assume that the only gene transcribed codes for a repressor protein. This protein binds to the operator gene on the viral genome, and thus prevents RNA transcription. As a consequence, the genome of the phage acts only as a part of the bacterial chromosome, being replicated together with this DNA, but not being transcribed for the bulk of its own genome. On induction, the repressor is inactivated in some way, so that the other viral genes can be expressed. New virions can then be formed, leading to the lysis of the host cell and the release of new infectious phage particles. A major shortcoming of this model, however, is the fact that it cannot account for prevention of the entry of other viruses of the same type into a lysogenized host cell. This problem can be overcome by assuming that a second gene is also transcribed; this gene product is a protein that can bind to cell receptors, preventing the attachment or entry of new phage particles.

Induction requires a recombinational event, as shown in Figure 4. The viral genome is excised by endonuclease cuts in the viral and bacterial genomes. Ligase, whether viral or host-specified, can then reseal the ends of both the phage and the bacterial genomes to give the original two molecules. Induction may be faulty, so that excision leaves some viral material while removing one or a few of the bacterial genes. In this case, a defective phage which may be capable of future transfer of genetic information from one host to another may be produced. These transducing phage particles can then infect other cells, but generally require a helper virus, since they are missing vital viral genes.

In order for ligase to reseal the ends of a phage genome, the viral DNA usually has complementary base sequences on the ends of the strands. These can be so-called sticky ends, where each strand has a single-stranded region that can overlap the end of the other strand to allow resealing. The result of the recombinational event involved in induction is the recovery of the circular genomes of the bacteria and the virus. Not all phage have a circular genome, but many can form circular molecules because of circular permutations in the sequences at the ends of the molecule (Figure 5.).

Mutations can arise in the structural gene for the repressor, so that the other viral genes could become active during lysogeny. This type of mutation gives rise to a virus that has lost the ability to allow a lysogenic infection. Such λ phage mutants, however, remain unable to productively infect host cells carrying an integrated λ prophage. This prophage continues to produce repressor, which binds to the superinfecting λDNA and prevents transcription of the viral genes. On the other hand, mutations localized to the postulated

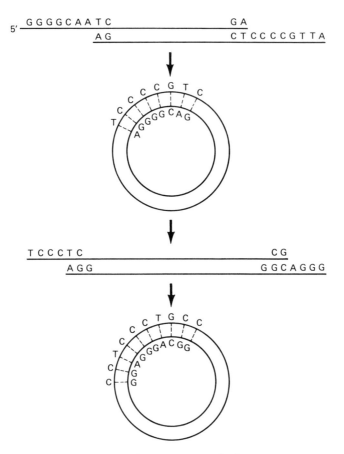

Figure 5. Some circular permutations of a linear genome.

viral operator region produce a lytic infection in all host cells, including those that contain a λ prophage. This behavior is a consequence of the inability of repressor to bind to the altered operator, owing to the pertubation introduced in the DNA composition of the operator. Since the repressor cannot bind, transcription of viral DNA proceeds, and viral products are formed.

Other mutations in these same regions might prevent prophage induction, an effect that could also be due to pertubations in binding capability, in this case preventing dissociation of the repressor–operator complex. If this occurs in the operator region of the prophage, an occasional superinfecting virus may escape inhibition. On the other hand, this type of alteration in the repressor itself would absolutely prevent any superinfection. In strains of bacteriophage that are completely resistant to induction by any means, such as the phage P2 in *E. coli*, available evidence suggests that inhibition of induction proceeds in a different fashion. No repressor has been identified in the host cell cytoplasm, and it is not clear that such a compound is formed. However, further studies are required for clarification of the mechanism of action of such noninducible prophages.

The normal pathways for induction include low dosages of ultraviolet light, X-rays, or chemical mutagens. It is known that induction requires protein synthesis, but no specific product has been identified. The mechanism of induction appears to be associated with DNA synthesis and/or repair, and requires a recombinational event. The protein whose synthesis is required might be a specific nuclease that nicks the DNA to allow the process of recombination to proceed. Alternatively, it might be that a viral polymerase must be produced to allow either replication or transcription. Even before induction, a very low level of specific viral functions is found in lysogenized bacteria, indicating that some transcription of the prophage genes takes place. On induction, specific mutations may be produced in the viral genome that allow viral functions to override the normal lysogenic controls.

SHORT BIBLIOGRAPHY

Gottesman, S., and Gottesman, M. 1975. *Proc. Natl. Acad. Sci. U.S.A.* 72:2188.
Nash, H. A. 1975. *Proc. Natl. Acad. Sci. U.S.A.* 72:1072.
Bernheimer, H. P. 1977. *Science* 195:66.
Landy, A., and Ross, W. 1977. *Science* 197:1147.

7.6. Recombination

GENERAL MECHANISMS

Recombination allows the exchange of genetic material from separate chromosomes to form a new, stable arrangement of genes. It is the process whereby nucleic acid fragments can be incorporated into a genome, and it is thus required for the completion of conjugation, transduction, and transformation in bacterial systems. In eukaryotic systems, allelic genes or homologous chromosomes can be rearranged, by recombination, into a pattern that differs from that of the parental cells. Repair of lesions in DNA from all organisms often is initiated with an exchange of genetic material (see Chapter 7.7). This process of recombination has been intensively studied in bacteria, viruses, and yeast. In bacteria and yeast, identification or recombinants is relatively simple, since they can be identified by easily defined biochemical or microscopic tests. Viral recombination can also be detected easily in some cases, but complete analysis of the processes requires statistical studies of large numbers of progeny. In those animals that produce few progeny and have long life spans, the detection of recombinants requires studies of populations rather than individuals.

Recombination can be reciprocal, resulting in the formation of two complete genomes, or nonreciprocal, so that one new chromosome and perhaps a nonviable fragment are formed. The processes described in the previous chapter often result in nonreciprocal recombination. Formation of prophages that are integrated into the bacterial genome (Chapter 7.5) requires recombination of two DNA molecules into a single, new genome. The same is true for integration of plasmids into the bacterial genome. In prokaryotic systems, only transduction actually proceeds through reciprocal recombination, since altered bacterial and viral genomes are both formed. In eukaryotic organisms, reciprocal recombination may take place between two similar chromosomes, resulting in the exchange of alleles between two heterozygotes. Nonreciprocal recombination can be detected more rarely, and is usually found between genes that are very closely linked. Both types of recombination are shown in Figure 1. Exchange of material between nonhomologous chromosomes, resulting in cytological detectable translocations, usually arises from faulty repair of chromosomal breaks rather than through recombinational events, and will not be discussed further.

Reciprical recombination

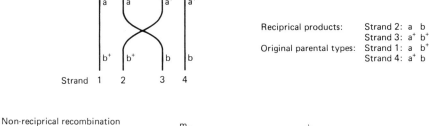

Reciprical products: Strand 2: a   b
                         Strand 3: a⁺ b⁺
Original parental types: Strand 1: a   b⁺
                         Strand 4: a⁺ b

Non-reciprical recombination

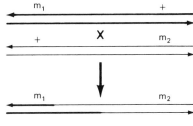

No ++ strand is recovered

Figure 1. Reciprocal and nonreciprocal recombination.

BACTERIAL RECOMBINATION

DNA molecules can enter a bacterial cell through several different mechanisms (see Chapter 7.4), but all pathways that result in hereditable changes in the genetic information carried by the cell (except in the case of plasmids), require the integration of the foreign DNA into the bacterial genome. The first necessary step in this integration is the pairing of homologous regions of the two DNA molecules. During conjugation, for example, those regions of the DNA carrying the same genes or alleles of each will align next to each other (Chapter 7.4). Then, an endonuclease will nick the two strands close to these allelic genes, and recombination will take place between the two strands (Figure 2). The process results in the incorporation of a fragment of the donor genome into the recipient DNA, with the loss of an equal segment of the original DNA of the female cell. When the parental strains each carry a marker that can be selected against by the growth medium, recombinant cells can be identified by their ability to grow in the selective medium which is lethal to both parental strains.

In transformation, also, the markers of the donor cells must differ from those of the recipients in order to allow detection of the integration of new genetic material. Although a large piece of donor DNA is absorbed onto

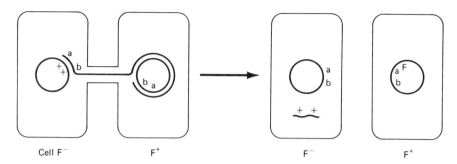

Figure 2. Recombination during conjugation.

the cell surface and enters the cell, only a small fraction of this material becomes integrated (Figure 3). The bulk of the exogenous DNA is eventually degraded by cellular nucleases. Plasmids also can be incorporated into a bacterial genome, although they generally are found as separate entities that replicate and are transferred independently of the parental DNA. Integration and excision of both plasmids and lysogenic viruses require a recombinational event. It is most probable that this event involves breakage and repair of the two strands, and requires the action of an endonuclease (see "Molecular Models," below). In *E. coli,* it has been shown that the *rec* genes which are required for recombination to take place code for both endonucleases and exonucleases (see Chapter 6.9).

The study of recombination in bacteria has been useful in mapping the bacterial genome. For example, the precise time of transfer of different genes during conjugation has made it possible to determine the linear arrangement of linked groups of genes in *E. coli,* and has helped to determine the circularity of the genome. Transduction and transformation have allowed the detection of close linkage between groups of markers. In general, very closely linked

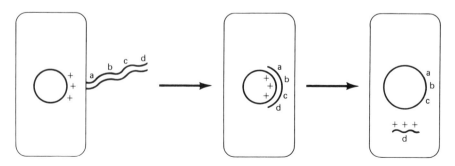

Figure 3. Recombination during transformation.

genes seldom if ever show recombination, whereas markers that lie very far apart almost invariably recombine during transfer from one cell to another.

VIRAL RECOMBINATION

When a host cell is infected simultaneously with two viral strains that differ genetically from each other, recombinant virions can be recovered after lysis of the host cell. In order to identify such recombinants, the infecting viruses must differ in at least two characteristics, and the host cell must be equally susceptible to infection with either virus. The frequency of recombination between any two markers varies widely and depends in part on the genetic distances between these markers. Studies of viral recombination using bacteriophage have been most useful in the development of molecular models to explain the process of recombination at the level of the participating DNA molecules.

During infection, the viral genome replicates, forming a pool of DNA molecules before encapsulation into new virions occurs. Recombination takes place between the viral genomes in this pool; each recombinant is capable of further replication before packaging. However, only a fraction of these DNA molecules may be used in the formation of complete viral particles; this fraction varies from 10 to 50% of the newly replicated DNA. Because of this, equal numbers of recombinant virions may not be found even if recombination is fully reciprocal. In addition, recombination between the molecules in a pool during replication allows multiple recombinational events to take place, further complicating analysis.

These factors, combined with the fact that large numbers of virions are formed, require that population genetics techniques be used to study recombination in viruses. Large numbers of progeny must be statistically analyzed, and the probability of a single recombinational event must be calculated. Studies of these types have allowed complete mapping of many viral genomes, including the bacteriophage λ and some of the T-even bacteriophages. The results of such studies with λ phage are compatible with a circular genome for this virus, as would be expected from its ability to be integrated into the bacterial genome during lysogeny. The T-even phages have been shown to have a linear genome, but there are repeated genes at both ends that allow circular permutations of the DNA of these viruses. Some eukaryotic viruses have also been at least partially mapped using recombinational studies.

Recombination in viruses requires the use of many bacterial gene products, since often the viral genome is too small to permit the encoding of all the proteins required for this process. Studies of viral recombination in host cells that are defective in one or another step in recombination show the influence of such host mutations. As in bacteria, several enzymes are required for successful completion of the recombinational event. These enzymes include nucleases, at least one of which is capable of introducing nicks into the DNA strands, and ligase, which is needed to join together the fragments of DNA into a complete genome. In animal viruses, the situation is less clear, but it seems probable that host genes will also be required in this case.

RECOMBINATION IN EUKARYOTES

In eukaryotic organisms, which have more than one chromosome, recombination takes place during meiosis in germ-line cells, and, very rarely, if at all, in somatic cells. Animals and plants may have many alleles for each gene; these alternate markers at a single locus on the chromosome allow the detection of recombination in these organisms. Genes can be shown to assort independently or as parts of linkage groups. If there is more than 50% recombination between two loci, the genes are not linked, but rather are independently assorted. This implies that the two loci are found on two separate chromosomes, although in practice some genes on the same chromosome may be widely enough separated, or may recombine so infrequently as to give such high percentages. Genes that show less than 50% recombination, on the other hand, are defined as linked, and are always found on a single chromosome. The analysis of the frequency of recombination between two or more markers defines the genetic distance between the genes. Such studies require the use of large samples which allows statistically valid comparisons, and/or the use of species with short generation times.

Two systems that have been very useful in the study of eukaryotic recombination are the fungi and dipteran flies, specifically the fungus *Neurospora* and the fruit fly, *Drosophila melanogaster.* These organisms combine both of the above-mentioned advantages. In each case, the organism has a short generation time, and large numbers of progeny can be produced and analyzed. In addition, the genetics of each has been extensively studied, and many markers are available for analysis. Homozygous strains may be mated to produce heterozygous progeny, and these can be crossed with each other or with the parental strains for complete analysis of linkage.

Fungi have a life cycle that consists of alternating haploid and diploid states (Figure 4). The diploid state is usually very short, and proliferation generally occurs in the haploid state. When a cell is fertilized, the two nuclei fuse, and replication takes place. In *Neurospora,* meiosis is confined to a structure, the ascus, that is narrow enough to hold the haploid nuclei in place, so that they remain in a linear arrangement that allows the products of each division to be clearly distinguished. The nuclei are then encased by rigid cell walls, and, in nature, the ascus will burst to release the haploid

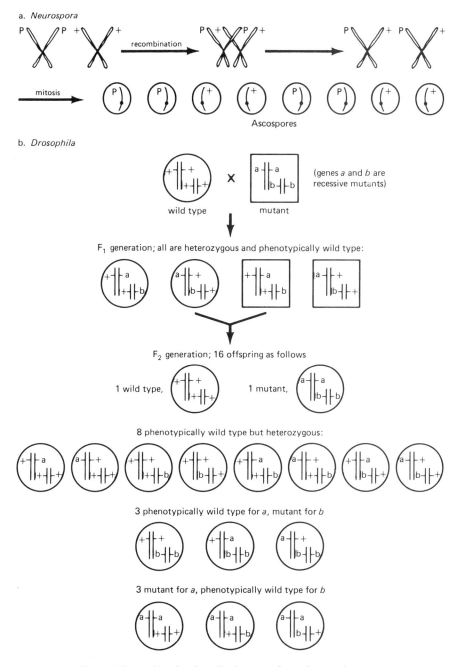

Figure 4. Recombinational studies in two eukaryotic organisms.

ascospores. If the asci are collected before they burst, and are carefully opened, the individual ascospores can be studied for the particular selected characteristics while retained in their original positions in the ascus. Recombinants can be easily scored in such a system. If the parental strains differ in two characteristics having the genotypes a^+b and ab^+, haploid products having only these two genotypes would result in the absence of recombination. In some percentage of the asci, however, the genotypes ab and a^+b^+ will be found in equal numbers, together with the parental types. This indicates that recombination has taken place between the two loci, and the number of recombinant ascospores gives a measure of the genetic distance between the loci.

Recombination can result also in unequal numbers of recombinant spores; this aberrant segregation is most often found with markers that are very closely linked, but it is a rare event. One-half of the ascospores within a single ascus will always be of the parental type; usually, the recombinant spores will be found in the ratio of $2:2$, but they are occasionally found in the aberrant ratios $1:3$ or $3:5$. This implies that recombination takes place in heteroduplex structures, and also supports the hypothesis, discussed for bacteria, that pairing of homologous chromosomes is not continuous along the whole genome, but rather that it occurs discontinuously in discrete segments of the genome.

Early studies in *Drosophila melanogaster* had established that genes could be assigned to one of four discrete linkage groups, which were shown to be associated with the four chromosomes of this organism. The genetics of this organism was established early, and many heterozygotes can be isolated for further study. Heterozygous individuals can be back-crossed to their homozygous parents, or can be mated to each other in order to study certain characteristics. In addition, the fruit fly has a specific property; no recombination takes place in males, but only in females. In combination with the fact that the generation time is very short, and the number of progeny is large, these factors have made this organism one of the best studied, and, as a consequence, it has been possible to obtain much useful information on recombination. The frequency of recombination between any two loci can be determined easily, and can be used as a measure of the genetic distance between these loci. Some recombinants derived from crosses in both *Neurospora* and *D. melanogaster* are shown in Figure 4.

Heterochromatic areas of the eukaryotic chromosome appear granular and complex under the microscope; these regions may be associated with changes in chromosome morphology due to breakage and repair processes. Recent evidence indicates that clusters of chromosomal breakpoints are closely associated with some heterochromatin, at least in *Drosophila* species. Banding patterns in these species are quite characteristic and can be easily identified in the giant chromosomes of the salivary gland cells. Inversions in gene order can be noted as changes in the banding characteristics of these chromosomes. Yoon and Richardson have found evidence to support the participation of heterochromatin in these inversions and in other chromosomal rearrangements, and have proposed a model to explain how such rearrangements are formed. This model is shown in Figure 5.

In man and other higher animals, the situation is more complex. Most early studies concentrated on statistical analysis of differences in allelic frequency in large populations. These studies have allowed the determination of many linkage groups in man, and in a few cases assignment to a specific chromosome could be made. This has been most noteworthy in the case of sex-linked genes, which can be assigned to the human X-chromosome. The frequency of recombination between such X-linked markers can be determined

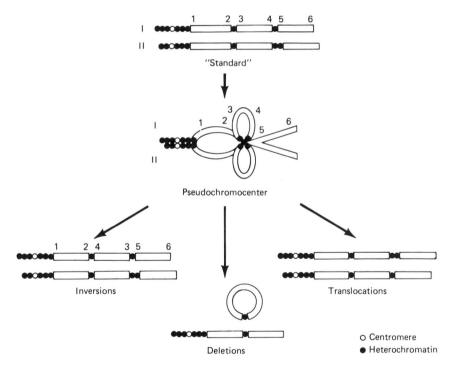

Figure 5. Pseudocentromere model of heterochromatin involvement in chromosomal rearrangements. The interstitial heterochromatic sites mark the location of breakpoints for inversions, deletions and translocations. Centromeric heterochromatin and the interstitial heterochromatin in the loci forming the pseudochromocenter are somewhat related, presumably having similar base sequences. Only two chromosomes (open and shaded) are used for this illustration, although the involvement of several chromosomes has been observed. (From J. S. Yoon and B. H. Richardson, 1978.)

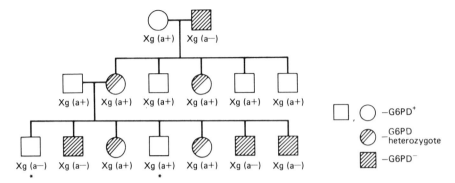

Figure 6. Recombination in human X-linked markers.

by the study of population genetics, and an estimate of the genetic distance between these genes can be calculated. Figure 6 shows a family in which two X-linked markers can be followed for three generations, and recombinants identified.

To some extent, recombinational studies in man depend on prior knowledge of linkage groups, some of which have been determined by population genetics and family studies. Other recombinations can be identified by studies of somatic cell hybrids. The studied products include enzymes that can be found in several allelic forms with different kinetic or electrophoretic properties. Many loci, however, can be identified in individuals because they give rise to disease states, but the biochemistry of these diseases has not been determined, and cell culture is not useful in further elucidating the genetic relationships.

A method that may be very useful in the next few years is the use of in situ hybridization. If an appropriate mRNA can be highly purified, it can be annealed to denatured chromosomes fixed on a slide. In the absence of contaminants, the location of the gene for this mRNA can be determined. At present, it is often a problem to purify the RNA to a high-enough degree, since very low levels of contamination with a rRNA, for example, will generate extra silver grains when the slide is coated with emulsion for autoradiography. However, it has recently been reported that histone genes may be localized by a statistical analysis of such slides, and perhaps various linkage groups can be located on their specific chromosomes using such a technique.

CYTOLOGICAL EFFECTS OF RECOMBINATION

The pachytene stage of the cell cycle follows DNA replication (see Section 12), and recombination appears to take place during this stage. Synaptinemal complexes can be microscopically identified at this point, and appear to be correlated with the process of recombination. Later, in the diplotene stage, chiasma form, which represent the physical exchange that has taken place during recombination. However, chiasma do not mark the site of a specific recombinational event, nor is it probable that even the physical location of the synaptinemal complex is of necessity directly correlated with the actual locus of recombination. These complexes, under the electron microscope, have the appearance of highly organized, ribbonlike tripartite structures that lie between paired homologous chromosomes at certain stages during meiosis. The structure is seen most completely during pachytene, although some elements of the structure can be seen earlier. Each pair of homologues normally has only a single synaptinemal complex associated with it. These complexes contain both protein and DNA; the relative roles of each in the function of the structures has not been determined. It is clear, however, that they are connected with recombination, and are indeed required for this process. Whether they are also sufficient for recombination is yet to be determined; they may indeed be merely a physical indication that the process has occurred.

Apparently, protein synthesis during the zygotene stage of meiosis is required for the formation of both synaptinemal complexes and chiasmata. DNA replication takes place prior to zygotene, during which stage the homologous chromosomes begin to pair. In addition to the requirement for protein synthesis, low-level DNA synthesis must also take place before formation of the complexes. This does not imply that replication must take place; indeed, the levels of synthesis required are more compatible with some type of repair replication. If it is assumed that recombination takes place during formation of the complexes, it is most probable that the repair of breaks induced in the DNA chain during recombination by the concerted action of ligases and polymerases is sufficient to account for this DNA synthesis.

MOLECULAR MODELS OF RECOMBINATION

In general, the molecular models that have been proposed for recombination fall into two general categories, one of which is essentially of historical interest only. This model, known as copy choice, assumes that recombination takes place during replication, when the enzyme that has been catalyzing the synthesis of one strand of the DNA, switches to copying the complementary strand. This model cannot be easily reconciled with information available from any system, or with the most current models of the mechanism of action of DNA polymerases. These enzymes appear to bind relatively closely with the strand being copied during replication, and to proceed until they reach a new replication fork. In addition, such a mechanism would give rise to hybrid chromosomes that would segregate into one parental and one recombinant genome, a situation not found *in vivo*.

The other general class of model is known as breakage and repair mechanisms. This model requires the introduction of nicks into the strands of DNA. This process may take place either during or after replication, an arrangement consistent with the evidence found in prokaryotes. Integration of plasmids, lysogeny, and recombination following transduction are not associated with replication. In addition, breakage and repair mechanisms require the action of nucleases and ligases, which are known to be essential components of prokaryotic recombination but would not be needed in a copy choice model. Models of this type account satisfactorily for all the evidence available from studies with bacteria, viruses, and eukaryotic organisms, although some aberrant segregations of fungal recombinants could be explained by either breakage and repair or copy choice models. However, the pattern of segregation of heteroduplex molecules formed during recombination is compatible only with the breakage and repair models.

Heteroduplex molecules are those in which the two strands of a duplex DNA molecule are not identical. Each strand, on replication, should give rise to two daughter chromosomes with identical sister chromatids. However, heteroduplexes have occasionally been found in viruses and, even more rarely, in haploid fungi. It is generally assumed that these molecules represent failures of the normal control mechanisms. Generally, mismatched regions of two sister chromatids would undergo repair if they did not segregate into two new separate chromosomes. Rarely, repair may not be complete in fungi, or, in viruses, packaging of the DNA into the virion may take place before

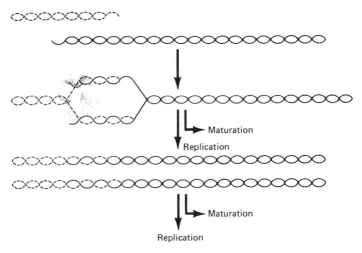

Figure 7. Breakage and repair model.

all the genomes have been repaired or before replication of some has taken place.

A general breakage and repair mechanism is shown in Figure 7. Some specific models have also been proposed, which generally assume that replication takes place before recombination. Some of them presume the participation of a polymerase in the repair of heteroduplexes formed during recombination (Figure 8), which appears likely, at least in prokaryotes where more informa-

a′ b′ c′ ──nuclease──► a′ c′ ──polymerase/ligase──► a′ b c′
─────   ── ──   ─────
a b c   a b c   a b c

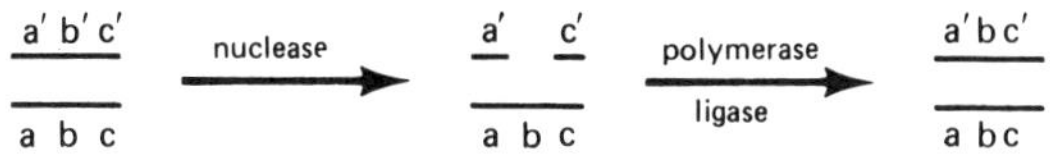

Figure 8. Correction of heteroduplex for one gene.

tion is available. The repair of heteroduplex formation may involve correction of the heteroduplex in the region of a single gene (Figure 8), or extensive repair that covers many genes (Figure 9). In both these cases, recombination requires the participation of nucleases, ligase, and a polymerase. It is probable that the process will be found to be similar in eukaryotic organisms, but not enough information is available at present to determine is this will be the case.

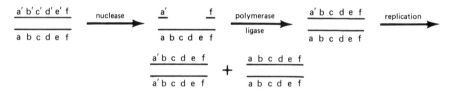

Figure 9. Extensive heteroduplex repair. The result after replication is one duplex recombinant for the internal markers, and the other duplex identical to the normal allele-bearing strand of the original heteroduplex.

BIBLIOGRAPHY

Barbour, S. D., and Clark, A. J. 1970. *Proc. Natl. Acad. Sci. U.S.A.* 65:955.
Clark, A. J. 1971. *Annu. Rev. Microbiol.* 25:437.
Wright, M., Button, G., and Hurwitz, J. 1971. *J. Biol. Chem.* 246:6543.
Sobel, H. M. 1972. *Proc. Natl. Acad. Sci. U.S.A.* 69:2483.
Daniell, E., Roberts, R., and Abelson, J. 1972. *J. Mol. Biol.* 69:1.
Goldmark, P. J., and Linn, S. 1972. *J. Biol. Chem.* 247:1849.
Clark, A. J. 1973. *Annu. Rev. Genet.* 7:67.
Rodding, C. M. 1973. *Annu. Rev. Genet.* 7:113.
Stadler, D. R. 1973. *Annu. Rev. Genet.* 7:87.
Monk, M., Kinross, J., and Town, C. 1973. *I. J. Bacteriol.* 114:1014.

Syvanen, M. 1974. *Proc. Natl. Acad. Sci.* 71:2496.

Skalka, A., Weissbach, A., and Barth, P. 1974. *Science* 18:1218.

Lee, M., and Miller, R. C., Jr. 1974. *J. Virol.* 14:1040.

Kerr, C., and Sadowski, P. D. 1975. *Virology* 65:281.

Broker, T. R., and Doerman, A. H. 1975. *Annu. Rev. Genet.* 9:213.

Miller, R. C., Jr. Lee, M. Seraba, D. A. and Paetkau, V. 1976. *J. Mol. Biol.* 101:223.

Sadowski, P. D., and Vetter, D. 1916. *Proc. Natl. Acad. Sci. U.S.A.* 73:692.

Takahashi, S. 1977. *Mol. Gen. Genet.* 150:43.

McGavin, S. 1977. *Heredity* 39:15.

Vlachopoulou, P. J., and Sadowski, P. D. 1977. *Virology* 78:192, 203.

Yoon, Y. S., and Richardson, R. H. 1978. *Genetics* 88:305.

Smith, C. A., and Hanawalt, P. C. 1978. *Proc. Natl. Acad. Sci.* 75:2598.

7.7. Mutation and Repair of DNA

MUTATION: DEFINITION AND CAUSATIVE AGENTS

Mutation may be defined as an alteration in one or more base pairs in a DNA molecule that results in a measurable, hereditary change in a gene as reflected in the gene product. Many mutations are corrected prior to replication by repair of the lesion, and thus do not alter the genotype of an organism. Other mutations are not detected, nor do they result in any measurable change in any gene product because they alter a codon in a manner that does not result in a change in the coding characteristics of the DNA. This is due to the degeneracy of the genetic code (see Section 10), whereby more than one codon can result in the incorporation of the same amino acid into a growing peptide. These alterations, together with alterations in DNA that do not seem to be functional, in that they appear not to be transcribed, will not be discussed further.

Other silent mutations result because they code for the incorporation of similar amino acids and therefore do not alter the function of the protein. Still others may introduce changes in amino acid sequence in regions of the protein that are not essential for function. These mutations, however, can be detected by analysis of the protein, or by DNA or RNA sequencing. In general, sequencing of nucleic acids is not a practical method of screening for mutations, since relatively little information on normal sequences is available. Screening of proteins for altered electrophoretic or kinetic properties is more practical.

Detectable mutations can be deleterious, neutral, or helpful. The largest class is the first, partly because deleterious mutations may often be discovered owing to a diseased state they introduce into an organism. Neutral mutations, on the other hand, may be discovered only by relatively sophisticated analysis of proteins from a large population, since they do not manifest themselves phenotypically. Few helpful mutations have been found, perhaps because of the selection that operated throughout evolution to restrict the gene pool of an organism to those genes that are most efficient under given growth conditions. Some deleterious mutations have also been retained because of selection; generally, these genes are of some aid to the organism in the heterozygous state, although they may be lethal in homozygotes. An example is

843

the gene for sickle cell anemia. Heterozygous children are protected against a particular form of malaria, whereas children who are homozygous for the normal allele of hemoglobin succumb easily to the malaria, and those homozygous for sickle cell anemia usually die young because of the altered properties of the hemoglobin. In general, the abnormal hemoglobins, of which there are many, tend to be less efficient than normal, although some are neutral under normal physiological conditions. No alterations in hemoglobin have been identified that increase the efficiency of oxygen transport.

There are basically two types of mutations: point mutations and frame shift mutations. The first class, the point mutations, can be further subdivided into transitions and transversions. These mutations involve a change in a single base within a gene; transitions refer to changes from purine to purine, or pyrimidine to pyrimidine, whereas transversions involve the substitution of a purine for a pyrimidine or vice versa. Frame shift mutations are caused by the addition or deletion of several bases (not a multiple of three) which alter the coding characteristics of a series of codons within a gene. These mutations will be discussed in further detail below. The causes of many mutations can be determined; others appear to be the spontaneous result of a change in the tautomeric form of a base, from the common form to one with altered base-pairing properties.

The agents that can introduce mutations into a DNA molecule include both physical and chemical agents. Physical agents such as ionizing radiation or ultraviolet (UV) light may cause breakage of the DNA chain, removal of one or more bases, crosslinkage (either within a single strand or between strands), and, to some extent, alterations due to the generation of free radicals, which then interact with the DNA. Some chemical agents function by similar mechanisms, whereas others directly modify the bases, or intercalate between the chains in such a way as to prevent local unwinding of a duplex molecule. These last may prevent either replication or transcription, or may cause the introduction of frame shift mutations. Many compounds act as chemical mutagens; in general, these molecules bind to the DNA in some fashion, or interact with the bases or with the phosphodiester backbone of the molecule.

Breakage of the DNA molecule may have several effects. If the breakage is extensive and cannot be repaired by the appropriate enzymes, the cell will be unable to replicate and will probably die if it is a bacterium or a germ-line cell in eukaryotes. Less extensive damage may be repaired prior to replication. In this case, the effects on the cell will be more complex. If the breakage involves a single strand, the other strand can serve as a template for repair, and no change could result. However, if there has already been replication, a segment of the DNA either may not be copied, introducing a frame shift mutation, or may not be copied accurately, resulting in one or more point mutations. Double strand breaks, on the other hand, require more extensive repair, and may indeed result in either deletion of the segment, or in complete inactivation of the DNA molecule.

POINT MUTATIONS

Most point mutations result either from random tautomeric shifts in bases, or from the action of a chemical mutagen. A general scheme for the introduction of a point mutation is shown in Figure 1. For some reason, more point mutations appear to be transitions than transversions, although theoretically both should occur at about the same frequency. The mechanisms whereby transitions arise are more clearly understood than those involved in the formation of transversions. These last would appear to require the removal of a base and its replacement by another base that cannot form stable hydrogen bonds with the corresponding base on the other strand. This could occur when the two strands are separated, as for example by local unwinding during replication or transcription, but it appears unlikely that it would take place when the DNA molecule is held together by hydrogen bonds.

One agent whose mode of action is reasonably well understood is nitrous acid. This compound, which forms on exposure of nitrates to low pH, can deaminate the bases G, C, or A, producing respectively xanthine, uracil, or hypoxanthine. The first change will not generally result in mutation, since the hydrogen-binding characteristics of xanthine are the same as those of guanine. Formation of uracil or hypoxanthine, on the other hand, will lead to mutations, since these compounds base-pair differently from the original. Naturally, if the incorrect base is identified and substituted by repair prior to replication, no mutation will be found. The actual fixation of such a mutation will require one cycle of replication. If U is substituted for C, on replication one daughter cell will receive a DNA molecule containing a U–A pair, while the other will have the correct C–G pair. The descendants of the first will all the carry the mutation, while the cells derived from the normal complement will all be wild type. Thus, two populations of cells will be found, which can be separated if the resulting mutation causes a change in growth requirements of the newly mutated cells.

Another chemical agent, bromo-deoxyuracil (BUdr), also causes the formation of point mutations. This compound is an analogue of cytosine, and is incorporated into the DNA in place of this pyrimidine. BUdr can then base-pair as either a C or a U, depending on the tautomeric form, leading to mutations in those cases where it hydrogen-bonds to an A during replication. Alkylating agents also introduce point mutations, often causing the change from a G–C pair to an A–T pair. In polar solvents, alkylating agents form

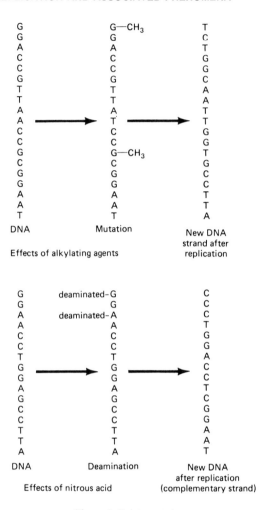

Figure 1. Point mutations.

carbonium ions which react very readily with nucleophilic groups such as the phosphate groups of the DNA backbone, or the ring nitrogen at position number 7 of the guanine base. The reaction consists of the addition of an alkyl group to this position, which changes the charge distribution of the base, allowing the incorrect base pairing.

In general, physical agents may play a role in the formation of point mutations, but they will more often result in mechanical breakage of the DNA chain. The mechanism for introduction of point mutations after damage with physical agents involves a copy error during the repair of the lesions involved. Repair of point mutations requires the excision of the incorrect base, and

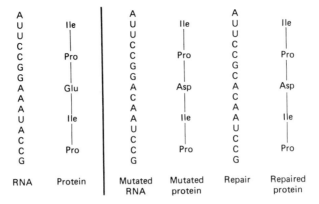

Figure 2. Repair of point mutations.

must take place prior to replication. The altered base must be recognized as incorrect, and the appropriate enzyme must then bind to the site of the lesion. A nick must be introduced close to this lesion; during this process, it is possible that the correct base may be excised and the incorrect base retained so that the mutation becomes fixed. This is thought to be possible because the repair enzymes may recognize the mismatching, rather than the incorrect base. Excision of the incorrect base must be followed by polymerase

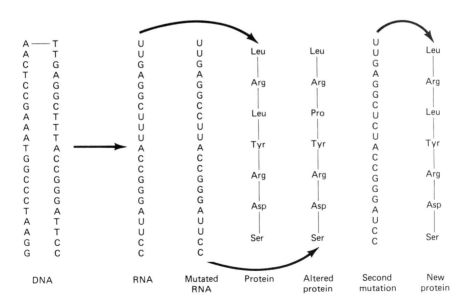

Figure 3. Phenotypic "repair."

activity to replace the base, and ligase activity to reconnect the segments of the DNA strand. This process may actually involve replacement of several bases, not just the mismatched one. A general scheme to illustrate this process is shown in Figure 2.

There may also be what appears phenotypically to be repair, even when the original lesion is retained. This involves the introduction of a second point mutation at a point close to but not identical with the site of the first point mutation (Figure 3). This situation can occur when the original mutation introduced an amino acid into the protein that caused a change in the tertiary structure of the peptide chain, thereby decreasing the efficiency of the protein function. The second mutation at some other site may restore the original folding of the peptide chain so as to allow tertiary structure similar or identical to the original, thus restoring function. Genotypic reversion, on the other hand, requires the precise repair of the mismatched base. This occurs with some low frequency, which may be characteristic of a particular mutation, and which may be altered by specific mutagenic agents.

FRAME SHIFT MUTATIONS

Some mutations result in a misreading of the codons due to the addition or deletion of bases in a gene. If three bases are added or deleted, the result will be a protein with one extra or one less amino acid than normal, and this is a special class of mutations that are not generally considered frame shifts. Addition or deletion of one, two, or some multiple of two, bases results in true frame shifts. The triplet codon is disrupted in this case, and incorrect reading of the following codons occurs (Figure 4). If this occurs at the beginning or in the middle of a gene, the result is often a completely nonfunctional peptide. If it occurs near the end of the gene, the protein will be less severely affected, and may be able to carry out its function in a manner close to normal.

Frame shift mutations can be introduced by several mechanisms. The introduction of free radicals into a solution containing DNA may cause the loss of a base, followed by breakage of the phosphodiester backbone in a limited region, deletion of the base, and repair of the chain so that it contains one (or more) base(s) less than the original molecule. In other cases, there may be mispairing of the two strands of a DNA molecule which contains homologous regions lying close to one another. This would lead to a looping out of a section of one chromosome; this region might then be more susceptible to nuclease activity and be deleted. Alternatively, the looped-out region could be duplicated by repair, leading to an addition to the genome.

Intercalating agents can introduce frame shift mutations by promoting the addition of single nucleotides. These agents, usually dyes, are planar,

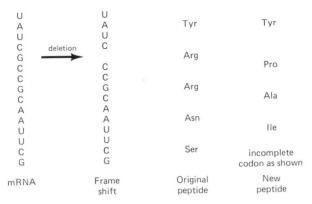

Figure 4. Frame shift mutations.

aromatic compounds that fit into the double helix, lying parallel to the bases, between two adjacent base pairs. On replication, an extra base can be added in the region of the dye, leading to a frame shift mutation. Among the best known intercalating agents are the acridine dyes (Figure 5).

Phenotypically, some of the effects of frame shift mutations can be reversed by further deletions or additions. If one base has been removed from a mRNA, for example, addition of a base at some point close to the original deletion may allow synthesis of a functional protein. Alternatively, deletion of two other bases close to the original mutation could lead to a protein with one less amino acid than normal, but perhaps capable of the normal function of the protein. It is, however, extremely difficult to introduce true genotypic reversion in frame shift mutations. This would require that the originally deleted base be reinserted, or that the added base itself be deleted. In general, frame shift mutations cause very severe effects on cells, since most resultant proteins are completely nonfunctional. This alteration can lead to cell death, or, at the least, to problems with cell growth. Only if the addition or deletion takes place near the end of a molecule is it at all likely that the protein may retain some function.

GENERAL MECHANISMS OF REPAIR

Repair processes require the coordinated function of several proteins, some of which were described earlier (see Section 6). The first step in repair involves nucleases, which generally nick the DNA strand in the region of the mutation. These nucleases may be the same as those required for recombination, or they may be independent nucleases. In the case of repair of ultraviolet lesions (UV damage) in *E. coli,* the nuclease used appears to be one of those associated

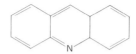

Figure 5. Structure of the acridines.

with DNA polymerase I. This same enzyme participates as a polymerase in the next steps of repair, involving the synthesis of oligomers to fill in the gaps introduced to remove the lesion (see below). After the strands are nicked, several bases may be removed by exonuclease activity to introduce the gap that will be filled by polymerase activity; it is probable that repair generally involves a short segment of the DNA rather than the single affected nucleotide.

All the known DNA polymerases of *E. coli* are capable of repair of lesions in the genome (see Chapter 6.8). Each of them may participate in the repair of a specific type of lesion. The only definite information available at present concerns the role of DNA polymerase I in the correction of the pyrimidine dimers introduced into *E. coli* DNA by UV light. It has been hypothesized, although not proved yet, that this same enzyme is involved in editing of mistakes introduced during replication; such a role for DNA polymerase II has also been suggested. Eukaryotic polymerases do not appear to carry associated nuclease activity but may be involved in gap filling much as the prokaryotic enzymes are.

Mutants incapable of repair have been described in many prokaryotic systems, and some of them have been useful in determining enzymes that are involved in repair. However, several different enzymes of the same type may be able to substitute for one another in such mutants, so that complete inhibition is not necessarily seen. The complete absence of repair will be lethal for an organism, especially because all organisms are subject to exposure to many mutagenic agents. These agents will introduce a certain number of mutations into the DNA, which will be transcribed to give rise to RNA molecules that are altered. Alterations in rRNA or tRNA could be immediately lethal; those found in mRNA will direct the synthesis of altered proteins. Since most such abnormal proteins will function less efficiently than the normal allelic form, the cell will grow less efficiently or may die. In some cases, such altered proteins may interfere with replication or transcription; it is also possible that such mutations may eventually result in neoplastic changes in eukaryotic organisms.

In general, most mutagenic agents studied have also been shown to be carcinogenic, and all carcinogens that have been studied result in mutations when tested in appropriate systems. One test that has been useful in screening compounds to test for mutagens is the "Ames" test, developed by Bruce

Ames. This test measures the extent of mutagenicity of such compounds in a bacterial strain; those found to be mutagens can then be tested in animals, and are often confirmed to be carcinogens. By the use of such tests, it has been found that many chemicals that have been used as food additives are mutagenic in bacteria and carcinogenic in rodents. A classical example is the use of nitrates to preserve the flavor and color of hot dogs and sausage; these compounds, as discussed above, can react with acids present in the intestinal tract to form nitrous acid, which is a potent mutagen, as well as a carcinogen.

ULTRAVIOLET LIGHT DAMAGE TO CELLS

Cells exposed to UV light have been shown to contain specific lesions in their nucleic acids. These lesions have been identified as pyrimidine dimers; a pair of pyrimidines in relatively close proximity to each other within the DNA molecule become crosslinked. These pyrimidines may either lie on the same strand (intrastrand) or on the opposite strands of the same double helix (interstrand). The replication of DNA and the transcription of RNA are both inhibited by the presence of such crosslinked dimers. These crosslinks are responsible for pertubations of the tertiary structure of the nucleic acid because they introduce minute bulges in the chains. In addition, the sequence containing such dimers cannot be copied by the polymerase, so that replication in the absence of repair would result in deletions in the DNA.

The most common dimer formed is T–T, although T–C and C–C dimers may also result. Both prokaryotic and eukaryotic cells can be affected by UV light, resulting in both cases in the formation of pyrimidine dimers. Mechanisms for the repair of such lesions have been described in all normal cells, but mutants incapable of such repair are found in bacteria, viruses, and man. Some of these mutants will be described in more detail below. In general, bacterial and viral mutants accumulate fragments, whereas the human mutant is more susceptible to skin cancers.

Ultraviolet light can also cause the formation of free radicals that can react with pyrimidine bases to cause the opening of the 5,6 double bond of the base (Figure 5). These bases can no longer base-pair, and may even cause breakage of the phosphodiester backbone. The final result will be inactivated DNA, or complete breakage of the molecule followed by cell death. This mechanism is less likely to occur in whole cells, but will account for much UV damage to DNA *in vitro*. The final result of most UV damage is the introduction of point mutations, caused by incorrect repair of part of the lesion introduced with pyrimidine dimers. Correction of T–T dimers, as noted above, involves the introduction of a gap that can cover 10 to 20 nucleotides; during filling of this gap, an error in copying may occur. This error might not be repaired and might result in the change from one base pair to another after replication. The possibility of such an occurrence is low, but there is some chance that it will happen.

REPAIR OF UV LESIONS IN BACTERIAL DNA

Bacteria contain two mechanisms for the repair of lesions introduced into the cell by the formation of pyrimidine dimers under the influence of UV light. The first is called photoreactivation, and it requires exposure to visible light for the activation of the specific enzyme(s) required. Binding of the enzyme to the lesion occurs in the dark; this binding is specific for UV-irradiated DNA. It will stabilize the lesion, preventing nonspecific degradation of the DNA. On exposure to the light, which must be in the visible range of the spectrum, the dimer is removed by the activated enzyme(s), but the mechanism whereby this occurs is not known. Not all bacteria possess such a photoreactivation system.

In contrast, the dark repair mechanism, which does not require visible light, has been described in detail. It has been established that the enzyme that participates in this mechanism is E. coli is DNA polymerase I; similar mechanisms have been described in other bacterial systems. The first step in the process involves the recognition of the structural distortion introduced by the dimer, followed by binding of the enzyme to this region. A nick is then introduced into the DNA by the endonuclease associated with the polymerase, and associated exonuclease activity removes about 20 bases, including bases on either side of the dimer. The original, undergraded DNA strand is then copied by the DNA polymerase I, and the repair is completed by ligase which joins the newly replicated oligomer to the original DNA. This process is shown in Figure 6.

Other mutations that prevent dark repair are also known, however, indicating that the above scheme may be only partially true. These mutations are known as *uvr*, and are located in widely separated areas of the genome. The gene products that are involved in *uvr* genes are not known. In addition, some *rec⁻* mutants, which are unable to undergo recombination, also show a sensitivity to UV light. These mutants show an exagerrated breakdown of the genome following exposure to UV light; repair of damage is also delayed in these cells. The mutants may prevent the action of DNA polymerase I by introducing gaps that are too long to be effectively repaired by this enzyme. Nucleases other than those associated with the polymerase might participate in the dark repair, and some of these mutants may code for altered forms of these enzymes. Ligase deficiency, too, will prevent dark repair, since this enzyme is required to connect the polymerase product to the original strand of the DNA.

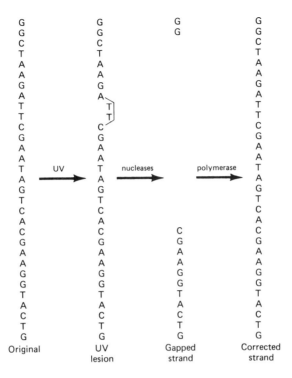

Figure 6. Dark repair of UV lesions in bacteria.

REPAIR OF UV DAMAGE IN HUMAN CELLS

In man, as in all eukaryotic systems that have been described to date, the polymerases do not have any associated nuclease activity. Repair of UV lesions thus requires separate nucleases and the polymerase which has not been specifically identified. The mechanism of action appears to be similar to that described in the bacteria. A nick is introduced in the vicinity of the lesion by an endonuclease, and a segment of the sequence around the lesion is removed by exonuclease activity. Polymerase and ligase activities are required to complete the repair. Since sunlight contains UV light, which may introduce lesions into the surfaces of the skin that are exposed, such a mechanism is important in epidermal tissue. Other tissues in the human body are reasonably well protected from contact with UV light under normal circumstances.

A recessive gene that can be identified in a small portion of the human population prevents this repair process. Individuals who receive one dose of the gene from each of their parents, and are therefore homozygous for the abnormal gene, suffer from a disease known as Xeroderma pigmentosum. These people show extreme sensitivity to sunlight, with visible skin lesions formed after very short periods of exposure. People with this disease show a high incidence of skin cancers, presumably due to the accumulation of mutations at a high rate. Studies have established that the gene defect involves a nuclease, preventing the excision and therefore the subsequent repair of the pyrimidine dimers.

BIBLIOGRAPHY

Drake, J. W. 1970. *The Molecular Basis of Mutation.* Holden-Day, San Francisco.
Cleaver, J. E., and Trosko, J. E. 1970. *Photochem. Photobiol.* 11:547.
Hollaender, A., ed. 1971. *Chemical Mutagens.* Plenum Press, New York.
Loprieno, N. 1971. *Scientia* 106:397.
Davies, J., and Komura, M. 1972. *Annu. Rev. Genet.* 6:203.
Cox, E. C. 1972. *Nature New Biol.* 239:133.
Drake, J. W. 1973. *Genetics Suppl.* 73:45.
Kondo, S. 1973. *Genetics Suppl.* 73:45.
Leigh, E. G., Jr. 1973. *Genetics Suppl.* 73:1.
Pietrzykowska, I. 1974. *Mutat. Res.* 25:273.
Van Sluis, C. A., Mattern, I. E., and Paterson, M. C., 1974. *Mutat. Res.* 25:273.
Witkin, E. M., and Parisi, E. C. 1974. *Mutat. Res.* 25:407.
Drake, J. W. 1974. *Symp. Soc. Gen. Microbiol.* 24:41.
Chaganti, R. S. K., Schonberg, S., and German, J. 1974. *Proc. Natl. Acad. Sci. U.S.A.* 71:4508.
Hand, R., and German, J. 1975. *Proc. Natl. Acad. Sci. U.S.A.* 72:758–62.
Mount, D. W., and Kosel, C. 1975. *Mol. Gen Genet.* 136:95.
San, R. H. C., and Stich, H. F. 1975. *Int. J. Cancer* 16:284.
Nishioka, H. 1975. *Mutat. Res.* 31:185.
Pietrzykowska, I., Lewandowsky, K., and Shugar, D. 1975. *Mutat. Res.* 30:21.
Ronen, A., and Rahat, A. 1976. *Mutat. Res.* 34:21.
Presber, W., Schroeder, C., and Krueger, D. H. 1976. *J. Theor. Biol.* 59:353.
Hutchinson, F., and Stein, J. 1977. *Mol. Gen. Genet.* 152:29.
Rydberg, B. 1977. *Mol. Gen. Genet.* 152:19.
Hand, R., and German, J. 1977. *Hum. Genet.* 38:297.
Marguardt, H., Rufins, F., and Weisburger, J. H. 1977. *Science* 196:1000.
Doniger, J. 1978. *J. Mol. Biol.* 120:433.

Mutagen Screening Tests:

Ames, B. N., McCann, J., and Yamaski, E. 1973. *Mutat. Res.* 31:347.
Epstein, S. S. 1974. *Cancer Res.* 34:2425.
McCann, J., Choi, E., Yamaski, E., and Ames, B. N. 1975. *Proc. Natl. Acad. Sci.* 72:5135.
Cairns, J. 1975. *Nature* 255:197.
Sirover, M. A., and Loeb, L. A. 1976. *Science* 194:1434.

SECTION 8
BACTERIAL PLASMIDS

AKIRA KAJI, TATSUO YAMAMOTO, AND
LAZAR M. SCHWARTZ

8. Bacterial Plasmids

PLASMIDS

Plasmids are extrachromosomal DNA present in some bacterial and eukaryotic cells. They are (1) nonlethal in most cases; (2) nonessential for the growth of the cell; (3) able to replicate; (4) inheritable by progeny; and (5) transmissible in many cases. Most varieties are present in an autonomous form, as circular DNA. However, other forms are integrated within the chromosome of the host.

Classification

Bacterial plasmids comprise several varieties:

1. Fertility factor (F), a classical plasmid that promotes the development of cell surface sites determining the conjugative ability of the host. This plasmid is efficiently integrated into host chromosomes.
2. Bacteriocinogenic factors that induce the production by the host of an extracellular antibiotic protein; the protein is lethal to members of the same or related species.
3. Drug resistance factors (R), which confer resistance to certain drugs upon host cells.
4. Cryptic plasmids—plasmids with unknown function; their presence in the host does not become manifest unless they have incorporated a segment of the host genome.
5. Other plasmids—plasmids with known functions other than above. For example plasmids which confer pathogenic capacity to bacteria.

Other criteria separate plasmids into: (1) transmissible—plasmids carrying the genetic determinants for their own intercellular transfer through conjugation; and (2) nontransmissible—plasmids that lack genetic determinants for their own transfer (which can, however, be transferred in association with other transmissible factors).

A different classification refers to their mode of replication: (1) plasmids whose replication is relaxed—their replication is not under specific control but is restricted by the availability of precursors, energy, replicating enzymes, or space; and (2) plasmids whose replication is under stringent control—

their replication is specifically controlled and occurs in concert with the cell cycle of the host.

Defective or lysogenic phages may also exist as autonomous particles and functionally can be considered plasmids. Their replication is usually under stringent control. When the control becomes relaxed, lysogenic phages can cause lysis of the cell.

Pili

The transmissible plasmids, in general, specify a product necessary for their own replication, and a protein called pilin. The protein is stored in an intracellular pool from which it is assembled and incorporated in filamentous structures of the cell surface called pili. The assembly step of pili requires energy, and therefore it can be stopped by energy poisons.

There are many kinds of pili, each specified by a given plasmid. The classical pili are F pili and I pili, but recent studies revealed various other pili such as W, E, N, and P pili, and so on. F pili are specified by F plasmid, and I pili are specified by the plasmids that belong to the I-incompatibility group (e.g., Col Ib). R plasmids, as described later, have a specific DNA region called RTF (resistance transfer factor) that can specify the type of pilus. The pili genes of R plasmid are thus independent of the drug resistance genes. The pili serve as sites for adsorption of some phages, called male specific phages. Specificity exists between the type of pili and kind of phages that can be absorbed.

Plasmid Incompatibility

Two plasmids belonging to the same incompatibility group cannot coexist *stably* within the same bacterial cell. This relationship is called incompatibility. Although the mechanism of incompatibility is not understood, it has been proposed that two incompatible plasmids have identical cell membrane sites for attachment of the plasmid. This concept however, has been challenged recently. Another possibility is that the product specified by the plasmid genome may cause inhibition of the DNA synthesis by the incompatible plasmid. Even when two plasmids are incompatible, they can coexist transiently, but during cell multiplication one of the plasmids is lost.

On the basis of plasmid compatibility, at least 23 compatibility groups can be defined among sex factors of the enteric bacteria (see Table 1). It has been shown that, except for a few cases, plasmids from different compatibility groups are much less similar with regard to size and DNA sequence than plasmids of the same incompatibility group.

Table 1. Compatibility Groups of Sex Factors Transmissible to *E. coli.*

COMPATIBILITY		SEX PILI	REPRESENTATIVES
Overgroup F			
	FI	F	F42, R386, ColV2
	FII	F-like	R1, R100, R538-1, R136
	FIII	F-like	ColB-K98, MIP240
	FIV	F-like	R124
	FV	EDP208	Fo*lac*
		(F-like, but serologically unrelated to F)	
Overgroup I			
	Iα	I	R64, R144, ColIb-p9
	I2	I-like	TP114, MIP241
	Iγ	I-like	R621a
	Iδ	I-like	R821a
	Iζ	I-like	R805a
Other groups			
	B	B	R16
	C	C	R40a, R57b-1
	D	D	R711b, R778b
	H (two groups)	H	R27, R726-1, R478
	J	J	R391, R391-3b-1
	K	K	R387
	M	M	R446b, R930
	N	N	N3, R447b
	P (several groups)	P	RP4, R702
	T	E (or T)	Rts1, R401
	V	V	R753
	W	W	S-a, R388
	X	X	R6K

Entry Exclusion (Surface Exclusion)

Entry exclusion (eex) was considered a phenomenon preventing isogenic transfer of plasmids that is different from incompatibility. Entry exclusion is determined by a specific alteration of the cell surface, and is seen only between two cells containing the same plasmid. Thus, F$^+$ cells are poor recipients of F plasmid from other F$^+$ cells owing to surface exclusion, which is under the control of two genes involved in the transfer of F plasmid, *tra T,* and *tra S.* Entry exclusion is caused by a lack of stable cell–cell association. It had been suggested that entry exclusion may occur at the stage of cell aggregation, in which another gene involved in the transfer of F, *tra G,* participates.

FERTILITY FACTOR

Fertility (F) factor, also called sex factor, has a molecular weight of about 64×10^6 daltons (determined by electron microscopy), which represents about 2.6% of the *E. coli* genome mass. It contains active genes coding for cell surface elements called sex pili, which promote the transfer of genetic material from one bacterium to another by conjugation (mating). Cells harboring the F factor are called F^+, and those lacking it are called F^-. F^+ cells act either as donors or as recipients (under special conditions), whereas F^- cells can act only as recipients. F^- recipient cells are converted to donors (F^+ cells) by conjugation.

Forms of F Factor

In host cells the F factor may be present in three forms:

1. As an autonomous element, existing mostly in a covalently closed circular form. In some cases attachment of protein to the circular DNA results in a relaxation complex.
2. As an integrated element, existing in a form in which the circular structure has been opened, and the plasmid is incorporated in linear form within the bacterial chromosome. This form is stable and is called Hfr.
3. As a larger circular structure containing fragments of the host's genetic material. This form called F', originates from Hfr cells when fragments of the host chromosome remain attached to the plasmid after it is excised from the chromosome.

F Factor Transfer

Mating of F^+ with F^- cells results in the transfer of F factor. The recipient (F^-) cell then becomes an F^+ cell. As described later, F^+ cells become Hfr cells if the F plasmid is integrated into the host chromosome. In the mating between F^+ and F^- cells, concomitant transfer of the bacterial chromosome is extremely rare. On the other hand, mating of Hfr with F^- cells is attended by a high frequency of concurrent transfer of the host chromosome (Hfr stands for high frequency recombinant). In this process, splitting of the integrated plasmid takes place, and a portion of F genome enters the F^- cell first, followed by host chromosome (Figure 1). The other portion of the integrated F plasmid enters F^- cell at the end. Since bacterial conjugation is usually interrupted, it is rare that the recipient cell (F^- cell) becomes an Hfr or F^+ cell. The bacterial chromosome that entered the recipient has to be recombined with the recipient chromosome for production of a stable transconjugant having the genome of the donor chromosome.

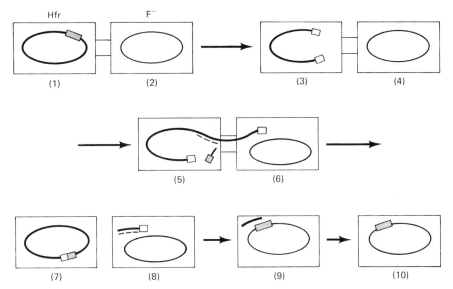

Figure 1. Schematic model of conjugation between Hfr and F⁻. (1) Hfr cell having F plasmid (☐) integrated into the chromosome. (2) F⁻ cell. (3) Splitting of integrated F plasmid. (4) F⁻ cell conjugated with Hfr. (5) Hfr cell synthesizing DNA and sending one strand of DNA with a portion of F plasmid at the tip into the F⁻ cell. The dotted line shows the newly synthesized strand of Hfr DNA with a piece of F on the tip. (6) F⁻ cell receiving a donor DNA having a portion of F plasmid at the tip. (7) After the breakage of conjugation, Hfr chromosome and integrated F plasmid remaining intact because a new strand is synthesized during the transfer. (8) F⁻ cell that has now received a portion of donor DNA and has synthesized a new strand of DNA complementary to this DNA. (9) Recipient cell (F⁻) that has just completed recombination of the donor DNA and excised its own DNA. (10) Recipient cell that has lost its own excised DNA. This is a stable transconjugant.

The production of F' is not dependent on the conjugation of an Hfr strain with F⁻. The F' is produced by a spontaneous excision of the F plasmid from the Hfr chromosome. During this excision, F plasmid often is excised with some of the host chromosome, and the resulting F plasmid is called F'.

During conjugation, the plasmid attaches to the cell membrane near a conjugation bridge. Cell pairing results in a formation of the conjugation bridge and triggers an extra initiation of replication, which then proceeds asymmetrically. One of the strands of the donor DNA goes into the recipient cell through the conjugation bridge; the other strand remains in the donor cell, and this strand is replicated. On the other hand, DNA synthesis of the recipient cell is necessary to convert the received single-stranded DNA into double-stranded DNA. The synthesis of plasmid DNA during transfer may be according to the rolling circle model, while vegetative replication probably occurs according to Cairn's model of concatenated DNA circles.

As described later, F factor may be repressed if an fi$^+$ (fertility inhibiting) R (drug resistance) plasmid is present in the same cell. The interference of transfer by fi$^+$ R factor is dependent on a repressor molecule, which suppresses the expression of the gene responsible for F pili production. If the R factor belongs to the fi$^-$ group, such an interference does not occur.

Integration of F Factor

Integration of the F factor within the bacterial chromosome may occur at least 16 different sites. The mechanism of integration involves a single reciprocal crossover between two DNA circles. Insertion sequences, (IS3, IS2, and γ-δ sequences) are present in F plasmid, and they play an important role in the integration of this plasmid into chromosome. The length of homology between the insertion sequence of F plasmid and the bacterial chromosome is much shorter than those between F′ and the chromosomes. Thus, F′, which has incorporated bacterial genes, integrates with a higher efficiency at the site of homology determined by those genes. Thus integration of F or F′ is dependent on the *rec A* gene (a gene indispensable for recombination of DNA, which is dependent on the homologous region of the DNA) product.

Lethal Zygosis

When an excess of Hfr cells is mixed with F$^-$ cells, up to 99% of the F$^-$ cells die within 1 to 2 hours. The physiological changes in the F$^-$ cells in such a case include defects in transport and membrane permeability. Only Hfr but not F$^+$ donors cause lethal zygosis. This is perhaps due to the fact that in an F$^+$ × F$^-$ mating, active disaggregation of conjugated cells takes place, disrupting the lethal cell contacts.

BACTERIOCINOGENIC FACTORS

Bacteriocinogenic factors are plasmids that induce the production of specific extracellular proteins acting as antibiotics on strains of the same or closely related species. Some of these plasmids exist as well-defined circular DNA molecules. In some bacteria, production of bacteriocin can be activated by ultraviolet irradiation or particular chemicals. Bacteriocins are produced by a large variety of bacteria and are named after the producer bacterial strain (Table 2). The best studied are the colicins, which were divided into 17 types based on their activity and on the specificity of their gene product. Frequently studied colicins are the following: Col E1, Col E2, Col E3, Col 1b, Col B2, Col V2. Colicinogenic factors are stable and may be isolated as covalently closed circular DNA monomers or complexed with protein

Table 2. Types of Bacteriocins and Producer Bacterial Species.

BACTERIOCIN	PRODUCER STRAIN
Colicins	E. coli, E. freundii, Paracolon, Shigella, Salmonella, Aerobacter
Alveicins	Hafnia
Caratovoricins	Erwinia
Arizonacins	Arizona
Cloacins	E. cloacae
Marcescins	S. marcescens
Pneumocins	K. pneumoniae
Aerocins	A. aerogenes
Pyocins	P. pyocyanea
Fluocins	P. fluorescens
Pesticins	P. pestis
Megacins	B. megaterium
Monocins	Listeria monocytogenes
Cerecins	B. cereus
Enterococcins	Streptococcus (enterococcus group)
Staphylococcins	Staphylococcus

as a relaxation complex. Although they may integrate within the bacterial chromosome, they rarely do so. In some species they may exist as dimers, or oligomers, especially in conditions of protein deprivation.

Colicinogenic factors exist in many copies per cell and replicate autonomously. In some E. coli strains, Col 1b acts as a sex factor, promoting the transfer of bacterial chromosome during conjugation. Colicinogenic factors are transferred through pili whose formation is specified by a region of the plasmid called transfer factor gene or TF. The pili specified by TF differ from the F pili and are called I pili. Col E1 and Col E2 lack the TF region, and their transfer requires the presence of a helper, in this case the F pili. Col V2 and Col V3 also lack the TF region and require as helper the presence of I pili specified either by Col 1b or by R plasmids. Col V2 is incompatible with the F factor and excludes autonomous F although it can stably exist in an Hfr host. The activity of colicins interferes primarily with DNA synthesis by either influencing energy requirements (Col E1), causing single strand nicks in DNA (Col E2), or removing terminal nucleotides from the 16S rRNA (ribosomal RNA) (Col E3).

R PLASMIDS

R plasmids are plasmids that confer resistance to antimicrobial agents such as antibiotics and synthetic chemotherapeutic drugs on host bacterial cells. Since the discovery of R plasmids in clinical isolates of Shigella in 1959, a wide variety of R plasmids have been reported, and now R plasmids seem to be ubiquitous in nature.

Genetic Information on R Plasmids

Drug resistances conferred by R plasmids are summarized in Table 3. Some R plasmids confer a single drug resistance, but usually R plasmids give multiple drug resistances. In addition, some R plasmids, isolated from Gram-negative bacteria, confer the following properties on their hosts: (1) phage restriction/modification (e.g., Eco R1 endonuclease or DNA methylase), (2) UV resistance, (3) Hfr, (4) lipopolysaccharide composition change, (5) altered cell growth, (6) colicinogeny (colicin production), (7) pathogenicity (entero-toxin production), (8) resistance to poisonous chemical agents (e.g., mercury, nickel, cobalt ions, and organomercurials), and (9) sensitivity to chemical agents (e.g., sodium dodecyl sulfate). Some R plasmids in Gram-positive cocci have been found to confer on host bacterial cells resistances to metal ions (e.g., mercury, cadmium, lead, bismuth, zinc, arsenite, and arsenate) and to dye (e.g., ethidium bromide). Thus, the presence of R plasmids permits bacterial cells to adapt to a wide variety of otherwise nonpermissive circumstances for bacterial cell growth.

Transfer of R Plasmids

In general, R plasmids are present in Enterobacteriaceae, *Vibrio, Pseudomonas, Bordetella, Haemophilus, Aeromonas, Neisseria* (Gram-negative), staphy-

Table 3. Drug Resistances Conferred by R. Plasmids.

R PLASMIDS	ANTIMICROBIAL DRUGS
in Gram-positive cocci	β-Lactam antibiotics (penicillins)
	Aminoglycoside antibiotics (e.g., kanamycin and streptomycin)
	Macrolide antibiotics (e.g., erythromycin and spiramycin)
	Lincosamide antibiotics (e.g., lincomycin)
	Streptogramin B-type antibiotics (e.g., vernamycin B)
	Tetracycline
	Chloramphenicol, sulfonamide.
	Fusidic acid
in Gram-negative bacteria	β-Lactam antibiotics (penicillins and cephalosporins)
	Aminoglycoside antibiotics (e.g., kanamycin, streptomycin, and gentamicin)
	Tetracycline
	Chloramphenicol
	Sulfonamide
	Trimethoprim

lococci, and streptococci (Gram-positive). The majority of conjugative R plasmids in Gram-negative organisms code for either one of two types of conjugative pili: F-like pili that can absorb F-specific phages, and I-like pili that can absorb I-specific phages. R plasmids specifying F-like pili and I-like pili are called F-like R plasmid and I-like R plasmid, respectively. Production of R pili is, in many cases, under control of the R plasmid itself specifying a repressor. Some R plasmids also repress production of F-pili (fertility inhibition+, fi+), but others do not (fi−).

In general, the mechanism of transfer of R factor is thought to be similar to that of F factor as discussed in the preceding section.

Replication and Molecular Nature of R Plasmid

In *Escherichia coli,* the class of R plasmids with relatively small molecular weight (less than 30×10^6 daltons) are present in multiple copies (relaxed replication). Certain R plasmids in this class resemble Col E1 plasmid in its mode of replication. Other R plasmids with larger molecular weight usually exist at one or two copies per chromosome (stringent replication).

Replication of some R plasmids in *E. coli* and in *Staphylococcus aureus* seems to proceed essentially according to Cairn's model (Figure 2). The presence of catenated molecules at the maturation step has been confirmed in both bacteria. In *E. coli,* at least one copy of R plasmid per chromosome equivalent seems complexed with the folded chromosome, and probably undergoes cosegregation with the chromosome into daughter cells upon cell division.

Conjugative R plasmids belonging to the FII-incompatibility group (F-like R plasmids such as R100, R6, and R1) consist of two separate segments: the RTF (resistance transfer factor) which carries genes for conjugative transfer, and the r-determinant (drug resistance determinant) which carries genes

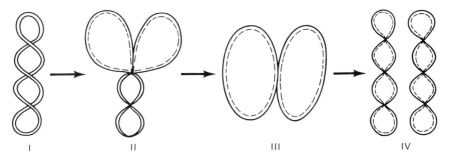

Figure 2. Replication of a typical drug resistance factor. I. Covalently closed circular (ccc) DNA. II, III. Concatenated intermediate in replication. IV. Newly formed ccc DNA.

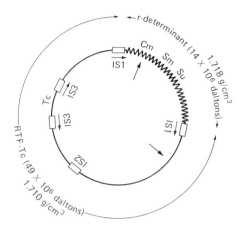

Figure 3. Structure of the composite R plasmid, R100. The symbol □ represents the insertion sequence, and arrows beside □ show the orientation of insertion. The other arrows indicate the site of replication origin. The composite form of R100 has a molecular weight of 63 × 10^6 daltons and a buoyant density of 1.712 g/cm^3.

for drug resistance. Each unit contains an independent origin of replication. Such R plasmids are called composite R plasmids. At the two junctions of the RTF and r-determinant, there occur insertion sequences (IS) in direct orientation, which play an important role in recombination events between RTF and r-determinant (Figure 3). RTF units of the composite, F-like R plasmids are similar to F plasmid in molecular structure. The DNA sequence of up to 90% of the region of F plasmid that contains transfer cistrons is present in the RTF of R factors (at least ten cistrons of F plasmid that are involved in transfer are substitutable with those of the R plasmid). The DNA sequence of r-determinant, however, is unique to R plasmid and not at all homologous with F plasmid.

The R plasmids existing in composite form in *E. coli* can dissociate into the RTF unit and the r-determinant unit in *Proteus mirabilis* (Figure 4a). Prolonged incubation of R$^+$ *Proteus mirabilis* in the presence of antibiotics, which can be inactivated by an enzyme coded by a gene on the r-determinant, results in amplification of the r-determinant unit to form poly-r-determinant R plasmid and multimeric r-determinant ("transition") (Figure 4b). The proportion of the R plasmids relative to the chromosome increases up to tenfold during this process. When the cells in the transition state are grown in a drug-free medium, the transitioned DNA molecules undergo dissociation of the r-determinant unit, and finally go back to the nontransitioned state (the composite form containing a single RTF unit and a single r-determinant unit) (back-transition) (Figure 4c). A tetracycline resistance plasmid in *Streptococcus faecalis* also undergoes amplification of the TC resistance gene after extended incubation of the cells in the presence of tetracycline.

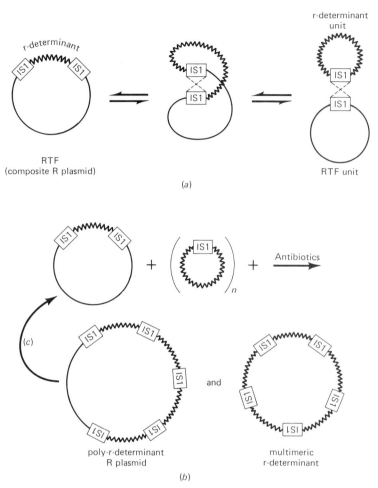

Figure 4. Possible mechanism for transition and back-transition observed with composite R plasmids in *Proteus mirabilis.* (a) Reversible dissociation. (b) Transition. (c) Back-transition.

Tn Elements

In many instances, DNA segments on R plasmids containing genes encoding for drug resistances can be transmitted from one R plasmid to other replicons, such as the host chromosome, bacteriophage DNAs, other R plasmids, and Col plasmid, coexisting in the same bacterial cell. These translocating genetic elements are termed "transposons" or "translocons," abbreviated Tn. Some properties of presently known drug resistance transposons are listed in Table 4. In addition to drug resistance transposons, there exist some other distinct transposons such as transposons manifesting lactose utilization, enterotoxin

Table 4. Properties of Transposons.

NAME OF ELEMENT		PHENOTYPE*	DNA SEQUENCE DUPLICATION AT THE ENDS			WHOLE LENGTH IN K BP
ORIGINAL DESIGNATION	ALTERNATIVE DESIGNATION		TYPE OF ORIENTATION	LENGTH IN K BP	IDENTITY TO IS	
TnA	Tn1	Ap	Inverted repeat	Similar to Tn3	None	Similar to Tn3
	Tn2	Ap	Inverted repeat	Similar to Tn3	None	Similar to Tn3
	Tn3	Ap	Inverted repeat	0.038	None	5.0
TnS	Tn4(contains Tn3)	Ap Sm Su	Inverted repeat	Not known	Not known	20
Tnk	Tn5	Km	Inverted repeat	1.5	None	5.3
	Tn6(or Tn903)	Km	Inverted repeat	1.1	Not known	3.1
TnC	Tn7	Sm Tp	Not known	Not known	Not known	13
Tncam	Tn9	Cm	Direct repeat	0.77	IS1	2.6
TnT	Tn10	Tc	Inverted repeat	1.4	None	9.3
Tn402	—	Tp	Not known	Not known	Not known	7.5
TnM	Tn501	Hg^{2+}	Not known	Not known	Not known	9.1
Tn917	—	Em	Inverted repeat	0.28	Not known	5.0

* Ap, ampicillin resistance (ampicillin[r]); Km, kanamycin[r]; Sm, streptomycin[r]; Su, sulfonamide[r]; Tp, Trimethoprim[r]; Cm, chloramphenicol[r]; Tc, tetracycline[r]; and Em, erythromycin[r].

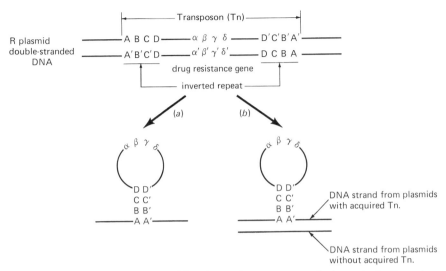

Figure 5. Detection of a transposon with an inverted repeat structure by heteroduplex formation. (a) Denaturation and intrastrand heteroduplex formation. (b) Heteroduplex formation between plasmids with and without acquired Tn.

production, and toluene or xylene degradation. Transposons consist of DNA segments containing one or more genes specifying drug resistance or other characteristics, and duplicated DNA sequences at the ends of these DNA segments, either in direct orientation or in inverted orientation along a genome (Figure 5). In certain cases, the repeated DNA sequences at the ends of the transposon are identical to insertion sequences IS1. Transposons containing an inverted repeat are detected by electron microscopy as a single-stranded DNA loop with a double-stranded DNA stalk (hairpin loop structure), when DNA is denatured and then allowed to anneal for short periods to form an intrastrand heteroduplex (Figure 5a). This structure can also be observed when heteroduplex formation is conducted between DNA having a Tn element and the same DNA not having Tn elements (Figure 5b). Transposition of these DNA segments does not require the bacterial *rec A* gene function, and can take place among DNAs that lack extensive nucleotide sequence homology. This results in the joining of the DNA segment at precisely defined sites on recipient plasmid ("illegitimate recombination"). Transposition of a Tn element is therefore different from the mechanism involved in general *rec A*–dependent recombination, which is reciprocal exchange of DNA in an area of extensive genetic homology. Although the mechanism of transposition is not known, unique DNA segments at the ends of transposons may provide highly specific recognition sites for enzymes involved in transposition.

On the other hand, insertion of a transposon into a structural gene is

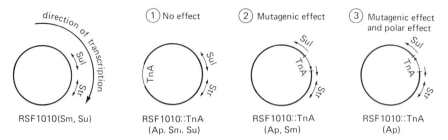

Figure 6. Mutagenic and polar effects of TnA insertion.

mutagenic, and the insertion of a transposon unit into a group of genes within a single transcription unit manifests a strong polar effect on the expression of genes distal to the promotor. The polar effect caused by insertion of a transposon may be dependent on the orientation of the inserted transposon (Figure 6). Transposons can also promote deletions of DNA sequences immediately adjacent to the termini of transposons.

Resistance Mechanisms

Biochemical mechanisms for drug resistance manifested by R plasmids, which are summarized in Table 5, can be divided into four categories: (1) inactivation (modification or hydrolysis) of antimicrobial drugs by inactivating enzyme specified by R plasmid, (2) production of a drug-resistant target enzyme by R plasmid, (3) modification of a target site such that a drug will not bind to the modified site, and (4) R plasmid–induced permeability change.

Expression of resistance genes on R plasmid is, in many cases, under negative control like the inducible system of the *lac* operon in *E. coli*. For example, resistance to tetracycline coded by R plasmid is an inducible resistance. Cyclic AMP does not participate in this induction. On the other hand, chloramphenicol acetyl transferase specified by R plasmids in Gram-negative bacteria is a constitutive enzyme, but its synthesis is stimulated by cyclic AMP and guanosine tetraphosphate.

PLASMIDS AND RECOMBINANT DNA

Recent developments in nucleic acid technology have made it possible to insert any gene into a plasmid and isolate the plasmid containing a certain gene in quantity. The basic principle of such a technique is illustrated in Figure 7.

The basic principle is to select an appropriate vector plasmid having a marker such as antibiotic resistance. Treat this plasmid with a restriction enzyme that introduces a specific staggered cut to the plasmid. Mammalian

Table 5. Some Mechanisms for Drug Resistance Conferred by R Plasmids.

	RESISTANCE TO	GRAM STAIN OF HOST	RESISTANCE MECHANISM	R PLASMID–CODED ENZYME OR PROTEIN RESPONSIBLE FOR RESISTANCE
Chloramphenicol	Cm	−	Inactivation by acetylation	Chloramphenicol acetyl transferase
	Cm	−	Permeability change	Not known
	Cm	+	Inactivation by acetylation	Chloramphenicol acetyl transferase
Tetracycline	Tc	−	Permeability change	TET proteins
	Tc	+	Permeability change	Not known
β-lactam antibiotics	Ap (ampicillin)	−	Inactivation by hydrolysis of the β-lactam ring	β-lactamase
	Ap	−	Permeability change	Not known
	Ap	+	Inactivation by hydrolysis of the β-lactam ring	β-lactamase
Sulfonamide	Su	−	Sulfonamide-resistant synthesis of dihydropteroate	Sulfonamide-resistant dihydropteroate synthase
	Su	−	Permeability change	Not known
	Su	+	Not known	Not known
Trimethoprim	Tp	−	Trimethoprim-resistant synthesis of tetrahydrofolate	Trimethoprim-resistant dihydrofolate reductase
Macrolide antibiotics	Em (erythromycin)	+	Inhibition of binding of Em to 50S ribosome subunit by methylation of 23S ribosomal RNA	Ribosomal ribonucleic acid methylase

Table 5. (continued)

RESISTANCE TO		GRAM STAIN OF HOST	RESISTANCE MECHANISM	R PLASMID–CODED ENZYME OR PROTEIN RESPONSIBLE FOR RESISTANCE
Aminoglycoside antibiotics	Sm (streptomycin)	–	Inactivation by phosphorylation	Aminoglycoside 3″-phosphotransferase
	Sm	–	Inactivation by phosphorylation	Aminoglycoside 6-phosphotransferase
	Sm	–	Inactivation by adenylylation	Aminoglycoside 3″-adenylyltransferase
	Sm	–	Inactivation by adenylylation	Aminoglycoside 6-adenylyltransferase
	Sm	+	Inactivation by adenylylation	Aminoglycoside 6-adenylyltransferase
	Km (kanamycin)	–	Inactivation by phosphorylation	Aminoglycoside 3′-phosphotransferase I and II
	Km and Gm (gentamicin)	–	Inactivation by adenylylation	Aminoglycoside 2″-adenylyltransferase
	Km	–	Inactivation by acetylation	Aminoglycoside 6′-N-acetyltransferase
	Km (or Km and Gm)	–	Inactivation by acetylation	Aminoglycoside 3-N-acetyltransferase
	Gm (or Gm and Km)	–	Inactivation by acetylation	Aminoglycoside 2′-N-acetyltransferase
	Km	+	Inactivation by phosphorylation	Aminoglycoside 3′-phosphotransferase
	Km	+	Inactivation by adenylylation	Aminoglycoside 4′-adenylyltransferase
	Km	+	Inactivation by acetylation	Aminoglycoside 6′-N-acetyltransferase
Metal ions	Hg^{2+}	–	Volatilization by reduction	Hg^{2+}- (or organomercurials-) volatilizing enzyme (mercuric reductase)
	Hg^{2+}	+	Detoxication	Mercuric reductase and organomercurial hydrolase

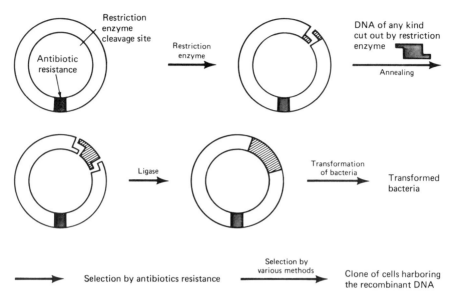

Figure 7. Preparation of recombinant DNA.

or any DNA of interest is then treated with the same restriction enzyme, and a small piece of DNA containing a gene of interest is isolated by either gel electrophoresis or other biochemical means. If there is a good selection method for the particular gene of interest, there is no need of isolation of the gene at this step. The treated plasmid and the foreign DNA are mixed, and the DNA ligase is added to seal together these two pieces of DNA. The resulting chimera DNA is added to bacteria (commonly *E. coli*) in the presence of Ca^{2+} or under appropriate conditions for introduction of circular DNA into the bacteria. The bacterium is first selected for resistance to antibiotics; and from the drug-resistant bacteria, clones of particular bacteria having the desired gene are selected. For the selection of a particular colony of interest, hybridization to the radioactive mRNA transcribed from the gene of interest may be used.

It is now possible, using this technique, to isolate in quantity any gene from eukaryotes or prokaryotes. This technique also has the potential of producing a large amount of a gene product in *E. coli*. It has been shown that certain bacterial enzymes can be made to occupy 40% of the total bacterial protein by introducing the gene into a relaxed plasmid. At least certain yeast genomes can be translated in *E. coli*. Thus, this newly invented technique has an enormous potential for practical as well as academic applications.

On the other hand, the technique can also present a biological hazard because one might create an artificial organism that is of potential danger to human beings.

GENERAL REFERENCES

Falkow, S. 1975. *Infectious Multiple Drug Resistance.* Pion Ltd., London.

Beers and Basset, eds. 1977. *Recombinant Molecules: Impact on Science and Society.* Raven Press, New York.

Achtman and Skurnay, 1977. *F-Plasmid in Cell–Cell Interaction.* Pion Ltd., London.

SECTION 9

RNA AND ASSOCIATED ENZYMES

THERESA CAMPANA AND
LAZAR M. SCHWARTZ

9.1. Ribonucleic Acids: Structure and Function

STRUCTURE AND SIZE RANGE

Ribonucleic acids are polymers of ribonucleotides that are held together by means of phosphodiester bonds. These molecules are generally single-stranded in most prokaryotic and eukaryotic organisms. In some viruses, single- or double-stranded RNA molecules serve as the viral genome, but most viruses contain no RNA. Once these DNA viruses enter a cell, RNA is synthesized that is specific for the virus, but the virion itself contains only DNA and protein.

RNA is a linear arrangement of heterocyclic bases linked to phosphorylated ribose molecules. The heterocyclic bases are essentially the same as those found in DNA except for the substitution of uracil for thymine. Some thymine, however, is found in a low percentage of RNA molecules. In addition to the normal bases, RNA contains several minor bases that are generally modifications of the normal nitrogenous bases. Unlike DNA, RNA does not usually show an equimolar distribution of purines and pyrimidines, since the molecule is generally single-stranded. The equimolar distribution in DNA is a consequence of the presence of complementary double strands. Those rare RNA viruses that contain a double-stranded RNA genome, of course, do show this characteristic. The backbone of RNA molecules, like that of DNA, is formed by phosphodiester linkages between the adjacent sugar moities.

Some RNAs show a large degree of secondary structure due to intramolecular hydrogen bonding between complementary sequences of bases found within the same molecule. The transfer RNA of all organisms, as well as some eukaryotic messenger RNA molecules, show such folding. All transfer RNAs can be folded into the characteristic cloverleaf form and then undergo further folding (see Chapter 9.6). This cloverleaf, which is found in both prokaryotic and eukaryotic tRNA molecules, may be required for the correct interactions between these and the other necessary components in protein synthesis (see Section 10).

The mRNA molecules from eukaryotic cells appear to have a certain degree of secondary structure, mainly in the form of multiple "hairpin" loops. This does not appear to be true for those molecules of mRNA found in prokaryotes, and may contribute to the apparently greater stability of the eukaryotic mRNAs. In addition, it has been postulated that this secondary structure may serve to protect the mRNA from degradation by cellular nucleases. Another possibility is that this highly structured form may be required in the correct alignment of the components of protein synthesis.

The size of RNA molecules varies widely, depending on the particular form of RNA. The smallest molecules are the tRNAs, which contain only about 80 to 90 bases. Other small RNA molecules are also found in the cell, including a small ribosomal RNA and some small mRNA molecules. In general, however, 4S RNA is composed almost completely of the tRNAs. The messenger RNA molecules and the nuclear RNA are the most heterogeneous in size, since their length depends on the protein product for which they code (see Chapter 9.4). The large molecules are those classified as ribosomal; they can be as large as 10^7 daltons in molecular weight. In general, prokaryotic and eukaryotic RNA molecules show about the same size range for each particular class. The rRNA molecules from prokaryotes are slightly smaller than those from eukaryotic cells (see Chapter 9.5), whereas organelle RNA molecules may be somewhat smaller, or may be essentially identical in size.

CLASSES OF RNA AND SPECIFIC FUNCTIONS

Different classification schemes can be devised for RNA; the one described is based on the function of cytoplasmic RNA molecules. It includes the following three types:

1. Messenger RNA: these molecules serve as the direct templates for protein synthesis, and vary in size depending on the specific protein for which they code.
2. Ribosomal RNA: these molecules are found in ribosomes, where they probably serve as structural components; within an organism, there are three size ranges of these RNA molecules.
3. Transfer RNA: these are the smallest RNA molecules; they serve as adaptors in protein synthesis, allowing the correct alignment of amino acids in the growing peptide chain by interaction with other RNA molecules.

The first class, mRNA, are the most heterogeneous in size, and the least stable of the RNAs. The half-life of mRNA varies from a few hours to at most a few weeks, after which they are degraded by cellular nucleases. The mRNA serves to transfer the genetic information encoded in the codons of the genes to the proteins required by the organism (see Section 10). After transcription of the mRNA, before protein synthesis can take place, the mRNA must associate with the ribosomes. With the assistance of tRNA molecules, the mRNA–ribosome complex then directs the synthesis of a specific protein in a consistent fashion, unless a mutation is introduced at some point.

Ribosomal RNA, rRNA, is found in three different sizes within the ribosomes of both prokaryotes and eukaryotes. In addition, there is a fourth species of RNA in eukaryotic ribosomes. These molecules are known to interact with the ribosomal proteins as well as with other RNA species. They may be the structural elements that hold the ribosomes together. In general, rRNA molecules are transcribed as large precursor molecules, which are then processed to give rise to the functional species (see Chapter 9.5). The prokaryotic species of rRNA have sedimentation coefficients of 5, 16, and 23S; the corresponding species in eukaryotic ribosomes are 5, 18, and 28S. The fourth eukaryotic component is a molecule of about 5.5S. The specific functions of each have not yet been determined, but all the components are required for the formation of functional ribosomes. Like mRNA, the rRNA molecules are complementary to specific sequences on the template DNA molecule. These genes, however, do not code for proteins as do those that are transcribed into mRNAs.

The smallest of the RNA molecules, the tRNAs, have a sedimentation coefficient of about 4S, and contain only about 80 bases per molecule. As noted above, these molecules show a high degree of secondary structure, with much intramolecular hydrogen binding between complementary regions in the molecule. Each cell appears to contain about 60 species of tRNA; some of these species are major, carrying different amino acids, while others appear to be minor modifications of one or another of them, which may be important in differentiation or in different nutritional states. The amino acids are esterified to the tRNAs, which then interact with the ribosomes and with mRNA to allow protein synthesis to proceed correctly (see Chapter 9.6).

Other RNA molecules are found in specific organelles like the mitochondria, and also in the nucleus of eukaryotic cells. These RNA molecules appear to serve similar functions to those described for cytoplasmic RNAs. Thus, there seem to be organelle-specific mRNA, rRNA, and tRNA molecules, which would serve to allow organelle-specific proteins to be synthesized. Each of these forms will be described together with the cytoplasmic forms in the following chapters. The RNA molecules found in the nucleus are called HnRNA (heterogeneous nuclear RNA); most if not all of them are formed and degraded within the nucleus, although a small percentage may be the precursors of mRNA, which is found in the cytoplasm. HnRNA molecules vary greatly in size, and some of these molecules contain specific base sequences whose function is at present speculative. Oligo-uridylic acid sequences have been described in some HnRNA molecules; some of these sequences contain polyphosphate groups at the 5' end of the molecule. The function of these groups is unknown. A certain number of HnRNA molecules are covalently linked to poly-adenylic acid sequences at the 3' end. These sequences may serve to identify those molecules that are the precursors of at least some of the mRNAs found in the cytoplasm. However, not all eukaryotic mRNA molecules have poly A sequences attached; some do, and, in these cases, the poly A may also serve some protective role, or may assist in the attachment of mRNA to other components required in protein synthesis. This is quite speculative; no specific role for poly A can be identified at present.

CELLULAR LOCALIZATION OF RNA

RNA molecules are all synthesized in the nucleus (see Chapter 9.2) in eukaryotic cells, and then are found in both the nucleus and the cytoplasm. In prokaryotic cells, RNA is found throughout the cytosol, generally closely associated with the ribosomes. Some eukaryotic RNA is also found in cellular organelles. The major part of the RNA found in any cell is associated with ribosomes in the cytosol. About 80% of the total cellular RNA is rRNA, and about 10% is tRNA; the remainder includes HnRNA, mRNA, and organelle-associated RNA.

In prokaryotic cells, since the DNA is not separated from the cytoplasm by a membrane, no transport processes are required before the RNA takes part in protein synthesis. The rRNA must be processed before it is of the correct size to associate with ribosomal proteins, but mRNA can immediately attach to ribosomes. The situation is quite different in eukaryotic cells; RNA molecules must be transported across the nuclear membrane into the cytoplasm before protein synthesis takes place. The mechanisms whereby this migration takes place are not well understood; it is especially difficult to visualize the transport of some of the larger mRNA molecules. Further experiments may implicate specific carriers in this process, but none is known at present.

SYNTHESIS OF RIBONUCLEIC ACIDS

Synthesis of RNA takes place by the copying of a segment of a DNA double helix (see Chapter 9.2). This process, called transcription, requires specific enzymes known as RNA polymerases, and the four appropriate ribonucleoside triphosphates as substrates. All RNA molecules are complementary to one strand of DNA, but obviously represent a small fraction of the total genome for any single molecule. In prokaryotes, replication, transcription, and protein synthesis are closely linked both temporally and spatially. Almost simultaneously with replication, RNA polymerase binds to the appropriate site on the newly synthesized DNA, and a mRNA is made. As it is elongating, the 5' end of the molecule associates with ribosomes, and directs the process of protein synthesis (see Section 10). In eukaryotic organisms, on the other hand, newly synthesized mRNA must be transported from the nucleus and may require some processing before it can associate with the ribosomes. This situation makes the whole process both longer and more complex as compared to bacteria, and may account for some of the complexities in the structure of eukaryotic mRNA.

During transcription, hybrid duplex molecules are transiently formed between the DNA of the genome and the RNA being transcribed. In general, they cannot be isolated, since the majority of the DNA strands remain hydrogen-bonded to each other, and because the newly synthesized RNA is quickly detached from the DNA. In the case of the bacteriophage φX 174, however, this hybrid duplex can be isolated. This phage belongs to a small subclass of DNA viruses whose genome consists of a single-stranded DNA molecule. The hybrid double strand is therefore very stable, and can be recovered during in vitro transcription. Chemical studies of the viral genome and its RNA products have shown that the viral RNA has a base composition exactly complementary to that of the single-stranded genome.

MODIFICATION OF COMPONENTS OF CELLULAR RNA

Both tRNA and rRNA contain modified bases; the percentage of such bases in tRNA is particularly high. The most usual modification found is the methylation of particular sites on uracil and cytosine. Methylation requires a one-carbon donor which is usually S-adenosyl methionine (SAM). Uracil can

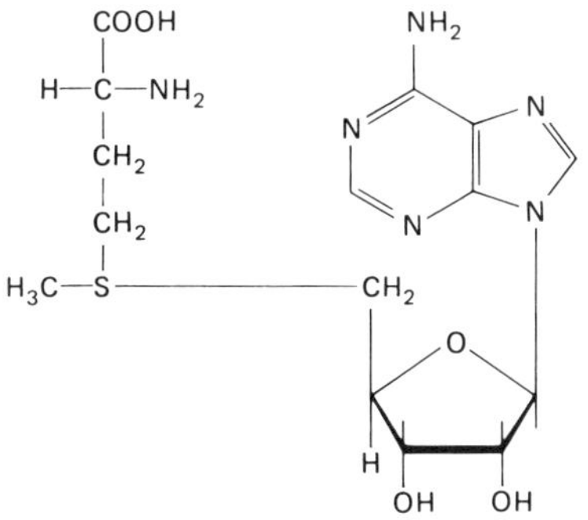

Figure 1. Structure of SAM.

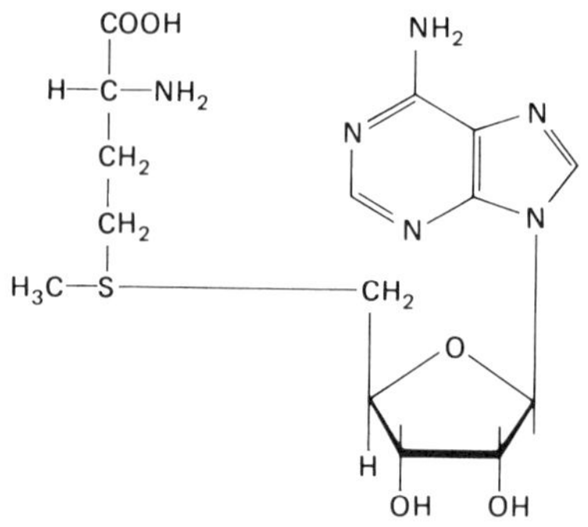

Figure 2. Some methylated bases found in RNA.

be modified at three sites; methylation at position 5 of the ring produces thymine, which is a normal component of DNA and is found to a small extent in some RNA molecules. Another common modification is the hydroxymethylation of some bases. In this case, the one-carbon carrier is usually a derivative of folic acid. Also, modification may proceed by the addition of thiol groups or methyl amino methane groups. Most methylations occur on pyrimidines, but some methylated purines have also been identified in RNA. Some of the more common methylated bases are shown in Figure 2.

RNA molecules also contain some molecules of xanthine and hypoxanthine. These purines result from the deamination of guanine and adenine, respectively, and the reactions are catalyzed by specific purine deaminases that normally participate in the metabolic degradation of the purines in vivo. These catabolic reactions are shown in Figure 3, together with a schematic representation of the interconversions of the purine bases. Other modified purines found in RNA include the isopentenyl derivatives such as triacanthine. This compound, shown in Figure 4, appears to have a hormone-like activity that, in vitro, facilitates the separation of the two daughter cells formed during mitosis.

At present, the specific functions of the modified bases in RNA are still subject of speculation. Some roles that have been postulated include: the conferral of resistance to nuclease digestion; the prevention of base-pairing in specific regions of RNA molecules; the folding of RNA molecules into specific secondary configurations. Support for this last hypothesis comes from studies of tRNA molecules which have a high concentration of modified bases and a specific, well-defined secondary structure. Another postulated role for modifications concerns the modified bases in rRNA; it is thought

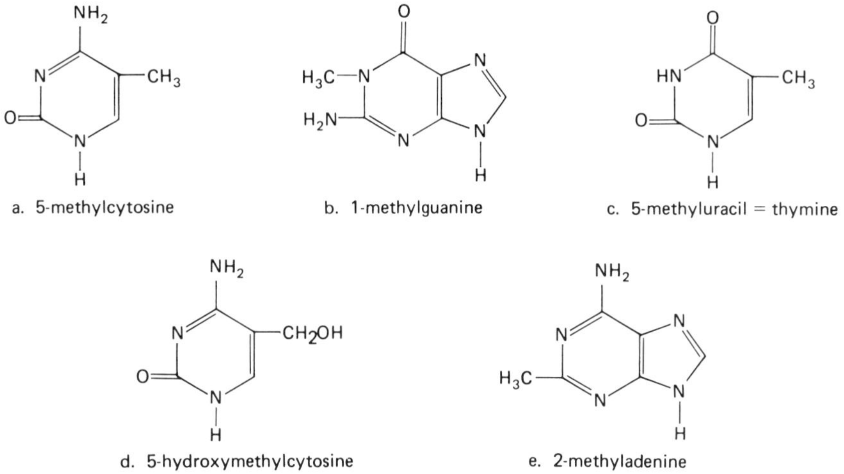

a. 5-methylcytosine   b. 1-methylguanine   c. 5-methyluracil = thymine

d. 5-hydroxymethylcytosine   e. 2-methyladenine

Figure 3. (a) Catabolic products of purine metabolism found in RNA. (b) Interconversions of the purines.

that they may in some way interact with ribosomal proteins to stabilize the structure of the ribosome itself. At present, there is no evidence that either supports or contradicts such a role.

Another hypothesis suggests that the methylation of eukaryotic rRNA may be directly related to the efficiency of processing of the large precursor molecules (see Chapter 9.5). If methylation is inhibited by the addition of cycloleucine, the last stage of processing of the precursor decreases in efficiency, and may even be completely inhibited. Cycloleucine does not alter the rate of protein synthesis, nor does it influence significantly the cleavage pattern of the precursor. The specific site of action appears to be the very last step in the processing. It has been suggested by Caboche and Bachellerie that this inhibition may be due to slight conformational changes at the specific cleavage site of this step. Further studies of this nature may help to clarify the specific role of modifications in the bases of RNA molecules.

BIBLIOGRAPHY

Books and Review Articles:

Gilham, P. T. 1970. *Annu. Rev. Biochem.* 39:227.
Burgess, R. R. 1971. *Annu. Rev. Biochem.* 40:711.
Bautz, E. K. F. 1972. *Prog. Nucl. Acid Res. Mol. Biol.* 12:129.

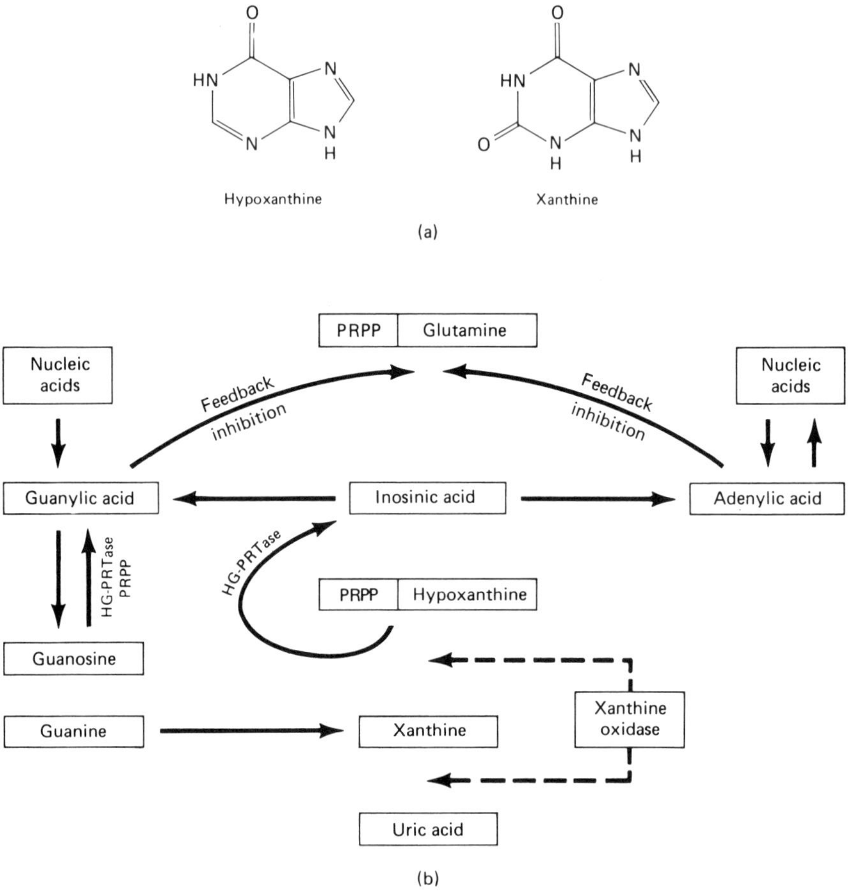

Hypoxanthine   Xanthine

(a)

(b)

Figure 4. Triacanthine structure.

Davidson, J. N. 1972. *The Biochemistry of the Nucleic Acids.* Academic Press, New York.
Watson, J. D. 1975. *Molecular Biology of the Gene.* W. A. Benjamin, Reading, Massachusetts.

Research Papers:

Roberts, J. W. 1970. *Cold Spring Harbor Symp. Quant. Biol.* 35:121.
Richardson, J. P. 1970. *Cold Spring Harbor Symp. Quant. Biol.* 35:127.
Sanger, F. 1971. *Biochem. J.* 124:833.
Cox, R. A., and Katchalsky, A. 1972. *Biochem. J.* 126:1039.
McReynolds, L., O'Malley, B. W., Nisbet, A. D., Fothergill, J. E., Givol, D., Fields, S., Robertson, M., and Brownlee, G. G. 1978. *Nature* 273:723.

9.2. Transcription

GENERAL MECHANISM

RNA is synthesized on a DNA template by the action of enzymes known as DNA-dependent RNA polymerases (see Chapter 9.3). The reaction requires the presence of the four ribonucleoside triphosphates as substrates, a DNA molecule as a template, and Mg^{2+} ions. Transcription proceeds in the 5' to 3' direction, adding the new nucleotides sequentially to the 3' end of the preceding phosphorylated ribose, and releasing pyrophosphate. It appears likely that the main energy source for the reaction is the breakage of the high-energy triphosphate bond in each nucleotide. In general, any RNA molecule represents a small fraction of the entire DNA genome of an organism, but is complementary to that segment. A few very small viruses may represent exceptions to this; in these cases, the bulk of the genome can be transcribed into one or a few RNA molecules which serve as messengers for the production of necessary viral proteins.

The template required for transcription is one of the two strands of a duplex DNA molecule; in vivo neither strand need be completely transcribed, but sections of each may serve as the actual template for various genes. The present theory which is most in accord with the available evidence is that RNA polymerases recognize specific initiation sequences on DNA molecules, bind to these regions, and begin the transcription of a particular gene. When another specific sequence is reached, which the polymerase recognizes as a stop signal, the RNA polymerase detaches from the DNA. The exact nature of these start and stop signals has not been determined, but may represent either sequences of bases or some as yet undefined physical characteristics. In the bacteria, it is probably that segments of both DNA strands serve as templates, with some genes transcribed from one strand and others from the complementary strand.

The initiation of transcription may be controlled by the recognition of specific DNA sequences. There is some evidence that newly transcribed RNA molecules start with either adenine or guanine; this 5' terminus can be identified with little difficulty, since it is the only one that carries a triphosphate group. This finding implies that the beginnings of genes contain sequences of several successive pyrimidines; evidence to support this has been found in studies of some viral DNA sequences. No primer is required for RNA synthesis, as contrasted with replication, which cannot proceed in the absence of a primer molecule (see Section 7). The binding of the first nucleotide substrate molecule to the DNA template may proceed by the formation of hydrogen bonds between them, with the enzyme serving a catalytic role. This binding would further local denaturation of the DNA duplex in the appropriate region and the local melting would be stabilized by the elongation of the nascent RNA chain.

The rate of elongation has been estimated to range from 15 to 55 nucleotides per second in vivo in bacteria and viruses. In vitro it is possible to attain similar rates. Both temperature and ionic strength of the media influence the rate of elongation in vitro, and may play a comparable role in vivo, but this has not been experimentally verified. Elongation itself consists of the sequential addition of nucleotides, with the formation of phosphodiester linkages between them, and the release of pyrophosphate molecules for each nucleotide added. It is not clear if any energy source other than the substrates themselves is required.

There appear to be specific termination signals, the nature of which is not known, that allow release of the polymerase from its binding to the template. Simultaneously or nearly so, the hydrogen bonds holding the hybrid duplex molecule must be broken so that the completed chain may be released. This process also appears to be sensitive to ionic strength. At ionic strengths lower than about 0.2 M KCl, no chains are released.

INHIBITORS OF TRANSCRIPTION

Many compounds may inhibit the synthesis of RNA by binding to the DNA template, whereas other compounds bind to the RNA polymerase and thus interfere with the catalytic action of this enzyme. In general, those inhibitors that bind to the template also interfere with replication. The binding of these molecules is not usually covalent; many of them intercalate into the double helix, thus altering its properties and preventing unwinding or attachment of the required enzymes. Compounds that bind to the template usually inhibit transcription in both prokaryotic and eukaryotic organisms. Those that bind to the enzymes, on the other hand, are specific for one or the other type, since these enzymes are different in different organisms. Some of these inhibitors are described in Table 1, and the structures of some are shown in Figure 1.

Other compounds that interfere with transcription in vitro are the nucleotide analogues. When incorporated into DNA, these analogues may prevent proper hydrogen bonding, thus introducing errors into both newly synthesized DNA and newly replicated RNA. Alternatively, they may also serve as substrates for either DNA or RNA polymerases. In these cases, the result may again be mutation, or specific ill effects such as the premature release of

Table 1. Inhibitors of Transcription.

COMPOUND	MODE OF ACTION
Actinomycin D	Intercalation into the duplex DNA adjacent to G–C base pairs; prevents binding of the polymerase.
Proflavine	Intercalation; prevents both binding of the polymerase and initiation of transcription.
Anthracycline	Probably intercalation; prevents elongation.
Distamycin A	Binds to A–T-rich regions of DNA; prevents the binding of the polymerase.
Luteoskyrin	Forms complex with Mg^{2+} ions; this complex binds to the DNA; appears to impair both the binding and the function of the polymerase.
Rifampicin	Binds noncovalently to bacterial RNA polymerases; inhibits transcription in general.
Streptolydigin	Binds to the bacterial polymerases; inhibits elongation.
α-Amanitin	Binds to many mammalian polymerases; selectively inhibits transcription catalyzed by these enzymes.
Pyrophosphate	Inhibits all polymerases, perhaps by an allosteric mechanism.

growing chains may result. Some nucleotide analogues lack a 3'-hydroxyl group on the ribose; these compounds prevent elongation of the growing chain. These compounds were useful in determining that base-pairing is required during transcription. More recently, they have been used in the nearest-neighbor analysis of RNA to help determine base sequence in specific RNA molecules.

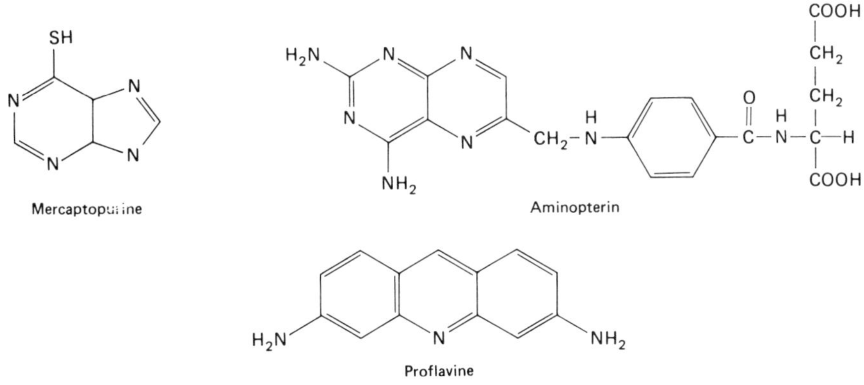

Figure 1. Structures of some inhibitors of transcription.

CONTROL OF TRANSCRIPTION IN PROKARYOTES

Transcription has been well studied in bacteria; control is mediated by protein factors that may act as repressors or activators of specific genes. Bacteriophage appear to be influenced by similar factors, which may be host-specific or may be coded for by the viral genome itself. Some of the components of the bacterial RNA polymerases may act as control mechanisms in transcription; this seems to be definitely the case for the σ subunit, which can be detached from the rest of the polymerase molecule and is required for initiation (see Chapter 9.3). Finally, there is some evidence suggesting a role for translation (see Section 10) in the control of transcription.

Repressor proteins were first isolated in 1966, but their existence had been postulated by Jacob and Monod in 1961. The system used as a model by these authors in their hypothesis was the *lac* operon of *E. coli,* a closely linked series of genes that permits the utilization of lactose as a carbon source for the growth of *E. coli.* The operon, or series of linked genes required for this process, is shown in Figure 2. The structural genes for the required enzymes are called *z, y,* and *a;* the other regions, named *i, p,* and *o,* are required for the regulation of transcription of the operon, and will be discussed in more detail below. The *z* gene codes for the main enzyme required in metabolism, a β-galactosidase. Normally, an *E. coli* cell contains only about five molecules of this enzyme; in the presence of lactose or similar sugars, the cell contains about 5000 molecules of this enzyme. Lactose is referred to as an inducer of the required enzymes, and the process by which the number of enzyme molecules is increased is known as induction.

Normally, lactose is not metabolized to any significant degree if glucose is present in the media. When, on the other hand, lactose is the sole or the major source of carbon, the cell is able to produce the required enzymes within 2 or 3 min. Jacob and Monod postulated that two types of genes were present in the *lac* operon: structural genes which code for protein products, and regulatory genes which allow or prevent transcription. The mechanism proposed was that a molecule, at first thought to be an RNA, would bind to the regulatory genes to prevent transcription. The region of binding is the *o* or operator gene; RNA polymerase binds to the *p* gene, but cannot proceed with transcription if the repressor is attached to the operator. The repressor is now known to be a protein that is coded for by the *i* gene; this protein was isolated by Gilbert and Muller-Hill. It is a tetrameric protein

1000			3420	760	810	Number of bases
i	p	o	z	y	a	Gene
repressor			β-galactosidase	permease	transacetylase	Gene products

Figure 2. The *lac* operon.

with a molecular weight of 155,000 daltons, and has a high affinity for DNA, so that it binds very tightly to the operator region. It appears likely that the N-terminal region of the protein actually binds to the repressor, since mutations at the C-terminal end of the repressor have little if any effect on the binding. Binding of the repressor appears to prevent the RNA polymerase from reading the structural genes; it does not prevent binding of the enzyme to the promotor *(p)* gene.

In the presence of glucose, the levels of the enzymes of the *lac* operon are reduced to as low as one-third those found in the absence of glucose, even when the medium still contains high levels of lactose. This catabolite repression is connected with the effects of glucose on the cyclic AMP levels of the cell. This repression, however, does not act directly through the *lac* operon genes, although cAMP is required for the induction of these genes. It appears that the levels of transcription of the mRNA are directly affected by the action of cAMP, but that there is no direct effect on the regulatory genes.

Addition of lactose or similar compounds derepresses the system, allowing transcription of the structural genes of the *lac* operon. A small amount of the sugar enters the cell by simple diffusion and binds to the repressor protein. Normally, the repressor–DNA complex is very stable, and will dissociate very slowly. In the presence of inducers, however, this stability is greatly reduced, and the repressor is easily removed from the complex. The inducer apparently interacts with the bound repressor, changing its conformation directly so that it is released from the complex. After detachment of the repressor, the RNA polymerase which is bound to the promotor region is able to transcribe the structural genes. These genes, as stated above, code for three enzymes, the first of which is the actual catalyst for the breakdown of lactose into simple sugars, which can be utilized by the cell's metabolic pathways. The second, a permease, allows the active transport of the lactose into the cell; the function of the third enzyme, β-galactosidase transacetylase, is not known in vivo.

Other operons have also been described; generally, they seem to be controlled in a more complex fashion, although some features of the positive control mechanism described for the *lac* operon are shared by some of them. The *gal* operon, for example, is required for the conversion of galactose to glucose-1-phosphate, and shows a similar type of control by a repressor protein, which can be removed from the operator region by induction. In addition, however, this operon also interacts with an unrelated series of genes, known as *cap,* which are required for the production of capsular polysaccharide. In certain *cap* mutants, all the *gal* operon genes are constitutively active; that is, these genes are no longer controlled by the operator region of the *gal* operon, but are always transcribed even in the absence of induction.

The *ara C* operon, which regulates the metabolism of arabinose, is controlled by a repressor protein that prevents transcription of these genes. The inducer for the system, however, appears to be an altered form of the repressor protein itself, which undergoes a change in the presence of arabinose. When no arabinose is found in the system, the repressor exists in a particular conformation that prevents transcription. In the presence of arabinose, an altered form of the repressor is found, which must bind to the operator region in order to allow transcription.

Other known operons are under negative control; that is, the genes are normally turned on and therefore transcribed. In the presence of certain, specific compounds, these genes may be turned off, or repressed, so that transcription is prevented. This appears to be the fashion in which the *his* operon is controlled; this operon regulates the synthesis of enzymes required for the cell to make histidine. The cell is able to synthesize histidine from ATP and phosphoribosyl pyrophosphate; in the presence of specific levels of histidine, which is added to the growth media, the *his* operon is repressed. The actual repressor appears to be histidyl-tRNA, not the amino acid itself. No regulatory gene has yet been identified for this operon; mutants that act in a regulatory manner have been identified, but are found dispersed throughout the genome, and do not have the classical characteristics of a regulatory gene. One mutant that is linked to the operon has been reported; this class, known as *hisO,* may represent an operator region defect, rather than a regulatory gene.

Regulatory schemes combining aspects of both negative and positive regulatory systems can be postulated. Many gene systems, however, have no identifiable operon, and in other systems there does not seem to be a close linkage between genes that code for related functions. Various activation factors have been postulated to play a role in control in many bacterial systems. The σ factor of RNA polymerase is involved in control of transcription. This subunit is readily detached from the core enzyme, and is required for the specific initiation of transcription of a given gene. In the absence of σ, both strands of the DNA may be transcribed, and a heterogeneous population of RNA molecules will be formed. The control of rRNA synthesis presents a case of special interest. Only a very small portion of the genome, less than 1%, represents DNA sequences coding for rRNA, yet this species represents the vast bulk of the transcription products in any cell. The synthesis of these molecules appears to be stimulated by a factor known as ψr, which has recently been identified as one of the bacterial factors required for the elongation of new peptide chains during protein synthesis (see Section 10). The exact mechanism responsible for the stimulation is not known, but there is some evidence that the specific promotors for rRNA synthesis undergo some conformational change before transcription of these genes takes place. The elongation factor may aid in local denaturation of the double helix in the appropriate region.

Cyclic nucleotides appear to play some role in the regulation of transcription. In the presence of low levels of cAMP, for example, some operons cannot be activated. High cAMP levels relieve the repression; this may be a direct effect of the nucleotide, or may be mediated by a cAMP receptor protein. The cAMP or its repressor protein will bind to the DNA, in some way stimulating the transcription of the particular gene. Another possibility is that the cAMP acts indirectly by influencing the phosphorylation of specific nuclear proteins so that they attach to or detach from the genome. The other cyclic nucleotide, cGMP, has also been postulated to be involved in control. However, the mechanism of action of this compound is less well characterized than that of cAMP.

Transcription may also be regulated by the end product of a series of reactions. Histidine, as mentioned above, will prevent the transcription of the *his* operon when present in the cell in high concentrations. Generally, this process requires the presence of another molecule, called co-repressor, which will form a complex with the end product. In the case of histidine, the tRNA specific for this amino acid must combine with it. The complex will then bind to the operator region of the operon, and will prevent transcription of the series of genes. This system is analagous to another system, called feedback inhibition, that controls the activity of enzymes by inhibition of a particular enzyme reaction due to the presence of excess end product of a series of enzymatic reactions. In the latter system, however, the interactions take place at the levels of the proteins, whereas in transcriptional control, the interactions occur on the genome.

REGULATION OF EUKARYOTIC TRANSCRIPTION

The control of transcription in eukaryotic cells is less well defined than that in bacteria because of the greater complexity of the eukaryotic genome. However, several stimulatory factors have been described that interact with specific eukaryotic polymerases. These factors appear to be species-specific, and perhaps even tissue-specific. One such factor has been described in frog ooctyes; it appears to inhibit specifically the synthesis of rRNA in these cells. In early stages of development, 97% of the RNA synthesized is rRNA; as development proceeds, the proportion of rRNA in the total RNA decreases significantly. This decrease correlates with the appearance of a protein that binds specifically to genes coding for rRNA. As such proteins are isolated and purified, they may allow the postulation of specific roles for such regulatory proteins.

Hormones, too, influence the rate of transcription; these compounds act by one of several mechanisms, depending on their chemical structure. Some hormones stimulate or repress cyclic nucleotide levels, thus acting indirectly, probably by mechanisms analogous to those mentioned above for prokaryotic systems. In eukaryotic cells, the mechanism almost certainly involves stimulation or inhibition of phosphorylation by cAMP-dependent kinases of nuclear proteins. Other hormones stimulate production of a particular RNA polymerase by unknown mechanisms. Still others increase both rRNA and mRNA synthesis; among these hormones is estrogen. Stimulation of rRNA synthesis by these compounds may be required during differentiation in order to produce the high numbers of ribosomes found in oocytes, for example. Estrogen also stimulates specific mRNA synthesis; in ova, all egg-white proteins are produced at high levels because of interactions between estrogen binding proteins and the genome.

The mechanism involved with such hormones appears to be the binding of the hormone to a cytoplasmic receptor. The complex then migrates to the cell nucleus and associates with DNA, where it acts as a positive modulator to increase transcription. The mechanism whereby this complex recognizes a particular gene is not known. An insecticide, Kepone, has been shown to bind to estrogen receptors and to stimulate specific mRNA transcription in chicken oviducts. This leads to the direct stimulation of some egg-white proteins. In addition, the insecticide also influences the metabolism of estrogen, causing an increase in the levels of active hormone, and thus indirectly stimulating synthesis of the mRNA molecules for the other egg-white proteins. This compound is not a structural analogue of the estrogen, and the chemical basis for the reported effects is not clear.

The nuclear proteins found associated with the eukaryotic genome may also be involved in the regulation of transcription. The basic proteins, the histones, have been shown to be required for maintenance of the nucleosome structure in chromatin. It is possible that DNA held in this conformation is unable to be transcribed, but this is still unclear from the experimental data available at present. It appears that attachment of histones to the genome may prevent binding of specific RNA polymerases, and therefore inhibit transcription. On modification of these proteins, perhaps by methylation or phosphorylation which could be controlled by hormones, the charge on the proteins may be altered so that they transiently detach from the chromatin to allow transcription of the mRNA. Histones from various organs and from different species have been isolated and compared; it seems that these proteins are organ-specific rather than species-specific. This seems to indicate that histones are not involved in the fine control of transcription, but rather may serve to prevent the synthesis of RNA from the bulk of the DNA. Thus, they could be modulators of transcription of blocks of inactive chromatin, but play no role in the fine control of RNA synthesis for specific mRNAs.

The acidic nuclear proteins have been postulated to carry out such a role. These proteins bind only to chromatin from homologous or closely related species, and appear to stimulate transcription. Unlike the histones, the acidic nuclear proteins have rapid turnover rates, and are specifically located in those regions of the chromatin that show high transcriptional activity. In many cases, phosphorylation of these proteins can be correlated with gene activation by specific hormones. The phosphorylated acidic nuclear proteins can bind to DNA, perhaps thereby promoting the binding of the RNA polymerases, which would allow specific gene transcription.

TERMINATION OF RNA SYNTHESIS

The genes on chromatin must be separated from each other and from nontranscribed spacers by some specific termination signals on the DNA. However, in the absence of a specific factor, rho (ρ), in prokaryotic cells, the newly synthesized RNA is not released from its interaction with the DNA. This protein is a tetramer, with a molecular weight of 200,000 daltons, and does not appear to interact with the RNA polymerase, but rather with the DNA template itself. It is possible that the factor somehow destabilizes the hydrogen bonds between the template and the new RNA, promoting the breakage of these bonds with the re-formation of the hydrogen bonds between the two strands of the DNA.

No comparable factors have been described in eukaryotic systems. The mechanism of termination in these cells is unknown, although it can be assumed that some specific signals on the DNA must exist. These signals could be recognized by the RNA polymerase itself, or perhaps require specific factors. On recognition, the enzyme would detach from the genome, the RNA–DNA hybrid must be broken, and the original double helix must be restored. It is probable that these mechanisms will be fully explored in the near future.

BIBLIOGRAPHY

General Mechanisms:

Goldberg, A. R., and Hurwitz, J. 1972. *J. Biol. Chem.* 247:5637.
Schafer, R., and Zillig, W. 1973. *Eur. J. Biochem.* 33:215.
Minkley, E. G., Jr. 1973. *J. Mol. Biol.,* 78:577.
Minkley, E. G., Jr. and Pribnow, D. 1973. *J. Mol. Biol.* 77:255.
Golbus, M. S., Calarco, P. G., and Epstein, C. J. 1973. *J. Exp. Zool.* 186:207.
Epstein, C. J. 1975. *Biol. Reprod.* 12:82.
Clegg, K. G., and Piko, L. 1977. *Biol.* 58:76.

Inhibitors of Replication:

Suhadolnik, R. J. 1970. *Nucleoside Antibiotics.* John Wiley and Sons, New York.

Goldberg, I. H., and Friedman, P. A. 1971. *Annu. Rev. Biochem.* 40:775.

Abraham, A. D., and Sekeris, C. E. 1971. *Biochim. Biophys. Acta* 247:562.

Salaman, D. F., Betteridge, S., and Korner, A. 1972. *Biochim. Biophys. Acta* 273:382.

Sobell, H. M., and Jain, S. C. 1972. *J. Mol. Biol.* 68:21.

Meilhac, M., Tysper, Z., and Chambon, P. 1972. *Eur. J. Biochem.* 28:291.

Onishi, T., and Muramatsu, M. 1972. *Biochem. J.* 128:1361.

Mauro, E. D., Hollenberg, C. P., and Hall, B. D. 1972. *Proc. Nat. Acad. Sci. U.S.A.* 69:2818.

Gianfranceschi, G. L., Amici, D., and Guglielmi, L. 1975. *Biochim. Biophys. Acta* 414:9.

Cozzarelli, N. R. 1977. *Annu. Rev. Biochem.* 46:641.

Control of Replication:

Martelo, O. J., Woo, S. C., Reimann, E. M., and Davie, E. W. 1970. *Biochemistry* 9:4807.

Roeder, R. G., and Rutter, W. J. 1970. *Biochemistry* 9:2543.

Sugiura, M., Okomoto, T., and Takanami, M. 1970. *Nature* 225:598.

Okomoto, T., Sugiura, M., and Takanami, M. 1970. *Biochemistry* 9:3533.

Teng, C. T., Teng, C. S., and Allfrey, V. G. 1970. *Biochem. Biophys. Res. Commun.* 41:690.

Teng, C. S., Teng, C. T., and Allfrey, V. G. 1971. *J. Biol. Chem.* 246:3597.

Ruddon, R. W., and Rainey, C. H. 1971. *FEBS Lett.* 14:170.

Greenblatt, J., and Schleif, R. 1971. *Nature New Biol.* 233:166.

Parks, J. S., Gottesman, M., Shimada, K., Weisberg, R., Perlman, R. L., and Pastan, I. 1971. *Proc. Nat. Acad. Sci. U.S.A.* 68:1891.

Luck, D. N., and Hamilton, T. H. 1972. *Proc. Nat. Acad. Sci. U.S.A.* 69:157.

Termination:

Beckman, J. S., Daniel, V., Tichauer, Y., and Littaner, U. Z. 1971. *Biochem. Biophys. Res. Commun.* 45:806.

Witmer, H. J. 1971. *J. Biol. Chem.* 246:5220.

Travers, A. A. 1978. Biochemistry of nucleic acids II. *Int. Rev. Biochem.* Vol. 17, B. F. C. Clark, ed. University Park Press, Baltimore.

9.3. DNA-Dependent RNA Polymerases

BACTERIAL RNA POLYMERASES

There appears to be but a single species of RNA polymerase for each bacterial species. These enzymes catalyze the formation of all types of RNA molecules, using DNA as the template. Most bacterial polymerases have five subunits, but phage polymerases apparently consist of a single polypeptide chain. Four of the bacterial subunits, α, β, β', and ω, form what is known as the core enzyme, while the fifth, σ, is required for initiation of transcription, and can be reversibly dissociated from the core. This dissociation has no influence on elongation of RNA chains after initiation, but influences the specificity of initiation, if it takes place before the start of transcription. Some data on the composition and molecular weights of prokaryotic polymerases are shown in Table 1 and Figure 1.

Most of the bacterial RNA polymerases contain two copies each of the α subunit, with a single copy of the others. The best-studied of these polymerases is the enzyme from *E. coli,* each cell of which contains about 7000 enzyme molecules during normal growth. This enzyme can form aggregates that are dependent on the ionic strength of the solution. At ionic strengths greater than about 0.1 M salt, the enzyme exists as a monomer containing stoichiometric quantities of the subunits. When the ionic strength is lowered, a dimer forms containing twice as many subunits. In the absence of the σ subunit, the core enzyme forms very large complexes that contain six or more of each core subunit. This aggregation takes place at ionic strength even higher than that at which the holoenzyme is formed, and will be retained up to ionic strengths of about 0.26 M. At these salt concentrations, the complexes will again dissociate.

The specific functions of each of the subunits are not clear at present. The two α subunits present in each monomer of the holoenzyme are required for polymerase activity. It has been suggested that the β' subunit may actually be a complex of the β and ω subunits, although this appears unlikely on the basis of the molecular weight of the holoenzyme. The functions of β and ω are not known; β' appears to be required for the binding of the enzyme to the DNA template. As noted above, σ is essential for the initiation of specific transcription; in the absence of this subunit, transcription occurs at

Table 1. Prokaryotic RNA Polymerases.

ORGANISM	MOLECULAR WEIGHTS					
	SUBUNITS					HOLOENZYME
	α	β	β	ω	σ	
E. coli	39,000	155,000	165,000	~10,000	90,000	~490,000
P. putida	44,000	155,000	165,000	~10,000	98,000	~500,000
A. nidulans	39,000	147,000	125,000	—	86,000	~440,000
Phage T3	—	—	—	—	—	110,000
Phage T7	—	—	—	—	—	107–110,000

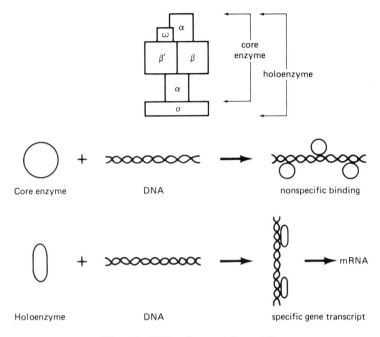

Figure 1. RNA polymerase (bacterial).

random at various sites on both strands of the DNA template. The enzyme also contains two tightly bound molecules of divalent zinc, which is required for enzyme activity. The average physical size of the holoenzyme is about 100 Å. About 30% of the amino acids in the molecule are found in the α-helical configuration.

In *E. coli,* the rate of growth of the RNA chain ranges from 13 to 90 nucleotides/sec. On the average, one RNA polymerase molecule is found attached per 600 base pairs in the genome, and each enzyme molecule seems to be in direct physical contact with about 20 bases in the DNA. This has been estimated from the observation that an oligomer of this size is resistant to digestion by DNase when the enzyme is bound to the genome. In phage T7 DNA, there appear to be two distinct types of RNA polymerase binding sites. One of these corresponds to specific promotor regions which are associated with the transcription of genes, while the other represents some random, nonspecific interaction of the enzyme with the DNA. On binding, the polymerase promotes a local denaturation of the double helix, allowing transcription of a specific gene on one of the two strands.

EUKARYOTIC RNA POLYMERASES

In eukaryotic cells, there are several different types of RNA polymerase that can be identified within each nucleus. These polymerases are compartmentalized, being found in either the nucleoplasm or the nucleolus, and differ in several important respects from each other. In general, three main types of RNA polymerases can be identified; each of these types also appears to be further subdivided into subclasses for which a role has been postulated in differentiation. Class I enzymes are found in the nucleolus, by definition, while the others, classes II and III, are localized in the nucleoplasm. All three classes require a divalent cation for activity; this ion can be divalent magnesium for all three, but class II enzymes prefer the divalent ions of manganese. Another difference between class II and the other types of RNA polymerases is that the former are sensitive to the inhibitor α-amanitin, while the others are insensitive to this compound. Some characteristics of the three types of polymerases are shown in Table 2.

Class I enzymes, which are localized in the nucleolus, are involved specifically in the transcription of the genes for rRNA; their location in this area correlates well with this function. These enzymes transcribe the large precursor molecules which are processed to form the 18 and 23S RNA molecules found in mature ribosomes (see Chapter 9.5), but do not participate in the formation of 5S RNA; their role in the synthesis of 5.5S RNA remains in dispute. The 5S RNA molecules, as well as the small tRNAs are all transcribed by the action of class III enzymes, which, as noted above, are found in the nucleoplasm. The other type of RNA polymerase, those that are referred to as class II enzymes, are known to transcribe mRNA; since it is thought that HnRNA molecules may be related to mRNA, it is assumed that these molecules are also transcribed by the class II enzymes.

Little is known about the subunit structure of eukaryotic RNA polymerases, and even less about the specific roles of subunits in these enzymes. These are now being studied; class III enzymes from mice and from toads appear to contain about ten subunits, but it is unclear whether these subunits are identical or different. The role of these possible subunits may be correlated with different subclasses of each polymerase type. There are indications in

Table 2.   Characteristics of Eukaryotic RNA Polymerases.

	CLASS		
	I	II	III
Preferred template	native DNA[a] or poly (dC)[b]	denatured DNA	poly (dC)[b]
Optimal salt concentration	0.05 M	0.06–0.08 M	not sensitive
Product	rRNA	mRNA; HnRNA	5S and tRNA
Preferred cation	Mg^{2+}	Mn^{2+}	Mg^{2+}

[a] When tested in a yeast system.
[b] When tested in sea urchins.

the literature that these subclasses, which appear to play a specific role in the differentiation of cells, may contain different subunits, or may differ in the size or composition of one particular subunit.

The action of RNA polymerases in eukaryotic cells appears to be influenced by many factors, including various hormones, the basic and acidic nuclear proteins, and specific protein factors. The basic protein histone III has been reported to interact directly with RNA polymerases, indirectly inactivating the enzyme through interactions with the DNA in chromatin. Binding of acidic proteins may, in general, enhance polymerase activity; these proteins have been postulated to play a role similar to that of the prokaryotic σ factor. In addition, these proteins often play a role in the effects of hormones on transcription, and may be the direct mediators of some hormonal effects.

Hormones from the pituitary gland may control the levels of the different RNA polymerases classes in the cell, which may be involved in embryogenesis and differentiation. Different embryonal stages have widely varying requirements for the types of RNA molecules that must be present. In very early embryos, little rRNA and mRNA are needed, since maternal supplies of ribosomes will be adequate for the limited protein synthesis that takes place. In the next stages of embryogenesis, many proteins must be synthesized; so the embryo requires many new ribosomes. This implies a coordinated increase in the synthesis of rRNA, 5S RNA, and ribosomal proteins, and therefore an increase in the amount of RNA polymerases required for these molecules to be formed. Initiation of protein synthesis to prepare the specific proteins required during each stage of growth requires a significant increase in the amount of class II enzyme found in the cell so that the specific mRNA molecules can be produced in large-enough quantities. In general, earlier stages require larger amounts of classes I and III, which eventually decrease, while class II enzymes show some increase in slightly later embryos.

Differentiation may also involve changes from one subclass of an RNA class to another. In sea urchin tissues, for example, subclass III B is the predominant form found in the blastula stage, replacing III A, which is present in unfertilized eggs. These changes may be controlled by hormonal signals. In chick embryos, 17 β-estradiol stimulates the activity of class I and II enzymes, resulting in increased synthesis of a specific protein, vitallogenin. Other hormones of the same type have been shown to increase the transcription of mRNA required for the synthesis of ovalbumin in chick oviducts. The hormones may, in some cases, act by stimulating or inhibiting the action of adenyl cyclase, thus controlling the cellular levels of cyclic AMP. This would influence in turn the activity of specific protein kinases, which phosphorylate nuclear proteins. Such a mechanism could result in increased or decreased transcription by influencing the binding of these nuclear proteins to DNA.

INHIBITION OF RNA POLYMERASES IN EUKARYOTIC CELLS

Since transcription requires the local denaturation of specific regions of the DNA double helix, any agent that interferes with this unwinding will prevent RNA synthesis. Not all inhibitors of transcription, however, interact with the RNA polymerases. Generally, intercalating agents and other inhibitors that interact with the genome rather than the polymerase can influence both prokaryotic and eukaryotic transcription. Those compounds that interact with the enzyme, on the other hand, usually do not show this type of cross-reaction, but are specific for one cell type, and sometimes even for a single RNA polymerase class.

Some compounds that are specific inhibitors of eukaryotic RNA polymerases are described in Chapter 9.2, specifically in Table 1 and Figure 1. Included among such compounds are antibiotics and hormone-like compounds. Antibiotics that interact specifically with prokaryotic RNA polymerases are useful in human diseases, since they act as bactericidal agents. Those compounds that inhibit eukaryotic RNA polymerases, on the other hand, are useful only in vitro, in the elucidation of the roles of the various classes of these enzymes, since cross-reaction between the classes is often not present.

A specific inhibitor of rat liver RNA polymerases has recently been described. It is a macromolecule, found in the smooth endoplasmic reticulum of rat liver. It does not appear to be an RNase, a DNase, or a protease. It interacts most strongly with class II polymerases, which require Mn^{2+} ions as the preferred cation. The mechanism of action appears to be a binding of this macromolecule to the complex formed by the manganese ions with the ribonucleotides. This complex would seem to be the actual substrate for the polymerase. The binding of the inhibitor to the complex prevents interaction of the substrate with the active site of the enzyme, perhaps by steric interference. Other inhibitors of this type may also exist that interact specifically with other RNA polymerases, but none has so far been identified.

ORGANELLE RNA POLYMERASES

Mitochondria contain specific RNA polymerases that are quite small compared to most other enzymes of this type. These polymerases have a molecular weight of about 64,000 daltons, and appear to contain a single polypeptide chain. They are generally inhibited by rifampicin but not by α-amanitin, except in the case of the yeast mitochondrial polymerases. Enzymes of this type have been isolated from the mitochondria of yeast, *Neurospora,* and rat liver; in each case, the preferred template is mitochondrial DNA. There do not appear to be different classes of mitochondrial RNA polymerases, but rather a single class that transcribes the mitochondrial genome at the

G2 and S phases of the cell cycle. It is not clear if these enzymes are coded for by the mitochondrial genome, or are made in the cytoplasm and transported into the organelle.

In chloroplasts, specific RNA synthesis appears to take place, but no purified chloroplast RNA polymerase has been described. RNA synthesis in the chloroplasts of simple plants is inhibited by rifampicin, as it is in prokaryotes and many mitochondria. No such inhibition has been demonstrated by this antibiotic in the chloroplasts of higher plants, however. Studies indicate that if a specific chloroplast RNA polymerase exists, it functions very tightly bound to the organelle DNA in vivo. This may indicate that the RNA synthesis in this system depends on a strict interaction of the enzyme with the genome of the chloroplast. However, the available evidence is also consistent with the hypothesis that no organelle-specific RNA polymerase exists, and that chloroplast RNA is synthesized by one of the cytoplasmic RNA polymerases of the plant.

PLANT RNA POLYMERASES

RNA polymerases from plants appear to exist as several different classes, which are generally known as RC-I, RC-II, and RC-III. Like prokaryotic and eukaryotic polymerases, but unlike the viral and mitochondrial enzymes, the plant polymerases contain several types of subunits (Table 3). In general,

Table 3. Plant RNA Polymerases.

PLANT TYPE	ENZYME	MOLECULAR WEIGHT, DALTONS	SUBUNIT TYPE	MOLECULAR WEIGHT, DALTONS
Wheat germ	II	$4–4.5 \times 10^7$	A	2.2×10^7
			A'	1.7×10^7
			B	1.4×10^7
			C	$\sim 0.45 \times 10^7$
			D	0.4×10^7
Coconut	RC-I	7.3×10^7	a	1.8×10^7
			b (2%)	1.5×10^7
			c	0.95×10^7
			d (2%)	0.80×10^7
	RC-II	6.3×10^7	a	1.8×10^7
			b (2%)	1.5×10^7
			c	0.69×10^7
			d (2%)	0.42×10^7
	RC-III	5.34×10^7	a	1.8×10^7
			b (2%)	1.12×10^7
			c	0.5×10^7
			d (2%)	0.4×10^7

these enzymes have a molecular weight range of 4×10^5 to 7×10^5 daltons, and each holoenzyme contains four to six subunits. These subunits range in size from 4×10^6 to about 2×10^7 daltons, and are not present in stoichiometric quantities in the holoenzymes.

Plant RNA polymerases are subject to control by specific plant hormones such as the auxins. These compounds appear to interact with receptor proteins to form a complex, and this complex stimulates the homologous RNA polymerase activity. The stimulation may involve binding of the hormone–protein complex to specific initiation sites on the plant DNA; such a mechanism could account for the transcription of specific plant genes. When the complex is bound, the appropriate RNA polymerase can attach to the genome to begin the transcription of the gene.

At present, no information is available regarding the specific roles of the different classes of plant polymerases. It appears likely, however, that there will be some correspondence to the specific functions of eukaryotic classes of the enzymes. Further work with plant polymerases may yield some clues to interesting work that can be carried out in eukaryotic systems in general.

BIBLIOGRAPHY

Matthysse, A. G., and Abrams, M. 1970. *Biochim. Biophys. Acta* 119:511.

Venis, M. A. 1971. *Proc. Nat. Acad. Sci. U.S.A.* 68:1824.

Polya, G. M., and Jagendorf, A. Y. 1971. *Arch. Biochem. Biophys.* 146:635.

Reid, B. D., and Parsons, P. 1971. *Proc. Nat. Acad. Sci. U.S.A.* 68:2830.

Kuntzel, H., and Schafer, K. P. 1971. *Nature New Biol.* 231:265.

Burgess, R. R. 1971. *Annu. Rev. Biochem.* 40:711.

Weaver, R. F., Blatti, S. P., and Rutter, W. J. 1971. *Proc. Nat. Acad. Sci. U.S.A.* 68:2994.

Kedinger, C., Gissinger, F., Gniazdowski, M., Mandel, J.-L., and Chambon, P. 1972. *Eur. J. Biochem.* 28:269.

Chan, V. L., Whitmore, G. F., and Siminovitch, L. 1972. *Proc. Nat. Acad. Sci. U.S.A.* 69:3119.

Sugden, B., and Keller, W. 1973. *J. Biol. Chem.* 248:3777.

Biswas, B. B., Ganguly, A., and Das, A. 1975. *Prog. Nucl. Acid Res. Mol. Biol.* 15:145.

Antonoglou, O., Salakidon, H., Haralambidon, E., and Traxatellis, A. 1977. *Biochim. Biophys. Acta* 474:467.

9.4. Messenger RNA

SIZE, STRUCTURE, AND FUNCTION

The molecules of mRNA within an organism are somewhat heterogeneous in size, but are all similar in structure. The size of the molecules depends on the size of the protein for which they code; a small protein will require a shorter mRNA than will a larger one. The molecules contain the codons that will be translated into the specific protein product, but also contain other nucleotides, which may include recognition signals for the interaction of the mRNA with other components of the ribosomal machinery. In addition, specific termination signals are present, several of which may be found in the same molecule, perhaps to ensure that the untranslated sequences found at both ends of the mRNA will not be translated. The actual function of these untranscribed sequences is not well defined; some may serve to hold the mRNA in correct alignment during association with the initiator tRNA and the ribosome, but no specific function can be ascribed to most of them.

In some viruses, the mRNA that is transcribed from the viral DNA may be polycistronic; the same is true for some bacterial genes, and perhaps the same situation will also be found in eukaryotic DNA. Polycistronic mRNA includes the message coding for more than one polypeptide. It may be translated into a single, large polypeptide that is then processed into the individual proteins; or, alternatively, translation could proceed at several initiation sites on the mRNA, so that the proteins would be made separately. The first hypothesis is probably more correct, since the proteins from polycistronic mRNA molecules are generally not translated at the same rate and to the same extent. This scheme would support the possibility that the ribosome attaches, translates the message for the first protein, and then reaches some termination signal that may sometimes be ignored. In this case, the second and subsequent peptide products will also be translated. Most mRNA molecules appear to code for a single polypeptide chain, however—not for several proteins. It is of interest to note that recent work with some viruses, immunoglobulins, ovalbumin, and hemoglobin indicates that the genes for these products, and possibly also the mRNAs produced from these genes, are discontinuous; that is, coding and nontranslated sequences appear to be interspersed within the molecule.

The situation can be well illustrated for the globin genes that code for the non-α chains of this polymeric molecule. In general, hemoglobin contains

Figure 1. Non-α globin gene cluster.

four chains, two of which are of the type known as α, and the other two of a different type. Normal adult hemoglobin contains two β chains, the minor adult form has two σ chains, fetal hemoglobin contains two γ chains, and embryonic hemoglobin has still another type, the ε chain. These non-α genes are known to be closely linked to each other, but not to the α genes. It was proposed by Kabat in 1972 that the non-α genes form a cluster that contains a single promoter gene with terminators (t) and operators (o) between the genes for ε and for γ, as well as between γ and β. This cluster is illustrated in Figure 1.

Kabat hypothesized that the shift in production of the different types of hemoglobins that occurs during differentiation is due to the excision of the inappropriate genes. That is, during embryogenesis, the ε gene is deleted so that the promoter gene allows transcription of the γ gene; late in fetal life, this gene is also excised, and the organism produces then only the two adult types of chains, the β and the σ. This occurs by the looping out of genes; the loop is susceptible to nuclease action and is removed. This scheme is illustrated in Figure 2.

Recently, several laboratories have attempted to discover evidence that would prove or disprove this theory. Benz et al. found that cells from sheep heterozygous for two types of adult hemoglobin can shift production of hemoglobin so that, under different physiological conditions, the same cell can produce one type or the other, implying that both genes are present within the individual cells, even though only one type of hemoglobin is normally produced by a single cell. Papayannopoulou and his coworkers tested a different implication of Kabat's theory. If the structure proposed by Kabat is correct, no cell can produce more than two types of hemoglobin, owing to

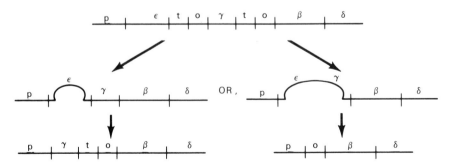

Figure 2. Looping out and excision of genes.

the presence of terminator genes. Using fluorescent antisera specific for various types of hemoglobin, this group was able to show that three different hemoglobins can be produced by a single cell. Mitchell and Williamson have shown that, contrary to the predictions of this hypothesis, normal adult human DNA contains the γ gene at about the same level as is found in fetal cells.

These results strongly support a mechanism of specific gene inactivation to account for the switching of cells from production of one type of gene product to another, at least in the case of the globin genes. They do not support the postulated theory of gene excision. Other laboratories have published evidence that implies a structural difference between actively transcribed genes and those that are inactive. Transcriptionally active genes are more susceptible to nuclease digestion than those that are switched off, and can also be physically separated from the latter. This behavior could be due to a less tight coupling of nuclear proteins in regions of active transcription, since it is thought that the nucleoprotein complex must be relaxed for RNA synthesis to take place (see also below).

As mentioned previously, in Chapter 9.1, mRNA molecules, at least in eukaryotes, appear to hydrogen-bond within the molecule, forming hairpin loop-type structures at several different points in the mRNA (Figure 3). These loops may be involved in resistance or sensitivity to nuclease digestion, and have been postulated to play some specific role in the identification of the ribosome-binding site on the mRNA molecule. Nontranslated sequences

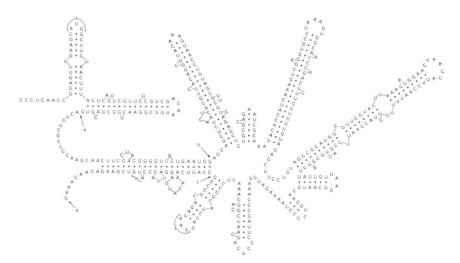

Figure 3. Hairpin loops in mRNA. A possible intramolecular hydrogen-binding pattern for a viral coat protein mRNA.

at the 5'-terminus of mRNA from viruses contain what appear to be initiation codons that are not recognized by the ribosome. This phenomenon might be due to the tertiary structure of the mRNA in these regions, a view supported by studies on protein synthesis using viral mRNA in vitro. If the mRNA is treated with heat before translation, the initiation pattern of translation is altered for two proteins coded for by the R17 virus. This heat treatment could cause breakage of hydrogen bonds forming the hairpin loops, especially in regions that are rich in A–T pairs. These results are consistent with the hypothesis that ribosomes bind to mRNA in regions that are not hydrogen-bonded, perhaps at the ends of loops, or in the linear regions between loops.

HALF-LIFE OF BACTERIAL mRNA

Jacob and Monod predicted that mRNA molecules should be rapidly degraded rather than being retained in the cell for long periods of time. This was found to be true for some bacterial messengers, but not for all. The half-life of the most rapidly degraded bacterial mRNA molecules appears to be of the order of 1 or perhaps 2 min at 37°C; at this point, nuclease digestion will break down the mRNA into its component ribonucleotides, which can be rephosphorylated and used to synthesize new RNA molecules. The break-down of the mRNA molecules proceeds almost simultaneously with transla-tion. As peptide chains are completed and ribosomes detach from the mRNA, nuclease can attack unless other ribosomes attach.

Some bacterial mRNA molecules are much more stable than this; the most stable appear to be retained for several hours prior to nuclease digestion. In *Bacillus cereus,* several mRNA molecules have been shown to be degraded only after several hours, whereas the mRNA for the *lac* operon genes appears to be much more quickly degraded in *E. coli.* The significance of these differ-ences may lie in the nature of the protein product. The least stable mRNA molecules appear to be those that code for inducible enzymes, which are usually required by the cell for a specific purpose. It would not be advanta-geous to the cell to continue to produce these proteins under normal physiolog-ical conditions; it may be more economical to continue to transcribe the mRNA when it is needed, rather than to retain the mRNA, which would continue to be translated. Constitutive proteins, on the other hand, must be continuously produced by the cell; retaining the same mRNA molecule will probably be more energy-efficient than retranscribing it each time. Nu-clease digestion may be prevented by the attachment of new ribosomes as the peptides are released; the mechanism whereby the ribosome would recog-nize the appropriate mRNA molecules is not known.

HALF-LIFE OF EUKARYOTIC mRNA MOLECULES

In eukaryotic systems, mRNA has a longer half-life than in bacteria. The molecules are synthesized in the nucleus, but must be transported into the cytoplasm for use in translation. Some time must be allowed for processing and transport of these molecules. The apparent half-lives of the eukaryotic mRNA molecules vary from several hours to several days, and perhaps several weeks in the case of embryonic tissues and oocytes. It is thought that the ova, which will be fertilized, may retain some "maternal" mRNA, which will be used to produce proteins in the early stages of development of the embryo. In oocytes, it has been postulated that the mRNA may be packaged in nucleoprotein complexes called "informasomes"; this same name has also been given to the postulated cytoplasmic particles that are involved in mRNA transport.

The stability of mRNA has important implications for theories of genetic regulation. It has been difficult to isolate and study single mRNA species, since many such molecules, each coding for a different group of proteins, can be produced in a single cell. If some ways were available to separate them, it might be possible to measure directly the stability of each. The shorter-lived molecules may share some common characteristics in structure that could help to explain the differences that are presumed to exist in control. At present, it is possible to isolate a few mRNA molecules, which generally are found to be produced by a single cell type in high concentrations. Examples of such mRNAs are those for the globin chains of hemoglobin, the immunoglobin molecules in certain disease states, and the lens crystalline protein in the eyes of calves. As more is learned of specific control processes that can stimulate the transcription of specific mRNA molecules, it may become possible to isolate other molecules, and to determine their properties with more precision.

HnRNA AS A POSSIBLE PRECURSOR FOR mRNA

HnRNA and mRNA share several characteristics. Both are rapidly labeled by short incubations (pulses) with radioactive precursors of ribonucleic acids, and have shorter half-lives than rRNA or tRNA molecules. Neither contains significant levels of modified bases, and they form stable RNA–RNA hybrids, implying a certain amount of sequence homology. In addition, the transcription of neither is influenced by Actinomycin D, which will prevent rRNA synthesis. Finally, poly A sequences have been found in both classes, although not every molecule of each class contains these stretches of adenine. The length of the poly A sequences is variable, ranging from about 10 to about

150 adenine residues, which are usually bound covalently to the 3'-terminus of the molecules.

This evidence supports a precursor role for HnRNA, but does not prove it. Some published evidence indicates a more complex relationship between these two classes. The antibiotic cordyceptin causes a significant reduction in the synthesis of mRNA, but has little or no effect on the transcription of HnRNA. In addition, incorporation of labeled uridine into RNA in the presence of low levels of Actinomycin D shows different patterns in mRNA and HnRNA. These observations can be reconciled with a precursor role for HnRNA by assuming that only a small fraction of it is actually processed into mRNA, and that the bulk of the HnRNA never leaves the nucleus. The presence of poly A sequences correlates with the actual precursor molecules, and cordyceptin could preferentially prevent their transcription. Even the actual precursor HnRNA molecules could contain nontranslatable sequences which are removed from these molecules during processing into mRNA.

Several lines of evidence have been reported that favor such a possibility.

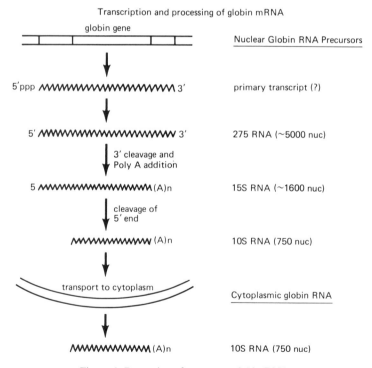

Figure 4. Processing of precursor globin RNA.

The largest HnRNA molecules do not contain poly A sequences, and indeed only a few such sequences are seen in HnRNA in general. These sequences are labeled prior to the appearance of adenylated mRNA molecules in the cytoplasm, and are similar in size to those found in cytoplasmic mRNA molecules. It has also been shown that ribosome-binding sites are present in a fraction of the HnRNA. Recently, it has been shown that globin precursor mRNA (i.e., large molecules that are processed to form the mRNA for globin chains) can be identified in the nuclear RNA. Bastos and Aviv have postulated a processing scheme for these globin mRNA precursors which is shown in Figure 4. The largest precursors are not adenylated; poly A is added at some stage during processing. Some evidence now available indicates that nontranslated sequences may be interspersed within the precursor with the actual codons, rather than being localized at the ends of the precursor as shown. In addition, evidence that only 10–20% of the HnRNA ever leaves the nucleus is now available. To sum up, the evidence supports the concept that a certain portion of the HnRNA serves as precursor molecules for the mRNA which will be transported to the nucleus to participate in protein synthesis.

BIBLIOGRAPHY

Size, Structure, and Function:

Kabat, D. 1972. *Science* 175:134.
Axel, R., Cedar, H., and Felsenfeld, G. 1973. *Proc. Natl. Acad. Sci. U.S.A.* 70:2029.
Gilmour, R. S., and Paul, J. 1973. *Proc. Natl. Acad. Sci.* 70:3440.
Nikolaev, N., Silengo, L., and Schlessinger, D. 1973. *J. Biol. Chem.* 248:7697.
Dunn, J. J., and Studier, F. W. 1973. *Proc. Natl. Acad. Sci. U.S.A.* 70:1559.
Ricard, B., and Salser, W. 1974. *Nature* 248:314.
Furinchi, Y., and Miura, K. 1975. *Nature* 253:374.
Wei, C. M., and Moss, B. 1975. *Proc. Natl. Acad. Sci.* 72:318.
Perry, R. P., Kelley, D. E., Frederici, K., and Rottman, F. 1975. *Cell* 4:387.
Adams, J. M., and Cory, S. 1975. *Nature* 255:28.
Perry, R. P., and Kelley, D. E. 1976. *Cell* 8:433.
Hunt, J. A., and Oakes, G. N. 1976. *Biochem. J.* 155:637.
Weintraub, H., and Groundine, M. 1976. *Science* 193:848.
Garel, A., and Axel, R. 1976. *Proc. Natl. Acad. Sci. U.S.A.* 73:3966.
Benz, E., Jr., Turner, P., Barker, J., and Neinhuis, A. 1977. *Science* 196:1213.
Papayannopoulou, Th., Nute, P. E., Stamatoyannopoulos, G., and McGuire, T. C. 1977. *Science* 196:1215.
Wallace, R. B., Dube, S. K., and Bonner, J. 1977. *Science* 198:1166.
Mitchell, G. J., and Williamson, R. 1977. *Nucl. Acids Res.* 4:3557.
Jeffreys, A. J., and Flavell, R. A. 1977. *Cell* 12:1097.
Brack, C., and Tonegawa, S. 1977. *Proc. Natl. Acad. Sci.* 74:5652.
Glover, D. M., and Hogness, D. S. 1977. *Cell* 10:167.
White, R. L., and Hogness, D. S. 1977. *Cell* 10:177.
Wellauer, P. K., and David, J. B. 1977. *Cell* 10:193.

Lai, E. C., Woo, S. L. C., Dugaiczyk, A., Catterall, J. F., and O'Malley, B. W. 1978. *Proc. Natl. Acad. Sci.* 75:2205.

Dugaiczyk, A., Woo, S. L. C., Lai, E. C., Mace, M. L., Jr., McReynolds, L., and O'Malley, B. W. 1978. *Nature* 274:328.

Half-life of mRNA:

Meyfalch, A. A. 1971. *Curr. Top. Dev. Biol.* 6:45.

Raff, R. A., Colat, H. V., Selvig, S. E., and Gross, P. R. 1972. *Nature* 235:211.

Schechter, I. 1973. *Proc. Natl. Acad. Sci. U.S.A.* 70:2256.

McKean, D. J., Potter, M., and Hood, L. 1973. *Biochemistry* 12:749.

Schechter, I., McKean, D. J., Guyer, R., and Terry, W. 1975. *Science* 188:161.

Ross, J. 1976. *J. Mol. Biol.* 106:403.

HnRNA as Precursor for mRNA:

Lim, L., and Canellakis, E. S. 1970. *Nature* 227:710.

Edmonds, M., Vaughan, M. H., and Nakazato, H. 1971. *Proc. Natl. Acad. Sci.* 68:1336.

Stavnezer, J., and Huang, R. C. C. 1971. *Nature New Biol.* 230:172.

Berns, A. J. M., de Abreu, R. A., van Kraaikamp, M., Beneditti, E. L., and Bluemendal, H. 1971. *FEBS Lett.* 18:159.

Lee, S. Y., Mendicki, J., and Braverman, G. 1971. *Proc. Natl. Acad. Sci.* 68:1331.

Greenberg, J. R., and Perry, R. P. 1972. *J. Mol. Biol.* 72:91.

Darnell, J. E., Jelinek, W. R., and Molloy, G. 1973. *Science* 181:1215.

Singer, R. H., and Penman, S. 1973. *J. Mol. Biol.* 78:321.

Macnaughton, M., Freeman, K. B., and Bishop, J. O. 1974. *Cell* 1:117.

Lewin, B. 1975. *Cell* 4:11.

Herman, R. C., Williams, J. G., and Penman, S. 1976. *Cell* 7:429.

Spohr, G., Dettori, G., and Manzari, V. 1976. *Cell* 8:505.

Ross, J. 1976. *J. Mol. Biol.* 106:403.

Curtis, P. J., and Weissmann, C. 1976. *J. Mol. Biol.* 106:1061.

Chan, L. N. L. 1978. *Nature* 261:158.

Tonegawa, S. 1976. *Proc. Natl. Acad. Sci. U.S.A.* 73:203.

Hozumi, N., and Tonegawa, S. 1976. *Proc. Natl. Acad. Sci. U.S.A.* 73:3628.

Stavnezer, J., and Buhop, J. M. 1977. *Biochemistry* 16:4225.

Kwan, S., Wood, T. G., and Lingrel, J. B. 1977. *Proc. Natl. Acad. Sci. U.S.A.* 74:178.

Bastos, R. N., and Aviv, H. 1977. *Cell* 11:641.

McReynolds, L., O'Malley, B. W., Nisbet, A. D., Fothergill, J. E., Givol, D., Fields, S., Robertson, M., and Brownlee, G. G. 1978. *Nature* 273:723.

Dugaiezyk, A., Wood, S. L. C., Lai, E. C., Mace, M. L., Jr., McReynolds, L., and O'Malley, B. W. 1978. *Nature* 274:328.

Poly A and mRNA Half-life:

Wilson, M. C., Sawicki, S. G., White, P. A., and Darnell, J. E. 1978. *J. Mol. Biol.* 126:23.

9.5. Ribosomes

GENERAL STRUCTURE AND FUNCTION

Ribosomes are ribonucleoprotein complexes, formed of specific RNA molecules complexed with certain proteins of a particular type. Each ribosome, whether isolated from prokaryotic, eukaryotic, or organelle systems, consists of two subunits of unequal size. In general, prokaryotic ribosomes are smaller than those from eukaryotes, but all are similar in structure and function. The complete ribosomes are found in the cytosol; in eukaryotic cells, association of RNA and proteins appears to take place in the nucleus.

The larger subunit of bacterial cells has a sedimentation coefficient of 50S, the small unit is a 30S particle, and the complete ribosome has a sedimentation coefficient of 70S. Eukaryotic 80S ribosomes consist of 40S and 60S subunits; the molecular weights of the two types being respectively 2.7×10^6 and 4.3×10^6 daltons. About 65% of the total bacterial ribosomes consist of rRNA, as opposed to about 55% in the eukaryotic ribosomes. Some of the general characteristics of eukaryotic, bacterial, and mitochondrial ribosomes are compared in Table 1.

The ribosome serves as a matrix for holding in place the various components necessary for protein synthesis. In addition, ribosomal proteins participate

Table 1.   Sedimentation Coefficients of Ribosomes from Different Sources.

	BACTERIA	EUKARYOTES	MITOCHONDRIA
Components	70S	80S	50–60S
Pseudouridine	0.2 mole %	1–2 mole %	
Methylated nucleotides	0.6–1.0%	1.2–1.7%	0–1.4%[a]
G + C content	54%	57–65%	37–45%
%RNA:% protein ratio	1.78	1.22	
Large subunit	50S	60S	35–45S
RNA	23S + 5S	28S + 5S + 5.5S	16–19S + 5S
proteins	32–34	50	30
Small subunit	30S	40S	25–35S
RNA	16S	18S	12–13S
proteins	21	30	23

[a] There is much disagreement on the presence of methyl groups in mitochondrial rRNA.

directly in certain steps of translation, during synthesis of the peptide bond between amino acids. The specific role of each ribosomal component is the subject of much study at present; much is known about several of the ribosomal proteins, some of which will be described below. The rRNA found in ribosomes is required for the structural and functional integrity of the ribosomal particles, and may participate in maintaining the proper configurations of the associated mRNA and tRNA molecules during translation. It is thought possible that divalent magnesium ions form bridges between non-paired bases in the various RNA molecules; this would aid in the maintenance of proper base-pairing between the codons of the mRNA and the appropriate anticodons of the tRNA. In addition, it would assure that each was held in position on the correct site of the ribosome.

Comparison of ribosomes from different organisms and from organelles is of interest in light of the speculation as to the origin of organelles. Mitochondria have been postulated to be remnants of parisitic bacterial cells; if this were true, the ribosomes should resemble prokaryotic rather than eukaryotic ribosomes. Instead, examination of the data shows differences in all three types. Chloroplast ribosomes, which are not shown in Table 1, show much greater similarities to bacterial ribosomes. Recently, however, a comparison of rRNA from bacteria, eukaryotes, and mitochondria has been published. The organelle 18S rRNA shows a strong structural homology with strongly conserved sequences in bacterial rRNA; this will be discussed in more detail below.

A major difference in eukaryotic ribosomes should be noted: they contain four different species of rRNA, as opposed to three types in bacteria and organelles. In addition, the site of methylation of nucleotides differs in eukaryotic ribosomes. The bulk of methyl groups that modify rRNA structure here are found on the sugar moiety, whereas the methylation in bacterial rRNA is generally found to occur on the bases themselves. The significance of these observations for the function of the ribosomes in the different groups is not known.

The proteins found in the ribosomes of *E. coli* have been extensively studied, whereas those of other species have been investigated to a lesser degree. Some ribosomal proteins have enzymatic activity, while others appear to function as structural components required for the maintenance of the integrity of the ribosomal particles. Ribosomes can be separated into their constituent proteins and nucleic acids, and then reconstituted in the absence of one of these components in an attempt to determine the function of each constituent. Using this technique, the functions of many of the proteins of the *E. coli* ribosome have been established. Other means of determining these roles have made use of altered proteins resulting from specific mutations. Still other approaches to the problem include the use of chemical agents to modify the structure of one or more ribosomal proteins, as well as the use of antibodies specific to one of these proteins.

TRANSCRIPTION AND PROCESSING OF rRNA

In both prokaryotic and eukaryotic cells, rRNA genes are transcribed as a single, large RNA molecule, with the rRNA from the small subunit at or near the 5' terminus. The large precursor molecule is then sequentially cleaved, giving rise to the specific rRNA molecules, and to other sequences, which are probably immediately degraded. Transcription of ribsomal RNA requires a specific RNA polymerase, as discussed in Chapter 9.2. In bacteria, processing apparently starts before transcription is complete, so that 16S RNA is released from the nascent precursor before 23S RNA has been completely synthesized. In eukaryotic cells, on the other hand, no processing takes place until the entire precursor molecule has been released from the template. The synthesis and preliminary processing of rRNA take place in the nucleolus of eukaryotic nuclei; the enzymes involved may include specific exonucleases localized in the nucleolus.

The eukaryotic precursor is originally synthesized as a piece of 45S RNA with a molecular weight of 4.1×10^6 daltons. This molecule is methylated during transcription; the presence of methyl groups may aid in the processing of the 45S molecule. The first step in processing reduces the size to 41S, a transient intermediate that is quickly cleaved to 35S and 20S fragments. The 20S is the direct precursor of the 18S rRNA molecule; this fragment migrates to the nucleoplasm, associates with the 30S ribosomal proteins, and is found as a complete small subunit in the cytoplasm within 30 min. The 32S fragment, associated with 5S RNA (Figure 1), and possibly already formed into a ribonucleoprotein complex, migrates to the nucleoplasm where final processing occurs. The fourth rRNA species may also be a product of the processing of the precursor, but little is known yet about the association of this molecule to the large subunit. After final processing, the large, 60S, subunit containing the final 28S rRNA molecule migrates to the cytoplasm. There is some evidence that ribosomal proteins may associate with the nascent precursor chains.

It appears that 5S rRNA is not formed in the nucleolus, and that complete 5S chains migrate to the nucleolus for association with the 28S precursor in a 1:1 ratio. Similarly, ribosomal proteins are formed in the cytoplasm, but form ribonucleoprotein complexes in the nucleus. Some control mechanism must exist to coordinate the synthesis of the three components at three different sites, but no such mechanism has yet been described.

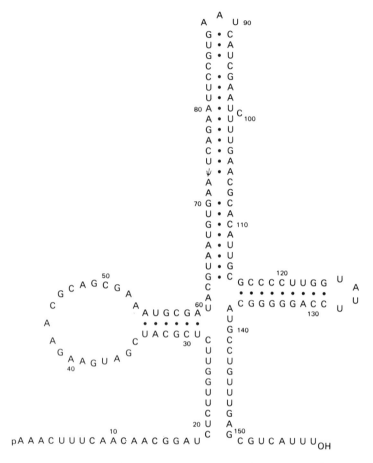

Figure 1. rRNA structure. Possible secondary structure of 5.8S RNA. The ends of the molecule do not seem to be involved in base-pairing. There is a ψp residue at position 73. (From G. M. Rubin, *J. Biol. Chem.* 248:3860, 1973.)

GENE MULTIPLICITY

Most bacterial genes are present in the genome in a single copy, while eukaryotic DNA contains many repeats of some genes. In both types of cells, rDNA, (i.e., DNA coding for rRNA sequences) is present in a relatively large number of copies. Prokaryotic cells show a multiplicity of 5 to 50 copies per genome, and the rDNA represents about 0.5% of the total coding sequences in the bacterial DNA. In eukaryotes, the multiplicity is much higher, with several hundred copies of the genes present per genome. With the genome, rRNA genes form tandem repeats, situated immediately next to each other. Eukaryotic rRNA precursors appear to have nonribosomal sequences at both the 5' and 3' termini, while the small rRNA of *E. coli* is apparently not connected to nonribosomal sequences at the 5' end.

During embryogenesis in some amphibians and insects, a large increase in the number of nucleoli found in certain cells is noted. This process, known as gene amplification, ensures the presence of sufficient ribosomes for rapid growth. There may be as many as 1500 extra, free nucleoli in oocytes, allowing production and accumulation of about 10^2 ribosomes in each egg. At normal rates of transcription, production of this many ribosomes would require 10^5 days. Assuming that the rate of transcription does not change, the presence of 1000 nucleoli will decrease the time required to 3 to 6 months, and an increased transcription rate will reduce it still further. The 5S genes do not show gene amplification, yet sufficient 5S RNA is produced, implying a greatly increased rate of transcription for these genes in this period. In certain other animals, extra rDNA genes are found, but they are not associated with extra nucleoli but remain within the original nucleolus. In these cases, there must be some specific stimulus to allow transcription of these copies at the appropriate time during development.

Cytological studies have established that the DNA coding for rRNA is located at specific sites on the eukaryotic chromosome; in some species, these sites can be easily visualized. A specific chromosome, or several of them, may contain one or more sites to which the nucleolus can attach; these nucleolar-organizing regions contain the rDNA genes. In situ hybridization of purified rRNA to denatured chromatin fixed on slides has allowed visualization of such sites in many eukaryotic chromosomes. Electron microscopy has confirmed the tandem arrangement of the reiterated rDNA genes. Segments of nucleolar DNA, each about 2–3 μm in length, can be seen to be coated with rRNA molecules which are being transcribed. Between each segment, there are nontranscribed sections that probably correspond to "spacer" DNA which lies between tandem repeats and does not seem to code for any RNA sequences. The arrangement of rDNA genes in *E. coli* appears to be similar, with tandem repeats of the genes separated by spacer regions.

RIBOSOMAL PROTEINS

The 21 proteins associated with the small subunit of the bacterial ribosome have been extensively studied in *E. coli*. Most of them have molecular weights that vary from 13,000 to 65,000 daltons, and they appear to be present in single copies in each functional ribosome. Several of them, including the proteins known as S-4, S-7, S-8, S-9, S-16, and S-17, have been shown to be required for the assembly of the functional 30S subunit. Some ribosomal proteins have been shown to form site-specific complexes with the rRNA; these proteins include S-4, S-7, S-8, S-15, and S-20. The resistance or sensitivity of organisms to certain antibiotics has also been correlated with the presence of certain ribosomal proteins. Streptomycin, for example, interacts with S-12, while spectinomycin resistance is correlated with S-5. On the other hand, some antibiotics interact with the RNA; kasugamycin resistance, for example, is dependent on the degree of methylation of 16S rRNA.

Studies involving the chemical modification of sulfhydryl groups indicate that the integrity of S-18 is absolutely essential for the maintenance of ribosomal function. Similar studies have shown that two proteins, S-11 and S-21, are required for the binding of rRNA and tRNA to the ribosome. An interesting protein of the small subunit is S-1; it can easily detach from the ribosome, and is thought to act as an initiation factor. No translation can be initiated in the absence of S-1, but the protein is not required for elongation of a peptide chain once chain growth has started.

The proteins of the large bacterial subunit have not been as well characterized. At present, even their number is still a matter of dispute, although it is generally accepted that there are more than 30, but fewer than 35 such 50S proteins. One of them is known to function as a peptidyl transferase, catalyzing the formation of peptide bonds between adjacent amino acids during translation. Two other proteins of the large subunit are known to be required for GTPase activity during elongation. No specific roles can be assigned the other proteins; some are required for the structural integrity of the subunit, while others are involved with interactions with the various rRNA species, as well as with the other components of protein synthesis. These proteins will be discussed at greater length in Section 10.

In eukaryotic ribosomes, the roles of individual proteins have been studied to a much lesser extent. It is known that there is no close structural homology between the bacterial and the eukaryotic ribosomal proteins, but it is very probable that functional homologies exist. There is an easily detached protein of the small eukaryotic subunit, for example, that appears to be similar to S-1. It appears to be responsible for the fact that both 40S and 43S ribosomal subunits can be found in eukaryotes; when it attaches, it changes the sedimentation coefficient of the subunit, and it may be required for the functional integrity of this subunit. Mitochondrial ribosomal proteins differ from both prokaryotic and eukaryotic proteins. Functional ribosomes cannot be reconstituted from a mixture of bacterial and mitochondrial components, or from eukaryotic and prokaryotic mixtures. The ribosomal components of the chloroplasts, on the other hand, are very similar to the bacterial ribosomes, and hybrid ribosomes made from these components are active in protein synthesis in vitro.

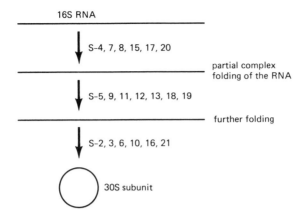

Figure 2. Assembly of the small bacterial subunit.

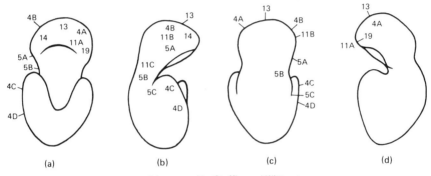

model proposed by Stoffler and Wittman

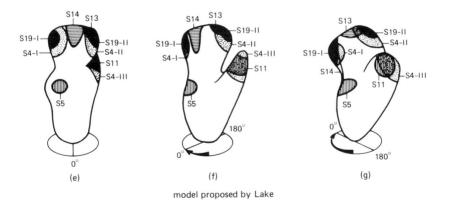

model proposed by Lake

Figure 3. Models of the 30S structure.

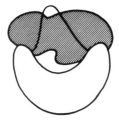
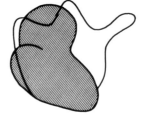

proposed by Stoffler and Wittmann   proposed by Lake

Figure 4. Models of the 70S subunit.

RIBOSOMAL ASSEMBLY

The assembly of the ribosome appears to be a cooperative process, wherein the binding of one protein to the complex facilitates the binding of others. Some proteins, notably S-4, S-7, S-8, S-15, S-17 and S-20, probably bind directly to the 16S RNA of the small subunit, and influence the subsequent formation of the ribonuclear complex. The assembly probably requires the formation of hydrogen bonds as well as hydrophobic interactions between the proteins, and between the proteins and the RNA. A diagram of a proposed scheme of the assembly sequence is shown in Figure 2; as shown, the actual binding of the S-1 protein, as well as its actual role in the integrity of the subunit, is still the subject of some doubt.

The proteins appear to be held to the RNA in a conformation best described as a monomolecular layer of proteins held together by the rRNA (Figure 3). Each of the 30S proteins has been shown to be at least partially accessible to the surface, since antigenic sites for each have been described. At the same time, the size and shape of the particle makes it unlikely that the proteins completely surround the rRNA. It is thought that the 16S RNA of the small subunit interacts with the other RNA components of the ribosome, which would not be possible if proteins completely surrounded the nucleic acid. A similar conformation has also been suggested for the 50S subunit, since antibodies against many of these proteins have also been described. The interactions of the rRNA with the ribosomal proteins may be responsible for the fact that ribonucleases have little if any effect on the RNA in the intact ribosome.

BIBLIOGRAPHY

General Structure and Function:

Warner, J. R., and Udem, S. A. 1972. *J. Mol. Biol.* 65:243.
Gorenstein, C., and Warner, J. R. 1976. *Proc. Natl. Acad. Sci. U.S.A.* 73:1547.

Spitnik-Elson, P., and Elson, D. 1976. *Prog. Nucl. Acid. Res. Mol. Biol.* 17:77.
Woese, C. R., Sogin, M., Stahl, D., Lewis, B. J., and Bonen, L. 1976. *J. Mol. Evol.* 7:197.
Brimacombe, R., Nierhaus, K. H., Garret, R. A., and Wittmann, H. G. 1976. *Prog. Nucl. Acid Res. Mol. Biol.* 18:1.
Bonen, L., Cunningham, R. S., Gray, M. W., and Doolittle, W. F. 1977. *Nucl. Acids Res.* 4:663.
Warner, J. R. and Gorenstein, C. 1977. *Cell* 11:201, 363.
Kurland, C. G. 1977. *Annu. Rev. Biochem.* 46:173.

Transcription and Processing:

Melli, M., Whitfield, C., Rao, R. V., Richardson, M., and Bishop, J. O. 1971. *Nature New Biol.* 231:8.
Warner, J. R., and Udem, S. A. 1972. *J. Mol. Biol.* 65:243.
Pace, N. R. 1973. *Bacteriol. Rev.* 37:562.
Dunn, J. J., and Studier, F. W. 1973. *Proc. Natl. Acad. Sci. U.S.A.* 70:3296.
Nikolaev, N., Silengo, S., and Schlessinger, D. 1973. *Proc. Natl. Acad. Sci. U.S.A.* 70:3361.
Gaubatz, J., Proshas, N., and Cutler, R. G. 1976. *Biochim. Biophys. Acta* 418:358.
Oostra, B. A., von Ooyen, A. J. J., and Gruber, M. 1977. *Mol. Gen. Genet.* 152:1.
Grummt, F., Paul, D., and Grummt, I. 1977. *Eur. J. Biochem.* 76:7.
Zingales, B., and Colli, W. 1977. *Biochim. Biophys. Acta* 474:562.
Szabo, P., Lee, M. R., Elder, F. B., and Prensky, W. 1978. *Chromosoma* 65:167.
Glover, D. M., and Hogness, D. S. 1977. *Cell* 10:167.
White, R. L., and Hogness, D. S. 1977. *Cell* 10:177.
Wellauer, P. K., and Dawid, I. B. 1977. *Cell* 10:193.
Arnheim, N., and Southern, E. M. 1977. *Cell* 11:363.

Ribosomal Proteins:

Baglioni, C. 1972. *Biochim. Biophys. Acta* 287:189.
Nomura, M. 1973. *Science* 179:864.
Nanninga, N. 1973. *Int. Rev. Cytol.* 35:135.
Held, W. A., Ballou, B., Mizushima, S., and Nomura, M. 1974. *J. Biol. Chem.* 249:3103.
Gorenstein, C., and Warner, J. R. 1976. *Proc. Natl. Acad. Sci. U.S.A.* 73:1547.
Warner, J. R., and Gorenstein, C. 1977. *Cell* 11:201.
Wu, B. C., Rao, M. S., Gupta, K. K., Rothblum, L. I., Mamrack, R. C., and Busch, H. 1977. *Cell Biol. Int. Rep.* 1:31.
Johnson, R., and Kumar, A. 1977. *J. Cell Biol.* 73:419.
Strycharz, W. A., Nomura, M., and Lake, J. A. 1978. *J. Mol. Biol.* 126:123.
Teraoka, H., and Nierhaus, K. H. 1978. *J. Mol. Biol.* 126:185.
Suryanarayana, T., and Subramanian, A. R., 1979. *J. Mol. Biol.* 127:41.

Gene Multiplicity:

Gall, J. G., Cohen, E. H., and Polan, M. L. 1971. *Chromosoma* 33:319.
Melli, M., Whitfield, C., Rao, R. V., Richardson, M., and Bishop, J. O. 1971. *Nature New Biol.* 231:8.
Hatlin, L. E., and Attardi, G. 1971. *J. Mol. Biol.* 56:535.
Hennig, W. 1972. *J. Mol. Biol.* 71:407, 419.
Sutton, D. 1972. *Nature New Biol.* 237:70.
Kram, R., Botchon, M., and Hearst, J. E. 1972. *J. Mol. Biol.* 64:103.

Ribosome Assembly:

Nomura, M., ed. 1973. *Ribosome,* Cold Spring Harbor Laboratory, Cold Spring Harbor, New York.

Held, W. A., Ballou, B., Mizushima, S., and Nomura, M. 1974. *J. Biol. Chem.* 249:3103.

Dokme, F., and Nierhaus, K. H. 1976. *Proc. Natl. Acad. Sci.* 73:2221.

Zingales, B., and Colli, W. 1977. *Biochim. Biophys. Acta* 474:562.

Shulman, R. W., and Warner, J. R. 1978. *Mol. Gen. Genet.* 161:221.

9.6. Transfer RNA

SIZE AND CELLULAR LOCATION

Transfer RNA molecules are those small RNAs that serve as adaptors in protein synthesis (see Section 10). Each molecule contains between 75 and 93 bases, and has an average molecular weight of about 25,000 daltons. Each cell contains 50 to 60 individual tRNA species, each of which is specific for an amino acid. Some degree of species specificity has been found for tRNA molecules, although cross-species reactions do occur, albeit at lower efficiency and with more mistakes in charging with the appropriate amino acid.

Like all other nucleic acid molecules, tRNA molecules are formed of nucleotides covalently linked to each other by phosphodiester bonds. The specificity of each molecule for a particular amino acid resides in the nucleotide sequence; this sequence has now been determined for at least 60 individual tRNA molecules. The sequences show differences between major tRNA molecules that carry different amino acids; these differences are found in several regions of the tRNA, rather than confined to one specific area.

Transcription of tRNA occurs in the nucleus, and the molecules then migrate to the cytoplasm. Some specific tRNAs are found in cellular organelles, and appear to be coded for by the organelle DNA, differing in sequence from the cytoplasmic tRNA molecules in the same cell. These organelle-specific tRNAs include one for N-formylmethionine, used in prokaryotic systems for the initiation of protein synthesis. This amino acid is apparently not required in eukaryotic protein synthesis.

STRUCTURE OF tRNA

The tRNA molecules share some common sequences; the 3'-OH end of the molecule always terminates in CCA, and is never base-paired to other regions. This is the site of attachment of the specific amino acid. All tRNA molecules contain four regions with a high degree of base-pairing, and a few contain a fifth such area. Three unpaired regions, usually represented as loops, have been found in all tRNAs; these, together with the base-paired stems, give rise to the generalized cloverleaf structure often used to represent tRNAs (Figure 1). The best-characterized region is the anticodon loop, which interacts with the mRNA during protein synthesis. Other invariant features of

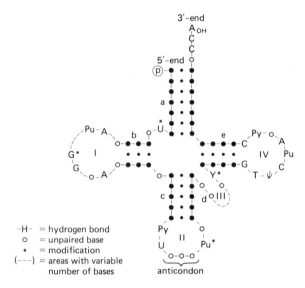

Figure 1.   General cloverleaf structure.

the tRNAs include the sizes of some of the stems and loops, as indicated below:

Amino acid arm: 7 base pairs
DHU (dihydrouridine) paired stem: 3–4 base pairs
Anticodon stem: 5 base pairs
TψC paired stem: 5 base pairs
DHU loop: 8–12 bases
Anticodon loop: 7 bases
TψC loop: 7 bases

Modified bases are found throughout the unpaired regions of the tRNA molecule. Loop I (DHU) often, but not always, contains dihyrouridine, and loop III almost invariably has the sequence TψC. Seldom if ever are modified bases found in the paired stem regions; it is thought that the modified bases interfere with normal hydrogen-bond formation. The stems show intramolecular complementarity, which allows base-pairing to occur. The extra arm is the most variable part of the structure; it may contain as few as 3 or as many as 14 nucleotides, some of which are base-paired.

While the cloverleaf has been useful in comparing different tRNA molecules, and has been generally accepted, these molecules exhibit a definite tertiary structure in nature. This structure exhibits extensive infolding of the arms, which appears to be a common feature. Many tRNA molecules have been crystallized; X-ray diffraction studies of the crystals confirm the

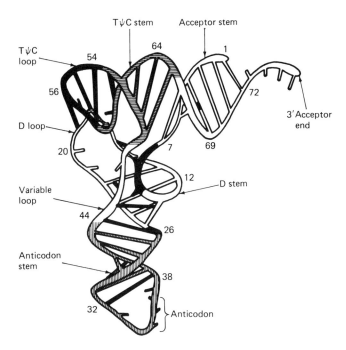

Figure 2.   Tertiary tRNA structure.

basic similarities as well as the structural regularity of the structure. One of the models for this folded molecule is presented in Figure 2; these models are consistent with the known characteristics of tRNA. The arms of the cloverleaf are folded and stacked into two regions, with the amino acid arm and the anticodon loop at opposite ends to facilitate protein synthesis. Stability is conferred on the molecule by interactions between the DHU, TψC, and extra arms.

The molecule is roughly L-shaped, with close interactions between the DHU and TψC arms, with the bases of the TψC loop essentially inaccessible to the external environment. The DHU loop, on the other hand, appears to overlap part of the TψC loop, and to be more accessible to the outside. The variable loop occupies the center of the molecule and interacts strongly with the DHU stem. The bases are stacked, in each part of the molecule, in such a way as to maximize stabilizing interactions.

THE ANTICODON LOOP AND THE WOBBLE HYPOTHESIS

The bases in the anticodon loop are stacked in a helical-type fashion that contributes to the required interactions with the appropriate triplet codon of the mRNA. As will be discussed in Chapter 10.2, there is some ambiguity in the third base of the anticodon. Bases 1 and 2 (see Figure 1) of the anticodon are invariant, but the third can be a mismatch for the codon; this is the "wobble" hypothesis proposed by Crick in 1966. Support for this hypothesis comes from studies that show that the same tRNA can recognize several codons, and that modification of one of the bases in an anticodon did not prevent the recognition of an appropriate codon.

The tertiary structure discussed above will allow this wobble in the pairing of the third base, because of a flexibility introduced by the proposed stacking into the anticodon loop. Not all mismatches can allow the recognition of the codon and the hydrogen bonding between codon and anticodon. The acceptable mismatches are:

$$
\begin{array}{cc}
\text{codon} & \text{anticodon} \\
\text{A} & \dots\dots\text{I} \\
\text{G} & \dots\dots\text{U} \\
\text{U} & \dots\dots\text{G}
\end{array}
$$

Other combinations would induce steric hindrance which would require distortion of both the mRNA and the anticodon loop. The interactions of the mRNA with the ribosomes prevent flexibility of the codon, whereas conformational changes in the bases adjacent to the anticodon will permit some distortion.

TRANSCRIPTION AND MODIFICATION

It appears probable that tRNA is invariably transcribed as a larger precursor molecule. Several such precursors have been sequenced, each having more than 40 additional bases, mainly added to the 5' end of the molecule. It is not clear whether modification of bases takes place during or after transcription. One precursor appears to be modified, while a second is not. The 3' CCA sequence is added after cleavage of the additional bases by a specific enzyme (Figure 3). Modification of the bases generally occurs after polymerization, rather than at the level of the precursor nucleotides. Modifying enzymes appear to act on all the tRNA molecules in a particular cell, and most of the modified bases are methylated. Methylation uses the one-carbon carrier S-adenosyl methionine, whereas cells grown in the absence of methionine contain tRNA molecules lacking methylated bases. The methylase is inhibited by nicotinamide and by certain cytokinins, but is stimulated by polyamines.

Other modifications have also been described. The most common altered nucleotide is pseudouridine, ψ, which differs from U in the position of the glycosidic linkage. Also common is thymidine riboside, a uridine base modified by addition of a methyl group to position 5 of the ring, but linked to ribose

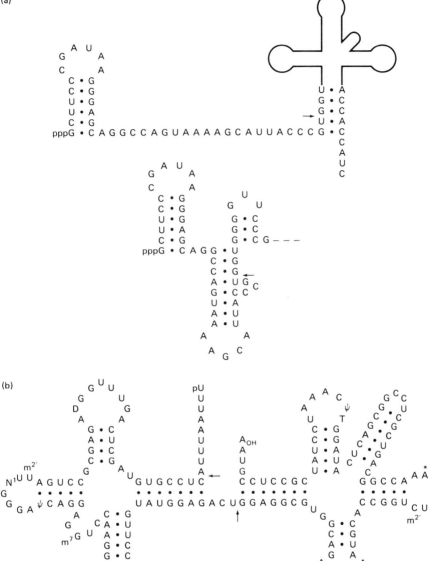

A* is ms²i⁶A and N_1 and N_2 are unknown modifications of U.

Figure 3. Precursor tRNA molecules. (a) *E. coli* su₃⁺ tRNA^Tyr precursor. Two possible configurations for precursor tRNA^Tyr. The arrows pointing toward the sequence indicate the beginning of the 5' end of the tRNA moiety and a cleavage point. (b) Bacteriophage T4 tRNA^Pro — tRNA^Ser precursor. A* is ms²i⁶A, and N^1 and N^2 are unknown modifications of U. (From S. Altman and J. D. Smith, *Nature New Biol.* 233:35, 1971.)

instead of deoxyribose. All DNA molecules contain the thymidine deoxyribo-side, but other RNA molecules do not contain thymidine. The thymidine can be further methylated in tRNA, as can inosine, the deamination product of guanine. Another modification of guanine, the formation of an extra ring, gives rise to the base "Y," often found in the anticodon loop. Modified bases are usually found in the open loops of tRNA, seldom in the base-paired arms. Some modified bases structures are shown in Figure 4.

Modifications may help to maintain the cloverleaf structure, since modified bases pair less efficiently than normal. In addition, they appear to be essential for proper interactions with the other components required in protein synthesis. When specific tRNA molecules, isolated from cells grown in the absence of methionine, are tested, several effects are noted, including decreased amino acid binding, reduced binding to ribosomes, and loss of specificity for the correct mRNA codon. One important site of modification, the bases in the anticodon loop, may be required for correct interaction with the mRNA codon, as shown by chemical modification of the base Y. When present, this base is usually adjacent to the triplet anticodon. After cleavage of Y, altered coding properties of the tRNA have been described. Thus, modifica-

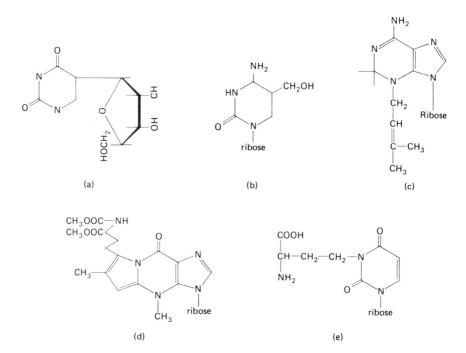

Figure 4. Some modified nucleotides of tRNA (a) Pseudouridine (ψ). (b) 5-Hydroxymethylcyti-dine. (c) 6-Amino-3-(3-methyl-2-butyryl) purine (triacanthine), a cytokinin. (d) Y. (e) X.

tions in tRNA may disrupt proper interactions with other nucleic acids, thus reducing the specificity normally found in protein synthesis.

FUNCTION

tRNA molecules interact with ribosomes and with mRNA in protein synthesis, and act as adapter molecules for appropriate amino acids. Each tRNA recognizes and binds to a single amino acid under normal conditions; this recognition and binding is mediated by an enzyme, an aminoacyl synthetase, also called amino acid–tRNA ligase. The enzyme has at least two binding sites, one specific for the amino acid, the other for the rRNA. Recognition of the correct tRNA appears to be mediated by the amino acid stem, since tRNA molecules from different species that specify the same amino acid share a similar sequence, while tRNAs from the same species that specify different amino acids show divergence in the sequence (Figure 5).

The enzyme first binds the amino acid; this binding requires ATP, and preserves the energy of the phosphate bond for use during protein synthesis. The activation of the amino acid is a two-step process:

$$\text{amino acid} + \text{ATP} \underset{\text{synthetase}}{\rightleftharpoons} \text{aa} \sim \text{AMP} + \text{P} \sim \text{P}$$

$$\text{tRNA} + \text{aa} \sim \text{AMP} \underset{\text{synthetase}}{\rightleftharpoons} \text{aa} \sim \text{tRNA} + \text{AMP}$$

where aa = amino acid, and $\sim$ represents a high-energy bond. The amino acid is esterified to the terminal adenine at the 3′ end of the tRNA; the amino acyl bond is formed between the amino acid and the OH group of the ribose group attached to adenine. Each amino acid–tRNA ligase catalyzes the formation of the amino acyl bond only for the specific amino acid–tRNA pair. However, chemical alteration of the amino acid after binding can take place; this does not influence the subsequent interactions of the tRNA in protein synthesis.

These later interactions are controlled by the sequence of the tRNA. Some characteristic, as yet unidentified, allows recognition of, and binding to, the ribosome. The amino acid sequence of the protein is determined by interaction of the anticodon loop with the mRNA; as mentioned above, the other nucleotides in the loop may exert some control over the specificity of binding. Cloverlead structures for four tRNA molecules (isoacceptor tRNAs), which are specific for phenylalanine, are shown in Figure 6. There are minor differences in the modified bases found in all three loops, as well as in the sequences of the base-paired stems. The differences can account for the lowered specificity seen when tRNA molecules from one species are used with components from some other organism, but the similarities are great enough to allow

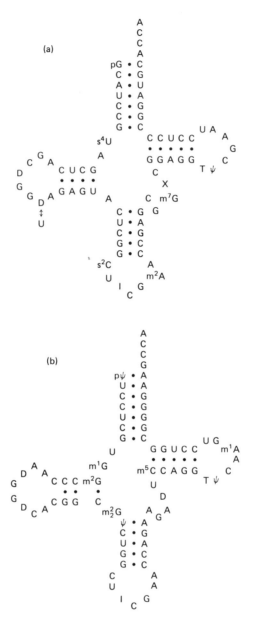

Figure 5. Differences and similarities in some tRNAs. (a) *E. coli* tRNA^Arg. (From K. Murao, T. Tanabe, F. Ishii, M. Namiki, and S. Nishimura *Biochem. Biophys. Res. Commun.* 47:1332, 1972.) (b) Yeast tRNA^Arg. (From J. Weissenbach, R. Martin, and G. Dirheimer *FEBS Lett.* 28:353, 1972.) (c) *E. coli* tRNA₁^Ser. N is unknown. (From H. Ishikura, Y. Yamada, and S.

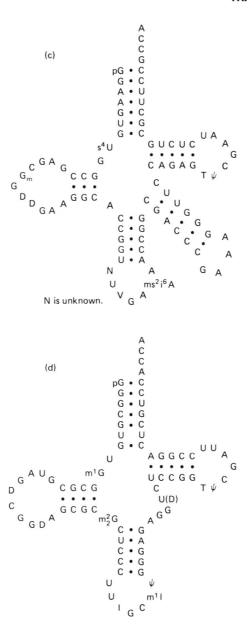

Nishimura, *FEBS Lett.* 16:68, 1971.) (d) Yeast tRNA$_1^{Ala}$. (From R. W. Holley, J. Apgar, G. A. Everett, J. T. Madison, M. Marquisee, S. H. Merrill, J. R. Penswick, and A. Zamir, *Science* 147:1462, 1965; and C. R. Merrill, *Biopolymers* 6:1727, 1968.)

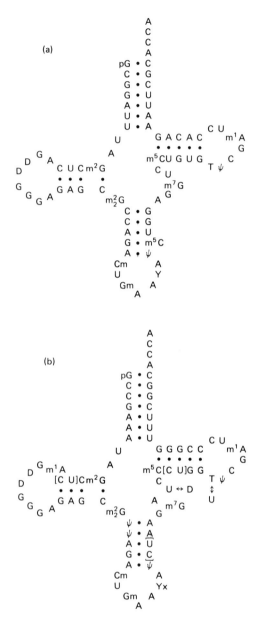

Figure 6. Some known tRNA^Phe structures. (a) Yeast tRNA^Phe. (From U. L. Raj Bhandary, S. H. Chang, A. Stuart, R. D. Faulkner, R. M. Hoskinson, and H. G. Khorana, *Proc. Natl. Acad. Sci. U.S.A.* 57:751, 1967; U. L. Raj Bhandary et al., *J. Biol. Chem.* 243:556, 565, 575, 584, 592, 598, 1968; and K. Nakanishi, N. Furutachi, M. Funamizu, D. Grunberger, and I. B. Weinstein, *J. Am. Chem. Soc.* 92:7617, 1970.) (b) Rabbit liver tRNA^Phe. Yx is a derivative of Y. (From G. Keith, F. Picaud, J. Weissenbach, J. P. Ebel, G. Petrissant, and G. Dirheimer,

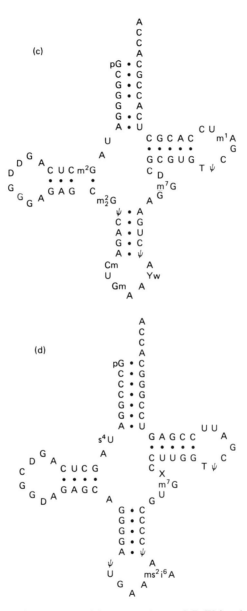

(c)

(d)

FEBS Lett. 31:345, 1973; and S. H. Blobstein, D. Grunberger, I. B. Weinstein, and K. Nakanishi, *Biochemistry* 12:188, 1973.) (c) Wheat germ tRNA[Phe]. Yw is a derivative of Y. (From B. S. Dudock, G. Katz, E. K. Taylor, and R. W. Holley, *Proc. Natl. Acad. Sci. U.S.A.* 62:941, 1969; G. Katz and B. S. Dudock, *J. Biol. Chem.*, 244:3062, 1969; and B. S. Dudock and G. Katz, *J. Biol. Chem.* 244:3069, 1969.) (d) *E. coli* tRNA[Phe]. (From B. G. Barrell and F. Sanger, *FEBS Lett.* 3:275, 1969; M. Uziel and H. G. Gassen, *Biochemistry* 8:1643, 1969; and M. Uziel and J. X. Khym, *Biochemistry* 8:3254, 1969.)

some interspecies cross-reaction. There is some tentative evidence that the TψC loop of the tRNA may interact with ribosomal RNA, specifically 16S rRNA or 5S RNA.

ORGANIZATION OF tRNA GENES

The tRNA genes in two organisms have been studied, and some information has been published. Unlike rDNA, which is found at a specific site on chromosomes of a species, tDNA genes appear to be found in several areas. Within the areas, however, the gene(s) appears to be present in several copies, containing sequences coding for the precursor and nontranscribed regions known as spacer DNA. In *Xenopus laevis,* the spacer regions contain less G + C then do the transcribed sequences, and there is a tandem repeat arrangement of the gene:

spacer	precursor	spacer	precursor	spacer	precursor	etc.
	tRNA		tRNA		tRNA	

In *Drosophila,* the site for tRNA^{Lys} has been localized to the right arm of chromosome 2, and studies are in progress to localize other tRNA genes. The method used is in situ hybridization; a specific tRNA molecule is isolated and purified. It is then labeled in vitro with a radioactive form of iodine, [^{125}I]. Chromosomes are denatured after fixation on slides, and are incubated with the iodinated tRNA under conditions that promote RNA–DNA hybridization. Autoradiography allows development and visualization of silver grains in regions where these hybrids have formed. Results obtained indicate that each tRNA gene is present in about eight copies per genome. Some problems arise, however, owing to low levels of contamination with other small RNA molecules, such as 5S rRNA, which are present in very high copy number. This gives rise to silver grains in regions that do not correspond to tRNA genes.

Present evidence indicates that each cell has about 60 tRNA species, some of which are isoacceptor molecules. For example, there may be as many as seven tRNA^{Ser} species. These isoacceptors need not map in regions very close to each other. Certain minor tRNA species, which arise by post-transcriptional modification, may, however, map with a parental major species. Some viruses carry a few genes for specific tRNA species that allow viral translation to occur. In these cases, the viral genome contains a single copy of each tRNA gene; those genes that are found are closely linked to each other.

CONTROL OF tRNA LEVELS IN CELLS

It appears likely that the physiological conditions within a specific cell may control the levels of tRNA molecules found in that cell. Litt and his coworkers have accumulated some data that bear on this point. In reticulocytes, immature red cells that can carry out hemoglobin synthesis, the levels of specific tRNA molecules correlate with the amount of the specific amino acids found in the hemoglobin produced by these cells. That is, if the hemoglobin contains high levels of isoleucine or methionine, there will be more of the specific tRNA molecules that carry these amino acids. Later work by this same group appears to have established that the mechanism involves the degree of charging of the particular tRNA with the appropriate amino acid. Increased levels of histidine–tRNA can be induced by decreases in the cellular levels of histidine. In the presence of fewer histidine molecules, all of these molecules will be attached to tRNA, decreasing the pool of free His–tRNA available. This condition in turn will either increase the rate of synthesis of the tRNA, or decrease the rate of degradation.

These studies have been carried out only for three specific amino acids, and only in two types of cells. If further work with other species and other cells confirms these conclusions, this mechanism will be well established. Other mechanisms may also be important, however. Little is yet known, for example, of the control mechanisms that dictate the rate of transcription of various genes. Processing of precursor molecules may also play a role in these controls. Further work in these areas should contribute to our knowledge of control mechanisms for RNA synthesis in general.

BIBLIOGRAPHY

Books and Review Articles:

Hall, R. H. 1970. *The Modified Nucleoside in Nucleic Acids.* Columbia University Press, New York.
Lizzardi, P. M., and Luck, D. J. L. 1971. *Nature* 229:140.
Arnott, S. 1971. *Prog. Biophys. Mol. Biol.* 22:181.
Gauss, D. H., von der Haar, F., Maelicke, A., and Cramer, F. 1971. *Annu. Rev. Biochem.* 40:1045.
Barrell, B. G. and Clark, B. F. C. 1974. *Handbook of Nucleic Acid Sequences.* Joynson-Bruvvers, Ltd., Oxford, England.
Richard, A., and Raj Bhandary, U. L. 1976. *Annu. Rev. Biochem.* 48:805.
Ladner, J. E. 1978. In Biochemistry of nucleic acids II. *Int. Rev. Biochem.,* B. F. C. Clark, ed. University Park Press, Baltimore.

Research Publications:

Holley, R. W., Apgar, J., Everett, G. A., Madison, J. T., Marquisee, M., Merrill, S. H., Penswick, J. R., and Zamir, A. 1965. *Science* 147:1462.

Crick, F. H. C. 1966. *J. Mol. Biol.* 19:548.

Raj Bhandary, U. L., Chang, S. H., Stuart, A., Faulkner, R. D., Hoskinson, R. M., and Khorana, H. G. 1967. *Proc. Natl. Acad. Sci. U.S.A.* 57:751.

Fuller, W., and Hodgson, A. 1967. *Nature* 215:817.

Dube, S. K., Marcker, K. A., Clark, B. F. C., and Cory, S. 1968. *Nature* 218:232.

Dudock, B. S., Katz, G., Taylor, E. K., and Holley, R. W. 1969. *Proc. Natl. Acad. Sci., U.S.A.* 62:941.

Barrell, B. G., and Sanger, F. 1969. *FEBS Lett.* 3:275.

Uziel, M., and Khym, J. X. 1969. *Biochemistry* 8:3254.

Sanger, S., and Brownlee, G. G. 1970. *Biochem. Soc. Symp.* 30:183.

Nakaishi, K., Furutachi, N., Funamizu, M., Grunberger, D., and Weinstein, I. B. 1970. *J. Am. Chem. Soc.* 92:7617.

Ishikura, H., Yamada, Y., and Nishimura, S. 1971. *FEBS Lett.* 16:68.

Altman, S., and Smith, J. D. 1971. *Nature New Biol.* 233:35.

Murao, K., Tanake, T., Ishii, F., Namiki, M., and Nishimura, S. 1972. *Biochem. Biophys. Res. Commun.* 47:1332.

Weissenbach, J., Martin, R., and Dircheimer, G. 1972. *FEBS Lett.* 28:353.

Litt, M., and Kabat, D. 1972. *J. Biol. Chem.* 247:6659.

Kim, S. H., Suddath, F. L., Quigley, G. J., McPherson, A., Sussman, J. L., Wang, A. H. J., Seeman, N. C., and Rich, A. 1974. *Science* 185:435.

Quigley, C. J., and Rich, A. 1976. *Science* 194:796.

Litt, M., and Weiser, K. 1978. 201:527.

Posarske, L. H., Cohn, M., Yanagisawa, N., and Auld, D. S. 1979. *Biochim. Biophys. Acta* 576:128.

9.7. Ribonucleases

GENERAL PROPERTIES

Many enzymes capable of breaking the phosphodiester bonds of RNA molecules have been described. Like the deoxyribonucleases, the RNases may be broadly grouped into endonucleases and exonucleases. In general, the ribonucleases are relatively small molecules that are quite stable to mild denaturation. Some require Mg^{2+} ions, while others show no dependence on the presence of any ions, and still others require both monovalent and divalent cations for maximal activity.

Ribonucleases from both prokaryotic and eukaryotic systems have been studied extensively. Among the endonucleases, some RNases result in the liberation of 3' nucleotides, while others produce 5' nucleotides; the mechanisms of action of the two types are not the same. The first group of endonucleases proceeds through the formation of a 2'–3' cyclic phosphate intermediate, which is then hydrolyzed to release the 3' mononucleotide. The 5' monophosphates, on the other hand, arise from a direct hydration of the 3' to 5' phosphodiester bond (Figures 1 and 2). Theoretically, 2' mononucleotides could be formed from the cyclic intermediate of the first type, but this mechanism invariably results in the formation of the 3' compounds. Exonucleases produce mononucleotides, generally containing a 5' monophosphate group, although some diphosphates are formed in certain cases.

Ribonucleases are present in all cells, and are also found on human skin. They can interfere during the isolation of RNA molecules from tissues unless the enzyme activity is inhibited to prevent digestion of the RNA. Several compounds can be used as inhibitors of RNase activity; the clay bentonite appears to be the most useful, since it seems to inhibit all RNase action. EDTA, a chelating agent, can be used to prevent activity by those enzymes that require divalent cations, but has no inhibitory action against pancreatic RNase, for example. Heparin, however, is an excellent agent to inhibit this enzyme. Another compound that has often been used as a general inhibitor of RNases is diethyl pyrocarbonate, known commercially as Baycovin, but some reports question its effectiveness.

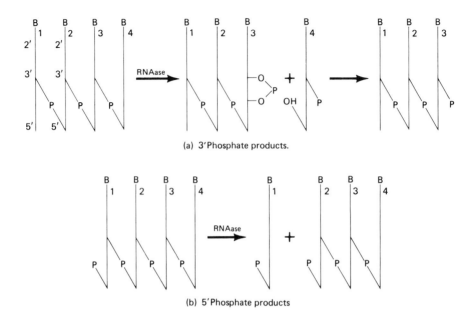

(a) 3' Phosphate products.

(b) 5' Phosphate products

Figure 1. Mechanisms of RNase activity. (a) 3' Phosphate products. (b) 5' Phosphate products.

BACTERIAL RIBONUCLEASES

More than ten ribonuclease activities have been identified in *E. coli;* of these, six are endonucleases, three are exonucleases, and the others have not yet been classified. The three known exonucleases each degrade RNA sequentially from the 3' end of the molecule. Some of the better-characterized *E. coli* enzymes are listed in Table 1, together with some of the known characteristics. Many of these enzymes can be isolated in association with ribosomes, and may also be so associated in vivo, although in some cases the isolation has been shown to cause an artifactual association. Some of these enzymes have been shown to participate in the processing of large, precursor RNA molecules, while the specific physiological role of many has not yet been clarified. Other bacteria have not been as extensively studied, but appear to contain at least some analogous ribonucleases.

RNase activity is required for several important cellular functions, including processing of precursors and degradation of mRNA. Some of these functions can be assigned to specific enzymes, but many questions remain unanswered. As noted previously (Chapter 9.4), bacterial mRNA molecules have a very short half-life; the nucleotides from degraded molecules are recycled to be used in the formation of new RNA. Several RNases have been postulated to be responsible for this digestion, specifically RNase II or III. RNase II

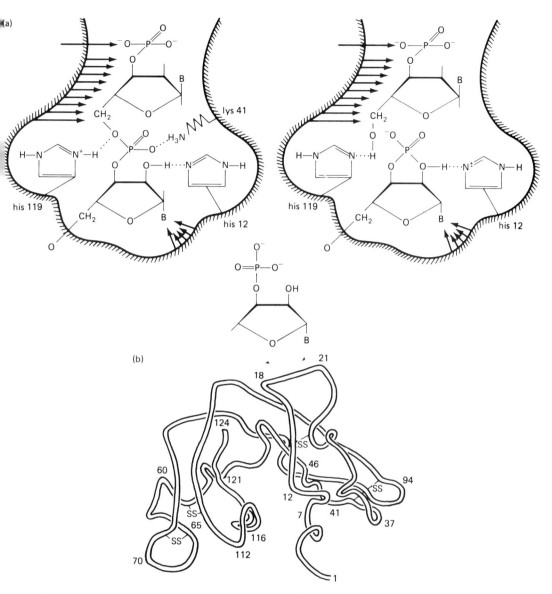

Figure 2. Structure of RNase. (a) Rabin's model of the catalytic site of ribonuclease. (b) Three-dimensional structure. His 12 and his 119 act catalytically. Lys 41 binds the phosphate.

C_2 oxygen of the pyrimidine aligns one of the imidazoles via a hydrogen bonded system including a water molecule bridge. Cyclization and hydrolysis are attended by reversion of the ionization state (acid and base) of the two imidazoles. Reproduced with permission from Findlay D., Herries D. G., Mathias A. P., Rabin B. R., and Ross C. A. 1962. *Biochem. J.* **85:** 152. Tridimensional configuration of ribonuclease reproduced with permission from Wyckoff H. W., Hardman K. D., Allewel N. M., Inagami T., Tsernoglou D., Johnson L. N., and Richards F. M. 1967. *J. Biol. Chem.* **242:** 3749.

Table 1. Some Ribonucleases from *E. coli.*

NAME	PH OPTIMUM	CATION REQUIRED	SUBSTRATE	PRODUCTS	MODE OF ACTION
RNase I	8.1	none	ssRNA*	3' mononucleotides	endonuclease**
II	7–7.5	Mg^{2+}, Mn^{2+}, K^+, NH_4^+	nonhelical ss RNA*	5' mononucleotides + resistant oligomer	exonuclease
III	9	"	dsRNA*	oligonucleotides	endonuclease
IV	6	none	ssviral R17 RNA	15S + 21S oligomers	endonuclease
P	8	Mn^{2+}, Mg^{2+}, K^+, NH_4^+	tRNA precursors	see text	
P_2	—	—			
P_3	8.2	Mg^{2+}, K^+, NH_4^+			
	7.5	Mg^{2+}, NH_4^+	16S precursor	mature 16S RNA	
H	—	Mg^{2+}	RNA in RNA:DNA hybrids	mono- and oligonucleotides	endonuclease

* ss = single-stranded; ds = double-stranded.
** This endonuclease proceeds through the cyclic 2'-3'-intermediate.

is required for viability, and cellular levels of the enzyme in temperature-sensitive mutants appear to be closely linked to the breakdown of mRNA. However, it is difficult to reconcile the fact that the available free end of mRNA is presumably the 5′ end, with the fact that RNase II begins digestion at a free 3′-OH terminus. This could be explained by assuming that the first step in mRNA degradation requires endonuclease activity, and that the oligomers formed are then attacked by RNase II. The consensus of opinion at present is that this enzyme probably participates in mRNA digestion, but is not the only RNase required in this process. The possible involvement of RNase III is not as well documented, but its endonuclease activity may fit the requirements of the degradation better. Perhaps the two enzymes work together; studies of temperature-sensitive mutants may resolve this question in the near future.

Another nuclease activity that is absolutely required for cellular viability is the processing of precursor molecules for rRNA and tRNA. The enzymes that are thought to participate in these maturation sequences have not yet been fully characterized. RNase M has been reported to excise some of the extra bases associated with the 16S precursor molecule, but its mechanism of action is not yet known. It has been reported that RNase II is also required in this process, since a temperature-sensitive strain of *E. coli* containing a thermolabile RNase II cannot synthesize ribosomes at the nonpermissive temperature. In addition, Corte and coworkers reported that RNase II can produce mature 16S rRNA from the precursor in vitro. This finding must be questioned, however, since endonuclease action would appear to be required, while RNase II is an exonuclease. RNase III may also participate in rRNA processing, based on studies with a mutant deficient in this enzyme. However, further studies on this mutant strain have found several other mutations in the strain, and it is not clear which of them is responsible for the defect in maturation.

The maturation of tRNA is somewhat better understood, although here, too, further studies will be required to clarify fully the role of various ribonucleases. Three enzymes, designated RNase P, P_2, and P_3, are known to be required in this maturation. The first, RNase P, specifically cleaves the precursor of tRNA^{Tyr}, but cannot cleave large, polycistronic molecules. Each of these enzymes catalyzes the endonucleolytic removal of bases at the 5′ end of the precursor. RNase II can remove the extra bases at the 3′ end, but the process is not very efficient in vitro. An enzyme that is capable of catalyzing this reaction efficiently has been identified by Bikoff and his coworkers; this RNase P III, or P_3 as it is referred to above, is not identical to RNase II, and appears to be required for complete processing of tRNA molecules.

The other RNase activities in *E. coli* for which a specific in vivo role has been postulated are RNase IV and H. The first is required during infection with the bacteriophage M17; it splits the viral RNA into two unequal segments and has been used in studies of the structure of this RNA. The two fragments formed are a 15S and a 21S piece; the 15S segment contains the original 5' end. It has been reported that the two fragments direct the synthesis of specific proteins. The 21S fragment is translated into the viral RNA synthetase, while the 15S piece appears to direct the synthesis of coat proteins. If this is the case, the specific cleavage may represent some type of control of protein synthesis. The separated mRNAs could be translated at different rates after separation, so that sufficient coat protein could accumulate for the viral progeny. Alternatively, the cut may be required to expose a start signal. The RNA transcript of phage T7 DNA also undergoes specific cleavage prior to translation, but the enzyme that catalyzes this reaction is RNase III. It has been determined that this cleavage is required for efficient translation of some specific mRNAs, but that not all protein synthesis is influenced. Some viral polycistronic mRNA molecules, on the other hand, appear to be translated well without processing.

RNase H is of interest since its preferred substrate is RNA that is found in a hybrid RNA:DNA molecule. This endonuclease is similar to an enzyme purified from animal sources, and is found in purified reverse transcriptase as well as in virions of RNA tumor viruses. This enzyme requires Mg^{2+} ions, is inhibited by ammonium sulfate concentrations greater than 0.1 M, and requires sulfhydryl groups for activity. The enzyme may not be a globular molecule; if it is, the molecular weight is in the range of 40×10^3 to 45×10^3 daltons, but a recent report indicates that the correct molecular weight may be about half that, or 21,000 daltons. This ribonuclease could participate in replication by removing the small RNA primers that are attached to nascent DNA. Mutant strains carrying an altered or a temperature-sensitive RNase H could be of great value in further defining the role of RNA in replication (see Chapter 7.1).

Several bacterial RNases have been identified as being extracellular in nature, among them the E. coli RNase I. It lies in the periplasmic space and may be required to degrade exogenous substrates to nucleosides, which can then enter the cell for utilization in the formation of new nucleic acids. This enzyme can associate with ribosomes during cellular breakage; in this case, it is inactive unless treated with EDTA, urea, salt, or agents that break apart ribosomes. When activated, this enzyme degrades rRNA, attacking all bonds as an endonuclease, RNase I does not influence breakdown of pulse-labeled RNA, nor does it appear to be required for cellular viability. Other "extracellular" RNases have been purified from B. subtilis strains. These enzymes have been useful for in vitro studies of complex RNA molecules, but no actual physiological role can be assigned.

EUKARYOTIC ENDORIBONUCLEASES

In general, eukaryotic ribonucleases include enzymes from the pancreas, the liver, and other organs of various animal species. Some of them are found in the nucleus and the nucleolus, while others are localized in the cytoplasm. Some participate in the processing of precursor RNA molecules, while other RNases appear to be active against RNA molecules in general. Most are endoribonucleases that are active at either acid or alkaline pH, and many are stable even at extreme temperatures. Some of these enzymes will be discussed in detail below.

Pancreatic RNase, or RNase I, is found in the pancreas of various animal species, and the bovine enzyme has been extensively studied. In vivo, the enzyme appears to have two distinct pH optima, at pH 4.5 and pH 7.5. RNase A, with a pH 7.5 optimum, is the major component; RNase B is a glycosylated form, active at much lower pH, and somewhat more resistant to proteolysis. The enzyme cleaves RNA through a cyclic 2'-3'-phosphate intermediate, at positions where the phosphate group is attached to the 3'-position of a pyrimidine nucleotide, and the 5'-position of the next nucleotide. The molecule is small, having a molecular weight of about 14,000 daltons, and consists of a single polypeptide chain. Under certain conditions, some of the molecules may dimerize; these dimers are relatively more active against double-stranded (ds) RNA molecules. Natural RNase A dimers have also been identified, and will also attack ds RNA more efficiently than does RNase A itself. In general, these RNases are localized in the cytoplasm of cells, specifically in or near the endoplasmic reticulum, the secretory ducts, and zymogen granules.

RNase II is an acid-stable enzyme that shows no base specificity and hydrolyzes both natural and synthetic RNA molecules to oligonucleotides carrying a terminal 2'-3'-cyclic phosphate group. This enzyme may be localized in lysosomes. There may be two separate enzymes of this type, one of which is lysosomal, while the other appears to be localized in the cytoplasm. It has been reported that acid RNase levels may change during neoplastic transformation. In mice with a genetic predisposition toward leukemia, elevated activity in the thymus and white blood cells has recently been demonstrated. This finding may be diagnostic for the detection of strains susceptible to cancer, and should be investigated further.

A ribonuclease activity that degrades RNA as an endoribonuclease has been isolated from the nucleoli of various animal cells. These enzymes can cleave rRNA precursor molecules in vitro; however, cleavage continues to limit digestion products of about 4S in size. If these enzymes participate in processing, control of digestion must occur. This control may be the result of association of the rRNA with proteins that would act as inhibitors of the RNase activity, and inhibition has also been noted in the presence of divalent cations. Further studies should clarify the possible role of such nucleolar ribonucleases in the formation of rRNA molecules.

Other enzymes have been definitely implicated in the maturation of mammalian RNA precursor molecules; these enzymes are RNase NU and RNase P. *Hsu*. Like *E. coli* RNase P, the mammalian enzymes may recognize the conformation of specific regions of RNA precursors. RNase NU has been isolated from a human cell line. In addition, it cleaves human tRNA precursor molecules, yielding fragments that migrate like tRNA on electrophoresis. Both RNase NU and P. *Hsu* are optimally active at pH 8.0; the first requires either a monovalent cation or Ca^{2+} ions, whereas the second requires both Mg^{2+} ions and a monovalent cation. Both enzymes appear to be localized in the cytosol.

An activity designated RNase H has been isolated from various mammalian cells. It is a large molecule, with molecular weight in the range of 65×10^3 to 90×10^3 daltons, and active on the RNA portion of DNA–RNA hybrids. This enzyme can nick a closed circular hybrid, but the subsequent activity may be exonucleolytic. At present, this behavior has not been clearly established, nor has the physiological role of RNase H been clarified, since the role of RNA primers in eukaryotic DNA synthesis is still the subject of debate (see Chapter 7.3). Further studies of this "hybrid nuclease" may help to answer these questions and thus clarify the mechanism of eukaryotic replication.

Other ribonucleases have been identified that have been useful in sequencing of RNA molecules. These enzymes split the polymer at defined sites, giving rise to small oligonucleotides which can be further analyzed using enzymes such as the phosphodiesterases. These enzymes include RNase T_1 from aspergillus and Physariem 1 from a slime mold. RNase T_1 preferentially cleaves adjacent to guanine residues, giving rise to a 3′ GMP and a 5′-OH on the next residue. This enzyme reacts only at linkages adjacent to unmodified guanine residues, and has been used in the analysis of the primary structure of tRNA and 5S RNA molecules. The Physariem 1 RNase is an interesting enzyme that will cut phosphodiester bonds adjacent to U, A, or G, but will not cut next to C, or, if it does, does so with much less than its usual efficiency. It can be used with other nucleases to study the sequence of small oligomers containing several C residues.

EUKARYOTIC EXORIBONUCLEASES

Relatively few enzymes of this type are known, although others probably will be identified in the near future. A 5′-exoribonuclease has been found in the nuclei of several mammalian species. This enzyme degrades RNA sequentially from the 3'-terminus, producing 5'-monophosphates. The enzyme is inhibited by the presence of methyl esters at the 2' position of the ribose, and appears to prefer rRNA precursors as substrates. However, endonuclease activity may be more consistent with the present models of rRNA processing than exonuclease activity; so the questions of the specific role of the 5'-exoribonuclease is still open.

Another such enzyme which has been identified in many eukaryotic systems is polynucleotide phosphorylase. Such enzymes, first described by Ochoa and his colleagues, catalyze the reaction:

$$n\text{NDP} \rightleftharpoons (\text{NMP})_n + n\text{P}_\text{i}$$

In vivo, the enzyme acts as an exonuclease, releasing diphosphates from RNA in the presence of inorganic phosphorus. Enzymes of this type have been purified from mitochondria of mammals, birds, and fish. The actual physiological role of polynucleotide phosphorylase in eukaryotic systems has not been established. In bacteria, there have been suggestions that this enzyme participates in mRNA degradation, but this possibility is not generally accepted.

Phosphodiesterases are exonucleases that accept either DNA or RNA as substrates. Many such enzymes have been described; often, phosphodiesterases are found in snake venom, and they have also been isolated from various animal tissues. The liver enzyme is a large glycoprotein localized in the plasma membrane, present in several forms that differ in subunit composition and can be identified on gel electrophoresis. The isoenzyme patterns found in hepatomas differ from those of normal liver, and these cancerous cells have also been reported to have higher phosphodiesterase levels than normal liver cells. These interesting observations may be useful in defining some metabolic differences in neoplastic disease, if confirmed in other systems. Phosphodiesterases in general catalyze the hydrolysis of nucleic acid molecules to mononucleotides. Enzymes isolated from snake venom generally give rise to 5'-monophosphates, while spleen phosphodiesterase produces 3'-phosphate; a 5'-phosphate end group inhibits the spleen enzyme. A specific phosphodiesterase that cleaves cyclic nucleotides has been described in the myelin sheath of nerve tissue. The physiological role of this enzyme is not yet clear.

Further research will undoubtly reveal many more eukaryotic ribonucleases that perform specific functions in metabolism. In addition, specific functions will be assigned to some of these enzymes. At present, the participation of a single enzyme in specific steps of RNA catabolism has been established only for a few ribonucleases, and many aspects of this breakdown remain unclear. Comparison of bacterial and eukaryotic enzymes shows many functional similarities. Properties of the better-characterized bacterial ribonucleases have been useful in the search for analogous eukaryotic enzymes. Many of the enzymes isolated have been useful in the study of RNA structure in vitro, although in vivo roles have not been fully clarified. Continued studies of this type, then, will lead to a deeper knowledge of both RNA metabolism and the exact structure of these molecules.

BIBLIOGRAPHY

Robertson, H. D. 1971. *Nature New Biol.* 229:169.
Corte, G., Schlessinger, D., Longo, D., and Venkov, P. 1971. *J. Mol. Biol.* 60:325.
Stavrianopoulos, J. G., and Chargaff, E. 1973. *Proc. Natl. Acad. Sci.* 70:1959.
Wyers, F., Sentenoe, A., and Fromagest, P. 1973. *Eur. J. Biochem.* 35:270.
Haberkern, R. C., and Cantoni, G. L. 1973. *Biochemistry* 12:2389.
Shedle, P., and Primakoff, P. 1973. *Proc. Natl. Acad. Sci.* 70:2091.
Dunn, J. J., and Studier, F. W. 1973. *Proc. Natl. Acad. Sci.* 70:1559.
Hercules, K., Schweiger, M., and Sauerbier, W. 1974. *Proc. Natl. Acad. Sci.* 71:840.
Roewekamp, W., and Sekeris, C. E. 1974. *Eur. J. Biochem.* 43:405.
Apirion, D., and Watson, N. 1975. *J. Bacteriol.* 124:317.
Studier, F. W. 1975. *J. Bacteriol.* 124:307.
Datta, A. K., and Niyogi, S. K. 1976. *Prog. Nucl. Acid Res. Mol. Biol.* 17:271.
Nikolaev, N., Folsom, V., and Schlessinger, D. 1976. *Biochem. Biophys. Res. Commun.* 70:920.
Sierakowska, H., and Shugar, D. 1977. *Prog. Nucl. Acid Res. Mol. Biol.* 20:59.
Ono, M., and Kuwano, M. 1977. *Mol. Gen. Genet.* 153:1.

SECTION 10
PROTEIN SYNTHESIS

THERESA CAMPANA AND
LAZAR M. SCHWARTZ

10.1. General Mechanisms of Protein Synthesis

CELLULAR LOCALIZATION AND REQUIRED COMPONENTS

The starting materials for protein synthesis are the amino acids present in all cells in solution. In eukaryotic cells, the polymerization of amino acids into proteins takes place in the cytoplasm but is directed ultimately by the cellular DNA, located in the nucleus. Formation of proteins requires mediation by the three major types of RNA described in Section 9, the mRNA, rRNAs, and tRNA, all transcribed from the DNA in the nucleus. In prokaryotes, where no nuclear membrane intervenes to separate the components, protein synthesis requires less time than in cells with a nucleus, but the general mechanisms are similar.

There is no direct homology between nucleotides and amino acids, so there must be an indirect mechanism to impart specificity to the polymerization of the amino acids. This specificity is conferred by the interactions of the various RNA components. The amino acid sequence is encoded in the mRNA, in the form of three-base codons (see Chapter 10.2), and also in the tRNA molecules that interact with these codons (see Chapter 9.6). Ribosomes provide the site where these interactions can take place, as well as a matrix for several enzymes that are required during the process. Energy is required for protein synthesis to occur; this energy is provided by the ATP used in the formation of the aa $\sim$ tRNA complex (Figure 1), and by GTP, which is hydrolyzed at several points in the process.

FORMATION OF THE INITIATION COMPLEX

The first step in protein synthesis is an association of the required components. The mRNA binds to the small ribosomal subunit, and a special initiator tRNA joins the complex. Several proteins known as initiation factors participate in these interactions, as well as, in the next step, the binding of the large subunit. Three initiation factors have been identified in the bacterium *E. coli,* and at least two are required in eukaryotic systems (see Chapter 10.5).

These associations are regulated in a complex manner. Interactions between the mRNA AUG initiator codon and the anticodon of the initiator tRNA

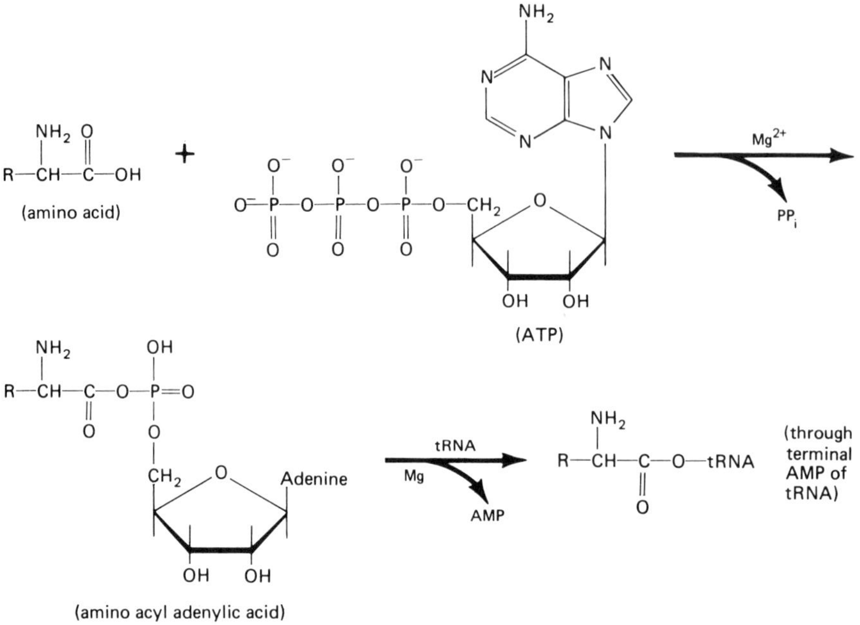

Figure 1. Formation of the aa ∼ tRNA complex.

are mediated by proteins of the small ribosomal subunit, and in e.g., *E. coli,* seven proteins of the 30S subunit appear to participate in this binding. In addition, nontranslated nucleotides preceding AUG appear to be necessary for initiation, implying that the recognition of AUG as an initiating codon by the ribosome involves the structure of the 5′ terminus of the mRNA.

The concentration of Mg^{2+} ions is very important in the formation of the initiation complex in vitro. Specific binding of the initiator tRNA requires low concentrations of Mg^{2+} ($\sim$ 4 mM). When Mg^{2+} concentrations of 20 mM are used, nonspecific binding of tRNA molecules to the ribosome can takes place. In prokaryotic systems the initiator tRNA species is a $tRNA_f^{Met}$, that is, a molecule specific for methionine, which allows formylation of the amino acid. Only N-formyl methionine can be incorporated into the N-terminal position of growing peptide chains, but it is usually removed sometime during chain growth. The specific $tRNA_f^{Met}$ can recognize only one of the two possible initiator codons, AUG and GUG. The first codes always for methionine; GUG, on the other hand, always allows incorporation of N-formyl methionine in the initial (N-terminal) position, but codes for valine in all internal positions.

In eukaryotes, two or three types of $tRNA^{Met}$ have been identified, but no transformylase activity has been found. One of these tRNAs can be formylated in vitro by *E. coli* transformylase, and this molecule appears to be required for the formation of the specific initiation complex. The difference between initiator tRNAs and other tRNA^{Met} molecules appear to lie in some modified bases in the anticodon loop, and some differences in sequence in other parts of the tRNA molecule. There is evidence that eukaryotic proteins also lose the initial methionine during chain growth. In most respects, initiation is very similar in the prokaryotes and eukaryotes, but there are differences in the components which normally prevent cross-reactions.

ELONGATION

The complete initiation complex, consisting of a complete ribosome, mRNA, and the initiator tRNA, can bind the second amino acyl–tRNA. This binding requires at least three proteins which act as elongation factors (see Chapter 10.3) and two molecules of GTP. The second amino acyl–tRNA enters the A site on the ribosome, a peptide bond is formed, and the growing chain is transferred to the A site (Figure 2). Translocation, the relative movement of the mRNA and the ribosome, takes place; the original tRNA, now empty, is removed, while the second tRNA, carrying the growing chain, is transferred to the P site. The GTP, which is required at this step is hydrolyzed and its energy released for completion of these reactions.

The large subunit contains a peptidyltransferase activity that catalyzes the formation of the peptide bond. The energy for this bond is probably released from the amino acyl bond holding the amino acid to the tRNA which has conserved some of the energy from the ATP originally used to form it (see Chapter 9.5). The hydrolysis of GTP provides more energy; this energy may be used for binding–release of elongation factors, and for translocation. The mechanism of translocation is not well understood, but it is a coordination of the movements of mRNA and ribosome relative to each other so that the tRNA carrying the growing peptide chain is moved to the P site, the empty tRNA is removed, and the next mRNA codon is aligned with the A site. The ribosome itself may participate in this coordination by conformational changes in its components, assisting in the translation of the chemical energy released by hydrolysis of GTP into mechanical energy required to allow the movement of components.

Peptidyltransferase activity has been shown to reside in one or two proteins of the large subunit. The 50S subunit of bacterial ribosomes can be partially dissociated into two core particles, β and γ, neither of which contains the peptidyltransferase activity. On reconstitution, the subunit regains the activity. This may imply that two separate proteins must interact to form a complete enzyme. Alternatively, the β and γ particles may each retain a subunit of a single protein. However, it is also possible that the conformation of the

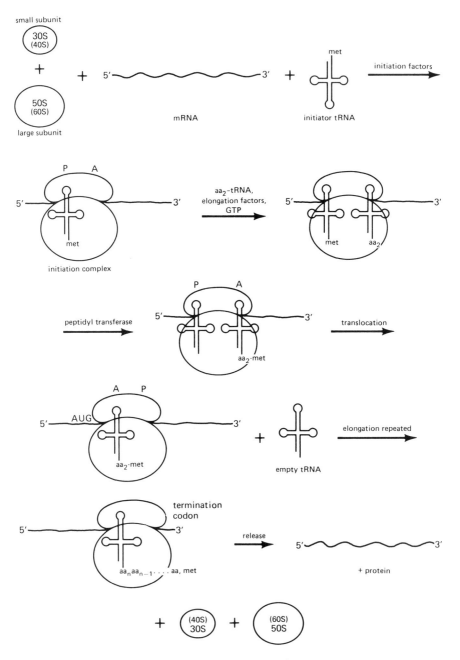

Figure 2. Protein synthesis, general scheme.

active site of the enzyme requires cooperative interactions with other proteins of the large subunit. In the separated particles, these interactions are disrupted, and the active site cannot be held in the proper conformation.

TERMINATION

Three codons do not specify any amino acids, and are called nonsense codons; they have been recognized to be specific termination signals. No tRNA binds when UAG, UAA, or UGA codons on the mRNA correspond in position to the A site on the ribosome. Release factors also appear to be required; they differ in their specificity of binding to one or another nonsense codon, and cannot bind to isolate subunits, but only to intact ribosomes. The termination factors may bind to the A site, thus triggering a conformational change in the ribosome. This, in turn, may cause the peptidyltransferase conformation to be altered in such a way as to allow this enzyme to function as a hydrolase.

Termination involves the release of the protein chain from its attachment to the tRNA held in the P site. Since antibiotics that interfere with peptide bond formation also interfere with this release, it is likely that the same enzyme is required for both processes. When converted to a hydrolase by appropriate interactions with the release factors, the enzyme catalyzes breakage of the amino acyl bond between the C-terminal amino acid and its tRNA. The peptide is then released, the tRNA separates, and the ribosomes detach from the mRNA. The detached ribosomes then apparently separate into the component subunits. Detachment requires two proteins and GTP, while dissociation into subunits may be mediated by a specific dissociation factor which may be identical to one of the initiation factors (see Chapter 10.3).

The mRNA may attach to another ribosome, or may be degraded by nuclease activity immediately on release from the complex. In nature, several ribosomes attach to a single mRNA sequentially (Figure 3), forming a complex known as a polysome. The number of ribosomes that constitute a polysome is dependent on the size of the mRNA. Ribosomes attach to the 5′ end of the molecule, and move to the 3′ end during translation. It is not known what factors determine whether another ribosome will attach or RNase will digest the free 5′ end of the mRNA. Different mRNA molecules have different half-lives; so each molecule may in some unknown fashion control this process.

THE tRNA ATTACHMENT SITES

As indicated above, the charged tRNA molecule binds to the ribosome at two sites during protein synthesis. Each site shows specificity for the charged tRNA molecules; a tRNA carrying a growing peptide chain is always transferred to the P site, whereas an entering tRNA carrying a single amino

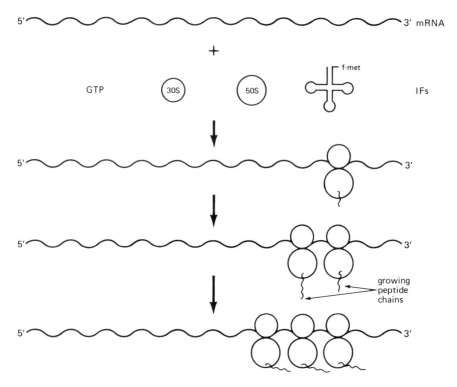

Figure 3. Polysome formation.

acid is bound to the A site. The only exception to this last is the initiator tRNA carrying N-formylmethionine (or initiator met–tRNA^{met} in eukaryotes). It can be postulated that this initiator tRNA differs in conformation from other tRNA molecules, and is similar to tRNA carrying a growing peptide chain. This conformation would be recognized by the ribosome, or other necessary constituents, as appropriate for the P site. Several proteins of the large ribosomal subunit do indeed show interactions with the initiator tRNA. In addition, there is evidence that initiator factors bind to the A site, and there is some A site–binding of elongation and termination sites.

Several studies have been interpreted as evidence that the P site lies largely or entirely on the large subunit. The A site, on the other hand, is closely linked to the small subunit. Isolated small subunits appear to be unable to bind more than one tRNA molecule, indicating that interactions between the subunits are required for both A and P sites to be available. There is also some evidence that, initially, f-met-tRNA$_f^{Met}$ may bind in two steps, the first of which may involve an intermediate binding site that is neither A nor P, before transfer to the P site. The sites may, then, include structural elements on both subunits, and may be controlled in some way by conformational changes resulting from subunit interactions. Such conformational changes could also be required for translocation and GTP hydrolysis.

POLYSOMES

Generally, mRNA molecules associate with several ribosomes during translation; the number of ribosomes that can attach to a mRNA, forming a polysome, depends in part on the size of the mRNA, but usually varies from three to seven. Each ribosome attaches at a different time, and is therefore at a different stage in protein synthesis. As the peptide chain is completed, ribosomes are detached from the 5' end of the mRNA; another ribosome may attach at the 3' terminus, or nuclease digestion may take place. The factors that determine the fate of the mRNA are not as yet known.

BIBLIOGRAPHY

Books:

Anfinsen, C. B., ed. 1970. *Aspects of Protein Biosynethesis.* Academic Press, New York.
Watson, J. D. 1975. *Molecular Biology of the Gene.* W. A. Benjamin, Reading, Massachusetts.
Weissback, H., and Pestka, S., ed. 1977. *Molecular Mechanisms of Protein Biosynthesis.* Academic Press, New York.

Research and Review Articles:

Guthrie, C., and Nomura, M. 1968. *Nature* 219:232.
Colombo, B., Vesco, C., and Bagliana, C. 1968. *Proc. Natl. Acad. Sci. U.S.A.* 61:651.
Lipmann, F. 1969. *Science* 164:1024.
Dube, S. K., and Rudland, P. S. 1970. *Nature* 226:820.
Lee-Huang and Ochoa, S. 1971. *Nature New Biol.* 234:236.
Metafara, S., Terada, M., Dow, L. M., Marks, P. A., and Bank, A. 1972. *Proc. Natl. Acad. Sci. U.S.A.* 69:1299.
Smithies, O. S., and Poulik, M. D. 1972. *Science* 175:187.
Keith, G., Picaud, F., Weissenbach, J., Ebel, J. P., Petrissant, G., and Dirkheimer, G. 1973. *FEBS Lett.* 31:345.
Blobstin, J. H., Grunberger, D., Weinstein, I. B., and Nakanishi, K. 1973. *Biochemistry* 12:188.
Schulman, L. H., and Goddard, J. P. 1973. *J. Biol. Chem.* 248:1341.
Egan, B. Z., Weiss, J. F., and Kelmers, A. D. 1973. *Biochem. Biophys. Res. Commun.* 55:320.
Delaney, P., Bierbaum, J., and Ofengand, J. 1974. *Arch. Biochem. Biophys.* 161:260.
Crothers, D. M., Cole, P. E., Hilbers, C. W., and Shulman, R. G. 1974. *J. Mol. Biol.* 87:63.
Kim, S. H., Suddath, F. L., Quigley, G. J., McPherson, A., Sussman, J. L., Wang, A. H. J., Seeman, N. C., and Rich, A. 1974. *Science* 185:435.
Weissbach, H., and Brot, N. 1974. *Cell* 2:137.
Lande, M. A., Adesnik, M., Sumeda, M., Tashiro, Y., and Sabatini, D. D. 1975. *J. Cell Biol.* 65:513.
Fitch, W. M. 1976. *Science* 194:1173.
Daniel, W. E., Jr. and Cohn, M. 1976. *Biochemistry* 15:3917.

Grunberg-Manago, M., and Gros, F. 1977. *Prog. Nucl. Acid Mol. Biol* 20:209.

Kurland, C. G. 1977. *Annu. Rev. Biochem.* 46:173.

Schulman, L. H., and Pelka, H. 1977. *J. Biol. Chem.* 252:814.

Sundari, R. M., and Pelka, H. 1977. *J. Biol. Chem.* 252:814.

Sundari, R. M., Pelka, H., and Schulman, L. H. 1977. *J. Biol. Chem.* 252:3941.

Barricelli, N. A., 1977. *J. Theor. Biol.* 67:85.

In situ Hybridization:

Steffensen, D. M., and Wimber, D. E. 1971. *Genetics* 69:163.

Hennig, W. 1973. *Int. Rev. Cytol.* 36:1.

Wimber, D. E., and Steffensen, D. M. 1973. *Annu. Rev. Genet.* 7:205.

Pardue, M. L., and Gall, J. G. 1975. *Methods Cell Biol.* 11:1.

Szabo, P., Elder, R., and Uhlenbeck, O. C. 1975. *Nucl. Acids Res.* 2:647.

Szabo, P., Elder, R., Steffensen, D. M., and Uhlenbeck, O. C. 1977. *J. Mol. Biol.* 115:539.

10.2.   The Genetic Code

TRIPLET CODONS

It is possible to construct a workable codon based on at least three bases; a one-base codon could only specify 4 amino acids, while codons containing two bases would be able to direct the incorporation of 16 amino acids normally present in proteins. A three-base codon will be required as a minimum in vivo. It is unlikely, from theoretical considerations, that more than three bases would be used, since this would require a larger genome than is found in viruses. Of course, an overlapping code could be used, but was ruled out when studies with synthetic polynucleotides were found to be consistent only with a three-base, nonoverlapping, and nonpunctuated codon. These early experiments used a poly U molecule; in the presence of *E. coli* ribosomes and Mg^{2+} ions (20 mM), a polymer containing three molecules of uridine was able to bind a tRNA molecule charged with phenylalanine. Larger polymers were no more efficient than U_3, indicating that this is the required codon size.

The early work of Nirenberg and his colleagues identified several specific codons. Later, Khorana, Ochoa, and others added more knowledge, finally permitting the determination of all the codons. Other evidence for a triplet code came from the work of Crick and his colleagues, who studied frameshift mutations in the phage T4. They found that when two such mutations occur within a single gene, separated by some relatively short DNA sequence, the correct amino acid sequence may be again found after the second mutation. The deletion or addition of any three nucleotides in the same gene could also have the same effect on amino acid sequences read after the third mutation.

The complete triplet code has been worked out, and each codon assigned a specific function. The code is "degenerate," so that more than one codon can specify a particular amino acid. This degeneracy is not uniformly distributed, since there are two amino acids that can respond only to one codon, while there are some amino acids that can be specified by four or six codons. In addition, no codon can specify two amino acids except for the very special case of the initiator codon GUG. In the initiator position, GUG allows the incorporation of methionine, but at all its other positions on the mRNA, only valine can be incorporated. There are three codons that do not specify

UUU	} Phe	UCU	} Ser	UAU	} Tyr	UGU	} Cys
UUC		UCC		UAG		UGC	
UUA	} Leu	UCA	} Ser	UAA	Ochre	UGA	Amber
UUG		UCG		UAG	} Amber	UGG	} Trp
CUU	} Leu	CCU	} Pro	CAU	} His	CGU	} Arg
CUC		CCC		CAC		CGC	
CUA	} Leu	CCA	} Pro	CAA	} Gln	CGA	} Arg
CUG		CCG		CAG		CGG	
AUU	} Ile	ACU	} Thr	AAU	} Asn	AGU	} Ser
AUG		ACC		AAG		AGC	
AUA	} Ile	ACA	} Thr	AAA	} Lys	AGA	} Arg
AUG	Met	ACG		AAG		AGG	
GUU	} Val	GCU	} Ala	GAU	} Asp	GGU	} Gly
GUC		GCC		GAC		GGC	
GUA	} Val	GCA	} Ala	GAA	} Asp	GGA	} Gly
GUG		GCG		GAG		GGG	

Figure 1. The genetic code.

the incorporation of an amino acid. These nonsense codons have been shown to code for termination of protein synthesis. The complete code is shown in Figure 1.

THE UNIVERSAL IDENTITY OF THE CODE

The genetic code shown in Figure 1 was determined originally from work in prokaryotic organisms. Later, the applicability of the code to eukaryotic protein synthesis was studied by Nirenberg and his coworkers. Binding of amino acyl–tRNA molecules, from E. coli, Xenopus laevis, and the guinea pig, to synthetic mRNA molecules, in an E. coli ribosome system, was studied. The correct amino acyl–tRNA molecules were bound in all three species, albeit with some differences in the strength of binding.

As mentioned previously, the initial amino acid incorporated is slightly different in prokaryotes and eukaryotes. The initiator codons, however, appear to be identical. Termination codons also appear to be identical in all species, although each may play some specific role, since UAA seems to be the most common terminator in vivo. Often, two or more nonsense codons have been shown to follow each other at the end of a translated region of a mRNA. This may be a protective mechanism to ensure termination in case a point mutation allows read-through of the first signal.

Differences in the strength of binding of tRNA molecules to synthetic messenger may reflect differences in the utilization of specific amino acids in the proteins of different species. It is also possible that these binding differences may reflect some control steps during differentiation.

Hb O_{INDONESIA}:	Glu → Lys;	GAA → AAA or
(also Hb C)		GAG → AAG
Hb S:	Glu → Val;	GAA → GUA or
		GAG → GUG
Hb Flatbush:	Ala → Glu;	GCA → GAA or
		GCG → GAG
Hb Rus:	Gly → Arg;	GGA → AGA or CGA
		or GGG → AGG or CGG
		or GGC → CGC
		or GGU → CGU
Hb Genova:	Leu → Pro;	CGA → CCA or
		CUG → CCG or
		CUC → CCC or
		CUU → CCU
Hb Köln:	Val → Met;	GUG → AUG

Figure 2. Codon changes resulting in abnormal hemoglobins.

MULTIPLE CODONS

Several amino acids have more than one codon, as noted above. Serine, for example, is specified by six different codons. Of these, four differ only in the third position, while the others are very different.

UCU	
UCC	AGU
UCA	AGC
UCG	

Six different anticodon sequences, then, could be found in tRNA^{Ser} molecules. The wobble hypothesis of Crick states that the first two bases of an anticodon must be exactly complementary to the corresponding codon sequence, but that the fit of the third pair need not be exact for correct reading of the message. It is possible that this arrangement may be a remnant of the evolution of the genetic code (see below), and it may be the basic reason why multiple codons exist. There is little direct evidence to bear on this point, however, and the exact reason why multiple codons are found is still open to debate. It is posssible that multiple codons, and the presence of isoacceptors, may be involved in specific control processes. If this were the case, one might expect to correlate the relative abundance of a particular codon or a particular isoacceptor tRNA with the state of differentiation of a particular cell, or with a particular cell type. More detailed knowledge of nucleic acid sequences may allow such correlations to be found.

MUTATION AND THE CODE

Many possible single base changes will have no effect on the amino acid incorporated in response to a particular codon. To return to the codons for serine, transitions or transversions in the last position of four codons will still result in coding for serine:

UCU → UCC or UCA or UCG

The same is true of the codons for glycine:

GGA, GGG, GGC, GGU

and many others. Changes in other positions of the condon will often have minimal effects because one neutral amino acid will be replaced by another, such as the change:

CUC (leucine) → UUC (phenylalanine)

or

AGA (arginine) → CGA (arginine)

or

GGA (glycine) → GCA (alanine)

Other transitions and transversions, however, may be more deleterious, as in the following:

GGC (alanine) → UGC (cysteine)

or

CAU (histidine) → GAU (aspartic acid)

or

AAA (lysine) → UAA (stop signal)

Many abnormal proteins in both prokaryotic and eukaryotic systems have been sequenced, and the specific mutation has been determined. In a large proportion of these abnormalities, the change is indeed an alteration in a single base of one codon. The abnormal hemoglobins have been extensively studied, for example, and all known variants can be correlated with a single point mutation (Figure 2). About half of them represent an A/G transition, but the reason for this is not known.

Special suppressor tRNA species have been identified. They misread specific codons that are nonsense or terminating signals, and they are called suppressors tRNAs because they counteract the effect of a premature termination induced by mutation to one of the nonsense codons. Thus, the "amber" codon UAG can be misread by a suppressor tRNA anticodon as:

UCG (serine)
CAG (glutamine)
UAU or UAC (tyrosine)
AAG (lysine)
UUG (leucine)

"Ochre," UAA, can be read as:

UAC (tyrosine)
AAG (lysine)
CAG (glutamine)

and "opal," UGA, can be read as:

UGG (tryptophane)

Such misreadings may still result in an altered protein, but it will be functional, in contrast to the prematurely terminated polypeptide.

EVOLUTION OF THE GENETIC CODE

The genetic code must have arisen before the bacteria became differentiated from their primitive ancestor cells—in other words, at least 3×10^9 years ago. It also appears likely that the code arose only once, in some cell that is the very remote ancestor of all living organisms, and has not altered since that time. Prior to the development of the code, direct interactions between nucleotides and amino acids may have provided some selectivity for protein synthesis in these primordial cells. However, such a system would not allow specificity.

The first code that arose might have been a doublet code, allowing for incorporation of 16 amino acids at most. Fifteen amino acids have been identified as possibly "primordial" in nature; they do not include asparagine, methionine, glutamine, tyrosine, and tryptophane, which would require a third nucleotide for coding. Interactions between dinucleotides and amino acids are stronger than those utilizing mononucleotides; trinucleotides permit even stronger binding.

It is interesting to note that none of the "newer" amino acids is specified by more than two codons. Indeed, methionine and tryptophane each has a single codon, and the other three can each be specified by two codons. An interesting speculation considers the possibility that the original code was punctuated. That is, the doublet codons were separated by single nucleotides that served as commas. Eventually, these nucleotides became the third base of the triplet codon.

The degeneracy of the code could be a protective device, to prevent point mutations from resulting in prematurely terminated polypeptides. If only 20 codons were used, 44 stop signals could arise by a single base change. Most mutations would then be lethal; instead, with 61 translatable codons, altered proteins that are as functional as the original will be found in a high proportion. Some such point mutations even increase the efficiency of the protein products, after which natural selection could act to improve the resulting strain.

BIBLIOGRAPHY

Nirenberg, M. W., and Matthaei, J. H. 1961. *Proc. Natl. Acad. Sci. U.S.A.* 47:1588.

Crick, F. H. C. 1963. *Prog. Nucl. Acid Res.* 1:164.

The genetic code. 1966. *Cold Spring Harbor Symp. Quant. Biol.,* Vol. 31.

Gorini, L. 1966. *Sci. Am.* 214:102.

Crick, F. H. C. 1966. *Sci. Am.* 215:55.

Yanofsky, C. 1967. *Sci. Am.* 216:80.

Woese, C. R. 1967. *The Genetic Code.* Harper & Row, New York.

Ycas, M. 1969. *The Biological Code.* Wiley (Interscience), New York.

Jukes, T. H., Holmquist, R., and Moise, H. 1975. *Science* 189:50.

Fitch, W. M. 1976. *Science* 194:1173.

Baricelli, N. A. 1977. *J. Theor. Biol.* 67:85.

Feinstein, S. D., and Altman, S. 1978. *Genetics* 88:201.

10.3. Cytoplasmic Factors Required for Protein Synthesis

HIGH-ENERGY COMPOUNDS

Protein synthesis requires energy at several points, and, as is true for most metabolic pathways, this energy comes from triphosphate nucleotides. In general, ATP is the source of energy used in almost all reactions. This compound is used for protein synthesis during the activation of the amino acid; the energy is stored in the ester bond between the amino acid and the tRNA, and is used during the formation of the peptide bond. However, the other steps in protein synthesis do not generally require ATP, although there are reports that ATP may also participate in the process. The exact role of ATP, and, indeed, even the requirement for this triphosphate, have not yet been established.

It is clear, however, that the source of energy for most of the steps in protein synthesis is another high-energy compound, GTP. At specific points during initiation and elongation, GTP must be hydrolyzed. The enzyme will not accept ATP, but nonhydrolyzable analogues of GTP can be bound. From experiments using such compounds as GMP-P (CH_2) P, it has been possible to determine the steps for which GTPase activity is required.

GTP participates in the formation of a ternary complex with the appropriate amino acyl–tRNA during both initiation (Figure 1) and elongation (Figure 2). After formation of a complex that, in prokaryotes, may consist of 30S subunits with mRNA and the initiation factor IF-3, GTP bound to IF-2 enters the complex to form a ternary complex. This is required for the proper positioning of the f-met–tRNA molecule in the complex. Binding of IF-1 also requires interaction with GTP, but the formation of the 70S ribosome is not dependent on the triphosphonucleotide. In eukaryotes, there are more factors, but GTP does not interact with all of them (see Chapter 10.5). Rather, it seems to interact specifically only with eIF-2, forming a ternary complex with the initiator tRNA and this factor; this complex then interacts with the other components of the system.

GTP must be hydrolyzed for the recycling of IF-2 during the first steps of protein synthesis in prokaryotes. If GTPase activity is inhibited, EF-Tu

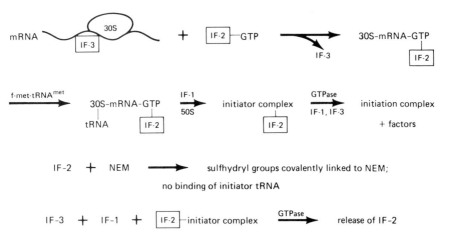

Figure 1. Formation of the prokaryotic initiation complex.

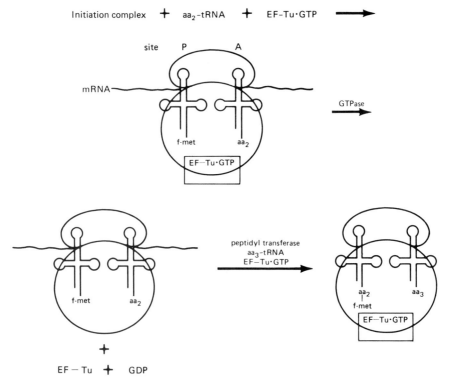

Figure 2. Participation of GTP in elongation.

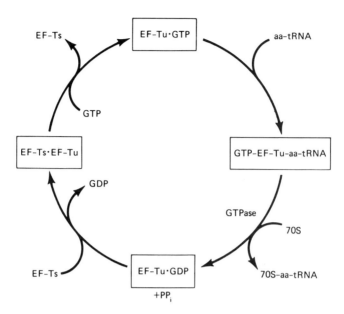

Figure 3. Recycling of EF-Tu.

cannot act to allow entry of a second amino acyl–tRNA into the A site. The enzyme appears to be activated by interactions between the ribosome and the appropriate factor. The same 50S subunit proteins appear to be at or near the site of the specific GTPase activities involved in both initiation and elongation. In *E. coli,* these proteins are L7 and L12; proteins that share at least some antigenic determinants exist in eukaryotic and other prokaryotic ribosomes. The conservation of these protein structures would appear to confirm the importance of GTPase activity in the course of protein synthesis.

GTPase activity is also required for the recycling of EF-Tu during elongation (Figure 3). In eukaryotic systems, the corresponding EF-1 factor apparently is not recycled, but GTP must still be hydrolyzed. Perhaps this hydrolysis allows a conformational change that in prokaryotes allows release of EF-Tu, but in eukaryotes simply creates a site where EF-2 may bind. The exact mechanism whereby GTPase activity allows other reactions to take place is not known, but, in general, conformational changes produced by the hydrolysis probably mediate these reactions.

BACTERIAL INITIATION FACTORS

These factors are proteins that can be isolated easily from ribosomes, to which the factors are loosely bound. IF-1 is a small basic protein with a molecular weight of about 9500 daltons; it contains about 90 amino acids and can be isolated as a tight complex with IF-3. The protein interacts with ribosomes, and may assist the dissociation of the 70S ribosome into the 30S and 50S subunits. It probably binds to a site on the 30S particle and interacts with the other factors during formation of the initiation complex. IF-1 is detached immediately prior to, or during formation of the 70S complex. This factor is also required for release of the ribosome-bound IF-2, which occurs before a second amino acid can be bound to the A site.

IF-2 has been described in two forms, one with a molecular weight of 107,000 daltons, the other of 84,000 daltons. It is possible that IF-2b is a product of proteolytic cleavage of the larger IF-2a molecule. The two forms are similar in chromatographic properties as well as in their specificity for the binding of mRNA to f-met–tRNA. IF-2 contains sulfhydryl groups that are protected on complex formation. If sulfhydryl-binding reagents are allowed to react with IF-2 in the absence of GTP, attachment of f-met–tRNA to the preinitiation complex cannot take place, but binding of the mRNA to the 30S subunit is not impaired. IF-2 also interacts with the specific GTPase required in initiation; this enzymatic activity may be activated by the combination of IF-2 with proteins on the 50S subunit. On hydrolysis of GTP, there is probably a conformational change that permits release of IF-2 from the complex. IF-1 stimulates the release of IF-2 from the complex. IF-1 also stimulates the IF-2–dependent GTPase, as does f-met–tRNA, but maximal activity requires some interaction of all the components.

The third bacterial initiation factor, IF-3, may not be a globular protein, since gel filtration and SDS (sodium dodecyl sulfate)–polyacrylamide gel electrophoresis give different molecular weight values for this protein. Gel filtration on Sephadex, which gives an accurate estimate of the molecular weight of globular proteins, indicates that IF-3 has a molecular weight of 32,000 daltons. In SDS–polyacrylamide gels, proteins are denatured and migrate according to size; such studies have determined the molecular weight to be 22,000 daltons. This figure accords well with the reported sedimentation coefficient of 2.2S, and is probably an accurate estimate of the size. IF-3 interacts with IF-1 to stimulate the release of IF-2 from the initiation complex. This factor is associated with the 30S subunit, and is probably released when the 50S subunit joins the initiation complex. IF-3 has also been reported to exist in two forms, α and β, which may control which phage MS2 genes are transcribed at any given point during lytic infection. It is not clear whether this represents a true specificity, since the repeated differences are small; in addition, other workers have not found two forms of this factor. Studies of mutant bacteria with altered IF-3 may resolve this problem.

EUKARYOTIC INITIATION FACTORS

In eukaryotic cells, at least seven initiation factors have been described. Some have been characterized; several of them appear to be composed of three to ten subunits, and, in general, they show a strong tendency to aggregate in solution. The molecular weights that have been ascertained are:

eIF-1	15,000 daltons
eIF-4A	50,000 daltons
eIF-4B	80,000 daltons
eIF-5	160,000 daltons
eIF-2	three subunits: 35,000, 50,000, and 55,000 daltons

The eIF-3 factor has a sedimentation coefficient of 17S, and on dissociation in SDS appears to contain nine or ten subunits.

Each of these factors appears to play one specific role during eukaryotic protein synthesis, unlike the bacterial factors, which may participate in several steps. The better-characterized reactions include the formation of a ternary complex between eIF-2, GTP, and the initiator met–tRNA$_f$. Formation of the 40S–met–tRNA$_f$–GTP complex requires interactions with eIF-1 and eIF-3. This last factor is also required for the addition of mRNA to the complex. Other factors that participate in this step include eIF-4A, 4B, and 4C, while eIF-5 catalyzes the addition of the large subunit to the complex. GTP must be hydrolyzed at this step, although the exact function of this GTPase is not yet understood. The factors may interact with either proteins or rRNA to stimulate the formation of specific complexes. The exact interactions may be more clearly defined in the future.

ELONGATION FACTORS IN BACTERIA

Three elongation factors have been described in bacterial systems, whereas eukaryotic cells apparently contain only two such proteins. These factors are proteins that participate in the process whereby the second and all subsequent amino acids are added to the growing peptide chain. They are required for binding of amino acyl–tRNAs, for the translocation of the peptidyl–tRNA from the A to the P site, and for the hydrolysis of GTP. The factors interact with the other components required for protein synthesis in specific ways.

EF-Ts and EF-Tu are required for the following reaction sequence (Fig. 4):

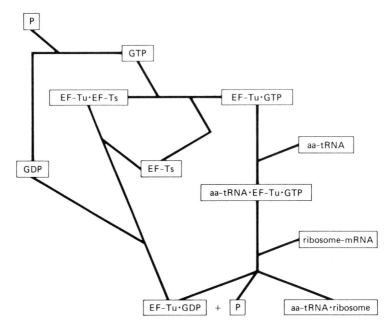

Figure 4. Protein synthesis in bacteria. Interactions between elongation factors.

These reactions permit the binding of the amino acyl–tRNA to the A site on the ribosome, and the recycling of the EF-Tu factor so as to permit interaction of this protein with the next amino acyl–tRNA. In vivo, EF-Ts is often isolated in a complex with EF-Tu, for which it has a higher affinity than does GDP. GTP, however, is able to replace EF-Ts in the complex, thus regenerating the [EF-Tu·GTP] complex required for binding of the aa–tRNA. EF-Tu has a molecular weight of 42,000 to 46,000 daltons, and contain one atom of zinc per mole. However, the zinc appears not to be required for binding of either GTP or the amino acyl–tRNA. It is not clear if this metal is a contaminant, if it is required for some other, as yet unspecified function, or if it plays a role in the structure of the factor.

EF-G, the third bacterial elongation factor, is a protein consisting of a single polypeptide chain with a molecular weight between 72,000 and 84,000 daltons. It is an acidic protein, containing about six sulfhydryl group, which are required for activity. In the presence of ribosomes, EF-G catalyzes the hydrolysis of GTP. The reaction requires Mg^{2+} ions and has optimal activity at pH 9.0. The EF-G factor interacts with the L7 and L12 proteins of the 50S ribosomal subunit. In the absence of these proteins in an in vitro system, GTP cannot bind to the ribosome when EF-G is present. Other functions have also been ascribed to EF-G. It may be required for the translocation of the peptidyl–tRNA from the A to the P site, and for removal of the empty tRNA from the P site when the A site is occupied.

Both EF-G and EF-Tu bind at or near the same site on the ribosome. The presence of one prevents binding of the other, indicating a careful orchestration of the interactions of each factor with the ribosome. These interactions may play an important role in the control of elongation.

EUKARYOTIC ELONGATION FACTORS

Two proteins required for elongation have been identified in several mammalian systems. They are called EF-1, analogous to EF-Tu, and EF-2, which carries out a function similar to that of the bacterial EF-G. EF-1 and EF-Tu can substitute for each other to catalyze the binding of the amino acyl–tRNA, but will not then interact with the heterologous EF-G or EF-2. This behavior indicates that the bacterial and mammalian factors differ in structure, and perhaps also in the exact mechanisms of interaction with the ribosome.

EF-1 appears to exist in multiple species that are polymers of a subunit with a molecular weight of about 50,000 daltons. One apparent exception to this situation is found in wheat germ, where the factor consists of three unlike subunits. These factors have molecular weights of 17,000, 47,000, and 52,000 daltons; doubt has been expressed, however, as to the actual involvement of the smallest subunit in the structure of the factor. The large aggregates appear to be associated with various lipids, including cholesterol. It has been suggested that the lipids stabilize these polymers.

EF-2 is a large protein, about 96,500 to 110,000 daltons in molecular weight, that contains essential sulfhydryl groups. It forms a stable complex with GTP:

$$\text{EF-2} + \text{GTP} \rightleftharpoons [\text{EF-2} \cdot \text{GTP}]$$

which interacts with the ribosome:

$$\text{EF-2} \cdot \text{GTP} + \text{ribosome} \rightleftharpoons [\text{ribosome} \cdot \text{EF-2} \cdot \text{GDP}] + \text{P}_i$$

This second complex is very stable, but it is possible that EF-2 cycles on and off the ribosome in order to catalyze both translocation and GTP hydrolysis. In general, EF-2 is involved in the same reactions as EF-G, that is, ribosome-dependent GTPase, translocation, and removal of the empty tRNA from the protein. The exact mechanisms by which it catalyzes these reactions, however, have not yet been clarified.

TERMINATION

This process also requires the cooperation of soluble cytoplasmic factors. In bacteria, three protein factors have been identified, known as release factors RF-1, RF-2, and RF-3. The first two have been studied in *E. coli;* they are proteins with molecular weights of 44,000 and 47,000 daltons, respectively. It has been calculated that each cell contains 500 molecules of RF-1 and 700 molecules of RF-2. Each of these factors interacts specifically with a particular termination codon, and both recognize the third, UAA; RF-1 is specific for UAG, while RF-2 interacts with UGA. The third factor, RF-3, is involved in both the binding and the release of the other release factors. RF-3 lowers the K_m of the RF-1 and RF-2 for the termination codons, to assist in the specific binding of these factors at the A site. It interacts with both GTP and GDP, indicating that hydrolysis of GTP may be required. However, no direct evidence of such a requirement has been found.

In eukaryotic systems, on the other hand, the hydrolysis of GTP has been shown to occur during termination. Only one factor has been identified in these systems; this protein recognizes all three termination codons. It has been isolated as a dimer, containing two subunits of 56,000 daltons. It is not yet clear whether the monomer or the dimer is the actual factor that interacts with the ribosome, nor is it known which form is required for the ribosome-dependent GTPase activity.

At present, termination is the least understood function of protein synthesis. Further studies are needed to clarify the interactions of the nonsense codons with the termination factors as well as with the ribosome itself. The specificities of the soluble factors, and the role of GTP in termination, are other areas that also require more detailed investigations.

BIBLIOGRAPHY

General References:

Lucas-Lenard, J., and Lipmann, F. 1971. *Annu. Rev. Biochem.* 40:409.
Weissbach, H., and Brot, N. 1974. *Cell* 2:137.
Weissbach, H., and Petska, S., ed. 1977. *Molecular Mechanisms of Protein Biosynthesis.* Academic Press, New York.
Grunberg-Manago, M., and Gross, F. 1977. *Prog. Nucl. Acid Res. Mol. Biol.* 20:209.

Initiation:

Lee-Huang, S., and Ochoa, S. 1971. *Nature New Biol.* 234:44.
Lee-Huang, S., Sillers, M. A. G., and Ochoa, S. 1971. *Eur. J. Biochem.* 18:536.
Baglioni, C., Jacobs-Lorena, M., and Meade, H. 1972. *Biochem. Biophys. Acta* 277:188.
Smithies, D., and Paulik, M. D. 1972. *Science* 175:187.
Macumder, R. 1972. *Proc. Natl. Acad. Sci. U.S.A.* 69:2770.
Dubnoff, J. S., Lockwood, A. H., Maitra, U. 1972. *J. Biol. Chem.* 247:2884.

Benne, R., Naaktgeboren, N., Gubbens, J., and Voorma, H. O. 1973. *Eur. J. Biochem.* 32:392.

Safer, B., Anderson, W. F., and Merrick, W. C. 1975. *J. Biol. Chem.* 250:9067.

Merrick, W. C., Kemper, A. M., and Anderson, W. F. 1975. *Proc. Natl. Acad. Sci. U.S.A.* 72:5556.

Trachsel, H., Erni, B., Schreier, M. H., and Staehelin, T. 1975. *J. Mol. Biol.* 116:755.

Safer, B., Adams, S. L., Kemper, W. M., Berry, K. W., Lloyd, M., and Merrick, W. G. 1976. *Proc. Natl. Acad. Sci. U.S.A.* 73:2584.

Kember, W. M., Berry, K. W., and Merrick, W. C. 1976. *J. Biol. Chem.* 251:5551.

Benne, R., and Hershey, J. W. B. 1976. *Proc. Natl. Acad. Sci. U.S.A.* 73:3005.

Benne, R., Wong, C., Luedi, M., and Hershey, J. W. B. 1976. *J. Biol. Chem.* 251:7675.

Sundari, R. M., Stringer, E. A., Schulman, L. H., and Maitra, U. 1976. *J. Biol. Chem.* 251:3338.

Benne, R., Luedi, M., and Hershey, J. W. B. 1977. *J. Biol. Chem.* 252:5798.

Schreier, M. H., Erni, B., and Staehelin, T. 1977. *J. Mol. Biol.* 116:727.

Elongation and Termination:

Goldstein, J., Milman, G., Scolnick, E., and Coskey, T. 1970. *Proc. Natl. Acad. Sci.* 65:430.

Miller, D. L., and Weissbach, H. 1970. *Arch. Biochem. Biophys.* 141:26.

Hachmann, J., Miller, D. L., and Weissbach, H. 1971. *Arch. Biochem. Biophys.* 147:457.

Modolell, J., Vazquez, D., and Monro, R. 1971. *Nature New Biol.* 230:109.

Brot, N., Boublik, M., Yamasaki, E., and Weissbach, H. 1972. *Proc. Nat. Acad. Sci. U.S.A.* 69:2120.

Arai, K., Kawakita, M., and Kaziro, Y. 1972. *J. Biol. Chem.* 247:7029.

Richter, D. 1973. *J. Biol. Chem.* 248:2853.

Nombela, C., and Ochoa, S. 1973. *Proc. Natl. Acad. Sci.* 70:3556.

Drews, J., Bednarik, K., and Grusmuk, H. 1974. *Eur. J. Biochem.* 41:217.

Nolan, P. D., Grusmuk, H., and Drews, J. 1975. *Eur. J. Biochem.* 50:391.

Cox, R. A., and Hirst, W. 1976. *Biochem. J.* 160:515.

Cox, R. A., Greenwell, P., and Hirst, W. 1976. *Biochem. J.* 160:521.

Slobin, L. I., and Moller, W. 1977. *Biochem. Biophys. Res. Commun.* 74:356.

Grusmuk, H., Nolan, R. D., and Drews, J. 1977. *Eur. J. Biochem.* 79:93.

Sander, G., Parlato, G., Crechet, J. B., Nagel, K., and Parmeggiani, A. 1978. *Eur. J. Biochem.* 86:555.

10.4. Prokaryotic Protein Synthesis

THE BACTERIAL RIBOSOME

As described previously (Chapter 9.5, 10.1), the subunits of ribosomes differ in size and specific function, but combine to form the structural component that permits protein synthesis. The two subunits found in bacterial chromosomes have sedimentation coefficients of 30S and 50S; each is a ribonuclear protein complex, which may include certain factors present in less than stoichiometric amounts. The smaller subunit is required for initiation, while certain functions of elongation are mediated by the 50S subunit. The whole process, however, requires cooperation between the subunits, bound together to form the 70S ribosome.

Many of the proteins in the 30S subunit have been identified, and specific functions can be assigned to some of them (see also Chapter 9.5). Protein S-1 of the 30S subunit deserves special mention. In the absence of this protein, which is easily dissociable from the subunit, no initiation complex can be formed. It is probable that this protein is required for recognition of the mRNA; an excess of this protein inhibits initiation. This behavior appears to be due to binding of excess S-1 to the mRNA, which can occur even in the absence of ribosomes.

Other ribosomal proteins are also required for the formation of the initiation complex. Of these, the role of S-12 is perhaps best understood. This protein, the site of interaction with the antibiotic streptomycin, is required for proper recycling of the initiation factor IF-2 (see Chapter 10.3). It is thought that interactions between the 16S RNA and S-12 protein are responsible for the recognition of initiation signals, though not of the specific initiation codon. Bacterial ribosomes from different species translate polycistronic phage mRNA molecules with different efficiencies for various components. Thus, *E. coli* ribosomes recognize the sites for three viral proteins at a ratio of $1:2.3:1.4$, whereas *B. stearothermophilus* ribosomes produce these products at a very different ratio, $1:0.06:0.4$. Goldberg and Steitz reconstituted ribosomes from the proteins of one species and the rRNA of the other; they found that the ratios were specifically responsive to the 30S proteins rather than to the 16S RNA. When single proteins of the *E. coli* ribosome were substituted by the analogous *B. stearothermophilus,* S-12 was shown to be responsible for the altered ratio.

The ribosomal proteins which are physically located in close proximity to the mRNA probably also include S-18 and S-21. Other proteins interfere with the binding of the initiation tRNA; antibodies to S-6 and S-12 have been shown to inhibit this step specifically. Antibodies to S-4, S-7, S-15, and S-16 do not interfere with binding of tRNA but prevent translation of mRNA. Proteins S-1, S-2, S-3, S-10, S-13, S-19, S-20, and S-21 appear to be required for both initiation and elongation; this has been interpreted to mean that these proteins may be involved in the A and P site formation, perhaps forming parts of both sites.

Some of the proteins of the 50S subunit have tentatively been assigned specific roles. The P site contains proteins L-2 and L-27; other 50S proteins (L-13, L-14, L-15, L-16, and L-32 or 33) are also in this region. L-18 and L-25 appear to be involved in the ribosomal GTPase activity, together with 5S RNA. Normally, the conformation of these components is such that no hydrolysis of GTP takes place. In the presence of the appropriate factors, which bind to proteins L-7 and L-12, a modification is induced in the conformation of L-18 and L-25 so that an active GTPase site is formed. The factors that bind to L-7 and L-12 include an initiation factor, IF-2, and two elongation factors, EF-T and EF-G. Another protein required for binding of EF-G is L-11; this protein also participates in the interactions between the amino acyl–tRNAs and the A site, and may be the protein responsible for peptidyltransferase activity. Peptidyltransferase, the enzyme that catalyzes the formation of the peptide bond, is an integral part of the large subunit.

If 50S subunits are treated in such a way as to remove groups of proteins and one basic protein while the γ pore lacks five additional basic proteins, the proteins that have been removed can also be recovered. Full peptidyltransferase activity is retained by the β core, but not by the γ core or the isolated protein fraction. When the five basic proteins are combined with the γ core, however, full activity is restored. This could imply that the enzyme is one of these five basic proteins, but requires interaction with other ribosomal components for the correct conformation. It is also possible, however, that the two fractions each contain part of the activity in the form of dissimilar subunits, both of which are needed for formation of the active site.

As described previously (Chapter 9.5), rRNA molecules are required for the structural integrity of the ribosome. Recent experiments have clarified the role of 5S RNA in *E. coli* ribosomes. The 50S subunit can be reconstituted in vitro from its components by a series of incubations:

$$23S\ RNA + 5S\ RNA + proteins \xrightarrow[\substack{4\ \text{mM} \\ Mg^{2+}}]{0°C} RI_{50}\ (33S)$$

$$RI_{50} \xrightarrow[\substack{4 \text{ mM} \\ Mg^{2+}}]{44°C} RI^*_{50} \text{ (41S)}$$

$$RI^*_{50} + 5S \text{ RNA} + \text{proteins} \xrightarrow[\substack{4 \text{ mM} \\ Mg^{2+}}]{44°C} RI_{50}(2) \text{ (48S)}$$

$$RI_{50}(2) \xrightarrow[20 \text{ mM } Mg^{2+}]{50°C} 50S \text{ subunit}$$

A similar series of incubations in the absence of 5S allows recovery of a 47S particle, which has lost much of the 50S activity, but can regain it on incubation at 50°C in the presence of 20 mM Mg^{2+}. These experiments, and characterization of the 47S particle, allowed Dohme and Nierhaus to tentatively assign certain functions to 5S RNA.

First, the 5S RNA is required to maintain an active conformation of the 50S subunit. In its absence, the binding of tRNA is significantly reduced, especially binding to the A site, as is chloramphenicol binding. Peptidyltransferase activity is completely inhibited in the absence of 5S, but GTPase activity of the subunit is not affected. This implies that proteins required for GTPase activity do not interact strongly with 5S RNA, but those that catalyze peptide bond formation may be closely associated with this RNA.

A defect in the maturation of rRNA has also been described by Johnson, Watson, and Aperion; the mutation prevents growth of *E. coli* at permissive temperature, and kills the cells at higher temperature. The mutant strain can be protected against killing by agents that prevent both protein synthesis and maturation of ribosomes. The molecular basis of the defect may involve an enzyme that normally modifies the structure of the rRNA, since the last step in processing of the 16S rRNA precursor is slowed significantly in this strain. In addition, the 16S rRNA appears to be degraded more rapidly than normal, again indicating a structural change in this component. The exact nature of the defect in protein synthesis induced by this altered rRNA has not been determined. It is clear, however, that profound consequences in ribosome function can be induced by alterations in the rRNA.

INITIATION

Initiation of bacterial mRNA translation requires the formation of a specific complex containing the mRNA, the specific initiator tRNA (Figure 1), the 70S ribosome, and three initiation factors, IF-1, IF-2 and IF-3. The first of these factors, IF-1, has only been found in *E. coli,* not in other bacterial systems. The interactions required for the formation of the initiation complex

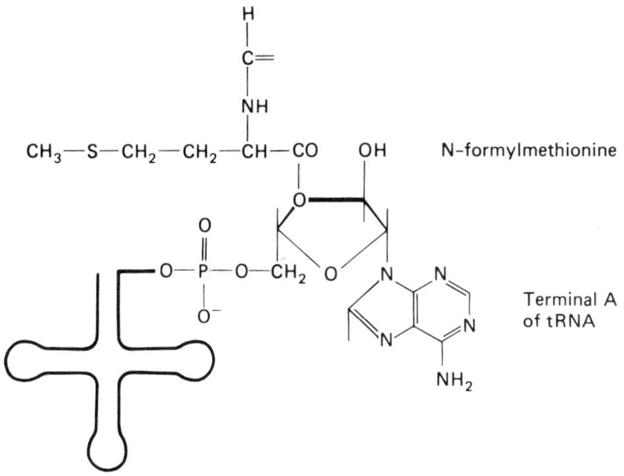

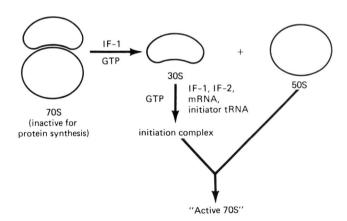

Figure. 1. Prokaryotic initiator amino acyl–tRNA.

involve the following components: initiation factors, 30S and 50S ribosomal subunits, GTP, mRNA, and f-met–tRNA. The initiation factors, which are associated to some extent with the 30S subunit, are IF-1, IF-2, and IF-3. IF-1 appears to facilitate the dissociation of 70S ribosomes to 30S and 50S subunits (Figure 2), required to allow participation of 30S subunits in the binding of the other components. IF-3 binds to a site on the 30S, possibly a site formed in consequence of a conformational change induced by IF-1. The exact sequence of events that follows this binding is not yet established, since two alternate pathways accord equally well with available evidence,

Figure 2. Dissociation of 70S ribosomes.

namely: (1) binding of 30S to mRNA or (2) f-met–tRNA binding to 30S in the presence of IF-2. It is clear that the result of interactions of tRNA, mRNA, 30S subunits, and IF-2 and IF-3 is the formation of a complex containing mRNA, the 30S particle, the factors, and f-met–tRNA. GTP binding is required at this step, and IF-2 remains attached. IF-1 and IF-3 may become detached during the formation of this complex, but IF-2 is not released until the 50S subunit is joined to the complex and the GTP has been hydrolyzed. It seems very probable that IF-2 binds at the A site on the ribosome, causing binding of the initiator tRNA at the P site; release of IF-2 from the A site allows the process of elongation to proceed. IF-1 also plays a role in the release of IF-2, possibly inducing a conformational change that allows the IF-2–dependent GTPase activity.

The initiator tRNA is bound at the P site in such a fashion as to allow interaction of the anticodon loop with the initiating codon of the mRNA. Since AUG and GUG each participate as codons for internal amino acid residues, as well as initiator codons, specific aspects of sequence and conformation must be involved in recognition of the initiation signal. The ribosome, with or without the associated f-met–tRNA, must bind to the mRNA in such a way as to permit alignment of the anticodon with the initiator codon; this may in part depend on interactions with IF-3. This factor is absolutely required for formation of the initiation complex with natural mRNA molecules, although the other factors may be able to substitute for it with synthetic messengers. These other factors, IF-1 and IF-2, can promote the binding of the f-met–tRNA to the AUG codon with a synthetic mRNA, but allow less than 10% of binding to natural mRNA in the absence of IF-3. However, IF-3 alone does not promote initiation, but rather interacts with the other two factors to permit the necessary reactions.

ELONGATION

Formation of the initiation complex is followed by binding of a second amino acyl–tRNA (aa–tRNA) to the ribosome. This binding is mediated by an elongation factor, EF-Tu; other factors, EF-G and EF-Ts, are required during the continuing process of elongation. The process involves the following: (1) binding of amino acyl–tRNA, with GTPase activity; (2) formation of the peptide bond; and (3) translocation of the growing chain to the P site with hydrolysis of GTP (Figure 3). EF-G is required for GTPase activity; both EF-G and EF-Tu interact with proteins of the 50S subunit. EF-Ts may catalyze the release of EF-Tu from ribosomes after binding of the aa–tRNA to the A site; in vitro, it forms a complex with EF-Tu.

Peptide bond formation is catalyzed by the peptidyltransferase that is found as an integral part of the 50S subunit. Some available information has implicated the L-11 protein in this reaction, yet experiments show that core particles

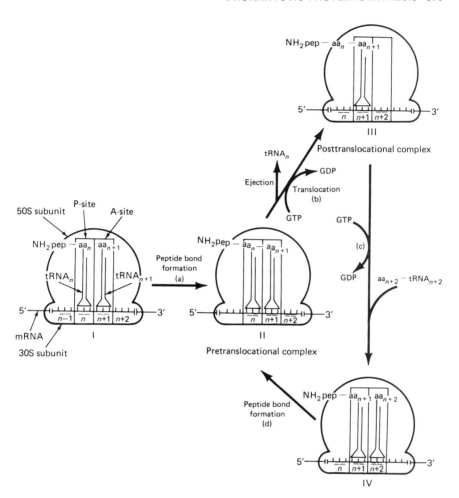

Figure 3. Elongation.

that lack L-11 retain peptidyltransferase activity. This could be explained by assuming that very few molecules of L-11, which cannot be detected by normal methods, are still retained in the core particle. Normally, a protein must constitute 5–10% of a mixture to be identified by two-dimensional electrophoresis, while levels as low as 1% of the total may suffice for activity. Another protein, L-16, may also be required for peptidyltransferase, but further studies are required to confirm this observation. It is possible that L-16 in some way stimulates the activity of L-11, and is therefore not essential to activity, although it may be required in vivo to maintain a maximal rate of elongation.

The hydrolysis of GTP, which is dependent on elongation factors, is essential for the process of translocation. Some proteins of the large subunit are also required for GTPase activity; these proteins are L-7 and L-12. In their absence, EF-Tu and EF-G binding is reduced drastically, and GTPase activity decreases. The same proteins participate in the binding of the IF-2 factor, as well as the termination factor, RF. These proteins seem to have changed little during evolution, since immunological and biochemical comparisons of such proteins from both prokaryotes and eukaryotes indicate structural homologies. This finding implies that L-7 and L-12 are essential for the function of all ribosomes. It is not clear whether they participate structurally in the formation of the GTPase, or whether their role is one of regulation of a factor associated enzyme. GTPase activity is not required in vitro for aa–tRNA binding, peptide bond formation, or translocation, in the poly U–directed synthesis of polyphenylalanine. It would appear, then, that GTP must be hydrolyzed simply in order to dissociate the EF-G factor from the ribosome. In addition, GTP participates in the formation of the EF-Tu–aa–tRNA complex formed before binding of the aa–tRNA to the A site. This could imply that GTP acts as a modulator of the conformation of EF-Tu; on hydrolysis, the GDP would cause dissociation of EF-Tu by allowing a second opposite, conformational change.

Translocation is the process of relative movement of the components, so that the tRNA carrying the growing peptide chain enters the P site, and the next mRNA codon moves to the A site. The exact mechanism of translocation is not well understood; GTP must be hydrolyzed, but this hydrolysis may have only indirect effects as described above. The process may be partially controlled by interactions between the mRNA codon and the tRNA anticodon. There is evidence that the loss of a positive charge on the aa–tRNA will modulate its interactions with the A and P sites. After peptide bond formation, the empty tRNA molecule leaves the P site, and the tRNA carrying the growing peptide chain moves from the A site to occupy the P site. The EF-G factor participates in this transfer, GTP is hydrolyzed, and EF-G dissociates from the ribosome. The next aa–tRNA can now bind to the A site; the mRNA has moved so that the next codon is in position to interact with the A site.

The tRNA molecule may interact with one of the rRNA molecules, perhaps the 16S or the 5S RNA. There are sequences in both these RNA species that are partially complementary to TUCG; however, interactions of these GAAC sequences with the loop appear to be impeded by the postulated tertiary structure of the tRNA. When 5S RNA is removed from the ribosome, and also when 16S RNA is modified by reaction with Kethoxal, binding of rRNA is inhibited. If conformational changes in the tRNA take place during complexing with EF-Tu and GTP, as has been reported, such interactions are much more likely. Further studies of the physical-chemical changes that occur on binding of tRNA to the factors, and studies of the ribosomes, may clarify the exact role of each component.

TERMINATION

Protein synthesis stops when a nonsense codon enters the ribosomal A site, requiring interaction with termination or release factors. Two of these factors, RF-1 and RF-2, are specific for one of the termination codons UAG and UGA, respectively. The third stop codon, UAA, can interact with either factor. In addition, a third factor, RF-3, enhances the activity of others. GTP is hydrolyzed during this process in prokaryotes. Termination codons seem to be often found in pairs in the RNA phages f2 and R17, as well as in *E. coli*. This may be a control mechanism to prevent accidental read-through of the stop signal.

The completed protein chain must be released from the tRNA during termination. This requires a hydrolysis of the ester bond linking the C-terminal amino acid to the adenine residue at the end of the amino acid arm of the tRNA. Available evidence indicates that the enzyme responsible for this ester-bond hydrolysis is the peptidyltransferase itself. Antibodies to L-11 and L-16, the 50S proteins associated with peptidyltransferase activity, inhibit the hydrolysis as specifically as they inhibit peptide bond formation. In addition, formation of a peptide bond implies the hydrolysis of the ester bond holding the amino acid to its specific tRNA. The peptidyl–tRNA that undergoes hydrolysis is always in the P site, while peptide bond formation results in addition at the A site. This seems to imply that the peptidyltransferase has two active sites, one of which interacts with each of the ribosomal binding sites. When no aa–tRNA is positioned at the A site, only hydrolysis at the P site can take place.

Termination also requires release of the empty tRNA, which is tied to translocation. The mRNA is also removed from its association with the ribosome. This may lead to digestion of the mRNA by nucleases, which are no longer prevented from action by the physical-chemical interactions between mRNA and the ribosome. In addition, the ribosome dissociates into subunits, which can be recycled and initiate protein synthesis anew. This dissociation requires a specific factor, DF, which may alter the conformation of ribosomal components, preventing interactions between the subunits.

BIBLIOGRAPHY

Jacob, F., and Monod, J. 1961. *J. Mol. Biol.* 3:318.
Lipmann, F. 1969. *Science* 164:1024.
Zubay, G., Schwartz, D., and Beckwith, J. 1970. *Proc. Natl. Acad. Sci. U.S.A.* 66:104.
Jibe, A., and Bourgeois, S. 1972. *J. Mol. Biol.* 69:397.

Jackson, E. N., and Yanofsky, C. 1973. *J. Mol. Biol.* 76:89.

Rose, J. K., Squires, C. L., Yanofsky, C., Yang, H. L., and Zubay, G. 1973. *Nature New Biol.* 245:133.

Englesberg, E., and Wilcox, G. 1974. *Annu. Rev. Genet.* 8:219.

Nierlich, D. P. 1974. *Science* 184:1043.

Bertrand, K., Korn, L., Lee, F., Platt, T., Squires, C. L., Squires, C., and Yanofsky, C. 1975. *Science* 189:22.

Dickson, R. C., Abelson, J., Barnes, W. M., and Reznikoff, W. S. 1975. *Science* 187:27.

Sundar, R. M., Stringer, E. A., Schulman, L. H., and Maitra, U. 1976. *J. Biol. Chem.* 251:3338.

Sundar, R. M., Pelka, H., and Schulman, L. H. 1977. *J. Biol. Chem.* 252:3941.

Grasmuk, H., Nolan, R. D., and Drews, J. 1977. *FEBS Lett.* 82:237.

Sander, G., Parlato, G., Crechet, J. B., Nagel, K., and Parmeggiani, A. 1978. *Eur. J. Biochem.* 86:555.

10.5. Protein Synthesis in Eukaryotes

GENERAL CONSIDERATIONS

Basically, protein synthesis in eukaryotes is quite similar to the process in prokaryotes (Chapter 10.4). There are differences in the required components, which, however, show functional homologies in the two systems. Some components appear to have been strongly conserved during evolution, and a few can be used interchangeably, albeit not efficiently in the heterologous system.

Differences between the two systems will be described in detail below. Much information has been obtained from studies of hemoglobin synthesis, since immature red blood cells can be obtained easily, and the process gives rise essentially to a single product, making analysis easier. Information about specific components required in the process has come from studies in yeast and mammalian livers, which can be obtained in high yield. Control processes in eukaryotic cells have been studied in some detail, and may participate in differentiation, but further studies will be required to clarify this possibility.

Unlike prokaryotes, eukaryotic cells are compartmentalized by internal membranes. Protein synthesis takes place in the cytoplasm, either on free ribosomes or on polysomes bound to the endoplasmic reticulum (ER). In cells with little ER, most protein synthesis must take place on the free ribosomes attached as polysomes to the specific mRNA molecules. On the other hand, in cells containing significant amounts of rough ER (that is, with ribosomes attached), the proteins made here may form a separate class of molecules. Studies have shown that growing peptide chains on ribosomes attached to the ER project into the lumen, or interior, of the ER. When the protein is completed, it can be transported through the ER to the Golgi apparatus where the proteins are packaged. In this way, digestive proteins, for example, can be prepared for use and stored until needed in a membrane-bound organelle. The other proteins, produced on the free ribosomes, would be those required immediately by the cell, and could include hemoglobin, structural proteins, and biosynthetic enzymes. The actual mechanism of protein synthesis, however, is probably identical at both sites; only post-translational transport and packaging differ.

As in prokaryotes, each mRNA molecule is attached to several ribosomes (Figure 1). This was first demonstrated for hemoglobin mRNA by Rich;

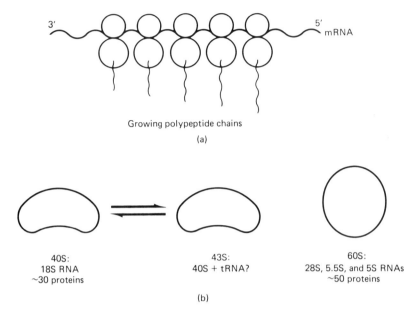

Figure 1. Polyribosomes. (a) Polysome complex, (b) Ribosomal subunits.

later studies also demonstrated the participation of such polysomes in *E. coli* protein synthesis. Since the size of the polysome is dependent on the size of the mRNA, it has been possible to isolate separate polysome fractions that are synthesizing the two types of immunoglobulin chains, or the two globin chains. Such separations may be useful in determining whether the subunits of a polymeric protein participate in the control of the synthesis of the polypeptides.

THE EUKARYOTIC RIBOSOME

As described previously (Chapter 9.5), the eukaryotic ribosome is larger than that of bacteria, having a sedimentation coefficient of 80S rather than 70S. Modified nucleotides are found in the 80S ribosomes, but many of the methyl groups are located on the ribose moiety, rather than on the bases themselves, as in the 70S particle. The ratio of RNA to protein is lower in eukaryotic cells; the significance of these structural difference in the function of the two types of ribosomes is unknown.

The large subunit of eukaryotic ribosomes, the 60S particle, contains three species of RNA: 28S, 5S, and 5.5S. This last component is specific to eukaryotic ribosomes, and is hydrogen-bonded to the 28S RNA. Except for the protein(s) specifying the peptidyltransferase activity, there appear to be few structural similarities between 50S and 60S subunit proteins. However, few of the 60S proteins have been isolated, and further studies may find other proteins whose structure is conserved. Functionally, the 60S subunit closely resembles the prokaryotic 50S particle. It interacts with the small subunit, forming the A and P sites, and contains peptidyltransferase activity.

The small subunit, the 40S, contains a single rRNA species, 18S RNA, and about 30 proteins. In vitro, this particle appears to be heterogenous, since two components differing slightly in size can be isolated on sucrose density gradients. The 43S component, however, may be an artifact due to strong interaction with the initiator tRNA. This has led Baglioni to postulate that the first step in eukaryotic protein synthesis involves binding of met–tRNA$_f$ to the small subunit, and that mRNA is associated later to this complex (see below).

INITIATION

Like prokaryotes, eukaryotic cells contain at least two tRNA^{Met} species, but no formylating enzyme can be identified in eukaryotes. Methionine attached to one species can, however, be formylated in vitro using the enzyme from *E. coli,* while the other tRNA does not show this ability. By analogy to the bacterial system, one of these species is called tRNA$_f^{Met}$, while the other is tRNA^{Met}. The first species is required for initiation. As mentioned above, mRNA is not required for the first step in initiation, which, on the basis of information now available, proceeds as shown in Figure 2. The initiation factor eIF-1 may play a role in the control of the interactions between the various factors. It seems to prevent association of the initiator tRNA to

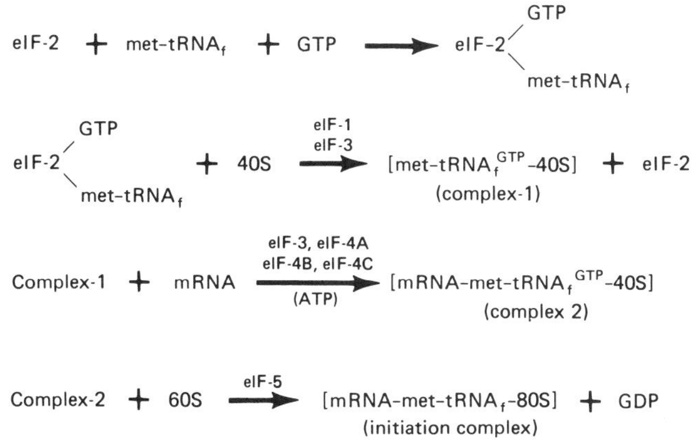

Figure 2. Eukaryotic initiation.

the 80S ribosome in the absence of mRNA, perhaps by some specific interactions with the various components. The role of ATP has not been defined, but it appears to be required during formation of the complexes in some plant and animal systems.

In comparison to bacterial systems, many more factors are required in eukaryotic protein synthesis. The significance of this is not known; if appears that some of these factors may play a role in the recognition of the 5' terminus of the eukaryotic mRNA. Most of these mRNA molecules have a "cap," added to the 5' terminus after transcription; this cap is a 7-methylguanosine (m⁷G) residue linked to the next nucleotide by a 5'-5' pyrophosphate bond. This m⁷G residue appears to be required for the initiation of translation; it is not known why a few molecules lack the cap. The direct interactions of m⁷G have not been clarified, but the residue may be involved in the recognition of mRNA by initiation factors.

Like the prokaryotic system, protein synthesis in eukaryotes requires the hydrolysis of GTP. This hydrolysis in prokaryotes is required for the release of initiation factors bound to the complex (see Chapter 10.3). In eukaryotes, GTP is apparently retained by the complexes until reaction with eIF-5. This factor may interact with some component of the ribosomes to induce a conformational change that allows a GTPase active site to be formed. ATP may also be required, at least in reticulocytes, and wheat germ, for mRNA binding, or for formation of a functional initiation complex. It is not clear whether ATP is hydrolyzed, or whether it is required in all systems. The role of each of the high-energy compounds, ATP and GTP, may be clarified in further experiments using isolated components in in vitro systems.

ELONGATION

At least two factors are required for elongation in eukaryotes: EF-1 and EF-2, which appear to be somewhat analogous to the bacterial factors. The general outline of the steps involved in elongation is similar to that observed in prokaryotic cells. A charged tRNA, carrying the anticodon appropriate for interaction with the mRNA codon at the A site, binds to the ribosome. The peptidyltransferase of the 60S subunit catalyzes peptide bond formation, with transfer of the growing peptide chain to the tRNA at the A site. Translocation takes place, the empty tRNA is removed, the tRNA carrying the peptide moves to the P site, and the next mRNA codon aligns with the A site.

In bacteria, EF-Tu leaves the ribosome on translocation, after GTP hydrolysis. The EF-1 factor of ascites tumor cells is similar in function to EF-Tu, but appears to remain attached to the ribosome throughout the whole process of elongation. This EF-1 factor has been isolated as an aggregate of three subunits; in some eukaryotic species, this trimer has been reported to be the active form. However, recent studies indicate that this may not be true, but rather that the individual monomeric subunits actually function in elongation. This point is not clear, however, since either form can be shown to promote amino acyl–tRNA binding in vitro when homologous ribosomes are used. In a heterologous system, using prokaryotic ribosomes, only the monomeric form of EF-1 allows binding of the aa–tRNA. Comparison of monomeric EF-1 with EF-Tu shows that the two factors can substitute for each other in heterologous systems, but that binding of aa–tRNA is slower and less efficient under these conditions.

In addition, such studies have led Grasmuk, Nolan, and Drews to conclude that the two factors bind to ribosomes in two different manners. EF-Tu associates to the 70S ribosome before addition of each amino acid, and dissociates during or immediately following translocation. On the other hand, EF-1 apparently binds after initiation, and remains bound until the termination codon is reached. The second elongation factor is required during each elongation step; in *E. coli* the dissociation of the first factor is a necessary prerequisite for elongation to proceed. When EF-1 and EF-G are used with *E. coli* polysomes, binding of the tRNA is not followed by further reaction. It is not possible to determine if this is due to altered interactions between the heterologous elongation factors. The second factor, EF-G in bacteria or EF-2 in eukaryotes, can function only within a homologous system. The inability of such mixed systems to carry out all the steps in elongation may be due to altered proteins in the ribosomes, or to structural differences in the elongation factors themselves. Functionally, EF-G and EF-2 are similar. Both participate in the GTPase reaction, as well as in translocation.

TERMINATION

In general, the main difference in the last step of protein synthesis in eukaryotes and prokaryotes lies in energy requirements. In prokaryotes, there is no apparent need for hydrolysis of GTP or ATP, while eukaryotic termination is accompanied by GTPase activity. The exact role of this hydrolysis is not known, however.

Only one release factor appears to be present in eukaryotic cells, whereas three, two of which have different specificities for termination codons, have been identified in *E. coli*. As yet, it is not clear if this may reflect differences in the utilization of the three nonsense codons between prokaryotes and eukaryotes. In general, the termination process has been less well studied in eukaryotic systems, so that little information is as yet available.

ORGANELLE-SPECIFIC PROTEIN SYNTHESIS

Insofar as has been determined to date, the ribosomes and factors required for protein synthesis in mitochondria and chloroplasts do not resemble those of the parent cell. These organelle-specific components generally are fully interchangeable with bacterial components, but not with those isolated from eukaryotic cells. Initiation appears to proceed through a formylated methionine, as in bacteria.

In general, only a few proteins are synthesized in organelles; there are only a small number of protein genes in mitochondrial or chloroplast DNA. The number of mitochondria-specific tRNA molecules varies with the particular parental species, from about 9 in *Saccharomyces cerevisiae,* to about 15 in animal cells, and a full complement of tRNA molecules in *Neurospora.* The amino acyl synthetases from the cellular cytoplasm do not interact efficiently with mitochondrial tRNAs, but the enzymes from the organelle use either cytoplasmic or mitochondrial tRNAs, as substrates, about equally well. This could imply that protein synthesis in mitochondria requires interaction with those cytoplasmic tRNAs for which no mitochondrial equivalent is available.

In chloroplasts, too, f-met–tRNA has been identified as the initiator tRNA. The mean size of chloroplast tRNA appears to be slightly larger than that of the parental cytoplasmic tRNA molecules. It is probable that these organelles contain a complete set of tRNA molecules specific for chloroplast protein synthesis. Polysomes have also been demonstrated in chloroplasts by analytical ultracentrifuge studies. The mRNA used in protein synthesis appears to be relatively stable, since the normal inhibitors of nuclear transcription have little or no effect on protein synthesis. Some of the ribosomal proteins may be synthesized within the chloroplast, but others appear to be made by cytoplasmic protein synthesis.

One interesting question that has not yet been resolved concerns the role of organelle-specific protein synthesis. It is not known whether this process is required for production of structural proteins, or whether organelle-specific enzymes are produced. Perhaps the proteins made in organelles play some role in the control of interactions between the organelle and its parental cell. The answers to these questions may also lead to a clearer understanding of the control of protein synthesis in general.

THE SYNTHESIS OF HEMOGLOBIN AS A MODEL

The red blood cell (RBC) is a highly specialized component of many animals; in man and in rabbit, the mature erythrocyte is essentially a sac containing hemoglobin and a few other proteins. Maturation of the stem cells involves sequential loss of the nucleus after transcription of RNA, followed by formation of cells that contain mRNA and ribosomes, and that carry out protein synthesis, and culminating in the release of mature RBCs into the circulating blood. The process normally occurs in bone marrow; under conditions of extreme anemia, reticulocytes, which are still capable of protein synthesis, can be released into the circulation. It is possible to make rabbits anemic, and then obtain blood containing a high proportion of reticulocytes, which can then be used for the study of hemoglobin synthesis, since about 95% of the protein produced will be globin chains.

Using such a system, Dintzis and his coworkers established the basic facts. Globin chains grow from the N-terminal amino acid to the C-terminal residue which is the last added. This same direction of growth has since been found to be true for all proteins. The independent but coordinated synthesis of the two subunits was also established; normally, equal numbers of both types of chains are produced. Synthesis proceeds on polysomes containing four to six ribosome monomers, as was established by Warner, Knopf, and Rich in their studies, which established that growing peptide chains are never isolated with monosomes.

Baglioni and his coworkers established that complete or nearly complete α chains can be found associated with polysomes, but complete β chains

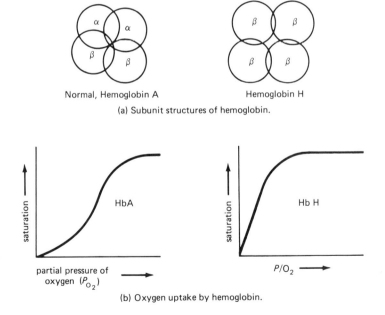

Normal, Hemoglobin A   Hemoglobin H

(a) Subunit structures of hemoglobin.

(b) Oxygen uptake by hemoglobin.

Figure 3. Subunit structures of hemoglobin.

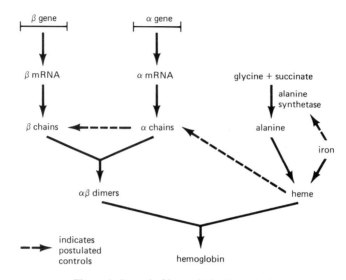

Figure 4. Control of hemoglobin biosynthesis.

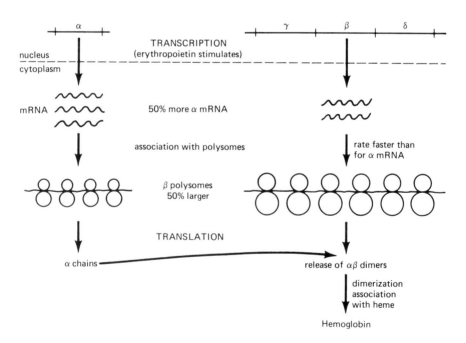

Figure 5. Translation control of hemoglobin synthesis.

are never found in this fraction. It had previously been established, by studies of patients with thalessemia, that a tetramer formed of β chains could be identified in patients with decreased levels of α chains, but no α_4 molecules could be detected in the absence of β chain synthesis (Figure 3). The thalessemias are a group of diseases in which there are deficiencies in the α or β genes (or the mRNA transcribed from these genes); these diseases result in the formation of only one of the two normal subunits of hemoglobin. It was also found that, in vitro, α_4 molecules precipitate because of instability. These facts led to the hypothesis that α chains are retained on polysomes until complete β chains are released; the β chains migrate to α chain–synthesizing polysomes, combine with the α chains, and the $\alpha\beta$ dimer is released. These dimers could then react with heme, eventually resulting in the formation of normal hemoglobin molecules that contain two α chains, two β chains, and four heme molecules, but with $\alpha_2\beta_2 \cdot 2$ heme the favored intermediate. This molecule is unstable, dissociating into two subunits on gel filtration, and could correspond to an $\alpha\beta$ dimer containing a single heme group in vivo. Heme also plays a more direct role in the control of globin biosynthesis; when concentrations of heme are high and those of $\alpha\beta$ dimers are low, globin synthesis is stimulated, and this stimulation may directly affect the translation of α chains. A general scheme of the control of hemoglobin biosynthesis is shown in Figures 4 and 5.

BIBLIOGRAPHY

Wilson, D. B., and Dintzis, H. M. 1970. *Proc. Natl. Acad. Sci. U.S.A.* 66:1282.

Holder, J. W., and Lingrel, J. B. 1970. *Biochem, Biophys. Acta* 204:210.

Jackson, R. J., and Hunter, A. R. 1970. *Nature* 227:672.

Baglioni, C. 1972. *Biochem. Biophys. Acta* 287:189.

Baglioni, C., Jacobs-Lorena, M., and Meade, H. 1972. *Biochem. Biophys. Acta* 277:188.

Gill, F., Atwater, J., and Schwartz, E. 1972. *Science* 178:623.

Whaley, W. G., Danwalder, M., and Kephart, J. E. 1972. *Science* 175:569.

Marks, P. A., and Rifkind, R. A. 1972. *Science* 175:955.

Hunt, T., Vanderhoff, G., and London, I. M. 1972. *J. Mol. Biol.* 66:471.

Kacian, D. L., Gambino, R., Dow, L. W., Grossboard, E., Natta, C., Ramirez, F., Spiegelman, S., Marks, P. A., and Bank, A. 1973. *Proc. Natl. Acad. Sci. U.S.A.* 70:3189.

Adamson, K. W., and Stamatoyannopoulos, G. 1973. *Science* 180:310.

Schwaber, J., and Cohen, E. P. 1974. *Proc. Natl. Acad. Sci. U.S.A.* 71:2203.

Harrison, P. R., Conkie, D., Affara, N., and Paul, J. 1974. *J. Cell Biol.* 63:402.

MacNaughton, M., Freeman, K. B., and Bishop, J. O. 1974. *Cell* 1:117.

Nienhuis, A. W., and Bunn, H. F. 1974. *Science* 185:946.

McKeehan, W. L. 1974. *J. Biol. Chem.* 249:6517.

Kabat, D. 1975. *J. Biol. Chem.* 250:6085.

Smith, D. W. E. 1975. *Science* 190:529.

Garrick, L. M., Dembure, P. P., and Garrick, M. M. 1975. *Eur. J. Biochem.* 58:339.

Ranu, R. S., and London, I. M. 1976. *Proc. Natl. Acad. Sci. U.S.A.* 73:4349.

Ross, J. 1976. *J. Mol. Biol.* 106:403.

Weatherall, D. J. 1976. *Johns Hopkins Med. J.* 139:205.

Kazazian, H. H., Jr., Van Beneden, R. J., and Snyder, P. G. 1976. *Johns Hopkins Med. J.* 139:211.

Grasso, J. A., Chromey, N. C., and Moxey, C. F. 1977. *J. Cell Biol.* 73:206.

Ballas, S. K., Atwater, J., and Burka, E. R. 1977. *Hemoglobin* 1:651.

Deisseroth, A., Nienhuis, A., Turner, P., Velez, R., Anderson, W. F., Ruddle, F., Lawrence, J., Creagan, R., and Kucherlapati, R. 1977. *Cell* 12:205.

Franco, R. S., Hogg, J. W., and Martelo, O. J. 1978. *Blood* 51:653.

Farace, M. G., Ullu, E., Fantoni, A., Rossi, G. B., Cioe, L., and Dolei, A. 1979. *Blood* 53:134.

Rubin, R. N., Ballas, S. K., Fischer, R., Winterhalter, K. H., and Burka, E. R. 1979. *Blood* 53:148.

10.6. Regulation of Protein Synthesis

GENERAL CONSIDERATIONS

Protein synthesis, as described in previous chapters, proceeds by a complex mechanism that is not yet fully understood. It is clear that all cells must exercise controls over this mechanism to retain a balance in the amount and types of proteins required at given times. Specific proteins may be either inducible or constitutive components of particular cells. Inducible proteins, those made only in response to a particular cellular environment, include many enzymes that are produced only as needed. Among these enzymes are thymidine synthetase, required only to produce thymidine for DNA synthesis prior to cell division, and the enzyme required for metabolism of lactose in *E. coli*. Since lactose is not the usual sugar included in media for laboratory growth of this bacteria, *E. coli* does not normally produce the enzymes used for the breakdown of this disaccharide. When lactose is present at high concentrations, synthesis of these enzymes is stimulated. Constitutive enzymes, on the other hand, are produced throughout the cell cycle; the control processes for the synthesis of these proteins are not known in as much detail.

Other proteins are produced only in specialized tissues, although all cells in the organism contain the necessary genes. Synthesis of these proteins is regulated in response to unknown stimuli that permit transcription and/or translation of these genes in one cell, but repress it in other tissues. Similar control processes may be involved in the synthesis of proteins required during specific phases of differentiation. Since it is clear that the DNA content of cells does not change during differentiation, and is identical in all somatic cells of a given organism, the control of specialized protein synthesis must be effected by factors that permit transcription, transport of specific mRNA molecules to the ribosomes, or the translation of such mRNA molecules.

In general, control processes may operate at specific levels to promote, inhibit, or modify protein synthesis. The first and most fundamental control is at the level of the DNA; controls may include the number of copies of a gene, the presence of operators and promotors, and the rate at which transcription occurs. At the RNA level, controls may include interactions with hormones and other effectors, the σ factors required for initiation of transcription, and the stability of the specific mRNA molecules. Another factor closely allied to this last might be the susceptibility of specific mRNA molecules to digestion by ribonucleases. Two possible mechanisms which might afford such protection are chemical modifications of the mRNA bases, and the physical folding of the RNA chain into specific conformations. At present, these speculations are the focus of various experimental approaches which may confirm such mechanisms.

The rate of translation of a given mRNA may also be amenable to control. The number of ribosomes that attach to a polysome–mRNA complex is at least partially controlled by the size of the mRNA. It is possible that the number of ribosomes may influence the rate of translation, but no information is as yet available to substantiate such a hypothesis. If different mRNA molecules are translated at different rates, it will be important to determine which factors play a role in this control.

In addition to the steps outlined above, it is clear that protein synthesis may also be regulated by other influences. Post-translational modifications of proteins are in some cases required for the synthesis of truly functional cell constituents. At present, it is possible only to speculate that such modifications may serve as regulatory steps during protein synthesis. However, attention has recently been directed at post-translational modifications, and more information may be available soon. Also, the synthesis of proteins containing several subunits, as well as those that include covalently linked cofactors, requires additional levels of control.

Finally, there are specific controls introduced either in vivo or in vitro by certain modifications in components of the protein synthesizing machinery. These include the mutations in ribosomal proteins that have been discussed previously (Chapter 9.5). In addition, various antibiotics have been shown to influence protein synthesis. In some cases, an altered ribosomal protein can interact with a specific antibiotic, modifying protein synthesis still further.

This chapter will consider some of the regulatory mechanisms listed above in greater detail. Certain aspects of these regulatory processes have not been fully amenable to experimental verification, but new approaches to these problems may permit great advances in the near future.

REGULATION AT THE LEVEL OF THE GENOME

The complexity and size of mammalian DNA permit gene duplication and gene amplification, the first of which can give rise to the raw material for the evolution of closely related genes, as has been postulated for hemoglobin (Figure 1). An original "primitive" globin gene, by the processes of duplication and mutation, eventually gave rise to genes that code for five or six different globin chains required at different times during development in humans. At the same time, however, the genes for the major globin chains have been

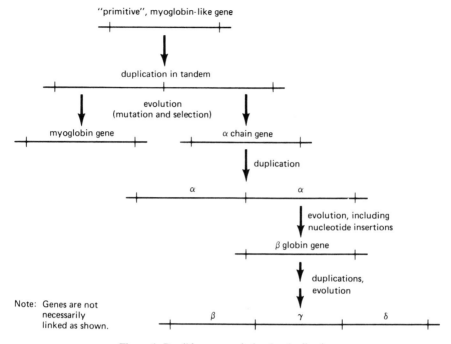

Figure 1. Possible gene evolution by duplication.

shown to be present in more than one copy; the exact number of such copies has not been absolutely determined. However, it appears that there are more β globin genes than copies of the gene coding for α globin. It has not yet been determined if this system influences the amount of specific mRNA produced and translated, although such a control system could be postulated.

The evolution of hemoglobin has received much attention from biologists. It has been shown that α and β genes share about 65 amino acid residues out of 141 residues in the α chain; the β chain is slightly larger. It is thought that α is the most primitive of the globin chains; it shares some structural homology with myoglobin chains, and is required for essentially all known hemoglobins. The precursor gene may have been duplicated during evolution, with one of the copies coded for a myoglobin-like chain, and the other developing into the α gene. A second duplication may have occurred, giving rise to a gene that underwent further mutation, eventually leading to primitive γ chains, required for fetal hemoglobin. This gene may have duplicated again, with further mutation in one copy eventually giving rise to the β gene, and the β gene, on duplication, giving rise as well to the gene for δ chains, found in a minor hemoglobin present in all cells. The close linkage of β, δ, and γ chains can be taken as support of this hypothesis.

The genes for α chains are not closely linked to those for β chains; genes for the other chains that replace β in minor or fetal hemoglobins are closely linked to β globin genes. It is probable that several copies of α gene are aligned in tandem on one chromosome, while the loci for β globin are on some other chromosome. In addition, there may be more α than β genes present in any cell. Globin mRNA molecules of high purity, as determined in in vitro protein synthesis assays, can be obtained. On fingerprinting, however, these molecules have been shown to be contaminated with other small RNA species, which probably represent highly reiterated genes like 5S RNA. For this reason, it has been difficult to localize the genes by in situ hybridization, since a high background, due to the contaminants, masks the specific labeling arising from the low-multiplicity globin genes.

In certain lower animals, gene amplification can be demonstrated; it is possible that large numbers of multiple copies of some genes may also be found in higher animals. During early stages of differentiation, the organism requires a burst of synthesis of components of the ribosome. This phenomenon may depend on the presence of very large numbers of the appropriate genes, all of which will be transcribed and translated during a short period of time. After the requirement for intense production has been filled, the genes present in high copy number may in some unknown fashion be repressed.

Many eukaryotic organisms have been shown to contain large areas of nontranscribed DNA, some of which consists of copies of genes. In addition, each cell within an organism contains the same gene complement, but some genes are transcribed only in certain specialized cells. The mechanism whereby this control is exercised is at yet unknown, but may reside in the other component associated with the DNA in chromatin. Alternatively, there could be minute changes in the DNA itself, so that only some copies contain the appropriate start signals for transcription. Such small alterations could not be detected by present techniques, but indirect methods do not appear to fully support this possibility. In vitro, specific protein synthesis can be induced in some cells that normally carry an inactive gene. However, other specific proteins can never be induced in any cells other than those of the specialized competent tissue. Further work may clarify some of these questions.

TRANSCRIPTIONAL CONTROL

The organization of the bacterial genome is better understood than is that of the more complex chromatin. In prokaryotes, there is clear evidence that operators and promotors, which regulate gene expression, are present as integral components of the DNA. Inducible operator regions may exist in both prokaryotic and eukaryotic DNA. Operators are found on inducible or repressible genes, but not on constitutive genes. A protein, the repressor, can bind to an operator, thereby preventing transcription. In bacterial systems, several repressors have been isolated, including the lactose and galactose repressor proteins. These repressors bind to specific operator DNA regions, but show greatly decreased affinity for this DNA in the presence of their inducers. Operator regions may control a single gene, but generally influence the transcription of several linked genes that code for a series of enzymes required for a specific reaction sequence. In several eukaryotic systems, there appears to be a coordinated transcription of genes that code for related proteins. In addition, many eukaryotic genes are repressed during much of the cell cycle and are turned on by specific stimuli at a given period. By inference, then, operons (i.e., groups of genes controlled by an operator region) probably exist in all cells.

DNA also contains specific regions that interact with the σ factor of RNA polymerase in bacteria. These promotor regions allow initiation of transcription. Modifications in such regions can have several effects: the gene may become repressed, or it may no longer respond to normal controls, or the rate of transcription could be altered. Evidence for similar regions in eukaryotic DNA is less convincing. In addition, σ-type factors have not been identified in eukaryotic RNA polymerases, and transcription appears to be controlled by the proteins associated with the chromatin.

In eukaryotic cells, control of transcription may involve hormones, acting in some cases through the cyclic nucleotides, cAMP and cGMP (Figure 2), which, in turn, may influence the acidic nuclear proteins by causing modifications, such as phosphorylation of specific amino acid residues. The latter alter the relative affinity of these proteins for DNA. On phosphorylation the acidic nuclear proteins may allow RNA polymerase binding to a specific region of the genome, thus permitting transcription of a particular mRNA. Constitutive proteins, on the other hand, may not be subject to such controls. Perhaps these DNA regions are not as tightly bound as nuclear proteins, allowing relatively free transcription. It is possible to speculate that all eukaryotic proteins show some inducibility, and that none are true constitutive proteins. Some in vitro studies of the synthesis of individual proteins in cell culture appear to be consistent with such a hypothesis, while others are not.

Hormones have been reported to influence protein synthesis, generally by modifying transcription of mRNA (Figure 3). The pituitary gland in mammals may control the relative proportions of the various RNA polymerases; the mechanisms whereby pituitary hormones exert this influence are not known. Certain hormones, including estrogen, increase the synthesis of rRNA, thus decreasing mRNA transcription and indirectly influencing translation of proteins. At the same time, estrogen has also been shown to increase the rate of transcription of certain specific mRNAs, and to produce differentiation

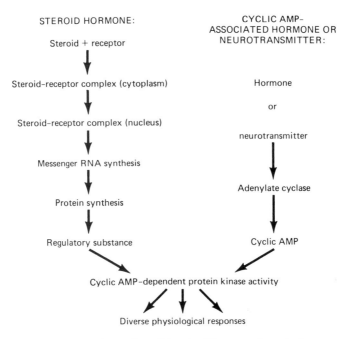

Figure 2. Scheme of possible role of hormones in control.

of chick oviduct epithelium. These last two effects may be related, but further work will be required to determine exact mechanisms. The hormones, in general, bind to cellular receptors; these receptors may be proteins found in the membrane, or in the cytoplasm of given cells. When the receptor is

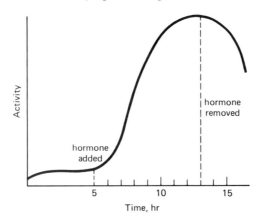

Figure 3. Effect of synthetic adrenal hormone on tyrosine aminotransferase. This effect is due to increased mRNA synthesis, followed by increased enzyme synthesis.

a membrane component, adenylate cyclase is often activated. This enzyme, which appears to be membrane-bound, will catalyze cAMP formation. The cyclic nucleotide in turn activates kinases, enzymes that are involved in phosphorylation of other proteins. The mechanisms involving cGMP are less well known, but are the focus of several ongoing studies.

TRANSLATIONAL CONTROL

Theoretically, the availability of specific components required for protein synthesis could control the rate of translation of a given mRNA. Initiator tRNA could be present in limiting amounts, for example, but there is no direct evidence that the levels of this nucleic acid are low enough to control the rate of protein synthesis. In bacteria, the initiating amino acid must be a formylated methionine, and formylation takes place after esterification of the methionine to the tRNA. It is conceivable that formylation is the limiting step, but again no evidence has been found to support such a hypothesis. Such measurements, however, are difficult to obtain accurately, and it remains possible that the availability of specific initiator tRNA molecules could be involved in control. Initiation also requires interactions with the specific initiation factors, which have been shown to be present in less than stoichiometric quantities. However, since these factors act catalytically, and recycle during translation, cellular levels need not necessarily be limiting.

The availability of amino acids, and of ribonucleoside triphosphates as an energy source, does control the rate of translation under certain growth conditions. When fewer nutrients are available, both protein degradation and protein synthesis decrease. If the cellular proteins are not broken down at normal rates, and fewer amino acids are available from exogenous sources, fewer tRNAs can be charged, resulting in a lack of substrates for protein synthesis. GTP is absolutely required also for translation; if cellular conditions are such that less ATP is formed, GTP levels fall. Generally, energy obtained during metabolism is stored in the form of ATP, which can phosphorylate other nucleotides (e.g., GDP) by a reversible reaction:

$$ATP + GDP \rightleftharpoons ADP + GTP$$

In most cells, aerobic catabolism makes much more energy available for storage as ATP than does anaerobic metabolism. For such cells, lack of oxygen during the breakdown of sugars will interfere with normal ATP levels, thus decreasing the amount of GTP required for translation. If purine biosynthesis is depressed, a similar effect will be noted, since GDP cannot be formed.

The ribosomal protein S-1 of bacteria may participate in control. This protein can be easily detached from the 30S subunit, leaving an inactive subunit. In addition, most studies have found that cellular levels of S-1 are not high enough to ensure that each ribosome contains one molecule of this protein, indicating that not all ribosomes are active in vivo. This protein is required during initiation, and may also pariticipate in elongation. Cellular levels of S-1 thus appear to control the availability of active 30S ribosomal subunits, which could limit the rate of translation. Similarly, a factor appears to be required to dissociate the ribosome into subunits after participation in translation. If this dissociation does not occur, the ribosome is removed from the pool that provides subunits for the initiation of translation. It is not yet clear if this dissociation requires a soluble factor that participates in initiation, or whether a separate protein is used. In either case, the concentration of this protein can control the rate of formation of initiation complexes.

Other possible control mechanisms might include the rate of attachment of ribosomes to the mRNA, the rate of movement of the mRNA, the rate of detachment of the completed peptide chain, and the rate of digestion of the mRNA. Little is known about the interactions responsible for each of these rates, but some speculations can be offered. The mRNA molecules which have been studied in detail have a variable number of nontranslated nucleotides at the 5'-terminus. These residues may fold into a tertiary structure which enhances ribosome recognition and binding, and may perhaps control the rate of interaction by this folding. The digestion of the mRNA by nucleases is most probably inhibited by interactions between mRNA and proteins in the ribosome. In hemoglobin synthesis, for example, it is conceivable that β globin may be longer-lived than the α globin mRNA because more ribosomes attach to the first than to the second. Similarly, if new ribosomes attach at the 5'-end as others detach after completion of translation at the 3'-end, the mRNA may be protected for a longer period. Detachment of completed proteins is probably dependent on several factors; if it is slow, translocation will proceed at a lower rate, thus preventing rapid translation.

Some possible mechanisms of control of detachment can be postulated for proteins consisting of subunits. In both hemoglobin and immunoglobulin synthesis, there appear to be interactions between subunits while one of them is still being translated. The postulated mechanisms assume that one subunit is dependent for completion and release on the presence of the other complete peptide. Thus, the rate of synthesis of the immunoglobulin heavy chain is controlled by the number of completed light chains available. Proteins that contain a cofactor may be synthesized at a rate dependent on the availability of this compound. The rate of synthesis of hemoglobin, for example, is partially controlled by the amount of the iron-containing heme moiety. In cases of diets deficient in iron, anemia can result because of a decreased synthesis of heme, which in turn depresses the translation of globin mRNA (see Chapter 10.4).

One special case of translational control can be described; this is the control of the comparative rates of synthesis of proteins coded for by a polycistronic mRNA. Each gene in such a mRNA is set off by initiation and termination signals; often the protein coded for by the nucleotides at the 5'-end of the mRNA is produced in much higher quantities than is that coded for at the 3'-terminus. The ribosomes attach at the 5'-terminus, and translation proceeds till the termination signal is reached, when the ribosome detaches. Theoretically, ribosomes could attach at any initiation signal but, in practice, attachment at such signals located within the mRNA is less efficient than attachment near the 5'-end. The result is a gradient in the efficiency of translation of the several genes encoded in a polycistronic mRNA. The *lac* operon, for example, codes for three proteins and is transcribed as a single mRNA molecule. The gene closest to the 5'-end is translated at a rate twice that of the middle gene, and five times greater than that of the gene closest to the 3'-end. This could also be explained by an occasional read-through of stop signals, but such a mechanism would then imply the production of a single protein chain that would require subsequent processing, and no evidence to support this has been found.

It should be clear that, at present, the mechanisms responsible for the control of translation are largely unknown. There remain many questions in this field, and few details can be described. With increased knowledge of the basic mechanism of translation, experiments can be designed to elucidate control steps. It is probable that the next few years will see rapid progress in our understanding of the factors that influence translation and maintain the homeostasis of cells.

POST-TRANSLATIONAL MODIFICATIONS

Often, the peptide chains released from polysomes on completion of translation are not fully functional until processing or modification takes place (Figure 4). Digestive enzymes, for example, are often synthesized as larger, inactive proteins that must undergo limited proteolysis before use. In addition, a similar mechanism holds for the proteins involved in coagulation, complement fixation, and the synthesis of certain hormones. Other proteins must have sugar moieties added; formation of glycoproteins takes place on ribosomes attached to the endoplasmic reticulum, which is connected to the Golgi apparatus. During transport through these membranous structures, many such modifications can be carried out.

Many proteins have also been found to contain modified amino acids, which may be of several types, including methylated or acetylated, oxidized, or halogenated amino acids, those conjugated to bases, or those containing additional amino or carboxyl groups. In all, about 130 such derivatized amino

(a) Processing by proteolytic cleavage.

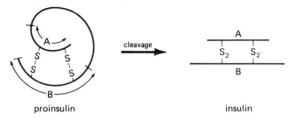

proinsulin   insulin

(b) Glycosylation.

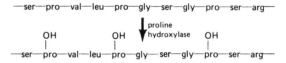

Cell wall peptidoglycan
(murein)

or

Protein + UDP–sugar ⟶ glycoprotein

(c) Addition of the —OH group (formation of hydroxyproline).

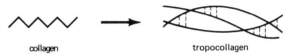

(d) Interchain hydrogen bonding.

collagen   tropocollagen

(e) Phosphorylation.

—ser—aa$_1$—aa$_2$—aa$_3$—ser—aa$_4$—

PO$_4$

PO$_4$ PO$_4$

—ser—aa$_1$—aa$_2$—aa$_3$—ser—aa$_4$—   casein, for example

Figure 4. Post-translational modifications. (a) Processing by proteolytic cleavage. (b) Glycosylation. (c) Addition of the —OH group (formation of hydroxyproline). (d) Interchain hydrogen bonding. (e) Phosphorylation.

acids have been identified to date in proteins isolated from different organisms. The identification and study of such modified amino acids is, to a large extent, a recent development. Some of them, however, have been known for longer periods, including hydroxyproline, hydroxylysine, and cystine, each of which involves a modification of an amino acid side chain. These amino acids are known to occur only after translation is complete, as is probably true for most of the modifications thus far identified. Protein kinases are found in every part of the cell, and modify preformed proteins by phosphorylation of specific amino acid residues.

In general, modifications are specific not only to a single amino acid species, but also to only certain of these residues within a given protein. This specificity may be linked to both the amino acid sequence and the tertiary structure specified by this sequence. Still unknown in many cases is the specific reason why some amino acids in a protein are modified. In a few proteins, modified amino acids have been shown to be required for the covalent attachment of coenzymes, for crosslinks that stabilize specific structures as in collagen, or for the regulation of transcription which appears to be linked to phosphorylation of acidic nuclear proteins. However, similar modifications in other proteins, such as in stable phosphoproteins, do not appear to play similar roles. In most cases, much remains to be clarified in reference to the role post-transcriptional modification plays in cellular processes.

MODIFICATIONS INDUCED BY ANTIBIOTICS

Many antibiotics in common use as antibacterial agents act by inhibiting protein synthesis of the microorganism. Other antibiotics can interfere with eukaryotic protein synthesis, and are not used clinically for this reason, but are helpful laboratory tools to probe the details of this mechanism. Some antibiotics that are commonly used in these in vitro studies are shown in Figure 5, and certain of their characteristics are listed in Table 1.

As noted in Table 1, specific antibiotics that interact with either the large or the small subunit of the ribosome are available. Streptomycin is known to bind to a specific protein of the small subunit (see Chapter 9.5). In *E. coli,* mutations that affect the amino acid sequence of this protein have been described. These mutations fall into two general catagories; the first class prevents binding of the antibiotic, while others induce an alteration such that protein synthesis requires the presence of streptomycin. The first group induces resistance, while the second class is known as streptomycin-dependent. This antibiotic, together with several other aminoglycosides, inhibits the binding of any amino acyl–tRNA to the A site of the 30S subunit, so that transpeptidation, translocation, and termination are also inhibited. In addition, those aminoglycosides that contain a streptamine residue also induce misreading of the codons. Thus, in the presence of streptomycin, *E. coli* will have an apparent mutation rate several times higher than normal.

Tetracycline and pactamycin also interfere with initiation by inhibition of the binding of all amino acyl–tRNAs to the A site, thus also inhibiting elongation and termination. Tetracycline interacts only with bacterial ribo-

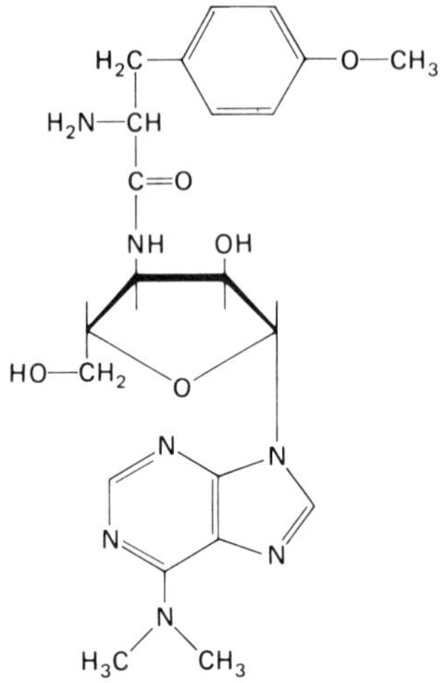

Puromycin

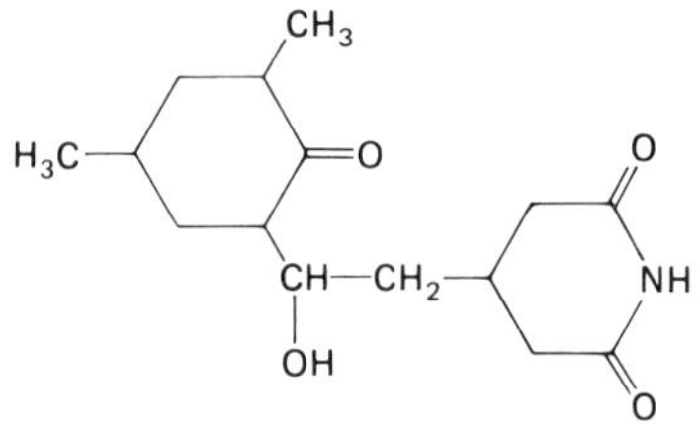

Cycloheximide

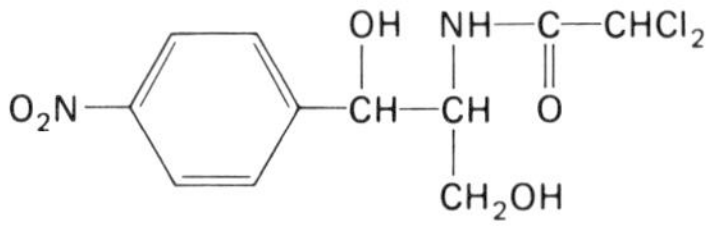

Chloramphenicol

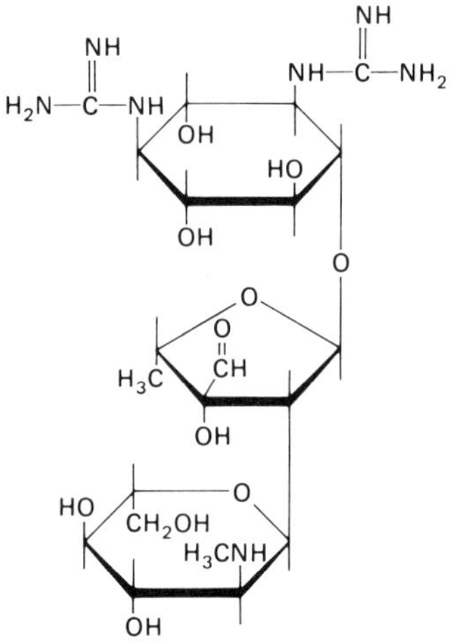

Streptomycin

Figure 5. Antibiotic inhibitors of translation.

Table 1. Inhibitory Characteristics of Selected Antibiotics.

ANTIBIOTIC	SUBUNIT AFFECTED	SPECIFIC INHIBITED FUNCTION(S)
Streptomycin	30S	Initiation, codon recognition
Tetracycline	30S	Initiation, codon recognition
Pactamycin	30S, 40S	Initiation
Chloramphenicol	50S[a]	Transpeptidation
Erythromycin	50S[b]	Transpeptidation, translocation
Fusidic acid[c]	50S	Translocation
Puromycin	50S, 60S	Transpeptidation, translocation
Cycloheximide	60S	Initiation, translocation

[a] Chloramphenicol also inhibits mitochondrial and chloroplast protein synthesis.
[b] Erythromycin inhibits protein synthesis in chloroplasts and yeast mitochondria, but has no effect on the mammalian mitochondrial system.
[c] The specific mode of action of fusidic acid has not yet been established.

somes, and is therefore clinically useful against bacterial infections of many types. Pactamycin presents a different picture. This antibiotic is specifically inhibitory for the binding of the initiator tRNA to the initiation complex, rather than for binding of any amino acyl–tRNA to interact with either bacterial or eukaryotic ribosomal initiation complexes, and so prevent initiation in both systems.

A few inhibitors of small ribosomal subunits are also effective against some organelle protein synthesis systems. As noted previously (Chapter 9.5), mitochondria from various eukaryotic organisms differ in size, ranging from those in yeast, which are 70–80S in size, down to the 50–60S ribosomes found in mammalian mitochondria. This size difference reflects alterations in rRNA and in ribosomal proteins, which may be responsible for the divergent responses to antibiotics. Several aminoglycosides, including neomycin, similar in structure to streptomycin, inhibit protein synthesis in yeast and insect mitochondria, but have no effect on mammalian mitochondria.

In general, antibiotic inhibitors of large ribosomal subunits prevent binding of amino acyl–tRNA molecules to the P site on the large subunit. Chloramphenicol interacts with all known mitochondrial systems as well as with prokaryotic 50S subunits, preventing attachment of the incoming amino acyl–tRNA. This in turn prevents transpeptidation, and inhibits continued growth of new peptide chains. Erythromycin and related macrolides act in a similar fashion, but have more variable effects on mitochondrial protein synthesis. Of the macrolides tested, all inhibit protein synthesis in yeast mitochondria, and some also inhibit mammalian mitochondria and chloroplasts.

Cycloheximide has no effect on either prokaryotic or organelle ribosomes, but inhibits elongation as well as initiation in eukaryotic protein synthesis. The effects on elongation are less pronounced; translocation of the growing peptide chain from the A to the P site is prevented in the presence of this antibiotic. More important, the initiator tRNA cannot be bound to the initiation complex of the eukaryotic ribosome. In vivo, the primary site of action of this antibiotic has not been determined.

Puromycin has been utilized intensively to study protein synthesis in both prokaryotic and eukaryotic systems. The antibiotic shares some structural features with the portion of tRNA that carries the amino acid (see Figure 4). Specifically, this antibiotic resembles the amino acyl–adenylyl end of the tRNA molecule, and competes with the amino acyl–tRNA for binding to the A site on the ribosome. Because of its structural analogy with the charged tRNA, puromycin can bind to both prokaryotic and eukaryotic ribosomes. Once bound, the antibiotic accepts the growing peptide chain, and can undergo translocation. However, no new amino acids can be added to the peptide; so premature termination takes place.

The use of specific antibiotics has led to a more complete knowledge of the different steps in protein synthesis. In addition, the use of certain antibiotics that differentially inhibit eukaryotic and mitochondrial ribosomes has allowed determination of the role of organelle protein synthesis. Proteins formed in organelles can be identified when cycloheximide is added to a mammalian system, for example, and as new antibiotics are tested, further information may be assembled. Clinically, these studies may also be useful, since they give some indication of the relative safety of new antibiotics in man.

BIBLIOGRAPHY

Litt, M., and Kabat, D. 1972. *J. Biol. Chem.* 247:6659.

Liarakos, C. D., Rosen, J. M., and O'Malley, B. W. 1973. *Biochemistry* 12:2809.

Marks, D., Park, W., and Borun, T. 1973. *J. Biol. Chem.* 248:560.

Samuels, H. H., Tsai, J. S., Cansanova, J., and Stanley, F. 1974. *J. Clin. Invest.* 54:853.

O'Malley, B. W., and Means, A. R. 1974. *Science* 183:610.

Kake, N., and Jordan, L. M. 1974. *Science* 183:663.

Goldberger, R. F. 1974. *Science* 183:810.

McMahon, D. 1974. *Science* 185:1012.

Hunt, T. 1974. *Ann. N.Y. Acad. Sci.* 241:223.

Lodish, H. F. 1974. *Nature* 251:385.

Suzuki, H., and Hayashi, Y. 1975. *FEBS Lett.* 52:258.

Murad, F., Kimura, H., Hopkins, H. A., Looney, W. B., and Kovacs, C. J. 1975. *Science* 190:58.

Palade, G. 1975. *Science* 189:347.

DeGroot, L. J., and Torresani, J. 1975. *Endocrinology* 96:357.

MacLeod, K. M., and Baxter, J. D. 1975. *Biochem. Biophys. Res. Commun.* 62:577.

Dickson, R. C., Abelson, J., Barnes, W. M., and Reznikoff, W. S. 1975. *Science* 187:27.

Lande, M. A., Adesnik, M., Sumida, M., Tashiro, Y., and Sabatini, D. 1975. *J. Cell Biol.* 65:513.

Ranu, R. S., and London, I. M. 1976. *Proc. Natl. Acad. Sci. U.S.A.* 73:4349.

Rothschild, H., Bickers, J., and Marcus, R. 1976. *Acta Haematol.* 56:285.

Hunt, T. 1976. *Br. Med. J.* 32:257.

Bradley, M. O. 1977. *J. Biol. Chem.* 252:5310.

Cozzarelli, N. R. 1977. *Annu. Rev. Biochem.* 46:641.

Lau, A. F., and Ruddon, R. W. 1977. *Exp. Cell Res.* 107:35.

Greengard, P. 1978. *Science* 199:146.

Wabl, M. R., Forni, L., and Loor, F. 1978. *Science* 199:1078.

Bunn, H. F., Gabbay, K. H., and Gallop, P. M. 1978. *Science* 200:21.

Caplan, A. I., and Ordahl, C. P. 1978. *Science* 201:120.

SECTION 11
CELL CYCLE

ELTON STUBBLEFIELD

11. Cell Cycle

1. HISTORY OF CELL CYCLE RESEARCH

For a long time we have known that organisms are composed of cells. It has also been apparent that the growth and reproduction of organisms is actually accomplished by growth and reproduction at the cellular level. Cell division, or *mitosis,* was described in detail about a century ago, so it is somewhat surprising to realize that very little new information about cell reproduction was discovered until about 25 years ago. During the early 1950s the groundwork was laid for the field of cellular kinetics, a rapidly expanding research area in cell biology that has provided most of the information to be presented in this chapter. It should be quite apparent to the reader that a true understanding of human health and disease is intimately entwined in the details of cell growth and reproduction, beginning with the reproductive cycle of invading viruses and bacteria and ranging ultimately to the reproduction of invading cancer cells. For the purposes of this presentation, however, we will restrict the subject to mammalian cell reproduction and leave the topic of prokaryotic cell reproduction to an appropriate microbiology text.

Until the modern era, about all that was known of cell replication was what was visible in a light microscope. The events of mitosis require only a small fraction of the time in a cell's life history, however, and the remaining part, the *interphase,* was a big mystery. Since nothing could be seen, it was assumed that nothing was happening. The chromosomes, which obviously doubled before mitosis, were assumed to reproduce in prophase, as the interphase chromatin condensed into visible chromosomes. The first clear evidence that this was not true came from the studies of Hewson Swift in 1950 (1), who measured the DNA content of individual nuclei by using photometric measurement of Feulgen-stained cells. At that time the concept of DNA as the genetic molecule was still uncertain, but the data of Swift tended to support this idea, since most cells had one, two, four, or eight times the basic amount of DNA. More germane to this discussion was the observation that mitotic cells all had the same DNA content, from earliest prophase until anaphase, at which time the ensuing cell division cut the DNA content per cell in half. Some interphase nuclei had the telophase amount of DNA, and others had the mitotic amount. Not enough data were accumulated to determine the occurrence of intermediate levels of DNA in nuclei, but the conclusion was inescapable—DNA synthesis occurred during interphase and not during prophase.

Alma Howard and S. R. Pelc (2) were the first researchers to determine at what time during interphase DNA synthesis occurred. They used the technique of autoradiography of an incorporated radioisotope, a technique that has continued to be a major method used in cell replication research. Roots of the broad bean *Vicia faba* were grown in water containing $^{32}PO_4$ for various periods up to 2 days. Root tips were fixed in acid alcohol and extracted in normal HCl at 60°C for 10 min. The major component containing ^{32}P was found to be DNA, which was removable by DNase. Their data showed that cells in mitosis do not make DNA and that only part of the interphase nuclei incorporated ^{32}P into DNA. Mitotic cells from roots exposed to $^{32}PO_4$ for 6 hr did not have an autoradiograph, so apparently a period of several hours must pass between the end of the DNA synthesis period and the start of mitosis. Further refinement of these experiments (3) led to a basic terminology that still remains in the cell cycle literature today. The visible period of mitosis is called the M phase, the detectable period of DNA synthesis is termed S, and the interphase periods before and after S, which represent *gaps* in our understanding, are called G_1 and G_2. Thus, a newly divided cell leaves M and enters G_1. At some later time it may pass into the S phase as it begins to make DNA, and then it goes on to G_2, at which time DNA replication is complete; and, thus, the cell eventually enters M to divide again.

2. DETAILS OF THE CELL REPLICATION CYCLE

Since growing populations contain cells that repeatedly pass through these four phases, G_1, S, G_2, and M have been traditionally diagrammed as parts of a cycle, as shown in Figure 1. The cell replication cycle has been adapted to many situations and cell types, and standard techniques for measurement of the duration of each phase of the cycle have evolved (for details see Appendix 1 of this chapter). As you might suspect, all such techniques for analyzing the cell cycle depend on some procedure for detecting DNA synthesis in cells; earlier methods used isotope uptake into DNA, while more recent approaches use sensitive fluorometric assays to determine precisely the DNA content of each cell. The other readily measured parameter is mitosis. Although some information about G_1 and G_2 events is now known, no definitive analytic techniques are available for these phases, so they are evaluated indirectly by subtracting S and M from the total cell cycle time.

In most mammalian cells growing at 37°C, the $S + G_2 + M$ part of the cell cycle is of similar length, averaging about 10–12 hr in most cell culture systems. In very fast-growing cells, this part of the cycle may be as short

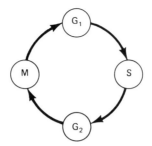

Figure 1. The cell replication cycle.

as 8 hr, while in slower growing cells it may last 20 hr; but such cases are rare and not well studied. The remaining phase, the G_1 phase, is much more variable in length, being completely absent in some cases and lasting days or even years in certain specialized cells. The reasons for this difference will become apparent later in this discussion (see section 11.11).

The most definitive cell kinetics work has been done with cell culture systems rather than intact organisms. Of course this is the advantage sought in the cell culture system, namely, the complete control of the cell environment. Cell culture systems tend to select for growing cells; otherwise the system is not productive. In a mixture of growing and quiescent cells, every subculture event dilutes the quiescent cells; so they are eventually lost from the system. Therefore, it follows that we know the most about cells that grow well in culture, and they all tend to be similar in their cell cycle parameters. For the purposes of this presentation, we can talk in terms of a *hypothetical* standard cell population that obviously does not exist but has cycle parameters similar to many of the cell systems reported in the literature.

Our standard cell takes about 8 hr to replicate its DNA, 2.5 hr for its G_2 phase, and about 0.5 hr to accomplish mitosis. Thus, the $S + G_2 + M$ part of the cycle requires about 11 hr; however, it must be emphasized that this is an *average* time and that the actual time required for each of the cells in the population will be normally distributed around this mean value. Even if the times in the various cell cycle phases are distributed according to some other scheme, e.g., lognormal or exponential, the sum of the phases tends toward a normal distribution. So, in addition to the mean value for time in $S + G_2 + M$ (11 hr), we also need to specify a standard deviation to describe the variability of our hypothetical standard cell population. If we establish the values of $S = 8 \pm 1.6$ hr, $G_2 = 2.5 \pm 1.2$ hr, and $M = 0.5 \pm 0.2$ hr, then the value for $S + G_2 + M = 11 \pm 2$ hr; this indicates that about 95% of the population will pass through $S + G_2 + M$ in a period ranging from 7 hr to a maximum of 15 hr (mean $\pm$ 2 standard deviations). Each phase may be normally distributed, but there is no conclusive evidence about this so far. Since S phase and mitosis are obviously task-oriented and involve molecular processes that can only proceed at a certain maximum rate, we can infer that each phase has a minimum time limit below which the task cannot be completed. In this case a lognormal distribution might be more appropriate; so we will assume this distribution for our standard cell population.

The G_1 phase of the cell cycle is an entirely different case. Rather than being task-oriented, the G_1 phase is more akin to an undetermined period of time with an off–on switch that is suddenly turned on at random to start the S phase. It has zero for a minimum and no maximum time. Smith and Martin (4) have proposed that the length of the G_1 phase is controlled by a probability factor. We can describe the G_1 phase of our standard cell population in equivalent terms by assigning it an exponential distribution with a mean of 4 hr and a standard deviation of $\pm$ 4 hr.

The end result is a standard cell population with an average time of 15 ± 4.5 hr from one cell division to the next. Since mitosis is a visible event, we can readily gather data on a real cell population by using time-lapse cinematography and thus actually measure the interdivision time for many individual cells. We usually call this time the generation time (T_g), and we usually try to distinguish it from the population doubling time (T_d). At first glance one might expect the mean T_g to equal the T_d, but in real populations such factors as cell death and differentiation cause T_d to be somewhat longer than T_g.

Because G_1 seems to be an entirely different kind of phase in the cell cycle, it is sometimes split away from the remaining phases, which all have relevance to cell reproduction. We will first examine the S + G_2 + M series of phases in some detail and save a discussion of the G_1 phase until later.

3. DNA SYNTHESIS PHASE

The beginning of DNA synthesis is the earliest known event in the reproductive sequence leading ultimately to mitosis. Once a cell begins to replicate its DNA, it is committed to an irreversible scheme that proceeds relentlessly toward cell division as a series of rote tasks that are accomplished one after the other. The sequence can be interrupted anywhere along the line, but if the hiatus lasts for more than a few hours, the cell is in trouble.

Clearly there is some molecular mechanism that starts the DNA replication process. This mechanism has been named the *trigger* and is thought to involve the synthesis of an mRNA for some specific protein(s). There will be more about this in sections 9 and 14. However, by definition, the S phase begins when the first DNA precursor molecules are incorporated into newly synthesized DNA. Fortunately, this process begins simultaneously in several thousand places along the DNA in the chromosomes of the S phase cell nucleus; so it is readily detected. If a radioactive precursor such as ^{3}H-thymidine is present in the environment of the cell, it is used in making the new DNA, and the radioactive nuclei in a population of cells can be readily detected by autoradiography. This approach, using tritium instead of ^{32}PO$_4$ as Howard and Pelc did, is now a standard technique for studying the cell cycle. The resolution of the tritium isotope is such that even the sites where DNA synthesis begins can be found in the chromosomes of the ensuing mitosis by autoradiography. A similar analysis with greater precision can be made by incorporating a bromine-containing precursor, BUdR (bromodeoxyuridine), into the DNA and detecting the sites of incorporation of the BUdR with a fluorescent stain in the chromosomes of the following mitosis (5).

Since only a part of the DNA begins synthesis at the start of the S phase, when are the remaining sites synthesized? It now appears (5) that there are three sets of sites in the chromosomes of mammals, classified as early-, middle-, and late-replicating DNA. In well-synchronized cell cultures it has been shown (6) that the kinetics of DNA synthesis during the S phase follows a three-step pattern, with the periods of synthesis separated by periods without synthesis. In Chinese hamster cells, the three sets of sites have been mapped in the metaphase chromosomes (5), and in the human, the late-replicating sites are known (7).

At the molecular level, the chromosomal DNA is organized into very long segments, perhaps centimeters in length, containing many replicating units (8). Replication proceeds in both directions along the molecule from the *origin,* and synthesis is terminated when two DNA replication forks meet. Origins are spaced along the DNA at intervals of 30 to 100 μm. All of the origins in a chromosomal replicating unit begin synthesis together, but no information about the junction between two adjacent replicating units is available. Also undetermined is the control mechanism that delays the start of middle- and late-replicating segments. The basic unit of replication, called a *replicon,* was at first thought to be one-half of a segment between two origins (8), but a more recent suggestion (5) defines a replicon as an entire replicating site on a chromosome. The replication units are similar in size to (and probably are identical to) the stainable bands on metaphase chromosomes (G-bands, Q-bands, etc.).

Once DNA synthesis is completed, the cell has by definition entered the G$_2$ phase. It is not known how the cell prevents synthesis of the DNA more than one time during the S phase; however, the cell does occasionally repeat the duplication of its DNA a second or third time, resulting in multiple copies of its metaphase chromosomes. This aberration is called *endoreduplication.*

4. BLOCKING DNA SYNTHESIS WITH DRUGS

It is possible to interrupt DNA synthesis by withholding from the cell precursor molecules required for DNA synthesis. This is usually done with certain drugs that induce an artificial block of a metabolic pathway needed for production of a deoxyribonucleotide, usually thymidylic acid. Many of the drugs used in such work are also valuable cancer chemotherapy agents because they affect cells primarily in the S phase; they are termed *cycle-active* agents. For cell cycle studies such agents are valuable because they permit partial *synchronization* of a random population. Methotrexate, also known as amethopterin, and a related drug, aminopterin, and the base analogue 5-FUdR have all been used to synchronize cells in culture. These agents all prevent the formation of thymidine in cells by blocking the methylation of deoxyuridine. On the other hand, an excess concentration of one precursor, such as thymidine, can block DNA synthesis by feedback inhibition of the synthesis of other precursors, such as deoxycytidine. The drug hydroxyurea has a similar effect. These agents are valuable for synchronization only because their effect is reversible. Upon removal of the agent by washing the cells or upon addition of the needed DNA precursor molecule, the cell resumes its S phase activities and proceeds through the replication cycle.

However, after drug blockage and rescue the cell is to some extent different from an unblocked cell. Since DNA synthesis was blocked but other metabolic processes continued, the cell has encountered a period of unbalanced growth (9), during which time RNA and protein synthesis continue unabated, and the cell grows larger. If the cell is rescued from its inhibited state within a time equal to one generation time, then it will usually survive and continue to grow without detectable ill effects. However, if the block is continued past the time limit, a strange phenomenon called thymineless death begins (9). Although the cells may survive metabolically for several days, they are unable to resume normal reproduction beyond one or two cell divisions; the population dies this reproductive death exponentially at a rate of about 95% of the population per generation time. The molecular mechanism of this curious phenomenon is not known, but it may somehow be related to the exponential nature of the G_1 phase.

5. G_2 PHASE

Upon successful completion of the S phase, the cell enters the G_2 phase of the cell cycle. This phase is generally envisioned as a transition period during which interphase chromatin is converted to the metaphase state, and the cell prepares in many ways for mitosis. Specific molecular details are lacking, however; so, true to its name, the G_2 phase remains a gap in our understanding.

The G_2 phase typically lasts from 1 to 4 hr in most cells. However, the elegant experiments of Johnson and Rao (10), in which they fused mitotic and interphase cells together, clearly demonstrated that only about 30 min was needed to prematurely condense the chromatin into chromosomes from *any* interphase state. During the G_2 phase it is possible to prevent the beginning of mitosis by blocking protein or RNA synthesis with such drugs as cyclohex-imide or actinomycin D (11). Thus, one would suspect that specific mRNAs and proteins are being made in preparation for cell division. Toward the end of G_2, specific cytological events occur, such as the laying down of the continuous metaphase spindle by the centrioles (see section 10) and the break-ing up of the Golgi apparatus and the nuclear envelope, but it is not known how these events are regulated.

Indeed, how does the cell "know" when it has finished DNA synthesis and should prepare for mitosis? There is some evidence (12) to support the concept that the completion of DNA synthesis in a particular chromosomal site(s) results in a signal (mRNA?) being sent from the nucleus, and this propels the cell on into the G_2 and M states. The G_2 phase ends when the events of mitosis begin to have a visible effect on the morphology of the cell.

6. MITOSIS

Mitosis begins with the first visible changes in the chromatin structure, leading ultimately to condensation of the chromosomes in *prophase*. The change is a continuous one without any perceptible abruptness until the end of prophase, when the nuclear envelope suddenly dissociates into vesicular subunits. At the same time, the cell usually loses its substrate attachment and rapidly rounds up into a sphere. The chromosomes, which were earlier immobilized within the nucleus, probably by attachment to the nuclear envelope, suddenly become free to move around within the cell. In the meantime, the centrioles have organized the metaphase spindle made of microtubules. The prometa-phase chromosomes begin to produce microtubules at their centromeres, and these chromosomal spindle fibers interact with the centriolar spindle to cause the chromosomes to move toward the equator of the spindle, a process called *congression*. The mechanism of chromosome movement is not yet known, but spindle fiber interactions are thought to provide the motive force. In *metaphase*, the chromosomes are aligned on the spindle equator, with the kinetochore of each chromatid aimed toward one pole of the spindle. *Anaphase* commences as the chromatids separate and begin moving toward the poles. The separation of the chromatids is the goal of *karyokinesis*, but a second process begins in anaphase—the cytoplasmic cleavage of the cell into two halves. This latter process is termed *cytokinesis* and occurs rather suddenly during anaphase and *telophase*. How the two processes are orchestrated, both in timing and position, is still a major mystery.

As the chromosomes approach the mitotic poles and cytokinesis begins, spindle enlongation doubles the length of the spindle. As the cell is cut in two by the cleavage furrow, the chromatids begin to aggregate into a cluster, and the vesicular components of the nuclear envelope reassemble on the surface of the chromatids to form the daughter cell nuclei. More detailed descriptions of the mitotic process can be found elsewhere (13), but this brief outline will serve to introduce more specific information later on.

7. BLOCKING OF MITOSIS WITH DRUGS

Many years ago the alkaloid *colchicine* was discovered to be a potent inhibitor of mitosis. This drug is of ancient origin and was used mostly for the treatment of gout. Its efficacy, in both cases, is related to its ability to block the assembly of microtubules, affecting cell motility and shape in gout treatment and preventing spindle assembly in mitotic cells (14). Certain cancer chemotherapy agents, namely, vinblastine (Velban) and vincristine (Oncovin), alkaloids isolated from the periwinkle *(Vinca),* have a very similar effect on mitosis. For cell cycle research a derivative of colchicine named Colcemid is most widely used because it is relatively free of side effects, and its action is readily reversible.

Colcemid blocks mitosis by preventing the formation of the metaphase spindle by the centrioles. Surprisingly, it does not completely prevent microtubule formation by the chromosomes, at least not at minimal effective dosage (14). Colcemid acts by binding competitively to a site on the protein *tubulin,* the protein monomer from which the microtubules are assembled. Upon removal of the Colcemid by washing the cells, microtubule assembly is resumed, and the cell proceeds through an apparently normal mitosis. Thus, Colcemid can be used as an effective synchronization agent (15). However, if cells remain in mitotic block for more than 3 or 4 hr and are then allowed to proceed, the ensuing mitosis may be abnormal, in that a multipolar spindle may form. There is more about this in section 12.

Mitotic blockage is in one way preferred to S phase block, because unbalanced growth does not happen. RNA and protein synthesis are minimal or absent in mitosis because no mRNA is transcribed from the DNA in condensed metaphase chromosomes.

8. SYNCHRONIZATION OF CELL POPULATIONS

Drugs that specifically block DNA synthesis or mitosis have been used extensively in cell cycle research to synchronize cell populations (16). An additional strategy often employed is the selective detachment of mitotic cells from monolayer cultures. Since mitotic cells tend to round up and detach from surrounding cells and the substrate surface, they can be differentially removed by shearing forces or short trypsinization (16). If millions of cells can be made to pass as one through the stages of the cell cycle, then biochemical analyses can be employed to determine molecular composition and enzyme activities (15). Morphological changes can also be monitored both inside (14) and on the surfaces (17) of cells.

A variety of additional synchronization procedures have been used in special cases, such as serum deprivation, isoleucine deprivation, cold shock, heat shock, and so on. All of these have also been used in conjunction with drug treatments and selective detachment to obtain highly synchronous cell populations.

Because of the biological variability in the time spent by a cell in each state of the cell cycle, synchronization rapidly decays. Consider our hypothetical standard cell population. If we start a population of these cells all at the beginning of mitosis and simulate their subsequent growth by computer (see Appendix 4), the effect of the synchronization is completely gone after two generation times (Figure 2). However, the synchronization of the first cell cycle is adequate for biochemical analysis of the population, so long as one remembers that synchrony is decaying more and more as time goes on.

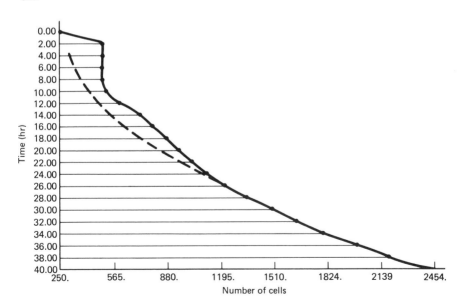

Figure 2. Decay of synchronization with time.

9. ENZYME FLUCTUATIONS IN THE CELL CYCLE

The first biochemical analyses to be made on synchronized cells were measurements of total DNA, RNA, and protein (9, 15). The accumulation of DNA is limited to the S phase, and, as one would expect, the original amount doubles during this period. On the other hand, protein and RNA are not conserved but exist in an equilibrium state, being simultaneously synthesized and broken down. The levels of RNA and protein are stable until the cell enters the S phase, whereupon they gradually rise twofold by the time the cell reaches mitosis (15).

Studies of specific RNAs, such as ribosomal RNA (rRNA), have been made (18); in this case the pattern is similar to total RNA, as one might expect, since rRNA is a considerable fraction of the total.

Enzyme analysis has been a favorite topic because one can readily assume that the activity levels reflect fluctuations in the total enzyme present in a sample. Of course, such things as inhibitors, cofactors, and so forth, must be considered, but, in general, enzyme analysis allows the quantitation of a protein that is a small part of the whole. The first enzyme to be examined in synchronized cells was thymidine kinase (19). In mitotic cells removed from Colcemid-treated cultures this enzyme activity is relatively high, but after the metaphase block is removed and the cells divide, the enzyme activity drops off rapidly to almost undetectable levels. Only after the S phase begins does the enzyme activity rise slowly to the levels seen in mitotic cells. Computer simulation suggests that this pattern could be produced by as few as 15 mRNA molecules per cell for this protein in steady-state production, and break down during the S and G_2 periods of the cell cycle (20). This pattern of enzyme activity, typical of many of the enzymes involved in DNA precursor synthesis (21), is termed a *peak* pattern. Other enzymes are known that increase gradually through the cell cycle but never decrease; such a pattern is termed *continuous*. A third possibility is that an enzyme might maintain a certain level until some particular point in the cell cycle, at which time the amount of enzyme abruptly doubles. This is considered a *step* pattern, and would be especially interesting if the synthesis of new enzyme correlated with the synthesis of the structural gene segment for that protein. A variety of enzymes have been examined (19, 21), and most seem to be of the peak or continuous varieties. We were especially curious about the possible fluctuations of DNA polymerases in the cell cycle, but the several known varieties of this enzyme all appear to be continuous (22). However, there is evidence of enzyme activation of DNA polymerase α by a protease (23); so DNA synthesis might still be controlled by availability of *active* enzyme. Section 14 of this chapter deals with this subject in more detail.

10. CENTRIOLE CYCLE

Once synchronous cell populations were available, it became possible to follow the growth and reproduction of cytoplasmic organelles during the cell replication cycle. Ribosomes, mitochondria, and the various membranous systems all appear to increase uniformly in growing cells. The Golgi apparatus, nuclear envelope, nucleolus, and polysomes all disaggregate during mitosis and reassemble in the two daughter cells early in the G_1 phase. However, centriole growth and reproduction is strikingly correlated with the cell cycle.

The centriole is a microtubule organizing center in cells. It is constructed of fused triplets of microtubules arranged to form a cylinder about three times as long as the diameter $(0.25\ \mu)$. In electron microscopic sections across the cylinder, the nine microtubule triplets are also cross-sectioned and appear in a characteristic pinwheel pattern. Additional fine detail associated with centrioles has been described (24) but is not germane to this presentation. It should be noted, however, that centrioles appear to contain RNA (24) and in many ways behave as autonomously replicating entities within the cell.

During mitosis each daughter cell receives a single mature centriole with a short immature daughter centriole attached to it. Only the mature parent centriole participates in spindle organization during mitosis. Within a few hours after mitosis the daughter centriole grows to full length but maintains a peculiar right-angle orientation to its parent. About the time that the cell commits itself to S phase and DNA replication, the two mature centrioles begin their replication cycle (25, 26). Centrioles reproduce *generatively* rather than by fission. A daughter is constructed near one end of each parent as an almost full-diameter cylinder that is very short. As time passes, it slowly lengthens at a rate such that it is about half grown by the time of the ensuing mitosis. The structural details of centriole replication may be found elsewhere (26). The early events of centriole replication can be blocked by RNA inhibitors but not DNA inhibitors (25, 27). As mitosis approaches, the two mature centrioles, each with an attached daughter, lose the right-angle orientation to each other, and in late G_2 or early M they begin to organize the mitotic spindle. As microtubules form an astral figure around each parent–daughter pair, they push away from one another, and, as the spindle grows between them, they constitute the spindle poles toward which the chromosomes will move in anaphase. Thus, the centrioles replicate and separate exactly in step with the cell nucleus, so that each cell receives a pair of centrioles (one immature) in mitosis. However, the centriole plays a second role in the cell. In addition to its function in building the mitotic spindle, the centriole can become the basal body of a cilium or flagellum (28). Ciliated cells may need hundreds of such basal bodies, whose production occurs as follows:

Whatever is involved in the generation of a single daughter centriole can apparently be produced in mass for the production of hundreds of centrioles in tissues like ciliated epithelium (29). In a single cell generation these newly formed daughter centrioles differentiate into basal bodies, migrate to the cell surface, and construct cilia as extensions of the two inner microtubules of the nine triplets that compose their walls. The details of this differentiation step can be controlled to some extent in cell culture, and the ultrastructural sequence has been described in mammalian cells (30). During ciliogenesis the cell retains a pair of undifferentiated centrioles for mitotic purposes, although in some lower organisms basal bodies with attached flagella have been observed to function in spindle generation and mitosis. It would appear that the two functions are not mutually exclusive in all cases.

11. DIFFERENTIATION: G_1 AND G_0

Ciliogenesis is just one form of cellular differentiation, of course. Cells usually enter into specialized differentiation during the G_1 phase of the cell cycle. Often, as in the case of neurons, the specialization is irreversible, so that under normal circumstances they will never reproduce again. In other cases, the process is reversible so that after some period of quiescence the cell may again enter the S phase and divide in a subsequent mitosis. In this latter category are the reserve stem cells involved in wound healing, cells that may lie dormant for long periods. Such cells usually provide the fibroblasts that grow so well when biopsy material is placed in culture. In all of these cases the cell is clearly postmitotic and not yet involved in DNA replication, so it should be classified as G_1. However, a second term has arisen in the literature to describe G_1 cells that are not likely to replicate; such cells are defined as being in G_0. This state is by definition nonreplicative, but the whole concept is confused by the phenomenon of recruitment, in which G_0 cells are pulled back into the division cycle. This phenomenon is known to be operative in many tissue systems.

Smith and Martin (4) have challenged the G_0 concept with their proposal of G_1 control by a probability factor. The molecular nature of this factor is unknown, but the concept does make sense in that cycling cells have a fairly high probability for entering the S phase, while G_0 cells have a much lower probability factor. The experimental evidence for such a concept is not extensive, but where it has been tested, it seems to be correct. An interesting corollary is that the replicative states $S + G_2 + M$ constitute a form of differentiation that is only one of many possible fates facing the G_1 cell. Presumably, both genetics and environment regulate the probabilities governing which pathway a cell will take.

As a cell differentiates, a spectrum of specialized proteins appears in its cytoplasm, each having been generated by an mRNA copied from a specific DNA segment somewhere in the chromosomes. How is this orchestrated? In prokaryotes some of the molecular details are known, but in mammalian systems the complexity of the genome has made things quite difficult; so the molecular details for transcription control are not yet demonstrated. An interesting speculation by Paul (31) compares the information stored in the DNA to the memory system of a large computer. Viewed as a random access memory, we immediately realize that the information stored in the DNA must be of two basic types: *addresses* and *data*. The only information that has been examined to date has been the primary data specifying the amino acid sequence of proteins; the addressing system remains almost untouched by scientific experimentation. However, it almost surely exists.

Consider how such a mechanism should function. Each differentiation pathway would be controlled by a program in the DNA. As the controlling event starts the program, the initial RNA transcript from the primary site must contain the information to direct transcription activities to a series of other addresses in the genome where related information is stored. These *subroutines* can in turn activate other sites where needed information, in the form of both protein sequences and additional addresses, is stored. It would not be surprising to find chemical analogies to all of the computer programming "tricks" used in binary computers, as well as a lot of new tactics we humans have yet to discover (we have only had computers to play with for 30 years). To complete the analogy, the mRNA synthesis and processing system constitutes the central processing unit (computer CPU), and the ribosome and protein synthesis system constitutes the output port interfacing the memory system to the production of catalytic enzymes.

12. CELL CYCLE MUTANTS

Anyone who has ever worked with computers realizes that a complex program must be carefully designed and debugged to get it to work correctly. A seemingly trival mistake introduced anywhere in the information will usually have dire consequences. Mutation, a random alteration of the information stored in DNA, is usually detrimental to the cell, and probably for the same reasons. However, the cell has two complete copies of the program [and perhaps four sets (32)] inherited from each parent, and since both copies are freely interactive, an error in one copy can be covered by the correct information in the other. There being two kinds of information, mistakes of two different types will occur. The defective sequence of a protein is a well-known example of one type. The other case is a misdirected call to a wrong address (or to an address that does not even exist). If this latter type of mistake happens to both program copies in the same step of a differentiation program, then the program will be interrupted before it is completed. It is interesting in this connection that certain leukemias can be arranged in a sequence that appears to be blocked at different stages of erythropoiesis (33). Perhaps these cells were misdirected by a defective address at different points in the program onto the reproduction pathway every time they started in the differentiation program.

When we view the reproductive pathway $(G + G_2 + M)$ as a process controlled by a computer program, we might expect to find mutants that become blocked in the various stages of the cell cycle, unable to proceed because of defective information. By definition, such mutants, in the ordinary sense, would be hard to find, since they could only exist as single cells and could not be grown into a productive culture. However, in certain special types of mutants, called temperature-sensitive mutants (T_s mutants), this restriction does not apply (34). If the expression of a mutation depends on temperature, then it is only seen at the *restrictive* temperature, and T_s mutants for cell cycle events have been isolated in several cases. They can be grown at the *permissive* temperature, where the mutation is not expressed, and then the defect is studied at the restrictive temperature. The effect is thought to be the result of an altered amino acid sequence in an enzyme, such that adequate catalytic effect is obtained at one temperature but not at the other because of changes in the peptide tertiary structure at the active center.

Most of the T_s cell cycle mutants in mammalian cells become blocked either in S phase or in mitosis when incubated at the restrictive temperature. In only a few cases have the actual molecular defects been studied. However, in yeasts a much more extensive investigation of T_s cell cycle mutants has been done by Hartwell and collaborators (35). This kind of study should yield great dividends in the near future.

Even without our knowing specifically how the T_s mutants are blocked, they can be extremely valuable to cell cycle research because they give us a new way to synchronize cells. If the block of a T_s mutant at the start of the S phase can be reversed by a change in temperature, then it should be possible to keep a stock culture at least partially synchronized by controlled temperature fluctuation. This can be readily accomplished by a clock and appropriate electronics. A double mutant, blocked twice in each cell cycle at S and M phases, should be even more useful, as computer simulation has readily demonstrated (36). Such a culture could be kept in strict synchrony indefinitely.

13. CELL CYCLE–ACTIVE CHEMOTHERAPY AGENTS

One characteristic that all types of cancers share is uncontrolled growth. Cell cycle research is therefore of very great importance both to the treatment of the disease and in attempting to understand the molecular defect in cancer cells. Many of the cancer chemotherapy drugs with useful clinical effects are agents that specifically block cells in some stage of the cell cycle. Many of these cycle-active agents introduce bogus precursors into the DNA or in other ways interfere with DNA synthesis. Cytosine arabinoside (Ara-C), 6-mercaptopurine (6-MP), methotrexate (MTX), 6-thioguanine (6-TG), and 5-fluorouracil (5-FU) are all examples of such agents. They are effective because they kill dividing cells, including cancer cells, but do not harm differentiated normal cells. However, they have serious side effects because some normal cells also divide; bone marrow, epithelial surfaces, hair roots, and gonads can also be severely damaged by these agents.

Agents that block the cells in mitosis may be effective for a different reason. If the cells can be delayed long enough for the daughter centrioles to reach maturity, then the daughter centrioles can establish an independent mitotic pole, and the mitotic spindle becomes multipolar (26). Random splitting of the genome three or four ways is not likely to produce viable daughter cells; so the daughters often fuse together to form a multinuclear cell. Such a tetraploid cell may be able to differentiate if it is a normal cell, but its reproductive viability is reduced if it is a cancer cell.

14. CANCER AS A CELL CYCLE DEFECT

The major mystery of cancer is a definition of the defect in the cell cycle that results in uncontrolled growth. The point of control is probably operative in the period immediately before the cell enters the S phase. We have attempted an evaluation of all of the molecular events at this interface. At first we thought that perhaps some key precursor might be missing until DNA synthesis is supposed to begin, but studies of the enzymes for precursor synthesis (21) and the precursor molecules themselves (37) have shown them all to be present in sufficient abundance before S phase begins. We next examined DNA polymerase enzymes themselves and came to the same conclusion: there was plenty of DNA polymerase. A complication, which has not been completely resolved, concerns the multiplicity of DNA polymerase enzymes; at least four are demonstrable in cells, one in the mitochondria, one in the cytoplasm, and two in the nucleus (38). Probably only one of these enzymes, one of the DNA polymerases found in the nucleus, is active in DNA replication, although it is possible that two or three different enzymes are needed for such a complex process. An additional complexity is that the assay system for these enzymes using purified DNA may force activity from enzymes that are not active when using native chromatin as template.

For some time it has been known that the entry into S phase depends on RNA and protein synthesis (39), suggesting that a specific protein factor may be involved in initiating DNA replication. Evidence for a positive initiation factor was also found by Rao and Johnson (40) in cell fusion experiments using synchronized cells. They found that when an S phase cell was fused to a G_1 cell, the G_1 cell entered S phase sooner than it would have if it had been fused to another G_1 cell or left single. There is even evidence in some studies of a factor of this sort that can diffuse from cell to cell (41). What is this factor?

Several years ago, Brown and Stubblefield (42) found that treatment of isolated nuclei with low levels of trypsin or chymotrypsin resulted in a marked stimulation of the nuclei to synthesize DNA in an in vitro assay system. In the same system, assay of nuclei removed from synchronized G_1 cells resulted in reduced DNA synthesis compared to S phase nuclei (as one would expect), but after trypsin treatment, the G_1 nuclei made DNA at the same rate as the S phase nuclei (23). Furthermore, trypsin treatment had no effect on the rate of DNA synthesis in S phase nuclei. Perhaps the factor that initiates DNA replication in G_1 cells is a protease. But how would a protease effect a start of DNA replication?

One possible mechanism is illustrated by the research of Moise and Hosoda (43) into the DNA replication of the T4 bacteriophage. A specific protein from gene 32 (called P32) acts to unwind the DNA during replication. The affinity of this protein for native DNA is markedly altered by the removal of a short peptide length from one end of the molecule by either trypsin or chymotrypsin. Even though these two enzymes act at different amino acid sites, the result is indistinguishable. The P32 protein becomes measurably smaller. A similar region on the other end of the molecule is also susceptible to cleavage with similar consequences.

The entrance of a cell into S phase could be mediated by the appearance of a specific protease that activates either DNA polymerase or an unwinding protein similar to P32 from T4 phage. The polymerase enzymes could be active in an assay system all along but be inactive in the cell nucleus until protein cleavage increases its molecular affinity for the sites of origin of DNA replication in the native chromatin.

Defects introduced into such a scheme at several points could result in malignant transformation. The beginning point of a normal cell for entry into the S phase program would be the formation of the specific nuclear protease to activate the DNA synthesis enzymes. By the time the cell completes mitosis, the protease must be gone, or the daughter cell will again enter the S phase. Thus, factors that prevent loss of the protease could cause cancer. One such factor could be mutation of the protease-induction mechanism; another could be altered protease structure, such that it defies normal degradation. Viruses induce cellular proteases for the processing of their proteins; so oncogenic viruses would in this scenario be those that integrate their genome into the cellular DNA and permanently derepress the protease that activates the DNA replication enzymes. Such a cell would reproduce again and again, unable to differentiate because of being shunted repeatedly into the S phase every time it reached G_1. Further discussion of this protease theory of cancer can be found elsewhere (44).

This completes a general introduction to the cell replication cycle. Many details and ramifications could not be included because of space restrictions, and much valid research by many workers has been neglected in this treatment. This attempt has been aimed mainly at providing an overall perspective for assisting the student in gaining a basic understanding of cell cycle research.

APPENDIXES

1. Measurement of Cell Cycle Parameters

A general method used almost universally for estimating the lengths of G_1, S, G_2, and M is the percent labeled mitosis (PLM) experiment introduced by Quastler and Sherman (45). A growing population of cells is given a short pulse label of a radioisotope, usually ^{3}H-thymidine, at time zero. The cells are then washed free of the radioisotope, and the samples are harvested for analysis at hourly intervals thereafter. The cells are spread onto microscope slides in such a way that mitotic and interphase cells can be distinguished, and then the slides are coated with a photographic emulsion and stored for several weeks in the dark. After development of the emulsion-coated slides, silver grains can be found over the cells that were in S phase during the labeling pulse. However, in this analysis only cells in mitosis are considered, and a graph of the percentage of mitotic cells that are labeled is plotted, as in Figure 3.

Initially, none of the mitotic cells are labeled, and only after a period reflecting the G_2 interval does this value rise. The value stays high during the interval corresponding to the S phase and then drops again as cells that were in G_1 during the labeling period reach mitosis. From the 50% values the various intervals for average G_2, S, and $G_1 + M + G_2$ can be estimated as shown in Figure 3. The value for M can be determined from the average percentage of mitotic cells in the samples, as described in Appendix 2.

2. Cell Cycle Math

In an exponentially growing population of cells, certain mathematical relationships hold that are useful for routine cell cycle experiments. Consider first the distribution of ages (46) in such a population; there are always more younger cells than older cells because each old cell that divides is replaced by two young cells. Therefore, in calculating the length of the mitotic interval

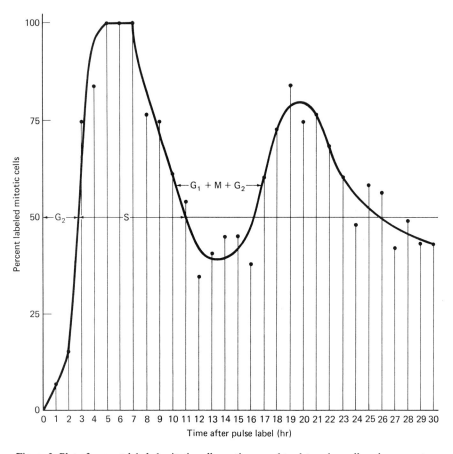

Figure 3. Plot of percent labeled mitotic cells vs. time, used to determine cell cycle parameters.

from the percentage of mitotic cells, such an age distribution must be taken into account (16).

If λ is the mean fraction of mitotic cells, and θ is the mean duration of mitosis as a fraction of T_g, then,

$$\theta = \frac{\ln (1 + \lambda)}{\ln 2}$$

and the mitotic period M can be calculated as

$$M = \theta T_g$$

For the more general case of an event that occurs between time t_1 and t_2, such that $t_0 \leq t_1 < t_2 \leq T_g$

$$\lambda = 2(e^{-kt_1} - e^{-kt_2})$$

3. Flow Microfluorometry

A new technique, called flow microfluorometry (FMF), is used extensively in cell cycle research (47). A population of cells in suspension is stained with a fluorescent dye that is quantitative for DNA. In a laminar flow stream the cells are passed single file through a focused laser beam at the rate of about 1000 cells/sec. As each cell passes through the laser beam, a pulse of fluorescent light is emitted from the cell, which is quantitatively related to the DNA content. These pulses are measured and stored electronically, and a histogram of DNA content versus frequency of occurrence is accumulated, as in Figure 4. G_1 cells all have a beginning amount of DNA that gradually increases as the cell passes through S phase. Cells in G_2 have a DNA content precisely double that of cells in G_1. FMF can therefore provide excellent quantitative information about a growing population, especially the relative numbers of G_1 and G_2 cells, which are not readily distinguishable otherwise. However, differentiated cells are not distinguishable from G_1 cells, so mixtures of growing and nongrowing cells, such as blood samples from leukemia patients, are more difficult to analyze. The G_2 peak includes mitotic cells as well. The FMF pattern is not sufficient in itself for complete analysis; some other method must be used to measure T_g and the mitotic fraction.

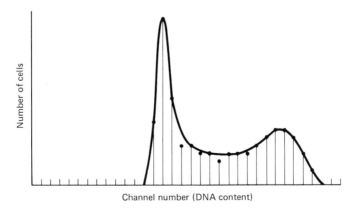

Figure 4. Analysis of DNA content by fluorescence detection.

4. Computer Simulation using CELLSIM

CELLSIM is a computer simulation language for cell cycle research (48). For cell biologists who have had no higher mathematics or computer experience, it provides a simple format to design and test complex models of cell populations. Most of the figures in this chapter are *simulated* results rather than actual experimental data. Computer modeling is valuable because it allows one to test his concepts about complex experiments; it readily locates inadequate assumptions and poor experimental design. In carefully controlled simulations, CELLSIM can provide data about unmeasurable parameters, such as the percentage of G_1 cells, so long as all of the measurable parameters are carefully matched to the experimental results. A typical CELLSIM program is shown in Figure 5.

CELLSIM requires no special hardware other than the standard computer facility usually found in any university or medical center campus. CELLSIM program tapes and user manuals are available from the designer, Dr. Charles Donaghey, Department of Industrial Engineering, University of Houston, Houston, Texas 77004.

```
CELL TYPES CEL1,CEL2;
STATES (1,2) G1,S,G2,M;
FLOW (1,2) G1-S (ALL),S-G2(ALL),G2-M(ALL),M-G1(ALL);
TIME IN STATES (1,2) G1:EXP(4.0),S:LOG(8.0,2.5),G2:LOG(2.5,1.4),
   M:LOG(.5,.04);
PROLIFERATION (1,2) M:2;
INOCULUM (1) 500;
MOVE,AT TIME = 20,S(1) TO S(2);
NUMBER OF GROUPS (1) = 400;
RANDOM NUMBER SEED = 46381;
NO PRINT*;
GRAPH M(2)/(M(1) + M(2)),M(1),M(2),TOTAL;
REPORTS 1 HOURS;
SIMULATE 60 HOURS;
```

Figure 5. A CELLSIM program.

REFERENCES

1. Swift, H. 1950. *Physiol. Zool.* 23:169.
2. Howard, A., and Pelc, S. R. 1951. *Exp. Cell Res.* 2:178.
3. Lajtha, L. G. 1957. *Physiol. Rev.* 37:50.
4. Smith, J. A., and Martin, L. 1973. *Proc. Natl. Acad. Sci. U.S.A.* 70:1263.
5. Stubblefield, E. 1975. *Chromosoma* 53:209.
6. Stubblefield, E., and Gay, M. 1970. *Chromosoma* 31:79.
7. Latt, S. A. 1975. *Somat. Cell. Genet.* 1:293.
8. Huberman, J. A., and Riggs, A. D. 1968. *J. Mol. Biol.* 32:327.

9. Rueckert, R. R., and Mueller, G. C. 1960. *Cancer Res.* 20:1584.
10. Johnson, R. T., and Rao, P. N. 1970. *Nature* (London) 226:717.
11. Arrighi, F. E., and Hsu, T. C. 1965. *Exp. Cell Res.* 39:305.
12. Stubblefield, E. 1964. *Symp. Int. Soc. Cell Biol.* 3:223.
13. Brinkley, B. R., and Stubblefield, E. 1970. *Adv. Cell. Biol.* 1:119.
14. Brinkley, B. R., Stubblefield, E., and Hsu, T. C. 1967. *J. Ultrastruct. Res.* 19:1.
15. Stubblefield, E., Klevecz, R., and Deaven, L. 1967. *J. Cell. Physiol.* 69:345.
16. Stubblefield, E. 1968. *Methods Cell Physiol.* 3:25.
17. Porter, K. R., Prescott, D. M., and Frye, J. 1973. *J. Cell Biol.* 57:815.
18. Klevecz, R. R., and Stubblefield, E. 1967. *J. Exp. Zool.* 65:259.
19. Stubblefield, E., and Murphree, S. 1967. *Exp. Cell Res.* 48:652.
20. Stubblefield, E., and Dennis, C. M. 1976. *J. Theor. Biol.* 61:171.
21. Stubblefield, E., and Murphree, S. 1974. In *Handbook of Experimental Pharmacology,* Vol. 38, Sartorelli, A. C., and Johns, D. G. eds. Springer-Verlag, Berlin.
22. Furlong, N. B., Novak, W. B., and Stubblefield, E. 1973. *Cell Tissue Kinet.* 6:303.
23. Brown, R. L., Clark, R. W., Chiu, J. F., and Stubblefield, E. 1977. *Exp. Cell Res.* 104:207.
24. Stubblefield, E., and Brinkley, B. R. 1968. *Symp. Int. Soc. Cell Biol.* 6:175.
25. DeFoor, P. H., and Stubblefield, E. 1974. *Exp. Cell Res.* 85:136.
26. Stubblefield, E. 1967. In *The Proliferation and Spread of Neoplastic Cells.* Williams and Wilkins, Baltimore.
27. Rattner, J. B., and Phillips, S. G. 1973. *J. Cell Biol.* 57:359.
28. Henneguy, L. F. 1897. *Arch. Anat. Microscop.* 1:481.
29. Kalnins, V. I., and Porter, K. R. 1969. *Z. Zellforsch.* 100:1.
30. Stubblefield, E., and Brinkley, B. R. 1966. *J. Cell Biol.* 30:645.
31. Paul, J. 1977. In *International Cell Biology 1976–1977,* Brinkley, B. R., and Porter, K. R. eds., p. 483. The Rockefeller University Press, New York.
32. Stubblefield, E. 1973. *Int. Rev. Cytol.* 35:1.
33. McCulloch, E. A., and Till, J. E. 1972. In *The Nature of Leukaemia,* Vincent, P. C. ed. Blight, Sydney.
34. Thompson, L. H., Mankovitz, R., Baker, R. M., Wright, J. A., Till, J. E., Siminovitch, L., and Whitmore, G. F. 1971. *J. Cell Physiol.* 78:431.
35. Hartwell, L. H., Culotti, J., Pringle, J. R., and Reid, B. J. 1974. *Science* 183:46.
36. Stubblefield, E. 1974. *Summer Computer Simulation Conference,* p. 697.
37. Nordenskjöld, B. A., Skoog, L., Brown, N. C., and Reichard, P. 1970. *J. Biol. Chem.* 245:5360.
38. Weisbach, A. 1977. *Annu. Rev. Biochem.* 46:25.
39. Mueller, G. C., Kajiwara, K., Stubblefield, E., and Rueckert, R. R. 1962. *Cancer Res.* 22:1084.
40. Rao, P. N., and Johnson, R. T. 1970. *Nature* (London) 225:159.
41. Dewey, W. C., Miller, H. H., and Nagasawa, H. 1973. *Exp. Cell Res.* 77:73.
42. Brown, R. L., and Stubblefield, E. 1974. *Proc. Natl. Acad. Sci. U.S.A.* 71:2432.
43. Moise, H., and Hosoda, J. 1976. *Nature* (London) 259:455.
44. Stubblefield, E., and Brown, R. L. 1977. In *Growth Kinetics and Biochemical Regulation of Normal and Malignant Cells,* Drewinko, B., and Humphrey, R. M. eds. Williams and Wilkins, Baltimore.
45. Quastler, H., and Sherman, F. G. 1959. *Exp. Cell Res.* 17:420.
46. Cook, J. R., and James, T. W. 1964. In *Synchrony in Cell Division and Growth,* Zeuthen, E. ed. Interscience, New York.
47. Horan, P. K., and Wheeless, L. L. 1977. *Science* 198:149.
48. Donaghey, C. E., and Drewinko, B. 1975. *Comput. Biomed. Res.* 8:118.

SECTION 12
THE EUKARYOTIC CHROMOSOME

RONALD A. ECKHARDT, SECTION
EDITOR

12.1. Structure and Function of Chromosomes

Kenneth S. McCarty, Sr. and Kenneth S. McCarty, Jr.

One of the principal characteristics of animal development is that those genes that become inactive in the course of somatic cell differentiation rarely revert to an active state. Some of the structural characteristics likely to dictate this functional state will be reviewed here.

EUCHROMATIN VERSUS HETEROCHROMATIN

Chromatin exists within the nucleus in either of two very distinct molecular aggregates. The first of these, heterochromatin, appears in parallel arrays as a highly condensed DNA–nucleoprotein complex. This complex is frequently observed to be attached to a specific nuclear organelle, the marginal lamella. Although the marginal lamella–associated DNA–heterochromatin is frequently in close contact with the inner nuclear membrane, this complex retains its integrity in detergent-isolated nuclei devoid of both inner and outer nuclear membranes. Thus, it can be concluded that the integrity of the lamella-associated heterochromatin complex is independent of nuclear membranes. The second form of chromatin (euchromatin) is less well delineated, appearing as extended irregularly spaced fibers localized within the nuclear matrix.

It should be emphasized that the definition of chromatin is operational, including as many methods for its isolation as there are laboratories engaged in these endeavors. These methods range from the simple lysis of whole cells followed by differential centrifugation, to the more stringent procedures using purified nuclei, extensive salt washes, and sedimentation through discontinuous high density sucrose cushions. In these preparations, approximately 80% of the genome DNA can be accounted for as heterochromatin. The euchromatin (20%) constitutes a potentially active complex. This activity (RNA transcription) is detected by ^{3}H-UTP incorporation into RNA, demonstrated by both electron microscopic autoradiography and RNA resolved by acrylamide gel electrophoresis. The fact that mRNA perichromatin granules may be seen in nuclear preparations of euchromatin represents additional evidence of transcriptional activity.

At least two transcriptionally inactive forms of heterochromatin can be defined in adult somatic cells. The heterochromatin characterized as *constitutive* represents an inactivation of the DNA genome as an essentially irreversible form of differentiation that occurs early in embryonic development. This feature of constitutive heterochromatin [by definition] represents a permanent structural alteration of chromosomes characteristic of a specific differentiated cell type. The second form of heterochromatin, defined as *facultative,* represents a transcriptionally inactive structure acquired at a late stage of development, as, for example, inactivation of the spermatocyte, or loss of function involved in reticulocyte maturation.

In the strict sense of the definition, all chromatin is facultative, since most, if not all, of the DNA genome can be considered in the heterochromatic state at the time of mitosis. Evidence of the reversibility of facultative heterochromatin is best illustrated by its potential for in vitro transcription cell fusion experiments, to clearly distinguish it from constitutive heterochromatin.

Of the 20% of the chromosomal DNA that exists in the extended or euchromatin configuration, less than 50% of the euchromatin is transcriptionally active at any particular instant. For purposes of discussion, we will define here four types of chromatin: (1) *constitutive heterochromatin,* as a permanently inactive structural feature of chromosomes (within the life span of the cell); (2) *facultative heterochromatin,* as inactive chromosomal components that define a differentiated state faithfully reproduced at each cell division; (3) *permissive euchromatin,* as a fraction of euchromatin in a potentially active state immediately responsive to specific signals, such as hormones, and so on; and (4) *active euchromatin,* as that portion of the genome actively engaged in RNA transcription. Some aspects of the super-macromolecular structure and function of these chromatin fractions will be reviewed.

Constitutive Heterochromatin

A prominent feature of the DNA associated with heterochromatin from a variety of organisms is that this fraction both initiates and completes its replication at the end of the S phase, much later than euchromatin.

Evidence for the presence of satellite DNA in association with constitutive heterochromatin is provided by in situ hybridization of this DNA fraction to the centromeric region of the metaphase chromosome and the analysis of DNA from heterochromatin fractionated by density gradient techniques. The in situ hybridization studies demonstrate a unique DNA species specificity.

When those DNA sequences shown to be associated with heterochromatin are subjected to denaturation and subsequently rapidly reannealed, the duplex that is formed has many of the properties of native satellite DNA. The C_{ot} renaturation curves correspond to 110–400 base-pair sequence lengths repeated a million times. Although the satellite DNAs differ widely in base composition (in different organisms or even different satellites within the same organism, e.g., guinea pig satellites I, II, and III), they all appear to share a common feature of low sequence complexity. The observation that satellite DNAs of eukaryotes have unusual silver salt binding characteristics has facilitated both fractionation and identification. In fact the complete sequence (370 base pairs) of satellite DNA from the African Green Monkey has already been established.

Many of the morphological features of chromosomal satellite structure are detected by banding (staining) techniques. Thus, cytological evidence of a centromeric structure is obtained by alkaline treatment of cells attached to coverslips, leading to a characteristic dense giemsa staining around the centromere. This alkaline treatment and giemsa stain is frequently referred to as C-banding (centromeric), presumed to be due to the greater concentration of chromosomal DNA remaining in the C-banded regions of the chromosome as a result of protein dissociation. Thus, trypsin treatment enhances C-banding. If chromosomes are incubated in the presence of 2X SSC* at 60°C, however, omitting the alkali, a pattern known as G-banding (giemsa) is generated along the arms of each chromosome with little or no reaction at the centromere. The fluorochromes, as, for example, quinacrine and quinacrine mustards, result in fluorescence characterized as Q-banding (quinacrine). These regions appear to be almost identical to that of G-banding. The fluorochrome-induced fluorescent regions are located in characteristic bands along the entire length of each chromosome, and interact intensively with the Y chromosome; thus, it has been shown that chromosomes can be classified by size and identified by their characteristic C- and Q-banding. Q-banding, and thus G-banding, appear to result from a quinacrine fluorescence enhancement with regions of DNA that are rich in adenine and thymine, whereas fluorescence quenching is the consequence of unstained guanine- and cytosine-rich regions of the chromosomes.

Using these simple cytological techniques, constitutive heterochromatin has been classified into three fractions: (1) centromeric heterochromatin constituting repetitive sequences of inactive satellite DNA responding only to C-banding, (2) heterochromatin within the arms of the chromosomes which responds to both G- and Q-banding, and (3) heterochromatin that responds to both C- and Q-banding.

Although the synthesis of main-band DNA takes place during the first half of S phase, the satellite DNA synthesis is confined to the second half of S phase. The rarity of intermediate patterns of DNA synthesis suggests an abrupt switch from main-band to satellite replication, observed to be temporally associated with the synthesis of heterochromatin.

The observation that transcriptionally inactive satellite DNA is confined to the constitutive heterochromatin in the centromere reflects its function as a structural entity. At least one structural function is suggested by its association with spindle fiber proteins (tubulin). It is presumed that the satellite DNA–tubulin interaction is required for chromosome migration during cytokinesis.

Facultative Heterochromatin

The inactivation of these specific regions of the DNA (facultative heterochromatin) may be the result of an early event, as, for example, the inactivation of the X chromosomes of the female mammalian cell. This inactivation takes place after the blastocyst stage (i.e., 3–5 days of embryogenesis), early in development and is reproduced at each cell cycle.

Other types of facultative heterochromatin may be the result of either early embryonic or late postembryonic differentiation. Examples of early modulation of heterochromatin are those events that inactivate regions of brain DNA in liver cells or liver DNA in brain cells. Examples of the acquisition of late facultative heterochromatin are spermatogenesis and erythropoiesis. The decision to inactivate a specific region of the DNA genome involves events of a limited number of specific centers, each of which results in a sequential inactivation of specific chromosome regions. This inactivation accounts for the heterochromatin bands (G- and Q-banding) observed along the entire length of the chromosome.

The exact molecular mechanism(s) that differentiates facultative heterochromatin from euchromatin will require more research. In the light of a number of recent concepts of isohistones of H1, and/or HMG nonhistones in nucleosome superstructures, some molecular mechanisms to account for the formation of facultative heterochromatin should now be reexamined.

Histone H1–Induced Heterochromatin in Nucleosome Superstructures

Recent attention has been concentrated on two levels of chromatin organization. The first is the presence of thin chromatin filaments approximately 100 Å in diameter, and the second consists of a thicker fiber with a diameter of 200 to 300 Å. It is reasonable to presume that the thin fiber is almost certainly a linear array of nucleosome core particles in contact with one another, and that the thick fibers are generated by coiling of the thin fibers.

Low angle neutron diffraction studies of the 300 Å chromatin fiber suggest that this structure represents a linear array of nucleosomes arranged in a "solenoid" with 100 Å pitch, a diameter of 300 Å, and a 100 Å hole down the central axis. The pitch is presumably determined by side-by-side packing of nucleosomes on adjacent turns of the solenoid. The presence of solenoid structures with these dimensions has been detected in electron micrographs of nucleosome oligomers prepared in the presence of magnesium. In the absence of magnesium, only the 100 Å thin filament is visible.

There is good reason to postulate that the interactions between nucleosomes are modified and stabilized by Mg^{2+}. The lysine-rich H1 histones in the presence of Mg^{2+} appear to be bound directly to the DNA within the spacer region between the nucleosome cores. Only four of the major histones are required to define the nucleosome core particle (Chapter 6.6). These included are the arginine-rich histones H3 and H4, and the moderately lysine-rich H2A and H2B held together by hydroprobic interactions between two molecules of each of the four histones. In fact, in chromatin reconstruction experiments only the arginine-rich histones are required to define the physical properties of the nucleosome core particles. Low angle X-ray scattering behavior of nucleosomes in solution has led to the conclusion that in the absence of histone H1 the nucleosome is best described as a flattened cylindrical structure about 110 Å in diameter and 57 Å in height, with the DNA wrapped around the 110 Å diameter to form a pair of rings at the top and bottom which enter and leave the particle on the same side.

The fifth histone, class H1, required for solenoid superstructure, can be selectively extracted from the chromatin using salt concentrations in the range of 0.3–0.6 M. Evidence of the unique location of H1 was first suggested in 1966 by the observation that only the antisera against H1 histones had the capacity to induce an immunofluorescent staining of cell nuclei. Although removal of histone H1 has no effect on the nucleosome subunit, in its absence an increase in nuclease susceptibility of the 10–60 base-pair DNA linker region is observed. In addition, the removal of histone H1 results in an increased accessibility of the chromatin to DNA polymerase I. The observations of Bradbury and others, using neutron contrast matching, extend these observations to imply that histone H1 is complexed directly with DNA, providing the DNA–protein complex required for heterochromatin structures.

In contrast to the highly conserved amino acid sequences of the nucleosomal core histones, the amino acid sequences of the H1 isohistones are much more heterogeneous. This observation first became apparent when the histone H1 class was eluted from Amberlite IRC-50 (Bio Rex P70) columns using shallow gradients of guanidinium chloride. Each tissue is characterized by multiple forms of H1 which vary quantitatively between tissues and qualitatively between species. For example, column chromatography of histone H1 from rat thymus or rat liver reveals the presence of five isohistones, each of which demonstrates immunological cross-reactivity with the corresponding isohistones of other rat tissues. As many as eight H1 isohistones have been resolved by chromatography of H1 preparations from spleens of calf, rat, cat, and chicken. The H1 isohistones have molecular weights of about 23,000. A precise assignment of this amino acid micro-heterogeneity is complicated, however, by postsynthetic modifications to be discussed below.

In solution H1 histones form a folded structure. Although this folded structure, which extends from residue 40 to 115, contains no β-structures, it does exhibit a significant amount of α-helix. The most likely location of the helical regions is from residues 42 to 55 and 58 to 75. There is both in vivo and in vitro evidence that H1 isohistones form direct crosslinks between DNA strands, a further implication of its role in heterochromatin structures. Thus an increase in ionic strength of the media induces a physical contraction of the chromatin that is absolutely dependent on the presence of both H1 and Mg^{2+}. As will be discussed below, histone H1 undergoes a peak of phosphorylation late in G2 phase of the cell cycle, which corresponds to chromosome condensation. This latter observation has led to the proposal that phosphorylation of this histone may be a part of a mitotic trigger mechanism. It should be emphasized that the removal of H1 histones has a minimal effect on the X-ray diffraction, circular dichroism, and hydrodynamic properties of chromatin, whereas the removal of H3 and H4 has profound effects on these parameters. This suggests that H1, H2A, and H2B do not contribute substantially to these properties of the core nucleosome subunit. In addition, these observations lend credence to the concept that histone H1 is associated with the regions of the DNA that do not contribute to the DNA–protein conformation of the core nucleosome.

In the absence of either histone H1 or magnesium, the repeat distance of the nucleosome and the DNA linker region assumes an extended configuration. Although the coil length (140 base pairs) of the core nucleosomal DNA particle is constant for all cells, the linker DNA bridge to which the histone H1 is bound varies with different cell types. The immediate significance of variations in this spacer distance is still obscure at this time.

The SV-40 minichromosomes (described in Chapter 6.6) represent useful models to investigate the mechanism of histone H1–induced nucleosome superstructure. Salt extraction of the SV-40 minichromosome, which removes histone H1, and/or the removal of Mg^{2+} allows the structure to open up into a linear form. Studies on the dependence of histone H1 binding on the number and size of the nucleosome oligomers show a steady increase in the affinity up to the octanucleosome, without further size dependence beyond this limit. This suggests that the octanucleosomes represent the most likely configuration of the solenoid nucleosome complex capable of forming a stable unit of higher ordered structure. Electron micrographs of oligonucleosomes containing histone H1 reveal the presence of spherical structures about 200 Å in diameter, containing six to ten nucleosomes each.

It is not clear at this time exactly how histone H1 contributes to the compaction of the solenoid structure observed in metaphase chromosomes. The isohistone of H1 may form bridges between spherical turns, and, indeed, it has recently been shown that when H1 is added to H1-depleted SV-40 minichromosomes, some of the H1 molecules link nonadjacent nucleosomes. It is reasonable to postulate that the H1 molecules connect spacer regions on either side of the nucleosome. Although the exact mode of H1–nucleosome binding is uncertain, it provides compaction of euchromatin to assume the heterochromatin configuration. One model that has been proposed is a thin (100 Å)-diameter filament in which adjacent nucleosome cores are in contact, in which the nucleosomes are rotated with respect to one another to permit inclusion of a variable length of spacer DNA without altering the fiber diameter. It is not clear if the spacer DNA is in partial contact with the nucleosome core proteins. This linker region is assumed to be complexed with histone H1 in a way that stabilizes "supercoiling" of the thin filament to form a 200–300 Å fiber. Still higher-ordered coil structures have been proposed to be formed from the fiber in such a way that the spacer DNA is always on the outside retaining its accessibility to nucleases (Figure 1).

As a consequence of these observations, it is reasonable to propose that heterochromatin (both constitutive and facultative) is represented by solenoidal nucleosome superstructures induced by histone H1 crosslinking. It should be noted in Table 1 that histone H1 modifications are evident at different phases of the cell cycle. These include phosphorylation of specific serine and threonine residues in late G1, S, and mitosis. As shown in Figure 1, phosphorylation of H1 has the potential to alter critical charge interactions between H1 and the DNA, with the consequent formation of euchromatin-extended structures.

EVIDENCE OF TRANSCRIPTIVE CAPACITY

The magnitude of the problem of the transcriptive capacity of chromatin is emphasized by the following observations: (1) As described above, 80% of the DNA is in a highly condensed transcriptionally inactive form (constitutive and facultative heterochromatin) with the remaining 20% of the DNA potentially active (euchromatin). (2) As discussed in Chapter 6.6, with very few exceptions eukaryotic DNA and mammalian viral DNA appear to be composed of repeating structural units called nucleosomes. (3) As will be emphasized here, postsynthetic modifications of nucleosomal histones are temporally related to transcriptional activity. (4) The processes of transcription and translation in eukaryotic cells are temporally separable and spatially distinct. (5)

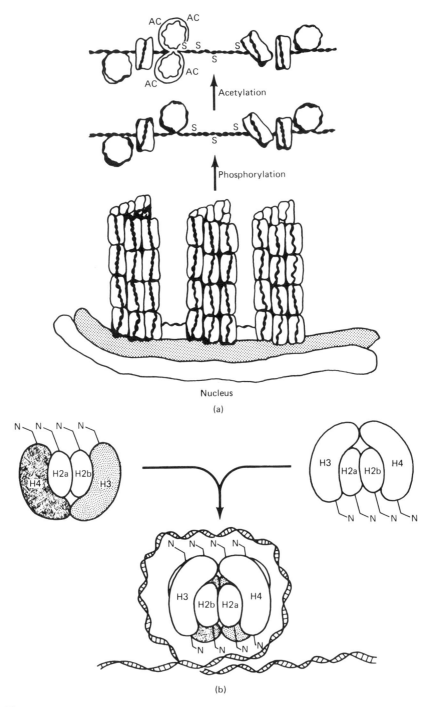

Figure 1. Diagrammatic representation of Salmine A1 protamine structure. This protamine is assumed to be composed of four *a*-helical segments joined by three partially flexible joints at residues just prior to two internal prolines and one joint before a pair of glycine residues. Arginines are shown as dark circles; and P and G stand for proline and glycine respectively.

Table 1. Phosphorylation and Cell Cycle.[a]

HISTONE	CELL CYCLE PHASE	RESIDUES PHOSPHORYLATED		
		SER	THR	TOTAL
H1	Late G_1	105	—	1
	S	105, 160, 180	—	3
	Mitosis	37, 105, 160, 180	16, 136	6
H2A	Late G_1	19	—	1
	S	1, 19	—	2
H3	Mitosis	10	—	1
	Interphase	28	—	1

[a] Phosphorylation has been shown to be related to the phase of the cell cycle. For example, histone H1 is phosphorylated in specific residues in late G_1, S, and mitosis; H2A is phosphorylated in late G_1; the mammary gland is phosphorylated on the amino-terminal series at the time that it is synthesized. H3 is phosphorylated during mitosis, and there is evidence that the residue that is phosphorylated is serine (58a).

Three or more polymerases are required for transcription. (6) Ribosomal genes are temporally amplified during oocyte maturation. (7) Some genes in eukaryotes may be amplified as a mechanism of drug resistance. (8) A significant proportion of the transcribed RNA is confined to the nucleus. (9) The DNA coding sequences for specific messenger RNAs including ovalbumin, immunoglobulin, and β-globulin may be discontinuous, with a single RNA-containing sequence transcribed from widely spaced regions of the DNA genome. Some aspects of these observations will be considered here.

Use of Specific Enzymes in the Identification and Fractionation of Active versus Inactive Nucleosomes

There are many lines of evidence to suggest differences in molecular organization between active and nontranscribed regions of the eukaryotic genome.

These molecular constraints appear to be the result of specific protein–DNA interactions. Three types of protein–nucleic acid interactions should be considered: (1) histone–DNA within the core nucleosome, (2) histone H1–DNA close to but outside the nucleosome, and (3) non–histone–DNA within the linker region.

Hybridization studies, using cDNA probes to globin mRNA, for example, have shown an increased nuclease sensitivity of transcriptionally active DNA resulting in a preferential loss of chromosomal DNA within the actively transcribing fraction. This suggests a fundamental structural difference between active and inactive core nucleosomes. Evidence that the nuclease sensitivity of core nucleosomes could be accounted for by postsynthetic modifications of histones and/or H1–DNA interactions will be discussed below.

The observation that DNase II produces double-stranded nicks in the DNA

Table 2. Amino Acid Sequences Surrounding Sites of Phosphorylation by Protein Kinases.[a]

PROTEIN MODIFIED	SEQUENCE	ORIGIN OF ENZYME
Histone H1	R-(K)-A-[S]-G-P (37)	Rat liver, calf liver, pig brain
	S-G-[S]-F-(K)-L (105)	Rat liver, calf liver, pig brain
	$\begin{smallmatrix}R\\K\end{smallmatrix}$-K-[S]-P-(K) (160)	Trout testis
Histone H2A	N-Ac-[S]-G-(R)-G (1)	Trout testis
	T-(R)-S-[S]-R-A (19)	Mouse mammary gland
Histone H2B	R-(K)-E-[S]-T-S-V (36)	Pig brain, lymphocyte
	K-(K)-G-[S]-K-A (14)	Pig brain, lymphocyte
	P-A-K-[S]-A-P-(K) (Ac 6)	Trout testis
Histone H4	N-Ac-[S]-G-(R)-G-K (1)	Trout testis
Protamines	(R)-R-[S]-S-S-R-P	Trout sperm
	(R)-V-[S]-R-(R)	Trout sperm
Phosphorylase B	Q-I-[S]-$\begin{smallmatrix}V\\I\end{smallmatrix}$-(R)-G	Rabbit, human muscle

[a] Serine residue bracket indicates locus of phosphorylation. Superscript indicates residue. A = alanine; E = glutamic; G = glycine; I = isoleucine; K = lysine; L = leucine; P = proline; R = arginine; S = serine; V = valine. Other abbreviations as in Table 1. Numbers represent residue number modified (e.g., S (38) = serine residue 38) by phosphorylation. N = amino terminal; Ac = acetylated residue.

linker region between nucleosome core particles has provided a technique for the fractionation of transcriptionally active chromatin. Thus, Gottesfeld and coworkers have combined differential nuclease sensitivity with a preferential solubility of the cleaved fragments in 2 mM Mg^{2+} to fractionate active nucleosomes. This combination of differential nuclease sensitivity and solubility in 2 mM MgCl$_2$ has been used to fractionate transcriptionally active chromatin. The magnesium-soluble chromatin has been found to contain those DNA sequences that are known to be transcribed, excluding much of the inactive DNA sequences. For these studies the Friend erythroleukemia cell was particularly well suited, since this cell could be induced by dimethylsulfoxide to synthesize globin messenger RNA. cDNA probes were used to detect globin DNA sequences in the magnesium-soluble chromatin fraction. An important control in these experiments is that they have the potential to differentiate between active and inactive nucleosomes. For example, when nucleosomes are isolated, there appears to be a selective nuclease sensitivity of transcriptionally active core nucleosomes. Thus, the nuclease DNase I preferentially cleaves the chromosomal DNA within the nucleosomes within the region of active genes. These studies have revealed the fact that actively transcribed globin and albumin genes are preferentially sensitive to DNase I digestion. All of these nuclease digestion experiments indicate that active genes are in a different conformational state from the bulk of the DNA and from the inactive genes.

Proposed Altered Nucleosome(s) Structures in Relation to Transcriptional Activity

Electron microscopic visualization of actively transcribing ribosomal genes indicates that the DNA comprising the transcribed segment is in a highly extended conformation. Both biochemical and electron microscopic evidence suggest that at least some of the actively transcribed DNA genome is associated with structures that closely resemble nucleosomes. Thus, there is evidence that both inactive and actively transcribed DNA is protected from micrococcal nuclease (staphylococcal nuclease) activity by the presence of nucleosomes. There is evidence, however, of differential nuclease sensitivity of those DNA fragments involved in hormone-induced RNA transcription. Thus, as described above, DNase I has been used to detect a preferential DNA sensitivity of regions of DNA actively engaged in either globin or ovalbumin mRNA transcription, preferentially sensitive to digestion in the respective cell types. At least one model has been proposed by Weintraub suggesting a tetrameric "half nucleosome" derived from an inactive octanucleosome. The unpairing and unfolding into half nucleosomes is presumed to be a prerequisite for DNA transcription and/or replication. This suggests a modulatory role for the nucleosome which may be the consequence of observed histone modifications (acetylations, phosphorylations, and methylations). The half-nucleosome concept of Weintraub retains a unique feature of DNA–histone interactions in that the histones are not essential to completely dissociate free of the DNA. This is consistent with many experimental observations that histones are never free within the nucleus, retaining their association with the DNA throughout the cell cycle.

It would be dangerous to extrapolate that the simple release of those constraints imposed by the core nucleosome are sufficient to override the histone–DNA complexes as a barrier to RNA polymerase activity. The observations on the half nucleosome will have to be reconciled with numerous electron microscopic observations stressing the total absence of nucleosomes from transcribing genes.

For example, the nascent ribosomal RNA fibrils of *Oncopeltus* appear to be attached to an unbeaded chromatin strand with a packing ratio significantly lower than for DNA in regions of beaded chromatin. Additional studies indicate that the ribosomal cistrons in *Xenopus* are underrepresented in nucleosomes from cells in which rRNA synthesis is high. The ribosomal genes of *Physarum polycephalum* are particularly well suited for these studies because: (1) the ribosomal genes are localized on a large, extrachromosomal cistron; (2) they exist in a palindrome-like DNA (therefore easily identified); (3) the DNA molecule constitutes a large portion (1–2%) of the total nuclear DNA; (4) *Physarum* can be grown in large batches, with either active or inactive rRNA genes; and (5) the subunit structure of the *Physarum* chromatin DNA has been described. In these studies, staphylococcal nuclease digestion of these rDNA cistrons demonstrates that the rDNA sequences are recovered primarily in two fractions containing monomer-sized DNA lengths (140–160 base pairs). The most significant aspect of these studies is the observation that the two fractions contained the same DNA fragment size, although one of the fragments (the A fragment) sediments at 5S and the other at 11S (normal for a mononucleosome). These studies provide evidence, substantiated by electron microscopy, that a high percentage of the 19S and 26S rDNA sequences are packaged in the 5S particle (A fragment), which appears to have a structural configuration that differs from the bulk of the chromosomal DNA and would explain the electron microscopic observations of the absence of nucleosomes (in tight conformation) in actively transcribing genes. This does not exclude the concept of half nucleosomes but rather serves to extend it, as representing an early stage of transcription, prior to the fully extended state observed in the active transcription of ribosomal genes.

In all of the examples discussed here one is still confronted with the problem of resolving a mechanism to permit a polymerase "read-through" of an extended euchromatin fraction in which the DNA is associated with histones in either the half nucleosome or the fully extended state.

Postsynthetic Modification of Nucleosomes and Transcriptional Activity

The real paradox concerning histones is that in spite of numerous molecular constraints (including sequence conservation, limited diversity in the number of classes, constant protein–DNA ratio, and metabolic stability), as many as 200–300 different molecules have been resolved, all of which demonstrate the same amino acid composition as the parent unmodified histone. These histone microheterogeneities represent the consequence of both single and multiple postsynthetic modifications (acetylation, methylation, phosphorylation, poly-ADP-ribosylation, etc.) It should be emphasized that all of these modifications are reversible, some are hormone-dependent, and many are cell-cycle-related.

As shown in Table 3, gene activation of each of the histones may be correlated with numerous postsynthetic modifications. A number of studies have emphasized the fact that phosphorylation may be temporally correlated

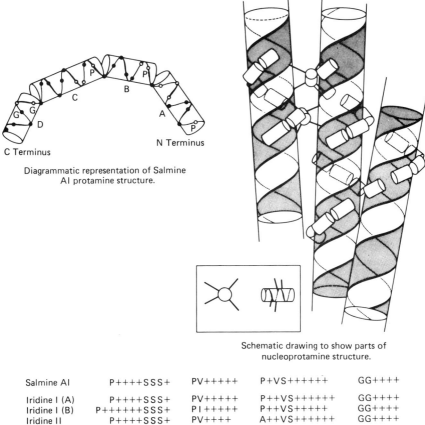

Diagrammatic representation of Salmine
AI protamine structure.

Schematic drawing to show parts of
nucleoprotamine structure.

	Helix A	Helix B	Helix C	Helix D
Salmine AI	P++++SSS+	PV+++++	P+VS++++++	GG++++
Iridine I (A)	P++++SSS+	PV+++++	P++VS++++++	GG++++
Iridine I (B)	P++++++SSS+	PI+++++	P++VS+++++	GG++++
Iridine II	P++++SSS+	PV++++	A++VS++++++	GG++++
Thynnin Y1	P++++EAS+	PV+++++	Y++STAA+++++	VV++++
Thynnin Y2	P++++QAS+	PV+++++	Y++STAA+++++	VV++++
Thynnin Z1	P+++++SS+	PV+++++	Y++STVA+++++	VV++++
Thynnin Z2	P+++++SS+	PV+++++	Y++STAA+++++	VV++++
Clupine Z	P++++S++AS+	PV++++	P++VS++++	A++++
Clupine YI	A++++SSS+	PI++++	P+++TT++++	AG++++
Clupine YII	P+++T++AS+	PV++++	P++VS++++	A++++

Sequences of protamines

Figure 2. Schematic drawing to show parts of nucleoprotamine structure. Protamine molecules are represented by several connected cylinders; each corresponds to an *a*-helical segment. They wrap around the major groove (shaded) of the DNA double helix shown as a long large cylinder. Inset, and *a*-helical segment with four consecutive arginine residues (represented as four rods radiating out from the cylinder) is shown in two-orthogonal orientations. Two types of possible cross-linking are shown. Between the left and middle DNA double helices, there are two *a*-helical segments with arginine side chains shown as straight lines. Each segment forms two contacts across a major groove of one DNA double helix and two across a minor groove of the other DNA double helix. Between the middle and the right DNA double helices, three *a*-helical segments from one protamine molecule are in contact on the major groove of the middle DNA double helix and the fourth segment on the major groove of the right DNA double helix. There are many other types of cross-linking possible.

Table 3.   Temporal Relation of Postsynthetic Modifications and Gene Activity.

HISTONE	MODIFICATION	ACTIVITY
H3, H4	Acetylation	↑ RNA synthesis, lymphocytes
H3, H4	Deacylation	(−) RNA synthesis, *Arbacia lixula*
H3	Acetylation	↑ RNA synthesis, HeLa cells
H3	Phosphorylation	Mitosis
H2A	Phosphorylation	↑ RNA synthesis, mammary gland
H1	Phosphorylation	

with the cell cycle, particularly the phosphorylation of histones H1 and H3. The induction of cell division and passage from the G_o phase of the cell cycle in mammary gland cultures results in the phosphorylation of histone H2A in serine residue 19. This serves to emphasize that only a limited number of specific (amino acids) serine and threonine residues are involved in this postsynthetic modification (Table 4).

Phosphorylation and acetylation represent postsynthetic modifications that take place in both the cytoplasm and the nucleus (Table 4). For example, the amino terminal serine is both phosphorylated and acetylated in histone H4, in a process that is tightly coupled to the translation of the messenger RNA. Immediately after the translation of histone H4 an additional lysine residue is acetylated, as a step likely to be essential in the cytoplasm prior to its transport to the nucleus. (At later stages acetylation of lysine residues 5, 8, 12, and 16 occurs, at the time when histone H4 is in the nucleosome configuration within the nucleus, representing a rapidly reversible process.) Methylation of lysine residue 20 and concomitant phosphorylation of a histidine residue represents, one of the many nuclear events modifying the charge residues of histone H4.

It should be emphasized that all of the postsynthetic modifications within the core nucleosome histones are rapidly reversible and limited to the amino terminal residues (1–40). The one exception appears to be the acetylation of the amino terminal serine residues of histones H2A and H4, which appears to be an early cytoplasmic event, closely coupled with the messenger RNA translation process. Since the acetylation of the amino terminal serine residues of histones H2A and H4 is specifically related to their synthesis, acetylation can be used to follow de novo synthesis.

Three cardinal features characterize the postsynthetic modifications of the core nucleosome histones: (1) the rapidly reversible postsynthetic modifications take place on the amino terminal residues which interact by a "charge–charge" interaction (positively charged lysine and negatively charged phosphate backbone of the DNA) within the wide groove of the DNA associated

Table 4. Residues Involved in Histone Postsynthetic Modification.[a]

| HISTONE | PHOSPHORYLATION | | ACETYLATION | | METHYLATION | |
	CYTOPLASM	NUCLEUS	CYTOPLASM	NUCLEUS	CYTOPLASM	NUCLEUS
H1	—	$S_{37,105,160,180}$ $T_{16,136}R, K_{212}$	—	—	—	—
H2A	S_1	S_{19}	S_1	K_5	—	—
H2B	—	$S_{6,32,36,38}$	—	$K_{5,12,15,20}$	—	—
H3	—	$S_{10,28}$	—	$K_{9,14,18,23}$	—	K_9, K_{27}
H4	S_1	—	S_1	$K_{5,8,12,16}$	—	K_{10}, K_{20}
H5	—	S	—	—	—	—
H6	—	S_5	—	—	—	—

[a] The letters refer to the amino acids that are modified, using the one-letter code designation for the amino acids. S, serine; T, threonine; R, arginine; K, lysine. The subscript designates the specific residue that it modifies when known. Specifically, in the case of histone H2A and H4, the modification takes place in the cytoplasm, as well as the nucleus on the amino terminal series.

on the outside of the nucleosome core particle; (2) the enzymes for acetylation and deacetylation and phosphorylation and dephosphorylation are tightly bound to the chromatin, and (3) the postsynthetic modification can be temporally related to gene activation or replication of the DNA (genome). Inhibitors of dephosphorylation such as phenylmethylsulfonylfluoride and/or inhibitors of deacetylation such as n-butyric acid result in postsynthetic modification of a significant fraction of the core nucleosomal histones. These modifications have the potential to result in extensive alterations in nucleosome structures as described above.

Macro- versus Micronuclei and Transcriptional Activity

Recent evidence suggests that the ciliated protozoan, *Tetrahymena*, may represent an evolutionary linkage between a "prokaryote-like" ancestor and eukaryotes. Within a single cell this organism contains a germinal diploid "micronucleus" to maintain the genetic continuity of the organism, as well as a polyploid "macronucleus," formed only after conjugation from the zygotic nucleus. The macronucleus functions as a somatic nucleus, directing most of the cell's transcriptional activity during vegetative growth and is destroyed at the end of each sexual generation.

Tetrahymena pyriformis presents a unique opportunity to study the relationship between histones (and their postsynthetic modifications), chromatin structure, and the genetic activity of macro- and micronuclei sharing a common cytoplasm. Although 80–90% of the DNA sequences found in micronuclei are also present in similar amounts in macronuclei, they are metabolically extremely different. Some of these differences include: (1) macro- versus micronuclei DNA content, 45%C versus 2%C; (2) macro versus micro replication during the cell cycle phases G_1, S, G_2 versus S, G_2; (3) macro versus micro dividing either amitotically at cell division or mitotically at cell division; (4) the chromatin structure having nucleosomes versus a fibrous chromatin coil; (5) the presence of nucleoli versus the absence of nucleoli; (6) the presence of ribonucleoprotein particles versus their absence; (7) a high RNA content versus little or none; and (8) the expression of dominant alleles versus no activity. In brief then, macronuclei are endoreplicated, amitotically dividing, transcriptionally active somatic nuclei, whereas the micronuclei are diploid, mitotically dividing, and represent transcriptionally inert germinal nuclei.

The histones from macronuclei can be fractionated into five distinct fractions. These include histones H1, H2B, H3, and H4, which are all clearly homologous with their counterparts in calf thymus. The fifth histone, referred to as HX, is sufficiently different from calf thymus H2A to identify it as specific for the macronuclear histone. Only the histones HX and H1 have an amino acid heterogenity as determined by SDS gel electrophoresis. The histones H2B, H3, and H4 appear to exist as clearly resolved homogeneous amino acid compositions. Most of the heterogenity seen in histones HX and H1 results from secondary postsynthetic modifications.

There are three important differences between macro- and micronuclear histone complements: (1) micronuclei appear to lack most if not all secondarily modified histones subspecies, (2) micronuclei appear to contain little or no histone H1, and (3) micronuclei contain little or no histone H3.

The difference observed in transcription between micro- and macronuclei cannot be attributed to the presence or the absence of nucleosomes which are clearly visible by electron microscopy in both of these fractions. The macronuclei of *Tetrahymena* contain the genes coding for ribosomal RNA (rDNA). The ribosomal genes in the macronuclei are amplified, they are extrachromosomal, and they are characterized as "palindromic dimers," which are capable of independent replication.

Refeeding a starved culture of *Tetrahymena* results in the preferential synthesis of ribosomal DNA (rDNA). For this reason preferential introduction of isotopic labels into *Tetrahymena* chromosomal rDNA provides a substrate whose structure can be probed at the nucleosome level by selective nuclease digestion studies. For example, limit digestion with staphylococcal nuclease followed by DNAase I digestion has already provided evidence to suggest that chromatin from the rDNA genome region is organized differently when compared with bulk chromatin. The active regions of rDNA genes appear as linear displays of DNA–histone complexes. Studies with this system under experimentally manipulative gene (rDNA) response (starvation vs. refeeding) serve to emphasize that active genes are characterized by a DNA–protein complex that is selectively sensitive to DNase I digestion. These studies of *Tetrahymena* rDNA lend additional credence to earlier concepts that the histone–DNA interaction plays an important role in transcription control. We suggest in addition that postsynthetic modifications of the nucleosomal histones account for these structural and functional alterations.

Spermatogenesis

Spermatogenesis represents an important example of a specialized mechanism of cellular differentiation as a result of selective facultative heterochromatization. Of considerable interest in these studies is the possible role of chromosomal proteins. As discussed in Chapter 6.6, the spermatocyte histones are eventually replaced by simpler polyamines, the high-arginine-containing protamines. Thus, in the rainbow trout at a late stage of spermatogenesis, a low-molecular-weight protein of high arginine content, protamine, is synthesized and has the capacity to progressively replace histones in a process that appears to be essential in the DNA packaging, as an inactive highly condensed

DNA–protamine complex confined to the small volume provided by the sperm head. The same type of DNA–protamine condensation is observed in the mature rat spermatid. The process of sperm maturation is the consequence of first a progressive increase in both histone X1 and histone X2, and later a progressive loss of both histone H1 and histone H5. In the spermatogonial stages, which are characterized by a high rate of mitosis in cell division, there is a high degree of phosphorylation of histone H1 and a high degree of acetylation of histone H4. At this stage histones X1 and X2 are present only in relatively low amounts. At 14 days, when the premeiotic phases and primary spermatocytes are appearing, histone fraction X3 is observed, and there are increases in the relative amounts of X1 and X2. The rapid increases in histone fractions X1, X2, and X3 during the prophase of the first meiotic division in the developing rat testis suggest that these histone fractions may play a role in meiosis.

CHROMATIN TRANSCRIPTION OF ACTIVE EUCHROMATIN

Despite intensive investigations for a number of years, our ignorance of the mechanism of gene expression in eukaryotes remains appallingly great. Two of the major difficulties in the analysis of gene expression are: (1) the difficulty of analyzing genes that may be represented only once in a huge complex genome, and (2) our failure to reconstitute in vitro systems in which the synthesis of messenger RNA or its precursors is initiated. As discussed above, however, it is now apparent that extensive control of gene expression occurs at the level of mRNA synthesis. In this regard two points should be emphasized. First, the mRNAs which code for specific differentiated products are detectable only in those cells that are committed to make those products. For example, globin mRNAs are limited to reticulocytes, ovalbumin mRNAs are limited to cells of the oviduct, and immunoglobulins are limited to plasmacytoma cells. Second, it is becoming increasingly evident that two levels of gene regulation may occur. Experience with prokaryotic systems shows that different regions of the cell's genome are transcribed into mRNA at different frequencies, and that mRNA is either the direct product of the transcription event or is derivative of precursors that need not be much larger than the mature mRNA. Gene transcription is somewhat more complex in eukaryotes, however; for example, large RNA precursors are found in nuclei, and these sequences are processed prior to their transport to the cytoplasm. These large RNA precursor products have been termed nuclear hnRNAs. Thus, we are now well aware of the requirements of a complex set of post-transcriptional steps involving specific endonucleolytic cleavages and modifications. Additional mRNA processing is also essential and requires the addition of poly A on the 3' end, as well as the addition of specific methylated bases, or "capping", on the 5' end of the mRNA.

Three systems will be discussed to illustrate some additional complexities (segmentation) involved in chromatin transcription.

Adenovirus mRNA Segmentation

A vast majority of the data that have been obtained concerning mRNA transcription is a result of work with adenovirus 2, a virus that grows well in cultured cells. The genome of the adenovirus consists of a linear complex of DNA of about 35,000 base pairs, sufficient to code for 30–40 average-size polypeptides. The expression of these polypeptides is under temporal transcriptional control; some of them are termed "early proteins," synthesized at all times during a lytic infection, whereas others, "late proteins," are synthesized only at later stages of adenovirus infection. The early genes are synthesized from four widely spaced regions of the DNA genome, and during the early stages of infection the only virus-specific mRNAs present in cells are complementary to one strand of the DNA sequence. Hybridization studies have shown that transcriptional controls still occur late in adenoviral infection, and that the site at which RNA synthesis is initiated is quite specific and very efficient. The most striking observation of the transcription of late messenger RNA, particularly the viral hexon protein mRNA, consists of four separate blocks of sequences. Measurements of the lengths of the single-stranded DNA and the DNA–RNA hybrids show that closest to the 5' end of the hexon mRNA, a small number of nucleotides complementary to a specific position on the R strand of the viral DNA are followed by approximately 80 nucleotides coded by a specific position. An additional 110 nucleotides represent a "mosaic" in which the DNA is transcribed into RNA as a large precursor molecule which is then cleaved at specific positions. The following observations have been made: Many if not all adenoviral late mRNAs contain an identical pentanucleotide (7Me Gppp AZU (C_4U_3) Grp) at the 3' end. Although these capped structures are not complementary to viral DNA sequences near the major late structural genes, they hybridize with DNA sequences that map between specific positions. The mRNAs for the fiber protein are 100K nucleotides in length. The mRNAs each contain sequences at their 5' end that can be seen by electron microscopy to hybridize into positions 16.7, 19.7, 26.7 on the R strand of the adenoviral genome. This suggests that certain base sequences are common for very different mRNAs.

Evidence now suggests that these mRNA precursors are synthesized and only later cleaved and ligated into the final mRNA product. These post-transcriptional events undoubtedly play a major role in RNA transcription.

Ovalbumin Gene mRNA Segmentation

The discovery of adenovirus mRNA segmentation as discussed above has raised the question of whether cellular mRNAs could also be coded by separate blocks of DNA sequences.

The elegant studies by Chambon and those of O'Malley in developing methods to fractionate and amplify the ovalbumin gene using the techniques of molecular cloning have now advanced our concepts of the DNA genome sequence complexities. Thus using the techniques of molecular cloning, an *Eco* RI fragment of chicken DNA (fragment "a") containing a sequence complementary to the 3' half of the ovalbumin mRNA has been prepared in large quantities. A detailed analysis of this cloned fragment now appears to prove conclusively that the chicken ovalbumin gene sequence is split. In fact the DNA coding sequences are interrupted at least twice in the chicken ovalbumin genome, and it is now becoming evident that several eukaryotic genes consist of blocks of coding sequences separated by intervening nucleotides. Three examples are: (1) the coding region of the rabbit and mouse β globulin genes; (2) the variable and constant sequences within the coding region of a cloned mouse plasmocytoma κ light chain, which are separated by an intervening sequence of 1250 base pairs; and (3) the fact that intervening DNA sequences are not confined to mRNA coding sequences, since they have been observed in both *Drosophila* ribosomal DNA insertions and intervening sequences in yeast tRNA genes.

At least two models have been proposed for the structural organization of the split ovalbumin gene. In one model, the insertion model, the different regions coding for the mRNA are all on the same DNA segment in the same order and orientation as in the in vitro synthesized double-stranded cDNA, but they are separated by intervening sequences (also termed introns) not represented in the ovalbumin mRNA. In another model the different regions are not necessarily in the same order and orientation as the double-stranded cDNA.

The significance of the split genes seen in eukaryotes is not clear at this time. This arrangement suggests multifunctional aspects of the DNA gene that have yet to be defined. Most evidence suggests that the RNA is first transcribed from an intact region of the DNA and is later processed by cleavage and splicing in very specific regions of the RNA product. These postsynthetic modifications must play important roles in gene regulation.

Drug-Induced DNA Genome Amplification in Transcription Control

Detailed analysis of the molecular mechanisms of drug-induced overproduction of specific enzymes has only recently yielded some important information fundamental to molecular biology. A promising approach has been the use of methotrexate-selected mammalian cell variants that possess a regulatory response in the overproduction of folate reductase. Of the several potential factors proposed to define the methotrexate resistance, the regulation of folate reductase activity represents the only mechanism to be clearly demonstrated. This folic acid analogue strongly and specifically inhibits dihydrofolate reductase in a competitive manner, to indirectly repress the de novo synthesis of purines, thymidine, and glycine. Hence exposure to sufficiently high concentrations of methotrexate kills dividing cells. Of the several potential factors to define methotrexate-induced drug resistance, the most frequently reported observation for mammalian cells has been an increase in the cellular content of dihydrofolate reductase. In this situation, resistant cells accumulate sufficiently high concentrations of this enzyme to maintain some free enzyme activity in the presence of the drug. Several avenues of evidence suggest that the highly resistant lines with greatly increased levels of dihydrofolate reductase are the result of selective pressures induced by culturing the cells in the presence of high levels of methotrexate. Evidence to suggest that methotrexate does not act directly to induce or maintain the increased synthesis of dihydrofolate reductase in resistant cell lines is as follows: (1) A simple single exposure of cells to the drug without selective pressure has no effect on dihydrofolate reductase synthesis. (2) In most resistant cell lines, increased dihydrofolate reductase synthesis is a stable property and does not decline when the cells are grown in the absence of the drug. (3) The kinetics of the decrease of the dihydrofolate reductase in the absence of methotrexate cannot be explained by a corresponding dilution of the drug. (4) Cells supplemented with purines, thymidine, and glycine show a decrease in dihydrofolate reductase synthesis. (5) There is no evidence that methotrexate is a mutagen.

Methotrexate induces a selection of those cells in which the folate reductase represents as much as a 200-fold increase in the levels of enzymatically active and immunologically cross-reactive folate reductase present in sensitive cells. This may represent as much as 6–8% of the total protein synthesis. An assay for the specific folate reductase mRNA activity in cells under a variety of conditions demonstrates both increased synthesis of the mRNA, detected by specific cDNA probes, and its increased activity, demonstrated by in vitro translation systems.

A detailed analysis of the molecular mechanism which accounts for the increased enzyme synthesis using cDNA probes has now shown that the DNA of the selected drug-resistant cells is also specifically amplified (200-fold increase in the amplified DNA) for the folate reductase gene. These results, if confirmed in other systems, are fundamental to our concept of gene amplification as a mechanism of drug resistance.

The most important aspect of these studies is that they add further evidence to support the concept that the genome of higher organisms can *no longer be considered to be static*. Thus the genome when placed under selective pressures, as in drug resistance, or oocyte development, undergoes a variety of changes. Many studies will be required to determine if the amplification of the methotrexate DNA genome is tandemly reduplicated, as seen in the classical example described in Chapter 6.6, in the amplification of the ribosomal genes in the developing amphibian oocyte. The amplification of the ribosomal genes appears to be specifically regulated as part of the developmental sequence and occurs extrachromosomally, apparently by either a rolling circle replication "mechanism," or a reverse transcription of the specific mRNA, or a disproportionate replication of a specific gene during one part of the S phase of the cell cycle. The common feature of all of these mechanisms is that large increases in the number of specific genes appear to be the consequence of selective environmental pressures.

BIBLIOGRAPHY

Phillips, D. M. P., ed. 1971. *Histones and Nucleohistones*. Plenum Press, New York.

Hnilica, L. S., ed. 1972. *The Structure and Biological Function of Histones*. CRC Press.

Huijing, F., and Lee, E. Y. C., eds. 1973. *Protein Phosphorylation in Control Mechanisms,* Vol. 5. Academic Press, New York.

Cameron, I. L., and Jeter, J. R., eds. 1974. *Acidic Proteins of the Nucleus*. Academic Press, New York.

Lewin, B., ed. 1974. *Gene Expression*, Vol. 2, *Eucaryotic Chromosomes*. John Wiley & Sons, New York.

Hidvegi, E. J., Sumegi, J., and Venetianer, P., eds. 1975. *Biochemistry of the Cell Nucleus Mechanism and Regulation of Gene Expression*. North-Holland/American Elsevier, New York.

Stein, G. S., and Kleinsmith, L. J., eds. 1975. *Chromosomal Proteins and Their Role in the Regulation of Gene Expression*. Academic Press, New York.

Fitzsimons, D. W., and Wolstenhome, G. E. W. eds. 1975. *The Structure and Function of Chromatin*. Elsevier/Excerpta Medica/North-Holland, Amsterdam.

Criss, W. E., Ono, T., and Sabine, J. R., eds. 1976. *Control Mechanisms in Cancer*. Raven Press, New York.

Davidson, E. H., ed. 1976. *Gene Activity in Early Development*. Academic Press, New York.

Stein, G., Stein, J., and Kleinsmith, L. J., eds. 1977. *Methods in Cell Biology,* Vol. XVI. Academic Press, New York.

Bradbury, E. M., and Javaherian, eds. 1977. *The Organization and Expression of the Eukaryotic Genome*. Academic Press, New York.

O'Malley, B. W., and Birnbaumer, L., eds. 1977. *Receptors and Hormone Action,* Vol. I. Academic Press, New York.

McCarty, K. S., Jr., and McCarty, K. S., Sr. 1977. Steroid hormone receptors in the regulation of differentiation. *Am. J. Pathol.* 86(3):

Clark, B. F. C., Klenow, H., and Zeuthen, J., eds. 1977. *Gene Expression*, Vol. 43, Symposium A2. (See Section B, RNA synthesis and control, and Section C, Chromatin structure and function.) Pergamon Press, New York.

Li, J. H., and Eckhardt, R. A. eds. 1977. *Chromatin and Chromosome Structure*. Academic Press, New York.

Ts'o, P. O. P. ed. 1977. *The Molecular Biology of the Mammalian Genetic Apparatus,* Vol. 1. North-Holland, Amsterdam.

Ts'o, P. O. P. ed. 1977. *The Molecular Biology of the Mammalian Genetic Apparatus,* Vol. 2. North-Holland, Amsterdam.

Stein, G., Stein, J., and Kleinsmith, L. J. eds. 1978. *Methods in Cell Biology,* Vol. XVIII. Academic Press, New York.

Jeter, J. R., Jr., Cameron, I. L., Padilla, G. M., and Zimmerman, A. M. eds. 1978. *Cell Cycle Regulation.* Academic Press, New York.

Garapin, A. C., Lepennec, J. P., Roskam, W., Perrin, F., Cami, B., Krust, A. Breathnach, R., Chambon, P., and Kourilsky, P. 1978. Isolation by molecular cloning of a fragment of the split ovalbumin gene. *Nature* 237:

Lai, E. C., Woo, S. L. C., Dugaiczyk, A., Catterall, J. F., and O'Malley, B. W. 1978. The ovalbumin gene: Structural sequences in native chicken DNA are not contiguous. *Proc. Natl. Acad. Sci. U.S.A.* 75(5):2205–9.

12.2. Mitotic Chromosomes

Michael S. Risley

The lengths of DNA comprising eukaryotic genomes are relatively enormous. For example, the nucleus of a human somatic cell contains approximately 2.2 meters of DNA. Somatic cell nuclei from the newt, *Triturus cristatus,* contain about 18 meters of DNA. Obviously, such long lengths of DNA must be compressed to a considerable degree to fit them within the relatively small volume of a nucleus. This compression is achieved through protein–DNA interactions which result in the coiling and folding of DNA into compact nucleoprotein masses (chromosomes).

Chromosomes are the most conspicuous cellular components observable during mitosis and meiosis. Because of this, descriptions of eukaryotic chromosome morphology and chromosomal events during the cell cycle have been available for nearly a century (1). In contrast to prokaryotic cells, eukaryotic cells have multiple chromosomes. *Ascaris megalocephala* possesses 4 chromosomes, human somatic cells have 46 chromosomes, and somatic cells from some crustaceans may contain as many as 200 chromosomes. Genetic analyses have demonstrated a 1:1 correspondence between the number of different linkage groups and the haploid chromosome number. Thus, the huge total lengths of DNA in the genomes of eukaryotes are subdivided into smaller fragments and packaged in separate chromosomes of various sizes (lengths). The fragmentation of the DNA does not relieve the cell of the necessity to compress the DNA, since even small chromosomes contain relatively large amounts of DNA. The smallest human metaphase chromosome is only about 2 μm in length and yet contains enough DNA to form a 1.4-cm linear duplex. What is the identity of the macromolecules that compact DNA into metaphase chromosomes? Is the DNA condensed into a highly ordered arrangement? Are there qualitative variations in the proteins associated with different chromosomes from the same cell or with the same chromosomes taken from different cell types?

During interphase of the cell cycle, individual chromosomes are not resolvable (see Figure 1). The chromosomes exist in a relatively extended configuration consisting of interspersed regions of diffuse (euchromatin) and condensed (heterochromatin) chromatin. Prophase is accompanied by a progressive condensation of each chromosome into a distinct slender filament. At metaphase,

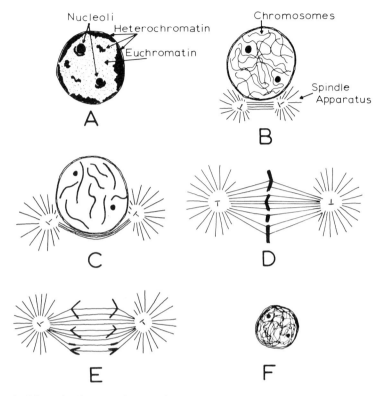

Figure 1. Schematic diagram of gross chromosomal morphology during the cell cycle. (A) interphase; (B) early–mid prophase; (C) late prophase; (D) metaphase; (E) anaphase; (F) late telophase.

the chromosomal filaments attain their highest degree of compaction and become readily resolvable as individual units. The compact chromosomes decondense during the final phase of cell division (telophase) to reestablish the configuration typically seen in interphase nuclei.

The various states of chromosome compaction represent structural adaptations required for specific functions (see Chapter 12.1). Euchromatin (diffuse chromatin) exists in an extended state to facilitate transcription of its DNA. Heterochromatic regions are not generally transcribed; thus they remain condensed throughout most of the cell cycle (with the exception of a relatively brief and localized decondensation during replication of heterochromatic DNA). Each chromosome is compacted into a small independent unit during mitosis to facilitate an orderly segregation of the relatively long lengths of DNA to each of the daughter cells. What are the molecular mechanisms that regulate chromosome compaction? How is the timing of the chromosome dispersal–condensation cycle controlled?

Despite a long history of research, a detailed understanding of mitotic chromosome structure is still lacking. However, light and electron microscopic, biochemical, and biophysical techniques are currently being employed in an intense multidisciplinary effort to resolve the questions stated above. It would not be surprising if several of the questions mentioned above were at least partially resolved prior to the release of this publication.

MORPHOLOGY OF MITOTIC CHROMOSOMES

Chromosome morphology may be examined in tissue sections, but detailed studies with the light microscope are generally performed on spread or squash preparations of cultured cells. The use of cultured cells with a high mitotic index maximizes the number of complete metaphase complements that can be observed in a reasonable time period. Colcemid or colchicine may be added to cultures to arrest cells at metaphase (see Section 10) and thereby increase the number of metaphase complements available for study. Generally, spreads are prepared with a cell concentration that maximizes the number of cells per slide without yielding a significant overlap between metaphase complements from separate cells.

Chromosome spreads are made by collecting the cultured cells by centrifugation, swelling them in a hypotonic solution (0.075 M NaCl or KCl; 0.8–1.2% sodium citrate), fixing the cells in 40–60% acetic acid or 25% acetic acid, 75% methanol (or ethanol), and then spreading them on clean glass slides that are subsequently dried. Squash preparations are made by squashing fixed cells or tissue (suspended in fixative or fixative and stain) between a coverslip and slide. Further treatments of squashed cells can be carried out after freezing the slide on dry ice and lifting the coverslip off the specimen. Use of subbed (coated with 0.1% gelatin, 0.01% chrome alum) or albuminized slides and siliconized coverslips reduces the chance that the specimen will be removed with the coverslip. Staining of spreads or squashes with Giemsa or orcein is a relatively quick and simple way to stain chromosomes for general morphological observations. Several detailed discussions of methods for preparing chromosomes for light microscopy are available (2–4).

Mitotic metaphase chromosomes consist of two, genetically identical *chromatids* (Figure 2). Resolution of each chromatid is frequently difficult because they are usually coiled and closely associated with each other. However, colchicine, hypotonic treatments, and, to varying degrees, staining procedures usually cause the chromatids to straighten and separate. The chromatids are held together at a primary constriction, a region of low DNA content per unit length of chromosome, which is usually lightly stained or achromatic.

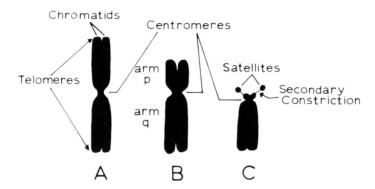

Figure 2. Schematic diagram of gross morphological features of mitotic chromosomes. (A) Metacentric chromosome; (B) submetacentric chromosome; (C) acrocentric chromosome.

This region, termed the *centromere,* is bordered by constitutive heterochromatin. This class of heterochromatin remains condensed and transcriptionally inactive throughout the life cycle of an organism. The connections between sister chromatids are maintained at the centromere until anaphase. At this time, the centromeric connections in all of the chromosomes of a dividing cell are lost.

The centromere also contains two dense elements resolvable with the electron microscope. These structures, termed *kinetochores,* function as sites for attachment of spindle microtubules to each chromatid. In fact, they are capable of initiating and directing the assembly of microtubules from unpolymerized tubulin in vitro (5, 6). Since the sister kinetochores are attached by microtubules to opposite poles of the spindle, sister chromatids migrate in opposite directions during anaphase when the interchromatid connections are broken.

Chromosomes containing multiple (7, 8) and diffuse (9, 10) centromeres have been described. Spindle microtubules attach at a few or many sites on such chromosomes. However, chromosomes with single centromeres are by far the most common in higher eukaryotes. The position of the centromere can vary between different chromosomes, but it normally occurs at a constant site on any specific chromosome. Chromosomes are grouped into four categories depending upon the location of the centromere. *Metacentric* chromosomes have centrally located centromeres that separate the chromatids into arms of approximately equal length. *Submetacentric* chromosomes possess arms of unequal length owing to the location of the centromere between the ends *(telomeres)* of the chromosome and the center. Short arms are designated p and long arms q. The centromeres of *acrocentrics* are positioned very near the ends of these chromosomes, and the arms differ greatly in length. If the centromere occurs at the very end of a chromosome, it is termed *telocentric.* The normal occurrence of telocentrics as a consistent feature of a karyotype is seriously questioned.

During the migration of chromosomes to the spindle poles, the centromeric regions usually precede the remainder of the chromosomes. Because of the freedom of chromatid bending at the centromere, anaphase chromosomes may appear V-shaped (metacentric), L-shaped (submetacentric), or rod-shaped (acro- or telocentric).

The *telomeres* of chromosomes should not be simply regarded as the ends of chromosome. These regions possess unique properties indispensable to chromosome structure and function and should be considered as specialized structural regions of chromosomes. On the one hand, telomeres prevent fusion between chromosomes (11). Chromosomes that have lost their telomeres are free to fuse with one another, but chromosomes with intact telomeres do not generally fuse with broken or intact chromosomes. On the other hand, telomeres promote transient end-to-end associations between chromosomes during interphase (see 12). Telomeres also appear to form associations with the inner nuclear membrane and may play a role in maintaining order within the interphase nucleus (13).

Some chromosomes also possess *secondary constrictions* and *satellites.* Like centromeres, secondary constrictions are regions of relatively low DNA content per unit length of chromosome which stain only lightly or not at all. These regions are unlike centromeres in that they do not permit free bending of the chromatid, nor do they function in spindle fiber attachment. Frequently, secondary constrictions such as those on human chromosomes are involved in nucleolus formation and are termed *nucleolus organizer regions.* These constrictions are the sites of genes for 18S and 28S ribosomal RNAs (14–16). The functions of other secondary constrictions are unknown, but one should be aware that they can be artifactually produced on chromosomes by a variety of treatments (17, 18). Satellites are rounded chromatin bodies attached to the rest of the chromosome by slender achromatic filaments, such as secondary constrictions.

CHROMOSOME BANDING

Following routine staining with Giemsa or orcein, the arms of meiotic prophase or polytene chromosomes exhibit regions of darkly stained chromatin alternating with regions of lightly stained chromatin (see Chapter 12.3). The bands or beads of deeply stained chromatin, referred to as *chromomeres,* are arranged in a readily resolvable pattern that is specific for individual chromosomes. The specificity of the chromomere patterns is of particular significance because it facilitates combined genetic, biochemical, and morphological analyses of particular chromosomal regions.

Unlike meiotic prophase and polytene chromosomes, mitotic metaphase chromosomes are highly compacted, and underlying structure in the chromosome arms is difficult to resolve following routine staining techniques (see Figure 3). However, special staining techniques that produce specific banding

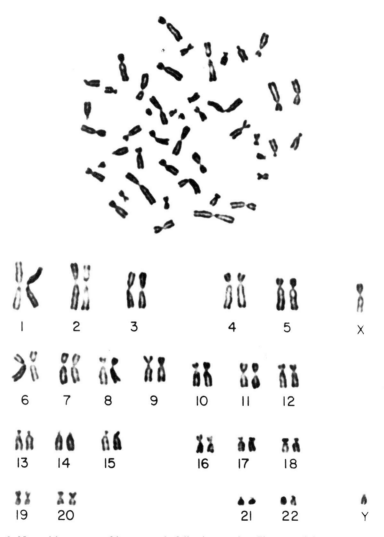

Figure 3. Normal karyotype of human male following routine Giemsa staining.

patterns on mitotic chromosomes have been developed during the past ten years (see Figure 4). These techniques provide the means for conducting the types of detailed cytogenetic analyses of mitotic chromosomes that could previously only be conducted with meiotic prophase or polytene chromosomes. Because of their importance, a brief discussion of the major banding

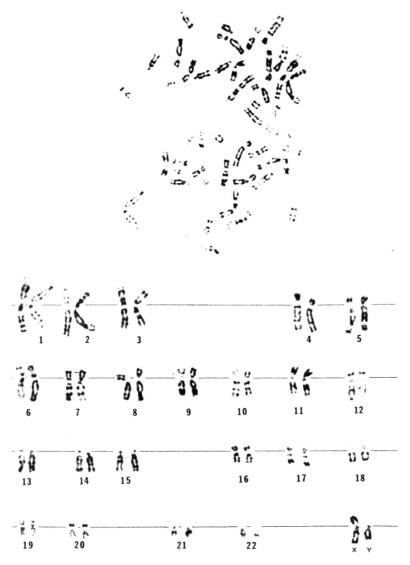

Figure 4. Normal G-banded karyotype of human male following Giemsa staining of chromosomes treated with protease.

techniques is presented below. Details of chromosome banding methods have been published in several recent reviews (19, 20).

In 1968, Caspersson et al. (21) reported that chromosomes stained with quinacrine mustard and viewed with a fluorescent microscope displayed a series of transverse fluorescent bands. It was later shown that the quinacrine band (Q-band) pattern was specific for each human chromosome (22, 23). At about the same time, Pardue and Gall (24) reported that chromosomes that had been partially denatured for in situ hybridization and subsequently stained with Giemsa were preferentially stained in regions containing constitutive heterochromatin (C-bands). The reports from Caspersson's and Gall's laboratories were quickly followed by a number of publications from different investigators describing procedural modifications for obtaining Q- or C-bands, as well as new methods for other banding patterns (G-, R-, and T-bands).

Q-Bands

Q-banding is obtained by passing chromosome spreads through a series of alcohol baths of decreasing concentrations to disodium phosphate–citrate buffer (pH 7.0) and then staining with 0.005% quinacrine mustard (25). Alternatively, slides may be directly stained in 0.5% aqueous quinacrine dihydrochloride (26, 27). The two methods yield similar results.

The Q-band pattern is observed with a fluorescent microscope. Fluorescence of the Q-positive bands varies in intensity from faintly fluorescent to brightly fluorescent. Negative bands do not fluoresce and therefore appear dark. The necessity of a fluorescent microscope and the relatively low contrast and clarity of Q-bands (relative to G-bands) are disadvantages in the routine application of Q-banding. However, the reproducibility of the method when applied to chromosomes from various sources is a distinct advantage. Moreover, quinacrine staining is a valuable tool for the study of the mammalian Y chromosome (20) and inactivated X chromosome (28), both of which fluoresce brilliantly.

G-Bands

Several different G-banding methods have been described. The procedures most often used fall into two categories: (1) the acid-saline-Giemsa (ASG, 29) or alkaline-saline-Giemsa (30) techniques, in which spread chromosomes are heat-denatured in concentrated saline prior to Giemsa staining, and (2) Giemsa or Leischman staining after partial proteolytic digestion of spread chromosomes (31, 32).

G-positive bands appear as densely stained regions on the chromosome, readily resolvable by ordinary light microscopy or phase contrast microscopy (see Figure 4). G-negative bands appear lightly stained or unstained. The majority of the G-bands appear in the same positions as Q-bands, the exceptions occurring at certain juxtacentromeric regions. Since G-band analysis does not require specialized equipment, it is an attractive procedure for routine chromosomal studies. However, the results of the G-banding methods are variable relative to the G-banding techniques. Published procedures must be optimized in each laboratory and often for different batches of slides.

R- and T-Bands

Reverse (R) banding can be obtained after spread chromosomes are heat-denatured (85°C for 10–60 min) in isotonic saline and subsequently stained in Giemsa (33) or acridine orange (34). More recently, fluorescent R-bands have been produced following the binding of chromomycin antibiotics to human chromosomes (35, 36).

As implied by their name, R-bands appear in regions corresponding to Q- or G-negative bands, including telomeres. Staining of telomeres is particularly advantageous for the study of structural rearrangements which frequently occur in these regions (37). R-bands stained with Giemsa are resolvable by routine light microscopy. Visualization of R-bands stained with acridine orange (or chromomycin antibiotics) requires a fluorescent microscope; R-bands fluoresce a brilliant green, while R-negative (Q- and G-positive) bands faintly fluoresce red.

Modifications of the pH and temperature of slide incubation in the R-banding procedure can be used to obtain T- (telomere) bands after Giemsa or acridine orange staining (38). The T-bands are actually a subset (those most resistant to denaturation) of the R-bands. Interestingly, T-bands stained with acridine orange vary in fluorescence intensity from one chromosome pair to another. This makes T-band analysis extremely useful for the detection of translocations.

C-Bands

Several methods have been used to produce C-band patterns (39–41). All of the methods require a prestaining treatment of slides which results in extensive denaturation of the chromosomes. This denaturation is often effected by incubation of slides in alkaline solutions (preferably 0.5% barium hydroxide, 41) or heated buffer solutions. Chromosomes are subsequently stained with Giemsa.

The C-banding procedure results in a selective staining of regions (rather than bands) comprised of constitutive heterochromatin, such as centromeric chromatin and the long arm of the mammalian Y chromosome. The rest of the chromatid appears faintly stained and often swollen or partially dispersed. The C-bands are usually poorly stained by other methods. Specific heterochromatic regions may be selectively stained after alkaline (pH 11) Giemsa staining (42).

The most obvious advantage of the banding techniques is that they provide a means to identify unequivocally each mitotic chromosome. Precise karyotypes can now be constructed by combining band analysis with the more classical criteria for chromosome identification, such as relative chromosome length, centromeric position, ratios of arm lengths, and occurrence of secondary constrictions and satellites. As many as 320 to 554 (depending upon the degree of chromosome condensation) light and dark bands can be localized on G-banded human metaphase chromosomes (43). Even greater resolution (2000–3000 bands) can be obtained following G-band analysis of human chromosomes from early–mid mitotic prophase (43). The banding techniques are also extensively used in combination with somatic cell hybridization and in situ hybridization to conduct detailed cytogenetic analyses. Of particular clinical importance is the fact that the banding techniques have provided the resolving power necessary for correlating structural rearrangements (e.g., translocations, insertions, deletions, duplications, etc.) with phenotypic abnormalities.

Chromosome banding has also provided important insights into the structure of mitotic chromosomes. It is now fairly clear that there is a quantitative variation in chromosome condensation along the arms of metaphase chromosomes, with the greatest concentrations of chromatin appearing in regions that are Q- or G-band-positive (44–46). It is also clear that each Q- or G-band is actually comprised of numerous smaller bands more readily visualized on meiotic prophase chromosomes (43). A particularly important observation was that the bands on mitotic chromosomes closely correspond to the chromomeres of pachytene chromosomes (47, 48). Therefore, the Q- or G-bands of mitotic chromosomes are formed by the coalescence of chromomeres, and it seems likely that the organization of meiotic and mitotic chromosomes is very similar.

Although the quantitative variation in the distribution of chromatin along the chromosome arm is likely to be a factor in banding (44–46, 48), it does not seem to be a sufficient reason for the degree of contrast that occurs between positive and negative bands. Moreover, quantitative differences alone cannot explain the mechanisms by which the various prestaining treatments elicit selective staining. As discussed in the next section, qualitative differences in the composition and interactions of chromosomal macromolecules may also play a significant role in chromosome banding.

MACROMOLECULAR CONSTITUENTS OF MITOTIC CHROMOSOMES

DNA

One of the long-standing problems in eukaryotic genetics is the *C-value paradox*. Eukaryotic genomes seem to consist of much more DNA than required to code for the number of structural genes estimated by genetic and biochemical analysis. Estimates of the percent of eukaryotic genomes coding for messenger RNAs range from 2 to 5% (see 49, 50). What is the function of the rest of the DNA? An additional, related problem that must be explained is the variability in the haploid DNA content between eukaryotes, even between some closely related species.

It is often assumed that most of the DNA that does not code for mRNAs is somehow involved in gene regulation and/or chromosome structure. This may be at least partially correct. However, such arguments fail to account for variations in DNA content between eukaryotes. Closely related species probably do not require extensive quantitative differences in the DNA sequences that control gene expression or chromosome structure. Moreover, there is no obvious reason why those amphibians with larger genomes than humans should require much more regulatory DNA. As yet, a role cannot be ascribed to the apparent excess DNA in eukaryotic genomes. Insights into this problem should become available as more is learned of the sequence organization of DNA and the arrangement of DNA in chromosomes.

As discussed in Section 6 and Chapter 12.1 (also see 49, 50), eukaryotic DNA is comprised of several distinct sequence classes, distinguishable by the techniques of nucleic acid hybridization. Briefly summarized, there are four sequence classes which differ in their degree of repetition and complexity. The unique, highly complex sequence class consists of many different sequences, each of which is present only once per haploid genome. This DNA class represents between 40 and 80% of eukaryotic genomes, with most genomes consisting of approximately 70% unique DNA. The middle repetitive-frequency class consists of sequences repeated up to approximately 60,000 times, as in the cow (51). Many organisms possess two groups of middle repetitive sequences with repetition frequencies ranging between 30–200 and 1000–4000 times (52). The middle repetitive class of DNA consists of several families of closely related sequences with a total complexity considerably less than that of unique sequences. Interestingly, a significant fraction of the unique sequences (and the majority of unique sequences that are transcribed) are located adjacent to middle repetitive sequences with an average length of 300 base pairs (see 49, 50). The third major sequence class is comprised of highly repetitive, relatively simple DNA sequences. These sequences may be repeated a million or more times per genome as in the cow, mouse, or crab (see 53). Generally, the highly repetitive sequences only represent a small (1–10%) percentage of the total genome. Frequently, they have a base composition distinct from the average base composition of the toal genome and will band as satellites during isopycnic centrifugation in cesium salts. The fourth sequence class consists of inverted repeats of DNA (palindromes). These sequences also represent a small fraction of the genome.

DNA may also be subdivided according to functional characteristics. Certain sequences, including many of the unique, as well as some of the middle repetitive sequences and inverted repeated sequences, are transcribed at some point during an organism's life cycle; other sequences, such as the highly repeated DNAs, are never transcribed. DNA sequences also differ in the timing of their replication during S phase (see Section 11). Generally, DNA in euchromatin is replicated early in S phase, while the sequences in heterochromatin are replicated later in the S phase.

In order to understand the arrangement of various types of DNA in mitotic chromosomes, it is important to determine the number of DNA molecules present in each chromatid. It is now generally accepted that each chromatid is composed of a single DNA duplex complexed with proteins. Several observations led to the acceptance of this principle of *uninemy* and the general rejection of arguments for the existence of multiple DNA strands per chromatid *(polynemy)*. First, DNA replication and segregation to sister chromatids was found to occur in a semiconservative, rather than dispersive, manner (54). Second, the longitudinal axis of a lampbrush chromosome (which probably has a similar genetic organization to mitotic chromosomes) was shown to consist of two continuous strands (one per chromatid). The linear integrity of these strands was disrupted by DNase but not protease or RNase treatments (55). Third, it was demonstrated that gentle lysis of *Drosophila* cells yielded DNA molecules sufficiently long to account for the total DNA content of their longest chromosome (56).

Attempts to localize the different classes of DNA sequences on mitotic chromosomes have relied heavily on the technique of in situ nucleic acid hybridization. Detailed reviews of the methodology and applications of this powerful technique have been published (57–59). Simply stated, in situ hybridization employs autoradiography to detect chromosomal sites that contain DNA sequences hybridized to radioactive DNA or RNA probes that were incubated with the chromosomes prior to autoradiography. In most cases, chromosome spreads or squash preparations (see above, under "Morphology of Mitotic Chromosomes") are first treated with RNase to remove RNAs which may compete with the probe. The chromosome preparations may also be extracted in acid (HCl) to remove basic proteins which may interfere with hybridization. The chromosomal DNA is then denatured by heating the slides in saline and/or formamide solutions or by incubation in solutions that are strongly acidic or basic. Slides are then incubated with the radioactive RNA or DNA probes under the appropriate conditions of salt concentration, temperature, and time required to achieve hybridization without loss of cytological detail. After removal of the unhybridized probe, the slides are autoradiographed and stained.

Currently, the principal limitation of the technique is that only repetitive DNA sequences can be localized on mitotic chromosomes with any certainty. The sensitivity of in situ hybridization depends upon the concentration of sequences complementary to the probe and the specific activity of the probe. Detection of unique sequences, which are represented at the lowest concentration, will require probes of extremely high specific activity, as well as technological advances in autoradiography to increase the efficiency of probe detection.

Using in situ hybridization, a great deal has been learned about the locations of highly repetitive satellite DNAs. Generally, DNA sequences belonging to this class are preferentially localized in regions consisting of constitutive heterochromatin or C-bands (24). These heterochromatic regions occur at centromeres, near nucleolar organizers, at some telomeres, and occasionally within the arms of chromosomes, such as the human Y chromosome. In some organisms, such as mouse, the satellite DNAs appear to be equally represented on nearly all chromosomes (24). Other organisms, such as man, contain a number of different satellite DNAs, which are preferentially located at certain sites on specific chromosomes (60). The satellite DNAs are never transcribed, but their discrete locations suggest that they serve structural roles, such as suppression of crossing-over and maintenance of linkage conservation and control of chromosome associations during interphase.

Support for the structural roles of constitutive heterochromatin comes from observations on the locations of ribosomal RNA genes at interphase and metaphase. The 18S and 28S rRNA genes are always located adjacent to blocks of constitutive heterochromatin, in the nucleolar organizing regions of chromosomes (14–16). These regions are usually on medium-sized chromosomes near the end of the short arms or on acrocentrics, close to the centromeres (61). At interphase, the nucleolar organizers of different chromosomes are closely associated, and adjacent heterochromatic regions appear fused into a perinucleolar mass. Genes for 5S rRNA are also frequently located close to telomeric or centromeric heterochromatin, but not at nucleolus organizers (see 59). Nevertheless, the 5S genes become closely associated with nucleoli and perinucleolar heterochromatin at interphase (62).

Much less is known of the relationships between other DNA sequence classes and mitotic chromosome structure. A class of middle repetitive DNA (C_{ot} 10^{-2} to 1) from the Algerian hedgehog has been localized to intercalary heterochromatin and Q-positive bands of mitotic chromosomes (62, 63). Human middle repetitive DNA also appears enriched at Q-positive bands (64).

Yunis and his colleagues have presented evidence for a preferential localization of inverted repeated DNAs (65) and DNAs complementary to poly A$^+$ messenger RNA (66) on G-negative (or R) bands.

Regions of chromosomes containing AT- or GC-rich DNA have been detected by indirect immunofluorescence (see 67, 68). In this technique, antibodies to specific nucleosides or oligonucleotides are elicited in rabbits, collected, and bound to cytological preparations of chromosomes, which were first denatured. The slides are then exposed to fluorescein-labeled sheep or goat anti-rabbit IgG antibodies which will bind to the rabbit antinucleosides. The sites of antinucleoside binding are located by fluorescence microscopy. In brief, the studies conducted by Miller and his associates have demonstrated that Q/G-positive bands are enriched for AT-rich DNA, while Q/G-negative (R) bands are enriched for GC-rich DNA. These results agree well with those of van de Sande et al. (69), which demonstrated the preferential binding of olivomycin (an antibiotic that preferentially binds GC-rich DNA) to R-bands.

The DNA sequences in different chromosomal regions have also been distinguished by their replication timing during S phase. BUdR (5-bromodeoxyuridine) is a thymidine analogue that is readily incorporated into DNA during replication. Regions of mitotic chromosomes that incorporated BUdR during S phase can be detected cytologically because they appear relatively elongate and weakly stained with either the fluorochrome Hoechst "33258" (70) or Giemsa (71). Localization of early- or late-replicating DNA can be accomplished by exposing cells to BUdR during different periods of S-phase. Generally, early-replicating DNA tends to be concentrated in Q/G-negative bands (72), while mid–late-replicating DNA is concentrated in Q/G-positive bands (73). The latest-replicating DNA is usually associated with the constitutive heterochromatin of C-bands. It thus seems that a correspondence exists between the transcribable, early-replicating DNA of euchromatin and Q/G-negative or R-bands, while Q/G-positive and C-bands are enriched for the nontranscribed, late-replicating DNA of heterochromatin.

The differential distribution of different types of DNA along chromosome arms probably plays a significant role in determining certain banding patterns. Quinacrine banding is likely to be a result of the preferential location of AT-rich DNA in Q-positive bands. In vitro, quinacrine fluorescence is enhanced by AT-rich DNA and quenched by GC-rich DNA (74). The pattern of acridine orange staining obtained by R-band techniques suggests that R-bands contain double-stranded DNA, while R-negative (Q/G-positive) bands contain single-stranded DNA. This result is expected from the greater resistance of GC-rich DNA to the heat denaturation step employed during R-banding.

All of the banding techniques cannot be completely understood in terms of DNA alone. Certain heterochromatic regions on human chromosomes

1, 19, and 16 contain an AT-rich satellite DNA, but exhibit little or no fluorescence when stained with quinacrine. G-bands can be produced by a variety of techniques that do not depend upon denaturation of DNA (e.g., protease treatments). C-banding requires extensive degradation of DNA in other chromosomal regions (75, 76), and yet many C-bands contain AT-rich DNA that should be subject to more rapid denaturation. It appears that chromosomal proteins also play a significant role in determining banding patterns (75, 77).

RNA

Little is known of potential RNA constituents in metaphase chromosomes. In fact, there is some doubt that RNA is a natural structural component of chromosomes. The difficulty arises as a result of uncertainty regarding the origin of RNA constituents on isolated metaphase chromosomes. Metaphase chromosomes are exposed to cytoplasmic constituents during their isolation. Therefore, cytoplasmic RNA could adsorb to the chromosomes during cell disruption. Chemical analyses from early studies of isolated chromosomes indicated that there were significant quantities of RNA associated with isolated metaphase chromosomes (78–81). However, several studies have demonstrated that most, if not all, of the RNA of isolated metaphase chromosomes is 28S and 18S ribosomal RNA (80, 81). The natural occurrence of RNA on metaphase chromosomes was placed in further doubt by the demonstration that RNA-free chromosomes could be isolated in a nearly neutral, PIPES buffered medium of hexylene–glycol (82).

Interestingly, a specific class of RNA molecules (SnRNA) have been localized by electron microscopic autoradiography to mitotic prophase chromosomes of *Amoeba proteus* (see 83, 84). These (shuttling) RNAs dissociate from metaphase chromosomes and then reassociate with anaphase chromosomes. It is entirely possible that a quantitatively minor species of RNA plays some role in the organization of mitotic chromosomes. If these RNAs undergo an association–dissociation cycle, their occurrence on isolated chromosomes would be highly dependent upon the phase of the cell cycle from which the chromosomes were isolated. Detailed analyses of minor RNA species extracted from highly purified chromosomes isolated from specific phases of the mitotic cycle should provide insight into the role of RNA in mitotic chromosomal structure.

Proteins

The DNA of interphase and mitotic chromosomes is associated with two classes of proteins, the histones and the nonhistone chromosomal proteins

(NHP or NHCP). Published values for the mass ratio of protein to DNA in isolated metaphase chromosomes range from 1.8 to 5.8 (see 85). In most cells, the ratio of histone to DNA approximates 1.0. This indicates that the variation in the total protein to DNA ratios is primarily due to differences in the nonhistone protein content of chromosomes isolated by different techniques. Such large variation probably reflects different degrees of contamination of isolated chromosomes by cytoplasmic constituents, as discussed earlier.

The histones are by far the most thoroughly characterized chromosomal proteins (see Sections 6 and 11). Histones are relatively small (11,300–22,000 daltons) basic proteins that have a major role in packaging DNA into chromosomes. There are five classes of histones associated with the DNA of most somatic cells: the lysine-rich histones H1, the slightly lysine-rich histones H2A and H2B, and the arginine-rich histones H3 and H4. In addition, there is a sixth histone class, H5, which is restricted to erythroid cells in organisms possessing nucleated erythrocytes. Each histone class, with the exception of H4, is comprised of several proteins that differ in primary structure. Some organisms may have as many as eight different H1 histones (see 86). Five different H2A histones and four different H2B histones have been identified in sea urchin embryos (87, 88). Cells from adult mammalian tissues contain two H2A histones, three different H3 histones, and two distinct H2B histones. [Thus far three H2B variants have been identified in mammals, but one of them is unique to mouse (89).]

Histones are usually synthesized in synchrony with DNA synthesis, during S-phase of the cell cycle (90, 91). Exceptions to this occur in developing gametes (92, 93) and early embryos (94). Following synthesis, the histones exhibit little, if any, turnover (95). The timing of histone synthesis and the high stability of histones indicate that the histone composition of mitotic chromosomes from any particular cell type is dependent upon the types and quantities of each histone synthesized during each S-phase in that cell type's lineage.

Electrophoretic comparisons of histones from interphase and mitotic chromosomes of tissue culture cells have demonstrated that the five histone classes are each present in similar amounts on both types of chromosomes (95–97). Each of the histone variants present on interphase chromosomes of tissue culture cells is also synthesized during S-phase (98), and thus the variants of mitotic chromosomes and interphase chromosomes of tissue culture cells are probably similar.

The results of studies using tissue culture cells may be typical of cells that are not differentiating. Comparisons of histone variants found in different mammalian tissues and organs indicate that significant quantitative differences occur (99), suggesting that the cell types in different tissues have had different amounts of each variant synthesized during their differentiation. In fact, dramatic changes in the types of histone variants synthesized do occur during embryogenesis (87, 88). It seems that histone composition may change considerably from interphase to mitosis in differentiating cells, and that the histone composition of mitotic chromosomes from different cell types may also differ.

Histones appear to be generally distributed on mitotic chromosomes, as one might expect from the fundamental role that these proteins play in chromosome structure (see Sections 6 and 11, refs. 86 and 105). Quantitatively, histone distribution probably parallels that of DNA in mitotic chromosomes, although this has not been directly demonstrated. While the five histone classes probably are evenly distributed, variants within each class may not be evenly distributed. Evidence has been presented to indicate that newly synthesized histones preferentially segregate with one of the two sister DNA duplexes resulting from replication of any particular segment of DNA (100, 101). The parental histones segregate with the other DNA duplex. If newly synthesized histones differed from parental histones (as occurs during embryogenesis), then copies of the same DNA sequences present in different chromatids could be complexed with different histones. A recent study has presented evidence suggesting that H1 histones synthesized during the blastoderm stage of embryogenesis in *Drosophila* preferentially associated with one of the two sister chromatids (88).

Additional structural heterogeneity occurs within each histone class as a result of enzymatic modifications such as phosphorylation, acetylation, methylation, and poly(ADP)-ribosylation (see 86, 102, 103). Histone H2A can also be modified by the covalent bonding of the protein ubiquitin to lysine residue 119 (104). Each of these modifications may alter histone–DNA and/or histone–histone interactions to bring about an alteration in chromatin structure. Comparisons of histone modification during interphase and mitosis have revealed that histones H1 and H3 become highly phosphorylated on mitotic chromosomes (see 86, 105, 106). Following mitosis, most of the phosphate groups are removed, and histones H1 and H3 assume an interphase level of phosphorylation. The other histones exhibit few modification differences during the cell cycle. These observations have led several investigators to propose that phosphorylation of histones H1 and H3 is involved in regulating chromosome condensation during mitosis (see 105, 106).

As yet, the nonhistone proteins of mitotic chromosomes have not been well characterized. The nonhistone proteins are extremely heterogeneous. Estimates of the number of different nonhistones associated with interphase chromosomes have been as high as 450 (108). This high degree of complexity, coupled with a certain degree of uncertainty regarding the purity of isolated metaphase chromosomes, has impeded progress. An additional problem has been that many of the methods used to solubilize nonhistones are denaturing and often preclude analyses of higher-order structure and enzymatic activities.

The nonhistones of interphase chromosomes include many chromatin-bound enzymes (e.g., RNA polymerase, DNA polymerase, acetylase, deacetylase, phosporylase, etc.), and structural proteins and proteins that may be involved in gene regulation (see 86). The nonhistones of mitotic chromosomes also include a number of different enzymes, including RNA polymerase (109). A specific set of nonhistones (scaffold proteins) has been shown to have a major role in maintaining the structure of metaphase chromosomes from HeLa cells (110–112; see below, next section).

Various enzymes and the proteins generally important to chromosome structure are probably present on all of the mitotic chromosomes. However, a recent study of nonhistones associated with different size classes of metaphase chromosomes suggests that certain nonhistones may be selectively bound to specific chromosomes (113). A specific structural protein (termed N) has been localized to nucleolar organizers (114, 115).

Several investigators have suggested that proteins of mitotic chromosomes are important in chromosome banding, along with the distribution of chromomeres and the differences in DNA base composition along the chromatid (75, 77). Unfortunately, little is known of the manner by which proteins affect chromosome banding. Banding may be related to a differential distribution of certain proteins. Nonhistones would be the most likely participants in such a mechanism, since histones are uniformly distributed. Banding may also be related to differences in protein–DNA and/or protein–protein interactions in various regions of chromosomes. Both histones and nonhistones could be important in such a mechanism. Resolution of the influence of chromosomal proteins on banding and identification of the proteins involved should enhance our understanding of the organization of mitotic chromosomes.

CHROMATIN FIBER FOLDING IN MITOTIC CHROMOSOMES

Numerous ultrastructural studies have demonstrated that interphase and metaphase chromosomes are principally comprised of irregular, knobby "thick" fibers with diameters varying from 200 to 300 Å, depending upon the source and method of preparation for electron microscopy (see 13, 116, 117). The "thick" chromatin fibers can be converted to "thin" ($\sim$100 Å diameter) fibers by exposure to chelators of divalent ions or solutions of low ionic strength. Over the past six years substantial progress has been made in achieving a thorough understanding of the structure of thin fibers and their organization into thick fibers.

Thin chromatin fibers consist of a linear array of closely packed, disk-shaped structures (110 Å dia. $\times$ 55 Å h.), termed nucleosomes (see 86, 107). These structures are considered to be the fundamental units of structure for nearly all eukaryotic chromosomes. Nucleosomes consist of a core region and a linker region that connects adjacent nucleosomes. The core is comprised of 140 base pairs of DNA wrapped around an octamer of histones consisting of two molecules each of histones H2A, H2B, H3, and H4. As yet, the exact path of the DNA around this histone complex is unknown. The linker region is more variable in structure than the core. It may contain as few as 14 base pairs of DNA, as in *Aspergillus* nucleosomes (118), or as many as 101 base pairs of DNA, as in sea urchin sperm (119). Linker DNA is associated with one molecule of histone H1.

Since the unit fiber of chromosomes appears to be the 200–300 Å diameter fiber, there is considerable interest in elucidating the manner in which the nucleosomal fiber, or thin fiber, is arranged into this unit fiber. Thus far, this level of structure has not been characterized. However, there are two strong proposals currently being considered. Finch and Klug (120) have suggested that nucleosomal fibers can coil into tubelike (solenoids) thick fibers in the presence of divalent cations. This model envisions the thick fiber as a continuous coil of the thin fiber. Other investigators have proposed that the thick fiber consists of large, repeating clusters (superbeads) of nucleosomes that are closely packed (121, 122). This organization would be discontinuous and provide a measure of flexibility to the thick fiber. It should be noted that these proposals are not mutually exclusive. The thick fiber may not have only one type of organization.

The packing ratio (length of DNA/length of fiber) of DNA in nucleosomes is approximately 7 (see 107). The formation of thick fibers will further increase the packing ratio to 25 (superbead model) to 40 (solenoid model). However, the packing ratio of DNA in metaphase chromosomes may be as high as 8000. Evidently, the thick fibers are arranged into higher orders of structure that permit an extreme compaction of DNA.

A number of early studies using light microscopic techniques have indicated a helical architecture for both meiotic (123) and mitotic chromosomes (124–126). Quantitative considerations, in addition to observed helical structures, prompted some investigators to propose that DNA undergoes several levels of coiling to attain the compaction typical of metaphase chromosomes (see 127). Such models are referred to as *helical-coil* models. Recently, Sedat and Manuelidis (128) have proposed a helical-coil model to explain observations obtained from a variety of microscopic techniques. In this model, DNA is first coiled into 100 Å diameter fibers consisting of a linear array of nucleosomes. The 100 Å fiber is then coiled to form a 300–500 Å diameter tube, which also coils to form a 2000 Å tube. The final level of coiling, suggested as the coiling level that differentiates interphase and metaphase chromosomes, results from the coiling of the 2000 Å tubes into 6000 Å tubes. Bak and his associates (129–131) have also observed tubelike structures as intermediates in the denaturation of isolated metaphase chromosomes. These investigators have proposed that 300 Å fibers are coiled into 4000 Å tubes that may also coil to form a tube with the dimensions of a chromatid from a metaphase chromosome.

Metaphase chromosomes usually appear as fibrous masses when examined by whole mount electron microscopy (see 13, 116). Most frequently, the fibers have dimensions corresponding to the "thick" fibers described earlier (200–300 Å diameter). Looplike projections of the fibers can be seen extending from the longitudinal axis of the chromatid. Moreover, a number of fibers are often observed to run parallel to one another in the longitudinal dimension. DuPraw (132, 133) proposed the *folded-fiber* model to account for these observations. In this model, the chromatin fiber is folded numerous times in both the transverse and longitudinal dimensions. Transverse folds were considered responsible for the looplike fiber projections, whereas longitudinal folds were invoked to explain the observed longitudinal fibers. Folding was considered to be a random process. A final twisting of the folded fiber structure was suggested as a means by which the coiling visualized by light microscopy could be achieved.

Recent studies suggest that the looplike projections visualized by electron microscopy are true loops that are constrained rather than transverse folds. Studies of the effects of ethidium bromide on the sedimentation rate of interphase chromosomes partially depleted of protein have demonstrated the occurrence of constrained loops of DNA in interphase nuclei (134–138). Estimates of the lengths of these loops range from 220 KB (kilobases) in HeLa cells (138) to 85 KB in *Drosophila* tissue culture cells (137). The loops appear to be constrained by nonhistones (134–137) and/or RNA (137).

Laemmli and his colleagues at Princeton recently demonstrated that the DNA of HeLa cell metaphase chromosomes is also constrained into loops (110–112). Chromosomes depleted of 90% of their proteins contain numerous loops of DNA 15–30 μm in length (45–90 KB) projecting from a more central scaffold consisting of about 30 nonhistone proteins. The origin and the insertion of each loop were adjacent in most cases. The scaffold maintains a considerable amount of the morphology of metaphase chromosomes and was therefore proposed to be a fundamental structural feature (core) of metaphase chromosomes. The existence of chromosome cores had been proposed previously by other investigators as well (139–141).

In summary, the chromatin fiber appears to be looped numerous times and constrained in that configuration by nonhistone proteins that may recognize specific DNA sequences located at the bases of the loops. Studies of polytene (142, 143), meiotic prophase (144, 145), and mitotic chromosomes (44–46) by electron microscopy have also demonstrated that the loops are most numerous in chromomeres. These observations led Bahr (see 117) to propose a modified folded-fiber model in which the principal mode of folding was the formation of fiber loops that project transversely from the chromatid axis. Looped fibers would form the ultrastructural basis of chromomeres. It was also suggested that longitudinal fibers are interchromomeric, nonlooped fibers that connect adjacent and perhaps distant chromomeres. The coiling seen by light microscopy, and sometimes electron microscopy, was considered an artifact resulting from chromomere alignment. The aspect of this model that is particularly noteworthy is that it emphasizes the occurrence of a specific folding or looping pattern to account for the regularity of chromosome structure as seen by banding and quantitative electron microscopy.

Laemmli et al. (146) have provided one possible model that may account for loops, coils, and scaffolds. In this model, the 200–300 Å chromatin fiber is coiled upon itself and then further coiled around a nonhistone protein scaffold or core. The base of each gyre in the coiled 200–300 Å fiber would be anchored to the scaffold and thus be constrained. If the gyres of this coiled fiber are close to one another (low pitch) and aligned, they may form a tube approximately 2000 Å–3000 Å in diameter. This would account for the 2000 Å tubes described by Sedat and Manuelidis (128). Successive twists of this tube as it wraps around the nonhistone scaffold would give the chromatid a coiled architecture similar to that described in early light microscopic studies (123–126). On the other hand, successive gyres in the coiled 200–300 Å fiber might appear as irregular chromatin loops if the alignment of the gyres were disturbed by preparative techniques such as fixation or spreading.

The regularity and specificity of chromosome structure may be explained by assuming that chromomeres are regions consisting of a 200–300 Å fiber that is more tightly constrained by scaffold proteins into higher-order coils than the fiber of interchromomeric regions. The chromomere patterns of different chromosomes could result from differences in the localization of DNA sequences which are strongly bound by the nonhistones in the scaffold. If the chromosome is stretched, as in preparation for whole mount electron microscopy, the interchromomeric coils might relax before the chromomeric coils, and appear as longitudinal fibers. Fixation or G-band techniques may also have the effect of denaturing the interchromomeric coils in such a way that they stain only faintly with Giemsa (G-negative), while chromomeres stain intensely.

REFERENCES

1. Flemming, W. 1965. *J. Cell Biol. (Suppl.)* 25:3. Translation of 1880 paper.
2. Hsu, T. C. 1972. In *Methods in Cell Biology*, Vol. 5, D. M. Prescott, ed., p. 1. Academic Press, New York.
3. Lubs, H. A., McKenzie, W. H., Patil, S. R., and Merrick, S. 1973. In *Methods in Cell Biology*, Vol. 6, D. M. Prescott, ed., p. 345. Academic Press, New York.

4. Schwarzacher, H. G. 1974. In *Methods in Human Cytogenetics,* H. G. Schwarzacher and U. Wolf, eds., p. 71. Springer-Verlag, Berlin.
5. Telzer, B. R., Moses, M. J., and Rosenbaum, J. L. 1975. *Proc. Natl. Acad. Sci. U.S.A.* 72:4023.
6. Gould, R. R., and Borisy, G. G. 1978. *Exp. Cell. Res.* 113:369.
7. Sears, E. R., and Camara, A. 1952. *Genetics* 37:125.
8. Angell, R., Gianelli, F., and Polani, P. E. 1970. *Ann. Hum. Genet.* 34:39.
9. Bayreuther, K. 1955. *Chromosoma (Berlin)* 7:508.
10. White, M. J. D. 1971. *Chromosoma (Berlin)* 34:183.
11. Roberts, P. A. 1975. *Genetics* 80:135.
12. DuPraw, E. J. 1970. *DNA and Chromosomes.* Holt, Reinhart and Winston, New York.
13. Comings, D. E. 1968. *Am. J. Hum. Genet.* 20:440.
14. Ritossa, F. M., and Spiegelman, S. 1965. *Proc. Natl. Acad. Sci. U.S.A.* 53:737.
15. Wallace, H., and Birnstiel, M. L. 1966. *Biochim. Biophys. Acta* 114:296.
16. Evans, H. J., Buckland, R. A., and Pardue, M. L. 1974. *Chromosoma (Berlin)* 48:405.
17. Brown, J. A., Palmer, C. G., and Yu, P. L. 1972. *Can. J. Genet. Cytol.* 14:81.
18. Rudak, E., and Callan, H. G. 1976. *Chromosoma (Berlin)* 56:349.
19. Dutrillaux, B., and Lejeune, J. 1975. In *Advances in Human Genetics,* Vol. 5, H. Harris and K. Hirschhorn, eds., p. 119. Plenum Press, New York.
20. Pearson, P. L., and van Egmond-Cowan, A. M. M. 1976. In *New Techniques in Biophysics and Cell Biology.* Vol. 3, R. H. Pain and B. J. Smith, eds., p. 213. John Wiley and Sons, London.
21. Caspersson, T., Farber, S., Foley, G. E., Kudynowski, J., Modest, E. J., Simonson, E., Wagh, V., and Zech, L. 1968. *Exp. Cell Res.* 49:219.
22. Caspersson, T., Zech, L., and Johansson, C. 1970. *Exp. Cell Res.* 62:490.
23. Caspersson, T., Zech, L., Johannson, C., and Modest, E. J. 1970. *Chromosoma (Berlin)* 30:215.
24. Pardue, M. L., and Gall, J. G. 1970. *Science* 168:1356.
25. Caspersson, T., Lomakka, G., and Zech, L. 1971. *Hereditas* 67:89.
26. Pearson, P. L., Bobrow, M., and Vosa, C. G. 1970. *Nature (London)* 226:78.
27. Lin, C. C., van de Sande, H., Smink, W. K., and Newton, D. R. 1975. *Can. J. Genet. Cytol.* 17:18.
28. Mukherjee, A. B., Moser, G. C., and Nitowsky, N. M. 1972. *Cytogenetics* 11:216.
29. Sumner, A. T., Evans, H. J., and Buckland, R. A. 1971. *Nature New Biol.* 232:31.
30. Schnedl, W. 1971. *Nature New Biol.* 233:93.
31. Seabright, M. L. 1971. *Lancet* 2:971.
32. Wang, H. C., and Fedoroff, S. 1972. *Nature New Biol.* 235:52.
33. Dutrillaux, B., and Lejeune, J. 1971. *C. R. Acad. Sci. (Paris)* 272:2638.
34. Bobrow, M., Collacott, H. E. A. C., and Madan, K. 1972. *Lancet* 2:1311.
35. Schweizer, D. 1976. *Chromosoma (Berlin)* 58:307.
36. Schnedl, W., Breitenbach, M., Mikelsaar, A.-V., Stranzinger, G. 1977. *Hum. Genet.* 36:299.
37. Lejeune, J., Dutrillaux, B., Rethoré, M. O., and Prieur, M. 1973. *Chromosoma (Berlin)* 43:423.
38. Dutrillaux, B. 1973. *Chromosoma (Berlin)* 41:395.
39. Arrighi, F. E., and Hsu, T. C. 1971. *Cytogenetics* 10:81.
40. Yunis, J. J., Roldan, L., Yasmineh, W. G., and Lee, J. C. 1971. *Nature (London)* 231:532.
41. Sumner, A. T. 1972. *Exp. Cell Res.* 75:304.
42. Bobrow, M., Madan, K., and Pearson, P. L. 1972. *Nature New Biol.* 238:122.
43. Yunis, J. J. 1976. *Science* 191:1268.
44. McKay, R. D. G. 1973. *Chromosoma (Berlin)* 44:1.

45. Bahr, G. F., Mikel, V., and Engler, W. F. 1973. In *Chromosome Identification*, T. Caspersson and L. Zech, eds., p. 280. Academic Press, New York.

46. Bahr, G. F., and Larsen, P. M. 1974. *Adv. Cell Mol. Biol.* 3:191.

47. Ferguson-Smith, M. A., and Page, B. M. 1973. *J. Med. Genet.* 10:282.

48. Okada, T. A., and Comings, D. E. 1974. *Chromosoma (Berlin)* 48:65.

49. Davidson, E. H. 1976. *Gene Activity in Early Development.* Academic Press, New York.

50. Davidson, E. H., Klein, W. H., and Britten, R. J. 1977. *Dev. Biol.* 55:69.

51. Britten, R. J., and Smith, J. 1970. *Carnegie Inst. Yearb.* 68:378.

52. Davidson, E. H., Galau, G. A., Angerer, R. C., and Britten, R. J. 1975. *Chromosoma (Berlin)* 51:253.

53. Southern, E. M. 1975. *J. Mol. Biol.* 94:51.

54. Taylor, J. H., Woods, P. S., and Hughes, W. L. 1957. *Proc. Natl. Acad. Sci. U.S.A.* 43:122.

55. Gall, J. G. 1963. *Nature (London)* 198:36.

56. Kavenoff, R., and Zimm, B. H. 1973. *Chromosoma (Berlin)* 41:1.

57. Gall, J. G., and Pardue, M. L. 1971. In *Methods in Enzymology*, Vol. 21, K. Moldave and L. Grossman, eds., p. 470. Academic Press, New York.

58. Eckhardt, R. A. 1976. In *Handbook of Genetics*, Vol. 5, R. C. King, ed., p. 31. Plenum Press, New York.

59. Steffenson, D. M. 1977. In *Molecular Structure of Human Chromosomes*, J. J. Yunis, ed., p. 59. Academic Press, New York.

60. Jones, K. W. 1977. In *Molecular Structure of Human Chromosomes*, J. J. Yunis, ed., p. 295. Academic Press, New York.

61. Lima de Faria, A. 1973. *Nature New Biol.* 241:136.

62. Willey, A. M., and Yunis, J. J. 1975. *Exp. Cell Res.* 91:223.

63. Yunis, J. J., Tsai, M. Y., and Willey, A. M. 1977. In *Molecular Structure of Human Chromosomes*, J. J. Yunis, ed., p. 1. Academic Press, New York.

64. Sanchez, O., and Yunis, J. J. 1974. *Chromosoma (Berlin)* 48:191.

65. Chandler, M. E., Chuang, C. R., Saunders, G. F., and Yunis, J. J. 1978. *J. Cell Biol.* 79:112a.

66. Yunis, J. J., Kuo, M. T., and Saunders, G. F. 1977. *Chromosoma (Berlin)* 61:335.

67. Miller, O. J., and Erlanger, B. F. 1975. In *Pathobiology Annual 1975*, H. L. Ioachim, ed., p. 71. Appleton-Century-Crofts, New York.

68. Miller, O. J., and Erlanger, B. F. 1977. In *Molecular Human Cytogenetics*, ICN-UCLA Symp. on Molec. Biol., Vol. 7, R. S. Sparkes, D. E. Comings, and C. F. Fox, eds., p. 87. Academic Press, New York.

69. van de Sande, J. H., Lin, C. C., and Jorgenson, K. F. 1977. *Science* 195:400.

70. Latt, S. A. 1973. *Proc. Natl. Acad. Sci. U.S.A.* 70:3395.

71. Perry, P., and Wolff, S. 1974. *Nature (London)* 251:156.

72. Kim, M. A., Johannsman, R., and Grzeschik, K. H. 1975. *Cytogenet. Cell Genet.* 15:367.

73. Grzeschik, K. H., Kim, A. A., and Johannsman, R. 1975. *Humangenetik* 29:41.

74. Weisblum, B., and de Haseth, P. L. 1972. *Proc. Natl. Acad. Sci. U.S.A.* 69:629.

75. Comings, D. E., Avelino, E., Okada, T. A., and Wyandt, H. E. 1973. *Exp. Cell Res.* 77:469.

76. Pathak, S., and Arrighi, F. E. 1973. *Cytogenet. Cell Genet.* 12:414.

77. Sumner, A. T., and Evans, H. J. 1973. *Exp. Cell Res.* 81:223.

78. Lin, H. J., and Chargaff, E. 1964. *Biochim. Biophys. Acta* 91:691.

79. Cantor, K. P., and Hearst, J. E. 1966. *Proc. Natl. Acad. Sci. U.S.A.* 55:642.

80. Hubermann, J. A., and Attardi, G. 1966. *J. Cell Biol.* 31:95.

81. Maio, J. J., and Schildkraut, C. L. 1967. *J. Mol. Biol.* 24:29.

82. Wray, W., and Stubblefield, E. 1970. *Exp. Cell Res.* 59:469.

83. Goldstein, L., and Ko, C. 1974. *Cell* 2:259.
84. Goldstein, L., Wise, G. E., and Ko, C. 1977. *J. Cell Biol.* 73:322.
85. Hanson, C. V. 1975. In *New Techniques in Biophysics and Cell Biology,* Vol. 2, R. H. Pain and B. J. Smith, eds., p. 43. John Wiley and Sons, London.
86. Elgin, S. C. R., and Weintraub, H. 1975. *Annu. Rev. Biochem.* 44:725.
87. Cohen, L. H., Newrock, K. M., and Zweidler, A. 1975. *Science* 190:994.
88. Newrock, K. M., Alfageme, C. R., Nardi, R. V., and Cohen, L. H. 1978. *Cold Spring Harbor Symp. Quant. Biol.* 42(1):421.
89. Franklin, S. G., and Zweidler, A. 1977. *Nature (London)* 266:273.
90. Robbins, E., and Borun, T. W. 1967. *Proc. Natl. Acad. Sci. U.S.A.* 57:409.
91. Borun, T. W., Scharff, M. D., and Robbins, E. 1967. *Proc. Natl. Acad. Sci. U.S.A.* 71:2900.
92. Adamson, E. D., and Woodland, H. R. 1974. *J. Mol. Biol.* 88:263.
93. Brock, W. A., Trostle, P. K., and Meistrich, M. L. 1978. *J. Cell Biol.* 79:180a.
94. Arceci, R. J., and Gross, P. R. 1977. *Proc. Natl. Acad. Sci. U.S.A.* 74:5016.
95. Hancock, R. 1969. *J. Mol. Biol.* 40:457.
96. Sadgopal, A., and Bonner, J. 1970. *Biochim. Biophys. Acta* 207:227.
97. Shih, T. Y., and Lake, R. S. 1972. *Biochemistry* 11:4811.
98. Borun, T. W., Gabrielli, F., Ajiro, K., Zweidler, A., and Baglioni, C. 1975. *Cell* 4:59.
99. Zweidler, A. 1976. In *Organization and Expression of Chromosomes,* Report of the Dhalem Workshop, V. G. Allfrey, E. K. F. Bautz, B. J. McCarthy, R. T. Schimke, and A. Tissières, eds., Life Sci. Res. Rep. No. 4, p. 187. Berlin.
100. Leffak, I. M., Grainger, R., and Weintraub, H. 1977. *Cell* 12:837.
101. Weintraub, H., Flint, S. J., Leffak, I. M., Groudine, M., and Grainger, R. M. 1978. *Cold Spring Harbor Symp. Quant. Biol.* 42:401.
102. Allfrey, V. G. 1971. In *Histones and Nucleohistones,* D. M. P. Phillips, ed., p. 241. Plenum Press, New York.
103. DeLange, R. J., and Smith, E. L. 1975. In *The Structure and Function of Chromatin,* Ciba Found. Symp., Vol. 28, p. 59. Associated Scientific Publ., Amsterdam.
104. Goldknopf, I. L., and Busch, H. 1977. *Proc. Natl. Acad. Sci. U.S.A.* 74:864.
105. Gurley, L. R., Walters, R. A., Hildebrand, C. E., Ratliff, R. L., Hohmann, P. G., and Tobey, R. A. 1977. In *Mechanisms and Control of Cell Division,* T. L. Rost and E. M. Gifford, eds., p. 3. Dowden, Hutchinson and Ross, Stroudsburg, Pennsylvania.
106. Gurley, L. R., D'Anna, J. A., Barham, S. S., Deaven, L. L., and Tobey, R. A. 1978. *Eur. J. Biochem.* 84:1.
107. Kornberg, R. D. 1977. *Annu. Rev. Biochem.* 46:931.
108. Peterson, J. L., and McConkey, E. J. 1976. *J. Biol. Chem.* 251:548.
109. Matsui, S., Weinfeld, H., and Sandberg, A. A. 1978. *J. Cell Biol.* 79:116a.
110. Adolf, K. W., Cheng, S. M., and Laemmli, U. K. 1977. *Cell* 12:805.
111. Adolf, K. W., Cheng, S. M., Paulson, J. R., and Laemmli, U. K. 1977. *Proc. Natl. Acad. Sci. U.S.A.* 74:4937.
112. Paulson, J. R., and Laemmli, U. K. 1977. *Cell* 12:817.
113. Wray, W., and Wray, V. P. 1978. *J. Cell Biol.* 79:129a.
114. Matsui, S. 1974. *Exp. Cell Res.* 88:88.
115. Matsui, S., Goyanes, V., and Sandberg, A. A. 1978. *J. Cell Biol.* 79:116a.
116. Ris, H. 1975. In *Ciba Foundation Symp.: Structure and Function of Chromatin,* D. W. Fitzsimmons and G. E. W. Wolstenholme, eds., p. 7. North-Holland Publ. Co., Amsterdam.
117. Bahr, G. F. 1977. In *Molecular Structure of Human Chromosomes,* J. J. Yunis, ed., p. 143. Plenum Press, New York.
118. Morris, N. R. 1976. *Cell* 8:357.
119. Spadafora, C., Bellard, M., Compton, J. L., and Chambon, P. 1976. *FEBS Lett.* 69:281.

120. Finch, J. T., and Klug, A. 1976. *Proc. Natl. Acad. Sci. U.S.A.* 73:1897.
121. Kiryanov, G. I., Manamshian, T. A., Polyakov, V. Yu., Fais, D., and Clentsov, Ju. S. 1976. *FEBS Lett.* 67:323.
122. Hozier, J., Renz, M., and Nehls, P. 1977. *Chromosoma (Berlin)* 62:301.
123. Matsura, H. 1938. *Cytologia* 9:243.
124. Kuwada, Y., and Nakamura, T. 1939. *Cytologia* 10:492.
125. Ohnuki, Y. 1965. *Nature (London)* 208:1916.
126. Ohnuki, Y. 1968. *Chromosoma (Berlin)* 25:402.
127. Bahr, G. 1970. *Exp. Cell Res.* 62:39.
128. Sedat, J., and Manuelidis, L. 1978. *Cold Spring Harbor Symp. Quant. Biol.* 42:331.
129. Bak, A., and Zeuthen, J. 1976. *Hereditas* 82:1.
130. Bak, A., Zeuthen, J., and Crick, F. H. C. 1977. *Proc. Natl. Acad. Sci. U.S.A.* 74:1595.
131. Bak, A., and Zeuthen, J. 1978. *Cold Spring Harbor Symp. Quant. Biol.* 42:367.
132. DuPraw, E. J. 1965. *Nature (London)* 206:538.
133. DuPraw, E. J. 1966. *Nature (London)* 209:577.
134. Ide, T., Nakane, M., Anzai, K., and Andoh, T. 1975. *Nature (London)* 258:445.
135. Cook, P. R., and Brazell, I. A. 1975. *J. Cell Sci.* 19:261.
136. Cook, P. R., and Brazell, I. A. 1976. *J. Cell Sci.* 22:287.
137. Benyajati, C., and Worcel, A. 1976. *Cell* 9:393.
138. Cook, P. R., and Brazell, I. A. 1978. *Eur. J. Biochem.* 84:465.
139. Mirsky, A. E., and Ris, H. 1951. *J. Gen. Physiol.* 34:475.
140. Taylor, J. H. 1957. *Am. Nat.* 91:209.
141. Stubblefield, E., and Wray, W. 1971. *Chromosoma (Berlin)* 32:262.
142. Sorsa, V. 1972. *Hereditas* 72:215.
143. Sorsa, V. 1974. *Cold Spring Harbor Symp. Quant. Biol.* 38:601.
144. Comings, D. E., and Okada, T. A. 1970. *Chromosoma (Berlin)* 30:269.
145. Comings, D. E., and Okada, T. A. 1974. *Cold Spring Harbor Symp. Quant. Biol.* 38:145.
146. Laemmli, U. K., Cheng, S. M., Adolph, K. W., Paulson, J. R., Brown, J. R., and Baumbach, W. R. 1978. *Cold Spring Harbor Symp. Quant. Biol.* 42:361.

12.3. The Meiotic Chromosome

W. Clark Lambert, and Muriel W. Lambert

INTRODUCTION; THE SIGNIFICANCE OF MEIOSIS

Recombination of Genetic Material

The law of natural selection dictates that, for a given environment, the fittest shall survive, and that new mutant genes are selected either for or against on this basis. Most new mutations, however, are deleterious, since they occur randomly and represent deviations from an already more or less successful genotype. Thus the acquisition of new, advantageous mutant genes among members of a species is an extraordinarily slow process, and the chance of more than one such mutant gene being present in a given individual is slight. The process of evolution, however, requires acquisition of increasing numbers of advantageous mutant genes within single individuals, which then reproduce more successfully than their peers to carry on the progressively evolving species. This process is therefore vastly accelerated by mechanisms that allow genes of different members of the species to recombine with each other in successive generations. In prokaryotes this is accomplished by a variety of mechanisms; in most eukaryotes it is accomplished by sexual mating. So important is this process that most species have developed more or less spectacular mechanisms, consuming large quantities of nutrients and energy, for its occurrence, as contemplation of the blooms in a field of wildflowers will readily attest. The specific mode of mating varies greatly between species, but the chromosomal structures and events are remarkably conserved.

Production of Haploid Gametes

In 1883 Van Beneden observed that the nuclei of the egg and sperm of *Ascaris* contain only two chromosomes, whereas the nucleus of the zygote contains four (1). This and similar observations at the time prompted Weismann, in 1887, to postulate a special form of nuclear division, in gametogenesis, leading to a haploid number of chromosomes which is restored to the full, diploid number upon fertilization (2). Weismann thus accurately predicted the discovery of meiosis by perceiving the necessity for a mechanism

MITOSIS

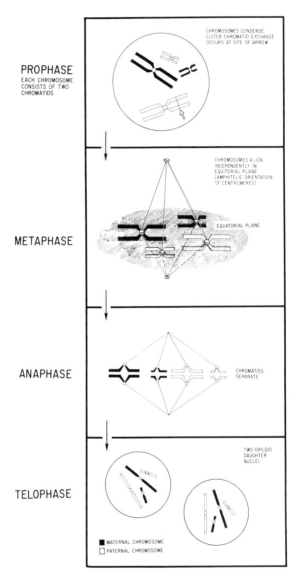

Figure 1. The stages of meiosis, contrast with mitosis (diagramatic representation of a hypothetical organism with four chromosomes (N = 4)).

MEIOSIS

FIRST MEIOTIC DIVISION

SECOND MEIOTIC DIVISION

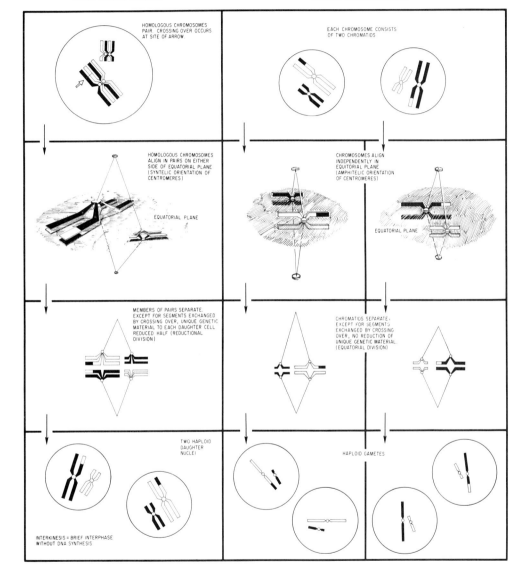

to carry out its second function, that of reducing the chromosome complement to the haploid state. This process occurs at very different times in the life cycle of different organisms. In humans, animals, and some plants, it occurs just before formation of the gametes, with cells of the organism otherwise being, for the most part, diploid. This is referred to as *terminal,* or *gametic,* meiosis. On the other hand, in some fungi, algae, and diatoms, meiosis occurs immediately after fertilization, so that only the newly fertilized ovum is diploid; this is termed *initial,* or *zygotic,* meiosis. When meiosis occurs at an intermediate time between fertilization and gametogenesis, as in most flowering plants, this is referred to as *intermediary,* or *sporic,* meiosis.

Functions of Meiosis; Contrast with Mitosis

In this chapter we will examine the process by which the genetic material of each member of most eukaryotic species is prepared for mating, which reaches its final stage in fertilization. In the flatworm, insect, and vertebrate this process is named *spermatogenesis* in the male and *oogenesis* in the female, together referred to as *gametogenesis,* the nuclear events of which are termed *meiosis.* In higher plants, sporogenesis is accomplished with similar nuclear developments, also called meiosis. The process accomplishes, by separate but overlapping mechanisms, two critical functions: (1) the donation of half the genetic "blueprint" of each of the mating members to the new member, with the guarantee (barring malfunctions) that the halves from each mate will be homologous to each other (i.e., one and only one of the genes in the parent for each autosomal locus is present in each gamete, and the sex chromosomes are appropriately distributed); and (2) recombination of the genetic material that is donated by each mating member, so that the material comprises an independent assortment of linkage groups, which may or may not be recombined, of each mating member's maternal and paternal genes (i.e., the genes derived from the grandparents of the new member). The process is thus very different from that of mitosis, to which it has certain superficial similarities. It is the function of *mitosis* to provide each daughter cell with an exact duplicate (except for the special case of somatic recombination) of the genetic makeup of the single parent cell; in meiosis the product is a gamete with half the genetic material of the parent cell, and different gametes derived from the same organism have completely different, randomized combinations of this material. Meiosis is the elegant process by which all of these important goals are achieved.

We will discuss information obtained using the light microscope—this includes most of the classical studies—and then more recent information obtained primarily using the electron microscope. Additional information obtained from biochemical and genetic studies will also be reviewed. Aspects of the meiotic chromosome common to it and to the mitotic chromosome (e.g., chromosome banding) have already been covered in the preceding chapter and will not be repeated here. The special topic of lampbrush chromosomes and transcription of meiotic chromosomes is discussed in a separate section in this chapter.

STUDIES WITH THE LIGHT MICROSCOPE

In 1887, Flemming reported two types of nuclear division, corresponding to the two successive divisions that make up meiosis, during the formation of pollen in flowering plants (3). At about the same time and during the following decades there were a number of reports of observations of different stages of the process, but the sequence of events remained more or less obscure. By 1900, however, von Winiwarter was able to follow these events in sequence by observing oogenesis in young rabbits, in which successive stages occur at different ages (4). The name "meiosis," meaning reduction, was proposed by Farmer and Moore in 1905 (5). Subsequently the stages of meiosis have been followed in a large number of organisms, including most plants, yeasts, and vertebrates, among them man (Table 1). The process is remarkably consis-

Table 1.   The Stages of Meiosis.

Mitotic Cell Cycle	$G_0 \rightarrow G_1 \rightarrow S \rightarrow G_2 \rightarrow$ Mitosis		Species differences appear to exist regarding time of commitment into the meiotic cycle (see text).
Premeiosis	Premeiotic G_1 / Premeiotic S / Premeiotic G_2		
Meiosis	Division I	Prophase I	Preleptotene (Preleptonema) / Leptotene (Leptonema) / Zygotene (Zygonema) / Pachytene (Pachynema) / Diplotene (Diplonema) / Diakinesis
		Premetaphase I / Metaphase I / Anaphase I / Telophase I	
	Interkinesis	(DNA synthesis occurs in organisms that have entered meiosis directly from G_0)	
	Division II	Prophase II / Metaphase II / Anaphase II / Telophase II	

tent in these varied organisms, and thus will be reviewed below as a general phenomenon, for the most part without further specific documentation. Reviews citing the voluminous bibliography of original contributions are readily available (6–11).

Premeiotic Cell Cycle Events

The process begins with a round of DNA replication by the gametogenic cells. Why this is necessary is not clear, since it would appear that the functions of meiosis—genetic recombination and reduction of the chromosome number to the haploid state—could just as easily be achieved by pairing of the unreplicated homologous chromosomes followed by a single division. In a very few species this actually takes place; an example is the genus *Comstockiella* of scale insects (12). In most, however, there is first a replication of each chromosome, so that when the first meiotic prophase appears, the chromosomes are already present as paired chromatids, even though this may not be apparent by light microscopy. It is for this reason that a series of two meiotic divisions, rather than one, is required, and that there are eventually four, rather than two, haploid gametes (or polar bodies) produced by each meiosis. There is, of course, normally no replication of DNA between these divisions; an exception is the red algae, which undergo DNA synthesis between meiotic divisions, but do not have the premeiotic S phase characteristic of most other species (13). This premeiotic DNA synthetic phase is, in at least some species, distinguishable from that of the mitotic cycle both by differences in timing and by certain mutants that enter premitotic S phase normally but fail to enter premeiotic S phase (14). Still other organisms may, following S phase, be experimentally induced to enter either mitosis or meiosis, however (15).

The First Meiotic Division: Reductional Division

Prophase I.   The first meiotic prophase is longer than that of mitosis, often extraordinarily so. In the human female, for example, oocyte precursor cells already exist in meiotic prophase I at birth, and remain so until puberty and through the childbearing years, during which, at each menstrual cycle, a few progress to metaphase I. Thus oocytes may remain in prophase I for over 50 years. This long existence in prophase I, with most of the genome in an inactive form as prophase I chromosomes, may be made possible by specialized structures, portions of chromosomes that extend out from the principal axis in loops, on which extensive RNA synthesis takes place *(vide infra)*.

The extraordinary length of meiotic prophase I has made it an excellent subject for study, and as a result much more is known about it than about the later stages of meiosis. It has, in fact, itself been divided into a number of parts. The stages of prophase I were recorded by von Winiwarter in female rabbits in 1900 as follows (4):

Leptotene; Chromomeres; The Meiotic Bouquet; The Synizetic Knot. On the first day after birth in the rabbit, in the middle layer of the ovary, there are cells containing chromosomes that appear as delicate single threads (i.e., the paired chromatids are seen as single structures). von Winiwarter termed this the *leptotene* (Gr., *leptos,* thin; *tene,* ribbon) stage. An alternate term is *leptonema* (Gr., *nema,* thread). Some authors also refer to a *preleptotene* or *preleptonema* stage during which autosomal chromosomes are very thin and are difficult to study, but sex chromosomes may stand out as dense, hyperchromatic structures. During leptotene, the chromosomes have a marked beaded appearance, the "beads" of homologous chromosomes exactly corresponding to each other in number, size, and orientation. These "beads" are known as chromomeres; little is known of their structure and function. Each chromomere was once thought to represent an individual gene, but it is now clear that this cannot be the case, simply because there are not nearly enough of them to account for the number of genes thought to be present in many of the species in which they have been observed. Chromomeres are also much larger than nucleosomes (beaded structures containing DNA and protein visible on chromatids with the electron microscope).

In many species, during leptotene, the chromosomes are all oriented with one or both of their ends, or *telomeres,* in contact with a single region of the nuclear membrane, altogether comprising a structure known as the *meiotic bouquet.* In other species this structure may form during the later stages of meiotic prophase (16–18). This region of attachment to the inner aspect of the nuclear envelope has been observed to correspond to the region of the centrioles outside the nuclear envelope. In yet other species, there is formed, instead of a metiotic bouquet, a complex accumulation of chromosomes in one small area of the nucleus. This structure, which persists throughout prophase I and sometimes longer, is known as the *synizetic knot.* The significance of these specialized structures is unknown, but they may be involved in mechanisms for subsequent pairing of homologous chromosomes. A similar bouquet phenomenon does not occur in mitosis; the configurations of chromosomes during all stages of meiosis are in general quite different from those of mitosis (11).

Zygotene; Synapsis. In diploid cells chromosomes are present as *N* pairs, one member of each pair derived from each parent (i.e., one from the father and one from the mother). Several days after birth (during zygotene in the rabbit) these homologous chromosomes begin to come together and then become associated, in a zipperlike manner, along their entire length. This association begins at the telomeres of the chromosomes in some species, and in others at both ends and at additional sites along the chromosomes. This process of association of homologous chromosomes is known as synapsis (Gr., coming together), and the stage during which it occurs was termed, by von Viniwarter, *synaptene,* although the term *zygotene* or *zygonema* (Gr., *zygon,* adjoining), introduced by Gregorie in 1907 (19), is more commonly used today. The visibly paired chromosomes (containing, however, four chromatids) are then known as bivalents (or tetrads). Within each bivalent, lying between the homologous chromosomes throughout their length, is an important structure, the *synaptonemal complex;* it is visible only by electron microscopy and thus will be discussed below in the section on ultrastructural studies.

Although synapsis may occur between nonhomologous chromosomes, and a synaptonemal complex may even be formed, a crossover *(vide infra)* arising from such a nonspecific synapsis appears to be an extremely rare event. Such crossovers between nonhomologous chromosomes are presumably a possible cause of translocations (21).

Pachytene; Crossing-Over; Chiasmata. This lateral association of chromosomes progresses to completion, at which point the cell enters *pachytene,* or *pachynema* (Gr., *pachus,* thick).

During pachytene, and possibly also in the latter part of leptotene, a special chromosomal event known as *crossing-over* occurs. Extensive studies in the early twentieth century demonstrated unequivocally the relationships between the observed cytological events and the genetic consequences, as follows:

Crossing-over is a process involving transverse breaks in the DNA sequence of homologous chromatids at precisely the same point, such that, after crosswise fusion of the sequences with each other, an exactly reciprocal exchange of segments takes place. Identical chromatids on the same side of the bivalent do not undergo crossing-over with each other, but each chromatid, of the four present in a bivalent, may undergo crossing-over with either of its two homologous chromatids on the opposite side. The point at which this occurs is called a *chiasma* (plural: *chiasmata;* Gr., *chiasma,* cross piece).

Note that homologous chromosomes are not paired prior to leptotene, but rather each chromosome is paired with its own duplicate, both newly semiconservatively synthesized from the same original. The steps up to this point thus resemble mitosis, and were the process to proceed as in mitosis, the chromosomes would line up on the metaphase plate—without homologous chromosomes pairing with each other—a step that would be followed by the separation of each chromatid from its newly synthesized duplicate and into the two different daughter nuclei. Instead, however, each already duplicated chromosome pairs, beginning in leptotene and during zygotene, with its homologous (and similarly duplicated) chromosome, so that, in pachytene, the bivalent (or tetrad) composed of *four* chromatids is observed. Several aspects of these synapsed homologous chromosomes merit our special attention at this point. First, consider the mitotic chromosome at metaphase. Each chromatid is paired with its own duplicate copy, both being newly synthesized semiconservatively from the same original, so that any exchange of segments that occurs at this point leads only to an exchange of identical genetic information unless a mutation has occurred in one of the chromatids in the brief moments since their duplication. Thus, this event, known as a *sister chromatid exchange* (reviewed in the previous chapter), does not, in general, lead to an alteration in the genome of the daughter muclei. At the first meiotic prophase, however, the bivalent is composed of pairs of homologous, rather than identical, chromatids (two identical copies of each of two homologous chromosomes), so that a crossover at this point does lead to genetic recombination. In this way a part of the function of meiosis, genetic recombination of material between homologous chromosomes, each originally separately derived from the parents of the mating organism (the grandparents of the organism being formed), is accomplished. The gamete receives neither the chromosome derived from the father nor that from the mother of each of the two mating organisms, but rather a randomized mix of linkage groups of both.

Toward the end of pachytene, which is usually a much longer stage than either leptotene or synaptene (it is the longest stage in mammalian spermatogenesis), the individual chromatids separate lengthwise, and for the first time all four chromatids of the bivalent become visible. This structure is now called a *tetrad* (it is still, however, considered also a bivalent). Following pachytene, the synaptic association between the homologous chromosomes lapses, and they begin to separate. At this point the chiasmata become visible as points of attachment between the separating homologous chromatids, the adjoined chromatids forming an X at the site of the chiasma as the remainder of the homologous chromosomes draw apart. This stage is known as *diplotene* or *diplonema (vide infra)*. Chiasmata are an almost universal feature of meiosis, although a few organisms in which they do not occur in one sex or the other are known. Genetic analysis shows that the interchromatid recombinations characteristic of crossing-over do not occur in the absence of chiasmata as observed during diplotene.

The Topological Mechanism of Crossing-Over; the Classical versus the Partial Chiasmatype Hypothesis. Classical geneticists regarded a chiasma, as observed during diplotene, as a site at which a chromatid has actually, in the literal topological sense, crossed over one of its homologous chromatids, which has undergone a similar, and reciprocal, crossover of the first chromatid. Thus, at the time of observation of the chiasma in diplotene, according to this model, no breakage of chromosomes has occurred, and on one side of the chiasma a paternal chromatid is paired (on the same side of the bivalent)

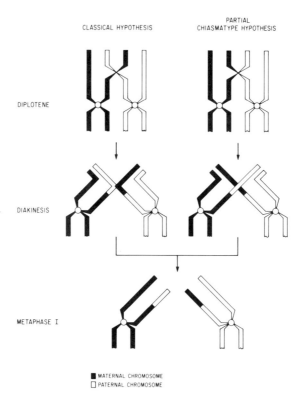

CLASSICAL HYPOTHESIS

PARTIAL
CHIASMATYPE HYPOTHESIS

DIPLOTENE

DIAKINESIS

METAPHASE I

■ MATERNAL CHROMOSOME
□ PATERNAL CHROMOSOME

Figure 2. Diagramatic representation of crossing-over and terminalization: the classical *versus* **the** partial chiasmatype hypothesis.

with the other paternal chromatid, and the maternal chromatids are similarly **together** (on the opposite side of the bivalent), whereas on the opposite side **of** the chiasma a paternal and a maternal chromatid are paired together on **both** sides of the bivalent. According to this model a chiasma *might give rise* to a genetic crossover, but only if it was followed by a breaking and **rejoining** of the two chromatids with each other.

An alternate model, now known to be correct, is the partial chiasmatype **hypothesis**, which proposes that, at the time a chiasma becomes visible during **diplotene**, breaking and rejoining of homologous chromatids has occurred, **but** no crossover in the literal sense has taken place. Thus, according to **this** model, at the time of formation of the chiasma, both maternal chromatids **are** paired together on the same side of the bivalent on both sides of the **chiasma**, and the paternal chromatids are similarly arranged. Thus a chiasma, **according** to this model, is firm evidence that a genetic crossover has **already occurred**. There are a number of topological proofs that the partial chiasma-

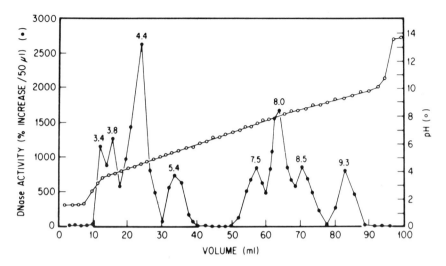

Figure 3. DNA endonucleases in chromatin protein of mouse melanoma cells. The non-histone protein has been isolated, fractionated by isoelectric focusing, and each fraction assayed for nuclease activity. (Lambert, M. W. et al., *Biochem. Biophys. Res. Commun.*, 91:1481, 1979).

type model is the correct one, the first convincing proofs having been put forward by the pioneering and very elegant work of Janssens (22) and Darlington (23, 24) in the 1920s and 1930s, all, of course, with the light microscope in the absence of sophisticated staining and banding techniques.

The Molecular Mechanism of Crossing-Over. The molecular events surrounding formation of chiasmata are completely obscure, although, on purely theoretical grounds, it is clear that one or more DNA endonucleases [enzymes that "cut" DNA within a strand, as opposed to DNA exonucleases, enzymes that attack DNA at the end of a strand and progressively digest the strand from that point (25)] must be involved (26). Recently it has been shown that a number of such enzymes are present in the chromatin of both mouse and man (25–30). These enzymes have a variety of substrate specificites, and there is some evidence that they recognize and cleave DNA only at specific sequences (28). Such enzymes, known in bacteria as *restriction* enzymes (because they restrict growth of certain strains of phage in the bacteria—the strains affected depending on the enzymes in question) have not yet been demonstrated in mammalian cells, but there is suggestive evidence that they may be present (28, 31). The demonstration of a whole group of these enzymes in chromatin—in intimate contact with DNA (28)—suggests that there is a complex spectrum of endonuclease-dependent mechanisms for control of DNA synthesis, repair, metabolism, and recombination. Studies of these enzymes in meiosis are in progress at present in our laboratory, as an initial attempt to decipher the molecular mechanisms responsible for crossing-over and genetic recombination. Virtually all that is known at present of these mechanisms is that the process involves a small amount of new synthesis of protein and DNA; a quantity corresponding to less than 1% of the total cellular DNA content is produced (32).

Terminalization. After the chiasmata become visible, they are, during the subsequent stages of the first meiotic division, observed to move gradually to the ends, or telomeres, of the chromosomes. This process is called terminalization, and it is during this period that the actual, topological crossing-over of the portions of the homologous chromatids that are destined to be exchanged (i.e., those distal to the chiasma) occurs.

Sites and Frequency of Chiasmata and Their Genetic Correlations: (1) Frequency of Chiasmata. The frequency of formation of chiasmata per chromosome per meiosis varies greatly between species, between chromosomes, and between sites on chromosomes. In general, one or a few chiasmata occur on a given chromosome in most species. The degree of correspondence between the frequency of observed chiasmata and of crossing-over as determined by genetic analysis is usually fairly good (33). A genetic length of 50 crossover units would be expected per chiasma, and this is approximately what is found. In maize, for example, the average total chiasma frequency (on all ten chromosomes) is 27.05, and the genetic length of the combined chromosomes is about 1100 units. In humans, the total chiasma frequency is about 55, suggesting a total map length of approximately 2750 units, but this latter figure has never been accurately determined.

(2) Sites of Chiasmata. The sites at which chiasmata tend to occur are also quite variable. In some chromosomes the chiasma frequency is uniform over their length, but in others it is much higher near the centromeres (*proximal* localization) or in still others it is higher near one or both telomeres (*distal* localization) (34). A combination of these frequencies may also occur. Such localizations, as expected, lead to a disparity between the locations of specific genes as determined by genetic mapping and (where known) as determined by cytological studies. One fairly constant finding, from both cytological and genetic studies, is that there is a minimum distance between chiasmata on the same bivalent. It is assumed that this is due to the first chiasma formed diminishing the chance for occurrence of a second one for a given distance on either side, an effect known as *chiasma interference.*

(3) Relationships between Multiple Chiasmata on the Same Chromosome. When two chiasmata are present in a single bivalent (a common occurrence), there are four possible relationships between them, each with its own cytological and genetic consequences. The second chiasma may occur between the same two homologous chromatids as the first (cytologically, *reciprocal chiasmata;* genetically, a *two-strand double exchange*); between the two homologous

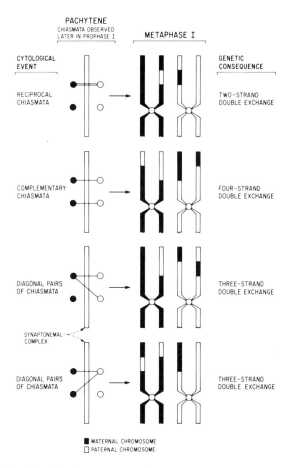

Figure 4. Possible relationships between two chiasmata occuring in a single bivalent (tetrad) on the same side of the centromere.

chromatids unaffected by the first chiasma (cytologically, *complementary chiasmata;* genetically, a *four-strand double exchange*); or between one of the chromatids involved in the first chiasma and the homologous chromatid not previously involved, there being two kinds of relationship, depending on whether two maternal or two paternal chromatids are involved (cytologically, *diagonal pairs of chiasmata;* genetically a *three-strand double exchange*). When more than two chiasmata are present on one bivalent, the possible relationships are simply combinations and permutations of the above.

Diplotene; Dictyotene. The stage, following pachytene, during which the homologous halves of the bivalents separate is known as *diplotene,* or *diplonema.* This is usually a long stage, and characteristically is extraordinarily long in oogenesis in most species. During diplotene, the ovum of most species becomes much larger, owing to extensive RNA synthesis (see final section of this chapter), leading to synthesis of protein and other cellular constituents. In mammals, including humans, the nucleus of the oocyte becomes several times its former size, the increase being due mostly to an increase in nucleoplasm (liquid) rather than an increase in nuclear macromolecules. Within the large pale-staining nucleus the chromosomes become fine and difficult or impossible to observe by light microscopy, even using the Feulgen stain. The nucleus at this point is sometimes referred to as the germinal vesicle, and this stage, really a variant of diplotene, is known as *dictyotene* or *dictyonema*. Dictyotene in the human female lasts from approximately the time of birth until ovulation, years later. The disappearance of the chromosomes, as observed by light microscopy during this period, is of historical importance because it was used as evidence for dissolution and subsequent resynthesis of genetic information in each generation, and thus was proposed as an argument for Lamarkian genetics (35). Dictyotene chromosomes are clearly visible by electron microscopy, however. Chiasmata, which become visible during diplotene, in addition to their function in crossing-over also have the function of stabilizing the structure of the partially separated bivalents during the later stages of meiotic prophase. This latter role is essential in some species, in which artificially or genetically induced absence of chiasmata causes a falling apart of diplotene chromosomes, leading to aneuploid and generally infertile gametes. In other species, however, chiasmata are clearly not necessary for maintenance of bivalent structure, since their absence has no effect.

Diakinesis. In diakinesis (Gr., *dia,* across or toward the periphery; *kinesis,* movement) the bivalents become much shorter and more condensed. They may also move toward the nuclear membrane, and this movement is the basis for the name given this stage. This stage blends into premetaphase in a manner resembling the events of mitosis.

Premetaphase I; Kinetochore Orientation.   The formation of the spindle and the disappearance of the nuclear membrane proceed in meiotic premetaphase I in a fashion quite similar to that of mitotic premetaphase. An important difference, however, is the manner in which the centromeres behave. In mitosis, there is one centromere per chromosome (i.e., per chromatid pair, both being newly semiconservatively synthesized during the previous S phase). The centromeres become localized rather precisely on the metaphase plate, each connected by spindle fibers to both poles, in what is known as *amphitelic orientation.* Then each centromere divides into two equal portions, one going with each chromatid into the separate daughter nuclei. This process contrasts sharply with meiosis, in which the chromosomes are not in the form of identical chromatids, but rather of bivalents, each composed of two homologous (not identical) pairs of newly semiconservatively synthesized identical chromatids, and therefore also known as a tetrad. Instead of a single centromere, each bivalent has two, one within each pair of chromatids. At premetaphase I these centromeres line up, not on the metaphase plate, but rather on either side of it, each with a spindle fiber to its nearest pole. This arrangement is known as *syntelic orientation*. The mechanisms responsible for this difference are entirely unknown. Unpaired chromosomes in meiosis, such as sex chromosomes, may be oriented either syntelically or amphitelically; chromosomes that are induced by radiation damage to pair in a manner resembling bivalents during mitosis nevertheless tend to undergo amphitelic orientation.

Metaphase I; Reduction Division. There is a smooth transition from premetaphase I to metaphase I, with the chromosomes lining up more evenly along the metaphase plate and becoming maximally condensed. The outlines of the chromosomes appear smooth, in contrast to earlier stages, particularly diplotene, during which a fuzzy outline is seen, due to strands of chromatin material extending out from the main mass to act as a substrate for RNA synthesis *(vide infra)*. The centromeres of homologous halves of bivalents appear to be stretched apart as far as incompletely terminalized chiasmata will allow. Between chiasmata, the chromosomes appear rotated 90°. Thus, if chiasmata exist on either side of a pair of centromeres, then they, with their adjoining chromosomal segments, form a ring. The plane of this ring is then perpendicular to that of the metaphase plate. Immediately beyond the chiasmata on either side, however, the chromosome segments are in a plane parallel to the metaphase plate. If there is another chiasma beyond the first, then the chromosome segments beyond it are again in a plane perpendicular to the metaphase plate and parallel to that of the ring formed by the centromeres and their adjacent segments. A 90° rotation thus takes place at each chiasma.

Anaphase I. In contrast to mitosis and the second meiotic division, the individual centromeres of anaphase I do not divide, but merely continue toward the poles toward which they were oriented during metaphase. As they do so, the chromosomes follow behind, the chiasmata completing terminalization at the telomeres. Whether a paternal or a maternal chromosome goes to a given pole is strictly a matter of chance at this point, and depends upon the orientation of the centromeres during premetaphase, also a matter of chance. Thus each daughter nucleus receives a random assortment of maternal and paternal chromosomes at this division, but gets *either* the maternal *or* the paternal half of each bivalent, never (barring nondisjunctions) both. There is, therefore, a reduction of the number of unique chromosomes in the daughter nuclei, leading to the term *reductional* division to describe the first meiotic division. For segments (i.e., linkage groups of chromosomes) that have been interchanged by crossing-over, however, the daughter nuclei each contain a single segment of *both* maternal and paternal chromosomes, so that no reduction in the number of unique segments occurs. For these segments the first meiotic division is therefore not reductional but is properly termed *equational*. Therefore, although the first meiotic division is often referred to as reductional and the second as equational, this terminology is not strictly correct.

The random separation of maternal and paternal chromosomes into separate daughter nuclei at this point is primarily responsible for the *Law of Independent Segregation (of Genes)* of Mendelian genetics. Crossing-over accomplishes recombination within chromosomes, and this process the recombination of chromosomes themselves. Thus the first goal of meiosis, genetic recombination, is accomplished by both processes operating in concert.

Telophase I and Interkinesis. The telophase of the first meiotic division resembles that of mitosis, except that each chromosome consists of two chromatids rather than one. The chromatids, except at their centromeres, are widely separated, so that metacentric chromosomes appear X-shaped and acrocentric chromosomes V-shaped. The nuclear membrane is re-formed as the daughter cells separate. In some organisms, telophase I blends directly into prophase II, but in others a brief interphase, known as interkinesis, during which DNA synthesis does not occur (except in red algae, *vide supra*) (13), supervenes before the beginning of the second meiotic division. During interkinesis the chromosomes become elongated and diffuse as in interphase of the mitotic cell cycle.

The Second Meiotic Division; Equational Division

Prophase II is short and does not include the complex structures or events characteristic of prophase I. Following rapid organization of the spindle, premetaphase II is reached. Premetaphase II differs from mitotic premetaphase by having chromatids that appear slenderer and, instead of paired lengthwise, widely separated except for the attachment site at the centromere. There are, of course, only a haploid number of chromosomes present, but each consists of two chromatids.

The centromeres of metaphase II are oriented amphitelically, as in mitosis, rather than as in metaphase I. In anaphase II, the centromeres divide as in an ordinary mitosis, except that the separation of chromatids has already been partially accomplished, since they lie apart in metaphase II rather than paired throughout their lengths. Telophase II proceeds in a manner quite similar to that of mitotic telophase, but, of course, with a haploid number of chromosomes.

Except for the effects of new mutations and of crossing-over during the first meiotic division, the chromatids that separate in the second meiotic division are identical, rather than homologous, and the number of unique chromosomes is not reduced. Therefore, the second meiotic division is often referred to as equational, rather than reductional. For those chromosomal segments where, owing to crossing-over, the first division was equational, however, the second division will necessarily be reductional.

Aspects of Meiosis Unique to Oogenesis or Spermatogenesis

The mitotically replicating precursors of sperm and ova are termed *spermatogonia* and *oogonia,* respectively; after they enter meiosis they are referred to as *primary spermatocytes* and *primary oocytes;* after the first meiotic division as *secondary spermatocytes* and *secondary oocytes* (and *polar bodies*); and after the second division as *spermatids* and *ova* (singular, ovum) (and *polar bodies*).

This process is known as *spermatogenesis* in the male and *oogenesis* in the female. The spermatids undergo extensive further differentiation to eventually form *spermatozoa* (singular, spermatozoan). This latter process, which involves radical alterations in chromosomal structure and proteins, together with spermatogenesis, is termed, in toto, *spermiogenesis.* The chromosomal alterations are discussed further in the section on biochemical studies *(vide infra).*

In many species, including humans, oogenesis does not progress through all of the stages of meiosis unless sperm comes into contact with, or even enters, the oocyte. The process is arrested at some earlier stage, such as metaphase I, until this occurs. Other differences in the timing of the various stages of meiosis have been referred to above.

In several species, such as *Drosophila melanogaster,* spermatogenesis proceeds synchronously in a number of spermatocytes, so that some multiple of 4, such as 64, spermatids are formed simultaneously, cytoplasmic bridges joining them during the process. Regardless of whether this synchronous development occurs, spermatogenesis leads ideally to the production of four spermatids per meiosis, with no chromosomes being wasted. In most species, however, considerable atresia occurs, so that fewer than four are normally produced. In oogenesis, moreover, only one ovum is produced. At the end of the first meiotic division, one of the daughter cells has only rudimentary cytoplasm, almost all of the cellular constituents being given to the future ovum. This rudimentary cell is referred to as the *secondary oocyte* or *first polar body;* it may divide again later to form two *second polar bodies.* The process is repeated after the second meiotic division, the new polar body also referred to, somewhat ambiguously, as the *second polar body.*

ULTRASTRUCTURAL STUDIES; THE SYNAPTONEMAL COMPLEX

As in the case of light microscopic studies, numerous reviews citing original references are readily available (6, 36–38). For the most part additional documentation will be provided in this section only where there is a special reason for it.

Thin section electron microscopy has shown that leptotene chromosomes process an axial filament, forming the core of each. The axial filament contains a large amount of protein in addition to DNA; when leptotene cells are treated with DNases, the axial filaments are not digested (6). Two separate fibrils, probably corresponding to the two chromatids, are seen. The chromatin fibrils are attached to the axial filaments as a series of loops extending laterally. The loops are not homogeneously distributed, but rather occur in a series of aggregates of varying, and often extensive, complexity. These aggregates correspond to the chromomeres observed by light microscopy (6).

During zygotene, as homologous chromosomes undergo pairing, a structure of utmost importance is formed between them. This structure, the *synaptonemal complex,* was discovered independently by Moses and by Fawcett in 1956 (39, 40). It consists of three parallel electron-dense strands, the lateral two of which are probably the axial cores of chromosomes between which the structure lies. The synaptonemal complex extends from end to end of each set of paired homologous chromatids, ending at the telomeres where they abut the nuclear membrane (41, 42).

Each synaptomenal complex has dimensions characteristic of its individual species, but considerable interspecies variation occurs. The overall width is about 160 nm in tomatoes and salamanders, 180 nm in mammals, and 200 nm in crickets. In general, the two lateral, electron-dense strands, known as *lateral elements,* are each about 30 to 40 nm wide; they are considered by many to represent the axial filaments formed in leptotene. Inconsistent with this idea, however, is the fact that, under certain circumstances, complete synaptonemal complexes have been observed where there was no chromosome to provide its axial filament to make up one or both lateral elements (36). The central strand, known as the *central element,* is about 12 to 20 nm in width. It may be seen as a simple dense line, as in humans, or may itself consist of several dense lines with superimposed transverse periodicity, as in grasshoppers. Between the central and lateral elements is an electron-lucent space traversed by *transverse filaments* about 2 nm in diameter.

There are several species in which one or the other sex does not have synaptonemal complexes, and, in each, crossing-over does not occur. This

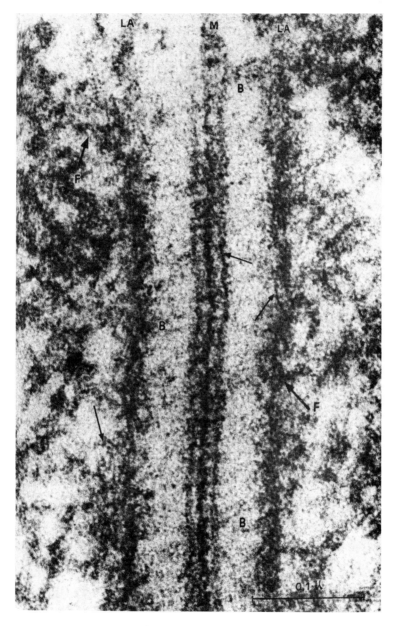

Figure 5. Frontal longitudinal view of a synaptonemal complex. M—trilayered medial component; LA—lateral arm; B—bridge between a lateral arm and the medial component; F (with large arrow)—demonstrates site of continuity between the lateral arms of the synaptonemal complex and the adjacent chromatids; small arrow—denotes site where the 1.5–2.0 nm filaments which constitute the basic morphologic units of chromosome complexes are seen. (Wettstein, R, and Sotelo, JR, *J. Microscop.* **6**:557, 1967).

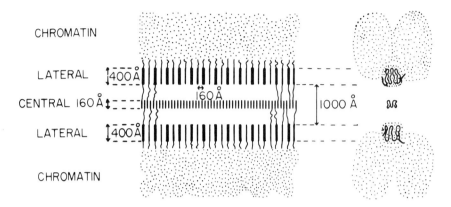

Figure 6. Diagramatic representation of a synaptonemal complex in *Neotiella.* (Westergaard, M., and von Wettstein, D, C. R. *Trans. Lab. Carlsberg* **35**:261, 1968).

feature may be genetically controlled, as in *Gowen's crossover suppressor gene* on chromosome number three of the male *Drosophila melanogaster.* On the other hand, synaptonemal complexes are rather consistently observed between nonhomologous chromosomes when they undergo synapsis, although crossing-over is quite rare. Thus the presence of a synaptonemal complex appears to be a required, but not a sufficient, condition for crossing-over to occur.

Although it has been demonstrated in lily anthers that a small amount of DNA synthesis is necessary for both formation of the synaptonemal complex in zygotene and its dissolution in diplotene, the central element does not appear to contain detectable DNA, and the lateral elements appear to be comprised principally of protein.

Prior to formation of the synaptonemal complex, the homologous chromosomes have already aligned themselves in a rather precise chromomere-by-chromomere fashion. This has led to the proposal that a premeiotic alignment of homologous chromosomes occurs, but there is no proof for this notion. This pairing is insufficiently precise to account for the exact exchange of segments that occurs in crossing-over (36). The basis for this exact matching is unknown. Most models propose a system for recognition of similar sequences on the DNA of the two chromosomes—these may or may not be repetitive DNA. Endonucleases of the *restriction* type, known at present only in bacteria, might be the mediators of this recognition *(vide supra).*

BIOCHEMICAL STUDIES; SPERMIOGENESIS; PROTAMINES

Although it is clear that meiotic chromosomes undergo a number of modifications that would be expected to require specialized macromolecules, such

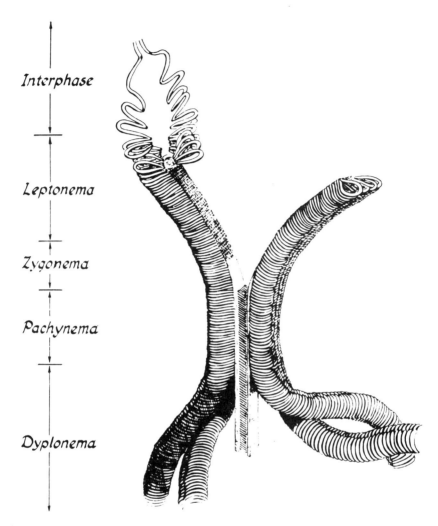

Figure 7. Diagramatic representation of the synaptonemal complex and of chromosome structure during the stages of meiotic prophase I. (Roth, T. G., *Protoplasma,* **61**:346, 1966).

as DNA endonucleases and ligases required for crossing-over, very little is known of the biochemistry of meiotic chromatin. Some investigators have reported a histone specific for meiosis, but other histones, also found in non-meiotic chromosomes, are found as well (43).

The heads of mature sperm in most species contain a very high percentage of DNA, higher than that of pure mitotic chromatin. This alteration serves the purpose of minimizing the weight of the chromatin and thereby increasing sperm mobility. It is made possible by extensive changes in nucleoprotein that occur following the second meiotic division, and therefore is a process unique to the later stages of spermiogenesis rather than spermatogenesis.

In some species, such as salmon and trout, the histones of sperm chromatin are entirely replaced by proteins known as *protamines*. These are small molecules (4000–5000 daltons) that have a strong positive charge ($pI = 10–11$) and in most species a very high percentage of *arginine* in their amino acid composition. The arginines fit into the shallow groove on the surface of the DNA double helix, providing a tight, geometrical structure, the positive charges of the arginines interacting with the negative phosphate groups on the DNA. The end result is a compact, sometimes almost crystalline structure that in some species is so regular that it has special optical properties, imparting negative birefringence to the nucleus when viewed by polarized light (36).

A large number of species, including man, do not have sperm containing true protamines [although mammalian sperm proteins are referred to as protamines, this terminology is not strictly correct (44)], but nonetheless have specialized sperm proteins (45, 46). Particularly in mammals, there is a considerable difference between these proteins in different species. The content of arginine, although lower than that in a protamine, is nevertheless usually high. Disulfide bonds play a role in the structure of these proteins. In some species, such as certain plants and carp, histones are found that appear to be identical with those of somatic chromatin. The species-specific nature of these basic nucleoproteins in sperm contrasts sharply with the markedly conserved structure of histones.

After fertilization, the sperm chromatin, now safely within the egg, undergoes a reversal of the alterations of late spermiogenesis, histones replacing the specialized nucleoproteins (47).

TRANSCRIPTIONAL ACTIVITY DURING MEIOSIS; THE LAMPBRUSH CHROMOSOME

The original description of the lampbrush chromosome was by Flemming in 1882 (48), but Rückert's more complete description of them in 1892 in sharks (49) is more frequently cited as the first report. They consist of diplotene chromosomes modified to allow for extensive RNA synthesis, needed to provide for *vitillogenesis* (yolk formation; growth of the precursor of the unfertilized ovum), and have been reported in oocytes of a large number of species, including a mollusc, a crustacean, an echinoderm, two species of sharks, several species of insects, and numerous mammals, reptiles, birds, and, particularly, salamanders and other amphibians (50). The name "lampbrush" was proposed by Rückert because their shape and fuzzy outline give them a

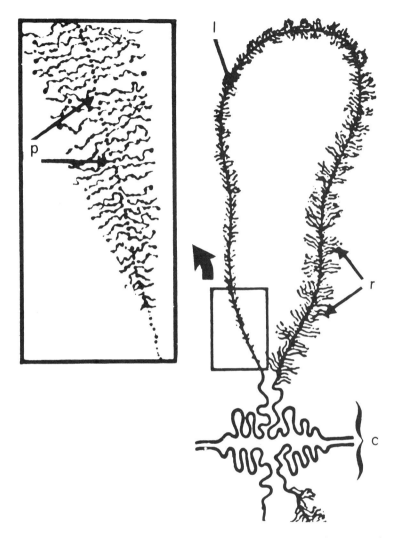

Figure 8. Diagramatic representation of a lateral loop of a meiotic prophase chromosome forming a "lampbrush" structure. l—lateral loop; r—RNA–protein fibrils; p—RNA polymerase molecules; c—chromomere. (Wischnitzer, S., *Endeavor*, **35**:27, 1976).

resemblance to *Lampencylinderputzer,* the brushes then used for cleaning chimneys of oil-burning lamps.

Like all diplotene chromosomes for which homologous pairs are present, lampbrush chromosomes consist of a tetrad, two pairs of homologous chromatids (the homology altered by crossover events) held together by a centromere

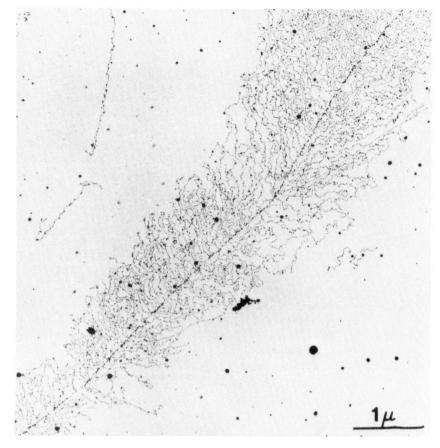

Figure 9. Portion of a lampbrush chromosome loop in *Triturus viridescens* showing gradient of RNA–protein complexes attached to loop axis. (Miller, O. L., and Hamkalo, B. A., Int. Rev. Cytol., **33**:1, 1972).

and by chiasmata where present. The chromatids are very extended, up to 500 to 800 μ in some instances, and the axes often become so thin that they cannot be resolved by the light microscope. Distributed along each chromosome (i.e., half-bivalent) are hundreds of chromomeres, from each of which extends a pair of very thin loops, each loop corresponding to one of the paired sister (not homologous) chromatids. Unlike chromatids elsewhere, however, the loops appear to lack typical nucleosomes.

The large size of the extended lampbrush chromosomes has made them amenable in certain species to manipulations not otherwise possible. Techniques developed by Duryee (51) and by Gall (52) in the late 1940s and

1950s, in which the nuclei are isolated and dissected under inverted phase-contrast microscopy, have vastly accelerated progress in our understanding not only of lampbrush chromosomes but also of many other areas of cell biology, such as transcription. These techniques are particularly well suited for combination with other more conventional cytological, biochemical, immunological, and ultrastructural methods to create elegant and informative experimental systems (50). Most of the studies described below used these special methods in one way or another.

A major finding regarding the structural relationships between the lateral loops and the chromomeres was obtained by simply stretching the chromosomes. Lampbrush chromosomes are quite elastic, and may be stretched about 2 1/2-fold without changing their morphology. Further stretching, however, causes some of the chromomeres to come apart, their lateral loops then remaining intact, as "loop bridges," to maintain the integrity of the chromosomal structure (50).

Extensive enzymatic digestion experiments combined with autoradiographic and ultrastructural studies (36, 50, 53–55) have shown that each lateral loop consists of a single double-helical strand of DNA upon which extensive RNA polymerization is occurring in a sequential fashion around the loop, with each strand of RNA beginning to be synthesized at one end (observed as the thin end cytologically) and becoming progressively longer as it continues along the strands toward the other end (observed as the thick end). Furthermore, the strand of DNA is itself in motion, spinning out from one portion of the chromomere at one end (that at which the RNA strands begin to be synthesized) and becoming wound into the other portion of the chromomere at the other end. The chromomeres themselves each thus appear to consist of four masses of coiled chromatid segments. Two of these masses belong to each chromatid, itself a single continuous double-helical strand of DNA. The DNA strand then is constantly being unwound from one part of the chromomere to extend the loop and being wound into the other part to reel it in again. In this way the entire contents of the DNA of the chromomere could, theoretically, eventually be extended into the loop to become substrate for transcription. Each loop is, in fact, comprised of one to several transcription units. The strands between chromomeres consist of dual strands of DNA and protein, one for each chromatid. This model, developed by Callan and Lloyd (57), appears to fit the available evidence quite well. It considers each chromatid as a single, continuous strand of DNA, a hypothesis for which there is additional evidence and which also satisfies theoretical considerations (36).

The extended lateral loops characteristic of lampbrush chromosomes appear to be present in all oocytes in diplotene, regardless of the species, and available evidence indicates that rather extensive RNA synthesis on such chromosomes is quite a general feature of oogenesis. It also may play a role in spermatogenesis in many, if not all, species. Lampbrush–like chromosomal structures have been shown in the diplotene stage of spermatogenesis in *Drosophila melanagaster*. Mutants lacking one or more of the loops are sterile (58).

REFERENCES

1. Van Beneden, E. 1883. *Arch. Biol. Paris* 4:265.
2. Weismann, A. 1889. In *Essays upon Heredity and Kindred Biological Problems,* p. 333. Clarendon Press, Oxford. (Written in 1887.)
3. Flemming, W. 1887. *Arch. Mikrosk. Anat.* 29:389.
4. von Winiwarter, H. 1900. *Arch. Biol. Paris* 17:33.
5. Farmer, J. B., and Moore, J. E. S. 1905. *J. Microsc. Sci.* 48:489.
6. Comings, D. E., and Okoda, T. A. 1972. Architecture of meiotic cells and mechanisms of chromosome pairing. *Adv. Cell Mol. Biol.* 2:309.
7. Moens, P. B. 1973. Mechanisms of chromosome synopsis at meiotic prophase. *Int. Rev. Cytol.* 35:117.
8. King, R. C. 1970. The meiotic behavior of the *Drosophila* oocyte. *Int. Rev. Cytol.* 28:125.
9. Guraza, S. S. 1977. Recent advances in the morphology, histochemistry, and biochemistry of the developing mammalian ovary. *Int. Rev. Cytol.* 51:49.
10. Stubblefield, E. 1973. The structure of mammalian chromosomes. *Int. Rev. Cytol.* 35:1.
11. Sasaki, M., and Makino, S. 1965. The meiotic chromosomes of man. *Chromosoma* 16:637.
12. Brown, S. W. 1963. The *Comstockiella* system of chromosome behavior in the armoured scale insects (Coccoidea: diaspididae). *Chromosoma* 14:360.
13. Krugens, P., and West, J. A. 1972. Synaptonemal complexes in red algae. *J. Phycol.* 8:187.
14. Baker, B. S., et al. 1976. The genetic control of meiosis. *Annu. Rev. Genet.* 10:53.
15. Stern, H., and Hotta, Y. 1969. In *Handbook of Molecular Cytology,* A. Lima-de-Faria, ed., p. 520. Wiley, New York.
16. Franc, J. M. 1973. Etude ultrastructurale de la spermalogenese en etenaire *Berol. Ovata. J. Ultrastruct. Res.* 42:255.
17. Gillies, C. B. 1975. An ultrastructural analysis of chromosomal pairing in maize. *C. R. Trav. Lab. Carlsberg* 40:135.
18. Moens, P. B. 1972. Fine structure of chromosome coiling at meiotic prophase in *Rhoeo Discolor. Can. J. Genet. Cytol.* 14:801.
19. Gregorie, V. 1907. *Le Cellule* 24:369.
20. Krush, G. S., and Rich, C. M. 1968. Cytogenic analysis of the tomato genome by means of induced deficiencies. *Chromosoma* 23:452.
21. Ford, E. H. R., 1973. *Human Chromosomes,* pp. 152–173. Academic Press, London.
22. Janssens, F. A. 1924. La chiasmatype dans des insects. *Cellule* 34:135.
23. Darlington, C. D. 1937. *Recent Advances in Cytology,* 2nd ed. Churchill, London. (Reprinted as *Cytology,* 1965.)
24. Darlington, C. D. 1934. The origin and behavior of chiasmata, VII: *Zea mays. Z. Indukt. Abstamm. Vererbungsl.* 67:96.
25. Lambert, M. W., and Studzinski, G. P. 1978. Methods for assessment of DNase activity. In *Methods in Cell Biology, Chromatin and Chromosomal Properties,* Stein, G., and Stein, J., eds., p. 43. Academic Press, New York.
26. Whitehouse, H. L. K. 1970. The mechanism of genetic recombination. *Biol. Rev.* 45:265.
27. Lambert, M. W., and Studzinski, G. P. 1979. Action of a partially purified deoxyribonuclease from mammalian melanoma cells on depurinated DNA. *Fed. Proc.* 38:994.

28. Lambert, M. W., and Studzinski, G. P. 1980. DNA endonuclease activities associated with melanoma cell chromatin. Biochem. Biophys. Res. Commun. 91:1481.
29. Lambert, W. C., et al. 1979. Nuclear DNA endonuclease activities of human lymphoblast cells in culture. Fed. Proc. 38,995.
30. Lambert, W. C., et al. A method for detecting defective DNA endonucleases in genodermatoses, J. Invest. Dermatol. 74:255.
31. Wang, E. C., and Furth, J. J. 1977. Mammalian endonuclease, DNase V. J. Biol. Chem. 252:116.
32. Hotta, Y., Ito, M., and Stern, H. Synthesis of DNA during meiosis. Proc. Natl. Acad. Sci. U.S., 56:1184, 1966.
33. White, M. J. D., The Chromosomes (6th ed), Chapman and Hall, London, 1973, pp. 76–100.
34. Watson, I. D., and Callan, H. G. 1963. The form of bivalent chromosomes in newt oocytes at first metaphase of meiosis. Qu. J. Microsc. Sci. 104:281.
35. Baker, T. G., and Franchi, L. L. The structure of the chromosomes in human primordial oocytes. Chromosoma, 22:358–377, 1967.
36. Du Praw, E. J. 1970. DNA and Chromosomes, p. 249. Holt, Reinhart & Winston, New York.
37. Wettstein, R., and Sotelo, J. R. 1971. The molecular architecture of synaptonemal complexes. Adv. Cell Mol. Biol. 1:109.
38. Gillies, C. B. 1975. Synaptonemal complex and chromosome structure. Annu. Rev. Genet. 9:81.
39. Moses, M. J. 1956. Chromosomal structures in crayfish spermatocytes. J. Biophys. Biochem. Cytol. 2:215.
40. Fawcett, D. W. 1956. The fine structure of chromosomes in the meiotic prophase of vertebrate spermatocytes. J. Biophys. Biochem. Cytol. 2:403.
41. Wettstein, R., and Sotelo, J. R. 1967. Electron microscope serial reconstruction of the spermatocyte I nuclei at pachytene. J. Microsc. 6:557.
42. Woollam, D. H. M., Millen, J. W., and Ford, E. H. R. 1967. Points of attachment of pachytene chromosomes to the nuclear membrane in mouse spermatocytes. Nature 213:298.
43. Sheridan, W. F., and Stern, H. 1967. Histones of meiosis. Exp. Cell Res. 45:323.
44. Dorlands' Medical Dictionary, 23rd ed., 1957. p. 1115. W. B. Saunders, Philadelphia.
45. Calvin, H. I. 1976. Comparative analysis of the nuclear basic proteins in rat, human, guinea pig, mouse, and rabbit spermatogonia. Biochem. Biophys. Acta 434:377.
46. Bellve, A. R., Anderson, E., and Hanley-Bowdain, L. 1975. Synthesis and amino acid composition of basic proteins in mammalian sperm nuclei. Dev. Biol. 47:349.
47. Bloch, D. P., and Hew, H. Y. C. 1960. Changes in nuclear histone during fertilization and early embryonic development in the pulmonate snail, Helix aspersa. J. Biophys. Biochem. Cytol. 8:69.
48. Flemming, W. 1882. Zellsubstanz, Kern and Zelltheilung. Vogel, Leipzig.
49. Rückert, J. 1892. Zur Entwidslungsgeschichte des Ovarialeies bei Selachiern. Anat. Anz. 7:197.
50. Wischnitzer, S. 1976. The lampbrush chromosomes: Their morphology and physiological significance. Endeavor 35:27.
51. Duryee, W. R. 1950. Chromosomal physiology in relation to nuclear structure. Ann. N.Y. Acad. Sci. 50:920.
52. Gall, J. J. 1966. Methods in Cell Physiology, Vol 2, p. 37, Academic Press, New York.
53. Snow, M. H. L., and Callan, H. G. 1969. Evidence for a polarized movement of the lateral loops of newt lampbrush chromosomes during oogensis. J. Cell Sci. 5:125.
54. Gall, J. G., and Callan, H. G. 1962. ^{3}H-Uridine incorporation in lampbrush chromosomes. Proc. Natl. Acad. Sci. U.S. 48:562.

55. MacGregor, H. C., and Callan, H. G. 1962. The active of enzymes on lampbrush chromosomes. *Q. J. Microsc. Sci.* 103:173.
56. Miller, O. J., Jr., and Hamkalo, B. A. 1972. Visualization of RNA synthesis on chromosomes. *Int. Rev. Cytol.* 33:1.
57. Callan, H. G., and Lloyd, L. 1960. Lampbrush chromosomes of crested newts *Triturus cristatus* (Lawenti). *Phil. Trans. R. Soc. B* 243:135.
58. Hess, O., and Meyer, G. F. 1968. Genetic activities of the chromosome in *Drosophila* during spermatogenesis. *Adv. Genet.* 14:171.

12.4. Gene Localization Using Interspecific Somatic Cell Hybrids

Richard E. Giles and Frank H. Ruddle

The genetic analysis of mammalian cells in vitro has been greatly facilitated by the production and analysis of interspecific cell hybrids (1–3). Different types of mammalian cells may be fused by treatment with inactivated Sendai virus (4–5) or polyethylene glycol (6) to produce heterokaryons. A fraction of the multinucleate heterokaryons give rise to mononucleate synkaryons (hybrid cells) in which the different parental genomes are reconstituted in a single nucleus. Hybrid cells are formed at a relatively low frequency (10^{-4}–10^{-6}), and biochemical selection is generally employed to eliminate parental cells (4). The most widely used biochemical selection system is the HAT system developed by Szybalski et al. (7). Parental cells lacking HPRT (hypoxanthine–guanine phosphoribosyltransferase, E.C. 2.4.4.8) or TK (thymidine kinase, E.C. 2.7.1.21) are fused and transferred to a medium containing hypoxanthine, aminopterin, and thymidine (HAT). Enzyme-deficient parental cells (HPRT$^-$ and TK$^-$) are killed because de novo purine and pyrimidine biosynthesis is blocked by aminopterin, and the enzymatic deficiencies prevent utilization of exogeneous sources of purines or pyrimidines. Hybrid cells survive because one parental genome provides HPRT, and the other provides TK. Other biochemical selection systems are available (1–2, 4).

If the parental cells are from different species, preferential chromosome elimination generally occurs, resulting in a reduction of the number of chromosomes derived from one of the parental cells (1–2). Preferential chromosome elimination exhibits two phases in interspecific human $\times$ mouse hybrids. During the initial phase (approximately 60 days) human chromosome loss occurs at a high rate. After the initial phase the chromosome complement appears to stabilize, and chromosomes are lost more slowly (8). Independently isolated human $\times$ mouse (HM) hybrid cell clones frequently differ with respect to the presence and absence of specific human chromosomes, and it is therefore possible to produce a panel of clones each of which retains a different combination of human chromosomes and which collectively represent the entire human genome (1).

GENETIC MARKERS

Interspecific variation between homologous proteins often permits analysis of the expression of homologous parental genes in hybrid cells. A substantial number of enzymes exhibit species-specific electrophoretic mobility and are valuable genetic markers of use in the analysis of hybrid cells (4, 9). A number of other markers have been analyzed in interspecific cell hybrids (1–4), such as auxotrophic markers, drug resistance, temperature resistance (10–11), surface antigens, specific proteins, virus susceptibility, tumor production, morphology, and toxin resistance.

CHROMOSOME IDENTIFICATION

Mammalian metaphase chromosomes may be stained with the fluorescent dye quinacrine (atebrin) or Giemsa stain to develop banding patterns (12–14) that permit the unambiguous identification of each chromosome in the normal karyotype of human (15), mouse (16), and Chinese hamster (17) cells. Cytogenetic analysis of interspecific hybrid cells is more difficult than analysis of normal diploid cells (18). Normal mouse cells possess 40 telocentric chromosomes. However, many of the permanent drug-resistant mouse cell lines used for the production of interspecific hybrids are heteroploid and exhibit marked deviations from the normal mouse karyotype such as an increased number of chromosomes per cell, biarmed chromosomes, and abnormal banding patterns. Established Chinese hamster cell lines such as CHO also exhibit substantial deviations from the normal hamster karyotype (17). A thorough cytogenetic characterization of parental cells is necessary if errors in chromosome identification are to be avoided.

Alkaline Giemsa staining (G-11) stains human chromosomes light blue and mouse or Chinese hamster dark purple (19–20), and may be performed after quinacrine staining to reduce the possibility of chromosome identification errors. The G-11 staining reaction also allows the detection of interspecific translocation chromosomes (20). Mouse chromosome centromeres fluoresce brightly when stained with the dye Hoechst 33258, whereas human and hamster chromosomes do not exhibit bright centromeric fluorescence (21–22). Giemsa banding procedures may be performed prior to Hoechst staining. Analysis of a metaphase plate by Hoechst staining after Giemsa banding markedly reduces the chance of chromosome identification errors in human × mouse and mouse × Chinese hamster hybrids. Established mouse cell lines may contain telocentric or biarmed chromosomes which do not exhibit bright centromeric fluorescence when stained with Hoechst stain, and some of the chromosomes in normal mouse cells exhibit weak centromeric fluorescence in comparison to other chromosomes in the normal mouse karyotype. Constitutive heterochromatin (C-bands) may be visualized by several procedures using Giemsa stain (12–14, 23). A number of human chromosomes polymorphisms have been detected which involve constitutive heterochromatin (24). C-band procedures result in dark staining of heterochromatin regions and light staining of euchromatic regions. Mouse centromeric heterochromatin may be used to distinguish mouse and human chromosomes in hybrid cells (24), but since several human chromosomes exhibit prominent C-band regions which do not stain brightly with Hoechst stain, it is preferable to use the Hoechst procedure in most instances for the analysis of human × mouse hybrid cells.

TYPES OF GENE ASSIGNMENTS

Marker expression data (i.e., isozyme phenotypes) and the presence and absence of specific chromosomes in a collection of hybrid cell clones are tested for concordant segregation by assembling the data in the format of 2 × 2 contingency tables as in Figure 1. Data from a number of 2 × 2 contingency tables testing the segregation of one marker against an array of other markers may be conveniently combined using the format of Table 1. The number of observations in the ++ and —— categories (concordant segregation categories) are compared to the number of observations in the +— and —+ categories (discordant segregation categories). Two basic tests for gene localization are performed using interspecific cell hybrids. *Synteny analysis* (Figure 1, Table A) tests for the concordant segregation of two phenotypic markers and is used to assign markers to a common chromosome and, indirectly, to a specific chromosome when the chromosomal locus of one of the markers is known. *Chromosome gene assignments* (Figure 1, Table B) are performed directly

	Table A				Table B	
	Marker 1 (HEX B)				Marker 1 (HEX B)	
	+	−			+	−
Marker 2 + Heat	18[a]	0		Marker 2 + Chromosome	6	0
Resist. −	1	14		5 −	0	11

[a] Number of clones + for marker 1 and + for marker 2.

Figure 1. 2 × 2 contingency tables.

Table 1. Marker Expression Data in a Collection of Hybrid Cell Clones

	TEST MARKER			
	++	+—[a]	—+	——
Isozymes 1	9[b]	0	2	15
2	6	4	4	8
3	10	7	2	7
Chromosome 1	6	0	0	9
2	4	5	3	3
3	6	3	2	4

[a] Positive for the isozyme or chromosome and negative for the test marker.
[b] Number of clones.

by testing for the concordant segregation of a phenotypic marker and a specific chromosome. *Regional mapping* or the assignment of a gene to a specific portion of a chromosome may be performed by employing a parental cell carrying a known translocation or by analyzing translocations arising during the propagation of hybrid cell clones (see also Chapter 12.5). A large number of human gene loci have been mapped using these experimental approaches (3). Goss and Harris (25) have performed regional gene localization by fusing X-irradiated human cells with mouse cells and analyzing the frequency at which known syntenic markers are co-transferred. This method of gene localization would be greatly facilitated if the catalog of selectable genetic markers in mammalian cells were expanded.

Theoretically, a clone panel composed of five clones would be sufficient to assign a marker to a specific human chromosome (1). In practice, a larger number of clones are examined using the clone panel approach described by Ruddle and Creagan (1). If a clone panel composed of clones selected for optimal retention of different human chromosome combinations is not available, more clones should be tested. For the assignment of nonselectable markers, Bengtsson and Bodmer (26) have suggested that 10–20 randomly chosen clones of independent origin be examined.

DISCORDANT CLONES

Obviously, clones may be discordant for any pair of phenotype markers or for a marker and a chromosome because the markers are asyntenic or the marker genetic locus is not on a particular chromosome. However, chromosome rearrangements, which may or may not be cytologically detectable, or technical artifacts may also lead to the observation of discordant segregation of syntenic markers or discordant segregation of a marker and the chromosome containing the genetic locus of the marker (18). Differential sensitivity of phenotype assays and the difficulty of detecting human chromosomes present in a hybrid cell population at a low frequency may lead to incorrectly scoring a clone discordant. Chromosome identification errors may also lead to clone scoring errors. Regulatory phenomena or cell culture artifacts may lead to erroneous phenotype determinations. In order to minimize technical errors it is highly desirable to: (1) analyze hybrid clones for phenotype and chromosome complement at the same passage number; (2) test hybrid clones of independent origin that have been subcloned after the initial period of rapid chromosome segregation; (3) determine the relative sensitivity of the phenotype assays employed; and (4) thoroughly characterize parental cells and hybrids for biochemical phenotype and chromosome complement.

BIOCHEMICAL SELECTION AND GENE ASSIGNMENTS

Utilization of biochemical selection systems which selectively fix the retention of a specific chromosome at a high frequency or which can be used to select against a specific chromosome can substantially reduce the chance of technical errors yielding clone scoring errors. Using the HAT selection system it is possible to selectively fix either the human X chromosome or chromosome 17 using a rodent parental cell deficient in HPRT or TK. Furthermore, it is possible to select against retention of the X (HPRT) by using 8-azaguanine or 6-thioguanine and against retention of chromosome 17 (TK) by using BrdUrd. Human chromosome 16 may also be fixed or eliminated using drug selection (1, 4). Human chromosome translocations involving the transfer of a selectable genetic locus to a nonselectable chromosome are particularly valuable for mapping purposes.

EXPERIMENTAL APPROACHES

Gene assignments may be performed by analyzing segregating interspecific hybrids produced by fusing intact cells. It is also possible to fuse subnuclear DNA containing particles such as microcells isolated by enucleation of colchicine-treated cells (27) or mini segregants isolated by cold treatment of mitotic cells (28) with intact cells by Sendai virus. Fournier and Ruddle (29) transferred small numbers of A9 mouse cell chromosomes into mouse B82, Chinese hamster E36, and human HeLa S3 recipient cells via mouse microcells using HAT or ouabain selection. Transfer of a portion of one cell genome to a recipient cell by subnuclear particles has two attractive features with respect to gene assignment studies: (1) the genetic complexity of the hybrid cell initially produced can be reduced; and (2) the direction of chromosome segregation may be controlled. Using cytoplasts produced by cell enucleation techniques, it is possible to test for cytoplasmic control of cell phenotypic markers. Bunn et al. (30) and Wallace et al. (31) have demonstrated that chloramphenicol resistance is controlled by a cytoplasmic element, presumably the mitochondrial genome, by fusing chloramphenicol-resistant cytoplasts with sensitive cells.

It is also possible to transfer genetic material between cells by purified metaphase chromosomes (32–38). The transferred genetic element (transgenome) is not cytologically detectable when purified metaphase chromosomes are used to transfer the human HPRT gene into HPRT⁻ recipient mouse cells (33) or the human TK gene into recipient mouse (36) or Chinese hamster (37) cells. No co-transfer of X-linked PGK (phosphoglycerate kinase, E.C. 2.7.2.3) or G6PD (glucose-6-phosphate dehydrogenase, E.C.1.1.1.49) was noted when human HPRT was transferred to mouse HPRT⁻ cells by purified metaphase chromosomes (33–34). Transfer of an intact human X chromosome and co-transfer of X-linked HPRT, PGK, G6PD, and alpha-Gal (alpha-galactosidase, E.C.3.2.1.22) were observed by Wullems et al. (35) when HPRT⁻ human × Chinese hamster hybrids containing human chromosomes other than the X were treated with purified HeLa metaphase chromosomes and selected in HAT medium. Co-transfer of TK and GK (galactokinase, E.C.2.7.1.6) in the absence of cytologically identifiable human chromosome material was observed when TK⁻ mouse cells (36) or TK⁻ Chinese hamster cells (37) were treated with purified human chromosomes. Co-transfer of Mtx^{RIII} (methotrexate resistance III) and Gat⁺ (glycine, adenosine, thymidine auxotrophy = Gat⁻) and Mtx^{RIII} and GlyB⁺ (glycine auxotrophy = GlyB⁻) was observed by Spandidos and Siminovitch (38) using purified Chinese hamster chromosomes and Chinese hamster recipient cells. Gene transfer by purified metaphase chromosomes is a valuable experimental approach of use in testing for close linkage of genetic markers.

Recent experiments have shown that it is possible to transfer the TK gene of herpes simplex virus to TK⁻ mammalian cells by restriction-endonuclease-generated fragments of viral DNA (39–40). Unpublished results from Silverstein's group indicate that several mammalian bulk DNA preparations can be used to transform mouse LMTK⁻ cells to the TK⁻ condition (personal communication). These observations indicate that DNA-mediated gene transfer is feasible in mammalian cells.

SUMMARY

Five basic experimental approaches are relevant to gene assignment problems in somatic cell genetics: (1) production of interspecific cell hybrids exhibiting chromosome segregation; (2) transfer of genetic material by subcellular elements such as microcells, mini segregants, and cytoplasts; (3) gene transfer by purified metaphase chromosomes which generally results in the transfer of cytologically undetectable genetic material and is very useful in testing for the close proximity of genes; (4) gene transfer by purified viral DNA; and (5) gene localization by nucleic acid hybridization (chapter 12.5). The potential usefulness of these experimental approaches as means of directly mapping genes in mammalian cells or placing selectable markers in appropriate positions for genetic manipulations appears high.

REFERENCES

1. Ruddle, F. H., and Creagan, R. P. 1975. Parasexual approaches to the genetics of man. *Annu. Rev. Genet.* 9:407–86.
2. Ringertz, N. R., and Savage, R. E. 1976. *Cell Hybrids.* Academic Press, New York.
3. McKusick, V. A., and Ruddle, F. H. 1977. The status of the gene map of the human chromosomes. *Science* 196:390–405.
4. Giles, R. E., and Ruddle, F. H. 1973. Production and characterization of proliferating somatic cell hybrids. In *Tissue Culture Methods and Applications,* P. F. Kruse and M. K. Patterson, eds. Academic Press, New York.
5. Giles, R. E., and Ruddle, F. H. 1973. Production of Sendai virus for cell fusion. *In Vitro* 9:103–7.
6. Gefter, M. L., Margulies, D. H., and Scharff, M. D. 1977. A simple method for polyethylene glycol promoted hybridization of mouse myeloma cells. *Somat. Cell Genet.* 3:231–36.
7. Szybalski, W., Szybalska, E. H., and Ragnie, G. 1962. Genetic studies with human cell lines. *J. Natl. Cancer Inst. Monogr.* No. 7:75–89.
8. Nabholz, M., Miggiano, V., and Bodmer, W. 1969. Genetic analysis with human–mouse somatic cell hybrids. *Nature* 223:358–63.
9. Nichols, E. A., and Ruddle, F. H. 1973. A review of enzyme polymorphism, linkage, and electrophoretic conditions for mouse and somatic cell hybrids in starch gels. *J. Histochem. Cytochem.* 21:1066–81.
10. Giles, R. E., and Ruddle, F. H. 1976. Replacement of a mouse cell heat sensitive function by the human X chromosome in interspecific cell hybrids. *Genetics* 83:s26.
11. Giles, R. E., Shimizu, N., Nichols, E., Lawrence, J., and Ruddle, F. H. 1977. Correction of a heat sensitive lesion associated reduced leucyl–tRNA synthetase activity in Chinese hamster cells by fusion with human leucocytes. *J. Cell Biol.* 75:387a.
12. Caspersson, T. and Zech, L., eds. 1972. *Chromosome Identification.* Academic Press, New York.
13. Detrillaux, B., and Lejeune, J. 1975. New techniques in the study of human chromosomes: Methods and applications. *Adv. Hum. Genet.* 5:119–56.
14. Lubs, H. A., McKenzie, W. H., Patel, S. R., and Merrick, S. 1974. New staining methods for chromosomes. *Methods Cell Biol.* 6:345–80.
15. Paris Conference (1971): Standardization in human cytogenetics. *Birth Defects: Orig. Artic. Ser.* 8(7):1, 1972. The National Foundation, New York.
Paris Conference (1971), Suppl. (1975): Standardization in human cytogenetics. *Birth Defects: Orig. Artic. Ser.* 11(9):1, 1975, or *Cytogenet. Cell Genet.* 15:201–38, 1975.
16. Nesbitt, M. N., and Francke, U. 1973. A system of nomenclature for band patterns of mouse chromosomes. *Chromosoma* 41:145–58.

17. Deaven, L. L., and Petersen, D. F. 1973. The chromosomes of CHO, an aneuploid Chinese hamster cell line: G-band, C-band and autoradiographic analysis. *Chromosoma* 41:129–44.

18. Pearson, P. 1972. The limits of recognition of human chromosomes in hybrid cells. In Ref. 12.

19. Bobrow, M., and Cross, J. 1974. Differential staining of human and mouse chromosomes in interspecific cell hybrids. *Nature* 251:77–79.

20. Friend, K. K., Chen, S., and Ruddle, F. H. 1976. Differential staining of interspecific chromosomes in somatic cell hybrids by alkaline Giemsa stain. *Somat. Cell Genet.* 2:183–88.

21. Kucherlapati, R. S., Hilwig, I., Gropp, A., and Ruddle, F. H. 1975. Mammalian chromosome identification in interspecific hybrids using Hoechst 33258. *Humangenetik* 27:9–14.

22. Kozak, C. A., Lawrence, J. B., and Ruddle, F. H. 1977. A sequential staining technique for the chromosomal analysis of interspecific mouse/hamster and mouse/human somatic cell hybrids. *Exp. Cell Res.* 105:109–17.

23. Chen, T. R., and Ruddle, F. H. 1971. Karyotype analysis utilizing differentially stained constitutive heterochromatin of human and murine chromosomes. *Chromosoma* 34:51–72.

24. Craig-Holmes, A. P. 1977. C-band polymorphism in human populations. In *Population Cytogenetics,* pp. 161–77. Academic Press, New York.

25. Goss, S. J., and Harris, H. 1977. Gene transfer by means of cell fusion. I. Statistical mapping of the human X chromosome by analysis of radiation induced gene segregation. *J. Cell Sci.* 25:17–37.

26. Bengtsson, B., and Bodmer, W. F. 1975. The strategy of gene assignments using hybrids: The number of lines needed to exclude chance associations. *Cytogenet. Cell Genet.* 14:232–36.

27. Ege, T., and Ringertz, H. R. 1974. Preparation of microcells by enucleation of micronucleated cells. *Exp. Cell Res.* 87:378–82.

28. Schor, S. L., Johnson, R. T., and Mullinger, A. M. 1975. Perturbation of mammalian cell division. II. Studies on the isolation and characterization of human mini segregant cells. *J. Cell Sci.* 19:281–303.

29. Fournier, R. E. K., and Ruddle, F. H. 1977. Microcell-mediated transfer of murine chromosomes into mouse, Chinese hamster and human cells. *Proc. Natl. Acad. Sci.* 74:319–23.

30. Bunn, C. L., Wallace, D. C., and Eisenstadt, J. M. 1974. Cytoplasmic inheritance of chloramphenicol resistance in mouse tissue culture cells. *Proc. Natl. Acad. Sci.* 71:1681–85.

31. Wallace, D. C., Pollack, Y., Bunn, C. L., and Eisenstadt, J. M. 1976. Cytoplasmic inheritance in mammalian tissue culture cells. *In Vitro* 12:758–76.

32. McBride, O. W., and Ozer, H. L. 1973. Transfer of genetic information by purified metaphase chromosomes. *Proc. Natl. Acad. Sci.* 70:1258–62.

33. Willecke, K., and Ruddle, F. H. 1975. Transfer of the human gene for hypoxanthine–guanine phosphoribosyltransferase via isolated human metaphase chromosomes into mouse L-cells. *Proc. Natl. Acad. Sci.* 72:1792–96.

34. Burch, J. W., and McBride, O. W. 1975. Human gene expression in rodent cells after uptake of isolated metaphase chromosomes. *Proc. Natl. Acad. Sci.* 72:1797–1801.

35. Wullems, G. J., van der Horst, J., and Bootsma, D. 1976. Transfer of the human X chromosome to human–Chinese hamster cell hybrids via isolated Hela metaphase chromosomes. *Somat. Cell Genet.* 2:359–71.

36. Willecke, K., Lange, R., Kruger, A., and Reber, T. 1976. Cotransfer of two linked human genes into cultured mouse cells. *Proc. Natl. Acad. Sci.* 73:1274–78.

37. Wullems, G. J., van der Horst, J., and Bootsma, D. 1977. Transfer of the human genes coding for thymidine kinase and galactokinase to Chinese hamster cells and human–Chinese hamster cell hybrids. *Somat. Cell Genet.* 3:281–93.

38. Spandidos, D. A., and Siminovitch, L. 1977. Linkage of markers controlling consecutive

biochemical steps in CHO cells as demonstrated by chromosome transfer. *Cell* 12:235–42.

39. Maitland, N. J., and McDougall, J. K. 1977. Biochemical transformation of mouse cells by fragments of herpes simplex virus DNA. *Cell* 11:233–41.

40. Wigler, M., Silverstein, S., Lee, L. S., Pellicer, A., Cheng, Y. C., and Axel, R. 1977. Transfer of purified herpes virus thymidine kinase gene to cultured mouse cells. *Cell* 11:223–32.

12.5. Gene Localization Using Nucleic Acid Hybridization

Richard E. Giles and Frank H. Ruddle

Nucleic acid hybridization has been extensively utilized in the analysis of the structure of genomes ranging from viruses to man since the introduction of the technique of DNA reassociation by Schildkraut et al. (1). Analysis of DNA reassociation kinetics led to the discovery that the DNA of eukaryotes contains three basic classes of DNA: unique sequences; moderately repetitious or related sequences; and highly repeated sequences such as the mouse satellite DNA (2). Repeated DNA has been found in a wide variety of eukaryotes and has been noted to constitute from 20% to over 80% of the genome in various organisms with reported repetition frequencies varying from 3 to 6.7×10^6 (3). Repeated DNA sequences may be interspersed with nonrepetitious DNA (4) or tandemly repeated (5). Some repeated-sequence DNA may be resolved from the bulk of the genomic DNA by density gradient centrifugation (6). DNA:DNA or RNA:DNA hybridization studies may be performed in solution, on nitrocellulose filters, in gels, or in situ on cytological preparations (2, 7–12). The reader should consult the references cited above for information on methodology. Nucleic acid hybridization was first utilized in gene localization experiments to demonstrate that the nucleolus organizer locus is the site of the genes encoding rRNA. Ritossa and Spiegelman (13) tested *Drosophila melanogaster* DNA prepared from stocks carrying duplications or deficiencies of the nucleolar organizer locus for the ability to form RNA:DNA hybrids with ^{3}H-rRNA in a filter hybridization system. They found that the amount of ^{3}H-rRNA hybridized to DNA was directly correlated with the number of nucleolar organizer loci. Correlation of nucleolar organizer number and the amount of ^{14}C-rRNA:DNA formed in solution nucleic acid hybridization experiments was observed by Wallace and Birnstiel (14), who studies *Xenopus laevis* toads containing zero, one, or two nucleoli. These results demonstrated that the genes encoding rRNA are located in the nucleolar organizer region of the chromosome in these two organisms. In situ nucleic acid hybridization was developed by Gall and Pardue (15), who hybridized *Xenopus laevis* ^{3}H-rRNA to *X. laevis* oogonia to study rDNA amplification. Label was detected over the nucleolus by autoradiography of the cytological preparations. Subsequent in situ hybridization studies on *X. laevis* by Pardue (16) clearly demonstrated localization of the 18S and 28S rRNA genes in the *Xenopus* nucleolar organizer region of diploid metaphase chromosomes, mapped 5S rRNA genes to the telomeric region of the long arms of most of the chromosomes, and detected a satellite DNA present in discrete bands in the middle region of the short arms of all chromosomes.

Since the introduction of the technique of in situ hybridization, cytological localization of 18S and 28S rDNA, 5S rDNA, and numerous satellite DNAs has been accomplished in a substantial number of organisms (3). The ability to localize genes using various nucleic acid hybridization approaches has been greatly expanded by the development of procedures for the cloning of DNA from higher organisms in prokaryotes (17, 18). In any nucleic acid hybridization experiment designed to localize genes indirectly by quantitative differences in hybridization between genetically different cells (i.e., interspecific human × mouse hybrids retaining different human chromosomes or *Drosophila* with gene duplications or deficiencies) or directly by in situ hybridization, the purity of the labeled nucleic acid probe is critical. For example, if a labeled nucleic acid probe complementary to a nucleotide sequence is present in the genome at a low frequency of repetition, the detected hybridization may be predominantly due to the contaminating sequence. The ability to clone eukaryotic DNA in prokaryotes promises to provide a source of large quantities of homogeneous specific eukaryotic DNA sequences which are not conveniently obtainable from bulk eukaryotic DNA or RNA using currently available chemical and physical methods of purification. Eukaryotic DNA cloned in prokaryotes has been utilized in analysis of the organization of the histone genes in the sea urchin genome (19, 20) and in analysis of the genome of *Drosophila melanogaster*.

GENE LOCALIZATION IN *DROSOPHILA* USING NUCLEIC ACID HYBRIDIZATION

Drosophila melanogaster (Dm) possesses a number of attractive features, reviewed by Gall (5), that facilitate analysis of the genome, such as: (1) small genome size; (2) a karyotype limited to four chromosomes; and (3) in the larval form, formation of giant polytene chromosomes exhibiting prominent bands, which consist of approximately 1000 chromatids aligned in parallel register. The extensive genetic data available on this organism and the attractive characteristics of the polytene chromosome as a substrate for in situ nucleic acid hybridization studies have been exploited by a number of investigators interested in gene localization.

Drosophila Satellite DNA and Repeated DNA

The range in the amount of satellite DNA exhibited by different *Drosophila* species is large (Ref. 5; a few % to 60%). Three satellite DNAs isolated from *Drosophila virilis,* in which satellite DNA constitutes 40% of the genome, were found by Gall (5) to be closely related repeating heptanucleotide sequences. In situ hybridization of *D. virilis* sat. I by Gall et al. (21) resulted in labeling of the chromocenter in polytene preparations and the centromeric heterochromatin of mitotic chromosomes. Hybridization of sat. I to polytene chromosomes from three other *Drosophila* resulted in labeling of the chromocenter and an additional specific band in two instances. Peacock et al. (22) isolated four major satellites and one minor satellite from Dm and observed labeling of the chromocenter and the 21CD region of the left arm of chromosome 2 when ³H-cRNA was hybridized to polytene chromosomes. Wensink et al. (17) cloned a segment of Dm DNA that was repeated 90 times in the genome and found the sequence was present in 15 different chromomeric regions and the chromocenter of polytene chromosomes, by in situ hybridization. Glover et al. (23) have localized a Dm DNA sequence repeated 33 times to the polytene chromosome chromocenter.

Drosophila rDNA and tRNA Genes

Localization of the 18S and 28S rRNA genes has been studied at two organizational levels. At the level of the polytene chromosome, Pardue et al. (24) demonstrated that the 18S and 28S rDNA sequences were located in the nucleolar organizer regions of the X and Y chromosomes by in situ hybridization. The genomic fine structure of rDNA has been examined by the analysis of cloned rDNA (25, 26), by analysis of density-gradient-purified rDNA (27), and by analysis of affinity-column-purified rDNA (28), using restriction endonuclease analysis (29), electron microscope heteroduplex analysis (30), and electron microscope R-loop mapping (9). From the results of these studies there appear to be two types of tandemly repeated rDNA sequences in *Drosophila:* (1) a sequence consisting of DNA coding for 18S and 28S rRNA in which the 18S and 28S genes are separated by transcribed and nontranscribed spacer sequences; and (2) a sequence similar to (1), but containing an insertion of variable size at a specific point in the 28S gene. These two types of rDNA sequences appear to be interspersed on the X chromosome (27, 28).

5S rDNA has been localized to region 56E-F on 2R by in situ hybridization (31), and it appears that the bulk of the 5S rDNA is located in this region (32). Analysis of cloned Dm 5S rDNA sequences by electron microscopy and restriction endonucleases (33, 34) indicates the 5S rDNA genes are arranged as a tandem repeat of approximately 380 base pairs (bp) of 5S rDNA + rDNA + 260 bp of spacer DNA.

The genes for tRNA (tDNA) are repeated in the genomes of eukaryotes and have been studied in Dm at the chromosomal and molecular level using the experimental approaches applied to the study of rDNA. Steffensen and Wimber (35) performed in situ hybridization studies with a tRNA probe and observed labeling of 68 distinct sites on chromosome 2. Labeling of the 56E-F region appeared to be due to contamination of the tRNA probe with 5S RNA. Using a purified ^{125}I-tRNA$_5^{Lys}$ probe and in situ hybridization, Grigliatti et al. (36) observed labeling of the 48F–49A and 56E-F regions of 2R. Dilution competition hybridization experiments indicated the probe was slightly contaminated with 5S RNA. Yen et al. (37) examined a cloned fragment of Dm DNA containing four tDNA genes. A cRNA probe prepared from the plasmid carrying the four tRNA genes hybridized to the 42A region of 2R. Three of the tRNA genes appeared to be identical, while the fourth gene was distinctly different. Intermingling of tRNA genes in a tandem repeat composed of tRNA genes + spacer DNA has been observed in *Xenopus* (38). This study (38) made the interesting observation that the tRNA$_1^{Met}$ and tRNA$_2^{Met}$ were not intermingled. Results demonstrating the presence of different secondary structures in the spacer regions between the cloned Dm tRNA genes suggested that the spacer regions were not identical repeats. Carroll and Brown (39) have detected heterogeneity in the spacer regions in *Xenopus* 5S rDNA, and Wellauer et al. (40) have described heterogeneity on the spacer of *Xenopus* rDNA.

Drosophila Histone DNA and Unique Sequence

Pardue et al. (41) have used a probe for histone coding DNA prepared from the sea urchin to localize the histone genes by in situ hybridization to the 39D-E region of 2L. A ^{3}H-cRNA probe prepared from cloned Dm histone DNA was observed to specifically hybridize to the 39D-E region of 2L (42), confirming the results of Pardue et al. (41). Analysis of the cloned Dm histone coding DNA by Lifton et al. (43) indicated that all five histone genes, separated by spacer DNA, are tandemly repeated. Lifton et al. (43) have noted that the arrangement of the histone genes in Dm differs from the organization of histone genes in the sea urchin in two characteristics: (1) the sequence of individual histone genes within the repeat is different; and (2) in Dm three histone genes are transcribed from one strand, and two histone genes are transcribed from the other strand, while in the sea urchin all five histone genes are transcribed from the same strand (20). Studies by Wensink et al. (17) suggest the feasibility of mapping unique genes in Dm using cloned Dm DNA and in situ hybridization of DM probes to polytene chromosomes.

GENE LOCALIZATION IN MAMMALIAN CELLS USING NUCLEIC ACID HYBRIDIZATION

Satellite DNA and Repeated DNA

A number of mammalian satellite and repeated DNAs have been mapped using in situ nucleic acid hybridization. Mouse satellite DNA was shown to be localized in the centromeric region by Jones (44) and by Pardue and Gall (45). In the human genome short repeated sequences appear to be interspersed with single copy sequences in approximately half of the genome (46). Some human repeated sequence DNA appears to be clustered (47). Several human satellite DNAs have been isolated and localized to regions of specific human chromosomes (48). Probes prepared from human satellites I–IV have been noted to label the Y chromosome (6, 48). Additional prominent labeling of other chromosome regions by various satellites has been observed, specifically: satellite I probes label 9, 15, and 22; satellite II probes label 1, 9, and 15; satellite III probes label 9, 15, and 22; and satellite IV probes label 9, D group, 20, and G group chromosome regions (6, 48). Probes prepared from each of the four satellites labeled other chromosome regions to a lesser extent, and some variability has been noted between results reported by different investigators (6). Macaya et al. (6), Jones (49), and Steffensen (11) have recently reviewed chromosomal localization of satellite DNAs. Marx et al. (50) prepared probes from highly repetitious human DNA and performed in situ hybridization. Three of the repetitious families appeared to correspond to satellites I, II, and III. Y chromosome–specific repeated DNA probes have been prepared and characterized by Cooke (51) and Kunkel et al. (52, 53). Singh et al. (54) have suggested that satellite DNA plays a role in the evolution of heteromorphic sex chromosomes.

Mammalian rDNA

Human 18S and 28S rDNA has been shown to be localized in the short arms of the D and G group chromosomes (55, 56). Hsu et al. (57) examined the distribution of 18S and 28S rDNA in several mammals and observed five basic patterns: (1) a single major site; (2) two sites; (3) multiple sites in or near centromeric heterochromatin; (4) multiple sites in heterochromatic short arms; and (5) multiple sites in telomeric regions. In *Mus musculus,* the chromosome locations of rDNA visualized by in situ hybridization exhibit some variation between different inbred strains. Henderson et al. (58) noted rDNA loci on mouse chromosomes 15, 18, and 19, while Elsevier and Ruddle (59) detected rDNA loci on chromosomes 12, 16, and 18 in different mouse strains. In a subsequent study, Henderson et al. (60) observed additional strain differences in the distribution of mouse rDNA loci. Human 5S rDNA is clustered at a site on the long arm of chromosome 1 (61, 62). Some human 5S rDNA may be located on 9 and/or 16 (62).

Localization of Human Hemoglobin Genes

In 1972, Price et al. (63) described in situ hybridization experiments localizing the human hemoglobin genes to chromosome 2 and a B group chromosome. Bishop and Jones (64) and Prensky and Holmquist (65) raised strong theoretical objections to this gene assignment based on the reported radioactivity of the ³H-RNA probe used by Price et al. (63). In a subsequent study, Price and Hirschhorn (66) described in situ hybridization studies with cDNA of much higher specific activity than the ³H-RNA probe used in 1972 and observed labeling of chromosome 4. Atwood et al. (67, 68) used ¹²⁵I-mouse reticulocyte mRNA and mouse hemoglobin loci (α or β) to test the feasibility of mapping hemoglobin loci by in situ hybridization. Atwood et al. (67, 68) observed labeling of the expected chromosomes. Deisseroth et al. (69, 70) have analyzed human × mouse hybrids (see above) with cDNA probes specific for human α-hemoglobin or β-hemoglobin by DNA∶cDNA solution hybridization and have assigned the human α-hemoglobin gene to chromosome 16 (69) and the human β-hemoglobin gene to 11 (70). Association of chromosomes 2, 4, or 5 with human α- or β-hemoglobin loci was excluded by the observation of clones positive for the chromosome but negative for the presence of α- or β-hemoglobin genes. In a recent review article, Steffensen (11) has indicated that he has observed labeling of C group human chromosomes but not A or B group chromosomes using ¹²⁵I-labeled human hemoglobin mRNA and an improved in situ hybridization method.

SV40 Integration Sites

Khoury and Croce (71, 72) have studied hybrids produced between SV40 transformed human cells and mouse cells for the presence of the SV40 genome by nucleic acid reassociation, T antigen expression, and human chromosome complement, and on the basis of their observations, assigned an SV40 integration site to chromosome 7. Croce (73) has assigned another SV40 integration site to chromosome 17. Botchan et al. (74) investigated the arrangement of SV40 sequences in several independently transformed rat cell lines by agarose electrophoretic analysis of restriction-endonuclease-cleaved cell DNA for the presence of SV40 genome sequences by the Southern technique. The pattern of SV40 genome–containing framents generated by a variety of restriction endonucleases observed by Botchan et al. (74) indicated that "there can be multiple copies of intact or partial viral genomes integrated at different chromosomal locations," and "the junction points between viral DNA and cellular DNA contain viral sequences which map at different positions on the viral genome." Such observations suggest that SV40 integration in the mammalian genome does not occur by a site-specific recombination process analogous to integration of λ in the *E. coli* genome. Additional studies will be necessary to determine if other human chromosomes in addition to 7 and 17 can integrate SV40 genomes, or if multiple different integration sites exist on single chromosomes.

CONCLUDING REMARKS

The elegant application of the techniques of nucleic acid hybridization and DNA cloning to the analysis of the *Drosophila* genome is impressive and suggestive of a future in which substantial progress can be made in dissecting other eukaryotic genomes. Generation of probes specific for individual tRNA genes from cloned eukaryotic tRNA would avoid problems associated with tRNA purification and should permit tRNA gene localization by in situ hybridization or by analysis of segregating interspecific cell hybrids. Preparation of nucleic acid probes for human α- and β-hemoglobin genes from cloned human DNA should provide a superior tool for analysis of the chromosomal localization of these genes by in situ hybridization.

REFERENCES

1. Schildkraut, C. L., Marmur, J., and Doty, P. 1961. The formation of hybrid DNA molecules and their use in studies of DNA homologies. *J. Mol. Biol.* 3:595–617.
2. Britten, R. J., and Kohne, D. E. 1968. Repeated sequences in DNA. *Science* 161:529–40.
3. Straus, N. A. 1976. Repeated DNA in eukaryotes. In *Handbook of Genetics*, 5:3–29. R. C. King, ed. Plenum Press, New York.
4. Davidson, E. H., Hough, R. R., Amenson, C. S., and Britten, R. J. 1973. General interspersion of repetitive with non-repetitive sequence elements in the DNA of *Xenopus. J. Mol. Biol.* 77:1–23.
5. Gall, J. C. 1973. Repetitive DNA in *Drosophila:* In *Molecular Cytogenetics*, B. A. Hamkalo and J. Papaconstantinous, eds., pp. 59–74. Plenum Press, New York.
6. Macaya, G., Thiery, J-P. and Bernardi, G. 1977. DNA sequences in man. In *Molecular Structure of Human Chromosomes*, J. J. Yunis, ed. Academic Press, New York.
7. McCarthy, B. J., and Church, R. B. 1970. The specificity of molecular hybridization reactions. *Annu. Rev. Biochem.* 39:131–50.
8. Britten, R. J., Graham, D. E., and Neufeld, R. R. 1974. Analysis of repeating DNA by reassociation. *Methods Enzymol.* 29:363–418.
9. Thomas, M., White, R. L., and Davis, R. W. 1976. Hybridization of RNA to double-stranded DNA: Formation of R-loops. *Proc. Natl. Acad. Sci.* 73:2294–98.
10. Pardue, M. L., and Gall, J. G. 1975. Nuclei acid hybridization to the DNA of cytological preparations. *Methods Cell Biol.* 10:1–16.
11. Steffensen, D. K. 1977. Human gene localization by RNA:DNA hybridization in situ. In *Molecular Structure of Human Chromosomes*, J. J. Yunis, ed. Academic Press, New York.

12. Eckhardt, R. A. 1976. Cytological localization of repeated DNAs. In *Handbook of Genetics* 5:31–53, R. C. King, ed. Plenum Press, New York.

13. Ritossa, F. M., and Spiegelman, S. 1965. Localization of DNA complementary to ribosomal RNA in the nucleolus organizer region of *Drosophila melanogaster*. *Proc. Natl. Acad. Sci.* 53:737–45.

14. Wallace, H., and Birnstiel, M. L. 1966. Ribosomal cistrons and the nucleolar organizer. *Biochem. Biophys. Acta* 114:296–310.

15. Gall, J. G., and Pardue, M. L. 1969. Formation and detection of RNA–DNA hybrid molecules in cytological preparations. *Proc. Natl. Acad. Sci.* 63:378–83.

16. Pardue, M. L. 1974. Localization of repeated DNA sequences in *Xenopus* chromosomes. *Cold Spring Harbor Symp. Quant. Biol.* 38:475–83.

17. Wensink, P. C., Finnegan, D. J., Donelson, J. E., and Hogness, D. S. 1974. A system for mapping DNA sequences in chromosomes of *Drosophila melanogaster*. *Cell* 3:315–25.

18. *Recombinant Molecules: Impact on Science and Society.* Miles International Symposium, Series No. 10. Raven Press, New York, 1977.

19. Kedes, L. H., Cohn, R. H., Lowry, J. C., Chang, A. C. Y., and Cohen, S. N. 1975. The organization of sea urchin histone genes. *Cell* 6:358–69.

20. Cohn, R. H., Lowry, J. C., and Dedes, L. H. 1976. Histone genes of the sea urchin *(S. purpuratus)* cloned in *E. coli:* Order, polarity and strandedness of the five histone-coding and spacer regions. *Cell* 9:147–61.

21. Gall, J. G., Cohen, E. H., and Atherton, D. D. 1974. The satellite DNAs of *Drosophila virilis. Cold Spring Harbor Symp. Quant. Biol.* 38:417–21.

22. Peacock, W. J., Brutlag, D., Goldring, E., Appels, R., Hinton, C. W., and Lindsley, D. L. 1974. The organization of highly repeated DNA sequences in *Drosophila melanogaster* chromosomes. *Cold Spring Harbor Symp. Quant. Biol.* 38:405–16.

23. Glover, D. M., White, R. L., Finnegan, D. J., and Hogness, D. S. 1975. Characterization of six cloned DNAs from *Drosophila melanogaster,* including one that contains the genes for rRNA. *Cell* 5:149–57.

24. Pardue, M. L., Gerbi, S. A., Eckhardt, R. A., and Gall, J. G. 1970. Cytological localization of DNA complementary to ribosomal RNA in polytene chromosomes of *Diptera. Chromosoma* 29:268–90.

25. Glover, D. M., and Hogness, D. S. 1977. A novel arrangement of the 18S and 28S sequences in a repeating unit of *Drosophila melanogaster* rDNA. *Cell* 10:167–76.

26. White, R. L., and Hogness, D. S. 1977. R loop mapping of the 18S and 28S sequences in the long and short repeating units of *Drosophila melanogaster* rDNA. *Cell* 10:177–92.

27. Wellauer, P. K., and Dawid, I. B. 1977. The structural organization of ribosomal DNA in *Drosophila melanogaster. Cell* 10:193–212.

28. Pellegrini, M., Manning, J., and Davidson, N. 1977. Sequence arrangement of the rDNA of *Drosophila melanogaster. Cell* 10:213–24.

29. Nathans, D., and Smith, M. O. 1975. Restriction endonucleases in the analysis and restructuring of DNA molecules. *Annu. Rev. Biochem.* 44:273–93.

30. Davis, R. W., Simon, M., and Davidson, N. 1971. Electronmicroscope heteroduplex methods for mapping regions of base sequence homology in nucleic acids. *Methods Enzymol.* 21D:413–28.

31. Wimber, D. E., and Steffensen, D. M. 1970. Localization of 5S RNA genes of *Drosophila* chromosomes by RNA:DNA hybridization. *Science* 170:639–41.

32. Procumier, J. D., and Tartof, K. D. 1975. Genetic analysis of the 5S RNA genes in *Drosophila melanogaster. Genetics* 81:515–23.

33. Hershey, D. N., Conrad, S. E., Sodja, A., Yen, P. H., Cohen, M., Jr., Davidson, N., Ilgen, C., and Carbon, J. 1977. The sequence of *Drosophila melanogaster* 5S DNA cloned in recombinant plasmids. *Cell* 11:585–98.

34. Artavanis-Tsakonas, S., Schedl, P., Tschudi, C., Pirrotta, V., Steward, R., and Gehring, W. J. 1977. The 5S genes of *Drosophila melanogaster*. *Cell* 12:1057–67.

35. Steffensen, D. M., and Wimber, D. E. 1971. Localization of tRNA genes in the salivary chromosomes of *Drosophila* by RNA:DNA hybridization. *Genetics* 69:163–78.

36. Grigliatti, T. A., White, B. N., Tener, G. M., Kaufman, T. C., and Suzuki, D. T. 1974. The localization of transfer RNA$_5^{lys}$ genes in *Drosophila melanogaster*. *Proc. Natl. Acad. Sci.* 71:3527–31.

37. Yen, P. H., Sodja, A., Chen Jr., M., Conrad, S. E., Wu, M., Davidson, N., and Ilgen, C. 1977. Sequence arrangement of tRNA genes on a fragment of *Drosophila melanogaster* DNA clones in *E. coli. Cell* 11:763–77.

38. Clarkson, S. G., and Kurer, V. 1976. Isolation and some properties of DNA coding for tRNA$_1^{met}$ from *Xenopus laevis. Cell* 8:183–95.

39. Carroll, D., and Brown, D. D. 1976. Adjacent repeating units of *Xenopus laevis* 5S DNA can be heterogeneous in length. *Cell* 7:477–86.

40. Wellauer, P. K., Dawid, I. B., Brown, D. D., and Reeder, R. H. 1976. The molecular basis for length heterogeneity in ribosomal DNA from *Xenopus laevis. J. Mol. Biol.* 105:461–86.

41. Pardue, M. L., Kedes, L. H., Weinberg, E. S., and Birnstiel, M. L. 1977. Localization of sequences coding for histone messenger RNA in the chromosomes of *Drosophila melanogaster. Chromosoma* 63:135–51.

42. Karp, R. W., and Hogness, D. S. 1976. Isolation and mapping of histone genes contained in cloned segments of *Drosophila* DNA. *Fed. Proc.* 35:1623.

43. Lifton, R. P., Goldberg, M. L., Karp, R. W., and Hogness, D. S. 1978. The organization of the histone genes in *Drosophila melanogaster*. Functional and evolutionary implications. *Cold Spring Harbor Symp. Quant. Biol.* 42:1047–1051.

44. Jones, K. W. 1970. Chromosomal and nuclear location of mouse satellite DNA in individual cells. *Nature* 225:912–15.

45. Pardue, M. L., and Gall, J. G. 1970. Chromosomal localization of mouse satellite DNA. *Science* 168:1356–58.

46. Schmid, D. W., and Deininger, P. L. 1975. Sequence organization of the human genome. *Cell* 6:345–85.

47. Ginelli, E., and Corneo, G. 1976. The organization of repeated DNA sequences in the human genome. *Chromosoma* 56:55–68.

48. Gosden, J. R., Mitchell, A. R., Buckland, R. A., Clayton, R. P., and Evans, H. J. 1975. The location of four human satellite DNAs on human chromosomes. *Exp. Cell Res.* 92:148–58.

49. Jones, K. W. 1977. Repetitive DNA and primate evolution. In *Molecular Structure of Human Chromosomes,* J. J. Yunis, ed. Academic Press, New York.

50. Marx, K. A., Allen, J. R., and Hearst, J. E. 1976. Chromosomal localization by in situ hybridization of the repetitious human DNA families and evidence of their satellite DNA equivalents. *Chromosoma* 59:23–42.

51. Cooke, H. 1976. Repeated sequence specific to human males. *Nature* 262:182–86.

52. Kunkel, L. M., Smith, K. D., and Boyer, S. H. 1977. Human Y-chromosome specific DNA. *Science* 191:1189–90.

53. Kunkel, L. M., Smith, K. D., Boyer, S. H., Borgaonkar, D. S., Wachtel, S. S., Miller, O. J., Breg, W. R., Jones, H. W., Jr., and Rary, J. M. 1977. Analysis of human Y-chromosome specific reiterated DNA in chromosome variants. *Proc. Natl. Acad. Sci.* 74:1245–49.

54. Singh, L., Purdon, I. F., and Jones, K. W. 1976. Satellite DNA and evolution of sex chromosomes. *Chromosoma* 59:43–62.

55. Henderson, A. S., Warburton, D., and Atwood, K. C. 1972. Location of ribosomal DNA in the human chromosome complement. *Proc. Natl. Acad. Sci.* 69:3394–98.

56. Evans, H. J., Buckland, R. A., and Pardue, M. L. 1974. Location of genes coding for 18S and 28S ribosomal RNA in the human genome. *Chromosoma* 48:405–26.

57. Hsu, T. C., Spirito, S. E., and Pardue, M. L. 1975. Distribution of 18S + 28S ribosomal genes in mammalian genomes. *Chromosoma* 53:25–36.

58. Henderson, A. S., Eicher, E. M., Yu, M. T., and Atwood, K. C. 1974. The chromosomal location of ribosomal DNA in the mouse. *Chromosoma* 49:155–60.

59. Elsevier, S. M., and Ruddle, F. H. 1975. Location of genes coding for 18S and 28S ribosomal RNA within the genome of *Mus musculus*. *Chromosoma* 52:219–28.

60. Henderson, A. S., Eicher, E. M., Yu, M. T., and Atwood, K. C. 1976. Variation in ribosomal RNA gene number in mouse chromosomes. *Cytogenet. Cell Genet.* 17:307–16.

61. Atwood, K. C., Yu, M. T., Johnson, L. D., and Henderson, A. S. 1975. The site of 5S RNA genes in human chromosome 1. *Cytogenet. Cell Genet.* 15:50–54.

62. Steffensen, D. M., Prensky, W., Mutton, D., and Hamerton, J. L. 1975. Mapping the human 5S RNA genes on chromosome 1 using translocations. *Cytogenet. Cell Genet.* 14:264–68.

63. Price, P. M., Conover, J. H., and Hirschhorn, K. 1972. Chromosomal localization of human haemoglobin genes. *Nature* 237:340–42.

64. Bishop, J. O., and Jones, K. W. 1972. Chromosomal localization of human haemoglobin genes. *Nature* 240:149–50.

65. Prensky, W., and Holmquist, G. 1973. Chromosomal localization of human haemoglobin structural genes: Techniques queried. *Nature* 241:44–45.

66. Price, P. M., and Hirschhorn, K. 1975. In situ hybridization of chromosomal loci. *Fed. Proc.* 34:2227–43.

67. Atwood, K. C., Henderson, A. S., Kacian, D., and Eicher, E. 1975. On the feasibility of mapping low-multiplicity genes by in situ hybridization. *Cytogenet. Cell Genet.* 14:59–61.

68. Atwood, K. C., Yu, M. T., Eicher, E., and Henderson, A. S. 1976. Feasibility tests for mapping low-multiplicity genes by hybridization in situ. *Cytogenet. Cell Genet.* 16:372–75.

69. Deisseroth, A., Nienhuis, A., Turner, P., Velez, R., Anderson, W. F., Ruddle, F. H., Lawrence, J., Creagan, R., and Kucherlapati, R. 1977. Localization of the human α-globin structural gene to chromosome 16 in somatic cell hybrids by molecular hybridization assay. *Cell* 12:205–18.

70. Deisseroth, A., Nienhuis, A., Lawrence, J., Giles, R., Turner, P., and Ruddle, F. H. 1978. Chromosomal localization of the human beta globin gene to human chromosome 11 in somatic cell hybrids. *Proc. Natl. Acad. Sci.* 75:1456–1460.

71. Khoury, G., and Croce, C. M. 1976. Assignment of the integrated SV40 DNA to human chromosome 7 in a SV40-transformed human cell line. *Cytogenet. Cell Genet.* 16:164–70.

72. Khoury, G., and Croce, C. 1975. Quantitation of the viral DNA present in somatic cell hybrids between mouse and SV40 transformed human cells. *Cell* 6:535–42.

73. Croce, C. M. 1977. Assignment of the integration site for simian virus 40 to chromosome 17 in GM54VA, a human cell line transformed by simian virus 40. *Proc. Natl. Acad. Sci.* 74:315–18.

74. Botchan, M., Topp, W., and Sambrook, J. 1976. The arrangement of simian virus 40 sequences in the DNA of transformed cells. *Cell* 9:269–87.

12.6. The Mammalian Nuclear Envelope

Randolph C. Steer, Akhouri A. Sinha, and Michael J. Wilson

Although the nuclear envelope was first demonstrated indirectly by Hertwig in 1893, it did not receive much attention until recently. For a long time it was considered as a static structure whose sole function was to provide a barrier between the nucleus and the cytoplasm. It consisted of two membranes separated by a perinuclear space and interspersed with pore complexes. However, owing to the introduction of electron microscopy, subcellular biochemistry, and methods for its isolation and characterization, the nuclear envelope is now considered as a dynamic organelle (1). It contains enzyme activities that suggest its participation in numerous processes. For example, there is sufficient experimental evidence for a role in nucleocytoplasmic exchange of substances, and in the organization of chromatin. Also of great importance is the possibility that the inner nuclear membrane is a site for the initiation of DNA synthesis and replication.

In this chapter we will discuss briefly the methods involved in obtaining mammalian nuclear envelopes, as well as some of the important aspects of their structure, biochemistry, and physiology. Although techniques have been developed specifically for the isolation of nuclear envelope from thymus, ventral prostate, and lymphocytes of different organisms, and from plants and primitive organisms, we shall largely restrict ourselves to observations on the mammalian liver nuclear envelope. It is also important to realize that nuclear envelopes obtained from avian, plant, and other sources differ significantly from those of the mammalian liver. Our purpose is to provide a general survey of this organelle. For a more extensive consideration we have included a list of excellent reviews (1–3) and original manuscripts (4–20).

METHODOLOGY

Isolation of the Nuclear Envelope

A variety of techniques exist to isolate this organelle; however, no method is completely satisfactory for all studies on the morphology or biochemistry of the nuclear envelope. Methods differ widely in several respects. Some require only 90 min to obtain a "final product" from purified parent nuclei, whereas others require 2 days. These differences result largely from disagreements regarding appropriate treatment of the nuclei to avoid contamination of the envelope preparation by chromatin, ribosomes, nucleoli, and other cellular substances.

It would seem appropriate to obtain a final preparation consisting of nuclear ghosts which display relatively little disruption of the inner and outer nuclear membranes and nuclear pore complexes. To this end, a mild procedure may be used such as digestion of nuclei by deoxyribonuclease along with a sequence of low-ionic-strength washes in 1 mM sodium bicarbonate (pH 7.2) or 0.1 mM magnesium chloride (pH 8.6). Some investigators employ repeated digestion by deoxyribonuclease to disperse the chromatin, while others use solutions of markedly different pH, or prefer to obtain the final nuclear envelope preparation by differential rather than isopycnic centrifugation. In contrast to the claims that low-ionic-strength conditions render the nuclear enve-

Table 1. A Method for Isolation of Purified Rat Liver Nuclear Envelope.

	Purified nuclei from 3 rat livers (20 g pulp)	
		Suspend in 4 ml 0.1 mM MgCl₂. Add DNase I (50 μg/ml), 4 vol. digestion buffer (10 mM Tris-HCl), 0.1 mM MgCl₂, 5 mM 2-mercaptoethanol, 0.25 M sucrose (pH 8.6, 37°C). Stir well; incubate at 23°C for 7 min; mix well in glass homog. tube; incubate at 23°C for 7 min. Terminate rx. with ¾ vol. ice-cold H₂O; mix; centrifuge 20 min at 29,000 × g.
PHASE I (90 min)	Discard sup.	
		Crude nuclear envelope pellet (0.5 ml)
		Suspend in 16 vol. digestion buffer, but at pH 7.4. Add DNase I (10 μg/ml). Gently mix; incubate at 23°C for 20 min. Terminate rx. with 2 vol. ice-cold H₂O; mix; centrifuge 20 min at 29,000 × g.
PHASE II (20 hr)	Discard sup.	
		Partially purified nuclear envelope pellet (0.5 ml)
		Suspend in 16 ml 0.25 M sucrose; mix well; add EDTA-Tris (20 mM). Keep on ice 10 min. Layer over sucrose gradient (1.5M/2.2M), 30 mM Tris HCl, 30 mM KCl, 1 mM MgCl₂ (pH 7.4, 1°C). Centrifuge 18 hr at 80,000 × g.
	Purified nuclear envelope (at 1.5M/2.2M sucrose interface)	

lope unstable, we provide an outline for isolating and purifying intact rat liver nuclear envelope (Table 1). This technique (4) is a modification of that of Kay et al. (5). An additional step to dissociate ribosomes adhering to the outer nuclear membrane is involved.

Other procedures exist to isolate the nuclear envelope, but most of them involve conditions that are more disruptive to the envelope than the above method. For example, methods using ultrasonication and high-ionic-strength extraction, deoxyribonuclease digestion accompanied by high-ionic-strength extraction, Triton X-100, or heparin provide a preparation of nuclear envelope relatively (sometimes completely) devoid of DNA. In addition, these methods generally disrupt nuclear envelope morphology and damage its pore complexes.

Subfractionation of the Nuclear Envelope

The nuclear envelope may be considered to be composed of four subfractions: the inner membrane, the outer membrane, the intermembranous region, and the pore complex. To date, no procedure has been presented that can isolate a homogeneous preparation of any of these subfractions. However, several laboratories appear to be making excellent progress toward that goal. The use of a nonionic surfactant such as Nonidet P-40 or Triton X-100 results in a sample of inner nuclear membrane that retains pore complexes. These reagents appear to remove the outer nuclear membrane and to cause loss of phospholipid from the inner membrane. When Triton X-100 extraction is followed by treatment with 0.3 M magnesium chloride to remove chromatin, pore complexes attached to inner membrane fragments remain. Ultrasonication, although not completely satisfactory, appears to offer promise in the attempt to subfractionate the nuclear envelope into homogeneous fractions of pore complexes, inner membranes, and outer membranes.

Assessment of Purity

The nuclear envelope preparations obtained by the above methods vary widely in composition and morphology. For example, morphologically some preparations have either a predominance of small circular single-membrane vesicles, or intact nuclear ghosts with abundant double-membrane sheets, or only small single- or double-membrane sheets, or combinations of the above. However, some preparations may contain a much higher amount of DNA than others, suggesting a contamination by chromatin. Examination of these preparations by electron microscopy may reveal intact nuclei containing chromatin. Preparations that contain a relative excess of RNA may be expected to be contaminated by ribosomes.

Since the preparations of nuclear envelope vary, its assessment for purity must be considered according to the specific aspect that is being studied. This is especially important because of disagreements in methods for obtaining this organelle as well as lack of a universally accepted definition of what constitutes a purified nuclear envelope preparation. Therefore, for practical purposes, a combination of acceptable values for chemical composition plus electron micrographs showing nuclear membrane sheets or ghosts with characteristic pore complexes (as in the intact cell) should be taken as acceptable criteria of nuclear envelope purity. Assessment of purity by enzymic marker has not been widely accepted.

STRUCTURE

Methods: Transmission Electron Microscopy, Negative Staining, Freeze Cleavage, Scanning Electron Microscopy

Electron microscopy of thin sections has provided much information on the nuclear envelope of intact cells, isolated nuclei, and preparations of nuclear envelope. It also reveals that the outer nuclear membrane is studded with ribosomes. In a pore complex the central granule stains intensely, and the inner membrane is attached to chromatin and heterochromatin (Figure 1). However, when the nuclear envelope is broken into ghosts or large sheets, the preparation shows numerous membranous vesicles or fragments, both of which are difficult to identify as a nuclear preparation without using other techniques, such as special staining. For example, negative staining is frequently used to study the ultrastructure of isolated nuclear envelope (17). It provides details of the annulus of the pore complex. The annulus is clearly observed when ammonium uranyl oxalate is used in staining. Freeze cleavage provides additional information on the identification of structures of the nuclear envelope in intact and isolated nuclei. This technique is very useful for studying the distribution of pore complexes and intramembranous particles (Figure 2).

High resolution scanning electron microscopy has recently been applied to characterize the nuclear envelope and associated pore complexes of mouse liver nuclei (6). It provides a three-dimensional view of the distribution of ribosomes on the nuclear surface. In addition, it has been claimed that several types of pore-complex-associated structures not reported by other techniques, may be demonstrated by scanning microscopy.

Nuclear Pore Complex, Annulus, and Peripheral Lamina Fraction

The structure and function of the nuclear pore complexes and peripheral lamina are currently receiving much needed attention by researchers. Early

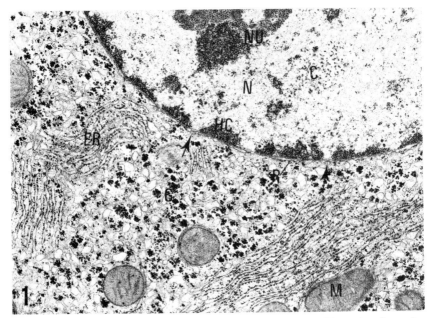

Figure 1. An electron micrograph of a hepatocyte from a rat liver, illustrating the nucleus (N), nucleolus (NU), chromatin (C), heterochromatin (HC), inner and outer nuclear membranes with nucleopores (arrows), glycogen (G), ribosomes on the outer membrane (R), rough endoplasmic reticulum (ER), and mitochondria (M). ×20,950.

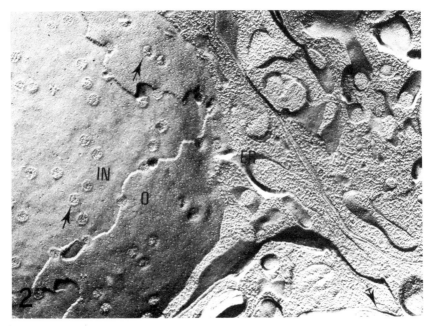

Figure 2. A freeze-fractured replica of a mouse prostatic epithelial cell, showing the fractured inner (IN) and outer (O) nuclear membranes. Also illustrated are nucleopores (arrows), and endoplasmic reticulum (ER), besides the intramembranous particles on the nuclear membranes. Crossed arrow shows direction of the shadow. ×39,660.

observations on the nuclear pore region generated an incomplete description of its features. Recent studies have shown that the nuclear pore complex is a distinct structure, and not merely an "empty space." Its dimensions have been reported to vary with the physiological status of the organ as well as with the preparation for electron microscopy. In most preparations, the nuclear pore complex is a more stable structure than the inner or outer nuclear membrane. Negative staining and freeze-fracture techniques have demonstrated its octagonal structure with an inner diameter of about 60 nm. However, a recent study employing high resolution scanning electron microscopy has shown that the complex contains eight globular subunits that form a generally round, rather than octagonal periphery. It has also been suggested that the organization of the peripheral nuclear chromatin (adjacent to the inner nuclear membrane) might determine the locations at which nuclear pores are formed. Therefore, the pore location may not be random.

The annulus is a sort of cylinder that extends through and beyond the pore and thus encompasses a portion of the nucleoplasm and cytoplasm. The high resolution electron microscopy methods employing both direct analysis and Markham rotation suggest that the annulus may consist of four paired subunits. The annular part of the complex is wider on both sides of the nuclear envelope, resulting in an hourglass shape.

Recently, in rat hepatocytes a nonmembranous lamina at the nuclear periphery to which the pore complexes attach, has been described (7). The lamina appears to be structurally distinct, associated with the inner membrane, and extends over the entire submembranous nuclear surface in a "shell-like" fashion. Dwyer and Blobel (7) have presented evidence that the isolated lamina is a 150 Å thick proteinaceous structure.

The protein of the nuclear pore complex–peripheral lamina fraction represents approximately 5% of the total protein of rat liver nuclei. It has been speculated that the lamina represents a polymeric crystalline assembly composed of a small number of monomeric subunits. It is made up of approximately equal amounts of three polypeptides as shown by analysis with sodium dodecylsulfate polyacrylamide gel electrophoresis. Whether this triplet comprises the lamina while other minor electrophoretic bands contain the proteins of the pore complex is not known.

Relationship of the Nuclear Envelope to Endoplasmic Reticulum, Chromosomes, and Chromatin

In most cells, the outer nuclear membrane is contiguous with the membranes of the endoplasmic reticulum. Both membranes are studded with ribosomes, and when isolated from the intact nuclei, they become indistinguishable morphologically. Freeze-cleavage techniques have shown similar patterns of intramembrane fracturing for both. Sodium dodecylsulfate polyacrylamide gel electrophoresis, however, has shown that the total polypeptide composition of nuclear envelope preparations significantly differs from that of the endoplasmic reticulum (see next section).

The inner nuclear membrane shows a stable association with chromosomes and their fragments. In most interphase nuclei, chromatin (predominately heterochromatin) is found adjacent to the inner membrane, and the attachment appears to be nonrandom, with preferential occurrence at particular chromosomal sites. An example of such a nonrandom association is the mammalian sex chromatin body originally described by Barr (8). A discussion of the possible significance of the attachment of DNA to the inner membrane of the nuclear envelope is included in the "Physiology" section, below.

BIOCHEMISTRY

Composition: Proteins and Amino Acids, Carbohydrates, Lipids, Nucleic Acids

The chemical composition of nuclear envelopes depends much on the isolation techniques as well as on the purity of the initial nuclear preparations. Fractionation of envelope proteins has been best accomplished by polyacrylamide gel electrophoresis in the presence of sodium dodecylsulfate using nuclear envelope solubilized in 2% sodium dodecylsulfate and 1% beta-mercaptoethanol. Bornens and Kasper (9) have conducted experiments to detect proteolysis during the envelope-solubilization procedure, and discovered no endogenous protease activity. They compared the electrophoretic patterns of similarly prepared nuclear envelope and microsomal membranes, and found that the former contained 23 individual zones which ranged in molecular weight from 16,000 to 160,000. The nuclear envelope has approximately 55% of its total protein distributed roughly equally in the molecular weight ranges of 47,000 to 60,000 and 64,000 to 74,000. The microsomal membrane contains about 50% of its protein in the range of 47,000 to 60,000. In both membrane systems, the polypeptides with molecular weight of approximately 160,000 stain strongest for carbohydrate, suggesting that the major glycoprotein(s) of the nuclear envelope and microsomal membrane may be similar or identical. In general, when expressed as a percentage of weight, protein accounts for approximately 60 to 80% of the liver nuclear envelope.

Bornens and Kasper (9) have provided information on the distribution of amino acid residues of nuclear envelope proteins. The ratio of polar to nonpolar residues varied within a restricted range for the individual molecular-weight classes, and had a value close to one. Furthermore, envelope proteins did not appear similar to histones (which characteristically have a ratio of basic to acidic amino acids of approximately two); the nuclear envelope fractions, with one exception, had ratios of less than one. In addition, the envelope did not appear to contain proteins characteristic of nonhistone chromosomal proteins. It should be noted, however, that other groups have obtained data somewhat dissimilar to the above in regard to the characteristics of envelope proteins. Such differences probably reflect the nature of the extraction procedures used by different authors.

Nuclear envelope obtained from rat liver contains about 3 to 4% carbohydrate by weight. Approximately 90% of the total carbohydrate is neutral sugar, predominantly glucose, glucosamine, and mannose, with lesser amounts of sialic acid and galactose. Most of the carbohydrate appears to be associated with the envelope proteins rather than the lipids. Most of the mannose and glucosamine is located in the outer membrane, while the glucose is present on both aspects of the nuclear envelope. The carbohydrate residues appear to be exposed on the surfaces of the membranes, as indicated by the binding of concanavalin A to both inner and outer nuclear membrane.

Lipids account for 15 to 30% of the weight of the nuclear envelope (3). Phospholipid represents about 80 to 95% of the total lipid. It is widely believed that most, if not all, of the nuclear lipid is located in the envelope. The lipid composition of the nuclear envelope closely resembles that of the microsomal membrane; both have a low content of sphingomyelin, cholesterol, and lysophosphatidylcholine. Phosphatidylcholine is the predominant phospholipid of both nuclear envelope and endoplasmic reticulum.

Various analyses of rat liver nuclear envelope prepared by different techniques have provided widely differing values for nucleic acid content. On a weight basis, the RNA has ranged from 1 to 10% and the DNA from zero to 8%. These differences are most likely due to the techniques used to isolate the envelope. It is, however, important to note that the entire envelope-associated RNA or DNA is not due to contamination by ribosomes or nuclear material, regardless of the technique employed. That some RNA present in the envelope is nonribosomal is supported by the fact that stripping of ribosomes by various methods from the outer nuclear membrane does not significantly reduce the envelope's RNA content. Furthermore, digestion with pancreatic ribonuclease does not reduce the RNA content.

The DNA content of the nuclear envelope is a topic of particular importance because of suggestions that the envelope may be involved in DNA replication and in the organization of chromatin. It seems likely that some portion of the DNA found in the inner nuclear membrane reflects an in vivo attachment at that site. This contention is supported by data that demonstrate the retention of some DNA in nuclear envelopes exposed to high-ionic-strength conditions and/or sequential digestions with pancreatic deoxyribonuclease.

Enzymes

In comparison to other cellular membranes, relatively little is known about the enzymic machinery of the nuclear envelope. This situation may in part be due to the lack of a universally accepted standard preparation of this organelle, but also likely results from problems in obtaining sufficient amounts of envelope from tissues of the small laboratory animals. Despite these drawbacks, many studies have reported on the enzyme activities in the preparations of nuclear envelope. For example, enzymes reported to be associated with mammalian liver envelopes include glucose-6-phosphatase, N-demethylase, mannose-6-phosphatase, aryl hydroxylase, Mg^{2+}–ATPase, monoamine oxidase, 5'-nucleotidase, alkaline phosphatase, acid phosphatase, and others (2). Steer et al. (4) have recently reported the presence of a protein phosphokinase activity in rat liver nuclear envelope. In addition, others have reported a DNA swivel (nicking–rejoining) enzyme activity in the nuclear envelope from a human lymphoid cell line (10). A steroid 5 alpha-reductase has been described in the nuclear envelope obtained from rat ventral prostate (11).

Most of the cytochrome c oxidase activity of the nuclear envelope appears to be endogenous to that organelle and not attributable to mitochondrial contamination, as some groups have suggested (2). Cytochemical studies demonstrate that its activity is associated primarily with the inner nuclear membrane. And it has been proposed that the presence of this activity may reflect a site of oxidative phosphorylation at the nuclear envelope. However, this is still a speculation.

PHYSIOLOGY

Nucleocytoplasmic Transport of Substances

The permeability properties of isolated nuclei and nuclear envelopes have been investigated (12), nonmammalian organisms having been used predominantly. However, data regarding permeability derived from tracer and morphologic studies have been interpreted generally as representative of eukaryotic envelopes. Many substances appear to be in continuous exchange between nucleus and cytoplasm. These substances include ions, chromosomal proteins, hormones, nucleic acids, and ribosomal and messenger ribonucleoproteins. Most ions, small molecules, and many macromolecules appear to traverse the nuclear envelope by diffusion alone. It is interesting to note that the potassium concentration of the nucleus is significantly higher than that of the cytoplasm, while the nuclear sodium concentration is less than that of the cytoplasm. This situation exists despite failure to demonstrate the presence of a Na^+–K^+ energy-dependent transport system.

Paine et al. (12) have examined the permeability of nuclear envelope in amphibian oocyte by microinjection of tritiated-dextran fractions, autoradiography, and mathematical methods. They demonstrated a patent radius of pores to be approximately 45 Å. Diffusible cellular metabolites and proteins with a radius less than 45 Å appeared to cross the envelope at rates influenced by solute size. Small changes in the effective radius of the solute profoundly affected the rates of envelope permeation. They presented three lines of evidence that support the view that these pore-complex channels are the sites of nucleocytoplasmic macromolecular exchange: (1) Colloidal gold particles in passage from cytoplasm to nucleus appear to be limited by the annular material to these central pore-complex channels; (2) ribonucleoprotein-containing particles in nucleocytoplasmic transit appear to reduce their diameter to the range of 100 to 200 Å as they traverse the central region of the pore complex; and (3) they proposed a model, based on restricted diffusion through pores, that could account for a 2500-fold difference in the rate of envelope permeation among solutes that differ only in size. Since most cellular proteins are of a size that makes their movement readily influenced by small changes in pore radius, it has been suggested that the nuclear envelope controls nucleocytoplasmic exchange by varying the patent pore radius. Harris (2) states that it is not unreasonable to propose that the nuclear pore complex might in fact provide independent passive and active transport systems for different substances.

Of particular interest are reports of an envelope-associated Mg^{2+}–ATPase activity that is not stimulated by $Na^+ + K^+$, and apparently is not involved in cation transport across the nuclear envelope. It appears to be involved in the nucleocytoplasmic transfer of ribonucleoproteins (13). The location of this activity, as revealed by cytochemical methods using lead phosphate, is controversial, with a recent report demonstrating the lead phosphate location near the pore complex (14), while another study (15) showed its even distribution along the outer leaflet of the nuclear envelope.

The role of the Mg^{2+}–ATPase of the nuclear envelope warrants intensive study because of the possibility of elucidating the envelope-translocation phase of the protein synthetic process. It has been suggested that RNA is transferred from the nucleus only in a ribonucleoprotein complex, thus implicating nuclear protein synthesis as a step essential to the ultimate transport of mRNA and rRNA. In support of this hypothesis, Eckert et al. (16) demonstrated that actinomycin D and cycloheximide both inhibited the nuclear release of preexisting nuclear RNA. It is noteworthy to mention that cytosol proteins and ATP are essential to the efflux of ribonucleoproteins from isolated nuclei.

Paine et al. (12) have suggested that ribonucleoprotein particles, which have a radius greater than 45 Å (and are thus too large to diffuse through the pores), would likely require in order to cross from nucleus to cytoplasm a conformational change in the ribonucleoprotein particles, or the pore complexes, or perhaps both. When taken in combination, it is not unreasonable to consider the possibility of an important role for the nuclear pore complex in the control of protein synthesis.

Role of the Nuclear Envelope in DNA Synthesis

One of the most exciting aspects of nuclear membrane biology involves the ongoing controversy as to whether the initiation of DNA synthesis and replication in mammalian cells occurs near or at the nuclear envelope. This notion was previously rejected by several groups; however, recent work indicates that DNA is likely replicated near or at the nuclear envelope. It is possible that early DNA replication occurs away from the inner nuclear membrane, while the late-replicating DNA occurs at the sites of attachment of the inner nuclear membrane to adjacent heterochromatin.

Sinha and Mizuno (17) have studied DNA synthesis associated with a DNA–nuclear membrane complex from rat liver. They employed the detergent sodium N-lauroyl sarkosinate (sarkosyl), which removed the outer nuclear membrane with its associated ribosomes during the preparation of an "M-band" fraction which contained fragments of inner nuclear membrane, some nuclear pores, and small amounts of dense chromatin particles. It was similar in composition to envelope fractions obtained by different techniques. They showed that the M-band contained the greatest proportion of newly labeled DNA and also supported DNA synthesis in vitro. Furthermore, a greater fraction of the newly synthesized DNA was associated with the M-band from 24-hour regenerating liver than with the normal liver, indicating that the DNA synthesis might be associated with the M-band during the proliferative stage of liver cells.

Yoshida et al. (10) have recently reported the presence of a DNA swivel (nicking–rejoining) enzyme activity in the chromatin and nuclear membrane fraction of a human lymphoid cell line. These enzymes are capable of untwisting supercoiled DNA by the nicking and rejoining of a single strand and are presumed to provide the "swivel action" essential to the unwinding of parental strands during the replication of long DNA molecules. Twenty percent of the total activity and less than 1% of the total nuclear DNA content were associated with the nuclear membrane fraction. The swivel enzyme appeared to be tightly and specifically bound to replicating DNA in the nuclear membrane, and its possible role as a replication factor was suggested. This group also reported the presence of a γ-like DNA polymerase in the nuclear membrane preparation.

Role of the Nuclear Envelope in Chromatin Organization

The idea that nuclear chromosomal DNA has specific sites of attachment to the inner nuclear membrane is based on experimental evidences. These sites are envisaged as being important in the orientation of chromosomes during interphase, and mitotic and meiotic prophase. The attachment of DNA to the inner nuclear membrane is almost certainly not artifactual. It most likely represents sites of chromosome–envelope union that occur in vivo. This claim is supported by the resistance of the attachment to various detergents, high-ionic-strength conditions, and a variety of mechanical spreading techniques.

Franke et al. (18) have demonstrated that after removal of all ionically bound proteins, a small amount of nuclear membrane DNA remains resistant to deoxyribonuclease cleavage, suggesting that such DNA is bound to and protected by membrane lipoproteins and thus serves as "anchor pieces" for chromosomal DNA molecules. Ultrastructural studies have shown that it is not only the terminal aspects of the DNA molecules that are attached to the inner nuclear membrane, but also there are loops of DNA that project from the membrane in a "garland-like" fashion. Similar studies also demonstrate that DNA attachment is not limited to the area of the pore complexes, since techniques that severely disrupt nuclear envelope morphology do not eliminate the DNA strand or loop attachment to the remaining small, fragmented areas between the pores.

During interphase and meiotic prophase, it is the centromeric or pericentromeric heterochromatin that appears to be selectively associated with the inner nuclear membrane. Attachment of telomeric heterochromatin to the envelope occurs at the ends of the synaptinemal complexes during the meiotic zygotene stage; this appears to be important for the pairing of homologous chromosomes. In addition, the perinucleolar heterochromatin of many cell types displays regular attachments to the inner membrane of the nuclear envelope. Whether the attachment of chromosomal material to the nuclear envelope is an absolute requirement for the initiation of chromosome replication is not certain. We are unaware of any report of replication of a chromosome that is obviously unattached to the nuclear envelope. Likewise, from other (nonmammalian) studies it is generally understood that such membrane attachment, in and of itself, is not sufficient for the DNA replication process.

CONCLUSIONS AND COMMENTS

The mammalian nuclear envelope is a dynamic entity that has been suggested to participate in the processes of nucleocytoplasmic transport, DNA synthesis, and chromatin organization, as well as other aspects of cellular function. Although studies on this cellular fraction have not yet provided a unified hypothesis of its functions, considerable experimental evidence to support its participation in the above events has been presented.

In addition to ongoing studies on the normal structures and functions of the nuclear envelope, recent papers (19) have shown that disruption of its morphology and synthesis occurs in response to certain hepatocarcinogens. In view of this, it seems plausible that future studies on nuclear envelope pathology may further help to define functions of this organelle. Recent work (20) has also shown that the nuclear envelope is the major site of insulin binding in the rat liver cells. These binding sites have high affinities and are hormone-specific. Accordingly, it would seem plausible to speculate that a nuclear-envelope-associated mechanism might exist whereby insulin exerts some of its effects, such as macromolecular synthesis. Further elucidation of the roles of the nuclear envelope in cell biology will probably depend on methodological progress in isolating and defining this organelle.

REFERENCES

1. Franke, W. W., and Scheer, U. 1974. Structures and functions of the nuclear envelope. In *The Cell Nucleus,* H. Busch, ed. Academic Press, New York and London.
2. Harris, J. R. 1978. The biochemistry and ultrastructure of the nuclear envelope. *Biochem. Biophys. Acta* 515:55.
3. Kasper, C. B. 1974. Chemical and biochemical properties of the nuclear envelope. In *The Cell Nucleus,* H. Busch, ed. Academic Press, New York and London.
4. Steer, R. C., Wilson, M. J., and Ahmed, K. 1979. Protein phosphokinase activity of rat liver nuclear membrane. *Exp. Cell Res.* 119:403.
5. Kay, R. R., Fraser, D., and Johnston, I. R. 1972. A method for the rapid isolation of nuclear membranes from rat liver: Characterization of the membrane preparation and its associated DNA polymerase. *Eur. J. Biochem.* 30:145.
6. Kirschner, R. H., Rusli, M., and Martin, T. E. 1977. Characterization of the nuclear envelope, pore complexes, and dense lamina of mouse liver nuclei by high resolution scanning electron microscopy. *J. Cell Biol.* 72:118.
7. Dwyer, N., and Blobel, G. 1976. A modified procedure for the isolation of a pore complex–lamina fraction from rat liver nuclei. *J. Cell Biol.* 70:581.
8. Barr, M. L. 1959. Sex chromatin and phenotype in man. *Science* 130:679.
9. Bornens, M., and Kasper, C. B. 1973. Fractionation and partial characterization of proteins of the bileaflet nuclear membrane from rat liver. *J. Biol. Chem.* 248:571.
10. Yoshida, S., Ungers, G., and Rosenberg, B. H. 1977. DNA swivel enzyme activity in a nuclear membrane fraction. *Nucl. Acids Res.* 4(1):223.
11. Moore, R. J., and Wilson, J. D. 1972. Localization of the reduced nicotinamide adenine dinucleotide phosphate: Δ^4-3-Ketosteroid 5α-oxidoreductase in the nuclear membrane of the rat ventral prostate. *J. Biol. Chem.* 247:958.
12. Paine, P. L., Moore, L. C., and Horowitz, S. B. 1975. Nuclear envelope permeability. *Nature* 245:109.
13. Agutter, P. S., Harris, J. R., and Stevenson, I. 1977. Ribonucleic acid stimulation of mamma-

lian liver nuclear-envelope nucleoside triphosphatase: A possible enzymic marker for the nuclear envelope. *Biochem J.* 162:176.

14. Chardonnet, Y., and Dales, S. 1972. Early events in the interaction of adenoviruses with Hela cells 3. Relationship between an ATPase activity in nuclear envelopes and transfer of core material: A hypothesis. *Virology* 48:342.

15. Sikstrom, R., Lanoix, J., and Bergeron, J. J. M. 1976. An enzymic analysis of a nuclear envelope fraction. *Biochem. Biophys. Acta* 448:88.

16. Eckert, W. A., Franke, W. W., and Scheer, U. 1975. Nucleocytoplasmic translocation of RNA in *Tetrahymena pyriformis* and its inhibition by actinomycin D and cycloheximide. *Exp. Cell Res.* 94:31.

17. Sinha, A. A., and Mizuno, N. S. 1977. DNA synthesis associated with a DNA-nuclear membrane complex from rat liver. *Cell Tissue Res.* 183:191.

18. Franke, W. W., Deumling, B., Zentgraf, H., Falk, H., Rae, P. M. M. 1973. Nuclear membranes from mammalian liver: IV. Characterization of membrane-attached DNA. *Exp. Cell Res.* 81:365.

19. Glazer, R. I., and La Via, M. F. 1975. Biochemical and morphological changes in hepatic nuclear membranes produced by N-hydroxy-2-acetylaminofluorene. *Cancer Res.* 35:2511.

20. Vigneri, R., Goldfine, I. D., Wong, K. Y., Smith, G. J., and Pezzino, V. 1978. The nuclear envelope: The major site of insulin binding in rat liver nuclei. *J. Biol. Chem.* 253(7):2098.

SECTION 13
PERSPECTIVES FOR
CELL BIOLOGY

GEORGE P. STUDZINSKI

13. Perspectives for Cell Biology

The importance of cell biology is increasingly being recognized. Journals devoted to this field are maintaining rapid-growth in both volume and number. Society for Cell Biology meetings are attended by increasing numbers of scientists, and cell biology research is on the whole well supported by our society. This feeling of excitement and optimism is due to several factors, and indications are that the future is indeed bright.

One of the reasons for the growth of cell biology as a research arena has been the gradual acquisition of new, highly sophisticated techniques. Section 1 of this volume describes the most important investigative tools available today; and while new methods are still being introduced, the current era may be characterized principally by refinements in existing technology. For instance, cell biology as a discipline probably owes more to the application of electron microscopy to biological materials than to any other single development. Recently, the capabilities of electron microscopy have shown a steady if not spectacular expansion, and this progress is likely to continue. Development of tissue culture (a misnomer) also has been fundamental to the emergence of cell biology as a recognized discipline. The ability to deal with cells as individual units, rather than with tissues, allows the investigator to reduce the complexity of the biological system by an order of magnitude. This technology, established for mammalian cells early in this century, has recently been advancing only by the realization of its pitfalls, such as silent microbial infections or contamination by other cell lines. The challenge in this area is to be able to grow cells in chemically defined media. This presently can be accomplished to a limited extent, but growth is poor unless the medium is supplemented with serum. Many growth factors have been isolated from sera and various animal tissues, but none of these factors appears to be the cell-division-promoting substance that the serum provides for mammalian cells. More recently, advances in immunology have led to the development of immunofluorescent methods, which permit visualization of cellular structures that previously could not be studied morphologically; an example is staining of bundles of actin filaments which form the cytoskeleton. These methods, which have not yet been fully exploited, offer considerable promise for the future.

Speculation regarding the future development of technology may not be particularly profitable. It seems safe, however, to suggest that one aspect of growth will be the conversion of existing descriptive tools to ones capable of quantitation, by making use of the increased capacities of transistorized computers. If successful, this work may revolutionize the field.

Perhaps even more important than advances in technology for the emergence of cell biology as a major discipline, are the conceptual advances taking place in the sister discipline of molecular biology, and the simultaneous evolution of concepts relating to the cell as a unit. Cellular-recognition elements represent a class of such recently developed concepts. These elements include cell receptors, described in Section 3, where 14 types of receptors are discussed; complementarity of biological macromolecules, which permits these molecules to seek out and interact with one another, a property utilized experimentally in nucleic acid hybridization; and restriction endonucleases, which, although so far found only in bacteria, represent a prototype of hydrolytic enzyme with very precise sequence recognition.

Structural organization of genetic information is becoming increasingly better understood, and is a problem peculiar to cellular as opposed to molecular biology. From a simple distinction of euchromatin and heterochromatin, the field has advanced to studies of repetitive versus unique DNA sequences, the study of histone–DNA interaction in the nucleosome, and investigation of the basis for bands that can be visualized in metaphase chromosomes. Questions addressed to the mechanisms of storage of genetic information and selection of segments for transcription are particularly relevant at this time. Although mammalian cells are much less amenable to attempts to define the organization of their genome than bacteria or yeast, since it is more difficult to obtain mammalian mutants, current studies with temperature-sensitive mutants of cultured rodent cells can perhaps be expanded and achieve more general importance for the study of the cell.

Cell damage that is not rapidly lethal can illuminate many aspects of cell function. The discovery that viruses can exist within cells without destroying these cells has led to key advances in biology. The demonstration that some DNA viruses can integrate with the host genome, and thereby modify the cell's replicative behavior, is probably of the most fundamental importance, since it points the way to genetic engineering, and it can also serve as a model for the study of neoplastic transformation under conditions that permit precise characterization of the transcriptive process. Equally intriguing is the introduction of genetic information by RNA viruses; and the portion of the viral genome that determines the sarcoma-like transformation of cultured chick fibroblasts has recently been determined.

Other forms of sublethal damage, such as are produced by moderate exposure to various forms of radiation and to diverse chemicals, are of particular relevance to studies of neoplastic transformation, but may turn out to be helpful to our understanding of degenerative diseases, and perhaps also be related to studies of the process of aging. These damaging agents exert their effects to varying degrees on different cells, and this variability is to some extent due to the reparative capacity of the cell in question. As discussed in Section 6 of this volume, a number of enzymes associated with the DNA of the cell can selectively hydrolyze internal bonds within DNA, and these enzymes, DNA nucleases, may have a special importance for the process of DNA repair. Incomplete or inappropriate repair could result in an altered cell capable of replication, and thus form a neoplastic clone. Studies in the author's laboratory indicate that the number of nucleases associated with DNA is quite large, and this may indicate complex functional interrelationships.

A concept that is rather special to cell biology is that of the cell cycle. It focuses on the repetitive sequence of DNA replication and cell division, which may be separated into distinct intervals of varying length. Of course, the repetitive or cyclic changes are not limited to DNA replication and mitosis, though these phenomena serve as the most easily visualized markers of the replicative process; and events that are preparatory to spindle formation could perhaps be utilized to construct a cell cycle with somewhat different parameters. Since neoplastic cells are characterized by their ability to continue to traverse the cell cycle under conditions that arrest the cell cycle progress of normal cells, studies of the cell cycle have helped to produce increased effectiveness of cancer chemotherapy, by optimizing conditions for selective killing of cycling cells. It now remains for us to find a means of effective protection of normal cycling cells, to achieve eradication of neoplastic cells from an organism. One approach toward this goal is to study the metabolic differences between normal and transformed cells. Differences have been found in the RNA metabolism of normal and SV40-transformed human fibroblasts, and such differences, and others, may prove to be exploitable for the chemotherapy of cancer.

This brief survey of some recent developments and an indication of trends for the future should indicate that the discipline of cell biology is making a two-pronged thrust. There is the preoccupation with expanding existing knowledge of the living cell, and with the harnessing of this knowledge for the conquest of disease. There is a reciprocal relationship here, however; studies of pathological conditions have repeatedly turned up information on basic processes common to all cells. For example, Warburg's studies of cellular metabolism were initiated to determine the basis for neoplastic behavior of cells, yet have taught us more about energy metabolism of cells in general.

The overall goal of understanding life processes is being steadily achieved. Perhaps in the not too distant future we will be able to advance from the analytical approach, exemplified by this book, of examining membranes, cellular organelles, chromosomes, and so on, to reconstructing the cell from its components. The groundwork for this is already available, since it has been shown that various subcellular components can function for a limited time in vitro, and cells can fuse with portions of cells of other types. Can we hope to create life from cell components?

SECTION 14
INDEX

Index